PHYSICS

PHYSICS

PHYSICAL SCIENCE STUDY COMMITTEE

D. C. HEATH AND COMPANY, BOSTON

LIBRARY OF CONGRESS CATALOG CARD NUMBER 60–13412

Published by D. C. HEATH AND COMPANY
under arrangements with
EDUCATIONAL SERVICES INCORPORATED

PREFACE

The Physical Science Study Committee is a group of university and secondary school physics teachers working to develop an improved beginning physics course. The project started in 1956 with a grant from the National Science Foundation, which has given the main financial support. The Ford Foundation and the Alfred P. Sloan Foundation have also contributed to the support of the program.

This textbook is the heart of the PSSC course, in which physics is presented not as a mere body of facts but basically as a continuing process by which men seek to understand the nature of the physical world. Besides the textbook there are the following closely correlated parts: a laboratory guide and a set of new and inexpensive apparatus; a large number of films; standardized tests; a growing series of paper-back books by leaders in related fields; and a comprehensive teacher's resource book directly related to the course.

The PSSC physics course is the work of several hundred people, mainly school and college physics teachers, over a period of four years. A brief account of this collaboration is given at the end of the book. Here it is appropriate, however, to recognize two of these collaborators. Professor Jerrold R. Zacharias, the Department of Physics of the Massachusetts Institute of Technology, called together a committee of leaders in physics and in education from which this project sprang. He has been active in all phases of the project. Professor Francis L. Friedman, also of the Department of Physics at MIT and a member of the Committee from the beginning, has played the major role in developing the textbook and has contributed significantly to all parts of the program.

In many ways this new course differs markedly from the beginning physics course usually taught in the United States. To be sure that the new approach was sound and teachable, the help of teachers and students was sought. In 1957–58, eight schools and 300 students tried out the early materials. Their comments and suggestions helped to improve and extend the content and approach. Then in 1958–59, nearly 300 schools and 12,500 students used the course, and in 1959–60, almost 600 schools and 25,000 students participated in the third test year. The course was thoroughly revised in the light of this experience.

The reactions of teachers and students show that a large percentage of students are intrigued by this course and do well with it. Their concepts grow through exploration in the laboratory, analysis in the text, and study of the films. The course appeals to students who are inclined toward the humanities as well as to those who are already interested in science.

The PSSC Course

The PSSC course consists of four closely interconnected parts. Part I is a general introduction to the fundamental physical notions of time, space, and matter: how we grasp and how we measure them. As the student learns of the almost boundless range of dimensions from the immensely large to the infinitesimally small, from microseconds to billions of years, he finds out how these magnitudes can be measured. He learns that instruments serve as an extension of his senses. Laboratory experience shows how we first measure by direct counting and then extend our range of measurements by calibrating and using simple instruments such as stroboscopes or range finders.

From these experiments measuring time and space, the student moves to an understanding of velocity and acceleration, of vectors and of relative motion. He then goes on to study matter, which we see moving through space in the course of time. In this first examination of matter, we develop the concepts of mass and of its conservation. We then use the evidence of physicists and chemists to find that matter is made of relatively few kinds of atoms. Direct experience is provided in the laboratory. There, for instance, the students compute the size of a molecule from measurements of thin films of oil. Moving pictures extend this direct laboratory experience by showing experiments which are beyond the reach of students.

Throughout, the student is led to realize that physics is a single subject of study. In particular, time, space, and matter cannot be separated. Furthermore, he sees that physics is a developing subject, and that this development is the imaginative work of men and women like him.

The topics in the PSSC course are selected and ordered to progress from the simple and familiar to the more subtle ideas of modern atomic physics. In Part I we have looked at a broad picture of the universe. Now as we examine certain fields of physics in more detail, we start in Part II with light. We live by light, and the student moves easily into a study of sharp and diffuse shadows, reflection in mirrors, and the refraction of light at optical boundaries. The natural development of the subject leads us to develop a particle theory (or model) of light. Its discussion illustrates repeatedly the manner in which virtually all scientific knowledge develops. Again films — for instance, the film on the pressure of light — help the student to go beyond the laboratory.

Under continued scrutiny the particle model proves inadequate, and the student finds that we need another model — a wave model. The laboratory again provides an unexcelled source of experience, and here the student becomes familiar with the properties of waves. He observes the behavior of waves on ropes and on the surface of water. He begins to recognize the group of characteristics that constitute wave behavior. Knowledge of interference and diffraction comes directly from a study of waves in a ripple tank. For the first time, perhaps, the smears of light around street lamps, the colors of oil slicks, and the formation of images by lenses appear as aspects of the wave nature of light.

During the first half of the course, the principal emphasis is on the kinematics of our world: where things are, how big they are, and how they move, not why. In Part III we turn to a closer look at motion, this time from a dynamical point of view. With simple laboratory apparatus the students discover Newton's law of motion. They learn to predict motions when forces are known and to determine forces when motions are known. Thus armed they follow the extraordinary story of the discovery of universal gravitation, Newton's educated guess with which he jumped from the known laws of motion to the law of gravitational attraction.

The laws of conservation of momentum and of energy are introduced through a combination of theory and laboratory exploration. These laws form a substantial portion of Part III, and we stress their use in situations where detailed observation of the motion is not possible, as in Chadwick's discovery of the neutron and in the kinetic theory of gases.

Part IV introduces the student to electricity and through it to the physics of the atom. Here the student uses the knowledge of dynamics gained in Part III. We begin with qualitative observations, then proceed to a quantitative study of the forces between charges. We learn how to measure very small electric forces and discover that electric charge comes in natural units. We then study the motion of charged particles in electric fields and learn how to determine the masses of electrons and protons.

Next comes a discussion of magnetic fields produced by magnets and currents, and a discussion of the forces they exert on moving charges. As a final part of electricity we discuss the induction laws and give the student a qualitative feeling for the electromagnetic nature of light. Many of the fundamental ideas are explored in the laboratory — Coulomb's Law, the magnetic field around a current, the force exerted by a magnetic field on a current-carrying wire are examples.

Now we use the knowledge gained on a large scale to probe the structure of atoms. Following the work of Rutherford, we establish the nuclear model of the atom. But some questions are unanswered. Why, for example, is such an atom stable? Why doesn't it collapse by emitting light? In searching for answers, we discover that light is both grainy and wavy. Furthermore, we find that although matter behaves like particles, in some respects it also behaves like waves. By combining both properties, we can understand the stability of the hydrogen atom and the structure of its energy levels. In this part of the course, because direct experimentation becomes harder and more expensive, films bring to the student such experiments as the Millikan experiment and the interference of photons. At the end of the course we have arrived at the modern model of atoms.

The PSSC course as now presented has proved to be thoroughly teachable. It is useful in a wide variety of schools. However, those who have collaborated in building this course wish to improve it further. As the Physical Science Study Committee continues this development, your comments will always be welcome.

James R. Killian, Jr.
Chairman, Board of Trustees
Educational Services Incorporated

CONTENTS

PART I THE UNIVERSE

PART II OPTICS AND WAVES

PART III MECHANICS

PART IV ELECTRICITY AND ATOMIC STRUCTURE

PART I

THE UNIVERSE

Colliding Galaxies. This photograph, made with the 48-in. Schmidt telescope at Palomar, shows two immense systems of stars colliding in space at a tremendous distance from the Earth. If we could observe all that is taking place during such a collision, on successively smaller scales down to where we could perceive sub-atomic particles, we would see all of the principles of physics demonstrated.

WHAT IS PHYSICS?

CHAPTER 1

PHYSICS is the fundamental science of the natural world. It tells us what we know about that world, how men and women found out what we know, and how they are finding out more today.

When a flash of lightning shatters the dark, the radio crackles and your eyes are dazzled for a few seconds. A moment later you hear the roll of thunder, and a loose windowpane rattles. Three states away in a storm-location center, a radio-locater can pinpoint the lightning stroke; and downtown the weather forecaster, hearing a far-away rumble, nods as if he had been expecting the storm.

Here is a chain of events, different events, taking place at different places and different times. They are all linked. How are they tied together, and just what is happening to eye, to ear, to the radio, and in the air itself?

Take another chain of events. In the test shops of a steel mill you can watch a thin bar of a new alloy pulled at its ends by the powerful jaws of a testing machine as big as a house, which is driven by a fast-whirring electric motor no bigger than a football. The solid bar slowly yields to the pull. It stretches out like a piece of taffy, and breaks a little later with a jangle of sound. How does it all work? What holds the bar together? Why did it finally give way? And, by the way, why is steel stronger than glass? Why is it more dense than aluminum? Why does it rust?

Men once feared the "illness of the sun," when the sun disappeared and the earth darkened. Then we learned about the complex motion of the moon. Eclipses became far easier to predict than tomorrow's weather. The moon has been circling our planet since long before the first dinosaur walked the earth. A man-made satellite can circle the globe for a long period without propeller, jet, or wings — a tiny synthetic moon. How do satellites move? How can we design our own? How can we visit the moon?

Physics enables us to answer such questions. It gives us the power to predict and to design, to understand and to adventure into the unknown. From what we learn in physics, new things are made. With new answers in physics, new questions are always arising. Many of these questions would never have been asked if physics itself had not been put to use.

Before the time of Galileo there were no astronomical telescopes. Once Galileo had put together two lenses to make an astronomical telescope and had discovered four moons revolving around Jupiter, more and better telescopes were designed and made. With their aid, new heavenly bodies were found, such as the many small planets called asteroids that move between the orbits of Jupiter and Mars.

New questions now arose. How could the complex motions of these moons and asteroids be explained? To answer questions like this, much of the special mathematical branch of physics called *mechanics* was developed. Beginning in the eighteenth century, rapid advances were made in this study of how objects move when subjected to complex forces. The new knowledge of mechanics led to the better design of machines. So we see that without the telescope, mechanics would have taken a slower course.

More recently, around fifty years ago, the beginnings of the understanding of atoms made it clear how to build much better air pumps than ever before. With these new pumps, a good vacuum was easy to obtain, and with a good vacuum experiments that formerly were impossible started researchers delving into the nature of electrons and atoms. This ability to produce a high vacuum, and the knowledge it brought, led to such varied practical achievements as radio and television tubes, concentrated orange juice, and atomic energy. This atomic research also clarified the very foundation of chemistry by making it possible to determine what holds two atoms together or what keeps them apart.

So the subject grows. It is like a great building under construction, not a finished structure around which you have only to take a guided tour. Though some parts are pretty well complete, and both useful and beautiful, others are only half-done. Still others are barely planned. New parts will be started and completed by the men and women of your generation, possibly by you or your classmates. Once in a while, a finished room in this structure known as physics is found unsafe, or no longer large enough for new discoveries, and the room is abandoned or rebuilt. This happens often, but the great foundations are well laid and stand on pretty solid ground. These remain unchanged though changes go on above them. It is the intent of this book to let you see the plan of the building, to show you what the builders have done, to look at some of the parts they are working on now, and notice occasionally where the design is still incomplete.

1–1. Physics and the Other Sciences of Nature

Physics is the fundamental science of the natural world, but it is not the only such science. Physics is fundamental because it deals with such features of the world as time, space, motion, matter, electricity, light, and radiation; and some feature of every event that occurs in the natural world can be seen in these terms. *Astronomy*, the science which tries to understand the moon, the planets, the stars, and the universe beyond the stars, is built on physics. *Geology* is a kind of detailed "astronomy" of the planet we know best, our own earth. *Meteorology*, the physics of our atmosphere, attempts to explain the causes of weather in terms of physics. *Chemistry* is a science nearly as fundamental for the others as is physics. Its specialty is understanding the many substances that surround us here on earth, and also the new ones made by chemists, which have never existed before. A major branch of chemistry, called *biochemistry*, the chemistry of life, deals with our own bodies, and the food we eat. And the whole living world itself is the object of many sciences, from anatomy to zoology, each specializing in a particular kind of physical object, such as plants and animals in all their diverse and wonderful forms.

Staying even closer to physics is a group of bordering sciences called by names like *astrophysics*, *geophysics*, and *biophysics*. Astrophysics is the physics of the astronomical world. You could say that the locations and the identification of the stars are problems of astronomy, but a study of what makes the stars shine is a part of astrophysics. Geophysics deals with the physics of our earth, and biophysics with the physics of living things.

1–2. Physics and Engineering

Technology — the whole collection of means and equipment which man has built to improve his lot on this planet — is based on science. All the sciences contribute — physics, indeed, very often. When physicists learn to understand and control a particular sort of event, say radio waves, then there begins to form a group of specialists whose work is to make this new gain useful. In this way *radio engineering* and *electronics* arose as a special offshoot of physics, and are now studied by more people and with more total effort than physics itself. So it has happened time after time: for electricity, for aviation, and for the motion of air and water (called aerodynamics and hydrodynamics).

Three hundred years ago the pioneer Italian physicist Galileo (1564–1642) tried to find out how to support heavy beams without breaking them. In those days long, painful, trial-and-error experience had produced people who were more or less skilled in the art of constructing buildings, but there was little scientific study of such matters. Nowadays, the understanding of this part of

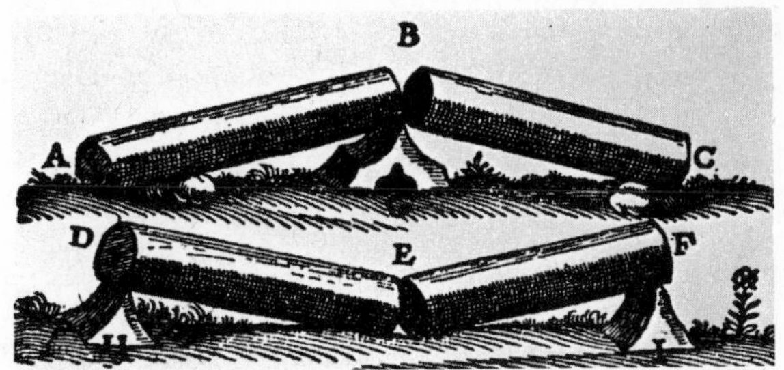

1–1. This drawing is from Galileo's book "Two New Sciences," written in 1638. He found that the length of a heavy beam may be the same, without breaking of its own weight, whether it is supported at both ends (D and F) or at the middle (B).

1–2. An engraving of the laboratory of Michael Faraday at the Royal Institution in London about 100 years ago. In the lower right-hand corner is some of the apparatus he used in his work on electricity. (From "Life and Letters of Faraday," by Dr. B. Jones; Longmans, Green.)

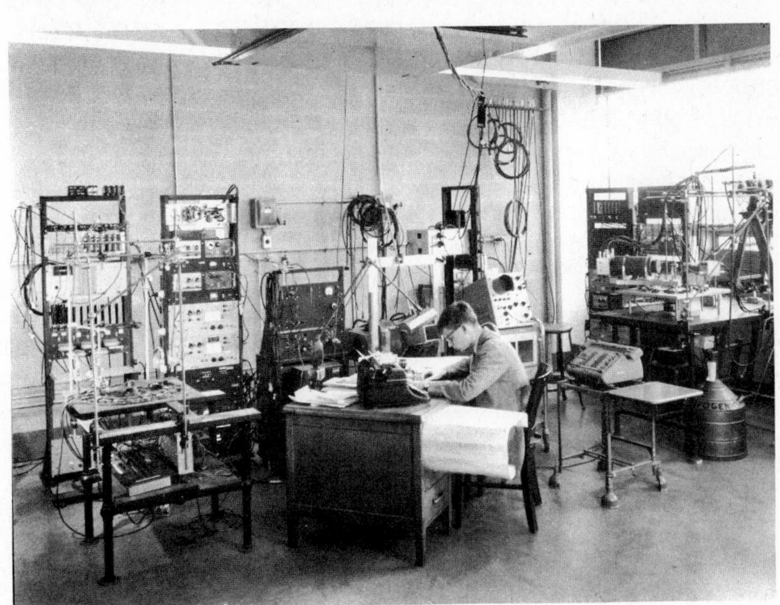

1–3. A typical American physics laboratory in 1959. Compare it with Faraday's lab shown in Fig. 1–2.

physics is so important in everyday life and so well developed, that it is left to a professional group of engineers, far removed from the general study of physics. These are the people who design and build skyscrapers, bridges, and roads. Their work is based on physical principles so well tested by three centuries of experience that the physicist no longer doubts their applicability. He feels that he can add little to them that is new. In the same way, the release of nuclear energy (atomic power), a recent product of the physics of the twentieth century, is now very near to becoming a specialized, important, and fascinating technical pursuit on its own, called *nuclear engineering.*

This is the way with physics. It fathers other sciences and their useful applications, which we can call technology. Like grateful children, these have often in their turn given back to physics new materials, new tools, and new ideas. Many of these new tools are now almost indispensable to physics. For example, radio and other electronic devices grew out of physics, and now these devices are used in solving modern problems in physics. Modern research in physical science and the television entertainment industry alike depend on electronics, which is the direct descendant of what seemed to be obscure and unimportant happenings in the physics laboratories of 1900.

1–3. The Tools of Physics

Physics requires tools — tools of every kind. As with nearly all activities of human beings, the key tool of the physicist is his mind. Next, he needs language to make clear to himself and to others what he thinks and has done, and what he wants to do. Mathematics, which can be thought of as a special, supremely clear and flexible international language of relation and quantity, is also an important tool in his kit — and his own eyes, ears, and hands are very important indeed. He regards these as the first instruments for collecting information about the events of the world, which he tries to understand and to control. Then, to aid his senses, and to produce the special circumstances he sometimes wants to study, he must make use of a rich variety of other tools, instruments, machines, or contrivances.

Our senses are often unreliable and are subject to error. For example, we generally have little trouble in telling whether one thing happened before or after another, but we find that our estimates of how long before, or how long after, are unreliable. (Look at a clock, then look away for what you believe to be five minutes and see how well or badly you do.) If you had no clock outside your body, you could roughly measure the flow of time by counting your heartbeats. You would find, however, that the rate of your pulse changed from day to day, from morning to evening, and sometimes from minute to minute. Without a clock you might not detect these changes unless you compared your pulse with another person's. The two of you would not agree exactly in measuring time intervals, and then you might try to find something outside yourselves that would beat more steadily than your pulse.

An example of the process that we have been discussing is given in a well-known story. While watching a great lamp swinging from the ceiling of a cathedral, Galileo noticed that the lamp seemed to take about the same length of time to complete each swing. He guessed that he could use the lamp, or any other pendulum having a similar motion, as a good timing device. The extent of the swing, however, changed greatly from the wide arc with which it started to an almost imperceptible motion later. Could it really be that the rate of swinging did not depend on the length of this arc? Although Galileo knew that his pulse beat was not steady, he felt sure that its rate was steady enough during the relatively short time taken for the motion of the lamp to die down. He found that the same number of pulses marked each swing, regardless of the distance that the lamp traveled during the swing. This observation of Galileo's led to the idea that a pendulum kept swinging by a spring or a slowly falling weight would keep accurate time. Such clocks could be tested by starting two or more of them together and then seeing if they swung through equal numbers of beats in the same time. From such experiments grew the familiar pendulum clocks that are still nearly as accurate and reliable instruments as any that man can build.

This is the typical story of how a basic notion may be established. We begin with a rough, personal experience, like that of the heartbeat, and transfer it to an instrument which appears to behave more simply and reliably. Then we test the instrument, to see if it really works as we have guessed. So physics is built, going outward from our own experience, making a bold guess, which

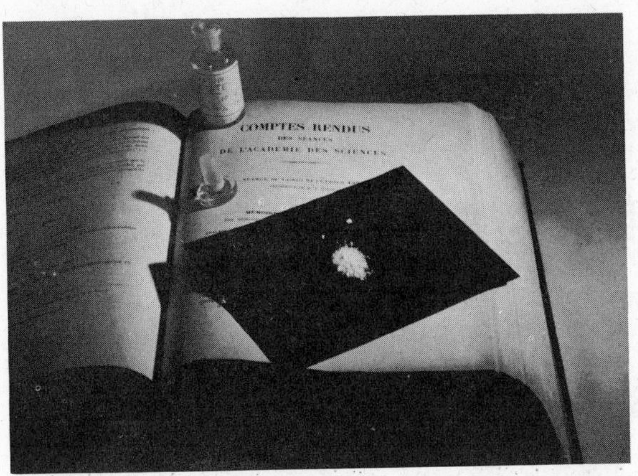

1–4 (a). In 1896, the French physical chemist Henri Becquerel discovered radioactivity by exposing a photographic plate to a uranium salt. The photographic plate was wrapped in black paper, and crystals of uranium acetate were laid on top.

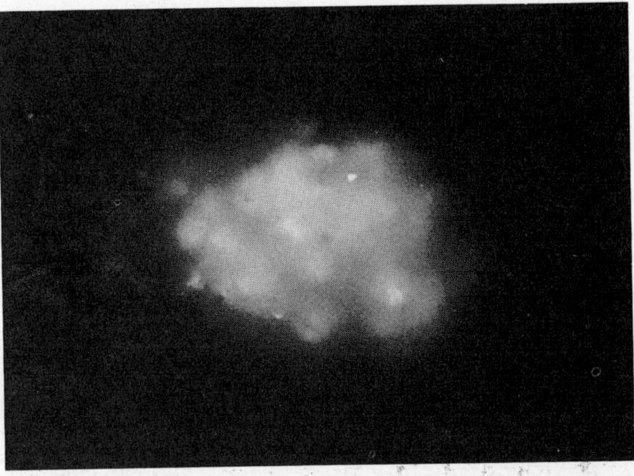

1–4 (b). The resulting exposure, like the one reproduced here, could only result from some invisible yet penetrating emanations from the salt, since light was never permitted to strike the photographic plate. Here is an example of a simple means used to obtain an important fundamental result.

is often a real step in the dark — Galileo could not be sure that the pendulum wasn't just matching his changing pulse — and then testing the guess by seeing what it must imply. In this way we have built microscopes which can make tiny atoms visible, and mammoth telescopes that plumb the depths of space.

The tools of physics may be simple. In 1896 Henri Becquerel discovered the strange radioactive properties of uranium, and began the branch called *nuclear physics,* with no other equipment than a photographic plate, wrapped in black paper, and a few crystals of a special chemical salt. In 1934 Fermi and his associates in Rome discovered the slow-neutron basis of atomic energy. They used simple apparatus — a hospital radium supply, a marble fountain basin of water, some pieces of silver and cadmium, and an instrument made of little pieces of thin metal leaf mounted on a small microscope. Following up the work of Fermi, five years later Hahn and Strassmann discovered the fission of uranium. They worked with simple chemical equipment and a commonplace Geiger counter. Who will next found a branch of science with simple equipment and a really good idea? We do not know, but it is bound to happen.

The tools of physics may become wonderfully complex. The instrument-filled satellite and its launching rockets can be thought of as the tools of the physicist who seeks to study the upper air and the rain of particles from outer space. To make an electron move through a spiral path such as is shown in the photograph in Fig. 1–6 (b) requires complex equipment. At the University of California Radiation Laboratory there is a huge ring-shaped magnet, weighing as much as a ship, and deriving its power from generators sufficient to supply the power needs of a small town. (Fig. 1–5.) Running through the magnet there is a tube, shaped like a tire, big enough so that a man could crawl around inside. Its rim is as far across as a basketball court. Because this chamber must be kept free of air, it contains a high vacuum like that inside a radio tube. The whole device is operated by a network of switches and tubes and meters, as complicated as a small telephone exchange. And for the picture itself, the big cameras must be focused on a tubful of liquid hydrogen, an extremely cold but intensely flammable liquid. [Fig. 1–6 (a).]

1–4. Who Builds Physics?

The people who design the kind of equipment you have been reading about are physicists. When their skills are primarily skills in designing and performing experiments, they are called experimental physicists. When, on the other hand, they are skilled primarily in the use of mathematics in the problems of physics, they are called theoretical physicists. Benjamin Franklin and Mme. Marie Curie were experimental physicists. Isaac Newton and Albert Einstein were theoretical physicists — perhaps the greatest.

1–5. The bevatron at the University of California Lawrence Radiation Laboratory is an example of a large and complex tool. The man in the lower right gives an idea of the dimensions of this giant accelerator. The huge ring-shaped magnet weighs as much as a ship and requires as much power as a small town. This large tool is used in obtaining evidence of the behavior of particles too small to be seen with any device so far developed by man. (Courtesy: University of California Lawrence Radiation Laboratory.)

In the earlier days, the tools, both experimental and mathematical, were so simple that a single man or woman could become skilled in the use of both kinds. Isaac Newton not only made the thrilling experiment of breaking sunlight into colors with a prism, but actually invented for his own use one of the most useful forms of mathematics, the calculus. Franklin contributed to electrical theory. Nowadays some of the tools are so complex that few physicists are versatile enough to become masters of all of them. But whether theorists or experimenters, the people who build physics are all physicists.

Physicists may be aided by engineers and by craftsmen of many sorts. All these — the physicists, engineers, and craftsmen — form a coordinated team. Clearly, no one man could have built, or even designed, the whole of a great modern laboratory like that at Berkeley. But the people who fix the purpose of the team are the physicists. The engineer finds his interest primarily in the design and operation of the instruments or machines or processes at hand. The physicist is interested in what he can find out by the use of these tools, whatever they are.

It will be clear that we have not given in this chapter a sharp, simple definition of what physics is. For physics grows and changes, just as what we know about the world, and what we can do with that knowledge, also changes. After you have finished this book, as you look back on what you have seen and learned and wondered at, you will have a much better view of what physics is than we could write in a chapter.

In the next few chapters we shall talk about time, space, motion, matter, and measurement. They are all related, and they are all essential to our discussion of physics. They form a foundation on which we will build — not something

1–6 (a). Here again is a very complex instrument to extend our senses. This liquid-hydrogen bubble chamber in conjunction with a source of high energy electrons (like the bevatron in Fig. 1–5) was used to obtain the picture of an electron helix shown in Fig. 1–6 (b). (Courtesy: University of California Lawrence Radiation Laboratory.)

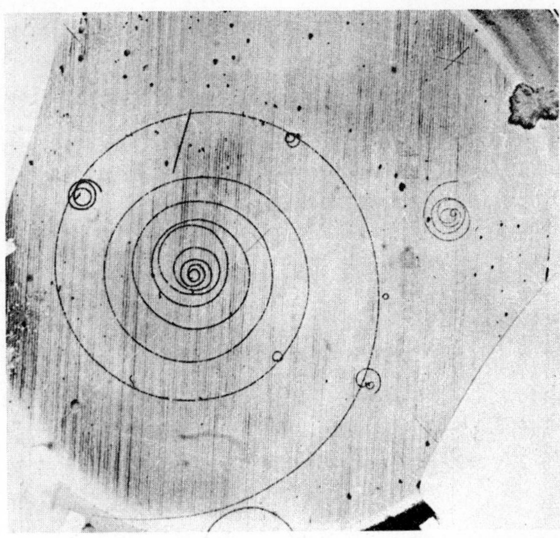

1–6 (b). The electron leaves a visible track as it passes through the liquid hydrogen, much as a jet airplane leaves a vapor trail in air at high altitudes.

we can study and then forget. Furthermore, what we say in the next few chapters is only a beginning; and the ideas we talk about will become clearer as we use them throughout the rest of the book. We shall see new meaning in them later on. This is particularly true of the ideas we have expressed in this introductory chapter. As you go further into physics, you should be prepared to look back at these early chapters from time to time later on.

Most of the people who study the fundamentals of physics do not go on to become physicists. Some will go on in physics or related work, in engineering or in other sciences. Whether you go on or not, you can find in the story of nature, as physicists see it, a good deal that will help you understand the changing world in which we all live. For physics lies behind the headlines, behind the gadgets that create the new jobs, and behind the new problems every citizen has to face. In studying this growing subject, one of the most significant in the history of man, you will have a chance to nourish that curiosity about the world which marks us humans off so sharply from the other animals, that wonderful feeling of *wanting to know*, which can be a deep satisfaction throughout a whole lifetime.

FURTHER READING

ANDRADE, E. N. DA C., *Sir Isaac Newton*. Doubleday Anchor Books, 1958.

CURIE, EVE, *Madame Curie*. Doubleday, 1949.

FERMI, LAURA, *Atoms in the Family*. University of Chicago Press, 1954. An account of Enrico Fermi's life and work.

FRANKLIN, BENJAMIN, *Autobiography*. Pocket Books.

GAMOW, GEORGE, *The Birth and Death of the Sun*. Mentor Books. (Chapter III: The Transmutation of Elements, Becquerel.)

HEATHCOTE, N. H. DE V., *Nobel Prize Winners in Physics*. Henry Schuman Co., 1953. Biographical sketch and summary of the prize-winning work of each.

JEANS, JAMES, *The Growth of Physical Science*. Cambridge University Press, 1951. (Galileo, pp. 145–150, 171–178. Newton, pp. 183–196, 204–210, 225–227. Einstein, pp. 293–301.)

TAYLOR, F. SHERWOOD, *A Short History of Science and Scientific Thought*. Norton, 1949.

TIME AND MEASUREMENT

CHAPTER 2

2–1. The Starting Point — the Senses

The most universal physical instruments are built into our bodies. Through our eyes we get most of our information about the world. Nearly as important are our ears, which bring us sounds. Then there are the various impressions of touch. These include the very delicate touch of our fingertips on which we rely for texture, the muscular senses of pushing and pulling, by which we form the impressions of weight and solidity, the feel of hot and cold, and our inner sense of balance. Smell and taste — more important to chemistry than to physics — are also important sources of what we know about the outside world. These tools, which continually bring information to us, are, as you know, called the *senses*. Moreover, we not only passively sense the world, but with our hands and back and legs we handle and move some parts of it.

It is true that no one has to manufacture or buy his eyes or his ears, but their use is not entirely given to us at birth. We all had to train ourselves to use them. We all had to learn to interpret the images we see and the sounds we hear, to learn that the little patch down the street is the school building, big as life when we get near it. As babies we spent much of our time learning these things. We cannot remember how hard it was, just as we cannot remember learning to talk.

The senses can be deceived. Optical illusions are familiar. Perhaps the most common one forms the basis of the "movies." If you examine a strip of movie film, you will see that it bears a sequence of slightly differing still pictures. Run them by fast enough, and the eye will blend them into a smooth succession, which we recognize as motion. Your sense of temperature can also be fooled: if you hold one hand in a pan of hot water and the other in cold water and then put both hands simultaneously into a pan of lukewarm water, the "cold" hand will feel hot, and the "hot" hand will feel cold. (If you haven't tried this, try it.)

Like the senses, all the other instruments of the physicist can be deceived — even the most accurate and sensitive, such as delicate balances, electronic meters, and timing devices. They all have their limitations. Testing the readings of his instruments, like questioning the first impression of the senses, is part of the cross-checking which has to go into every conclusion made by the physicist. But this careful cross-checking gives him confidence in his instruments, just as our sense of touch can be a valuable cross-check to confirm what we see with our eyes.

2–2. The Key Concepts of Physics; the Need to Extend the Senses

Let us consider a few of the most basic notions of physics, *time* and *space*, and their combination in what we call *motion* and *matter*. No doubt we gain our first impressions of these through our senses. But it is pretty clear that in order to learn all that we want to know about time, space, and matter we must extend and sharpen our sense impressions by the use of other tools.

Consider first what we call *time.* Lying in bed, running down the hall, riding in a plane, we are always aware (if we are aware of anything) of the passage of time. We all have a measure of time built into us: the heartbeat. About once a second — sometimes slower, sometimes faster — it beats for our whole lifetime. We have other measures of time, too, which we all know. The sun marks day and night. The four seasons pass, and we all hope to see a few hundred of them come and go. Much longer than that, or much shorter than a heartbeat, or the blink of an eye, we cannot directly grasp. But certainly time extends far beyond these bounds — back to before we were born, ahead to after we die — and for moments too fleeting for us to capture. Our parents recall what we cannot; the historians tell us more than that; big trees go back centuries; and we do not doubt that the hills and the rocks themselves are far older. All these things are beyond the direct grasp of our personal time sense.

A second important notion in physics is *distance,* or *space.* We can pace off a mile, with a little effort. We can span a short distance with our fingers, or with our extended arms. We can even hold our fingertips close together to show a hairsbreadth of space between them, but it is hard to measure off less. How can we measure distances greater than we can pace off or smaller than we can feel? As we shall see, the measurement of extremely short and extremely long distances is important for understanding the way the world works. To gain this understanding, physicists have developed methods of measuring the distance to the planets and the stars, and the means of measuring the size of atoms.

The third key notion is substance or material, or *matter* as it is more commonly called. It is one of the main successes of physics in our times that we have learned a great deal about the inner nature of matter. We have learned that all the differing materials — skin, bone, blood, rock, steel, nylon, air, even the sun — are composed of the same tiny building blocks, the atoms. Their combinations "spell out" the nature of the complex world in which we live, and even the nature of our bodies. Just as a couple of dozen letters of the alphabet make up all the books that have ever been written in the English language, so the combination of a few building blocks makes up all matter with its great variety. We did not discover these atoms by the direct use of our senses. They are far too small for us to see in everyday experience. We learned of their existence by extending our senses, using the ideas and techniques of physics and chemistry.

Here we have not sharply defined space, time, and matter. These fundamental concepts are familiar enough to everyone, and yet they are hard to define. The main point is that we take these three key concepts from everyday experience. We establish them by the use of our own built-in detecting devices — eyes, muscles, and so on. For example, we sense big pieces of matter: mountains, perhaps a stretch of ocean; and small ones: down, it may be, to the fine grains that make up white flour, or the motes of dust that we see in a sunbeam.

It is our first job to find how we can go beyond these ordinary experiences. We must find out how to talk in an orderly fashion about things far away from the familiar experience of everyday life. Doing this will bring us into the heart of the subject.

2–3. Time and Its Sweep

Close your eyes for a short time. Then open them while you count "one, two, three." Close them again. Now what did you see while your eyes were open? If you were in a normal room, not much happened. Things appeared unchanging. But if you sat for a few hours with your eyes open you would find people going in and out, shifting chairs, opening windows. The whole activity of the things in the room appears to depend on the time interval over which you watch. Watch for a year, and the plant in its pot will grow up, flower, and wither.

Keep the experiment going, at least in thought. Watch for a hundred years, and the building may have come down about you. A thousand years? No American town has lasted for a thousand years, except possibly for the Pueblo Indian villages of the Southwest. Ten thousand years? In that time the Niagara River will have cut away the rock, and the falls will have receded far upstream. In a million years much of the American landscape will be unfamiliar. (Fig. 2–1.)

2–1. Niagara Falls illustrates the slow changes that time brings to the face of our world. The dotted line in the photograph shows the shape of the American Fall before a slide carried away about 15,000 tons of rock from its lip in 1954. This process, continuing over long periods of time, has caused the falls to move miles upstream to their present location, and in 10,000 more years will carry them far beyond in the direction of Lake Erie. (United Press Photo.)

We can try now to go from long time intervals to short ones. Imagine the same room, but now open your eyes for briefer and briefer times — "quick as a wink," as the saying goes. Of course, this is exactly what a camera does. Now that blur over there where the electric fan is whirring stands still, and sharpens into a set of four fan blades. A little faster, and the wings of a fly, which you cannot see normally even as a blur, will also appear clearly. At this stage your eye — or its camera-shutter stand-in — is opening for only a few thousandths of a second.

2–4. Time Intervals, Long and Short; Multiple-Flash

Of course, you cannot blink your eyes fast enough to notice the effects mentioned in the last section. However, the shutter of a motion-picture camera can be opened and closed very rapidly. For ordinary movies the camera exposes either sixteen or twenty-four frames (individual pictures) in each second, and the pictures are shown on a screen at the same rate. (Fig. 2–2.) These rates were chosen because our eyes actually retain images for a time somewhat longer than a twentieth of a second. This retention is called *persistence of vision* and is responsible for the appearance of smooth, continuous motion we see in a movie.

In many instances the entire motion that we want to photograph takes place while an ordinary motion-picture camera shutter is open for just one frame. To photograph such motions we often use a more refined technique — the multiple-flash — which enables us to measure very short time intervals. Here, instead of opening and closing a camera shutter, we turn on brief, intense flashes of light at regular intervals in a darkened room. A camera, with its shutter open, then takes pictures only when the light flashes. Repeated flashes produce a sequence of pictures which is recorded on the camera film. Since the time between successive flashes is known, examination of the series of still pictures thus obtained enables us to determine the time interval of the action photographed.

For example, Fig. 2–3 shows a series of thirteen pictures of a bullet as it punctures a toy balloon. In this case the time between successive flashes was $\frac{1}{4000}$ sec; therefore, the total time elapsed between the first and last pictures is $\frac{12}{4000} = \frac{3}{1000}$ sec. Also, by examining the third, fourth, and fifth pictures, you can see that it took the bullet less than $\frac{1}{2000}$ of a second to enter and leave the balloon. Thus, from these flash pictures we get two physical measurements — the time interval for the bullet to pass through the balloon and the time interval for the balloon to collapse. Neither of these measurements could possibly have been made without a method of extending our senses.

With multiple-flash photography, we can make pictures of many rapidly moving objects — familiar things from raindrops to machine parts, baseballs, and bullets. We can also take pictures of things that we may want to measure as part of our investigation in physics. In this book you will find many examples of the use of the flash technique to study motion. This technique, and a similar technique that you will develop in laboratory, will be among our most important tools. It is not necessary to take each successive flash picture on a separate frame. We can make a multiple exposure at equal time intervals on one piece of film. See Fig. 6–19 for an example.

Taking photographs at regular time intervals not only allows us to analyze motions that would otherwise be mere blurs to our eyes; it also allows us to see these motions slowed down. For example, frames taken at a rate of 4000 per second may be shown at a rate of 24 per second. We use this technique in reverse to study motions which take place slowly. The growth of a flower, the motion of the tides, and the movement of a glacier are all motions that span long time intervals. These intervals are so long that normally we get no feeling of motion by direct observation.

2–2. Producing the effect of motion with still pictures. These five photographs were taken with a 35-mm motion-picture camera at the rate of 24 pictures, or frames, a second. The holes at the left of the strip are sprocket holes by which the film is pulled past the lens in a series of jerks. Note the changing position of the diver from frame to frame. All the action took place in $\frac{1}{6}$ sec. When the film is projected, we actually see a series of still pictures in rapid succession. However, because the eye retains a given image for a fraction of a second, we get the impression of motion.

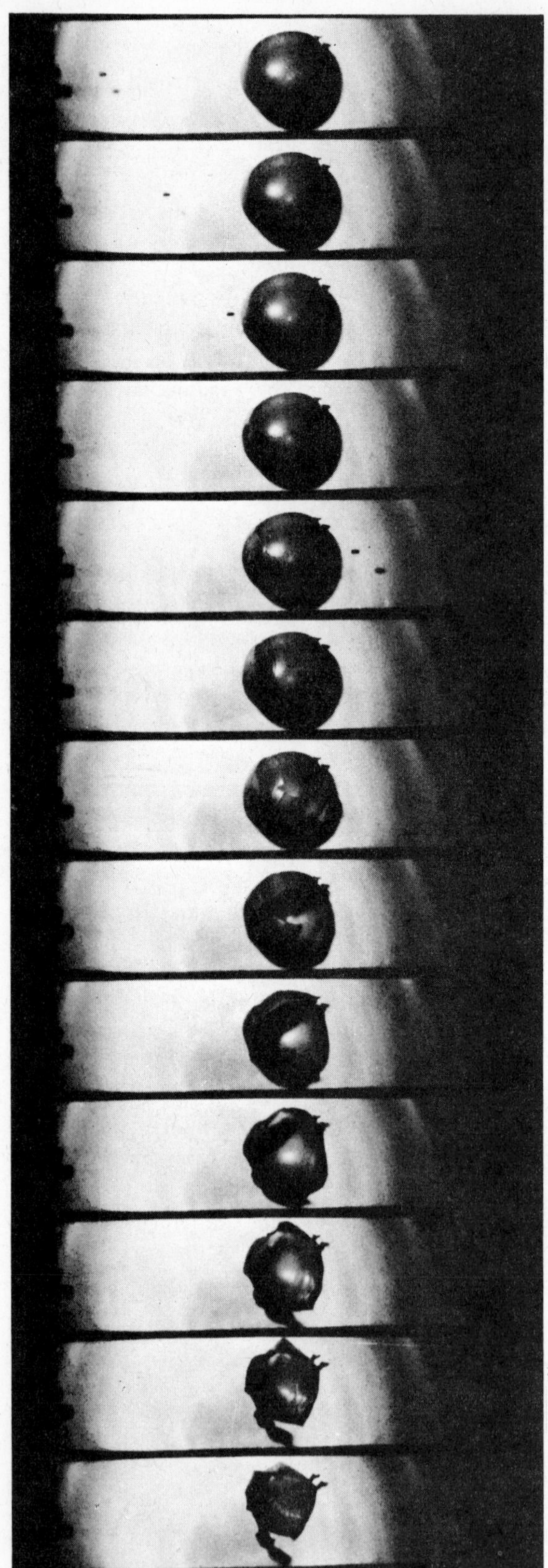

2–4. This high-speed photograph shows a .30-cal bullet as it smashes into a light bulb. The duration of the flash was less than one-millionth second. Note the rifling marks on the body of the bullet as well as the cracking of the glass. (Courtesy: Harold E. Edgerton.)

To allow us to observe these motions as a whole, we use time-lapse photography. In this case, a photograph is taken of a blossoming flower say, every hour. This series of photographs is then projected on a screen at the normal projection rate. We thus see in minutes a motion that may have happened in days.

In discussing multiple-flash photography we have talked only about the time intervals between flashes. You have probably realized that each individual flash must last for a very short period of time. We can often learn a great deal from a picture made with a single flash such as that of Figs. 2–4 and 2–5. Because of the brief duration of the flash, the motion, in each case, appears "frozen." Figure 2–6 is a photograph of the laboratory where these high-speed pictures were made.

2–3. These pictures taken at a rate of 4,000 a second show a bullet as it punctures a toy balloon. A total time of $\frac{3}{1000}$ sec elapsed between the first and last pictures. Note the slow rate at which the balloon collapses when compared with the speed of the bullet, which is out of the frame of the picture in less than $\frac{1}{1000}$ sec after it punctures and leaves the other side of the balloon. (Courtesy: Harold E. Edgerton.)

2–5. The human eye is not fast enough to catch the rapid motions (60 a second) of a hummingbird's wings. In this high-speed photograph, taken with a flash stroboscope, the flash lasted only $\frac{1}{100,000}$ sec. Therefore we see the wings apparently motionless. A motion picture, taken at the usual 24 frames a second, would show only blurred images of the wings. (Courtesy: Harold E. Edgerton.)

2–6. This apparatus was used to make the high-speed photographs of the bursting balloon shown in Fig. 2–3. From left to right, note the gun, balloon, strobe light (under balloon), electronic timer, and camera. (Courtesy: Harold E. Edgerton.)

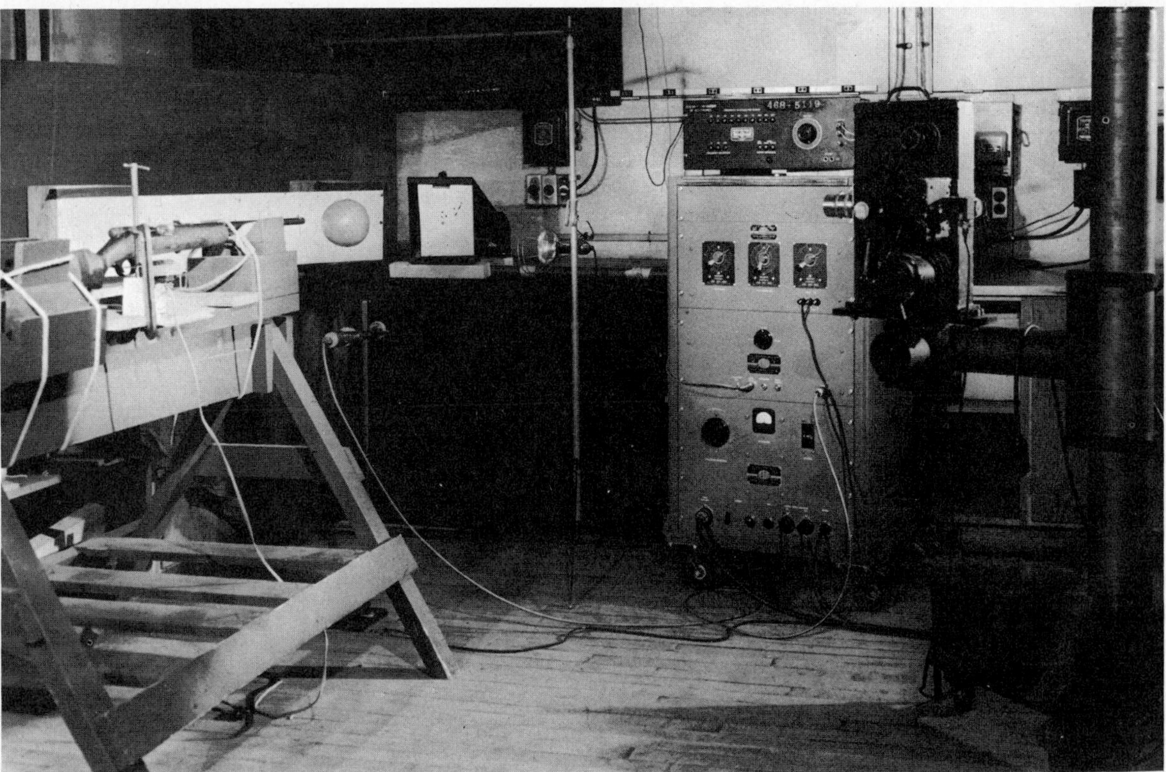

2–5. The Stroboscope

The blades of an electric fan and the clapper of an electric bell both exhibit a motion that repeats over and over in exactly the same way. You can measure the short time intervals involved in these motions by a simpler method than multiple-flash photography. For this purpose we use a stroboscope. One form of this instrument is shown in the Laboratory Guide. It consists of a large disc with slits spaced at equal intervals around the circumference.

To see how this device allows us to measure short time intervals, consider first a disc stroboscope with only one slit. We can use this one-slit stroboscope to measure the time it takes the turntable of a record player to go through one rotation. First we mark the turntable with an arrow and let the record player settle down to its steady motion. Then we set the stroboscope spinning and look through the slit as shown in Fig. 2–7. Each time the slit passes we get a glimpse of the turntable.

Now suppose that we spin the stroboscope so that the slit goes all the way around in exactly the time of rotation of the turntable. Then, each time that we can see through the slit the arrow on the turntable will be in the same position. It will appear to stand still even though it is really rotating. In this instance, then, the time for one rotation of the stroboscope measures the time for one rotation of the turntable. On the other hand, if the stroboscope spins faster than the turntable, the arrow on the turntable will not get all the way around between glimpses, so it will not seem to stand still. Also, if the stroboscope goes too slowly, the arrow will move around by more than one rotation between glimpses; so again it will appear to move. Consequently, by adjusting the speed of the stroboscope to make the arrow stand still, we automatically set the times of rotation equal; and we can use the stroboscope speed — at our control — to measure an unknown time of rotation.

The stroboscope can be used to measure the time for one rotation of an object that is turning too fast for this time to be measured directly. If the disc has twelve equally spaced viewing slits then the viewer gets twelve glimpses for each rotation of the disc. This means that a stroboscope with many slits can measure a time interval much shorter than the disc's rotation time — as many times shorter as there are equally spaced slits in the disc.

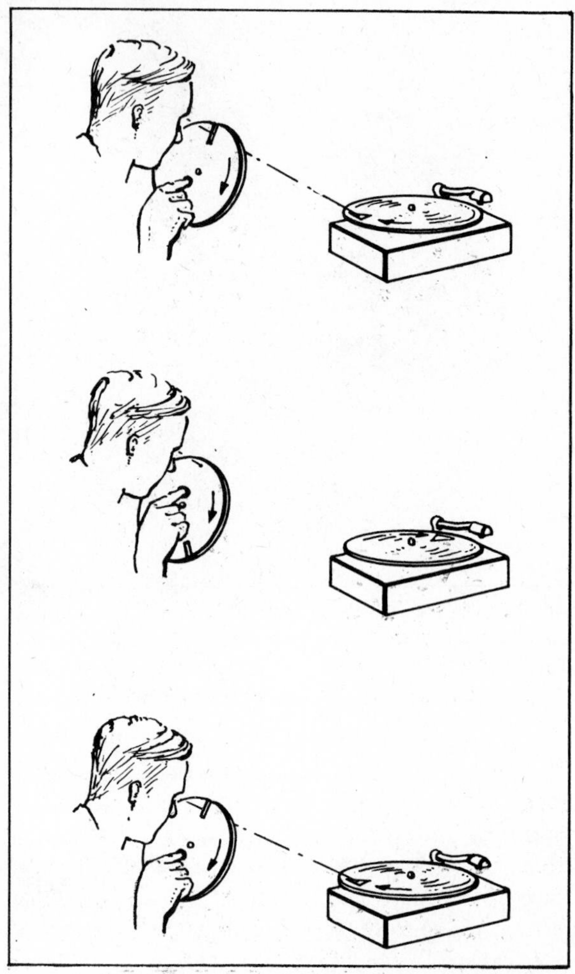

2–7. The principle of the stroboscope. When the disc in front of the observer's eye is rotating at the same rate as the turntable, the observer will see the arrow only when it is in a particular position. The motion is then "stopped." What are the limitations of this device?

As an example, suppose we use the stroboscope to watch a small ball being whirled around on the end of a short string. We find that the ball appears to stop when the disc makes one rotation every two seconds. If our instrument has ten slits, then in 2 seconds we get ten glimpses — the time between glimpses is $\frac{1}{5}$ sec. Since the ball appears stopped at each glimpse, the time for one rotation of the ball is $\frac{1}{5}$ sec.

A stroboscope, like any other instrument, has its limitations. If the disc is spinning too fast or the slits are too numerous and small, so little light may pass through the slit that you cannot see.

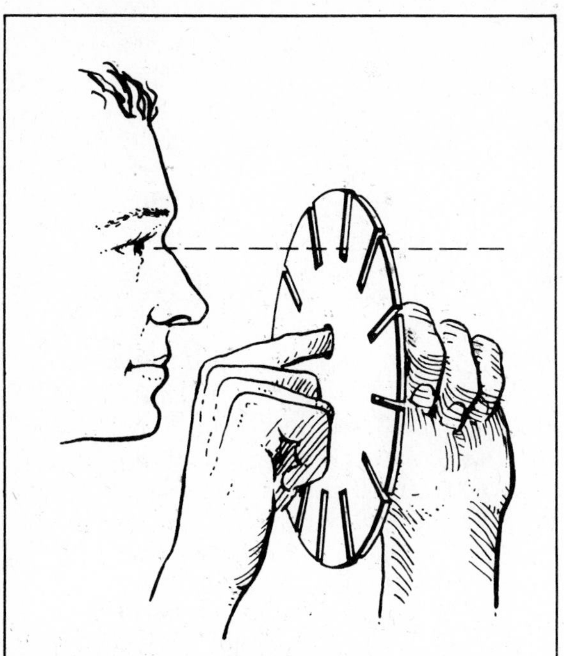

2–8. Using a hand stroboscope. With twelve slits you can measure a time interval one twelfth of the time of one rotation of the disc.

There is a kind of confusion possible, too. Consider our example of the one-slit stroboscope "stopping" the motion of a record-player turntable. Since the turntable appeared at the same place each time we could see it, we assumed that its time for one rotation was equal to that of the disc. There are, however, other possibilities. The turntable could have gone around two, three, four . . . times during one rotation of the stroboscope; and we still would have observed the same effect. How can we be sure that we really see the turntable on successive rotations? This problem occurs quite frequently when using a stroboscope, but there is a simple way to get around it. When you have the motion stopped, simply increase the speed of the stroboscope. The motion may or may not appear to be stopped again at some higher speed. If it does not, then you know that the original speed of rotation of the stroboscope was the correct one. If it does, then continue increasing the speed of the stroboscope until you can no longer stop the motion. The highest speed of the stroboscope which stops the motion will give the time of rotation of the turntable.

2–6. Comparing Times; Counting Units

One of the physicist's big tasks is to find a way to talk clearly about all these time intervals. He must be able to compare them, to use them, to predict them, however large or small they may be. He needs a measure.

The measurement of time is familiar to everyone. We all know about the second, the day, week, month, year, century. All of these are built on a single simple principle: counting. The part of mathematics most important in physics is counting. To measure time intervals, physicists simply count off seconds.* Every time interval can be expressed as so many seconds. It is sometimes convenient to use days, just as it is sometimes convenient to count by dozens instead of by ones. A day is shorthand for 86,400 seconds. For time intervals shorter than one second we have to count by fractions of a second. The physicist uses decimal fractions, like tenths, hundredths, thousandths, and so on.

All of our time counts are in terms of seconds. What is a second and why was it chosen? There is no particular reason for the choice. It is completely arbitrary. We might as well have chosen a time unit twice as long, or half as long. It would have worked just as well. There is no natural division of time known to us that would apply throughout the universe. Perhaps the second is convenient because it is not very far from the interval between heartbeats. This is not fundamental, however. What is important is that a unit be clearly defined and easily reproduced so that it is available to everybody.

A second is approximately defined as the time between "ticks" on a clock which makes 86,400 ticks while the sun moves from its noon position on one day to its noon position the next day. From measurements of the sun's motion, astronomers can calculate with great accuracy just when it crosses the highest point in its journey, and from that they fix the time. Because the sun moves at somewhat different speeds across the sky during the year, an average is taken over all days, and this average defines the second.

The earth is ever changing. Earthquakes, floods, eruptions, freezing, and melting take

*A "minute" is a tiny part of an hour; $\frac{1}{60}$ of a minute is a kind of minute of a minute. In old time it was called a *second minute*. We have shortened our speech, and call it just a "second."

place. Even the earth's rotation, which causes the apparent motion of the sun in the sky, is not really unchanging. We know it changes a little, because some very good clocks agree among themselves better than any of them agree with the observations of the sun. Therefore the physicist usually defines the second by the careful maintenance and cross-checking of the best observatory clocks. Any laboratory time measurement must in the end be referred to them if high accuracy is needed.

Just what makes a clock keep accurate time is a very hard and deep question. This is not simply a matter of the complicated works you see in an ordinary watch or clock. It is rather what you mean by time itself. Let us be satisfied with the idea that very carefully protected beating pendulums, or the newer electronic clocks which depend on the vibrations of a thin slab of quartz crystal, all count off accurate time. If they are compared over years and years, they agree with one another with high precision all over the world. Still newer ones, using as vibrators certain atomic vibrations themselves, are now being built. No one knows if there may not be some slight differences among all these means of marking time. We know that so far there have been none big enough to notice. One of the tasks of future physics is to press this question further.

Time measurement gives rise to what appear to be two different questions: "How long did it take?" and "When was it?" The first question we answer by giving a time interval: "The race took four minutes." The second question is answered by a statement such as "The race started at five o'clock yesterday afternoon." For the first measurement, a stop watch is good enough; it ticks off, starting at zero, and measures the length of a time *interval.* In the second case, the reading on a correct clock is needed. But this is really much the same thing, for a clock simply measures the interval from some arbitrary starting time, say midnight. The exact date is just another interval of time, measured from an agreed fixed point of time, say New Year's, while we count the years themselves from A.D. 1. In both kinds of question, a time interval must be stated in the answer. In the answer to "when," however, one end of the interval must be agreed upon. In physics, we most often need to answer the question "How long does it take?" because the things we talk about happen over and over. But if you want to catch a train on a particular day, you also need to know when the time count begins. The problems of standard and daylight time, of time zones, and so on, are really problems of agreeing on such a starting time. Once you agree on a starting time, the questions are really the same. We must measure an interval.

2–7. Times Large and Small — Orders of Magnitude

The span of time since the first animals came to live on dry land includes something like 12,000,000,000,000,000 seconds. The time it takes a light ray to pass through a windowpane is about 1/100,000,000,000 part of a second. Such numbers are impossibly clumsy to learn or to use. But since we must be prepared to use large and small numbers, large and small counts, throughout physics, we must find a way to handle them.

There is an easy, compact way. Any number can be written as the product of a number between one and ten and a number which is a power of ten. For example, we can write 769 as 7.69×100; and 0.0043 is $4.3 \times \frac{1}{1000}$. The number at the beginning of this section is $1.2 \times 10{,}000{,}000{,}000{,}000{,}000$. We shall usually write our numbers this way, but in order to avoid writing zeros till our hands hurt, we shall use an abbreviation. Instead of 100 we write 10^2; in place of $\frac{1}{1000}$, which equals $\frac{1}{10^3}$, we write 10^{-3}, and in place of the long one we write 1.2×10^{16}. The exponent, at the upper right of the 10, tells how many zeros in the power of ten, and we use the minus sign to say that we deal with thousandths instead of with thousands.

A few more examples should make the system clear:

$$3270 = 3.27 \times 10^3.$$
$$0.124 = 1.24 \times 10^{-1}.$$
$$652{,}000 = 6.52 \times 10^5.$$

We also have a standard way of reading these numbers: "Three point two seven times ten to the third," "one point two four times ten to the minus one," "six point five two times ten to the fifth," etc. The big *plus* powers of ten indicate huge numbers and the big *minus* powers of ten indicate tiny numbers. The time since land animals came into being is then about 10^{16} seconds; the time for light to penetrate a windowpane is 10^{-11} second. Scientists make frequent use of this notation, as it offers a convenient method of communication. You should get used to it very early in your work.

Now, multiplying and dividing the powers of ten is easy. You simply add or subtract the exponents. For example, the time required for light to pass through ten thousand thicknesses of glass would be the time to pass through one pane (10^{-11} sec) multiplied by the number of panes (10^4), or

$$t = 10^{-11} \text{ sec} \times 10^4 = 10^{(-11+4)} \text{ sec} = 10^{-7} \text{ sec}.$$

Positive and negative exponents will be freely used in this book. If the methods for handling them are unfamiliar to you, practice on the last few problems at the end of this chapter. You can make up more problems yourself.

We do not always deal with round numbers, like 10^{11}. Suppose you have numbers like 172 and 32,500. These can be written as 1.72×10^2 and 3.25×10^4. Then multiplication and division can be carried out separately for the powers of ten and for the numbers between unity and ten which stand before them. For example, when we multiply these two numbers we get

$$1.72 \times 10^2 \times 3.25 \times 10^4 = 1.72 \times 3.25 \times 10^2 \times 10^4 = 5.59 \times 10^6.$$

If we divide the first of these numbers into the second, we have

$$\frac{3.25 \times 10^4}{1.72 \times 10^2} = \frac{3.25}{1.72} \times \frac{10^4}{10^2} = 1.89 \times 10^2.$$

As another example, 1.36×10^3 multiplied by 2.00×10^{-5} is

$$1.36 \times 2.00 \times 10^3 \times 10^{-5} = 2.72 \times 10^{-2},$$

and similarly

$$\frac{1.36 \times 10^3}{2.00 \times 10^{-5}} = 0.68 \times 10^8 = 6.8 \times 10^7.$$

This way of writing numbers is very convenient for multiplication and division, but be careful with addition and subtraction. Suppose you want to add

$$1.20 \times 10^2$$
$$\text{and } 5.63 \times 10^3.$$

Both numbers must be expressed with the *same* power of ten before addition. Thus

$$1.20 \times 10^2 = 0.12 \times 10^3.$$

Therefore, we write

$$0.12 \times 10^3 + 5.63 \times 10^3 = (0.12 + 5.63) \times 10^3 = 5.75 \times 10^3.$$

Notice that when you add two numbers, the answer is always close to the number with the larger power of ten. For example, $10^{11} + 10^2$ is very nearly 10^{11} and not at all close to 10^{13}!

This way of writing numbers makes it easy to determine what is called the *order of magnitude*. The order of magnitude is the power of ten closest to the number. This is, of course, an approximate statement about the number. It serves to put you "in the right ballpark." So we can say that the order of magnitude of 137 is 10^2; that is, 137 is closer to 100 than it is to 1,000. Similarly, the order of magnitude of 0.00262 is 10^{-3}; that is, 0.00262 is closer to 10^{-3} than it is to 10^{-2} or 10^{-4}. Estimating by rounding off to orders of magnitude is one of the most helpful ways to begin any computation in physics. Sometimes it is good enough for the entire purpose you have in mind. In our work we shall use this technique frequently; and you should become familiar with it now. However, we do not always use power-of-ten notation. For example, to write the speed of a plane as 455 mi/hr, or the time for a certain trip as 0.2 hr is often more convenient than 4.55×10^2 mi/hr and 2×10^{-1} hr. The choice of what notation to use is a matter of convenience.

Table 1 gives us the order of magnitude of the time duration of many things. Many of these intervals are somewhat variable — the human life span or the time for light to cross different rooms, for example. Consequently, it would not make sense to specify them precisely. Giving their orders of magnitude as we have done in the table is appropriate. Furthermore, the table shows an enormous range of time intervals, the longest a billion billion seconds and the shortest less than a billionth of a billionth of a second. To compare such widely different intervals it is convenient to compare orders of magnitude. For example, we see from the table that a day is eight orders of magnitude greater than (that is, 10^8 times as long as) the time for a fly to make one wing-beat.

Table 1. Orders of Magnitude of Times

Each interval is one-tenth of the preceding interval.

Time Interval in Seconds	Associated Event
10^{18}	Expected total life of the sun as a normal star
10^{17}	Age of the oldest rocks
	Time elapsed since first fossil life
	Time elapsed since first land life
10^{16}	Time for the sun to revolve around the galaxy
	Age of the Appalachian Mountains
10^{15}	Time elapsed since dinosaurs
10^{14}	Remaining life of Niagara Falls
10^{13}	Time elapsed since earliest men
10^{12}	
10^{11}	Time elapsed since earliest agriculture
	Time elapsed since earliest writing
	Time elapsed since the beginning of the Christian Era
10^{10}	Time elapsed since the discovery of America
10^{9}	Human life span
10^{8}	Time elapsed since you began school
10^{7}	Time for the earth to revolve around the sun (year)
10^{6}	One month
10^{5}	Time for the earth to rotate once on its axis (day)
10^{4}	Duration of average baseball game
10^{3}	Time for light from the sun to reach the earth
10^{2}	One minute
10^{1}	
10^{0}	Time between heartbeats (1 second)
10^{-1}	Time for bullet (.30 caliber) to cover the length of a football field (300 ft)
10^{-2}	Time for electric fan to complete one turn
10^{-3}	Time for fly to beat its wings once
	Time that a fired bullet is in the barrel of a rifle
10^{-4}	Time for one vibration of the highest-pitched audible sound
10^{-5}	Time during which firecracker is exploding
10^{-6}	Time for high-speed bullet to cross a letter of type
10^{-7}	Time for electron beam to go from source to screen in TV tube
10^{-8}	Time for light to cross a room
10^{-9}	Time during which an atom emits visible light
10^{-10}	
10^{-11}	Time for light to penetrate window-pane
10^{-12}	Time for air molecule to spin once
10^{-13}	
10^{-14}	
10^{-15}	Time for electron to revolve around proton in hydrogen atom
10^{-16}	
10^{-17}	
10^{-18}	
10^{-19}	
10^{-20}	Time for innermost electron to revolve around nucleus in heaviest atom
10^{-21}	
10^{-22}	Time for proton to revolve once in nucleus

Notice that our own personal experience of time covers about ten orders of magnitude, from about 10^{-1} second, the smallest interval we can comprehend directly, to some 10^{9} seconds, our life span. Another two orders of magnitude to 10^{11} seconds includes all we can learn from history, which is only a few hundred generations old. Beyond that, we must devise special indirect methods to fix times. For example, from the kind of fossils we find in a geological formation we can learn something about the age of the formation, and from the order in which fossil-bearing rock was laid down we learn about the evolutionary sequence. To go back still further we must build intricate instruments and learn to interpret their readings. In this manner, for example, we can measure the age of the earth by methods that depend upon the laws of radioactivity. See, for example, the book by Patrick Hurley mentioned in the reading references at the end of the chapter.

For very short times, below direct perception, about three or four orders of magnitude to 10^{-5} second cover the ordinary motions and changes of the fastest-moving things men can make, even explosions. For still smaller orders of magnitude, we can use the much more responsive electrons as the "parts" of a clock and go to time intervals as short as 10^{-10} second. Below that, all the way down to the shortest time intervals which are of physical interest — more than ten orders of magnitude beyond the reach even of electronics — we are in the realm of the atom. Here indirect arguments alone give us the time intervals that enable us to conjecture about what is going on in these tiny and swiftly changing parts of the world around us. To tell how all these time intervals are detected, and how the world appears when regarded not with our senses alone, but with instruments which allow us to split seconds — these are among the main goals of this book.

We have not stopped in either direction in measuring time. We continue to press outward from our senses, both to the very slow and to the incredibly quick. And as we do, we learn more and more about the world.

2–8. The Direction of Time

Our whole lives hinge on the difference between past and future. Time moves on relentlessly. We easily recall the past but we can hardly predict the future, except for a short time in advance. Time seems to have a natural direction. How this direction arises is a very deep and difficult question. We shall not try to settle it. Nevertheless, it is worth noting that we can predict eclipses of the sun for thousands of years in the future. And in the same way, we can "predict" that on some date in the past an eclipse was visible in such and such a place. A search of the historical records usually confirms our mathematical conclusions. For example, we have dated by astronomical calculations the documents and monuments of peoples like the Mayans of Central America who had excellent calendars, but whose starting point for time reckoning was originally unknown to us.

The difference between past and future is not really important in astronomical calculations. The solar system, regarded simply as a big, moving machine which takes up one position after another, would run just as well "backward" as "forward." However, the distinction between past and future is important in the lives of men and women. Apparently, "time's arrow" is to be found in complicated phenomena, like people or plants where birth comes first and death last and the process of life never runs in reverse.

FOR HOME, DESK, AND LAB

Note: Items marked * are projects to be done at home.

1. Compare the apparent heights of columns 1, 2, and 3 in Fig. 2–9. What is the actual relationship of heights? Did you use a device to check up on your senses?

2. Check your time sense by trying to estimate when an interval of $\frac{1}{2}$, 1, or 3 minutes has elapsed.
   (a) Record your error in each case.
   (b) Are the errors appreciably different fractions of the time intervals involved?

3. Since it is difficult to see a watch in a photographic darkroom, some photographers have learned to measure time in seconds by counting at their normal conversational rate but interspersing a long word between numbers, as "Mississippi one, Mississippi two, Mississippi three . . ." Try this method and compare its accuracy with that of Question 2.

4. * Make a pendulum from a piece of string and a small weight. Adjust the length until it takes one second to make a complete swing to and fro. How great is the error of your pendulum over a one-minute period? What fraction of the total time is the error?

5. * A project for a homemade timepiece. Galileo performed some of the first important experiments with the motion of falling bodies before the days of accurate clocks. To measure the short time intervals involved in his experiments, he used a simple clock that you can make for yourself. In the bottom of a tin can, punch a small hole with a nail. Keep the can nearly full of water and measure the amount of water that falls out in 10, 20, and 30 seconds. In this way you can learn to read the clock in seconds.

   What are the major sources of error in this device? Can you reduce the errors? Remember Galileo used a clock like this in discovering some of the major principles of physics. (See "Two New Sciences" by Galileo.)

6. * Galileo, in observing the swinging of a cathedral lamp, "found that the same number of his pulse beats marked each swing regardless of the distance the lamp traveled during each swing." Check on the correctness of this statement by constructing and timing a simple pendulum. If you find difficulty in counting your pulse beats and pendulum swings at the same time, try working with a partner or using a watch (which Galileo did not have available).

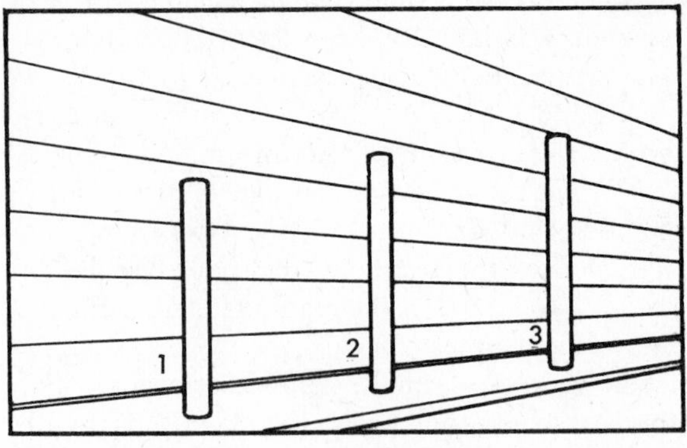

2–9. For Problem 1.

7. How many times per second should a light flash to show images 10 inches apart of a projectile traveling 1000 yards per second?

8. A study of the entire series of pictures of which the strip in Fig. 2–3 is only a part would show that the balloon was completely deflated 12 frames after the bullet entered it. What period of time does this represent?

9. A student has a movie projector which shows pictures at the rate of 16 frames per second. His movie camera can take pictures at various speeds. He wishes to take pictures of a football game so that the action will be slowed down to $\frac{1}{2}$ normal speed when projected. He wants to set the speed of the movie camera at 8 frames per second but his friend insists he should set it at 32 frames per second. Who is correct? Why?

10. In time-lapse photography, plants and their blossoms may be seen to develop at a rate comparable to that of the motion of animals. If the total growth of a plant which would require 50 days is to be shown on a 10-minute film, what interval should elapse between the successive pictures? (Assume that the film is to be shown at 24 frames/sec.)

11. The shutter speed of a camera is $\frac{1}{25}$ of a second. How far would a rifle bullet travel while a student attempts to take its picture with a $\frac{1}{25}$-second exposure? (The bullet's speed is 3500 ft per sec.) What shutter speed would be necessary to limit the bullet's movement to 0.1 inch during the exposure?

12. A 10-slit stroboscope is rotated at a constant rate for 20 seconds to determine that a motor shaft takes $\frac{1}{40}$ sec to make one rotation. How many rotations does the stroboscope make?

13. A stroboscope disc with 4 openings must be rotated 80 times in 10 seconds to make a fan with

four identical blades appear to stand still. What are the possible rates of motion of the fan? How would your answer be different if one of the blades was a different color from the others?

14. A disc stroboscope contains 4 slits and is turned 6 times in 10 seconds. What time interval can be measured by it?

15. * Use a stroboscope (see Laboratory Guide) to look at a phonograph turntable, a dripping faucet, a fluorescent lamp, a fan, a TV screen, a small weight tied to a string and whirled about someone's head, and a falling weight. For which of these motions can you measure the time interval?

16. (a) How many human life spans have elapsed since earliest man?

(b) Approximately how many times would an air molecule spin around its axis while the earth revolves once around the sun? See Table 1.

17. (a) In 1959 the population of the United States was about 176,000,000. Express this number in powers-of-ten notation. What is the order of this magnitude?

(b) Express as a power of ten the budget of the United States for a year when it is 71 billion dollars.

(c) Use the powers-of-ten notation to determine the average amount of the budget that must be paid by an individual citizen.

18. Express only the order of magnitude of your answer to the following:

(a) Light travels on the order of 10^5 miles each second. How far will light travel in a year?

(b) Calculate the length of time it takes the light from the sun to travel the 93 million miles to the earth.

19. Using powers-of-ten notation, find the following:

(a) 0.00418×39.7

(b) $\dfrac{6000}{.012}$

(c) $\dfrac{.703 \times .014}{280{,}000}$

20. A watch ticks 5 times each second. Expressing only the order of magnitude of your answer, find how many times it ticks:

(a) during a day.

(b) during a year.

21. Suppose that there are 1.7×10^8 people living in the United States and that 7.5×10^6 of these people live in New York City. How many live in the rest of the country?

FURTHER READING

BOLTON, L., *Time Measurement.* Van Nostrand, 1924.

BROWN, HARRISON, "The Age of the Solar System," *Scientific American*, April, 1957 (p. 80).

EDDINGTON, SIR A. S., *The Nature of the Physical World.* Cambridge University Press, 1953 (pp. 36–62).

HOOD, PETER, *How Time Is Measured.* Oxford University Press, 1955.

HURLEY, PATRICK M., *How Old Is the Earth?* Doubleday, 1959: A Science Study Series paperback.

LYONS, HAROLD, "Atomic Clocks." *Scientific American*, February, 1957 (p. 71).

SPACE AND ITS MEASURES

CHAPTER 3

We began the last chapter by describing time as "one of the basic notions of science," and went on to speak at some length about time. Perhaps you noticed that we were unable to confine the discussion to time and time alone. We were speaking also of positions and distances, of motion, of matter.

These, too, are basic notions. Each of them is intertwined with all the others. It is impossible to deal with one without dealing with all the rest. To discuss them intelligibly, it is necessary to deal with them one after another, although they do not appear in nature one after another. They come together.

To use these notions skillfully, we must refine our understanding of each of them, and we must do this even though, strictly speaking, we have no place to start. The procedure — and all our history has shown it to be a very practical procedure — is to move back and forth among these basic notions, registering gains wherever we can and using these gains in turn to register further gains. We use our crude notions of space, for example, to refine our notion of time. Then we are able to use our refined knowledge of time to improve our notion of space. But while we carry on this process, we must remember that physics itself is one indivisible subject dealing with the whole universe of which we are part. We subdivide it for our own convenience, but only so that later we may put it together again.

What we can say with assurance is that size and distance, as divisions of space, determine the nature of the world just as much as does time. Think of the sun, whose bright glare showers the earth with light, makes our crops grow, and keeps our earth from being a dead, frozen planet. It appears to us as a large, bright disc, too brilliant to look at directly. Compare it with a star which appears as nothing but a tiny bright spark in the dark night. The difference is one of distance. The sun is a star we happen to live "near." The little twinkling star, though a furiously hot sun like our own, is relatively far away from us.

Or consider the very small. You know that a drop of pond water looks a little cloudy perhaps to the unaided eye, but nothing more. Under the microscope, it is a jungle of plants and animals, living, hunting, fleeing. Beyond the microscope's grasp is a still more wonderful part of the world, the world of the atom, which we are going to probe.

When we say the sun is "near," compared to any other star, or that Bombay is "far," compared to any place in our state, we have started to measure intervals of distance, or size. Intervals of space — sizes or distances — can best be compared by the same scheme we used in comparing time intervals. We have only to make a count. We count how many times we have to span with our fingertips, or lay off with a ruler, or pace out with equal steps, and we have measured a distance.

3–1. The Unit of Distance

Every people has had a unit of length. Hunting folk, like the North American Indians, used the pace, the bowshot, and the day's journey. When it became necessary to measure off land for irrigation and for plowing, standard rods were made. As early as ancient Egyptian times, when great buildings were made of stone, rather wide use was made of a standard of length, a cubit, or the distance from the elbow to the tip of the middle finger. In the times of the Ptolemies, there were professional pacers who helped make maps by pacing out the roads in units called stadia. By medieval times, with the growth of the European nations, there were many measuring units. In England, length was measured by the inch, foot, yard, fathom, rod, furlong, mile, and league. These units reflect convenient early standards.

The French Revolution brought to power a government set sharply against all that was traditional and old-fashioned. An early action of the new government of France was the establishment of a group of learned men ("experts," we would say nowadays) to produce a rational set of units for all measurements, the common, everyday ones as well as those of science and the blossoming technologies. They set up standards of length, among many others, which have become world-wide in science, and nearly world-wide in everyday life. They called their scheme of units the metric system, and its fundamental length unit is the meter (from the Greek *metron,* to measure). They felt it was better to adopt a length standard which had some more lasting significance than the length of the pace, and they were convinced of the value of the decimal system. They therefore chose the meter to be one ten-millionth (10^{-7}) of the distance from the equator to the North Pole. In the 1790's, this dimension was rather well known in terms of carefully laid out base lines surveyed in Europe. This is the origin of the metric system, which we employ throughout physics in all countries today.

It was one thing to say that the meter was to be 10^{-7} of a quadrant of the earth's circumference, but quite another to lay off this distance on a short metal bar. However, it is not important that the standard meter be related to the earth's circumference. As our standard of length we now employ the standard meter bar the French made. Many careful copies have been produced.

The Founding Fathers of our own American republic, very much steeped in the same climate of opinion that later produced the metric system of weights and measures in France, introduced a kind of "metric system" in currency which we use to this day. They established our decimal system of coinage, with 100 cents = 1 dollar, and a few other multiples, like dimes and quarters, to replace the traditional English system in which 12 pence = 1 shilling, and 20 shillings = 1 pound sterling. Anyone who struggles to calculate a 10 per cent discount on the price of an English book will see the virtue of a system of units which matches the number system. This is the great value of the metric system, which has made it universal in science. Even our inch is now legally defined in terms of the meter: it is defined as exactly 2.54×10^{-2} meters.

It is worth remembering that a meter is roughly a yard and a foot is about 30 cm, while a millimeter is about the thickness of a pencil lead.

Names and Definitions of Metric Units of Distance

Unit			
1 kilometer (km)	= 10^3 meters (m)		
1 centimeter (cm)	= 10^{-2} m		
1 millimeter (mm)	= 10^{-3} m	= 10^{-1} cm	
1 micron (μ)	= 10^{-6} m	= 10^{-3} mm	
1 Angstrom (A)	= 10^{-10} m	= 10^{-8} cm	

Note that in the table the prefix *kilo* means 10^3, *centi* is 10^{-2}, *milli* is 10^{-3}, and *micro* is 10^{-6}. Another prefix, often used, is *mega,* which means 10^6. A widespread habit has grown up among American physicists in recent years of referring to a large sum of money as a "megabuck." This use of Greek and Latin prefixes for multiples and submultiples of a unit has been extended to many different units. Have you ever heard of a *megohm* or a *microfarad?* What is a *millisecond?*

Throughout this book, to save time and space, we shall follow the practice of physicists and, whenever convenient, use the abbreviations given in the table instead of writing out the full name of the unit.

3–2. Measuring Large Distances — Triangulation

The method of laying standard lengths end to end can be used to measure quite large distances on the surface of the earth. It is sometimes used

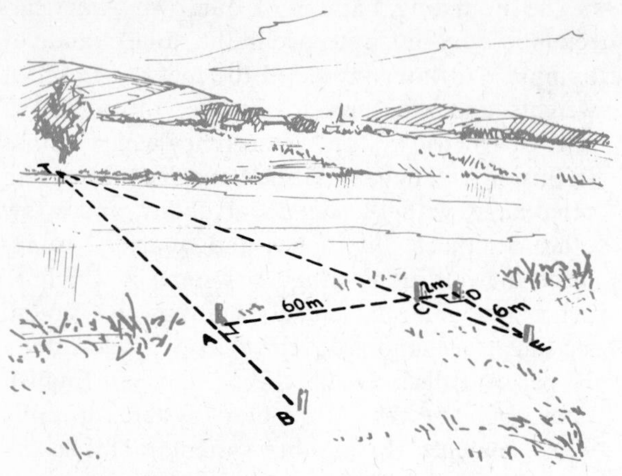

3–1. Measuring a distance by triangulation.

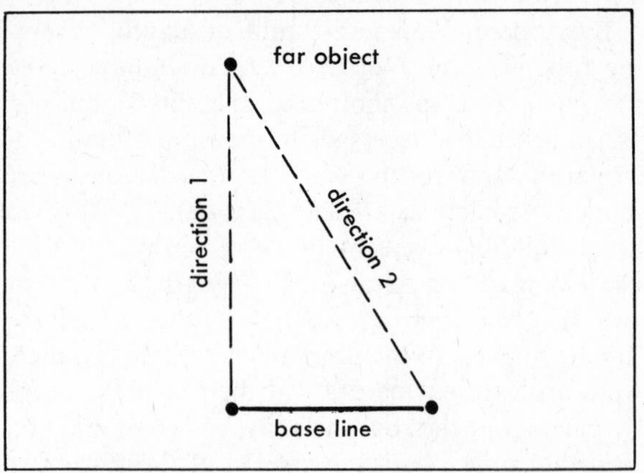

3–2. When we have measured the length of a base line and know the direction of an object from each end of the base line, we can find the distance to the object.

in surveying, but often it becomes inconvenient. To measure the distance across a river, or the height of a mountain, or indeed the distance to a star, we can use a simple, indirect method. This method is based on the geometry of a triangle and is called *triangulation*.

One way to measure a distance by triangulation is illustrated in Fig. 3–1. We wish to measure the distance AT across the river. To do so we line up the tree, T, on the far side of the river, with two stakes A and B. We then construct the right angle BAC. (To do this we can use a large carpenter's square.) We drive a stake into the ground at C, a measured distance from A. Then we continue along line AC and drive another stake, D, into the ground a measured distance farther on. Now we construct a right angle CDE. We drive in a stake at E so placed that it is in line with the tree, T, and the stake, C. Finally we measure the distance DE.

As you can see in the figure, the triangles TAC and EDC are similar because they have two pairs of equal angles, the right angles TAC and EDC and the vertical angles TCA and ECD. Therefore the corresponding sides are in the same ratio. In particular

$$\frac{AT}{DE} = \frac{AC}{DC},$$

and the distance AT across the river is

$$AT = \frac{AC}{DC} \times DE.$$

Since we have measured AC, DC, and DE, we can now determine the distance AT across the river. For example, if we suppose that the measured distances are $AC = 60$ m, $DC = 2$ m, and $DE = 6$ m, then the width of the river is

$$AT = \tfrac{60}{2} \times 6\text{m} = 180\text{m}.$$

We can simplify the procedure. All we need to do is to construct the right angle TAC; measure off a convenient distance, AC, called the base line; and measure the angle TCA. By making a scale drawing we can get the answer.

An instrument can be constructed that will measure the angles and work out the geometry automatically. An example of such a triangulating instrument, for measuring distances by simple sighting, is the range finder found in almost all good cameras. The base line of the range finder is no larger than the camera, and distant objects will appear at almost the same angle from both ends of it. Just where the sight lines cross is then difficult to say. The camera range finder, therefore, measures only the distances to near-by objects. You can make range finders with longer base lines, and you will find that the bigger you make the base line, the greater the distance you can measure.

The big range finders on warships have base lines limited by the size of the ship. To measure the distances of planets, astronomers use base lines extending over half the earth. The largest base line we can use is the diameter of the earth's orbit, the distance from one point on its path around the sun to the point reached a half year later. This sets the limit for measuring big distances geometrically.

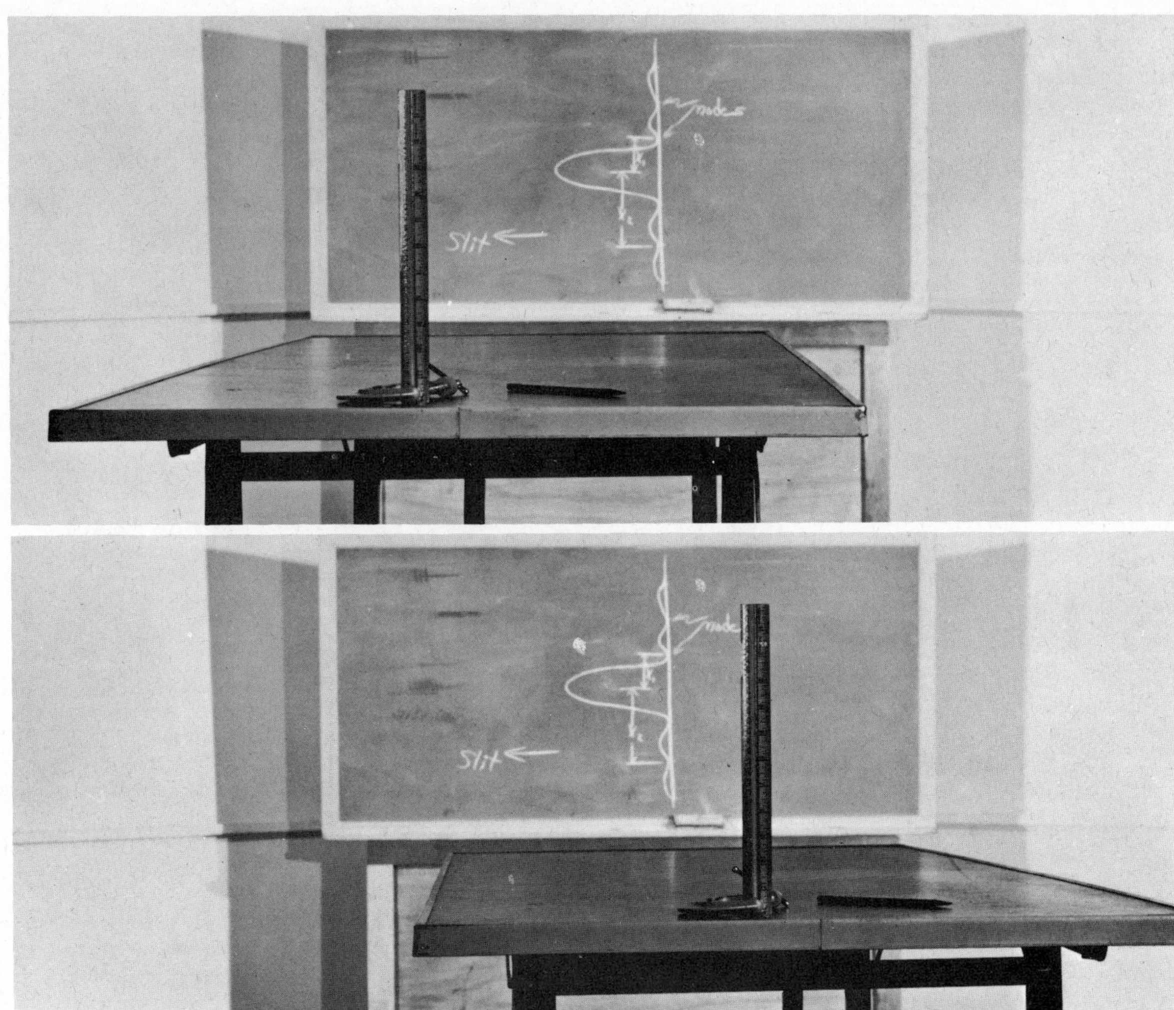

3–3. In these photographs the two positions of the camera were somewhat less than a meter apart. Note the apparent shift of the ruler with respect to the more distant blackboard.

To use a base line to find the distance to an object, we must measure the direction of the object from each end of the base line. (Fig. 3–2.) To measure these two directions, an astronomer who uses the diameter of the earth's orbit as a base line must have a way of establishing a reference direction when he takes his observation at one end of the diameter and when he takes it at the other end. To fix this reference direction, he uses the most distant stars. He can pick them out because they do not change their apparent positions with respect to one another. Here he is using something very familiar to you. As you watch through a window of a rapidly moving car, the objects near you apparently move rapidly backward but the distant features of the landscape do not seem to move at all. In the same way, the most distant stars stand still relative to each other and show little or no apparent motion even over thousands of years. For this reason, we call them the fixed stars and we can use them to give us known directions from any point on the earth's orbit.

Unlike the extremely distant stars a near-by star will appear to move relative to the distant ones as we go from one point to another on the earth's orbit. This shift in the apparent direction of the near-by star is just like the shifts you see looking out the car window or the shift you see when you hold out a finger before your eyes and look at it first with one eye open and then with the other. The finger appears to shift its position along a distant wall; and the nearer it is to your face the

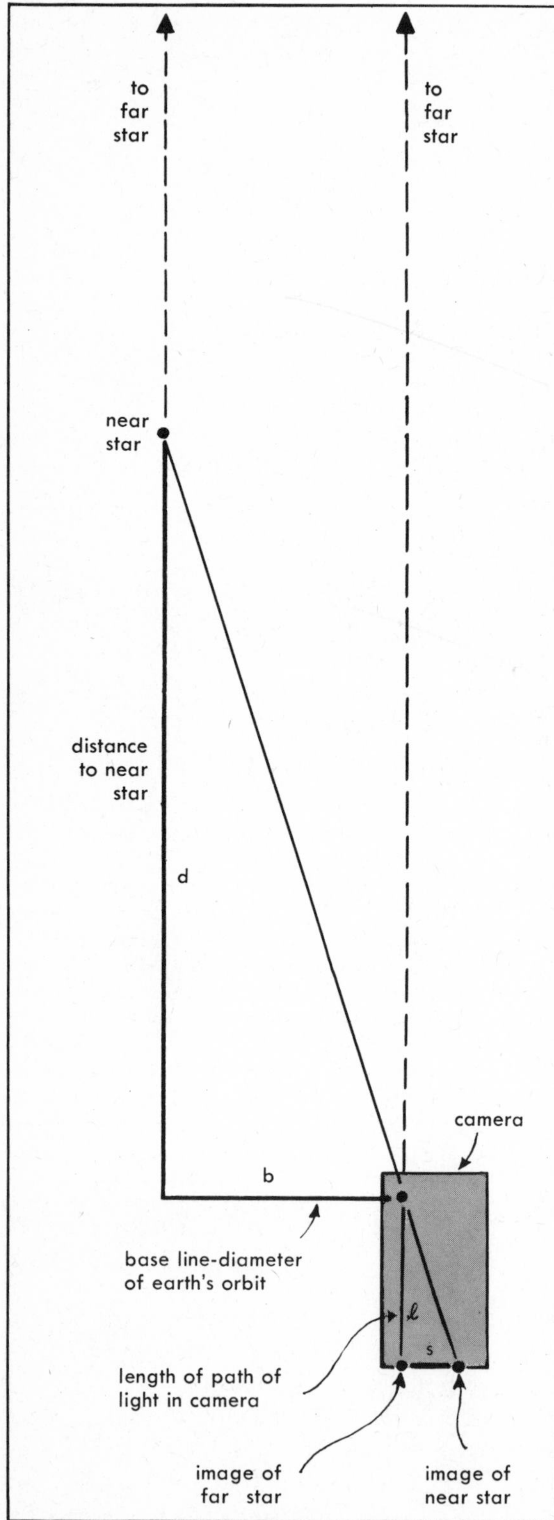

3–4. Finding the distance to a near star by geometry. The triangles in the figure are similar, therefore

$$\frac{d}{b} = \frac{l}{s} \quad \text{or} \quad d = b \times \frac{l}{s}.$$

3–5. The shift in position of a near star (Barnard's Star) with respect to the very distant "fixed" stars. Three pictures were made at six-month intervals with the 24-in. telescope at Swarthmore's Sproul Observatory. In this illustration, the pictures have been superimposed. The images of the two very distant fixed stars in the upper right coincide, while the three images of Barnard's Star (lower left) show a horizontal and vertical separation representing two motions of the star. One, indicated by the vertical separation of the three images, is the star's own "proper motion" in a straight line with respect to the fixed stars. The other, the horizontal displacement, is the apparent shift of the star's position as viewed from the two extremes of the earth's orbit. Notice that it goes to the right and then back to the left in successive six-month intervals. It is this displacement that enables us to calculate the distance to the star. The actual shift in the original photo was about 0.03 mm, giving a distance of about 6×10^{13} km.

farther it shifts. Fig. 3–3 is another example of such a shift.*

In Fig. 3–4 we see a simplified version of how an astronomer can fix the distance to a near-by star using the diameter of the earth's orbit as a base line. In order to get the fundamental idea, we assume that the astronomer is lucky: at one moment he finds the near-by star directly lined up with a distant star. The astronomer then waits for half a year so that the earth is now at

*This apparent shift of one object with respect to another is called parallax. Only when two objects are both extremely far away or both at the same position do they show no parallax. Only then is there no shifting with respect to each other when we move.

the other end of the base line. Then he takes a picture, pointing his camera at the far star so as to get the same direction again. Because the earth has moved, the two stars are no longer in line; and consequently he obtains two separate images on his photographic plate. Because the direction to the distant star is the same, the separation of the images on the photographic plate is related to the length of the earth's orbit in just the same way that the length of the path of light in the camera is related to the distance to the near-by star. You can see this from the similar triangles in the figure. Of course, if no distant star ever lines up with the near-by star (Fig. 3–5), the job is a little bit harder, but the method is essentially the same.

To make things clear in Fig. 3–4 we have used a near "star" whose distance is only a few times the diameter of the earth's orbit. In fact, there are no such stars. Even with the earth's orbit as the base line, the change in direction of the nearest star is very small, for that star is about 135,000 orbital diameters (about 4×10^{16} meters) away. The distances to only a few hundred stars are small enough to be measured in this way. For greater distances in the universe, we must use other methods, one of which is discussed briefly in Section 4–3.

The planets are close enough so that even a small telescope will show most of them as round discs. (Fig. 3–6.) This is clearly what you would expect if they are really globes whose sizes are of the same order of magnitude as our earth. But not even the Palomar telescope shows up any such clear discs for the stars. They are too far away. Astronomers have special means of measuring the sizes of stars. For the present we want to stress that we have a consistent picture. The stars are very far away, and hence they show no parallax, no disc. Closer to us they would be so many glowing suns.

Table 1 on page 28 shows the range of distances from our own size to larger and smaller sizes that can be measured with rulers, geometry, and light. The large distances beyond those that can be measured in this way are shown in Table 2 on page 30. The methods by which the geometrical measurement of distance has been extended to these distances beyond the reach of our best base line and best angle measurements are many and ingenious.

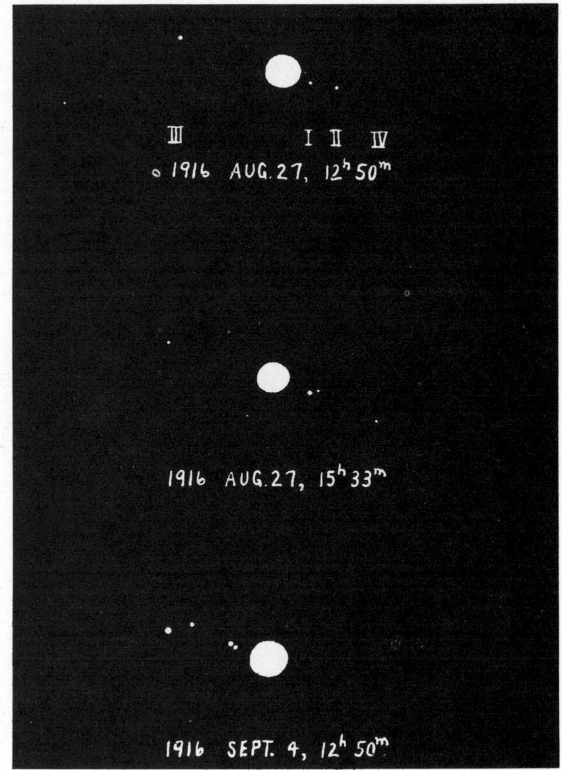

3–6. Jupiter and its moons. As we go to distances beyond the earth it is necessary to use telescopes to extend our senses. The planet Jupiter is visible to the unaided eye, but looks like a bright star. Have you ever noticed in viewing it that it doesn't seem to twinkle as much as a star? The illustration above shows the planet as photographed at three different times with a small telescope. The four satellites that show up are the ones discovered by Galileo and are often referred to as the Galilean moons. (Courtesy: Clyde Fisher and Marian Lockwood, "Astronomy," John Wiley & Sons, Inc.) In the illustration below, we see the planet as photographed through Palomar's 200-in. telescope. Note how much more detail is visible. Even the shadow of one of the moons can be seen. Jupiter has a diameter of the order of 10^8 m and is at a distance of the order of 10^{12} m from the earth.

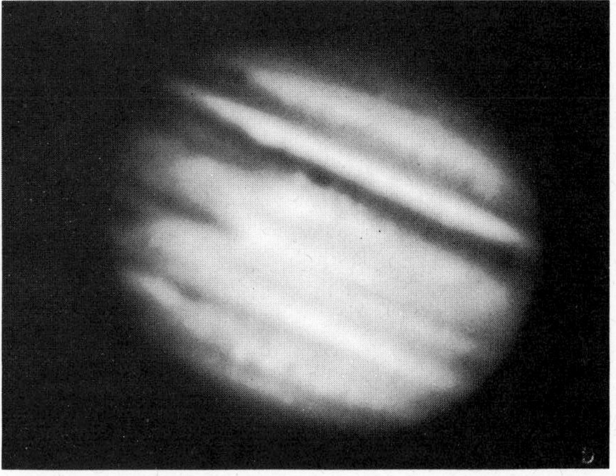

3–7. The globular star cluster in the constellation Hercules is so far from the earth that its distance cannot be measured by geometric methods. This photograph, made with the 200-in. Palomar telescope, shows one of the finest examples of a globular cluster in the northern sky. It is visible to the naked eye, under good conditions, as a small hazy patch of light. Its diameter subtends an angle of about 18 minutes at the eye. Actually, as you can see in the photograph, it consists of thousands of stars, most of which are larger and more brilliant than the sun. Although they seem to be crowding one another, in reality they are separated from each other by an average distance that is about 50,000 times the distance from the earth to the sun. The great distance between the cluster and the earth makes the stars appear close together. How could we go about measuring how far from the earth these stars are located?

Table 1. Distance

Orders of Magnitude of Lengths Found with Rulers, Geometry, and Light

Length in Meters	Associated Distance	Length in Meters	Associated Distance
10^{18}	Greatest distance measurable by parallax	10^{7}	Air distance from Los Angeles to New York
10^{17}	Distance to nearest star		
10^{16}		10^{6}	Radius of the moon
10^{15}		10^{5}	Length of Lake Erie
10^{14}		10^{4}	Average width of Grand Canyon
10^{13}	Distance of Neptune from the sun	10^{3}	One mile
10^{12}	Distance of Saturn from the sun	10^{2}	Length of football field
10^{11}	Distance of Earth from the sun	10^{1}	Height of shade tree
10^{10}	Distance of Mercury from the sun	10^{0}	One yard
10^{9}	Mean length of Earth's shadow	10^{-1}	Width of your hand
	Radius of the sun	10^{-2}	Diameter of a pencil
10^{8}	Mean distance from Earth to the moon	10^{-3}	Thickness of windowpane
	Diameter of Jupiter (Fig. 3–6)	10^{-4}	Thickness of a piece of paper
10^{7}	Radius of Earth	10^{-5}	Diameter of red blood corpuscle

A collection of a hundred billion distant suns make up what is known as our galaxy. Our own star, the sun, is probably a quite ordinary, though rather elderly, family member. Beyond our galaxy comes a great collection of other galaxies, cousins of our own, dotting the heavens as far as our greatest telescopes can reach. They spread out in all directions, looking fainter and smaller the greater their distance, but they are recognizably similar to our own. The nearest of these is the Great Nebula of Andromeda, which you can just see with the naked eye on a dark, clear night. (See Figs. 3–8 and 3–9.) Nearly a billion distant galaxies are scattered throughout the universe, according to estimates based on photographs of the sky taken with the big Palomar telescope. How many more there may be we are unable to say.

3–8. The Great Nebula in the constellation Andromeda. This enormous island universe of stars, which is similar to our own galaxy, is visible to the unaided eye under favorable conditions as a hazy patch of light, subtending an angle of about 3 degrees. It is the most remote object that is visible to the unaided eye. It is of the same order of size as the Milky Way, about 100,000 light-years in diameter. This photograph, made with the 48-in. Schmidt telescope at Mt. Palomar in California, also shows two satellite galaxies of the Great Nebula (center right and center left).

3–9. Cluster of galaxies in the constellation Coma Berenices. This photograph was made with Palomar's 200-in. Hale telescope. If we examine closely the light specks visible in this picture, we note that some of the images have a shape that resembles that of the Andromeda Nebula or one of its satellite galaxies in Fig. 3–8. These are indeed nebulae. They show different shapes and orientations. From the size of these images, this cluster of galaxies can be estimated to be about 20 or 30 times farther away from us than the Great Nebula in Andromeda. To an observer in one of these galaxies, the Andromeda Nebula and our own galaxy, the Milky Way, would appear as two neighboring members of a distant cluster.

Table 2

Orders of Magnitude of Distances Too Large to Measure by Geometric Means

Length in Meters	Associated Distance
10^{25}	Distance to farthest photographed object (a galaxy)
10^{24}	Domain of the galaxies
10^{23}	Domain of the galaxies
10^{22}	Distance to the Great Nebula in Andromeda (nearest galaxy)
10^{21}	Distance to the smaller Magellanic Cloud
10^{20}	Distance of the sun from the center of our galaxy
	Distance to globular star cluster in Hercules (Fig. 3–7)
10^{19}	Distance to the North Star (Polaris)

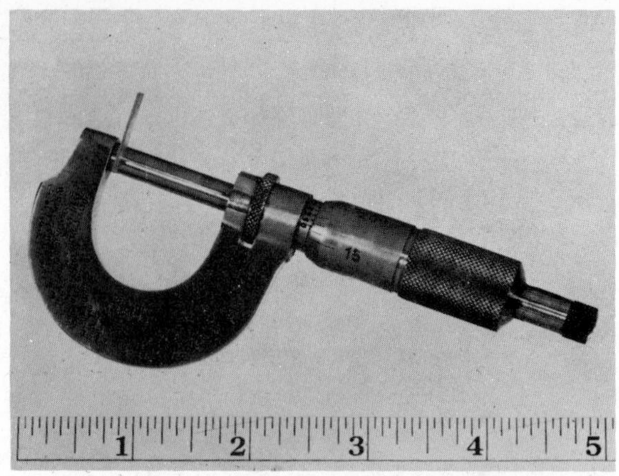

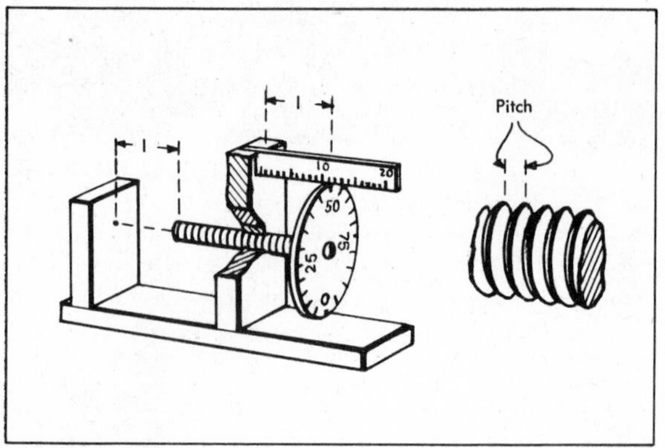

3–10. A micrometer caliper (above). Very small lengths, such as the thickness of a piece of paper, can be measured with this instrument. The basic part of this device, as shown in the simplified version sketched below, is a screw. Note the scale around the barrel, corresponding to the disc below, which enables us to measure a fraction of a turn. How does a screw help us to measure a small distance accurately?

3–3. Small Distances

If we go in the other direction toward the very small, we can still use straightforward geometrical methods. It is not hard to measure the thickness of a thin sheet of paper, if you have many of them. Stack up a hundred sheets, use a ruler to measure the stack; then you have marked off on the ruler a hundred times the thickness. This obvious indirect method is similar to what is often done in physics. Of course if the sheets of paper are very different in thickness, the result will refer not to any real sheet, but to an average of the thicknesses present. For many purposes this is good enough. What we obtain is the thickness of a sheet, assuming them all to be alike.

This page-thickness example shows how we can extend the basic idea of counting or spacing off to small distances. Another extension of counting to small distances is found in the use of a screw thread. If a screw is turned through one revolution in a fixed nut, it advances only by the distance between successive threads, the pitch of the screw. By dividing the turn into say a hundred parts, you can divide the advance of the screw into a hundred equal parts as well. This is the basis of the machinist's micrometer (Fig. 3–10). Other similar tricks will help a little, but to go further toward the very small we need to use amplifying devices, of which the most familiar is the microscope. With it, we can see small objects, and measure them by placing tiny "rulers" right beside them (Fig. 3–11). Again, the laying-off and counting method is at work.

The atom and its sub-units are so small that the ordinary microscope is no longer of help, for light itself is not a delicate enough probe. Newer sorts of instruments, and again a set of still more indirect but convincing methods, carry us down to the smallest distances about which we have any real knowledge. Some of the methods are simple enough for you to carry out. See your laboratory guide. Table 3 gives some idea (in terms of orders of magnitude) of the amount by which we can extend our everyday notions of distance and size into the very small.

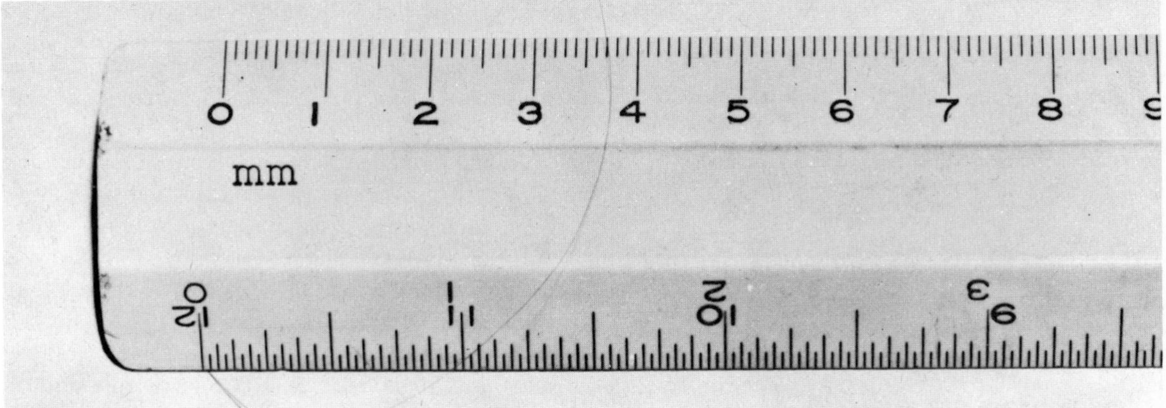

3–11 (a). The size of a human hair. In this photograph a hair has been placed across a millimeter scale. It is barely visible. How many hairs would have to be placed side by side to fill the space between two adjacent millimeter marks on the scale?

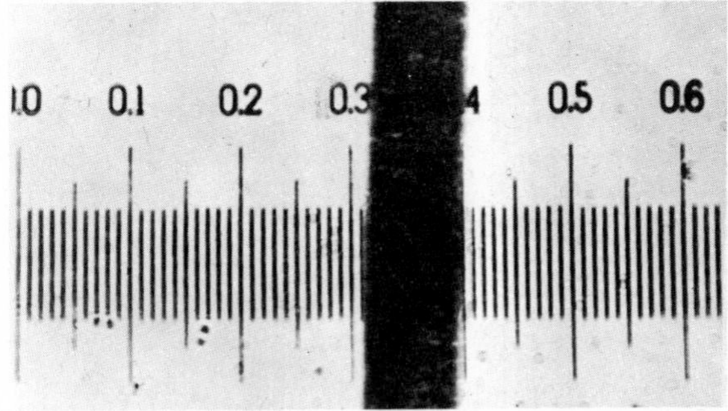

3–11 (b). Here the hair has been photographed on a very small ruler with the aid of a microscope. Each of the smallest divisions on the ruler is one hundredth of a millimeter. The microscope has made it possible for us to measure the diameter of the hair more accurately. How accurate was your estimate from Fig. 3–11 (a) of the number of hairs that would be required to cover a millimeter?

Table 3

Orders of Magnitude of Distances Too Small to Measure by Geometric Means

Length in Meters	Associated Distance
10^{-6}	Average distance between successive collisions (mean free path) of molecules in the air of a room
10^{-7}	Thickness of thinnest soap bubble still showing colors
10^{-8}	Average distance between molecules of air in a room
10^{-9}	Size of molecule of oil
10^{-10}	Average distance between atoms of a crystalline solid
10^{-11}	
10^{-12}	Average distance between atoms packed in center of densest stars
10^{-13}	
10^{-14}	Size of largest atomic nucleus
10^{-15}	Diameter of proton

3–4. The Dimensions of Space

The fact that space has three dimensions is usually demonstrated by pointing out that three separate measurements are needed to locate an object in space. In the room in which you are now sitting, for example, you can locate any point by specifying its distance from one wall, its distance from a second adjacent wall, and its height from the floor. We can say this with complete confidence, even though we may not know the shape of the room. We assume that it has at least two straight walls that meet in a corner of some kind. If walls and floor meet at right angles, they represent what are called rectangular or Cartesian coordinates. If the corners are all right-angled, the calculations may be simpler, but they are no better or no worse than any other kind. If the room is circular, three numbers will still do the job, although the calculation is different.

In any case, three numbers — and the rules that say what they mean — define any point, and only that point. This is merely one way of expressing the fact that space is three-dimensional. It is, however, not always the most interesting or the most informative way.

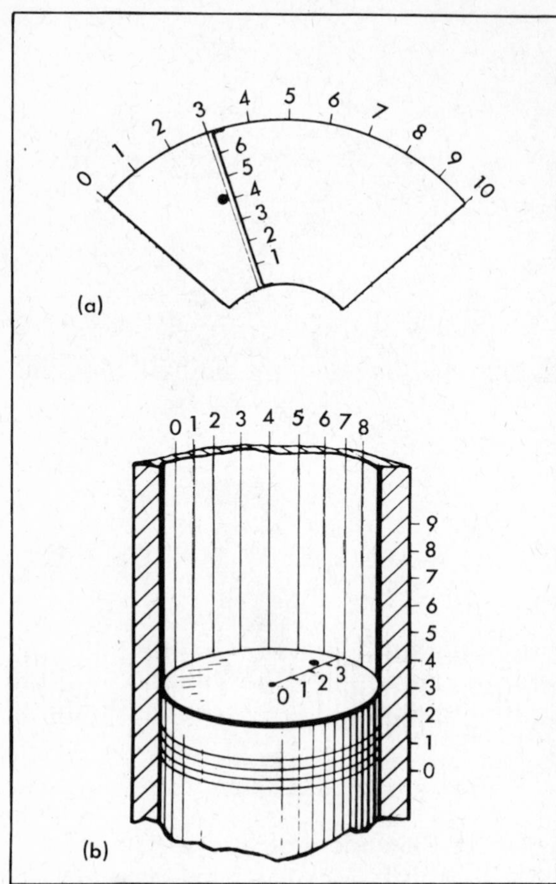

3–12. (a) Locating a point on a surface. (b) Locating a point in a volume.

We may approach the three dimensions of space in another manner. If you take a point — the point of your pencil is ideal — and move it, you create a line. Any position on the line can then be specified by stating its distance from the beginning of the line. The line, in other words, has one dimension.

If you now take the line, and move it, you create a surface. A windshield wiper is an excellent example of this: the line of its rubber edge, on each sweep, marks out a surface on the windshield of the car. To locate a point on this surface, you need two numbers, one to give the position of the wiper when it lies across the point, and the other to state how far out along the wiper the point is. The surface, in other words, is two-dimensional. [See Fig. 3–12 (a).]

In the engine of your car there are cylinders and pistons. The piston head is a surface. As it moves up and down from one position to another inside the cylinder, it sweeps out a volume. To find a point in this volume, we need three figures — two to define a point on the piston head, and a third to tell how far the piston is from one end of its stroke. [See Fig. 3–12 (b).]

Having now seen how a moving point generates a line, how a moving line generates a surface, how a moving surface generates a volume, what happens if we take the next step? What if we move a volume? The result is not what we might expect. A volume only sweeps out another volume, no different in kind from the volume swept out by a surface. We have run out of dimensions. Space, it seems, offers us only three upon which to work. Space is apparently three-dimensional, and no more.

There is still another way of looking at dimensionality. In this view, the pertinent characteristic of a line is that we can move along it from point to point without interruption — without lifting our pencil, as it were. But if one point is removed, we can no longer move directly from a point on the line to any other point beyond the gap. In effect, the line now is cut.

Removing a point from a surface, such as the floor of the room, does not hinder us. We can move from any point on the floor to any other point merely by going around the missing point. But cut the floor along a line so that it now has two disconnected areas. If we are on one side of the cut, we cannot go directly to the points on the other side of the boundary.

Finally, within the room as a whole, a full surface — a wall — is needed to prevent crossing from one point to another. But here again we come to the end. Any closed volume can be walled into two separate volumes, but we can go no further (unless the mathematicians invent new spaces, and they often do exactly that).

What we have just done can be stated in simple form: a point (with zero dimension) cuts a line; a line (with one dimension) cuts a surface; a surface (with two dimensions) cuts a volume or space. A volume (with three dimensions) merely cuts another volume.

All this may appear unimportant, or at best not important enough to warrant three repetitions. As we go along, however, we shall find reasons to use each of these aspects of dimensionality. We will be working in physics with things of no dimensions, of one dimension, and of two dimensions, as well as with physical space and its three dimensions.

Time, for example, has one dimension. It is specified by one number. We say, "Ten minutes from now." It is measured out by the passage of zero-dimensional instants. And in passing through time, we must pass through all the instants, one after another. For example, there is no way of getting from 8:30 a.m. to 8:32 a.m. without passing through 8:31 a.m. Each of these facts is significant; each is a characteristic of something having only one dimension.

3–5. Measuring Surfaces and Volumes

The clue for the measurement of surfaces and volumes lies in the way we measured distance. Lay off a convenient unit of area and simply count how many times the unit fits into the surface to be measured. By subdividing sufficiently, it is possible to fit the unit, or its subdivisions, into all the corners and curves of any surface with as much accuracy as you wish. (Fig. 3–13.) The process is similar to laying a tile floor.

The convenient unit always used for surfaces is a square whose edge is a standard unit of length. Since we use meters for length, we have as a unit of surface the square meter (m^2).

We can measure volume in the same way, fitting little cubes into every portion of the volume to be measured, until it is filled up. Here the unit we shall use is the cubic meter (m^3). Familiar divisions of these basic units are the square centimeter (cm^2) for area and the cubic centimeter (cm^3) for volume. How many square centimeters are there in 3 m^2? We know

$$1 \text{ m} = 100 \text{ cm};$$

$$\text{so} \quad 3 \text{ m}^2 = 3 \times 100 \text{ cm} \times 100 \text{ cm} = 3 \times 10^4 \text{ cm}^2.$$

Of course, the fitting of these little squares or cubes into irregular surfaces or volumes is not the only way to measure area or volume. Standard containers of convenient shape are usually on hand, and an odd-shaped volume, such as a milk bottle, might be measured by filling it with water and then pouring the water into a standard container or two, eventually using subdivisions made in some geometrical way on a container of simple shape like the familiar graduated cylinder.

The area of an irregular surface can be found by weighing a paper pattern cut to fit the surface neatly. One then compares the weight of the cut pattern with the weight of a measured square of the same material to find the area.

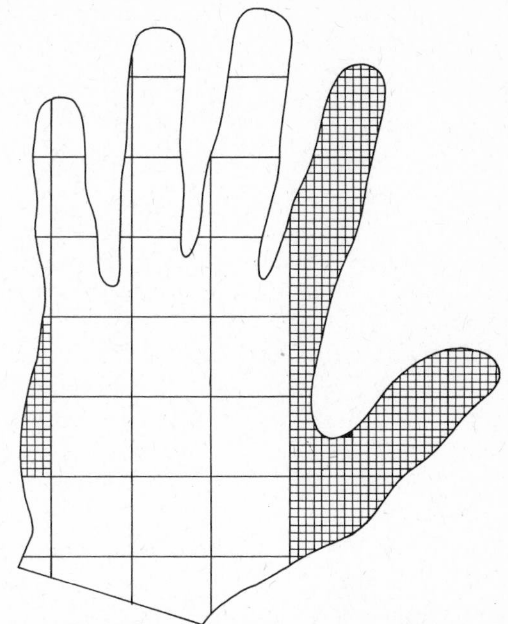

3–13. Measurement of a surface. In measuring the area of an irregular surface, such as the hand pictured above, we use the same method that we used in measuring a distance. First we lay off our units on the surface. To measure areas smaller than our unit area, we subdivide our unit. In the illustration, the unit is being subdivided to measure small irregularities. As you can see, there are additional small areas that will not fit these subdivisions. In such cases, we can subdivide the units as many times as we wish until we reach a point beyond which it is useless to go because the subdivisions become too small to see.

3–6. On the Limitations of Measuring

We have founded all our measurements on one simple scheme. To measure the size of some physical quantity, length, or time, you first choose a unit — any length or time you wish will do. Then to measure an interval larger than the unit, just "lay off" the unit as many times as it will go into the required interval. This is what we naturally do with a ruler. For anything left over after the count, or for any amount we want to measure which is smaller than the unit, we simply divide the unit into smaller equal parts, sub-units you may call them, and take as many of them as we need to match the given magnitude. We measure a box and find its length to be 20 cm and something left over. Dividing our centimeter unit into tenths, we find that the part left over contains three of these sub-units; so we say the box is

20.3 cm long. It is not hard to see that this method will work for any length that we want to measure. For we can make the divisions finer and finer until irregularities in the edge of the box we measure, or in the markings on our ruler, limit the fineness of our measurements of its length.

Some measurements are not subject to the process of making smaller and smaller subdivisions for greater and greater accuracy. The counting of the number of people in a room, for example, has a natural unit, the individual. Here the whole question of smaller and smaller subdivisions is irrelevant. Unlike time and space, matter does have known natural units. This is the real essence of modern physics. The natural units of matter are its building blocks, atoms and their few parts, which combine in so many ways to make up the whole of the material world — stars and sea, pencil and paper, skin and bone. We do not know whether space and time do or do not have such natural units. We only know that we have not run into them. Until we find such units (if we ever do) we will freely use any subdivision of our arbitrary unit of measurement to represent time and space.

We have just looked at the problems involved in the basic method of measurement by counting. In many real measurements a second type of problem arises. A measurement that is made by an indirect method is always based on special assumptions. In measuring the thickness of a piece of paper, for example, we made an assumption that the paper was uniform. The measurement of large distances by triangulation also involves an assumption — one we are pretty familiar with in everyday life. We assume that the line of sight — which is the line that light travels to get to the eye from the object — is a straight line. Only if this is right will our method of sight-triangulation work. Commonly we check the straightness of a board by sighting along it. We seem to accept the straightness of the path of light. Of course, it can deceive us and often does. The heat-shimmer you see above a hot radiator or a sun-warmed surface tells you that here are sight-paths which are not straight and are constantly changing. If we wish a reliable answer when measuring long distances by triangulation, we must avoid looking through heated, disturbed air. We cannot measure the distance to a star by this means on a night when the star is twinkling very much as a result of changing air currents from the warm surface of the earth. We want a clear, still night, with the star well up in the sky.

Another assumption involved in measuring by triangulation is that the laws of geometry are correct. They cannot be taken for granted, however. All assumptions that we make in measuring must be tested. The results of geometry and the straight path of lines of sight have been well tested, largely by the success of the whole picture we can build up. But we must always be on the watch, especially when using indirect methods in measuring things far from everyday experience, to see if such traditional assumptions can still be relied upon.

We noted earlier that we must do our best to understand the limitations of our instruments, including our senses. The problem of measuring the sizes of planets and stars illustrates this point. When we look through a telescope at various planets, they have various sizes; they appear as discs of various diameters. Stars seen in telescopes also appear to have some diameter, but the diameter does not change as we look from star to star. Instead it depends on which telescope we use and on which way we point it. The apparent size of stars seen in telescopes arises from the behavior of telescopes, not from the real size of stars. (See Fig. 3–14.) We have run into a limitation of our instrument, one which we can later understand, and we must get the information about the size of stars some other way. All indirect methods of measurement have limitations, and no one method works for all cases.

Even the method of using standard lengths has its problems. In very precise land surveys, for example, the temperature of the steel tapes used is measured meter by meter in order to correct for expansion or contraction. Here, because we employ physical objects, the direct method must be carefully scrutinized.

3–7. Significant Figures

Numbers and their combinations by means of arithmetic give us an exact way of speaking about quantity. In physics, however, there are limits to our accuracy of measurement, and they in turn place limits on our use of numbers to record our measurements.

We have learned that the use of a large string of zeros on either side of the decimal point, to express the order of magnitude of a quantity, is unnecessary. Every quantity can be written as a decimal number between one and ten multiplied by the appropriate power of ten. Instead of writing the radius of the earth as about 6,370,000 meters, therefore, we write it as 6.37×10^6 meters. Likewise, the diameter of a hair is about 0.00003 meter, which we write as 3×10^{-5} meter.

Now, in this way of writing numbers, we show the limited accuracy of our knowledge by omitting all digits about which we have no information. Thus, for the earth's radius, when we write 6.37×10^6 m and not 6.374×10^6 m or 6.370×10^6 m, we are saying that we are reasonably sure of the third digit but have no idea of the value of the fourth. The number of digits about which we do feel reasonably sure is called the number of *significant figures.* In the example of the hair, we have indicated only one significant figure. This means that we think three is a reasonable value, but we are not at all sure of the next digit (second significant figure).

A physicist who makes a measurement must estimate its reliability, and the simplest way of expressing that reliability is by writing the proper number of significant figures. To write additional figures that have no meaning is worse than a waste of time. It may mislead people who use those figures into believing them.

It is clear that the greater the accuracy of our measurements, the larger the number of significant figures we can use. When we write four significant figures, we imply that a fifth digit would have no meaning. If our accuracy were ten times greater, we would use another significant figure. The most careful physical measurements, using the highest available accuracy of the primary standards, still fall short of having twelve significant figures.

Because the numbers used in physics reflect the limitations of measurement, we modify our ideas of arithmetic slightly so as to make sure that we do not write meaningless digits in our answers. Suppose we make the following time measurements — 27.8 hr, 1.324 hr, and 0.66 hr — and we want to find their sum. Paying no attention to significant figures, we might write

$$\begin{array}{r} 27.8\ \text{hr} \\ 1.324\ \text{hr} \\ \underline{0.66\ \text{hr}} \\ 29.784\ \text{hr} \end{array}$$

3–14. This illustration, an enlargement of a small section of Fig. 3–7, shows two star images in detail. The images of the two brightest stars display four rays, while the smaller stars appear as small, irregular shapes. The four neat rays on the bright stars are due to the out-of-focus image of a four-armed support within the telescope. Even the roundish shapes of the images of the fainter stars do not depend on the stars, but on the nature of the telescope, the atmosphere, the photographic plate, and the light. These cause the light from a distant star to blur rather than focus to a sharp point. The true star image in each case would be considerably smaller than the blurry spot. For this reason, the star images of Fig. 3–7 appear much more crowded than the stars which make them. In the same way, the stars that form our Milky Way cannot be separated by the unaided eye.

What is the meaning of this result? In any number obtained by measurement all the digits following the last significant one are unknown — for example, the hundredths and thousandths place in the first measurement above. These unknown digits are not zero. Clearly if you add an unknown quantity to a known quantity you get an unknown answer. Consequently, the last two digits in the sum above are in fact unknown. In this case, then, we should round off all of our measurements to the nearest tenth so that all the digits in our answer will be significant. This gives

$$\begin{array}{r} 27.8\ \text{hr} \\ 1.3\ \text{hr} \\ \underline{0.7\ \text{hr}} \\ 29.8\ \text{hr} \end{array}$$

Since the first measurement is known only to the nearest tenth of an hour, we know the sum only to the nearest tenth of an hour.

Subtraction of measured quantities works the same way. It makes no sense to subtract known and unknown quantities. Particular care must be taken in subtracting two numbers of nearly equal magnitude. For example, suppose you wish to find the difference in length of two pieces of wire. One you have measured to be 1.55 meters long and the other 1.57 meters long.

$$1.57 \text{ m} - 1.55 \text{ m} = 0.02 \text{ m} = 2 \times 10^{-2} \text{ m}.$$

Notice that we do not write the answer as 2.00×10^{-2} m, since we are somewhat uncertain about each of the last digits in the original measurements. The difference certainly has only one significant figure, and we would not be too surprised if the difference were either twice as large or zero instead of 2 cm. Subtraction of nearly equal quantities destroys accuracy. For this reason, you sometimes need measurements much more accurate than the answers you want. To avoid the difficulty of making more accurate measurements, we would put the two wires side by side if possible and measure the difference directly with a micrometer screw rather than use the difference between two large numbers.

Now what about multiplication? How do we modify it to take account of the limitations of measurement? Suppose we wish to find the area of a long strip of tin. With a meter stick we measure its width to be 1.15 cm and its length to be 2.002 m. Here we have three-significant-figure accuracy in our width measurement and four-significant-figure accuracy in our length measurement. To get the area we multiply length by width. Paying no attention to significant figures, we get

$$\begin{aligned} A &= 2.002 \text{ m} \times 1.15 \times 10^{-2} \text{ m} \\ &= 2.30230 \times 10^{-2} \text{ m}^2. \end{aligned}$$

But now think of the meaning of this answer. When we measured the width we wrote 1.15 cm because we were not sure that the real width might not be a bit bigger or a bit smaller by perhaps 0.01 cm. If in fact the width is that much bigger, we have made a mistake in the area by the product of this extra width times the length, that is,

$$\begin{aligned} \text{Error} &= 0.01 \times 10^{-2} \text{ m} \times 2.002 \text{ m} \\ &= 0.02 \times 10^{-2} \text{ m}^2. \end{aligned}$$

Thus we see that we have an uncertain number in the hundredths place, which means that our original evaluation of the area may already be in error in the third significant figure. All the figures we write beyond the third have no significance. The proper way to express the answer is 2.30×10^{-2} m², for when two numbers are multiplied together, their product cannot have more accuracy (or more significant figures) than the less accurate of the two factors. Don't think that your results are improved by carrying out simple arithmetical operations to many figures.

What has been said about multiplication applies equally well to division. Never carry a division out beyond the number of significant figures in the least accurate measurement you are using.

It should be noted that numbers that are not the result of measurement may have unlimited accuracy and may be taken to any degree of accuracy required by the nature of the problem. For example, if an area was measured and found to be 3.76 m², twice that area would be $2 \times 3.76 \text{ m}^2 = 7.52 \text{ m}^2$.

We have seen how to handle numbers when they represent physical quantities. But we have by no means told the whole story of accuracy in measurement. The use of significant figures sometimes raises difficulties that would lead us into a detailed study of the theory of errors. However, the idea of significant figures helps us avoid misleading numbers and unnecessary calculation.

Every physical quantity must have: a unit, to tell what was counted; an order of magnitude; and a statement about its reliability, which for the present we can make in a rough way by writing only the correct number of significant figures. There is no technique in physics more important than the writing of physical quantities with all these facts made clear.

FURTHER READING

GAMOW, GEORGE, *One, Two, Three . . . Infinity*. Mentor Books, 1957 (pp. 257–261).

HELSON, W. H. I., and KILPATRICK, F. D., "Experiments in Perception." *Scientific American*, August, 1951 (p. 50). Some remarkable optical illusions illustrating the fallibility of our senses.

LEE, OLIVER J., *Measuring Our Universe*. Ronald Press, 1950. How physicists and astronomers measure distances within the atom and in outer space.

MOORE, PATRICK, *The Story of Man and the Stars*. Norton, 1954.

WHIPPLE, FRED, *Earth, Moon and Planets*. Harvard University Press.

FOR HOME, DESK, AND LAB

Note: Items marked * are projects to be done at home.

1. Choose an arbitrary unit such as the length of the first joint of the thumb or the length of a fingernail. Mark off a scale, using this unit, along the edge of a piece of paper. Use this scale to measure the length and the width of this page. Determine the ratio of the length to the width. What are the units of this ratio? Compare the ratio that you obtained with the ratios that others obtained for this same object using different units. What is the effect of different units in measuring ratios?

2. * Stand 75 to 150 yards from a building with a fairly flat front and several stories high (an alley between buildings with one dead end is also suitable). Clap your hands sharply and listen to the echo, which is, of course, much fainter than the original clap.

   Now clap in rhythm and adjust your rate of clapping until you cannot hear the echo because it comes back at the same time the louder sound is being created. Have someone count the number of times you clap in ten seconds. Measure the distance and compute the speed of sound (not forgetting to double the distance to get the path traversed).

3. * Find the height of a tree or a building on a sunny day. The information you need is the length of both your shadow and that of the tree and your own height. From these data the tree's height may be found by using similar triangles. Does the sun's position affect your results?

4. In using the triangulation method of measuring a distance, an observer sights upon an object directly opposite him on the far bank of a river. He places a stake where he is standing and then moves 50 meters upstream parallel to the river. Here he places a second stake. Then he moves 10 meters farther upstream and places a third stake. From this stake he walks directly away from the river until he is on a line with the second stake and the object on the far side of the river. He finds that he is 44 meters from the third stake. What is the width of the river? See Fig. 3–1 of the text for a diagram of this method.

5. * It is possible to determine your distance from a landmark by measuring two angles and a base line. Choose for a base line the side of a building or a football-field side line of known length. By sighting to an object from each end of the base line, the angle which each line of sight makes with the base line may be determined by using two sticks and a protractor. If these results are scaled so as to fit on a piece of paper, the distance may be roughly measured. The distance may also be determined trigonometrically, since two angles and a side are known.

6. * What is the diameter of the moon? Assuming that the moon is 3.8×10^5 km from the earth, you can determine its diameter by the following method. Place two strips of opaque tape 2 cm apart on a windowpane. Make a pinhole in a card and then observe the moon through the pinhole and between the two strips. Back away from the window until the moon just fills the space between the two strips. Measure the distance from the card to the window. Using the geometry of similar triangles, calculate the diameter of the moon. Do **not** attempt to use this method to determine the diameter of the sun. The bright sun will be harmful to the eye. Could this method be used to determine the size of a star?

7. * Cover one eye with your hand and try to judge distances with only one eye. Observe that most of the hunting animals and birds have a unique placement of the eyes which permits them to estimate the striking distance to their prey. Consider the difficulty of almost any of the many tasks we perform if we were denied this depth perception.

8. * A camera with one lens cannot show relative distance unless the picture it takes shows the depth of space which separates objects. Show how this could be used to make a camera "lie." Take a picture of objects on a table, from slightly below the edge. Notice that similar objects appear to be of different size depending upon their position on the table. Effects such as this are used to show the illusion of a person seemingly inside a bottle or larger than a tree.

9. (a) A simple range finder may be improvised by using two meter sticks to establish sight lines to the object. The amount these deviate from parallel positions is a measure of the nearness of the object sighted. If the meter sticks form equal angles with their base line, and are separated by one meter at the near end and 96 centimeters at the end away from the observer, what is the distance to the sighted object?

   (b) If the meter sticks are not sufficiently straight to give an accurate reading on the separations, an error in range estimation will result. What difference in the estimated range would result if the front measurement had been 96.2 instead of 96.0 cm when the backs of the sticks remained at 1 meter? Express this error as a per cent.

(c) As the sticks are made more nearly parallel, failure to sight the sticks exactly produces a much larger error of range estimation. Compare the ranges when the fronts of the sticks are 99.0 and 99.2 cm apart while the backs remain at one meter.

10. * Constructing a scale model of the solar system: A volleyball representing the sun and placed near one end of a football field will give a scale on which an inch will equal approximately 10^5 miles (0.1 megamile). To such a scale, the earth will be only a little more than $\frac{1}{16}$ inch in diameter and 930 inches (77 feet) away from the sun. Distant Neptune would be almost half a mile away and only a little over $\frac{1}{4}$ inch in diameter. What sizes will our other planets and their satellites have on our model? By what factor must all dimensions be reduced if this scale model is to fit easily on your football field? What object could you use to represent the earth on this new scale?

11. Determine the thickness of the leaves in one of your books by measuring the thickness of 200 pages (100 sheets). Why is it suggested that you use 100 sheets? What assumptions are made in this measurement?

12. A straight line 5.0 cm long is rotated in a plane about one end. What is the area swept out by this motion?

13. A straight line 20 cm in length is moved to a new position parallel to and 10 cm from its original position. What is the area of the surface that is swept out in moving the line?

14. A circle whose radius is 5.0 cm is moved along its axis to a new position parallel to the original plane. If it has been moved 10 cm, what volume has been generated by this motion?

15. A piece of cardboard whose dimensions are 12 cm by 8.0 cm is tilted about the 8.0 cm edge through an angle of 90 deg. What volume has been swept out by this motion?

16. An indirect method for determining the area of an irregular surface was mentioned in this chapter. What is assumed in this method?

17. A 12-inch LP record which plays for 25 minutes at $33\frac{1}{3}$ RPM has 4 inches of grooved surface along the radius. What is the average distance between grooves?

18. A person reports seeing a "flying saucer" 200 feet long, at an altitude of 6000 feet and flying at an estimated speed of 2000 miles per hour. Discuss the accuracy of this observation.

19. Two students made the following length measurements in the lab and wished to find their sum — 3.52 m, 4.213 m, and 5.034 m. One student insisted that they should round off to the nearest hundredth of a meter first and then add, while the other student argued that they should be able to add the measurements directly and then round off their sum.

(a) Try both of these methods and compare the results.

(b) Which student was correct?

20. Solve the following problems with due consideration to significant figures.

(a) $\dfrac{1.4 \times 10^3}{2.6 \times 10^5} = ?$

(b) $3.7(6.27 \times 10^{-2}) = ?$

(c) $46.7 - 10.04 = ?$

(d) $\dfrac{8.34 \times 0.659}{12.03} = ?$

21. A student measures a block of wood and records the following results: length = 6.3 cm, width = 12.1 cm, and height = .84 cm.

(a) What is the volume of this block?

(b) Assume the length and width measurements to be correct; however, you can see that the height measurement may be off by 0.01 cm either way. How would this change your answer for the volume?

(c) What fraction is this of the total volume?

22. If a circular piece of tin has a measured radius of 2.6 cm, what is its circumference?

23. A bag contains 25 identical marbles. A student makes measurements on one of them and determines its volume to be 1.76 cm³. What should his estimate for the total volume of all the marbles be?

24. A bus driver clocked the following times for portions of his route:

Station A to Station B	1.63 hr
Station B to Station C	4.7 hr
Station C to Station D	0.755 hr
Station D to Station E	2.00 hr

(a) How long did it take him to drive from Station A to Station E?

(b) What part of the whole trip does the time between Stations B and D represent?

(c) The time to go from Station A to Station C is how much more than the time to go from Station C to Station E?

FUNCTIONS AND SCALING

CHAPTER 4

4–1. Mathematical Relations

Many of the laws of physical science are most usefully expressed by mathematical relations, which show how one thing that we can measure depends upon other things that we can measure. In this section we shall discuss some of these relations.

Direct Proportion

One of the simplest relations between two quantities is called direct proportion. For example, let us look at the relation between the volume of a piece of iron and its weight. If we make measurements on pieces of iron we find that 1 ft^3 weighs 440 pounds, 2 ft^3 weighs 880 pounds, 3 ft^3 weighs 1320 pounds, and so on. This kind of relation, in which doubling the volume doubles the weight, tripling the volume triples the weight, etc., is what we mean by direct proportion. You will meet many cases of direct proportion in physics, so it is well to understand the various ways of describing this relation. We can say weight "is proportional to" volume of iron, or weight "varies directly as" volume of iron. Both mean the same thing: twice the volume, twice the weight; ten times the volume, ten times the weight, and so on.

We can write the relation in the shorter form

$$W \propto V,$$

where W is the weight of a piece of iron, V its volume, and the symbol $\propto$ means "is proportional to." If we have two different volumes of iron, V and V', the fact that their weights W and W' are proportional to their volumes can also be expressed as

$$\frac{W'}{W} = \frac{V'}{V}.$$

$W \propto V$ is just another way of making this statement.

Another useful form of this relation expresses the fact that when weight and volume are related by direct proportion they have a constant ratio. If we divide the weight of a sample of iron by its volume, the result will be the same as that obtained by dividing the weight of any other sample by its volume.

$$\left(\frac{W}{V}\right)_{\text{one sample}} = \left(\frac{W}{V}\right)_{\text{another sample}} = k.$$

The constant ratio k is called the *proportionality constant.* In our example of iron, $k = 440$ pounds per cubic foot. We can express this relation as an equation for *any* piece of iron:

$$\frac{W}{V} = k$$

or

$$W = kV.$$

Notice that this expression is very similar to the relation $W \propto V$. Indeed, if we do not know the numerical value of k it is just the same thing.

But when k is known, $W = kV$ tells us more; it is an equation which gives us the numerical relation between W and V.

We can illustrate this relation between weight and volume for iron by a graph. We must choose scales — one for the vertical direction, marking off some number of pounds for each vertical division of the paper, and one for the horizontal direction, marking off volumes in ft^3. Now we can mark a point on the graph for each of the pairs of values that we know.

Volume	*Weight*
1 ft^3	440 pounds
2 ft^3	880 pounds
3 ft^3	1320 pounds

The graph is the straight line shown in Fig. 4–1. On it are shown two values of V and the corresponding values of W. You can see from the similar triangles that the ratio W/V is the same in both cases. Such a graph presents to the eye the meaning of the equation $W = kV$. It is said to represent this equation. All direct proportions are represented by straight-line graphs such as the one we have just drawn. Different straight lines or different vertical scales correspond to different values of the proportionality constant k.

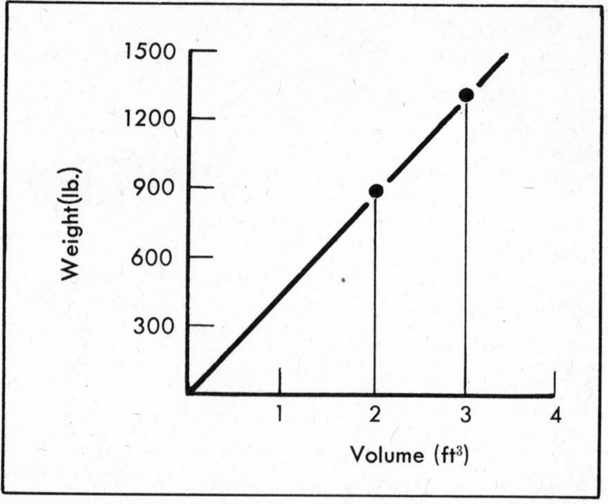

4–1. Graphic representation of a direct proportion. If the weight of 1 ft^3 of iron were less, would the graph be steeper? or less steeper?

Variation with the Second and Third Powers; Similar Figures

Another type of relation occurs when one quantity varies as the square of another. For example, the area A of a square of side L is equal to L^2:

$$A = L^2 \qquad (k = 1).$$

If L is measured in meters, the area A will be in square meters (m^2). Also, the area A of a circle of radius R is given by

$$A = \pi R^2 \qquad (k = \pi).$$

Both of these equations show that one quantity, an area, varies with the square of another, a length.

All circles are similar figures: all have the same shape. They are just magnified or reduced copies one of another. Also all squares are similar figures. But they are not the only similar figures. All sorts of figures may be made in magnified or reduced copies. The two curious areas in Fig. 4–2 are similar. One was made by magnifying the other until every linear dimension was tripled. You can check this statement by seeing that the sides of every square in the larger area are just three times what they are in the small one. This means that every square in the large area has just nine times the area of the corresponding small one. The total area of the large figure is therefore also nine times that of the smaller one. Just as in the case of circles and squares, the areas

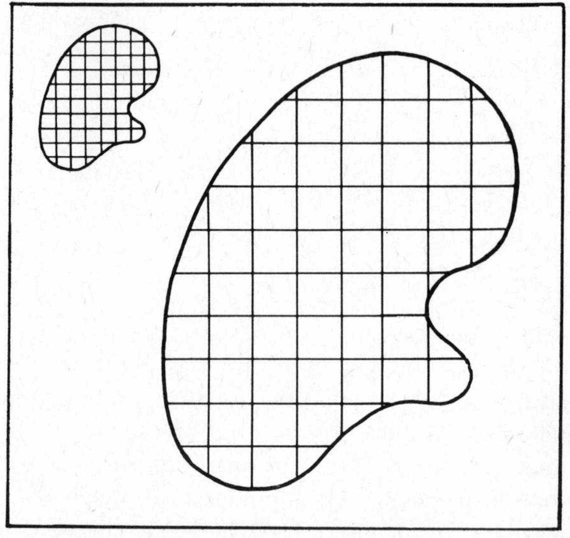

4–2. These two figures are similar; every linear dimension of the larger figure is the same multiple of the corresponding dimension of the smaller. In this case the dimensions of the larger figure are three times those of the smaller. You can check this by measuring corresponding squares.

of any similar figures "go up as" (vary as) the square of a linear dimension. When the linear dimension is multiplied by 3, the area is multiplied by 9. In general, then, for similar figures

$$A \propto L^2.$$

Notice that it does not matter which linear measurement you take for L, as long as you use the corresponding measure for all the similar figures you are comparing. For example, for a square you could use the diagonal just as well as the side. When the side of one square is n times as long as that of another, the diagonals are in the same ratio. And the area of the first square is n^2 times as large as that of the second. The same thing applies to the corresponding lengths in any two similar figures. (See Fig. 4–3.)

Some figures that have the same name may *not* be similar. Not *all* rectangles, for example, are similar. We can have two rectangles with the same base b but different heights h. The area is given as the product of the two linear dimensions: $A = bh$. Although such examples are different from similar figures, they have in common the fact that the area is always measured in units of the square of a length. If we use the meter as the measure of all lengths, the areas will be specified in terms of the number of meters squared.

Just as all areas are the product of two lengths, all volumes are the product of three linear dimensions. Again we must distinguish between solid figures like cylinders which may have the same base and different heights, and sets of similar solid figures like spheres or cubes in which every linear dimension is magnified or shrunk by the same factor. For similar solid figures, when the linear dimensions are multiplied by the factor n, the volumes are multiplied by the factor n^3, one n for each linear dimension. For example, the volume of a sphere is

$$V = \frac{4\pi}{3} R^3,$$

where R is its radius. Then a sphere of radius $R' = nR$ has a volume

$$\begin{aligned} V' &= \frac{4\pi}{3}(R')^3 \\ &= \frac{4\pi}{3} n^3 R^3 \\ &= n^3 V. \end{aligned}$$

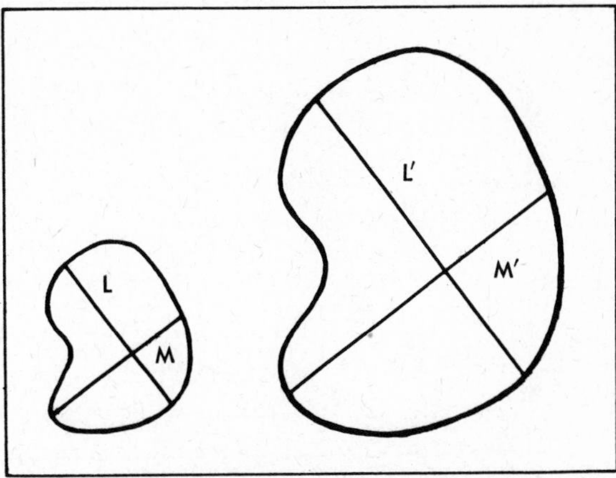

4–3. Because these two figures are similar, the ratio of their areas is the same as the ratio of the squares of *any* two corresponding dimensions. Here, since L' is twice L (M' is also twice M) the area of the larger figure is four times the area of the smaller.

This is just a particular example of the general rule: the ratio of the volumes of similar solids is the cube of the ratio of their linear dimensions. Check this yourself for cubes or for some curious solid that you build. One good way is to make the figure of blocks or bricks, then find the ratio of the numbers of bricks you must use to make a similar solid with every linear dimension doubled. You will find that you use eight times — that is, 2^3 — the original number of bricks.

Equations — Graphical Representation; Power Laws; Functions

For particular similar figures such as squares or circles, we can do more than show the proportionality of area and linear dimension: $A \propto L^2$. We can write equations including the proportionality constant: $A = L^2$ for the square and $A = \pi R^2$ for the circle. Just as we could represent the equation $W = kV$ by a graph, so we can represent these equations by graphs. The relation between length of edge and area for a square is shown in the table.

Length of Edge	Area
1 m	1 m²
2 m	4 m²
3 m	9 m²
4 m	16 m²
.	.
.	.
.	.

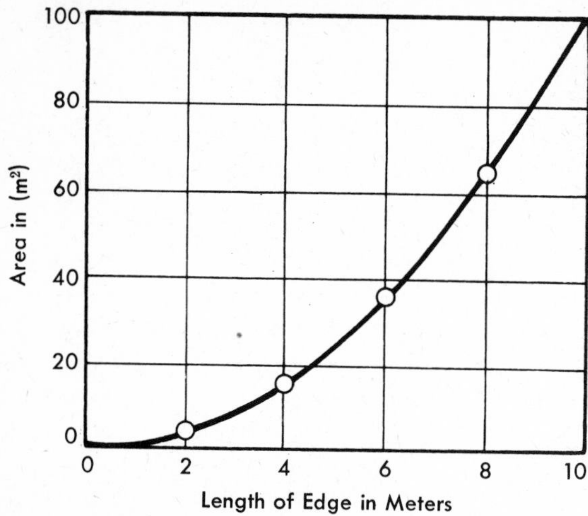

4–4. Graphic representation of the area of a square versus the length of a side. How can you use this graph to find the area of a square if you know the length of a side? How would you use it to find the length of a side, knowing the area?

In Fig. 4–4 we have used the values in this table to draw the graph of $A = L^2$.

Since the equation for the areas of any set of similar figures can always be written $A = kL^2$, we can use the graph of Fig. 4–4 for the relation of area and linear dimension for any set of similar figures. All we have to do is to change the vertical scale to account for the different values of k. For example, since $A = \pi R^2$ for a circle, we can read the radius on the horizontal scale and the area on the vertical one by multiplying every vertical reading by π.

We can make the same kind of graphical representation for the volumes of similar figures. The table shows a few values of the relation for the volume of a cube, $V = L^3$.

Length of Edge	Volume
1 m	1 m^3
2 m	8 m^3
3 m	27 m^3
.	.
.	.
.	.

We have graphed these values in Fig. 4–5. Again we can use this figure for all sets of similar volumes by adjusting the vertical scale for the value of k in $V = kL^3$. For example, if we read the radius of a sphere on the horizontal scale, the volume is $4\pi/3$ times the number on the vertical scale.

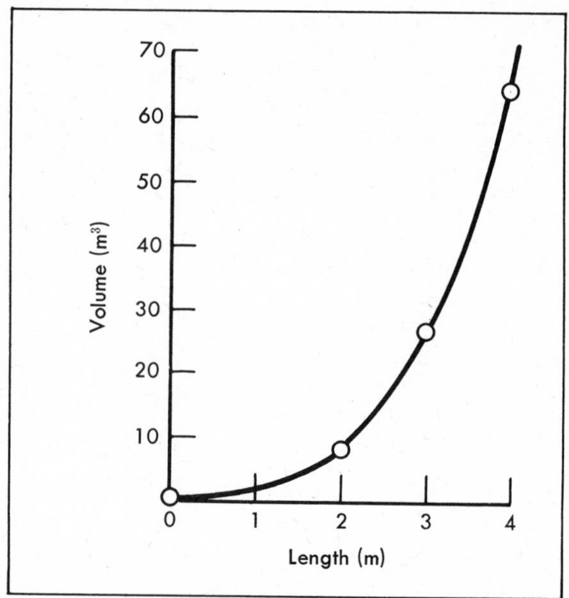

4–5. Graphic representation of the volume of a cube versus the length of its side.

Relations in which one quantity is proportional to a power, like the square, cube, etc., of another occur often in physics. They are called power laws. In addition to first, second, and third power laws, such as $W = kV$, $A = kL^2$, $V = kL^3$, which we discussed here, we also find inverse-power laws, such as $I = k/L^2$ — intensity of light is inversely proportional to the second power of the distance from the light source. We shall discuss the inverse-square relation in Section 4–3.

Whenever we have a relation between the values of one quantity in terms of the values of another, we have what is called a *mathematical function.* The area of a square is a *function* of the length of its side, and the volume of a sphere is a *function* of its radius.

The idea of functional relation is a very general one. For example, the expected time of arrival of a train at any station along a route is a function of the station's position along the route. A railroad timetable represents a set of such functions, for various trains and routes. Equations, tables, and graphs, as we have seen, are all useful ways of representing mathematical functions. Mathematicians have extended the ideas of function and relation far beyond what we have indicated here. If you are interested, see some of the references at the end of the chapter.

4–2. Interpolation and Extrapolation

Suppose we measure the volumes and corresponding radii of a number of spheres and plot the results (volume against radius). From the measurements, we are sure of the positions of a number of points on this plot, one for each sphere. If we now draw a smooth curve through these points, we obtain a curve from which we can find the volume of a sphere for any radius — not only for the values of the radii we have measured. The process of finding from this plot new values located between the measured ones is called *interpolation.* Such a process is meaningful and useful when there are good reasons to believe that the curve is valid for values between the measured ones. Then one gets information which is not immediately available from the measurements.

In the example of the relation between the volumes and radii of spheres, we know from the equation $V = \frac{4\pi}{3} R^3$ that the volume changes smoothly with the radius. So a smooth curve through a few computed or measured points is reasonable. When no formula is known, however, we depend only on experimental measurements. Then drawing a smooth curve expresses our belief that things change smoothly in nature. Interpolation always carries with it some element of risk. Even if things do change smoothly, we must get experimental values quite close together if we want to know how the graph goes in any region where it curves sharply. Interpolation is of no use at all for graphs of functions which cannot be represented by smooth curves.

Extrapolation, carrying the plot out beyond the range of the data, is even more risky. Error can arise here more easily, but so can discovery. For example, the problems encountered by aircraft in breaking the sound barrier were foreseen by extrapolation of equations which describe the exact behavior of aircraft at speeds well below that of sound. Extrapolation from the behavior of gases at normal temperatures leads to the idea of a lowest possible temperature, absolute zero, but about objects traveling close to the speed of light, extrapolation from ordinary experience leads to nonsense.

In our examples of the volumes of a series of spheres and the areas of squares, extrapolation would be quite as safe as interpolation, for we know the equations to hold according to the geometry of Euclid for spheres or squares of any size, however large. But the physicist has to admit that he has no certain test for the validity of Euclid's geometry beyond the distances to the galaxies. Indeed, theoretical physicists have invented proposals to change the laws of Euclid whenever enormous distances are involved. From the point of view of physics, the geometry of space is subject to experiment. Euclid's geometry may not be an accurate description of our measurements if the shapes we study range in size over many orders of magnitude. Naturally, we shall not change our description unless it gets us into trouble. In this course the geometry of Euclid will serve us well.

4–3. The Inverse-Square Relation

Look at a row of street lights that stretch away from you in the distance. The lamps themselves are all the same — that is, each gives off the same amount of light each second — but the closer each one is to you the more intense it appears. If the light spreads out equally in all directions (which is nearly true for a street lamp and a star and many other sources), it can be pictured as shown in Fig. 4–6. Here we consider just a portion of the light moving out through a sort of "pyramid" from the point P. As the distance

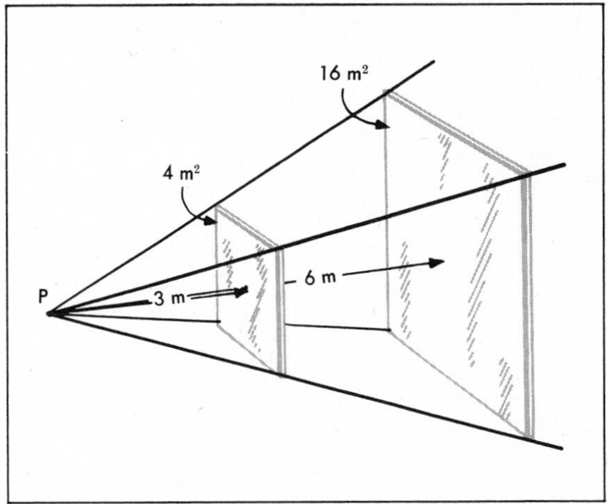

4–6. The inverse-square relation. Light from a point (P) radiates in all directions. Since the light spreads out to cover four times the area at twice the distance, it follows that it can be only $\frac{1}{4}$ as intense. Thus, when the distance is doubled, the intensity decreases to $\frac{1}{4}$, or the intensity is inversely proportional to the square of the distance.

from the source increases, the light is spread over a greater area and the light appears less intense. This suggests that the intensity of the light is inversely proportional to the area it falls on.

$$I \propto \frac{1}{A},$$

where I represents the intensity and A the area. For the moment let us assume that this relation holds for light. Later you will study light intensities experimentally.

Each of the sides of the squares in Fig. 4–6 is proportional to its distance from P. Therefore, the area of each square is proportional to the square of that distance. If we call the distance d, this can be expressed as

$$A \propto d^2.$$

Combining this relation with $I \propto \frac{1}{A}$ we find that

$$I \propto \frac{1}{d^2}.$$

This is the inverse-square relation, which for light says that the intensity is inversely proportional to the square of the distance from the source.

In detail you can see that $I \propto \frac{1}{d^2}$ by remembering that

$$I \propto \frac{1}{A}$$

means $$\frac{I'}{I} = \frac{A}{A'} \qquad (1)$$

and that $$A \propto d^2$$

means $$\frac{A}{A'} = \frac{d^2}{(d')^2}. \qquad (2)$$

So, combining (1) and (2) gives

$$\frac{I'}{I} = \frac{d^2}{(d')^2}. \qquad (3)$$

This is the same as

$$I \propto \frac{1}{d^2}.$$

Note that relation (3) holds for a single source at distances d' and d. It also holds for two identical sources, one at distance d' and the other at distance d. For example, suppose we have two street lamps, which we call 1 and 2, at different distances d_1 and d_2 from a white wall which they illuminate. Then, their intensities at the wall are in the ratio

$$\frac{I_1}{I_2} = \frac{d_2^2}{d_1^2}.$$

This relation enables us to estimate the distance of one lamp if we have another equal lamp at a known distance. For example, suppose we find that a lamp 10 meters (d_1) away gives an intensity that is 16 times that of an identical lamp at some unknown distance d_2. (Photoelectric cells, camera light meters, and photographic plates can give accurate measures of relative intensity. So can the eye with the aid of a special screen on which to make comparisons.) How can we find d_2? We know that I_1/I_2 is 16 and we know that d_1 is 10 meters.

$$16 = \frac{I_1}{I_2} = \frac{d_2^2}{(10 \text{ meters})^2}.$$

Solving for d_2 we get

$$d_2 = \sqrt{16 \times (10 \text{ meters})^2} = 4 \times 10 \text{ meters} = 40 \text{ meters}.$$

This is just the method which gives us our knowledge of the distance of far-off stars, whose distance from us is too great to be measured by the geometric methods using the diameter of the earth's orbit as a base line. The measurement is made by comparing the intensity of the faint image of a faraway star on a photographic plate with the intensity of a near-by star which appears to give off the same amount of light. The measurement is at best a rough one, because we do not expect that the two stars are really equally strong sources of light. But in this rough way we can go far beyond the possibilities of triangulation methods and at least determine the order of magnitude of the distance to far-off stars.

We can see how the inverse-square relation works by measuring the distance of a near-by star, using the inverse-square relation and comparing our result with the distance measured geometrically. There is a good star for this purpose, α Centauri A. Judging from its color and calculated mass, this star is very similar to the sun. But the intensity of illumination here at the earth is 10^{11} times greater from the sun than from α Centauri A. From the inverse-square relation we learn that α Centauri A must be about $\sqrt{10^{11}} = 3 \times 10^5$ times as far away from us as the sun is. The sun is 1.5×10^{11} m away, so the star must be about 4.5×10^{16} m away. And this is almost exactly what a geometrical measurement also tells us. In this case the inverse-square relation proves itself as a method of distance measurement. When we apply the inverse-square relation to measurement of distances of stars farther away, our confidence is strengthened because it agrees with other indirect methods of measurement.

We were able to find the distance to a star by two methods, but we do not have much hope of finding the size geometrically. The angle subtended at our eye is much too small to be measured visually or even with the best instruments. If the star is the same size as the sun, this angle is about the same as the angle a dime would subtend at a distance of 300 km. That is about the distance from New York to Washington. No wonder the sizes of stars cannot be measured directly even through the largest telescopes.

The inverse-square relation has given us a powerful new way to measure great distances. Many other mathematical relations in physics can be exploited to tell us things about the physical world. Often these do not appear to be closely related to the experiments which gave us the relation in the first place. We have introduced the inverse-square relation here to illustrate the use of such relations in physics, not to discuss the nature of light. Light will be our topic later on.

We must realize, however, that the inverse-square method of distance measurement has its limitations. The inverse-square relation will certainly not apply if there is anything between the eye and the source that makes light deviate from a straight-line path or absorbs some of it. Obviously, a patch of fog would reduce the intensity from a distant lamp and upset any calculations based on the inverse-square law. There must also be some definite meaning given to the distance between eye and source. This sounds obvious — and it is, if we think of a street lamp in the next block. We measure from where we stand to any point on the lamp. Since the lamp is so far away, all these measurements give essentially the same distance d. Thus you can see that the inverse-square relation will be true if the physical dimensions of the light source are small (less than 5 per cent, say) compared with the distance between eye and source. The inverse-square relation describes many situations in nature where something — light, particles, or lines of electric force — radiates from a point in straight lines uniformly in all directions. Many experimental verifications of this law for light and other effects have proved its truth and verified the deductions we made from geometry.

4–4. Scaling — The Physics of Lilliput

The fictional traveler Lemuel Gulliver spent a busy time in a kingdom called Lilliput, where all living things — men, cattle, trees, grass — were exactly similar to our world, except that they were all built on the scale of one inch to the foot. Lilliputians were a little under six inches high, on the average, and built proportionately just as we are. Gulliver also visited Brobdingnag, the country of the giants, who were exactly like men but twelve times as tall. As Swift described it, daily life in both kingdoms was about like ours (in the eighteenth century). His commentary on human behavior is still worth reading, but we shall see that people of such sizes just could not have been as he described them.

Long before Swift lived, Galileo understood why very small or very large models of man could not be like us, but apparently Dean Swift had never read what Galileo wrote. One character in Galileo's "Two New Sciences" says, "Now since . . . in geometry, . . . mere size cuts no figure, I do not see that the properties of circles, triangles, cylinders, cones, and other solid figures will change with their size. . . ." But his physicist friend replies, "The common opinion is here absolutely wrong." Let us see why.

We start with the strength of a rope. It is easy to see that if one man who pulls with a certain strength can almost break a certain rope, two such ropes will just withstand the pull of two men. A single large rope with the same total area of cross section as the two smaller ropes combined will contain just double the number of fibers of one of the small ropes, and it will also do the job. In other words, the breaking strength of a wire or rope is proportional to its area of cross section, or to the square of its diameter. Experience and theory agree in this conclusion. Furthermore, the same relation holds, not only for ropes

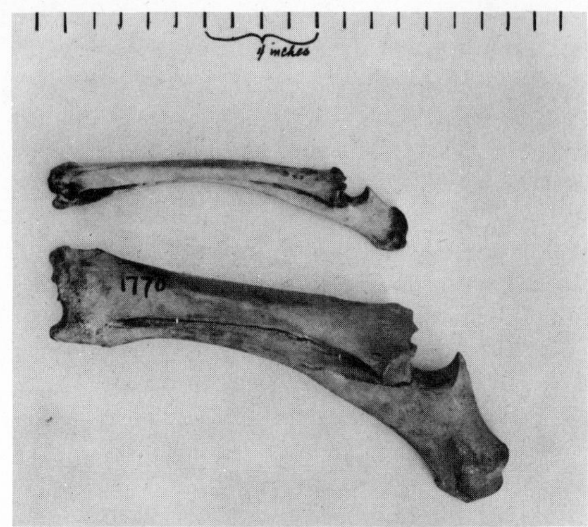

4–7 (a). The front leg bones of a bison and a gazelle. The animals are related, but the gazelle is much smaller. The photos show the approximate relative sizes of the bones.

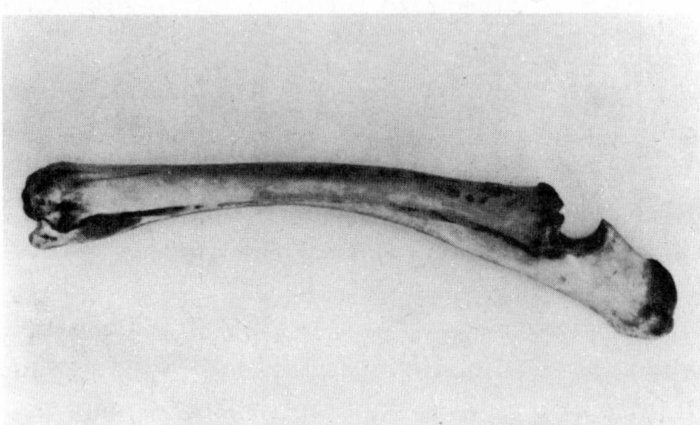

4–7 (b). The leg bone of a gazelle enlarged to the same length as the bison bone. Note that the bone of the larger animal is much thicker in comparison to its length than that of the gazelle. The small deer is generally more lightly and gracefully built. Can you visualize how much different Lilliputians must have been from men of normal size?

or cables supporting a pull, but also for columns or struts supporting a thrust. The thrust which a column will support, comparing only those of a given material, is also proportional to the cross-sectional area of the column.

Now the body of a man or an animal is held up by a set of columns or struts — the skeleton — supported by various braces and cables, which are muscles and tendons. But the weight of the body which must be supported is proportional to the amount of flesh and bone present, that is, to the volume.

Let us now compare Gulliver with the Brobdingnagian giant, twelve times his height. Since the giant is exactly like Gulliver in construction, every one of his linear dimensions is twelve times the corresponding one of Gulliver's. Because the strength of his columns and braces is proportional to their cross-sectional area and thus to the square of their linear dimension (strength $\propto L^2$), his bones will be 12^2 or 144 times as strong as Gulliver's. Because his weight is proportional to his volume and thus to L^3, it will be 12^3 or 1728 times as great as Gulliver's. So the giant will have a strength-to-weight ratio a dozen times smaller than ours. Just to support his own weight, he would have as much trouble as we should have in carrying eleven men on our back.

In reality, of course, Lilliput and Brobdingnag do not exist. But we can see real effects of a difference in scale if we compare similar animals of very different sizes. The smaller ones are not scale models of the larger ones. Fig. 4–7 shows the corresponding leg bones of two closely related animals of the deer family: one a tiny gazelle, the other a bison. Notice that the bone of the large animal is not at all similar geometrically to that of the smaller. It is much thicker for its length, thus counteracting the scale change, which would make a strictly similar bone too weak.

Galileo wrote very clearly on this very point, disproving the possibility of Brobdingnag, or of any normal-looking giants: ". . . if one wishes to maintain in a great giant the same proportion of limb as that found in an ordinary man he must either use a harder and stronger material for

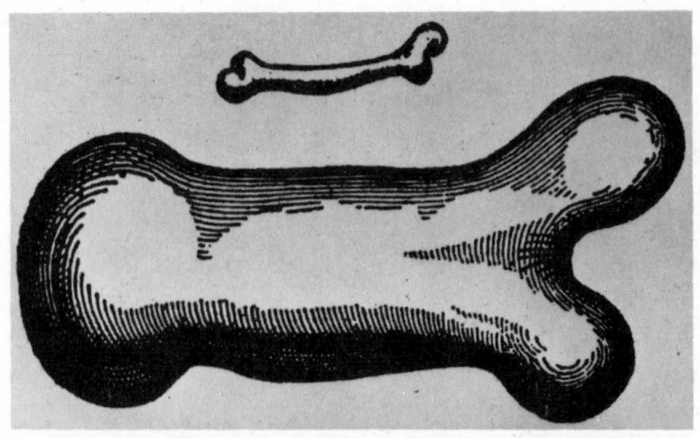

4–8. Galileo's drawing illustrating scaling. Over 300 years ago, Galileo wrote concerning the fact that a bone of greater length must be increased in thickness in greater proportion in order to be comparably strong. The large bone in this illustration from his book is about three times as long as the small bone and almost nine times as thick. Actually, this old illustration is in error. The large bone should be only about 5.2 times as thick. Do you agree? Why?

making the bones, or he must admit a diminution of strength in comparison with men of medium stature; for if his height be increased inordinately he will fall and be crushed under his own weight. Whereas, if the size of a body be diminished, the strength of that body is not diminished in the same proportion; indeed, the smaller the body the greater its relative strength. Thus a small dog could probably carry on his back two or three dogs of his own size; but I believe that a horse could not carry even one of his own size." The sketch of Fig. 4–8 is taken from Galileo, who drew it to illustrate the paragraph just quoted.

An elephant is already so large that his limbs are clumsily thickened. However, a whale, the largest of all animals, may weigh forty times as much as an elephant; yet the whale's bones are not proportionately thickened. They are strong enough because the whale is supported by water. What is the fate of a stranded whale? His ribs break. Some of the dinosaurs of old were animals of whalelike size; how did *they* get along?

Following Galileo, we have investigated the problems of scaling up to giants. Now let's take a look at some of the problems that arise when we scale down.

When you climb dripping wet out of a pool there is a thin film of water on your skin. Your fingers are no less wet than your forearm; the thickness of the water film is much the same over most of your body. Roughly, at least, the amount of water you bring out is proportional to the surface area of your body. You can express this by the relation

$$\text{amount of water} \propto L^2,$$

where L is your height. The original load on your frame is as before, proportional to your volume. So, the ratio *extra load/original load* is proportional to L^2/L^3, or to $1/L$. Perhaps you carry out of the pool a glassful or so, which amounts to about a 1 per cent increase in what you have to move about. But a Lilliputian will bring out about 12 per cent of his weight, which would be equivalent to a heavy winter suit of clothing with an overcoat. Getting out of the pool would be no fun! If a fly gets wet, his body load doubles, and he is all but imprisoned by the drop of water.

There is a still more important effect of the scale of a living body. Your body loses heat mainly through the skin (and some through breathing out warm air). It is easy to believe — and it can be checked by experiment — that the heat loss is proportional to the surface area, so that

$$\text{heat loss} \propto L^2,$$

keeping other factors, like the temperature, nature of skin, and so on, constant. The food taken in must supply this heat, as well as the surplus energy we use in moving about. So minimum food needs go as L^2. If a man like Gulliver can live off a leg of lamb and a loaf of bread for a day or two, a Lilliputian with the same body temperature will require a volume of food only $(\frac{1}{12})^2$ as large. But his leg of lamb, scaled down to his world, will be smaller in volume by a factor of $(\frac{1}{12})^3$. Therefore, he would need a dozen of his roasts and loaves to feel as well fed as Gulliver did after one. Lilliputians must be a hungry lot, restless, active, graceful, but easily waterlogged. You can recognize these qualities in many small mammals, like a mouse.

We can see why there are no warm-blooded animals much smaller than the mouse. Fish and frogs and insects can be very much smaller because their temperature is not higher than their surroundings. In accord with the scaling laws of area and volume, small, warm-blooded animals need relatively a great deal of food; really small ones could not gather or even digest such an enormous amount. Certainly the agriculture of the Lilliputians could not have supported a kingdom like the one Gulliver described.

Now we see that neither Brobdingnag nor Lilliput can really be a scale model of our world. But what have these conclusions to do with physics?

Let's start again with the very large. As we scale up any system, the load will eventually be greater than the strength of the structure. This effect applies to every physical system, not just to animals, of course. Buildings can be very large because their materials are stronger than bone, their shapes are different, and they do not move. These facts determine the constants like K in the equation

$$\text{strength} = KL^2,$$

but the same laws hold. No building can be made which will look like the Empire State but be as high as a mountain, say ten thousand meters. Mountains are solid structures, for the most part, without interior cavities. Just as the bones of a giant must be thick, an object of mountainous size on the earth must be all but solid, or else built of new materials yet unknown.

Our arguments are not restricted to the surface of the earth. We can imagine building a tremendous structure far out in space away from the gravitational pull of the earth. The load then is not given by the earth's gravitational pull, but as the structure is built larger and larger each part pulls gravitationally on every other and soon the outside of the structure is pulled in with great force. The inside, built of ordinary materials, is crushed, and large protuberances on the surface break off or sink in. As a result any large structure like a planet has a simple shape, and if it is large enough the shape is close to a sphere. Any other shape will be unable to support itself. Here is the essential reason why the planets and the sun tend to be spherical. The pull of gravity is important for us on earth, but as we extend the range of dimensions which we study, it becomes absolutely dominant in the very large. Only motion can change this result. The great masses of gas which are nebulae, for example, are changing in time, and hence the law that large objects must be simple in shape is modified.

When we go from our size to the very small, gravitational effects cease to be important. But as we saw in investigating Lilliput, surface effects become significant. If we go far enough toward the very small, surfaces no longer appear smooth, but are so rough that we have difficulty in defining a surface. Other descriptions must be used. In any case, it will not come as a complete surprise that in the domain of the atom, the very small, scale factors demonstrate that the dominant pull is one which is not easily observed in everyday experience.

Such arguments as these run through all of physics. Like order-of-magnitude measurements, they are extremely valuable when we begin the study of any physical system. How the behavior of a system will change with changes in the scale of its dimensions, its motion, and so on, is often the best guide to a detailed analysis.

Even more, it is by the study of systems built on many unusual scales that physicists have been able to uncover unsuspected physical relations. When changing scale, one aspect of the physical world may be much emphasized and another one may be minimized. In this way we may discover, or at least get a clearer view of, things which are less obvious on our normal scale of experience. It is largely for this reason that physicists examine, in and out of their laboratories, the very large and the very small, the slow and the rapid, the hot and the cold, and all the other unusual circumstances they can contrive. In examining what happens in these circumstances we use instruments both to produce the unusual circumstances and to extend our senses in making measurements.

It is hard to resist pointing out how much the scale of man's own size affects the way he sees the world. It has been largely the task of physics to try to form a picture of the world which does not depend upon the way we happen to be built. But it is hard to get rid of these effects of our own scale. We can build big roads and bridges which are long and thin, but are essentially not three-dimensional, complex structures. The very biggest things we can make which have some roundness, which are fully three-dimensional, are buildings and great ships. These lack a good deal of being a thousand times larger than men in their linear dimensions.

Nor can we, as yet, build anything complex like a watch or a radio tube which is scaled down to 10^{-3} of our own length. In this range of magnitudes lies all our engineering. Physics goes much beyond, outward to the galaxies and inward to the nucleus of the atom. The extension of our engineering technology to the very small and to the really giant belongs to the future. Power plants a mile high, or radio circuits built into a pinhead, would represent enormous new possibilities for technology. They may come, but for the foreseeable future the human scale will fix the physical nature of most of our endeavors.

Even within our present technology our scaling arguments are important. If we design a new large object on the basis of a small one, we are warned that new effects too small to detect on our scale may enter and even become the most important things to consider. We cannot just scale up and down blindly, geometrically; but by scaling in the light of physical reasoning we can sometimes foresee what changes will occur. In this way we can employ scaling in intelligent airplane design, for example, and not arrive at a jet transport that looks like a bee — and won't fly.

FOR HOME, DESK, AND LAB

1. The total thickness of 500 sheets of a particular sample of paper is 40 mm. Assuming that they are of uniform thickness, plot a graph of the total thickness against the number of sheets. From your graph determine the thickness of 200 sheets. Of 300 sheets. Of 600 sheets.

2. A book is to have a total of 600 pages.

(a) Plot the thickness of the book against the thickness of each sheet of paper (1 sheet is 2 pages), assuming that the paper is available in *any* thickness from 0.060 mm to 0.120 mm.

(b) Actually, paper is available only in certain specified thicknesses. If we assume that the thicknesses are multiples of 0.005 mm between these two limits, can we connect the points of our graph with a smooth line? Why?

3. The total surface area of a rectangular solid is the sum of the areas of the six faces. If each dimension of a given rectangular solid is doubled, what effect does this have on the total surface area?

4. Carefully plot the area of a square against length of side for lengths from 1 to 10. (This may be used as a square-root table in solving other problems.)

5. The volume of one cylinder is eight times the volume of another similar cylinder.

(a) If the circumference of the base of the smaller cylinder is 0.5 m, what is the circumference of the base of the larger cylinder?

(b) If another cylinder, also having eight times the volume, has the same height as the smaller cylinder, what is the circumference of its base?

6. A hollow metal sphere has a wall thickness of 2 cm. If you increase both the diameter and thickness of this sphere so that the overall volume is three times the original overall volume, how thick will the shell of the new sphere be?

7. The range of a television station is a function of the height of the antenna. The range is given by the formula $D = 3.56\sqrt{h}$, where D is the range in kilometers and h is the height of the antenna in meters.

(a) Calculate the range for antenna heights of 10 meters, 20 m, 30 m, and 50 m.

(b) Plot the range against the antenna height.

(c) Can you determine from the graph the range for an antenna height of 40 m? Of 70 m?

(d) How would you plot the data to get a straight-line graph?

8. * Solid materials resist the application of forces tending to distort them. Clamp a meter stick to a table and hang various known weights from the end. Measure the amount of bending in each case and plot these values against the corresponding weight.

(a) Does your graph suggest that the amount of distortion is directly proportional to the weights applied?

(b) Does this relation hold for extremely small weights? Large weights?

9. (a) The temperature at which a liquid boils depends upon the air pressure acting on its surface. Plot the pressures and the corresponding boiling temperatures of water from the data in the following table.

(One atmosphere is the pressure exerted by the air at sea level.)

TEMP. (*deg. C.*)	PRESSURE (*atmospheres*)	TEMP. (*deg. C.*)	PRESSURE (*atmospheres*)
0	6.05×10^{-3}	70	3.12×10^{-1}
10	1.21×10^{-2}	80	4.67×10^{-1}
20	2.30×10^{-2}	90	6.92×10^{-1}
30	4.20×10^{-2}	100	1.00
40	7.30×10^{-2}	110	1.43
50	1.22×10^{-1}	120	1.96
60	1.97×10^{-1}	130	2.67

(b) Notice that your graph does not present the data for low pressures clearly. Make a special plot for temperatures up to 60°. What do you observe?

(c) The starch in potatoes will not convert to the edible form at temperatures of less than about 90°C. What is the lowest pressure where potatoes may be cooked by boiling in an open pan?

10. The pressure of the atmosphere decreases as the altitude increases. At sea level the pressure is one atmosphere and at approximately 5500 meters, the pressure is 0.5 atmospheres. It continues to decrease by approximately half with each increase of 5500 meters up to 16,000 m.

(a) Plot the pressure P in atmospheres as a function of altitude A in meters.

(b) Is the representation improved by plotting $1/P$?

(c) What is the pressure at the top of Mt. Everest (8800 meters)?

(d) What is the pressure in atmospheres at an altitude of 100 kilometers? Do you believe your answer?

11. If two identical lamps are 60 cm apart, where should a screen be placed between them so that the intensity on one side of the screen is four times the intensity on the other side?

12. A small source of light is placed between two parallel, white screens (S_1 and S_2). It is 15 cm from S_1 and 45 cm from S_2. An absorbing filter that allows one half the light that falls upon it to pass through is placed between the light source and S_2. What is the ratio of the intensities of the light that falls on S_1 and S_2?

13. A ship sends out a sonar signal (a short pulse of sound that radiates uniformly in all directions). There are two nearly identical icebergs nearby. One is 500 m to the north and the other is 800 m to the east. In reflecting this signal back to the ship, each iceberg acts as a new sound source.

(a) What is the ratio of the intensity of the sound received at the nearer iceberg to that received at the further iceberg?

(b) What is the ratio of the intensity of the echo received at the ship from the near iceberg to that received from the far iceberg?

14. A fireman holds a high-pressure hose 2.5 meters from the midpoint of the wall of a building and finds that he can wet a circular area of 0.5 square meter on the wall. If the building is 7 meters wide, how far must he stand from the building so as to wet its entire width?

15. If your height and all your other dimensions were doubled, by what factor would this change

(a) your weight?

(b) the ability of your leg bones to support your weight?

16. The leg bones of one animal are twice as strong as those of another closely related animal of similar shape.

(a) what would you expect to be the ratio of these animals' heights?

(b) what would you expect to be the ratio of their weights?

17. A square column 15 cm by 15 cm can barely support a cube 1.0 m on an edge. What size cube can be supported by a column 30 cm by 30 cm made of the same material?

18. A hummingbird must eat very frequently and even then must have a highly concentrated form of food such as sugar. What does the concept of scaling tell you about the size of a hummingbird?

19. According to the zoo, an elephant of mass 4.0×10^3 kg consumes 3.4×10^2 times as much food as a guinea pig of mass 0.70 kg. They are both warm-blooded, plant-eating, similarly shaped animals. Find the ratio of their surface areas, which is approximately the ratio of their heat losses, and compare it with the known ratio of food consumed.

20. Horror movies sometimes present a creature such as a spider large enough to devour a human being. Is such a creature a possibility? Why?

21. A sphere of iron is suspended from a wire, 0.1 cm in diameter, which is just strong enough to support it. What must be the diameter of the wire needed to support a similar iron sphere having

(a) five times the original volume?

(b) five times the original diameter?

22. A rectangular water tank is supported above the ground by four pillars 5 meters long whose diameters are 20 cm. If the tank were made ten times longer, wider, and deeper, what diameter pillars would be needed? How much more water would the tank hold?

FURTHER READING

BOCKE, KEES, *Cosmic View: The Universe in 40 Jumps.* Day, 1957. Illustrations of changing scale from atoms to galaxies.

HALDANE, J. B. S., "On Being the Right Size." *World of Mathematics*, Vol. II, edited by James R. Newman. Simon & Schuster, 1956.

LEE, OLIVER J., *Measuring Our Universe.* Ronald Press, 1950. How physicists and astronomers measure distances within the atom and in outer space.

"Sets, Relations, and Functions." *Report of the Commission on Mathematics (Appendices)*, College Entrance Examination Board, New York (pp. 8–17).

SMITH, CYRIL S., "The Shape of Things." *Scientific American*, January, 1954 (p. 58).

THOMPSON, D'ARCY W., "On Magnitude." *World of Mathematics*, Vol. II, cited above.

MOTION ALONG A PATH

CHAPTER 5

A FREIGHT TRAIN is rolling down the track at 40 miles per hour. Around the bend a mile behind, a fast express appears, going at 70 miles per hour on the same track. The express engineer slams on his brakes. With the brakes set he needs two miles to stop. Will there be a crash? What we are called upon to do here is to predict where the two trains will be at subsequent times, and to find in particular whether they are ever at the same place at the same time. In a more general sense, we are asking about the connections between speeds, positions, and times.

The general subject of such relationships is called *kinematics.* In studying kinematics we do not concern ourselves with questions such as "Why does the express train need two miles to stop?" To answer such a question we would need to study in detail how the brakes slow down the train. Such questions as these will be considered in Part III on Mechanics. Here, we just consider the description of motion. We shall start with the discussion of motion along a given path without considering the position and direction of the path in space. Then in the next chapter we shall extend the discussion to describe the path.

In both of these chapters we shall draw on our ability to measure time and distance, for all motion is the changing of distance as time goes on. Usually we shall not think consciously of the time and distance measurements, but without them we would in fact be talking words without meaning.

5–1. Speed and Distance

For a body moving with a constant speed, the relationship of time, speed, and distance is expressed simply. If we let d stand for the length of the trip, v for the speed, and t for the time needed for the trip, the equation

$$d = vt$$

relates these quantities for all cases of constant speed.

It is often convenient to use a graph to represent motions. Fig. 5–1 shows a graph of the speed versus time for a car which travels at 45 mi/hr. Taking some horizontal position on the graph, such as that corresponding to 0.20 hr, we find a reading on the vertical (or speed) axis of 45 mi/hr. In fact, we find 45 mi/hr for *any* time we select.

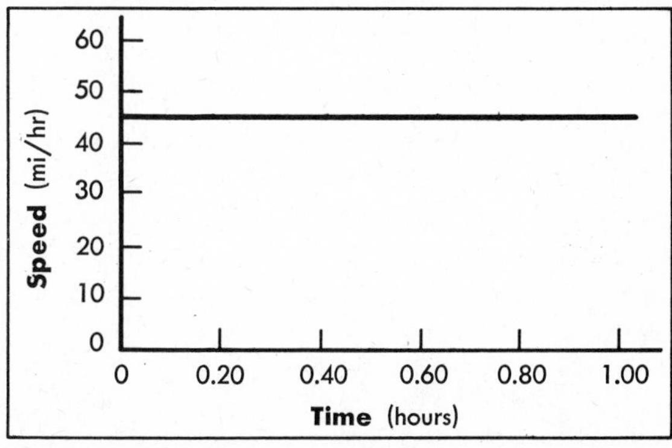

5–1. The speed of a car moving steadily may be graphed as a horizontal line.

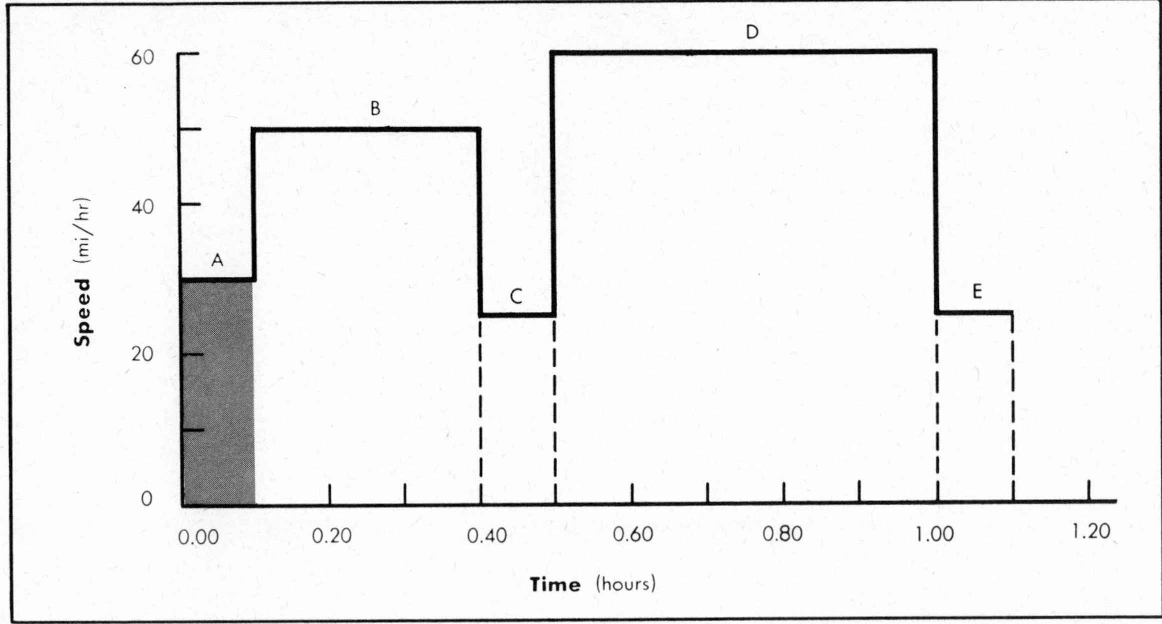

5–2. The motion of a car moving at different speeds during different time intervals. The distance covered in any interval is measured by the area enclosed.

A more complicated motion is described in Table 1. To compute the distance traveled during the first time interval (0.10 hr long) we use the equation $d = vt$. The result is 3 miles. We can perform a similar calculation for each succeeding interval, and add the results to find that the total length of the trip is 53 miles.

Table 1

Motion of a Car at Variable Speed

Time interval number	Duration of interval	Speed during interval	Distance in miles
A	0.10 hr	30 mi/hr	3
B	0.30 hr	50 mi/hr	15
C	0.10 hr	25 mi/hr	2.5
D	0.50 hr	60 mi/hr	30
E	0.10 hr	25 mi/hr	2.5

This motion is represented in Fig. 5–2. Actually, a real object could not move *exactly* according to this graph. Speed cannot increase in such sudden "jumps." However, a real car can make its changes of speed relatively rapidly. In that case, the graph of its motion will look very much like Fig. 5–2. We shall ignore the impossibility of sudden jumps in this discussion, so that we can keep our graph simple.

One great convenience of graphical presentation is that it enables us to see quickly when the car is going fast and when it is going slowly. Thus, the higher speeds occur "high" on the graph of speed versus time. Can the graph also tell us how far the car goes in each interval? The answer is "yes." Let us see how. During any one of the five intervals the car travels a distance given by the equation $d = vt$. In any interval, the height of the graph tells us the speed during the interval, and the horizontal length gives us the time. Thus v times t is the height times the base, or the "area" of the rectangle. This area is shaded for the first interval in Fig. 5–2. The units of these "areas" are different from the more common cm^2 or in^2 because one side of the rectangle is measured in hours, and the other is measured in mi/hr. The product in this case has units of hours $\times$ mi/hr = miles traveled.

The vertical axis of the graph represents the speed in mi/hr. But taking a ruler and actually measuring the vertical length in Fig. 5–2 to be 3.0 cm tells us nothing until we know that, for the particular scale of this graph, 3.0 cm represents 30 mi/hr. It is helpful to remember that the graph is a sort of scale drawing. Unlike a map which simply "scales down" distances, the graph

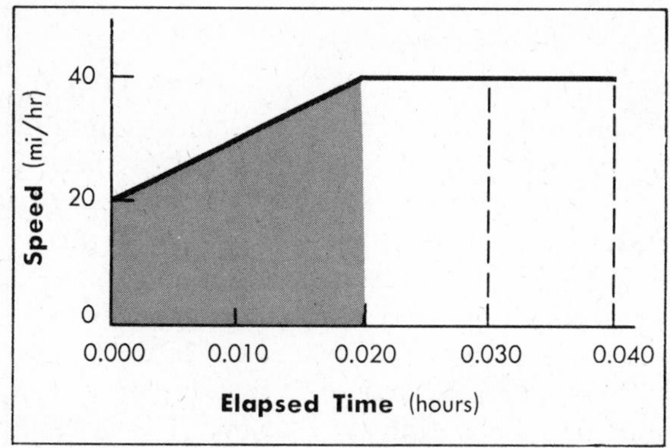

5–3. The speed-time graph for a car which is changing speed during part of its trip. Does the shaded area give the distance traveled during the time interval from 0.000 to 0.020 hours?

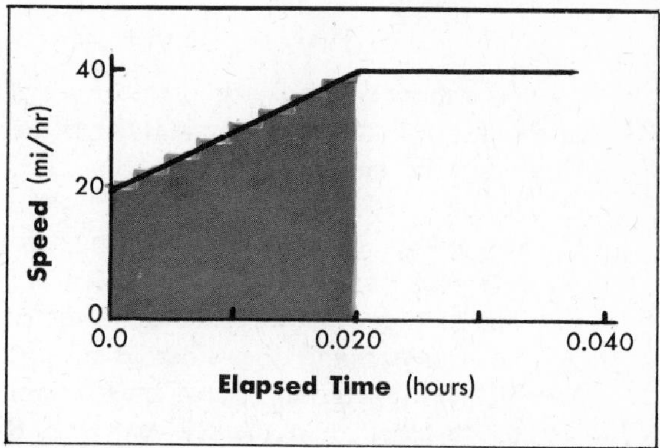

5–4. In this figure an imaginary car is alternately moving a little faster and then a little slower than the car of Fig. 5–3 so that, eventually, it covers the same distance.

has different scales in the horizontal and vertical directions — scales which may differ not only numerically, but also in the nature of the physical quantities that they represent and therefore in their units. When we talk about the "height" being 30 mi/hr, we are using the graph in a way that gives the same answer no matter what scale we use in the actual drawing. For example, it makes no difference whether we use 0.5 cm or 1.0 cm to represent 10 mi/hr, but we must know which, and stick to it on any one graph.

Since heights and horizontal distances that we plot on the speed and the time scales of our graph are proportional to the actual speeds and times involved, any two areas on the graph are exactly proportional to actual distances the car moves. This fact often allows us to decide at a glance in which time interval the greatest distance is covered. For example, we can see that the area of the rectangle marked *D* in Fig. 5–2 is greater than that of any of the other rectangles. Therefore, we know without calculations that the car travels farther in the interval *D* than in any of the other intervals.

The total distance the car travels in 1.10 hr is obtained by adding up the "areas" of all the intervals in Fig. 5–2.

5–2. Varying Speeds

For the case we have considered, the graph did not give us any really new information because we had a method of computing distances without the aid of a graph. Now we shall use our graphical ideas to help analyze a more difficult problem.

Fig. 5–3 gives a graph of the speed of a car versus elapsed time. Can we tell how far the car goes in the first 0.020 hr? We can try to multiply the speed by the time, but we get into trouble, for we must now choose from a whole range of speeds. On the other hand, using the area under the graph, which worked as an alternate method for motion at constant speed, might also serve here, allowing us to solve graphically a problem that presents difficulties when tackled algebraically. Using the area to find our distance looks reasonable because we can approximate the sloping graph of Fig. 5–3 closely by the one in Fig. 5–4.

The graph of Fig. 5–4 represents the motion of an imaginary car that changes speed in steps (keeping constant speed during each step). Each step brings it to a speed a little greater than the speed of the real car at that instant. Then, while the imaginary car's speed remains constant, the speed of the real car gains on it and passes it. Next the imaginary car's speed increases by another step. The distance covered by the imaginary car is given by the area shaded under the stepped graph of Fig. 5–4. If we make the steps smaller, and more frequent, the two cars would never differ much in speed. Then the shaded area which gives the distance covered by the imaginary car would practically give the distance covered by the real car. And that shaded area, for many steps, is practically the shaded area under the graph of Fig. 5–3 for the real car. If you want to see another discussion which leads to a rigorous proof that the area under this speed-time graph gives the distance traveled, read the material in the box on the next page.

Distance as the Area under the Speed-Time Graph

Here is a more rigorous argument to prove that the distance moved by the real car is the area under the sloping graph in Fig. 5–3. We can bracket the distance covered by the real car between two limits by having two imaginary cars that change their speeds in steps, one of them *A* always traveling faster than the real car and the other *B* always slower. Then in a given time *A* must travel a greater distance than the real car and *B* must travel a shorter distance than the real car. The distance traveled by the real car lies between those traveled by *A* and *B*. First imagine *A* and *B* each changing speed in large steps as in Fig. 5–5. *B* starts with the real car's initial speed. For the first 0.010-hour period, it travels at 20 mi/hr while the real car speeds up from 20 to 30 mi/hr, and for the next 0.010 hour *B* travels at 30 mi/hr. Meanwhile, *A* runs at 30 mi/hr for the first 0.010-hour period and then at 40 mi/hr. In a total time of 0.020 hr, *B* travels 0.20 mi + 0.30 mi or 0.50 mi; while *A* travels 0.30 mi + 0.40 mi, or 0.70 mi. The distance traveled by the real car must lie somewhere between these two values since it never moves faster than *A* or slower than *B*. Thus we have bracketed the real car's travel between the limits 0.50 and 0.70 mi.

Now make the steps smaller and more frequent, as in Fig. 5–6. If you calculate the distances traveled by *B* and *A* in the first 0.20 hr (the area under the graphs) you will find they are 0.55 mi and 0.65 mi. This gives a smaller interval between the upper and lower limits than we obtained before. We can continue to decrease the interval between the upper and lower limits for the distance by making the cars change speed in shorter and shorter time intervals. The area representing the upper limit of the distance and the area representing the lower limit become more and more nearly the same, and both of these areas get nearer and nearer to the area under the sloping curve. Mentally continuing this process, we prove that the "area" under the speed-time graph does give the distance traveled by the original car.

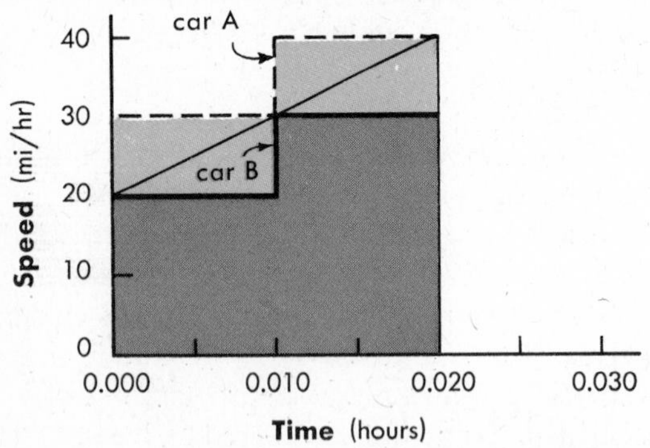

5–5. We can "bracket" the distance covered by the car in Fig. 5–3 by imagining two other cars, A and B, that travel with different speeds as shown in this figure.

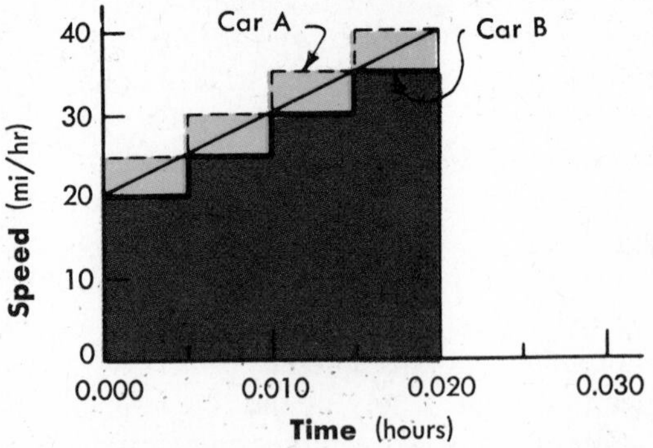

5–6. If the two cars of Fig. 5–5 change their speeds more frequently, it is clear that they approximate the motion of the real car more closely.

Since the "area" under the slant line of Fig. 5–3 is that of a trapezoid with a base of 0.020 hr, and the two heights, 20 mi/hr on the left and 40 mi/hr on the right, we can now say how far the original car goes. The area of the trapezoid gives the distance

$$d = \left(\frac{20 \text{ mi/hr} + 40 \text{ mi/hr}}{2}\right) \times 0.020 \text{ hr} = 0.60 \text{ mi}.$$

(You get the same answer by breaking the trapezoid up into a rectangle and a triangle and adding their areas.)

In general, even for more complicated speed-time graphs, such as that of Fig. 5–7, the distance is still given by the "area." For example, for the time interval 0.5 hr to 1.0 hr the distance is given by the shaded area of Fig. 5–7. Even if we are not able to compute the "area" from a

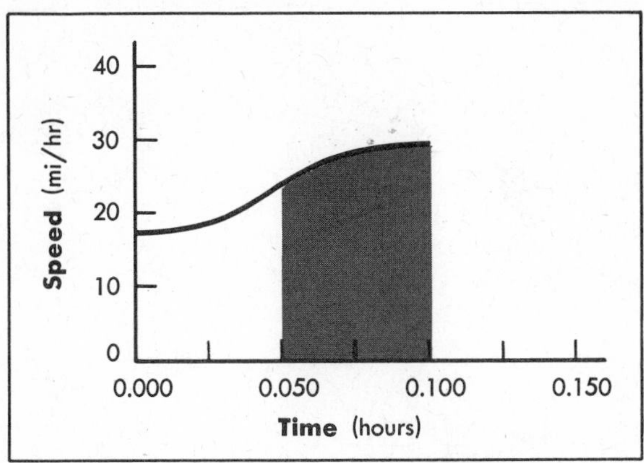

5–7. In general, the distance covered is given by the area under the speed-time graph, no matter how the speed changes.

formula, we can arrive at an approximate answer in other ways. For instance, we can divide the area into small squares and then multiply the area of each square by the number of squares counted, as suggested in Section 3–5.

5–3. Graphs of Distance versus Time

When we drive at a steady speed, the distance we go is proportional to the time we travel: $d = vt$. In other words, since v is constant, the area under the v versus t curve varies with t. At the speed of 60 mi/hr, for instance, in 0.10 hr we go 6 miles; in 0.20 hr, 12 miles, and so on. We can present this information in a table such as Table 2. Or we can use a new graph, the graph of distance d versus time t. The graph will make it easy to find the distance even at a time that is not included in the table.

Fig. 5–8 is the d versus t graph for a speed of 60 mi/hr. Like all direct proportions (see Section 4–1), it is a straight line.

What makes this line correspond to 60 mi/hr is its steepness. How steeply the line rises depends on the speed, which is the proportionality factor between d and t. For example, if the speed were greater, say 80 mi/hr, the straight line would be steeper. It would rise the same distance in a shorter time.

If your car breaks down and you phone the garage, you will probably tell the repairman the location of your car by telling him its distance and direction along the road from some landmark. "It is 5 miles from the blinking light, going toward California," you might say. From now on we shall measure d in a definite direction from some place on which we agree. In this way we can use d to specify position. Motion will still be described by the changes in d as time goes on.

When you drive on a superhighway, you may see a post every mile of the road. For example, the Pennsylvania Turnpike has mileposts which are numbered consecutively 1, 2, 3, etc., starting at the Ohio state line. When we pass a post labeled 176, we know we are 176 miles from the Ohio state line, measured along the road. If at that moment another car is opposite the post labeled 186, it is 10 miles along the road from us, in the direction away from Ohio.

We shall use this idea to help us make a graph which shows the positions of *two* cars. We describe the position of either car by giving its distance d along the road from some reference point like the state line or the place where a trip begins. We can then make a graph of d for each car at various times, as is done in Fig. 5–9 for one example.

Table 2

Distance-Time Relations for Steady Speed

Elapsed time	Distance covered
0.10 hr	6 mi
0.20 hr	12 mi
0.30 hr	18 mi
0.40 hr	24 mi
0.50 hr	30 mi

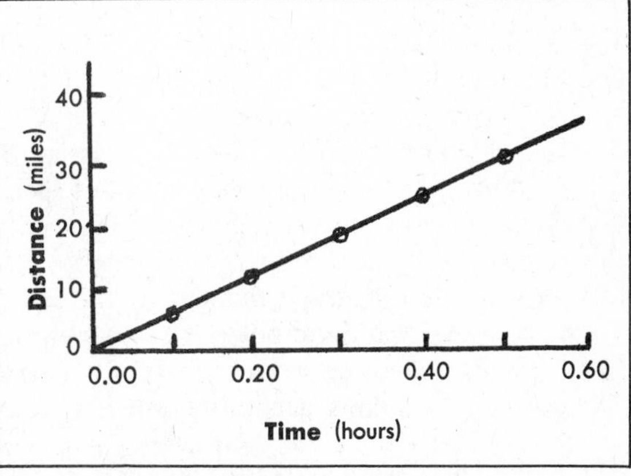

5–8. The distance-time graph for a steady speed is a straight line.

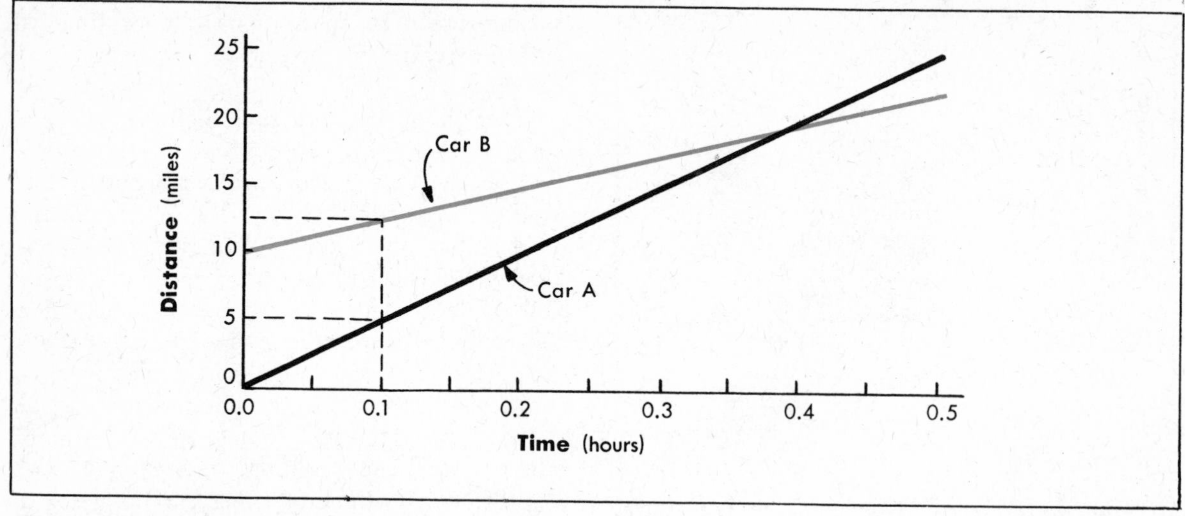

5–9. At what time will car A overtake car B?

From the graph we can calculate the speeds of the cars. In 0.1 hr, for example, car A goes from the position $d = 0$ to $d = 5$. It moves 5 mi and its speed is therefore 50 mi/hr. In the next 0.1 hr, it again goes 5 mi from $d = 5$ to $d = 10$; its speed is still 50 mi/hr. Because the graph is a straight line, the distance car A moves is the same for every 0.1 hr; therefore the speed of A is 50 mi/hr all the time. Car B also has constant speed. In each 0.1 hr it moves 2.5 mi, from $d = 10$ to $d = 12.5$ in the first 0.1 hr, from 12.5 to 15 mi in the second, and so on. Its speed is therefore 25 mi/hr.

In addition to the speeds, the graph tells us more. It says that car B starts 10 mi ahead of A, but A catches up. After 0.1 hr A is at $d = 5$ and B is at $d = 12.5$. A is therefore only 7.5 mi behind B. By the time 0.5 hr has passed we see that A is ahead of B. It is at $d = 25$, while B is only at $d = 22.5$. Just by looking at the graph we can tell how long it took A to catch up. At 0.4 hr both cars are at the same position, actually at $d = 20$; at 0.4 hr, therefore, A was just passing B.

In Section 5–1 we saw that on a graph of speed versus time we could tell at a glance at what times the speed was the greatest. The higher up the line occurred on the graph the greater the speed it represented. Now, however, we are dealing with a quite different graph — that of *distance* versus time. The speed is involved only indirectly in such graphs and is *not* shown by the height of the line above the time axis. For example, in Fig. 5–9 the line for car B is above that for car A in the entire interval from 0.00 hr to 0.40 hr, although car B is being overtaken during this interval and is certainly the slower of the two.

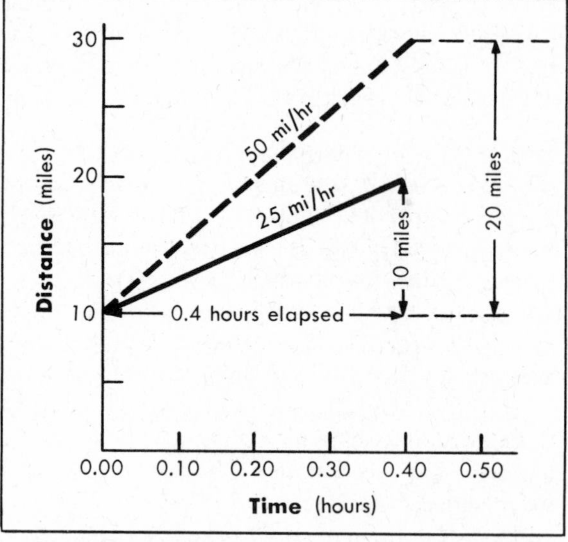

5–10. Higher speeds give steeper graphs of distance vs. time.

How can we tell from Fig. 5–9 which car is going faster? The answer is simple. One curve climbs more steeply than the other. For a given time interval, the steeper curve spans a greater interval of distance. Since the car which travels the greater distance in any given time is the faster, the faster car must be the one with the most steeply sloping graph. Car A is certainly going faster than car B. (That is why it passed B.)

Fig. 5–10 again illustrates the relationship between the steepness and the speed. The solid line is drawn for a car traveling at 25 mi/hr. We

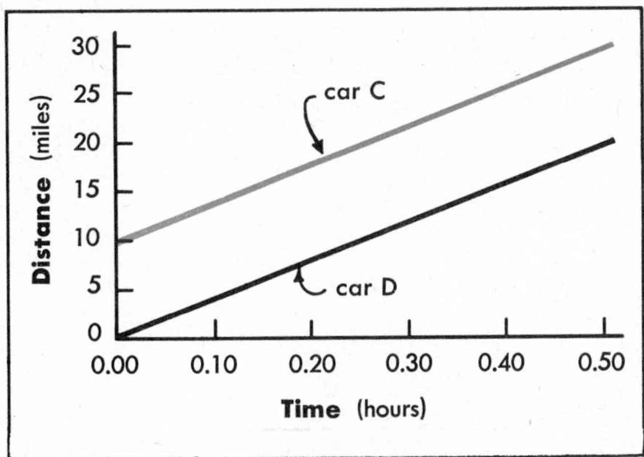

5–11. Since the distance-time graphs for the two cars are parallel, they represent the same speed even though the positions of the graphs are different.

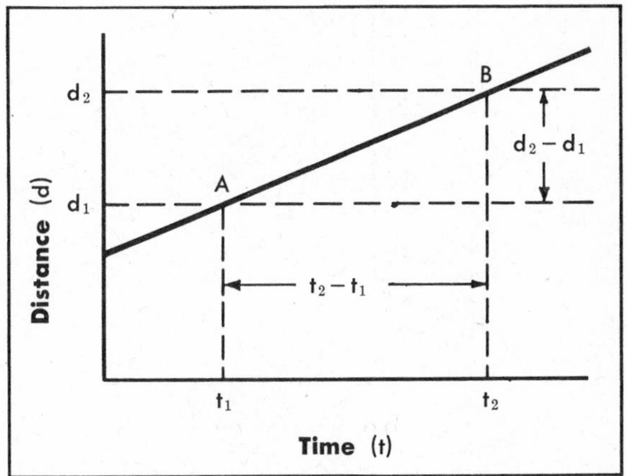

5–12. The slope of a straight line is found by dividing $d_2 - d_1$ "up" by $t_2 - t_1$ "over."

see that it has traveled a distance of 10 mi during the first 0.40 hr. A car going 50 mi/hr travels 20 mi during the 0.40-hr interval, and is described by the steeper dashed line of the graph.

On a *d* versus *t* graph it is the steepness alone that tells the speed. Position on the graph (or on the road) does not matter. In Fig. 5–11 the curves for cars *C* and *D* are equally steep. They are parallel to each other; therefore they describe a situation in which car *D* neither catches up to nor drops behind car *C*. It always keeps 10 miles behind *C*. The graphs will never cross as they did when one car passed the other (Fig. 5–9). The graphs of car *C* and of car *D* are in different positions, but they correspond to exactly the same speed.

We shall now express the connection between the speed and the steepness of the *d* versus *t* graph in mathematical language. To do so we shall begin by restating the connection between speed, time, and distance.

Imagine that while driving along a turnpike you check your speedometer, using the mileposts and a watch. The watch reads 3:25:00 at the post labeled 247 miles, and 3:26:00 at 248 miles. You have traveled one mile in one minute, and your speed is a mile a minute, or 60 mi/hr. Let d_1 stand for 247 miles and d_2 for 248 miles; also let t_1 stand for the time 3:25:00 and t_2 for the time 3:26:00. In this language you can express the speed v by the equation

$$v = \frac{d_2 - d_1}{t_2 - t_1}.$$

In general, if we pass from position d_1 at time t_1 to position d_2 at time t_2, this equation gives the average speed with which we move.

We can now give this equation for speed a precise geometrical meaning. In Fig. 5–12, if *A* and *B* are any two points on the graph, then the vertical interval between these points is obviously $d_2 - d_1$ and the horizontal interval is $t_2 - t_1$. These two intervals, $(d_2 - d_1)$ and $(t_2 - t_1)$, completely define the steepness of the graph, for they tell how far "up" and how far "over" one point on the line is from another. As we have already discovered, the speed depends upon the steepness of the distance-time graph; and the steepness of the graph depends upon how far up the graph goes in a certain interval over. The ratio of "up" to "over" is such a useful measure of the steepness that we give it a special name. We call it the *slope* of the line. For the distance-time graph, as Fig. 5–12 shows, the slope is $d_2 - d_1$

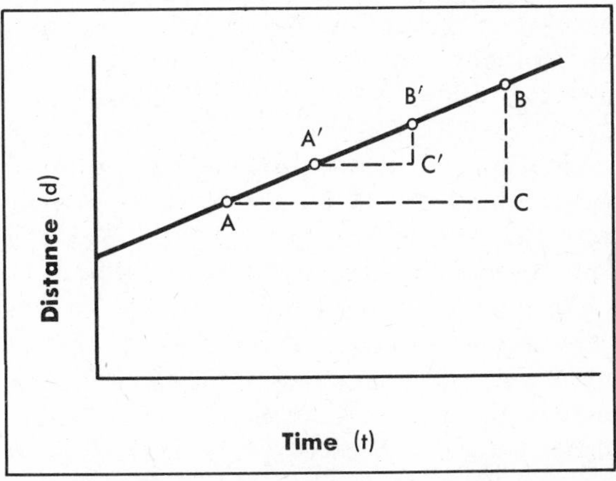

5–13. A straight line has the same slope all along its length.

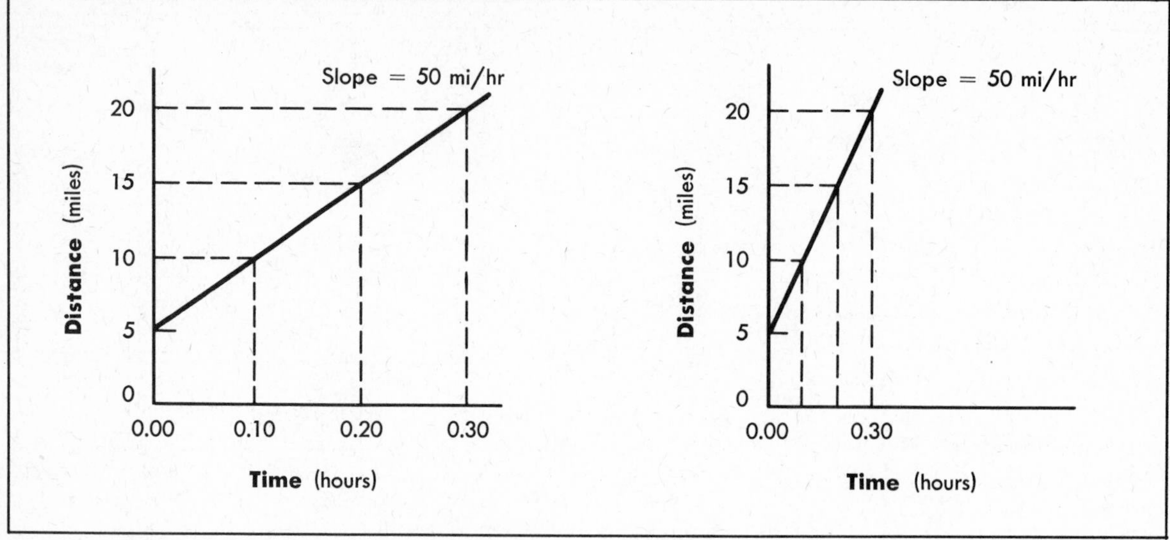

5–14. The slopes of the two graphs are the same, although their appearances differ. They will appear the same only when plotted to the same scale or on the same graph.

"up" divided by $t_2 - t_1$ "over." The slope of the distance-time graph is the speed of the car as we see from the last equation.

We determined the slope of the line in Fig. 5–12 from the ratio of "up" to "over" in going between the two points A and B. If we take any other two points such as A' and B' (Fig. 5–13), we can see from the similar triangles dotted in the figure that the ratio of "up" to "over" in the one case is exactly equal to the ratio of "up" to "over" in the other. Therefore we can use *any* pair of points on a straight line to compute its slope.

It is important to recognize that although the slope is related to the "steepness" of a graph, the angle between the graphed line and the horizontal has no particular significance since we could change the angle by replotting the data to different scale, as shown in Fig. 5–14. It is only when we are comparing lines on the same graph, as in Fig. 5–9, or on graphs plotted to the same scale, that the angle between the line and the horizontal axis helps us compare slopes. In general we must measure the vertical and horizontal intervals between two points on the graph and compute their ratio in the appropriate units — mi/hr, for instance — as in Fig. 5–14.

Our discussion of slope applies to other graphs; nothing restricts us to the graph of distance versus time. We shall shortly see the significance of the slope of a graph of *speed* versus time. In fact, we shall be dealing with slopes so often that it will be worth while to introduce a shorthand notation to indicate the process used in finding them. For instance, the slope of the distance-time graph is always equal to the ratio of an interval of distance $(d_2 - d_1)$ to an interval of time $(t_2 - t_1)$. Mathematicians and physicists often use the Greek letter delta, written as Δ, as an abbreviation for the phrase "an interval of." Δ is a Greek capital D chosen to stand for "difference," or "change of," or "increase of," or "an interval of." Thus, Δd means "an interval of distance" and Δt means "an interval of time." We read them "delta dee" and "delta tee."

We might compare the symbol "Δ" with some other algebraic symbol, for instance with "$\sqrt{\ }$," which means "take the square root of." In the expression $\sqrt{a}$, the symbol a stands for a number (or physical quantity) and $\sqrt{\ }$ tells us what to do with a. In a similar manner, in the expression Δt, t stands for a physical quantity, and Δ tells us what to do with t. It says "take an interval" of t or "take the difference between two values" of t.

When the ratio of two intervals is involved, as it is in determining a speed, it is customary to write the ratio as a fraction, with the understanding that the interval in the numerator takes place during the time interval of the denominator. Thus

$$v = \frac{\Delta d}{\Delta t},$$

which is read "vee equals delta dee over delta

tee," means "to find the speed, take the interval of distance traveled in the time interval Δt and divide that distance interval by that time interval."

In general, when we write $\frac{\Delta a}{\Delta b}$, we always mean that we shall use the interval of a that corresponds to a given interval of b. After all, we are interested only in the ratios of related intervals. Please note that there is no sense in separating the Δ from the a or b. The whole symbol Δa has a special meaning; an interval of a. It does not mean Δ multiplied by a.

5–4. Speeds and Directions

We have learned that the speed $v = \frac{\Delta d}{\Delta t}$ is given by the slope of the distance-time graph. In Fig. 5–15 we have the distance-time graph of a complete trip made by a car. Let us interpret it by calculating the three slopes of the graph.

During the first 0.20 hr the car was traveling at constant speed, as is indicated by the constant slope. The speed may be found by taking the ratio of the distance covered and the time elapsed at any point within the interval, for example

$$v_1 = \frac{\Delta d}{\Delta t} = \frac{6.0 \text{ mi} - 0.0 \text{ mi}}{0.20 \text{ hr} - 0.00 \text{ hr}} = 30 \text{ mi/hr}.$$

What was the car doing from 0.20 hr until 0.50 hr? Here the slope of the graph is zero — the car was stopped. From 0.50 hr until 0.80 hr the slope is

$$v_2 = \frac{\Delta d}{\Delta t} = \frac{0.0 \text{ mi} - 6.0 \text{ mi}}{0.80 \text{ hr} - 0.50 \text{ hr}} = -20 \text{ mi/hr}.$$

Notice that the result is negative. The distance (0.0 mi) at the later time (0.80 hr) is less than the distance (6.0 mi) at the earlier time (0.50 hr). The minus sign just tells us that the car was traveling along the road in the opposite direction from that taken at the start of the trip. In fact, the car returned to its starting point, $d = 0$, arriving there 0.80 hr after it left. The graph indicates at a glance both the approximate speed and the direction of travel. We have now derived from it the information needed to plot the graph of Fig. 5–16.

We have seen that the quantity v can be either positive or negative. The positive sign refers to one direction of motion and the negative sign to the opposite direction.

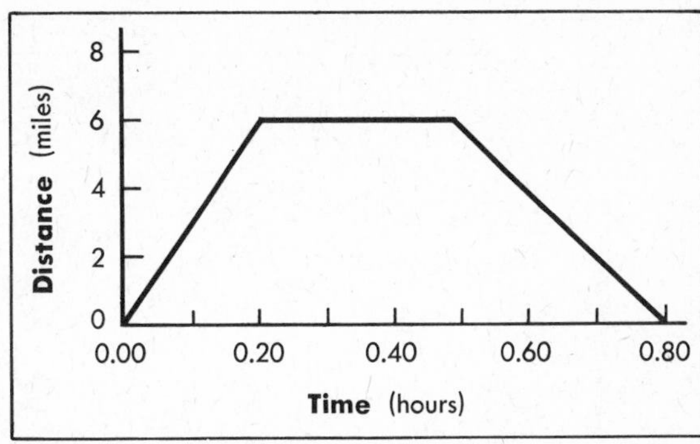

5–15. Distance-time graph of a complete trip made by a car. Between which times was the car going the fastest?

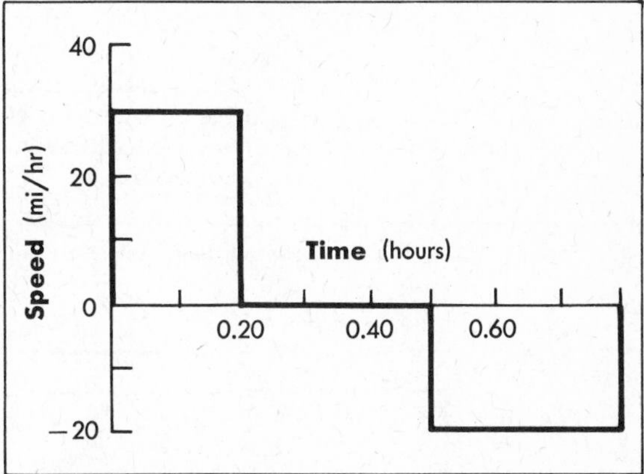

5–16. Speed-time graph of the motion shown in Fig. 5–15. The portion of the graph below the horizontal axis indicates that the car is traveling opposite to its original direction.

5–5. Instantaneous Speed — The Slope of the Tangent Line

We have been thinking of trips in which the speed is constant either throughout the trip or for different portions of the trip. The distance-time graphs were therefore made of straight lines. Fig. 5–17 is a distance-time graph of a car with continually changing speed. How can we find the speed of the car at any particular time? Here there are no straight lines, and it is not obvious how to apply the methods we have been discussing. On the other hand, if we were riding in the car, the speedometer would be able to tell us our speed. So let us think of the speedometer reading at a definite time, for instance 0.50 hr after we started our trip. How do we calculate it from the graph of Fig. 5–17?

50
40
30
20
10
0
Distance (miles)
0.00
0.20
0.40
0.60
0.80
1.00
Time (hours)

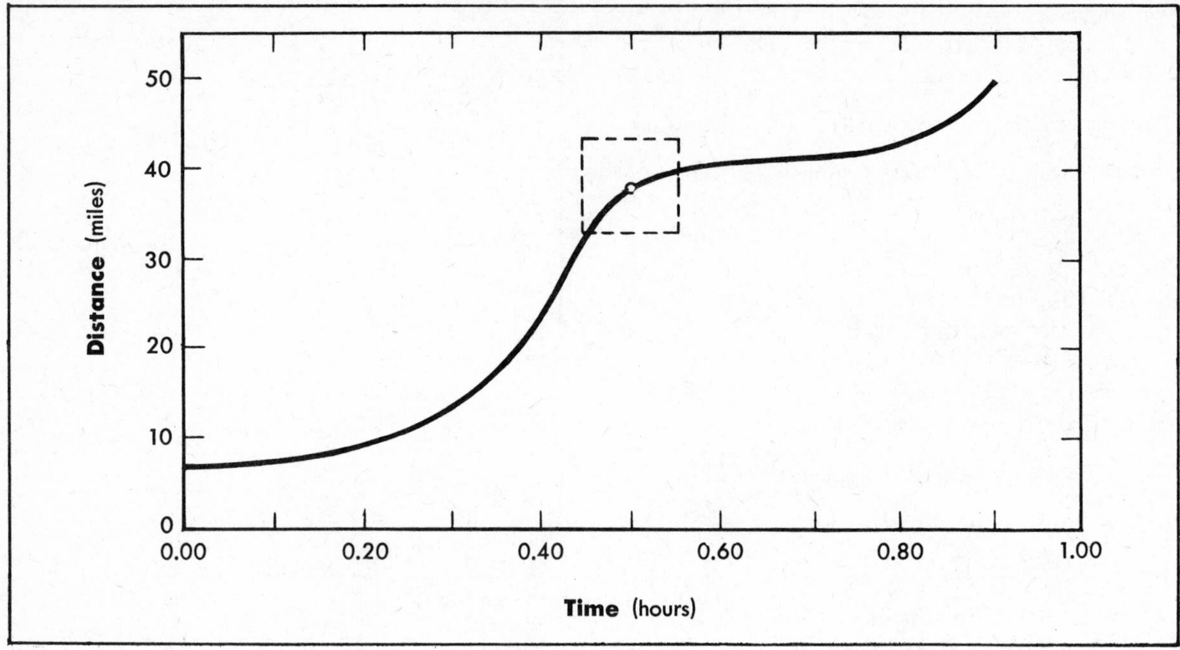

5–17. Distance-time graph for a car with continually changing speed.

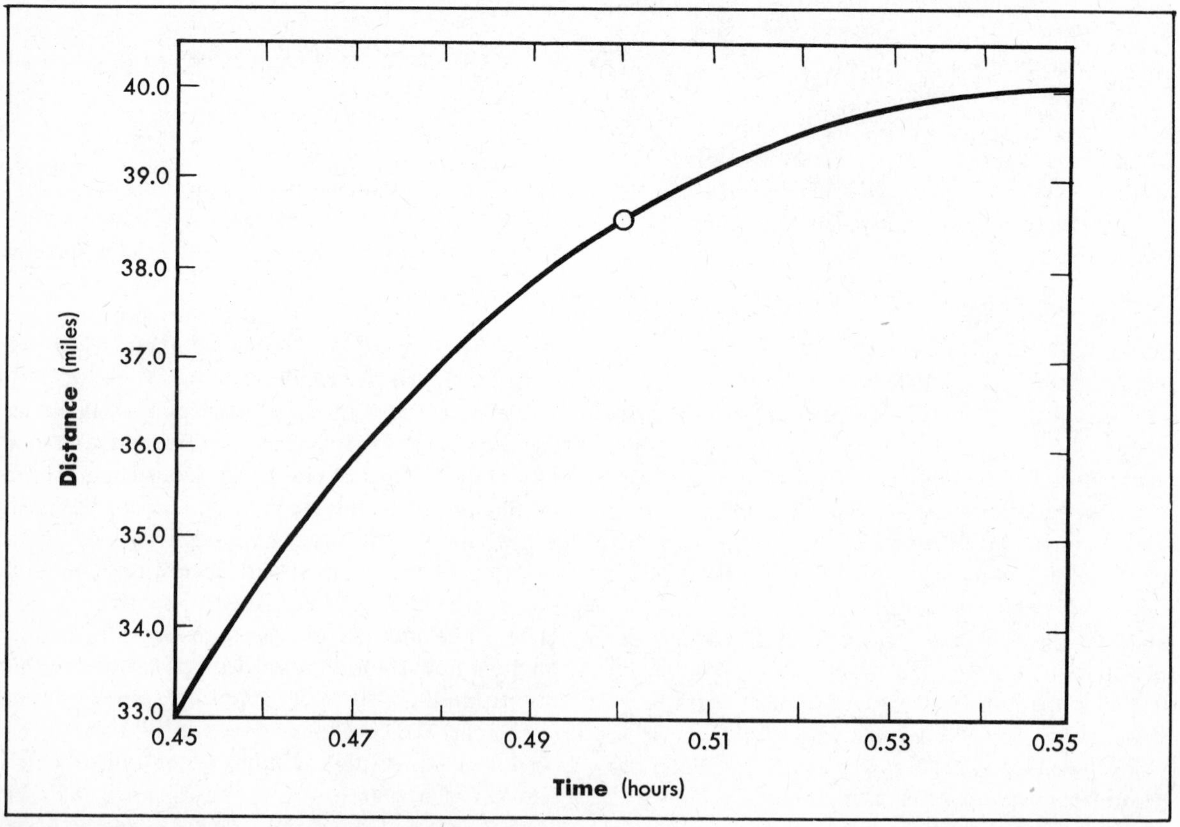

40.0
39.0
38.0
37.0
36.0
35.0
34.0
33.0
Distance (miles)
0.45
0.47
0.49
0.51
0.53
0.55
Time (hours)

5–18. In this figure, the part of the graph enclosed in the dashed rectangle of Fig. 5–17 is enlarged ten times.

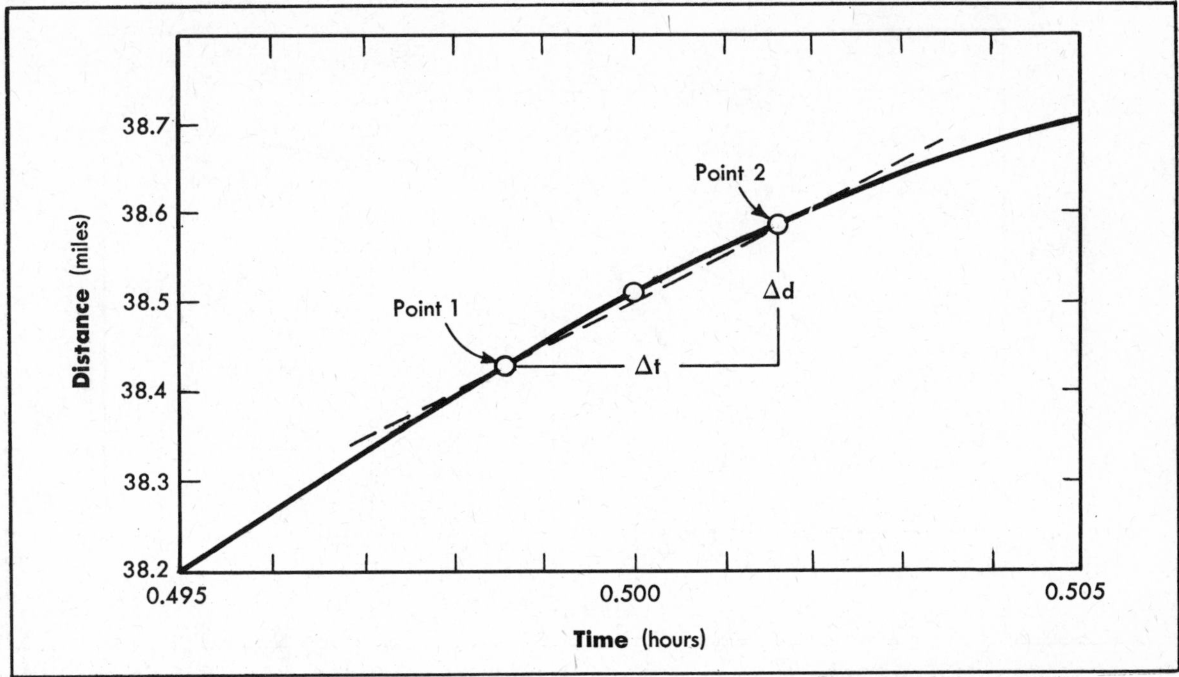

5–19. At a magnification of 100, a small portion of the graph within the dashed rectangle of Fig. 5–17 appears to be almost straight.

Let us look with a magnifying glass at the part of the graph within the dashed rectangle. If we magnify it tenfold, we obtain the graph of Fig. 5–18. Note how much straighter the curve on this new figure looks, compared with that of Fig. 5–17. A still greater magnification of the dotted rectangle in Fig. 5–17 shows us the interval which covers only 0.005 hr before and after the 0.50-hr mark (Fig. 5–19). With this graph, we can tell the speed by measuring the slope of the "straight" line. We choose two points near 0.50 hr, for example, 1 and 2 in Fig. 5–19; then reading from this graph, we find

$$t_1 = 0.4986 \text{ hr}, \qquad d_1 = 38.42 \text{ mi};$$
$$t_2 = 0.5016 \text{ hr}, \qquad d_2 = 38.58 \text{ mi}.$$

Consequently the slope is given by

$$\frac{\Delta d}{\Delta t} = \frac{d_2 - d_1}{t_2 - t_1} = \frac{0.16 \text{ mi}}{.003 \text{ hr}} \approx 53 \text{ mi/hr},$$

and the speed at the point 0.5 hr from the start is very closely 53 mi/hr.

The magnified part of a graph looks straighter than the whole graph because in the magnified picture we look at only a small portion of the unmagnified graph. When we magnify sufficiently, we look at only a small interval of d and t. In effect, therefore, we find the slope of a small portion of the curve by taking the ratio

$$\frac{\Delta d}{\Delta t} = \frac{d_2 - d_1}{t_2 - t_1}$$

for a pair of points 1 and 2 which are very close together. The points we use must be close enough together so that the graph is essentially a straight line in between.

When the part of the graph we use is nearly straight, we find the same slope and thus the *same* speed no matter which points we take to evaluate it. In Fig. 5–19, for example, if we let points 1 and 2 move along the curve until they are closer to the 0.50-hr mark, we get almost the same result as before. Try it for yourself. Furthermore, the points we use to find $\Delta d/\Delta t$ will be close together when Δt is small; and if Δt is small enough, $\Delta d/\Delta t$ will have a definite value for a smooth distance-time curve around a given point. We therefore say that the speed at a particular instant is given by the limit of $\Delta d/\Delta t$ as Δt "approaches zero," that is, as Δt gets smaller and smaller. Symbolically this statement is written

$$v = \lim_{\Delta t \to 0} \frac{\Delta d}{\Delta t}.$$

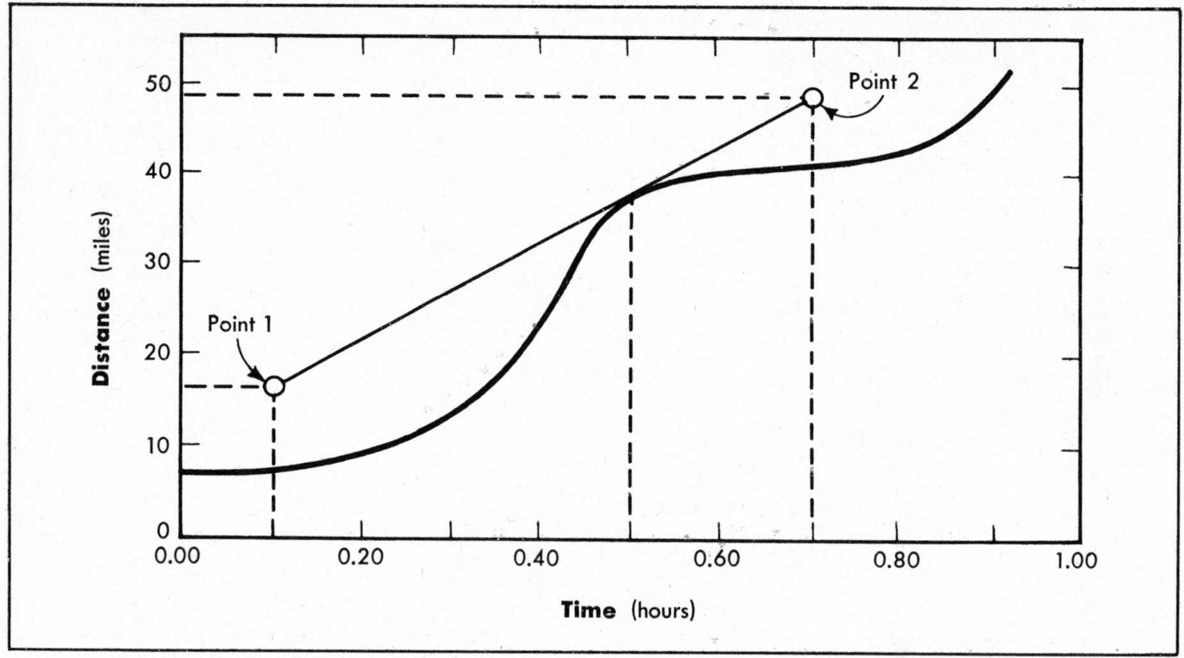

5–20. To find the speed at any instant, draw a line tangent to the curve at the point being considered. Then, by taking any two points on the tangent line, find the slope. The value of the slope is the speed.

(We read "$\lim_{\Delta t \to 0}$" as "the limit as Δt approaches 0 of . . . .") The word "limit" here stands for the result obtained when we take t_1 and t_2 close enough together so that there is no noticeable change produced in the value of the ratio by using a still smaller interval between t_1 and t_2. We make the interval Δt shorter and shorter until "in the limit," as we say, we get a definite result. This procedure lies at the heart of the branch of mathematics called the calculus.

There may be special cases when this procedure is hard to apply or when it has no meaning. A plot of positions which changed suddenly from one straight-line slope to another would have no slope at the point of abrupt change; no speed could be defined there. In fact, however, no matter how wide we open the throttle of a car, the speed changes smoothly, even if rapidly. Therefore, the slope of the position plot does not change instantaneously; and we can take short-enough time intervals to get the speed at any given instant.

To use the procedure we have outlined, we need to have a magnified picture of the distance-time graph, obtained, for example, by using a magnifying glass. Is there any simple way of getting the speed without going through the steps of magnifying? The answer is "yes": draw a tangent and measure its slope. Suppose we drew a straight line tangent to the curve of Fig. 5–17 at the point for which $t = 0.50$ hr as in Fig. 5–20. In this figure we can easily distinguish the tangent from the graph of d vs. t; but at hundredfold magnification in Fig. 5–21 we see that the tangent line and the curve are hardly distinguishable over a small-enough interval around the point of tangency. In this region they have the same slope. We can therefore use the slope of the tangent line to determine the slope of the graph at any particular point. Fig. 5–20 shows us how we can use this method to get the speed of the car at $t = 0.50$ hr. First, we draw the tangent line to the curve at the point chosen. Then we choose two convenient points (labeled 1 and 2) on the tangent line. We read the values of d_1, d_2 and of t_1, t_2 to find $d_2 - d_1 = 32$ mi and $t_2 - t_1 = 0.60$ hr, so that the slope is

$$\frac{d_2 - d_1}{t_2 - t_1} = \frac{32 \text{ mi}}{0.60 \text{ hr}} \approx 53 \text{ mi/hr}.$$

Therefore, when 0.50 hr has elapsed, the car has a speed of 53 mi/hr in the direction of increasing d.

The speed at a given instant is called the instantaneous speed. This is what we read on a speedometer. Also it is the instantaneous speed

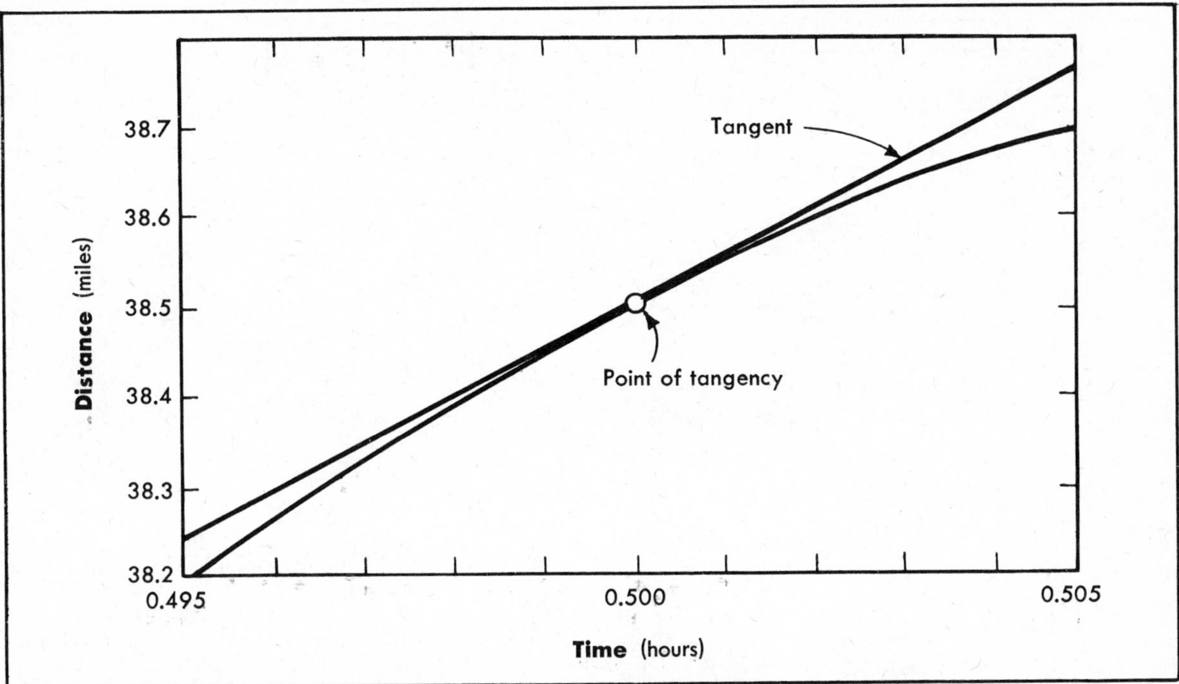

5–21. With 100-times magnification of Fig. 5–20, the curve and its tangent are indistinguishable near the point of tangency.

that we have calculated by using the slope method on our graphs:

$$v = \lim_{\Delta t \to 0} \frac{\Delta d}{\Delta t}.$$

When you say "he was going 70 when he passed me," you mean that his instantaneous speed was 70 mi/hr at the moment he passed.

We use the word *instantaneous* to distinguish the speed at one moment from the *average* speed over an interval of time. The average speed in the time interval Δt is defined as $v_{\text{av}} = \dfrac{\Delta d}{\Delta t}$. It is that constant speed which would move us through the actual distance Δd in the actual time Δt. If we move faster for part of the time and slower for another part, the instantaneous speed at almost every moment in Δt may be different from the average speed. But from Figs. 5–19 and 5–21 we can see that for a body moving with variable speed the instantaneous speed is nothing but the average speed over an interval of time which is so short that the speed changes during the interval may be neglected.

5–6. Acceleration Along the Path

A driver might observe that his car can reach 50 mi/hr in 10 seconds starting "from a standstill." He would be talking about the acceleration of his car, how fast its speed increases. Let us suppose that Fig. 5–22 is the graph of the speed versus time for the car. For simplicity we start with a straight-line graph; for a real car the graph might not be straight, but we shall consider more complicated graphs shortly. Fig. 5–22 says that the car speeds up to 50 mi/hr in 10 seconds, or 5 mi/hr in each second. (We write this as 5 mi/hr/sec or 5 mi/hr-sec and read it "5 miles per hour per second.") The quantity 50 mi/hr in 10 seconds or 5 miles per hour per second is a measure of the acceleration along the path of travel of the car. (The reason that we

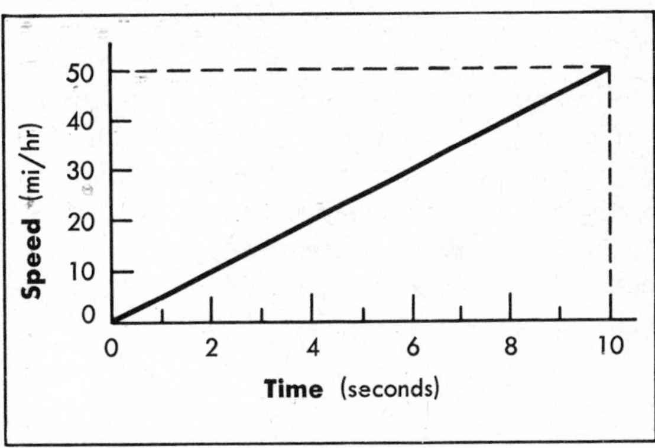

5–22. Graph of speed vs. time.

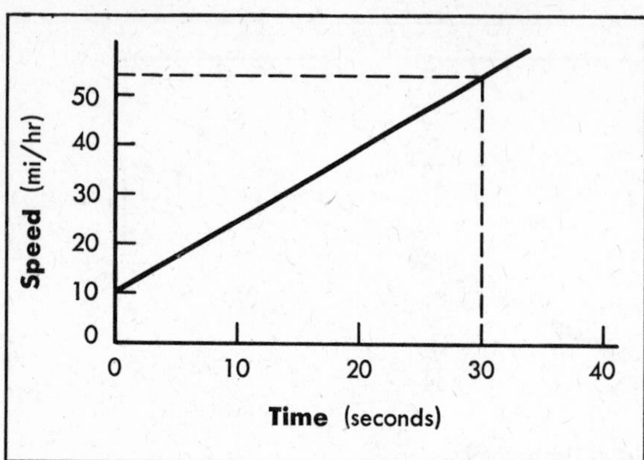

5–23. Graph of speed vs. time for a car that is in motion at $t = 0$.

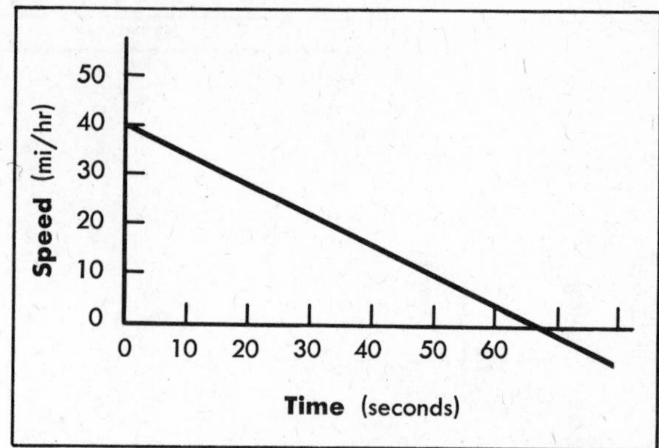

5–24. Deceleration is shown by a negative slope on the speed vs. time graph.

call this "acceleration along the path" is that there are many cases where the acceleration is not along the path. In the next chapter we shall see how to handle such cases.)

Fig. 5–23 is the graph of the speed versus time for another car. Notice that at "zero" time the car is going 10 mi/hr and that 30 seconds later it has a speed of 55 mi/hr. The speed has therefore increased 45 mi/hr in 30 seconds. The acceleration along the path is therefore given by $a_p = 45$ mi/hr in 30 seconds or $a_p = 1.5$ mi/hr-sec.

If we choose symbols for the quantities, we can use them in writing an algebraic expression for this calculation. Call the two times t_1 and t_2, and use v_1 and v_2 for the corresponding speed at these two times. The acceleration along the path is then given by the relation

$$a_p = \frac{v_2 - v_1}{t_2 - t_1} = \frac{\Delta v}{\Delta t},$$

where we use the Δ notation that was introduced in Section 5–3.

There is a simple geometrical significance to this equation. Just as $\frac{\Delta d}{\Delta t}$ is the slope of the d versus t graph, so the right-hand side of this equation is the slope of the speed vs. time graph. Therefore, we can say that the acceleration along the path is equal to the slope of the graph of v versus t.

If a graph of speed vs. time is of the type shown in Fig. 5–24, we see that the car is slowing down. At the initial time $t = 0$, it is going 40 mi/hr. Fifty seconds later it is going 10 mi/hr. In this time interval, $\Delta t = 50$ sec, the change in speed is $\Delta v = -30$ mi/hr. Consequently,

$$a_p = \frac{-30 \text{ mi/hr}}{50 \text{ sec}} = -0.60 \text{ mi/hr-sec.}$$

When $\frac{\Delta d}{\Delta t}$ has a minus sign, it means that the motion is backward, in the opposite direction from that in which we originally agreed to measure distances along the path. What does a minus sign mean here for the acceleration along the path? In this case the minus sign tells us that the car is slowing down; and, in general, the minus sign means that the change in speed Δv is in the backward direction. This happens either when an object which is moving forward slows down, or when an object is moving backward more and more rapidly. Indeed, if an object moves with a negative value of a_p and starts out going forward, it will slow down, stop momentarily, and then go backward, retracing its path at an increasing pace. In Fig. 5–24, find the instant when the car is standing still and the time during which it speeds up in a backward direction.

So far we have talked about constant acceleration along the path, that is, about uniform changes of speed. Let us now consider Fig. 5–25, which shows another graph of speed against time. What is the acceleration along the path when 20 seconds have elapsed? In other words, what is the *instantaneous acceleration* along the path at $t = 20$ seconds?

We know that if we magnified the portion near $t = 20$ seconds sufficiently, it would appear to be straight. The slope of this straight segment would then be the acceleration along the path. Furthermore, as we have seen, instead of magni-

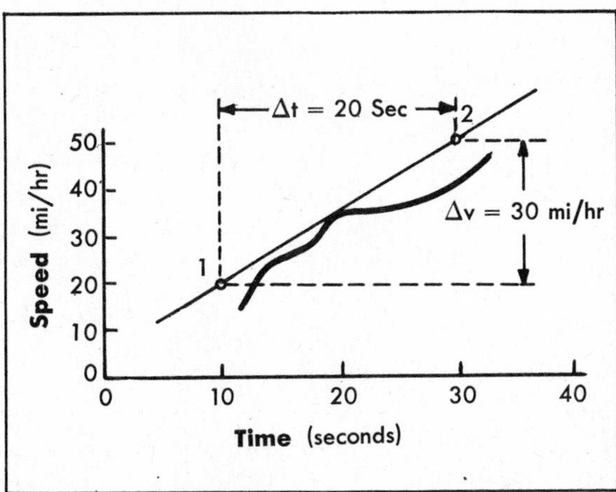

5–25. To find the instantaneous acceleration along the path, find the slope of the tangent line at the point being considered.

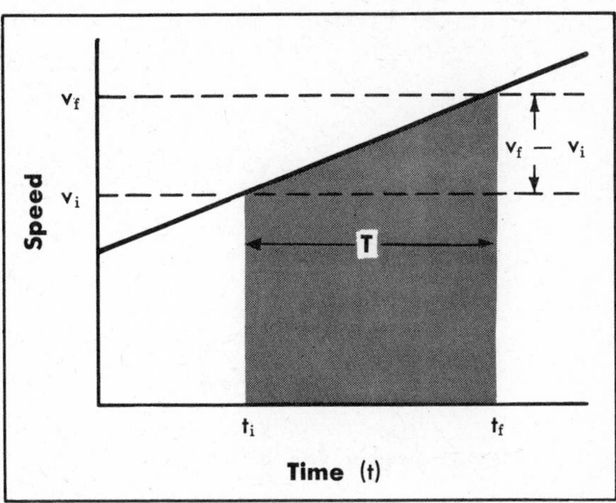

5–26. The speed vs. time graph of a motion with constant acceleration along the path. The slope $\frac{v_f - v_i}{t_f - t_i}$ of the graph is the acceleration along the path, and the area under the graph is the distance covered.

fying, we can draw a straight line tangent to the graph at $t = 20$ seconds, and we can find the slope of the curve by measuring the slope of this tangent line. In view of the definition of the slope, the instantaneous acceleration along the path at a time t equals the slope of the graph of speed versus time. In Fig. 5–25, by choosing two points (1 and 2) on the tangent line we find the instantaneous acceleration to be

$$a_p = \frac{v_2 - v_1}{t_2 - t_1} = \frac{50 \text{ mi/hr} - 20 \text{ mi/hr}}{30 \text{ sec} - 10 \text{ sec}}$$
$$= 1.5 \text{ mi/hr-sec.}$$

We can also express the instantaneous acceleration along the path in the language of Section 5–5 as

$$a_p = \lim_{\Delta t \to 0} \frac{\Delta v}{\Delta t}.$$

In addition to the instantaneous acceleration at each moment, we define the average acceleration for any time interval Δt as

$$a_{av} = \frac{\Delta v}{\Delta t}.$$

This tells us the over-all change of v in that particular time interval. The instantaneous acceleration along the path at time t is the average acceleration along the path for a very short time interval which includes t. If the acceleration does not change as time goes on, the average acceleration and the instantaneous acceleration are equal at any time.

5–7. Useful Results for Motion with Constant Acceleration Along the Path

When the acceleration along the path is constant, the methods that we have been developing enable us to express several useful relationships in the form of equations. Consider an object whose speed increases uniformly with time as shown by the graph in Fig. 5–26. Let us see what happens during a certain time interval. At the beginning of this time interval the speed is called v_i (the subscript "i" means initial), and the corresponding time is called t_i. At the end of this time interval the speed is called v_f (the subscript "f" means final), and the corresponding time is called t_f. Because the acceleration along the path is constant, we have

$$v_f - v_i = a_p(t_f - t_i) = a_pT, \tag{1}$$

where T is the time interval between the initial time t_i and the final time t_f. To find out how far the car has gone during this interval we can compute the shaded area in Fig. 5–26. From the trapezoid formula (or by adding the "area" of a rectangle and a triangle), we get

$$d = \tfrac{1}{2}(v_f + v_i)T, \tag{2}$$

a relationship between the distance traveled, the initial and final speeds, and the duration of the time interval.

We can also find a relation between the speeds

and the distance traveled. Solving Equation 1 for T we get

$$T = \frac{v_f - v_i}{a_p}.$$

Now, substituting this expression for T in Equation 2, we get

$$d = \tfrac{1}{2}(v_f + v_i)\frac{(v_f - v_i)}{a_p}.$$

Finally, on carrying out the multiplication, we have

$$2a_p d = v_f^2 - v_i^2$$

or

$$v_f^2 = v_i^2 + 2a_p d. \qquad (3)$$

This relation between the squares of the speeds and the distance is often useful. It will be essential in our discussion of kinetic energy in Part III.

Also if we solve for the final speed, v_f in Equation 1, and substitute it into Equation 2, we get a relation connecting the distance of travel, the acceleration along the path, the time interval, and the initial speed

$$d = v_i T + \tfrac{1}{2}a_p T^2. \qquad (4)$$

There is a simple meaning to the two terms on the right-hand side of Equation 4. The term $v_i T$ gives the distance the car would travel if its speed had stayed constant at v_i during the time interval, while the second term gives the distance the car would travel if it had started from rest at the initial time. You can verify these statements by first setting $a_p = 0$, then v_i equal to zero, in Equation 4.

Some examples will show you the use of these equations. Suppose a sports car accelerates at a constant rate, changing its speed in 6.0 seconds from 10 m/sec to 28 m/sec. What is its acceleration and how far does it go in this time interval?

We find its acceleration along the path from Equation 1

$$a_p = \frac{v_f - v_i}{t_f - t_i} = \frac{28 \text{ m/sec} - 10 \text{ m/sec}}{6 \text{ sec} - 0 \text{ sec}}$$
$$= 3.0 \text{ m/sec/sec or } 3.0 \text{ m/sec}^2.$$

We find the distance traveled from Equation 4

$$d = (10 \text{ m/sec} \times 6.0 \text{ sec}) + \tfrac{1}{2}(3.0 \text{ m/sec}^2 \times 36 \text{ sec}^2)$$
$$= 114 \text{ m}.$$

You can check this result for d by using Equation 3. (Try it.)

As another example, suppose a car starts from rest and accelerates at 2.0 mi/hr-sec for a distance of $\frac{1}{9}$ mi. How fast will it then be traveling and how long does it take to cover this distance?

We have two units of time, hours and seconds. It is convenient to eliminate one in favor of the other. In the following calculations we choose to express all time in hours. For this purpose we write

$$a_p = 2\,\frac{\text{mi}}{\text{hr-sec}} = 2 \times \frac{1 \text{ mi}}{1 \text{ hr} \times 1 \text{ sec}}.$$

Then we replace 1 sec by $\frac{1}{3600}$ hr; therefore

$$a_p = 2 \times \frac{1 \text{ mi}}{1 \text{ hr} \times \frac{1}{3600} \text{ hr}} = 7200 \text{ mi/hr}^2.$$

Now to find the final speed we use Equation 3, which becomes

$$v_f^2 = 2a_p d, \quad \text{because } v_i = 0.$$

The result is

$$v_f^2 = 2 \times 7200 \frac{\text{mi}}{\text{hr}^2} \times \tfrac{1}{9} \text{ mi} = 1600 \text{ mi}^2/\text{hr}^2$$
$$v_f = 40 \text{ mi/hr}.$$

We can find the time from Equation 1, which becomes

$$v_f = a_p t_f \quad \text{since } v_i \text{ and } t_i = 0.$$

Therefore

$$t_f = \frac{40 \text{ mi/hr}}{7200 \text{ mi/hr}^2} = \frac{1}{180} \text{ hr or 20 sec.}$$

5–8. Ranging by Speed: Radar and Sonar

Once we form the notion of speed, we can use it as a tool for measuring distance. Many people know how to gauge the distance of a lightning stroke in this way. Since sound travels a mile in about 5 sec (or a kilometer in 3 sec), while light takes less than 10^{-5} sec to cover the same distance, all we do is count the seconds between the flash and the bang and divide by 5 for miles (or 3 to get kilometers).

Because of its great speed, light is used to give a new unit of distance, the *light-year*. This is the distance light travels in a year. It is a big unit indeed, about 10^{16} m. The sun is only five hundred light-seconds or about 2×10^{-5} light-years away, and the nearest star is about 4.3 light-years away. You might try translating some of the

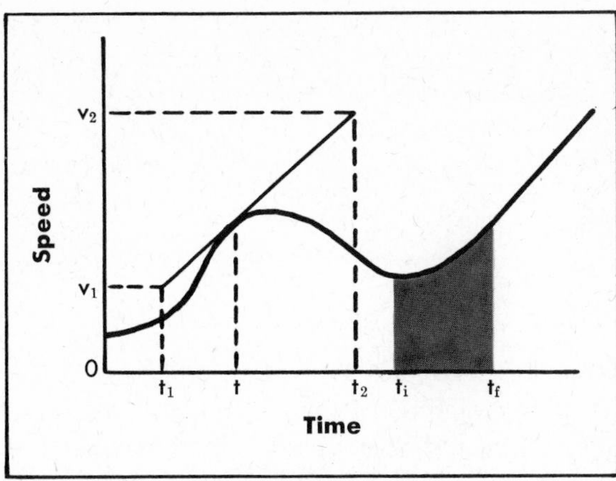

5–27. Uses of the speed vs. time graph.

distances in the first two tables of Chapter 3 into light-years.

Suppose you project into space some "object" which has a known and unchanging speed. If that messenger can go out and return to you along the same path without delay in turning around, then the distance is given to you by

$$2d = vt,$$

where d is the distance to the destination which it reached with a known speed v, and t is the time for the round trip.

Sound and light are such "messengers." In still air they travel with constant speeds, and they are reflected from objects of all sorts. By projecting sound in a definite direction, and detecting the time of arrival of the delayed weak echo, you can establish the distance of the object which reflects the sound. Echoes from the sound of our shuffling feet, of our voices, or even of our breathing, instinctively warn us of a wall when we approach it in the dark. People who are blind often develop such skills to a fine point which compensates for the loss of sight. Bats navigate with great accuracy in the dark by listening to the echoes of their high-pitched squeaks.

You can perform an echo-ranging experiment for yourself quite easily. Measure the speed of sound by timing over a known distance, and then use sounds to measure other distances. For more precise measurements over greater distances, sound can be projected directionally and echoes timed electronically. Such echo ranging, using underwater sound, is called *sonar.*

Light is harder to time, though its "echoes," which we call reflections, are everywhere. No unaided human sense can notice the round-trip time for light anywhere on earth. Light simply travels too fast for our senses. But with electronics, light echoes can be timed and, even more usefully, so can radio echoes which travel at the same speed as light. The use of radio echoes to locate objects is called *radar.* Knowing the velocity of the pulse sent out — its direction and magnitude — we can detect and time the echoes from every direction in turn. If these are collected by a rotating antenna and displayed to scale and in proper direction on a fluorescent screen, we have a radar map of the surrounding objects that reflect the radio pulses. Radar is very valuable in modern navigation.

In astronomy the radar-ranging method has rarely been used, but it can serve as a cross-check on optical measurements of the position of the moon or of an artificial satellite, and as a means of locating the temporary trails of meteors, high in the atmosphere.

5–9. Summary

In this chapter we have been studying kinematics — the story of motion and of the relationships of speed, time, and distance. Our starting point was the equation that we all learned early in our school days: at constant speed, the distance traveled is equal to the product of speed and the time of travel. We cannot use this relation if the speed is not constant, because we do not know in advance by which of the various speeds the time should be multiplied. However, we have been able to show how the distance can be obtained with the help of a graph of speed versus time, such as that shown in Fig. 5–27. The shaded "area" in the figure shows the distance covered between the times t_i and t_f.

This graph can do more for us. By drawing a tangent to the graph at any particular time, such as t, we can determine the slope of the graph, at this point. This quantity is the acceleration along the path — the rate at which the speed is changing. Thus, the acceleration at the time t in Fig. 5–27 is

$$a_p = \lim_{\Delta t \to 0} \frac{\Delta v}{\Delta t} = \frac{v_2 - v_1}{t_2 - t_1}.$$

When the curve is a straight line, as at the right of Fig. 5–27, the acceleration along the path remains constant. Under such circumstances, it is very easy to compute the "area" under the graph, and we have been able to arrive at algebraic equations that tell the full story of motion at constant acceleration. The use of graphs is not limited to this simple case, however. They furnish a quite general way of studying motion.

Another valuable graph is that of distance versus time, such as is shown in Fig. 5–28. From this graph we can find the speed as well as the distance. The slope of this graph at any particular time is the speed:

$$v = \lim_{\Delta t \to 0} \frac{\Delta d}{\Delta t} = \frac{d_2 - d_1}{t_2 - t_1}.$$

Although we have gone far in our study of motion, there are still questions we cannot answer. In the next chapter we shall get away from the restriction of motion to a fixed path such as a road. The introduction of vectors in the next chapter will allow us to consider motions in all directions — up-down; north-south; and east-west. For this purpose, speed must be replaced by velocity, which indicates the direction of the motion as well as how fast it is. Acceleration will then take on a more general meaning as the rate of change of the velocity.

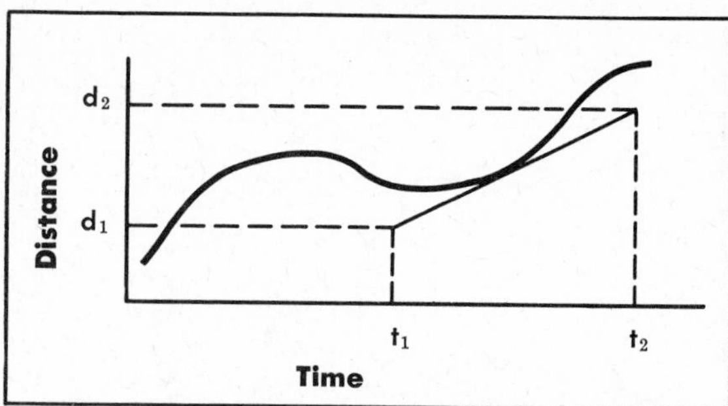

5–28. Speed can be determined from the distance-time graph.

FOR HOME, DESK, AND LAB

1. A runner makes one complete lap around an 800-meter track in 2 min 1.2 sec. What was his average speed in m/sec?

2. Two cars, one traveling at 40 mi/hr and the other at 60 mi/hr, start a trip of 120 miles at the same time. How much sooner does one car arrive at its destination than the other?

3. A man knows that by one route between two towns he must go 400 miles, and can average 45 mi/hr. By another route he can travel on a 400-mile stretch of superhighway, averaging 60 mi/hr, but he must travel an extra 80 miles on roads where he can average only 40 mi/hr. Which route takes the shorter time?

4. A Volkswagen and a Cadillac are driven on the same 80-mile trip. The Volkswagen travels at 50 mi/hr all the time. The Cadillac starts at the same time, driving at 60 mi/hr, but the driver stops for ten minutes after he has traveled for half an hour.
   (a) Make a graph of speed versus time for the two cars.
   (b) Which car is the first to arrive at the destination?

5. Data for a trip made in a car is given in the accompanying table:

Time Interval	Duration of Interval (hr)	Speed (mi/hr)
1	0.10	20
2	0.40	60
3	0.20	20

   (a) How far does the car go in the first interval?
   (b) What is the total distance of the trip?
   (c) Make a graph of speed versus time for this trip.
   (d) How long does it take the car to travel the first 14 miles?
   (e) Indicate the area on your graph which corresponds to the first 14 miles of travel.

6. A car travels at the speeds given in the accompanying table, where *T* is a particular time interval and *V* is a particular speed.

Time Interval	Duration of Interval	Speed
1	T	V
2	3T	4V
3	T	2V
4	2T	V/2
5	T/2	2V

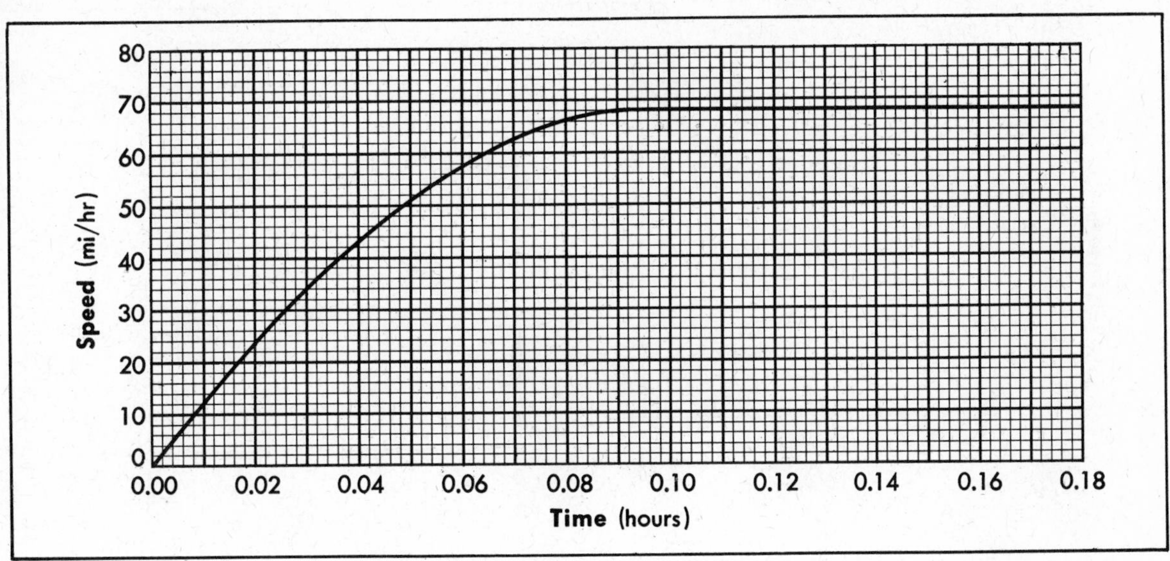

5–29. For Problem 8.

(a) Make a graph of speed versus time for this trip.

(b) What is the total distance of the trip?

(c) How long after the start of the trip is needed for the car to travel a distance of 7VT?

(d) How long a time does it take for the car to make the first half of the trip?

(e) What is the average speed for the entire trip?

7. The accompanying data show the instantaneous speed of a car at intervals of 1 second. Plot the speed versus time, and use your graph to answer the following questions.

(a) How fast is the car going at 2.6 sec? At 4.8 sec?

(b) How far did the car travel between the two instants in part (a)?

(c) What is the slope of the graph?

Time (sec)	Speed (m/sec)
0.0	10.0
1.0	12.4
2.0	14.8
3.0	17.2
4.0	19.6
5.0	22.0
6.0	24.4

8. A train speeds up according to the speed-time graph shown in Fig. 5–29. How far does it travel in the first six minutes?

9. Car A is stopped at a traffic light. The light turns green and A starts up. Just as it does so, car B passes it, going at a steady speed. Their speed-time curves are shown in Fig. 5–30.

(a) How long does it take car A to be going as fast as car B?

5–30. For Problem 9.

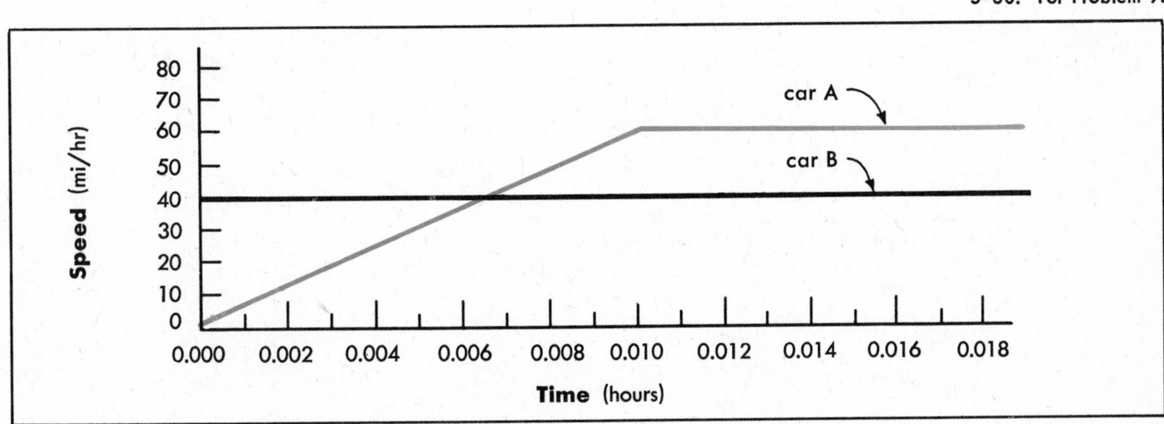

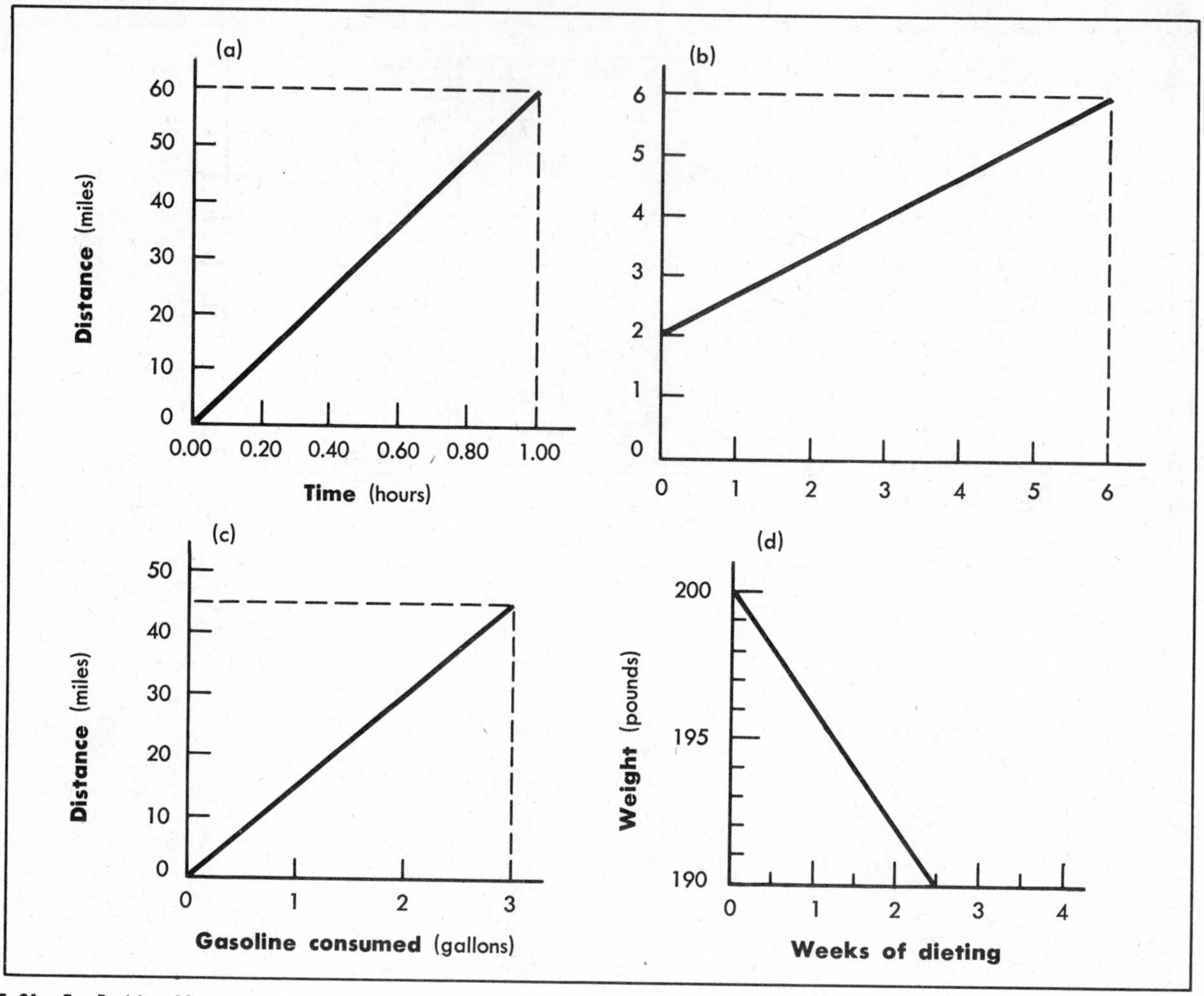

5–31. For Problem 10.

5–32. For Problem 11.

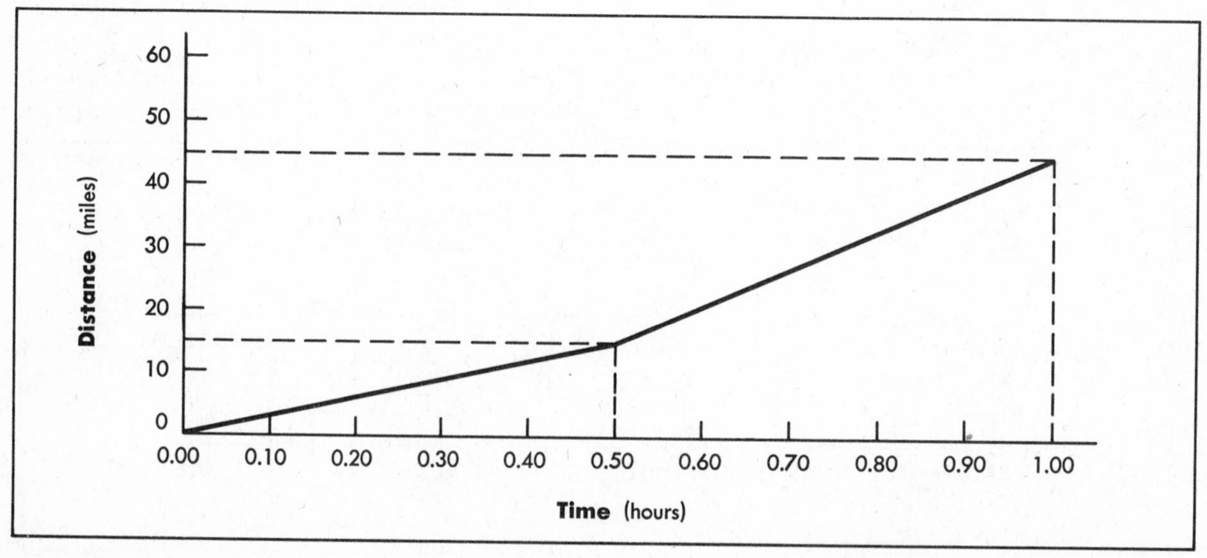

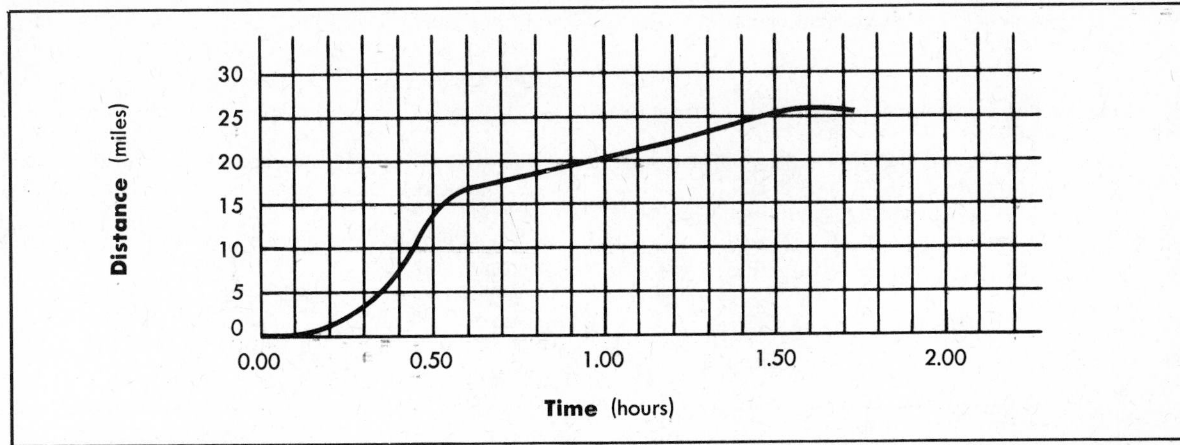

5–33. For Problem 12.

(b) At that time, how much is car B ahead of car A?

(c) Which car is ahead, and by how much, at the end of 0.010 hours?

(d) At what time does car A catch up with car B?

(e) How far have they traveled from the traffic light by the time car A catches up?

10. Find the slopes of the graphs in Fig. 5–31. State the units in each case.

11. The distance-time graph of a car traveling along a road is shown in Fig. 5–32. Make a graph of its speed versus time.

12. The distance-time graph of a car is shown in Fig. 5–33.

(a) At what time is the car going at the greatest speed?

(b) How fast is it traveling at that time?

(c) How fast is the car going at 0.70 hours?

(d) What is the average speed for the first half hour?

13. During a trip along a turnpike, a passenger sitting beside the driver recorded the following times at which they passed various mileposts.

Time hr:min	Milepost
10:05 a.m.	40
10:25	45
10:40	52
10:50	62
11:00	66
11:10	68
11:25	78
11:40	82
11:50	82
12:05 p.m.	76
12:15	70
12:30	56
1:15	40

(a) Plot the distance traveled by the car versus time.

(b) Between which mileposts was the car traveling at the greatest speed?

(c) What was the average speed on the return portion of the trip?

(d) What was the speed between 12:15 and 12:30 p.m.?

(e) During a part of the outgoing trip they were forced to slow down to 12 mi/hr by a slow-moving truck. Between which mileposts did this occur?

14. A train travels 60 mi/hr for 0.52 hr, 30 mi/hr for the next 0.24 hr, and then 70 mi/hr for the next 0.71 hr. What is its average speed for the trip?

15. A car going at 20 mi/hr accelerates to 60 mi/hr in 6.0 seconds. What is the average acceleration along the road?

16. From the graph of *speed* versus *time* for a car shown in Fig. 5–34, deduce the graph of *acceleration* versus *time*.

5–34. For Problem 16.

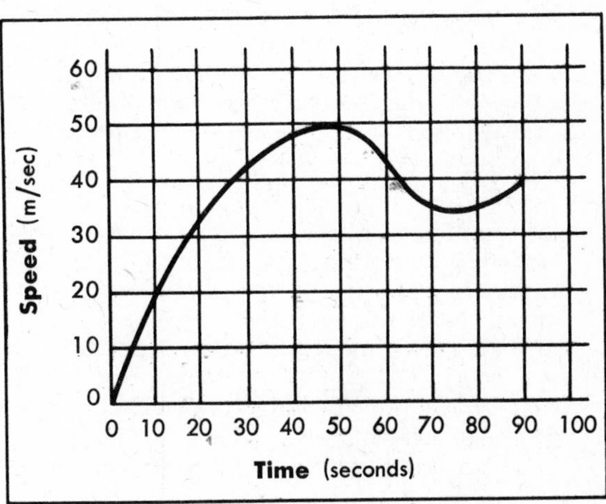

17. Make a graph of *distance* traveled versus *time* for the car of Problem 16.

18. A bobsled has a constant acceleration of 2.0 m/sec^2 starting from rest.
(a) How fast is it going after 5.0 seconds?
(b) How far has it traveled in 5.0 seconds?
(c) What is its average speed in the first 5.0 seconds?
(d) How far has it traveled by the time its speed has reached 40 m/sec?

19. A car, initially traveling at uniform speed, accelerates at the rate of 1.0 m/sec^2 for a period of 12 seconds. If the car traveled 190 meters during this 12-second period, what was the speed of the car when it started to accelerate?

20. A ball starting from rest rolls with uniform acceleration down an inclined track 216 cm long. A multiple-flash photograph shows that it took the ball 1.2 sec to cover this distance.
(a) What was the acceleration?
(b) Plot the velocity of the ball versus time.

21. Assume that the express train mentioned at the very beginning of the chapter stops with uniform acceleration.
(a) How long does it take to stop?
(b) What is the acceleration along the path during the braking?
(c) Plot the position of each train versus time on the same graph and from this find whether or not a collision takes place.

22. An automobile starting from rest increases its speed (accelerates) at a constant rate for 10 seconds. Its speed at the end of 5.0 seconds is 48 km/hr.
(a) What is the acceleration?
(b) What will be its speed after 10 seconds?
(c) How far will it travel in 10 seconds?
(d) How far does it travel during the eighth second?
(e) Derive an equation for finding the distance a body, starting from rest and accelerating uniformly, travels during the nth second. ($n = 1, 2, 3$, etc.)

23. A driver of a car going 52 km/hr applies the brakes, decelerates uniformly, and stops in 5 seconds. Another driver going 34 km/hr puts less pressure on his brakes and stops in 10 seconds. On the same graph plot speed versus time for each of the two cars.
(a) Which of the two cars traveled farther after the brakes were applied?
(b) Add a line to the graph which shows the second car decelerating at the same rate as the first car. How long does it take the car to stop at this rate of deceleration?

24. A car is traveling along a highway at 30 mi/hr. The driver then "steps on the gas" and accelerates at a uniform rate to a speed of 60 mi/hr in 10 seconds.
(a) What was the acceleration during this 10-second interval?
(b) How far did the car travel during these 10 seconds?

25. A rocket which placed a satellite in orbit attained a speed of 2.90×10^4 km/hr in 2.05 minutes.
(a) What was the average acceleration in km/hr sec? In m/sec^2?
(b) If the rocket had enough fuel to maintain the same rate of acceleration for an hour, what speed would it have at the end of the hour starting from rest?
(c) How far would it travel during this hour?

26. Plot the speed-time graph of a car traveling at a uniform speed of 40 mi/hr. On the same graph plot the speed-time graph for a second car starting from rest and uniformly accelerating to a maximum speed of 40 mi/hr.
(a) What relationship do you find between the distances covered by the two cars during the time in which the second car is accelerating?
(b) Would this relationship hold if you chose a different acceleration for the second car?
(c) Can you prove this mathematically?

27. A rocket-test sled is accelerated along a track for 10 sec with an acceleration of 100 m/sec^2. It then moves without acceleration for 5.0 sec, after which it moves with an acceleration of -150 m/sec^2 until it comes to rest.
(a) What is the maximum speed of the sled?
(b) How long does it take the sled to come to rest from the time it starts decelerating?
(c) What is the distance traveled during the first 10 sec? During the period of deceleration? During the entire trip?
(d) Plot a graph of the acceleration of the sled versus time. Find the "area" under the graph during the first 10 sec. How does this "area" compare with the maximum speed of the sled?
(e) Show that the change of speed of a body during any time interval is equal to the "area" under the acceleration-time graph for the same interval.

28. Look through the chapter and list all the places where the discussion must be limited to motion in a straight line — all the places when motion along a curved path would not do equally well.

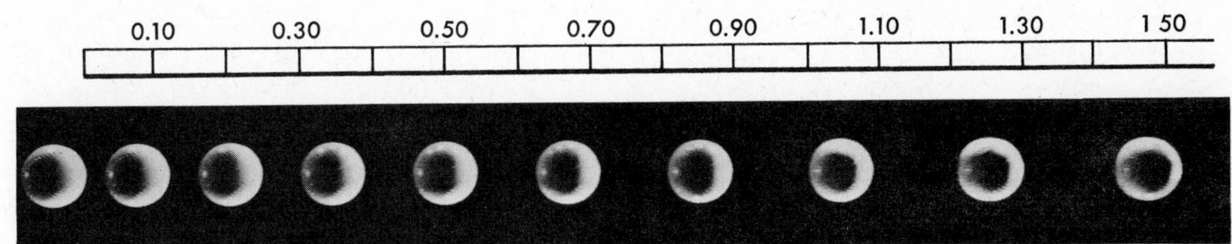

5–35. For Problem 29.

29. Fig. 5–35 is a multiple-flash photograph of a moving ball taken at 1/30 sec intervals. The ball is moving from left to right and the zero point on the scale lines up with the right-hand edge of the ball's initial position.

(a) Measure the distance from the zero point for each position of the ball, and plot a graph of distance against time to describe this motion.

(b) From your graph in (a), construct a speed-time graph.

(c) What does your speed-time graph tell you about the acceleration of the moving ball?

FURTHER READING

GRIFFIN, DONALD R., *Echoes of Bats and Men.* Doubleday, 1959. A Science Study Series paperback.

HORNUNG, JULIUS L., *Radar Primer.* McGraw-Hill, 1948.

RUSH, J. H., "The Speed of Light." *Scientific American*, August, 1955. A simple summary of methods that have been used for measuring this fastest of all possible speeds.

THOMPSON, SILVANUS P., *Calculus Made Easy.* Macmillan, 1944.

VECTORS

CHAPTER 6

A CAR moving along a road travels on a predetermined path, but there are many motions in nature for which the path or road is not fixed in advance. If you drive a motorboat on a lake, pilot an airplane, or want to find out about the motion of a satellite moving across the sky, you are facing a new situation. There are no roads or paths on the surface of the water or up in space.

To describe motion in general, we must know more than the speed. We must extend the ideas of Chapter 5 to include the direction of motion. We therefore introduce quantities which have both a magnitude and a direction. We shall represent these quantities by straight line segments. The length of the line gives the magnitude, and its direction specifies the direction in space. We shall now find out how to work with these new quantities, which are called vectors.

6–1. Trips and Vectors; Addition and Subtraction of Vectors

The simplest situation involving vectors arises when we consider motion along a straight line. Suppose you take a trip in a car along a straight road. Fig. 6–1 shows a line representing the road; the points *A*, *B*, *C* . . . on the road are equidistant — for example, one mile apart. If you start at *C* and stop at *H*, this trip is evidently represented by the arrow labeled *CH* in the figure. It is 5 miles long. Now, if you turn around and ride back to *F*, this second trip is represented by the arrow labeled *HF*. It is 2 miles long and in the opposite direction. The result of these two trips is the same as if you made a single trip from *C* to *F*, represented by the arrow *CF*, 3 miles long. This says that

$$\text{Trip } CH + \text{Trip } HF = \text{Trip } CF.$$

If we try to use the length of each trip to represent it in this equation, we will be led to an incorrect conclusion, since 5 mi + 2 mi $\neq$ 3 mi. On the other hand, from the figure you see that we can represent the trip *HF* by the negative number (−2 miles). Then we get the correct result:

$$5 \text{ miles} + (-2 \text{ miles}) = 3 \text{ miles}.$$

As this example shows, we can represent the two directions possible for trips along a straight line by positive and negative numbers; for example, positive numbers for arrows pointing to the right and negative numbers for arrows pointing to the left. Addition and subtraction of such vectors is the same as addition and subtraction of positive and negative numbers.

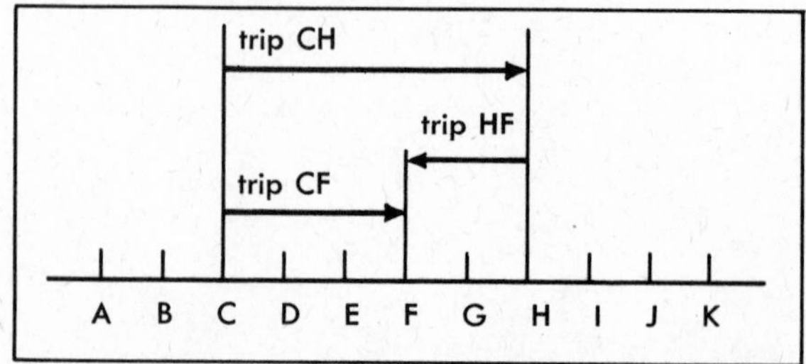

6–1. Trip *CH* followed by trip *HF* leads to the same result as trip *CF*.

By considering trips in any direction on a flat surface instead of restricting the trips to a straight line, we meet a new problem. Suppose we start at a point *A*. We make a trip 2.7 km north to *B* and follow that by a trip 2.7 km east to *C* as shown in Fig. 6–2 (a). A trip directly *from A to C* gives the same result as these two trips separately, as shown in Fig. 6–2 (b). Therefore we can write

$$\text{Trip } AB + \text{Trip } BC = \text{Trip } AC.$$

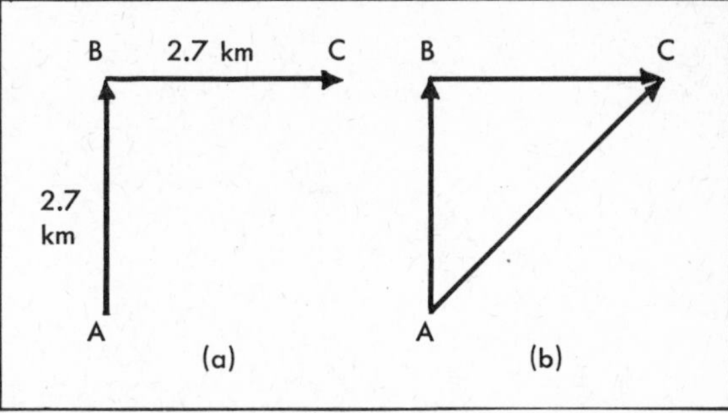

6–2. Trips on any surface, such as that of this page or that of the earth, may be added by the use of scale drawings.

We can add trips at any angle, such as those in Fig. 6–3. Notice that adding trips that are not along the same line is a different kind of addition from adding numbers. In particular, the *distance* we would walk going from *A* to *C* via *B* is longer than the distance going straight from *A* to *C*.

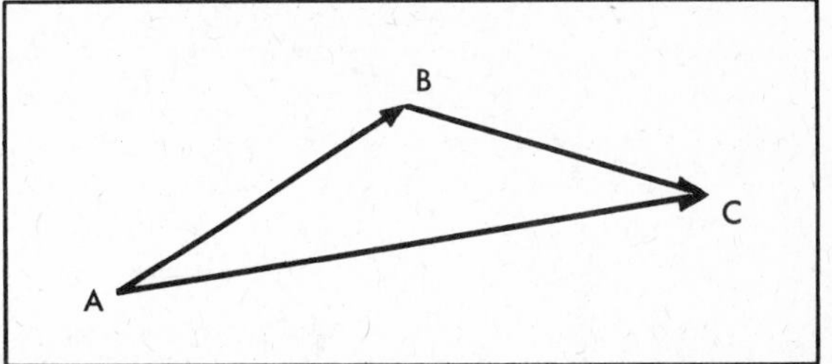

6–3. Trip *AB* + trip *BC* = trip *AC*.

In order to indicate a trip *from* a point *A to* a point *B*, we have drawn an arrowhead at *B* in the direction from *A* to *B*. The direction of the arrowhead tells us the direction of the trip, and the length of the arrow tells us the distance we have traveled. When we want to discuss this trip from *A* to *B*, instead of writing "Trip *AB*" we write the vector symbol $\overrightarrow{AB}$. Thus in Fig. 6–4 (a) we conclude that $\overrightarrow{LM} + \overrightarrow{MN} = \overrightarrow{LN}$. Usually it is more convenient to use a single letter to denote a vector. The trip from *L* to *M* can be represented either by the symbol $\overrightarrow{LM}$ or by the new symbol $\vec{R}$, and the description of Fig. 6–4 (b) is $\vec{R} + \vec{S} = \vec{T}$.

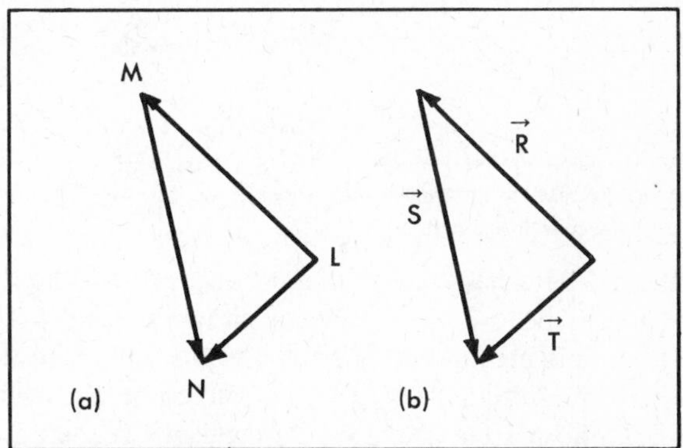

6–4. The same addition is shown in (a) and (b), although the vector notations are different.

To describe a straight-line trip completely, you need to know its length, its direction, and either its starting point or its end point. However, we shall often want to think of two such trips as being equivalent if they cover the same distance in the same direction, even though they start from different points. When we are interested only in the distance and direction, we shall use the name *displacement*, instead of trip. The statement that you have traveled 1.4 miles in a direction 15° west of north describes your displacement completely. Two vectors of the same length and the same direction represent the same displacement. When you displace a book one meter east and one meter north, it ends up $\sqrt{2}$ meters northeast regardless of where it started.

In general we shall define a vector without specifying where either end is, and we shall add vectors by putting them head to tail as in Fig. 6–4. Thus, if we want to find the sum of the two vectors shown in Fig. 6–5 (a), we can move one of

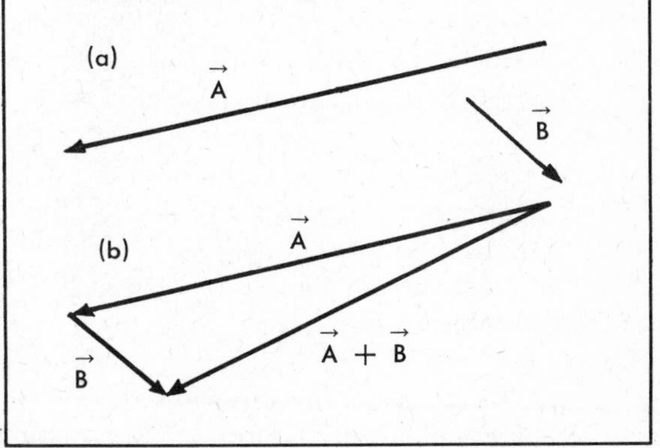

6–5. Addition of two vectors after moving one parallel to itself.

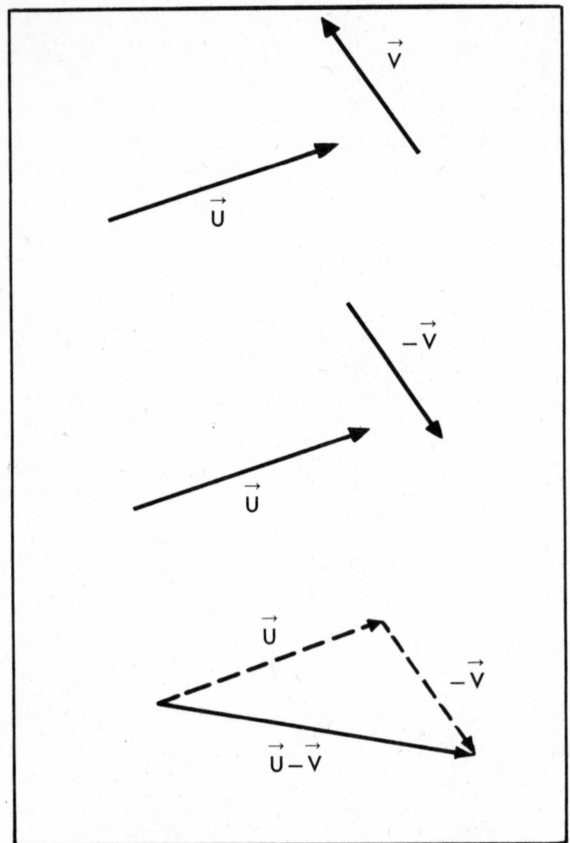

6–6. To find the difference of two vectors we add the negative of the second to the first.

them "parallel to itself" until its tail coincides with the head of the other, as shown in Fig. 6–5 (b). This means that two vectors are the same if their magnitude (length) and direction are the same, no matter where we draw them. If the position of one end of a vector is important we shall add that information when we use it.

Now we know how to add vectors. Is there a corresponding process for subtracting them? Recall that when we deal with positive and negative numbers the answer to the problem

$$6 - 8 = ?$$

is the same as the answer to the problem

$$6 + (-8) = ?$$

or to the problem

$$6 = 8 + ?$$

There are similar procedures for subtracting vectors. To see why, let us go back to trips for a moment. If you add the trip $\overrightarrow{BA}$ to the trip $\overrightarrow{AB}$, you get back to your starting point. The result is a "zero trip." We therefore say that $\overrightarrow{AB}$ and $\overrightarrow{BA}$ are opposite trips, whose sum is zero, and we write:

$$\overrightarrow{AB} = -\overrightarrow{BA} \quad \text{or} \quad -\overrightarrow{AB} = \overrightarrow{BA}.$$

In general, adding the trip $\overrightarrow{BA}$ is the same as taking away the trip $\overrightarrow{AB}$, and $\overrightarrow{CB} - \overrightarrow{AB}$ is the same as $\overrightarrow{CB} + \overrightarrow{BA}$ or as $\overrightarrow{CB} + (-\overrightarrow{AB})$.

For vectors the end points do not matter. The opposite of the vector $\vec{V}$ is any vector $-\vec{V}$ that is equal to $\vec{V}$ in length and opposite in direction. We can therefore subtract $\vec{V}$ from $\vec{U}$ by adding $-\vec{V}$ to $\vec{U}$. The procedure is illustrated in Fig. 6–6. We can also subtract $\vec{V}$ from $\vec{U}$ by answering the question $\vec{U} = \vec{V} + ?$ In Fig. 6–7 we show the vector $\vec{U}$, the vector $\vec{V}$, and the difference $\vec{U} - \vec{V}$. Notice that this vector in Fig. 6–7 is parallel to the corresponding vector of the same length and direction in Fig. 6–6. Therefore they are the same. Both methods give the same answer; use the method most convenient for you.

We have used displacements and the addition of displacements as examples of the new quanti-

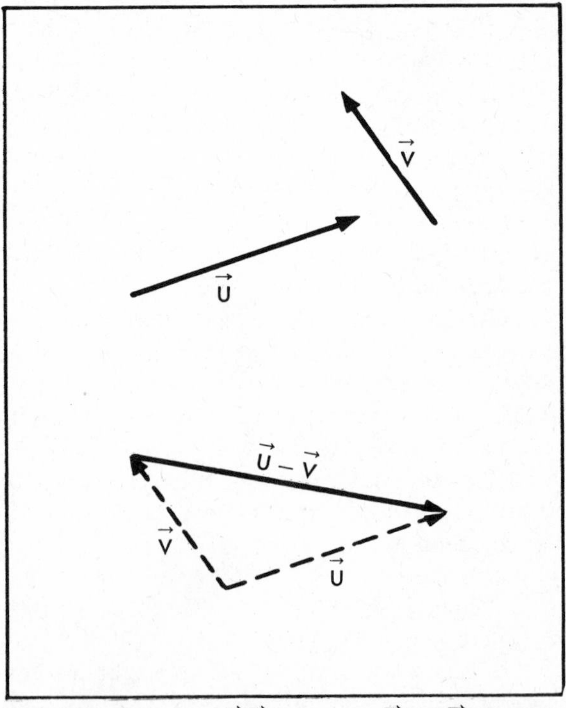

6–7. We can also find $\vec{U}-\vec{V}$ by drawing $\vec{U}$ and $\vec{V}$ tail to tail, then drawing a vector from the head of $\vec{V}$ to the head of $\vec{U}$. You can check that you have drawn this vector in the right direction by remembering that $\vec{V} + (\vec{U} - \vec{V}) = \vec{U}$.

ties we call vectors. We can represent these quantities by straight line segments, each with an arrowhead to indicate the direction and the length to give us the magnitude. This gives us a standard way of representing vectors. But what do we really mean by a vector? Vectors are any quantities which add and subtract in the same way as displacements. Notice that vectors are really new quantities and cannot be described by single numbers. The physical magnitudes which can be given with single numbers we shall call *scalars.* The temperature of a room is a good example of a scalar physical quantity just as a displacement 3 kilometers northeast is a good example of a vector quantity. We shall meet several types of vectors in physics.

6–2. Velocity Vectors

If an airplane has a speed of 250 km/hr through the surrounding air and flies in a wind of 50 km/hr, how fast does the airplane go over the ground? This question cannot be answered without further information, such as whether the wind is a head wind, a tail wind, or a cross wind. Because the direction of motion as well as the speed is important in problems like this, we need vectors to represent motions, just as we needed them to represent displacements.

In Chapter 5 we saw how to find the instantaneous speed of an object, such as a car, moving along a fixed path. We even took direction into account by using a plus sign for one direction and a minus sign for the other. Now we shall represent the direction of motion of a body by the direction of a vector, and represent the instantaneous speed (regardless of direction) by the magnitude of the vector. We call this vector the *instantaneous velocity.*

When we determine the speed of a car by reference to mileposts along a road, we find the speed *relative to the road.* To take into account the direction of the road, we specify it with respect to some real or imaginary fixed line on the ground, such as a line pointing north. When the speed and direction are both described, we have specified the velocity of the car *relative to the ground.*

It is important to recognize that we are using the two words "velocity" and "speed" in a technical sense which is different from everyday usage. When we are interested only in how fast a body is moving, we shall speak of *speed.* When we are concerned with both the magnitude and the direction, we shall use *velocity.* Thus, velocity is a vector and speed is a scalar.

Let us turn back to the example of the airplane mentioned at the beginning of this section. How can we find out how fast the airplane moves relative to the ground? To see what is involved, let us start with a simpler situation. Suppose we are in a free balloon, a few hundred feet in the air. If the air is perfectly still, the balloon will not move at all. If the whole mass of air is moving at 10 mi/hr — in other words, if there is a 10 mi/hr wind — the balloon moves right along with it. Only when the air mass changes velocity does the air "blow against" the balloon, speeding it up or slowing it down until it again moves at the same speed as the air.

Now let us imagine ourselves in a blimp, a large balloon with engines. With the engines off, the blimp moves only as the wind moves. But when the engines are going, the propellers pull us through the air at a certain velocity — a velocity with respect to the whole mass of air. Our motion relative to the ground now results from the combined effect of the motion of the air relative to the ground and of the motion of the blimp through the air.

In an airplane, the same thing happens. The airplane is supported by the air. Its engines give it a velocity through the air which must be added to the wind velocity to obtain the airplane's velocity relative to the ground. In particular, let us go back to the example of the airplane headed north, traveling through the air at 250 km/hr. Suppose the 50-km/hr wind is blowing toward the east. By "headed" north we mean that the nose of the airplane is due north of the tail. A few minutes later the nose is still due north of the tail, but the airplane is not due north of its former position. As well as going north, the airplane has moved east along with the whole mass of air. In Fig. 6–8 (a) the airplane is shown headed north at A. *If there were no wind,* the airplane would move in the direction in which it is pointed and would later be located at B. But during the time t while the plane would advance the distance $t \times 250$ km/hr from A to B, the air has moved east by an amount $t \times 50$ km/hr, and so the plane arrives at the position C.

The addition of the two displacement vectors $\overrightarrow{AB}$ and $\overrightarrow{BC}$ leads to the vector $\overrightarrow{AC}$, the displace-

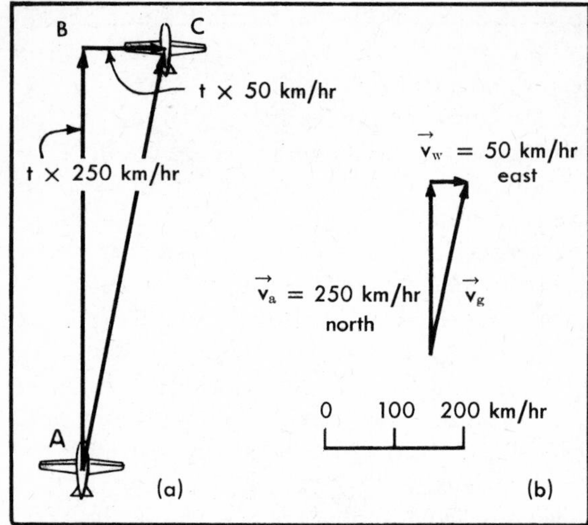

6–8. Part (a) shows the addition of the displacement vector $\overrightarrow{AB}$, which represents the airplane's motion through the air, and $\overrightarrow{BC}$, which represents the displacement of the air. Their sum is the vector $\overrightarrow{AC}$, the displacement of the airplane relative to the ground. On dividing by the elapsed time, the velocity vectors are found as shown in part (b). The velocity of the airplane relative to the ground is the vector sum of its velocity relative to the air and the velocity of the wind relative to the ground.

ment of the plane relative to the ground. These three vectors form a triangle. Each vector is proportional to a speed in a particular direction; $\overrightarrow{AB}$ to the speed north, $\overrightarrow{BC}$ to the speed east, and $\overrightarrow{AC}$ to the speed of the plane in the direction of motion with respect to the ground. On dividing each of these displacements by the elapsed time, we get a similar triangle representing the corresponding velocities. Since we now see that these velocities add exactly as the displacements, we have proved that velocity is a vector. In Fig. 6–8 (b) the velocity vector diagram is shown. The velocity $\vec{v}_a$ of the plane relative to the air is plotted in the same direction as $\overrightarrow{AB}$. It is a line north of length proportional to 250 km/hr. To this velocity we must add the velocity of the wind relative to the earth ($\vec{v}_w$ = 50 km/hr pointed east). We then obtain the velocity $\vec{v}_g$ of the plane relative to the ground. Both its direction and its magnitude can be obtained directly from its graphical representation.

Because $\vec{v}_a$ and $\vec{v}_w$ are at right angles in this example, it is easy to calculate the magnitude of the velocity relative to the earth (called the ground speed). Using the Pythagorean relationship, we see that

$$v_g = \sqrt{v_a^2 + v_w^2}$$

$$v_g = \sqrt{(250\text{ km/hr})^2 + (50\text{ km/hr})^2} = 255\text{ km/hr}.$$

Notice that the various speeds are indicated by v_g, v_a, and v_w, the same symbols that are used for the velocities, except that they do not carry the vector sign over them. This is a very convenient and commonly used notation. You can practice up on vectors and in particular on relative velocities by working through the practical navigation problem discussed in the boxed material. It is more complicated than the problem we just discussed, but the basic ideas are the same.

A Navigation Problem

As a practical example of the relations that we have found, suppose that the navigator of an airplane wishes to go from a city *C* to another city *D* which is 900 miles from *C* in a direction 30° east of north. The meteorologist tells him that there is a wind blowing from west to east with a speed of 50 mi/hr, and he knows that the pilot plans to maintain an air speed of 240 mi/hr. To get to *D*, the airplane must move over the earth in a direction 30° east of north. It is the navigator's problem to give the pilot his heading — to tell him the direction in which the airplane must be pointed.

The navigator solves his problem by constructing a velocity vector diagram like that shown in Fig. 6–9 (a). Here the velocity $\vec{v}_g$ of the airplane over the ground is made up as the vector sum of the wind velocity $\vec{v}_w$ and the airplane's velocity relative to the air $\vec{v}_a$. The navigator starts drawing his diagram from any point *O*, as in Fig. 6–9 (b). He knows the direction in which the airplane must go, that is, the direction of $\vec{v}_g$; and he lays this direction out from *O*. Also he knows the wind velocity completely so he lays out that vector. It runs directly east from *O* and its length *OP* represents the wind speed of 50 miles per hour. Now to get the velocity vector $\vec{v}_g$ of the airplane with respect to the ground, the navigator must add the velocity vector $\vec{v}_a$ of the airplane with

A NAVIGATION PROBLEM (continued)

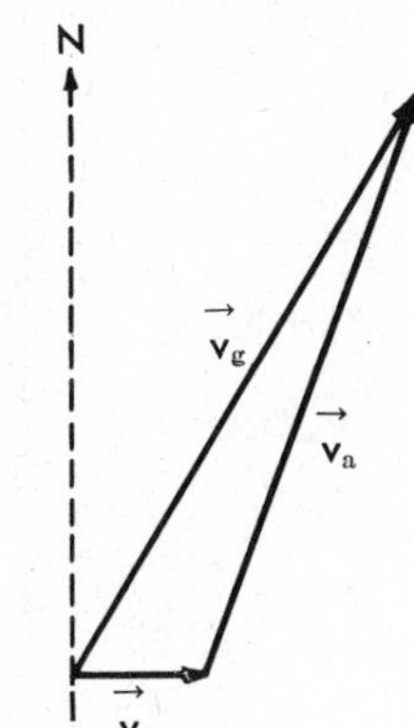

respect to the air. The vector $\vec{v}_a$ must therefore start from the point P, and its length (given by the speed of the airplane) must represent 240 miles per hour. But the navigator does not know the direction of $\vec{v}_a$. All he can do, therefore, is to draw a circle with its center at P and its radius the right length to represent the speed of 240 miles per hour. In Fig. 6–9 (b) we see the direction of $\vec{v}_g$ drawn 30° east of north; we see the vector $\vec{v}_w$ representing the wind velocity; and we see the circle showing the possible end points of the vector $\vec{v}_a$ drawn from the center P. Notice that this circle intersects the direction $\vec{v}_g$ of the airplane with respect to the ground in only one point, the point R on the figure. The airplane's velocity with respect to the air must have just the direction which carries it from the point P to the point R. This is the only way to get the correct direction of motion of the airplane over the ground. The vector $\overrightarrow{PR}$ is therefore $\vec{v}_a$.

The complete solution of the problem which we have just found is shown in Fig. 6–9 (c). By making measurements on this velocity vector diagram we find that the heading of the airplane (the direction of $\vec{v}_a$) is 19.8° east of north. This is the answer to

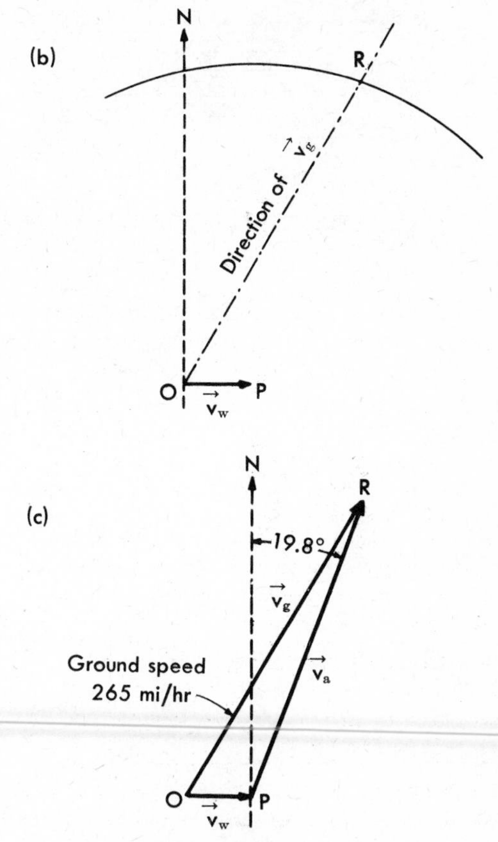

6–9. The solution of a navigation problem.

the navigator's problem. He can now tell the pilot which way to fly.

Determining the heading is the navigator's most important preflight job, but the pilot may also ask him how long the flight will take. To answer this question, the navigator measures the magnitude of the ground speed as constructed in his diagram. He finds that v_g will be about 265 mi/hr, and on dividing the 900 miles between C and D by this speed, he predicts that the trip will take about 3 hours and 25 minutes.

6–3. Components of Vectors

Suppose you want to swim across a river $\frac{1}{4}$ mile wide. The current in the river flows at $\frac{1}{2}$ mi/hr. You can swim at an average speed of 1 mi/hr, but only for 15 minutes.

What is the best plan to follow?

Suppose that you swim so as to keep your body always pointed at right angles to the bank. You will then be moving through the water perpendicular to the current, which will carry you steadily downstream. What will your velocity be with respect to the bank of the river? If we repre-

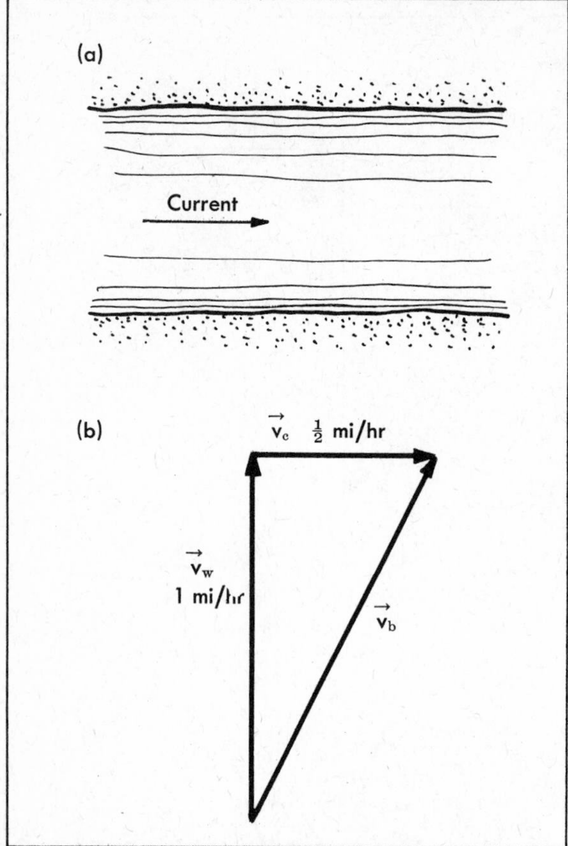

6–10. If you swim across a river with a velocity $\vec{v}_w$ through the water at right angles to the current $\vec{v}_c$, your velocity relative to the bank will be $\vec{v}_b$. Does the current help you reach the other side?

sent your velocity through the water by $\vec{v}_w$ and that of the current by $\vec{v}_c$, your velocity with respect to the bank is $\vec{v}_b$ in Fig. 6–10.

You can see that the magnitude of $\vec{v}_b$ is greater than that of $\vec{v}_w$, but does this get you across the river faster? No, your motion perpendicular to the banks of the river (which determines the time of crossing) is still the same. You will just make it. The velocity $\vec{v}_b$ tells us only that you will reach the other side downstream from the starting point.

The velocity $\vec{v}_b$ is made up of two parts, perpendicular to each other; these are called the rectangular components of $\vec{v}_b$. In this case, only the component $\vec{v}_w$ perpendicular to the bank affects the time of crossing. The other component $\vec{v}_c$ does not affect your progress to the other shore. Such rectangular components are mutually independent; they do not affect each other. No matter what the $\vec{v}_c$ is, you would still make it in 15 min.

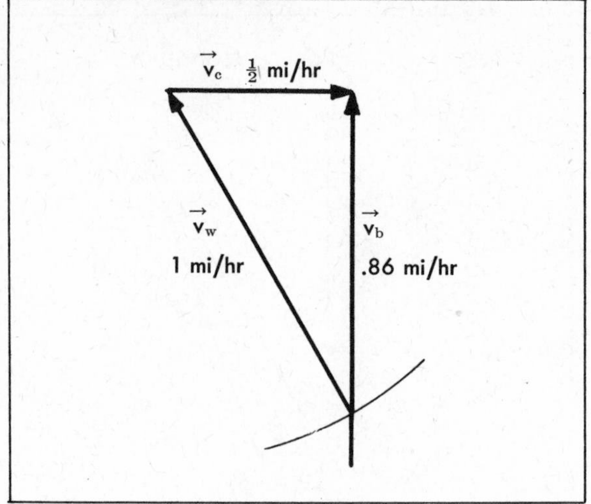

6–11. If you swim so that the component of $\vec{v}_w$ parallel to the banks is equal in magnitude but opposite in direction to $\vec{v}_c$, then $\vec{v}_b$ will be at right angles to the bank.

Suppose you're faced with a tougher problem; you can get ashore only at a beach which is directly opposite your starting point. Then your velocity $\vec{v}_b$ relative to the bank must be at right angles to it. This says that the component of $\vec{v}_b$ parallel to the bank must be zero. You must point your body upstream so that the component of $\vec{v}_w$ (Fig. 6–11) parallel to the bank is equal in magnitude and opposite in direction to $\vec{v}_c$.

Now your velocity *across* the river is only about 0.86 mi/hr and you won't make it. Perhaps you can wade the rest of the way.

We have seen that heading upstream makes it harder to get across the river. What would happen if you headed somewhat downstream? Of course, you won't get to the beach, but will you even get across the river? Do you agree that a current across your intended path cannot possibly help you?

Any vector $\vec{A}$ in a plane can be represented by two rectangular components. First we choose two perpendicular reference directions — for example, the directions given by OX and OY in Fig. 6–12. Then to construct the vector component of $\vec{A}$ along the direction OX, we construct a line through the head of $\vec{A}$ perpendicular to OX. Now we draw the vector which extends parallel to OX starting from the tail of $\vec{A}$ and ending at the perpendicular. This gives the component vector along OX (sometimes called the vector component of $\vec{A}$ along the X direction). To get the component vector in the direction OY (the

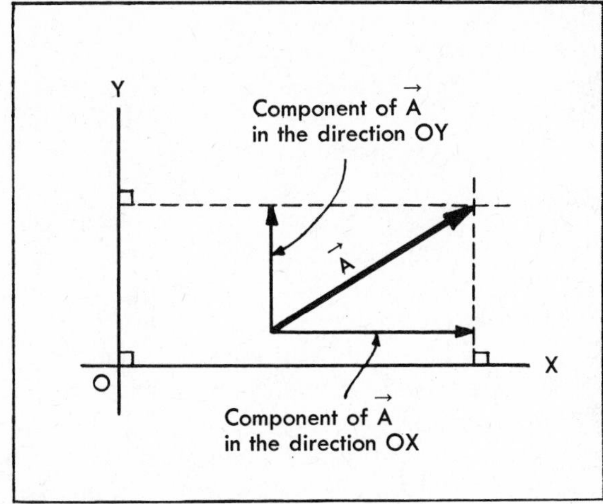

6–12. How to construct the rectangular components of a vector in a plane.

Y vector component of $\vec{A}$) we follow a similar process. (See Fig. 6–12.) Some examples of the components of vectors are shown in Fig. 6–13.

We can always build a vector from its components. To say that a ship moves 20 mi/hr northward and 10 mi/hr eastward tells us its velocity: there is only one possible magnitude and direction of velocity with this pair of components. Fig. 6–14 illustrates the point. As we see, the vector sum of the north and east components is the velocity. Notice the similarity between locating points on a graph by giving the coordinates and specifying a vector by giving its east and north components. When we give the coordinates of points on a graph, we are telling how far across the graph paper and how far up the graph paper we must go from the origin to locate the point.

We could represent a vector, using reference directions that are not at right angles. But rectangular components have an important advantage over any other choice. As we saw in the case of the swimmer, they are independent of each other. All sets of rectangular reference directions have this property of independence. If a vector $\vec{R}$ is perpendicular to a reference line AB, what is the component of $\vec{R}$ along AB? Does the component of $\vec{R}$ along AB change when the component perpendicular to AB is doubled?

We have needed only two components to specify a vector because we have been considering vectors in a plane — that is, in two dimensions. In three dimensions we can specify a vector by giv-

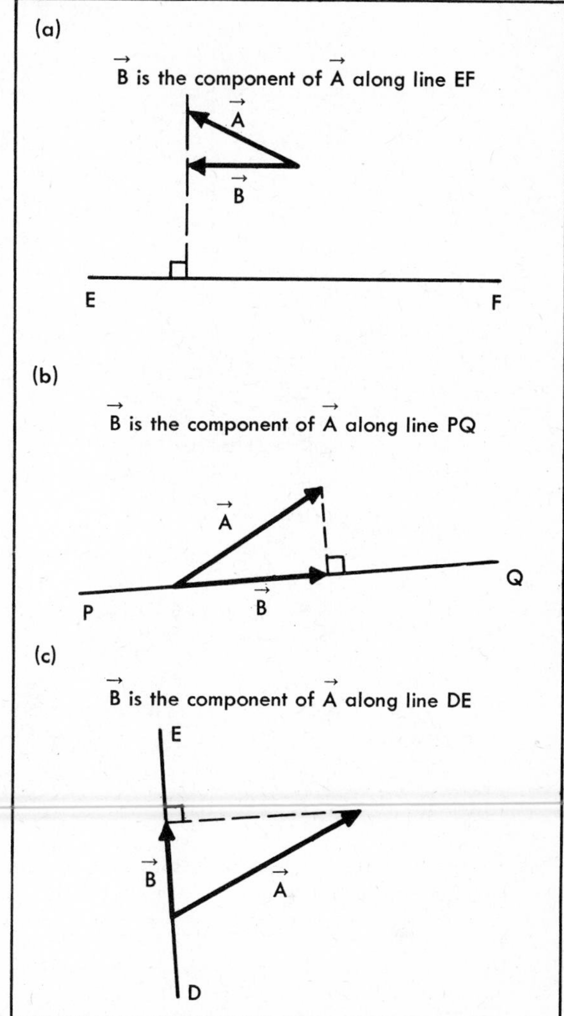

6–13. Examples of components of vectors along various directions.

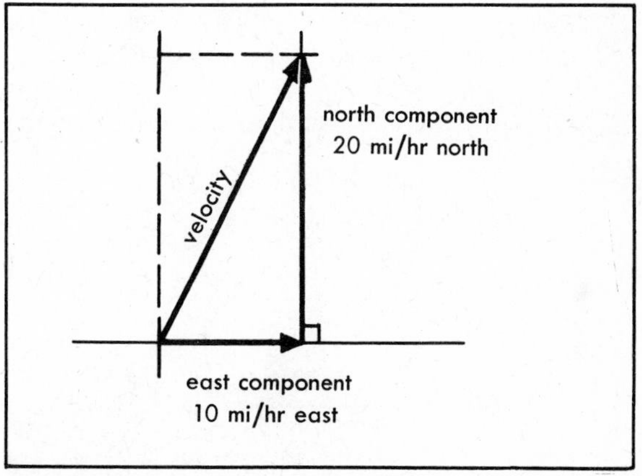

6–14. Finding a vector whose components are known. The velocity is 22 mi/hr, 27° east of north.

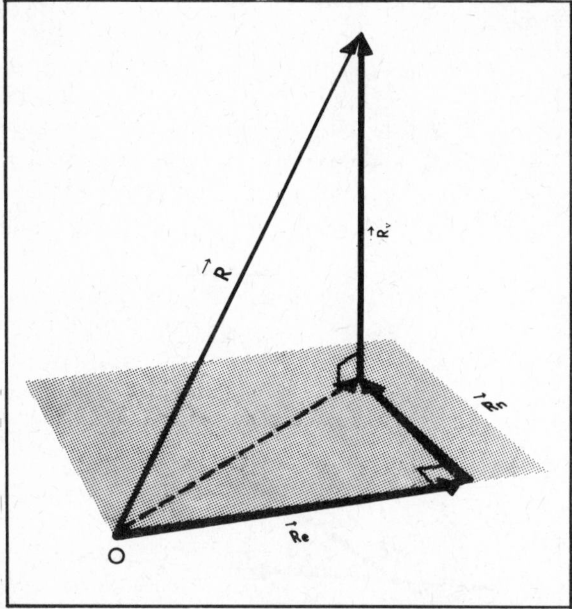

6–15. $\vec{R}_e$, $\vec{R}_n$, and $\vec{R}_v$ are the east, north, and vertical components of vector $\vec{R}$.

ing its components along three mutually perpendicular directions. As illustrated in Fig. 6–15, these three rectangular components added together give the vector.

6–4. Multiplying Vectors by Numbers and Scalars

Suppose that you have a vector $\vec{A}$, as shown in Fig. 6–16. What do you think is meant by $2\vec{A}$? Because multiplying a quantity by two means adding the quantity to itself, we conclude that $2\vec{A} = \vec{A} + \vec{A}$; and we see that $2\vec{A}$ is a vector twice as long as A pointing in the same direction. In general $k\vec{A}$, where k is any positive number, means a vector parallel to $\vec{A}$ and k times as long. What would you expect if k is negative?

What do we mean by $k\vec{A}$ when, for instance, $k = \frac{1}{4}$? In algebra $\frac{1}{4}x$ means a number which added four times over gives x. Here by $\frac{1}{4}\vec{A}$ we mean a vector which added four times over gives $\vec{A}$. The vector $\frac{1}{4}$ as long and in the same direction as $\vec{A}$ will do this job. You can show that no other vector will do, since any other vector differs in direction or in magnitude.

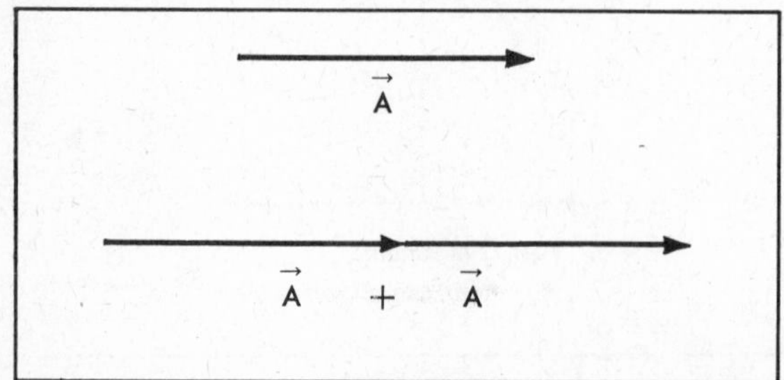

6–16. Multiplication of a vector by the number 2.

Briefly then, multiplying or dividing a vector by an ordinary number means multiplying or dividing the magnitudes while leaving the direction unchanged.

The rule that we have just found for multiplying a vector by a number such as 2 works just as well when a vector is multiplied by any scalar quantity such as a time interval. There is, however, one important difference between multiplication by a simple number and multiplication by a scalar that has units. When a vector is multiplied by a number, the new vector has the same units as before. It can be drawn on the same diagram as the original vector and to the same scale. When a vector is multiplied by a scalar having units, the units of the product are different from those of the original vector. To avoid confusion, it is best to represent the new vector on a new diagram.

Suppose, for example, that an airplane is flying northeast at 300 mi/hr. We can represent its velocity vector as in Fig. 6–17. If the plane flies for $\frac{1}{2}$ hour it will undergo a displacement, $\vec{R} = \vec{v}t$, of (300 mi/hr, northeast)($\frac{1}{2}$ hr) = 150 mi northeast. We can represent this displacement vector on another vector diagram, as in Fig. 6–18 (a), with a different scale to represent a distance instead of a rate of motion. If the airplane now continues for another $\frac{1}{2}$ hour, it undergoes a second equal displacement, and the sum of the two displacements must be just two times the original one. The total displacement is then found

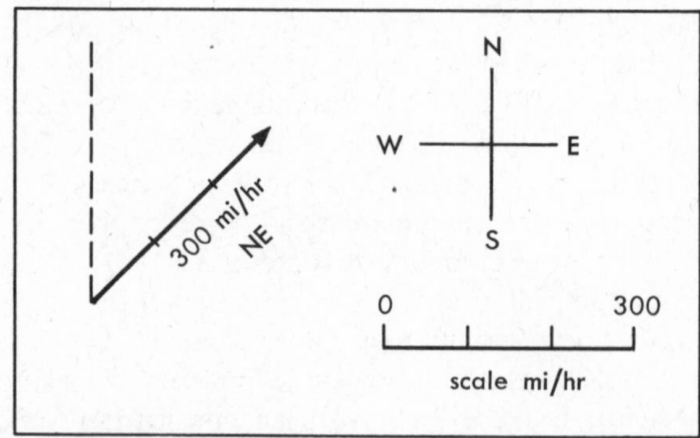

6–17. The velocity vector of an airplane flying northeast at 300 mi/hr.

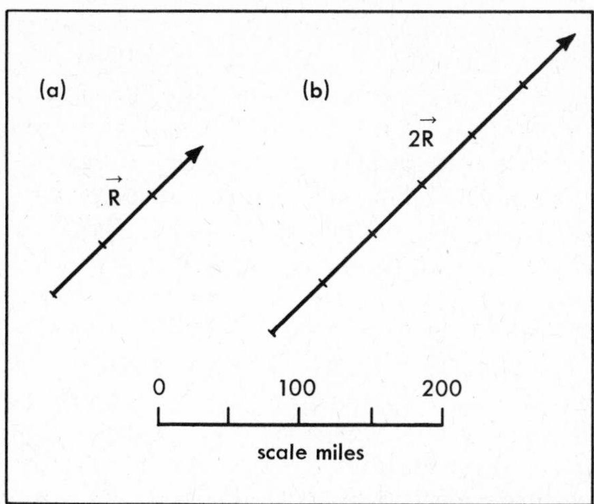

6–18. Displacement vectors for $\frac{1}{2}$ hour (a) and for two $\frac{1}{2}$ hours (b). The vector in (a) is obtained from that in Fig. 6–17 by multiplying $\frac{1}{2}$ hour by the velocity, a quantity with dimensions. The vector in (b) is obtained from that in (a) by multiplying by the pure number 2.

by multiplying the original displacement vector by the number 2. The total displacement of 300 miles northeast, as in Fig. 6–18 (b), can usefully be represented on the same vector diagram as the original displacement. It should not be placed on the same diagram as the velocity vector of 300 mi/hr because they are two different things, different physical quantities with different units.

6–5. Velocity Changes and Constant Vector Acceleration

Fig. 6–19 is a multiple-flash photograph of two balls. The ball at the left is falling straight down. Let us analyze its motion by finding the velocity vectors at successive intervals as the ball falls. We can get the average velocity vector for a given time interval by measuring the distance between two images of the ball and dividing by the time between the flashes which made those images. This gives us the length of the velocity vector; its direction is the direction of motion of the

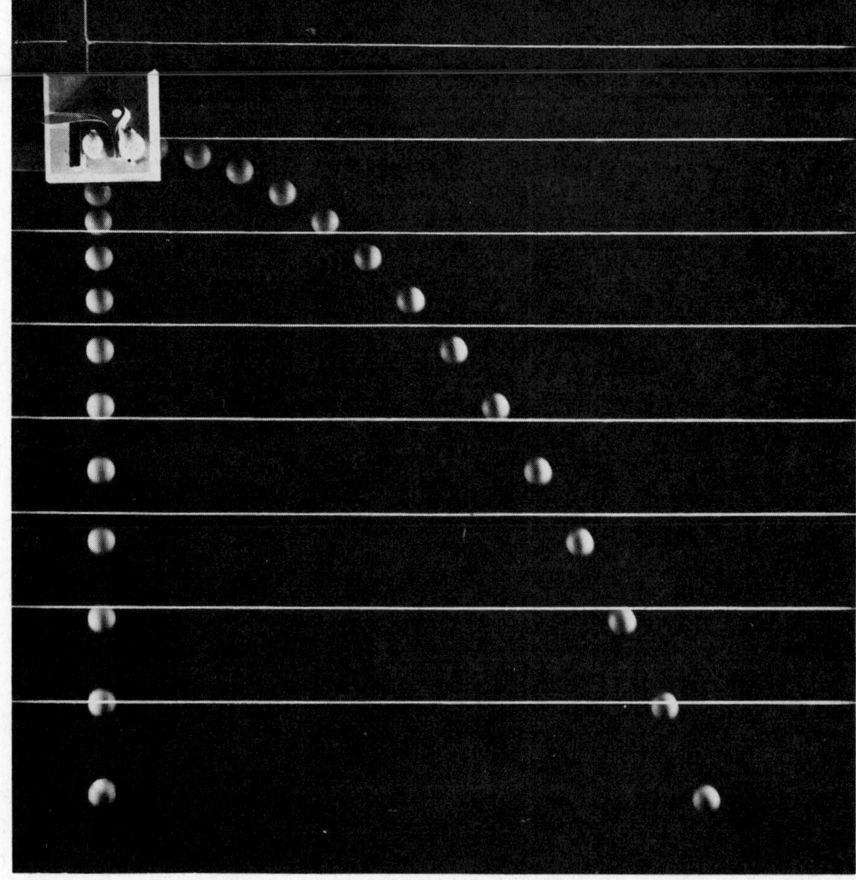

6–19. A flash photograph of two golf balls released simultaneously from the mechanism shown. One of the balls was allowed to drop freely, and the other was projected horizontally with an initial velocity of 2 m/sec. The light flashes were $\frac{1}{30}$ of a second apart. The white lines in the figure are a series of parallel strings placed behind the golf balls, six inches apart. Why do the strings appear to be in the foreground?

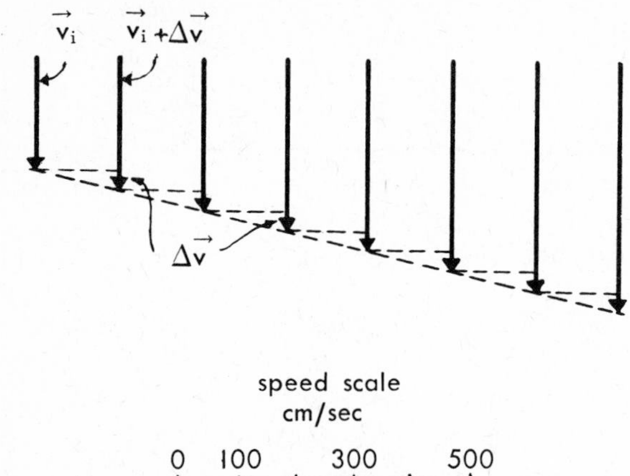

6–20. The length of the arrows is equal to $2\frac{1}{2}$ times the displacements of the left-hand ball in Fig. 6–19 during the last eight successive intervals of $\frac{1}{30}$ of a second. Because we know the actual separations of the white lines in Fig. 6–19 and the time intervals, we can turn the magnitudes of these displacements into speeds. The scale enables you to read the lengths of the arrows directly as speeds in cm/sec.

ball from one image to the other. In Fig. 6–20 we have measured off the successive displacements and put them side by side. The white strings in Fig. 6–19 are 6 inches apart and the interval between flashes is $\frac{1}{30}$ of a second. Using these facts, we have computed a scale so that we can read these vectors directly as the average velocities.

A glance at Fig. 6–20 shows that the velocity vector changes steadily. In each successive interval it increases by the same amount. Consequently, we can find the velocity as $\vec{v}_n = \vec{v}_i + n\,\Delta\vec{v}$. Here $\vec{v}_i$ is the velocity vector with which we start. $\Delta\vec{v}$ is the constant change in velocity that occurs in each interval. By adding n of these changes to the original velocity, we get the velocity n intervals further along.

We can rewrite the last equation so that it more closely resembles the equations we developed for the description of motion along a preassigned path. (See Chapter 5, especially Sections 5-6 and 5-7.) There we defined $a = \Delta v/\Delta t$, that is, the acceleration along the path. Here by dividing $\Delta\vec{v}$ by Δt we shall introduce the vector acceleration $\vec{a} = \Delta\vec{v}/\Delta t$. Using it, our last equation becomes

$$\vec{v}_n = \vec{v}_i + n\,\Delta t\,\frac{\Delta\vec{v}}{\Delta t}$$
$$= \vec{v}_i + \vec{a}t.$$

In the last line of this equation we have replaced $n\,\Delta t$ by t, the time during which the velocity has changed from its initial value $\vec{v}_i$ to its value in the nth time interval.

The velocity of the falling ball really increases steadily, as we can show by taking flash pictures at smaller and smaller time intervals. Therefore, after any time interval t it is $\vec{v}_t = \vec{v}_i + \vec{a}t$.

We have just described the motion of a falling ball in vector language. But since the ball moves on a predictable straight downward path, we hardly need the vectors. With speed and acceleration along the path we could have done the analysis equally easily. We would only need to add a statement that the motion is always straight down. The vector language, however, becomes far more useful when we analyze a more complicated motion. To see this let us get back to Fig. 6–19 and study the motion of the other ball, the one which moves out to the right in the figure.

The second ball in Fig. 6–19 moves both to the right and down. From the fact that the distance between the positions of the ball at successive flashes of the strobe light is greater for the later pictures, we see that the speed is increasing. Since the path is not a straight line, the direction of the velocity is changing too. We can analyze Fig. 6–19 to get the instantaneous velocity of the ball at various points along the path.* The

*One way of finding the instantaneous velocity in this case is to note that the horizontal component of the velocity is constant. This follows from the fact that the horizontal displacement is the same in each time interval. We then get $\vec{v}$ from this fact and the fact that the instantaneous velocity vector always points in the direction of the path. (See Fig. 6–21.) Other methods of analysis may give more precise results.

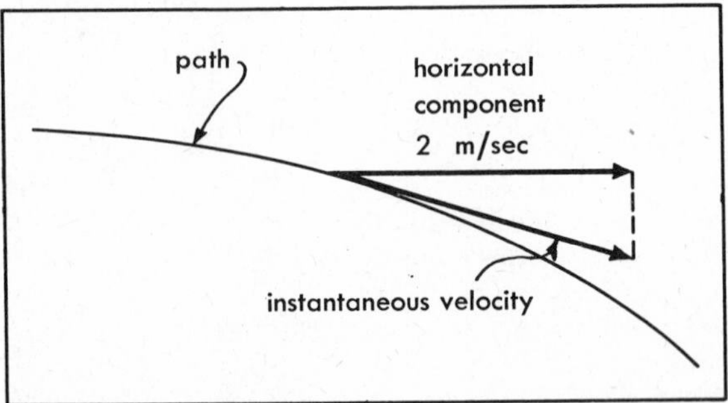

6–21. How to find the instantaneous velocity vector. It is tangent to the path and of such length that its horizontal component is equal to the initial horizontal velocity of the projectile.

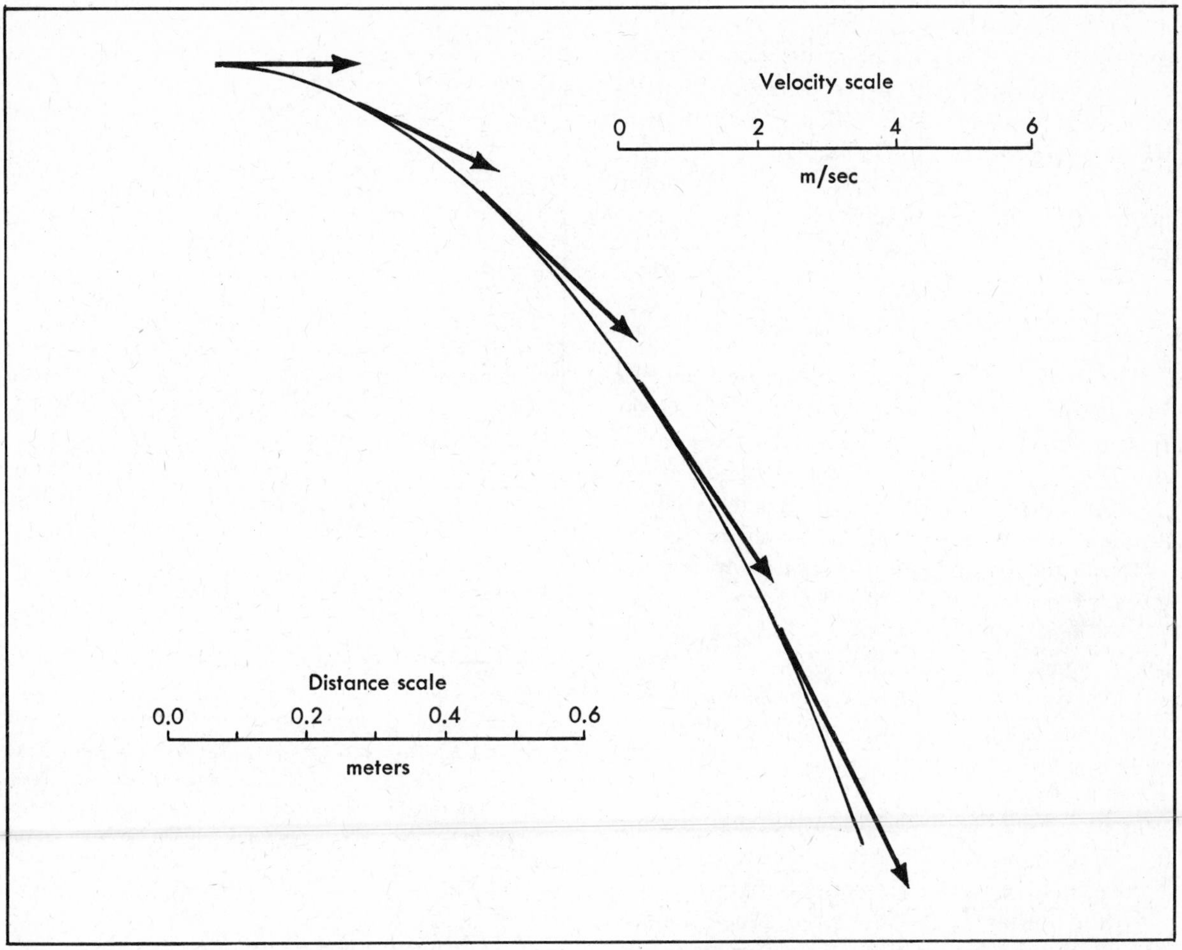

6–22. The position and velocity of the "thrown" golf ball in Fig. 6–19 are shown here on a single graph.

results of such an analysis are shown in Fig. 6–22. There both the position of the ball and its instantaneous velocity at 0.10-sec intervals are shown in the same graph. Note the two scales, one for distance and the other for velocity.

Fig. 6–23 shows only the sequence of velocity vectors of Fig. 6–22. Here, however, we have drawn the velocity vectors from the same starting point. Examination of this figure shows us that the successive vectors are obtained by adding a velocity vector of about 1 m/sec (actually it is 0.98 m/sec) directed vertically downward. We can express this rule in equation form. To do this we first express the components of the velocity. The horizontal component of velocity

$$\vec{v}_h = 2.00 \text{ m/sec, to the right}$$

stays constant throughout the flight. On the other hand, the vertical component is zero at

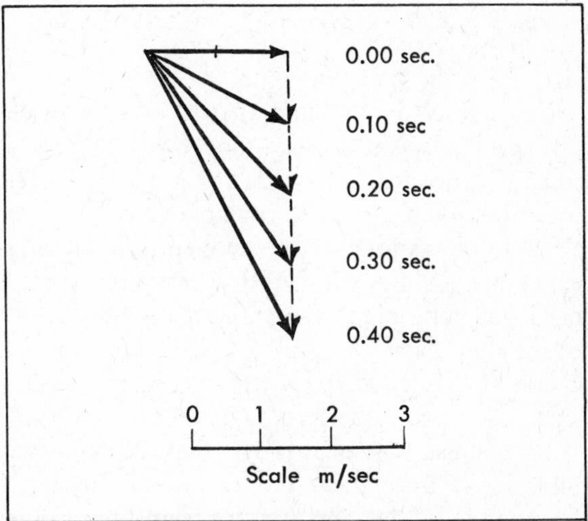

6–23. A sequence that shows only the velocity vectors of Fig. 6–22. Successive vectors are found by adding a constant vector directed vertically downward.

$t = 0.00$ sec and increases by 0.98 m/sec during each 0.10 sec. This is a uniform increase at the rate of 9.8 m/sec², so the vertical component of velocity at any time t is $\vec{v}_v = (9.8 \text{ m/sec}^2)t$, downward, where t is the time in seconds.

Now, combining the two rectangular components to give the vector velocity at any time t, we get

$$\vec{v}_t = (2.00 \text{ m/sec}), \text{ to the right} + (9.8 \text{ m/sec}^2)t, \text{ downward.}$$

The downward component of this vector is the product of a time and an acceleration. Since the time is measured in seconds and the acceleration in m/sec², the product has the units of m/sec, appropriate to a component of velocity. This is another illustration of the fact stated in Section 6–4, that the multiplication of a vector by a scalar gives a new vector, having the same direction, but of magnitude equal to the product of the scalar times the original vector.

We can put our equation for the motion of the ball thrown to the right into just the same form as we did for the ball falling straight down. Here (2.00 m/sec, to the right) is the initial velocity $\vec{v}_i$, and (9.8 m/sec², down) is the constant acceleration $\vec{a}$. So we get $\vec{v}_t = \vec{v}_i + \vec{a}t$ again. Notice that the acceleration of both balls is down. Also the downward motion is the same for both, as you can see by looking across the picture to check that one moves down the same amount as the other in each time interval. The only thing different in describing the motion of the two balls is the value of $\vec{v}_i$. The acceleration vector $\vec{a}$ is the same for both.

In Chapter 5 we found that $v_t = v_i + at$ described the speed at any time when there was constant acceleration along the path. The equation $\vec{v}_t = \vec{v}_i + \vec{a}t$ describes the velocity vector at any time as long as the acceleration vector is constant. Notice that the acceleration vector need not point along the path, as in the example of the right-hand ball in Fig. 6–19. Furthermore, $\vec{a}$ can be any constant vector of the right units. The 9.8 m/sec², down, which we found for the balls, is just a special value that occurs when balls move freely near the surface of the earth. In studying other motion we shall find other constant values of $\vec{a}$—and also acceleration vectors that change as time goes on. For instance, by pushing a ball we can get any $\vec{a}$ we wish.

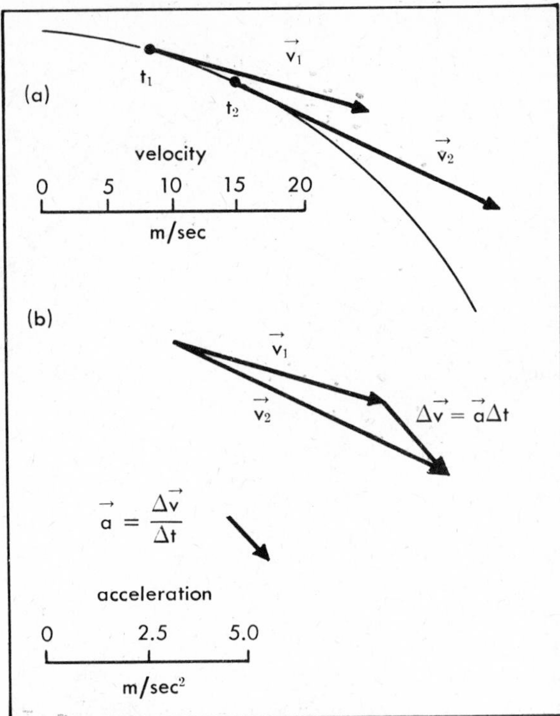

6–24. To find the average acceleration in the interval $\Delta t = t_2 - t_1$: First find $\Delta\vec{v} = \vec{v}_2 - \vec{v}_1$ and divide the vector difference by Δt. The result is the average acceleration vector $\vec{a}$, which can now be plotted with an appropriate scale as shown above.

6–6. Changing Acceleration and the Instantaneous Acceleration Vector

In the last section we described motion with constant vector acceleration. We introduced the vector acceleration to describe how the velocity vector changes. Even when the acceleration vector is not itself constant, we can introduce it in just the same way. We define it by $\vec{a} = \Delta\vec{v}/\Delta t$, where $\Delta\vec{v}$ is the vector change in v during the time interval Δt. Notice that this vector acceleration has the same direction as the change $\Delta\vec{v}$ of the velocity; since this change need not be in the same direction as $\vec{v}$, the acceleration $\vec{a}$ may point in any direction with respect to the motion. As we saw in the case of the right-hand ball in the last section, it need not be along the motion.

The vector acceleration we have just defined is the average acceleration over the time interval Δt. If the acceleration is itself changing as time goes on, $\vec{a}$ will depend on the time interval we choose. Let us take an example. Suppose a speedboat moves along the path shown in Fig. 6–24 (a).

At time t_1 it is moving with the vector velocity $\vec{v}_1$, and at the later time, t_2, it is moving with vector velocity $\vec{v}_2$. What is the average acceleration in the time interval $\Delta t = t_2 - t_1$? To find out we must determine the vector change $\Delta\vec{v} = \vec{v}_2 - \vec{v}_1$ in the velocity. Then the average acceleration is $\vec{a} = \Delta\vec{v}/\Delta t$. The procedure is indicated in Fig. 6–24 (b). We take the vector difference between $\vec{v}_2$ and $\vec{v}_1$, divide $\Delta\vec{v}$ by Δt, and plot the average acceleration vector $\vec{a}$ for the time Δt on a new diagram with an appropriate scale.

As the speedboat moves on, its acceleration may change. In fact we do not expect that it has remained constant even over the time interval from t_1 to t_2. In such situations we need to know the instantaneous vector acceleration at various times t rather than only the average acceleration vector over various intervals.

To find the instantaneous acceleration vector at any particular time t, we determine the average acceleration vector for shorter and shorter time intervals which include the time t. We define the instantaneous acceleration at a given time as the limit of the average acceleration $\Delta\vec{v}/\Delta t$ as the interval Δt becomes smaller and smaller. Usually this limiting vector has a definite size and direction.

Suppose, for example, that Fig. 6–25 shows the successive velocity vectors of our speedboat at time intervals of 10 seconds. If we make a composite picture in which the tails of these vectors coincide, we get Fig. 6–26. The changes in velocity during each successive time interval are also shown in this figure. We see that the velocity changes $\Delta\vec{v}$ in each of the four intervals differ both in magnitude and in direction. Therefore, since the time intervals are the same, the average accelerations are different.

If, instead of using 10-second intervals, we had used 2-second intervals, we would have gotten the pictures shown in Fig. 6–27. Since it is difficult to see the details of Fig. 6–27, a magnified portion of the first 10 seconds is shown in Fig. 6–28, using fivefold magnification. Notice that all five of the velocity changes have more nearly the same magnitude and direction than those of Fig. 6–26 (b).

If we had chosen a time interval shorter than 2 seconds, the successive velocity changes would have been even more alike. Usually we can

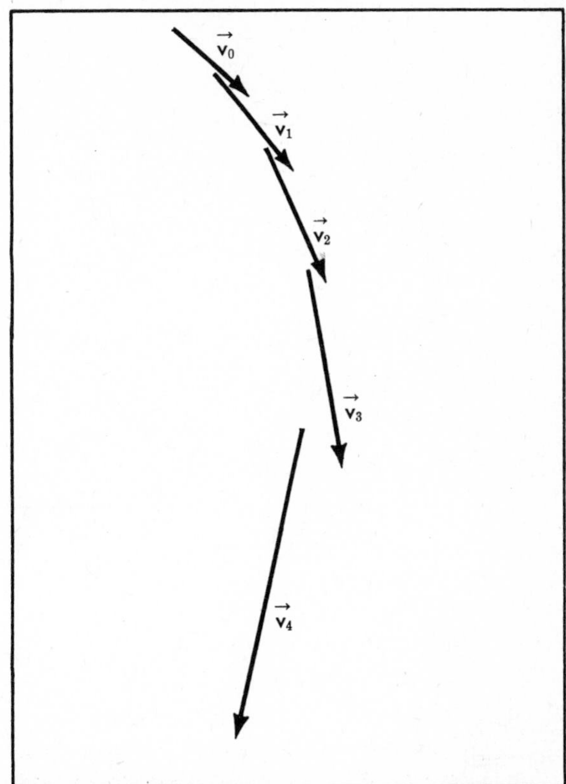

6–25. Successive velocity vectors of the speedboat at 10-second time intervals.

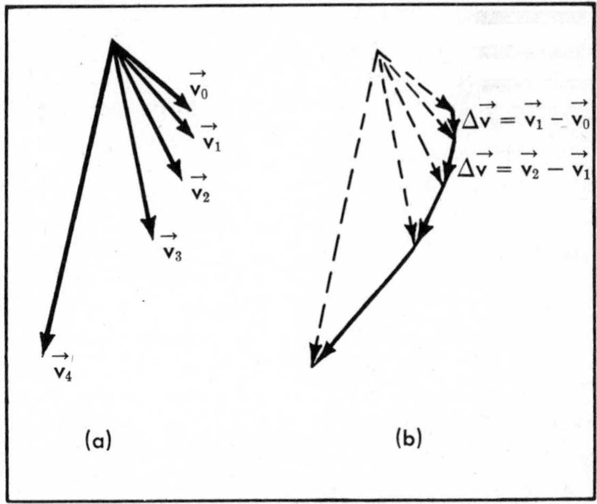

6–26. The vectors of Fig. 6–25 are shown here drawn from the same origin. The acceleration is not constant in direction or magnitude, as shown in (b).

choose time intervals so short that the acceleration does not change appreciably either in magnitude or direction in going from one interval to the next. With this understanding of "very short" we see that the instantaneous vector acceleration

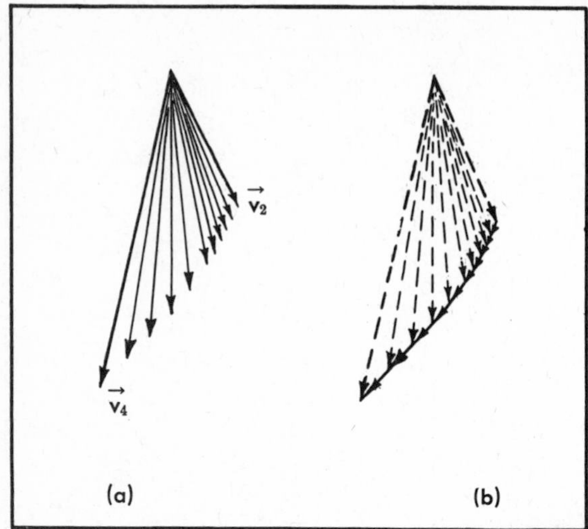

6–27. If we take 2-sec time intervals, the motion described in Fig. 6–25 looks like this when the vectors are drawn from the same origin. By taking a shorter time interval, the changes of velocity become more nearly equal.

at time t is the average acceleration for a very short time interval that includes the time t. We can therefore say that the instantaneous acceleration is the limit of the ratio $\Delta\vec{v}/\Delta t$ as Δt becomes very small. Just as the instantaneous acceleration along the path is

$$a_p = \lim_{\Delta t \to 0} \frac{\Delta v}{\Delta t}$$

(see Section 5–6), so the instantaneous vector acceleration is

$$\vec{a} = \lim_{\Delta t \to 0} \frac{\Delta \vec{v}}{\Delta t}.$$

The really new thing that we learn by considering vector acceleration as compared with acceleration along the path is that *changes in the direction* of the velocity give rise to an acceleration. Even if a body moves along a curved path at constant speed, it is accelerated. The simplest and most important example of this is a body moving in a circular path at constant speed. This is accelerated motion and the acceleration is a changing one. In Fig. 6–29 the circular path is shown and on it a sequence of velocity vectors at equal time intervals. These vectors are all the same length, but each points in a direction different from any other. If we construct a velocity diagram, as in Fig. 6–29 (b), in which the velocity vectors are plotted from a common origin, we see that the successive changes $\Delta\vec{v}$ in velocity are also different in direction one from the other. Because the successive changes in velocity are not parallel to each other, the vector acceleration which measures the change of velocity with time cannot be constant. By taking smaller and smaller time intervals, as in Fig. 6–29 (c), we can see that the instantaneous acceleration vector is directed perpendicular to the velocity vector at each instant of time. The fact that the angle between the acceleration and velocity vectors stays constant (it is always 90°) means that they rotate at the same uniform rate.

This example of constant-speed motion shows that acceleration may result from a change in direction without any change in speed. For motion along a straight line, on the other hand, the acceleration is the rate of change of speed. In general, if a body moves on a curved path, its acceleration vector stands at an angle to the motion. Then the component of acceleration along the path gives the rate of change in the speed (Fig. 6–30), while the component perpendicular is related to the change in direction of the velocity vector (Fig. 6–31). Can you use this fact to prove that the acceleration in uniform circular motion (Fig. 6–30) must be directed along the radius of the circle?

6–28. When the time intervals become very short, the successive velocity changes are nearly equal in magnitude and direction. Here are the first 10 secs from Fig. 6–27. The vectors are magnified 5 times and rotated to fit the page.

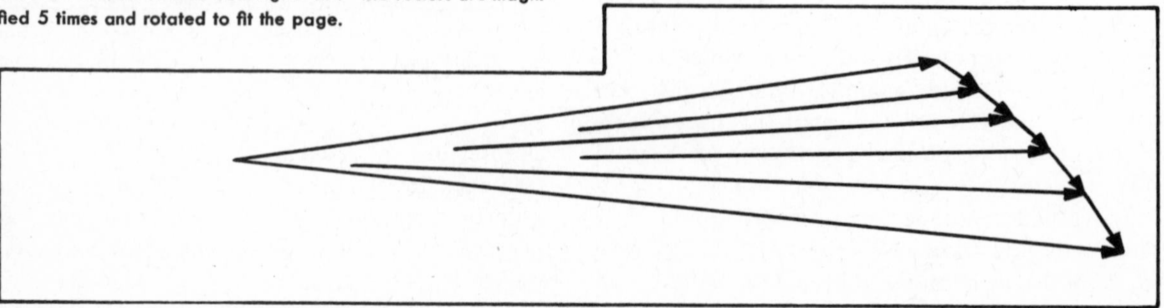

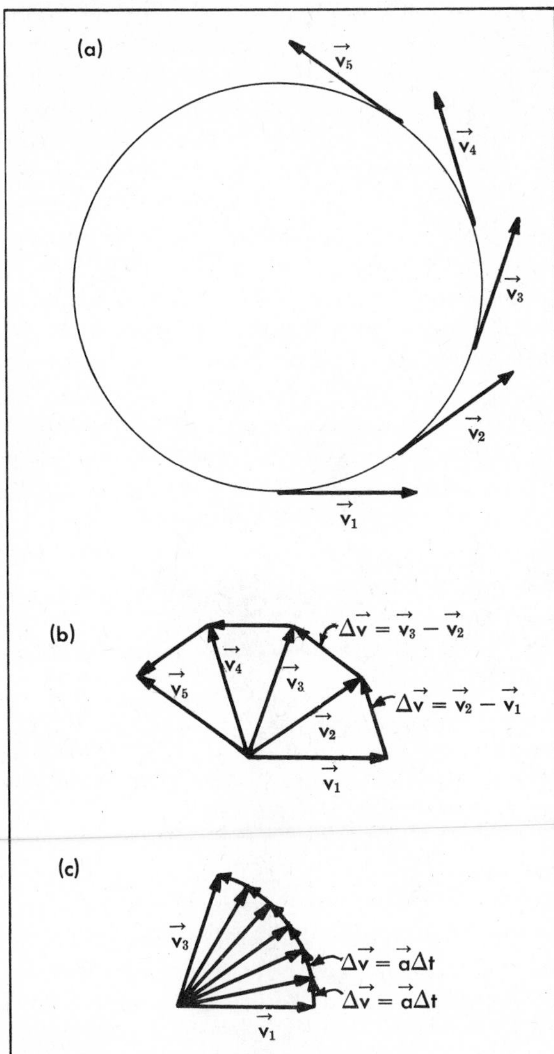

6–29. Part (a) shows the velocity of a body moving at constant speed in a circular path. In (b) the velocity vectors are drawn from a common origin, showing that the changes in velocity are in different directions. By taking shorter time intervals, as in (c), the instantaneous acceleration vector is seen to be perpendicular to the velocity vector.

We can make an object move with constant speed along any path. Because the speed does not change, the instantaneous acceleration then can have no component along the path. The acceleration vector is perpendicular to the direction of motion, that is, perpendicular to the path at all points. Motion at constant speed on a circular path is therefore only one of many motions in which the velocity vector and the acceleration vector are perpendicular to each other. Circular motion is the special case in which the magnitude of the acceleration stays constant. When, on the other hand, a body moves on a more complicated path at constant speed, the magnitude of the perpendicular acceleration changes. The acceleration is greater where the path curves more sharply.

6–7. The Description of Motion; Frames of Reference

We have studied vectors largely in order to describe motion, to describe the successive positions of an object in space and how fast it moves through them. The graceful motions of a waltz can be described fully, if somewhat dully, as a sequence of positions of the hands, the feet, and the rest of the bodies of the dancers, an appropriate position for each instant of time. In fact, dancing to music implies a manner of time measurement. For each note, there is a correct figure of the dance; and to each note, a proper instant of time.

The simplest and most fundamental motion is the motion of a single object, whose parts we do

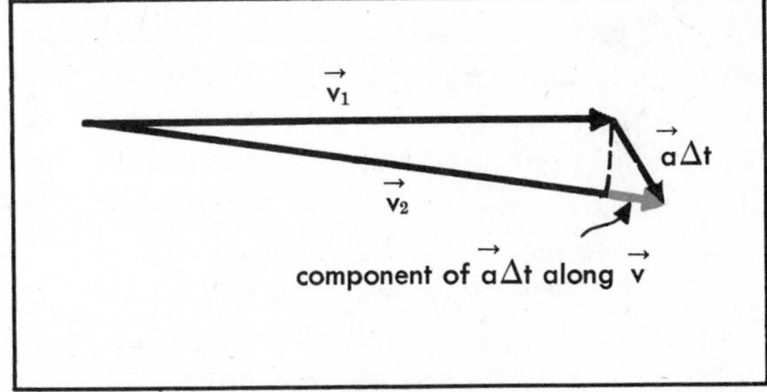

6–30. The component of $\vec{a}\Delta t$ along $\vec{v}$ is the change in magnitude of $\vec{v}$. When the component is zero there is no change in speed.

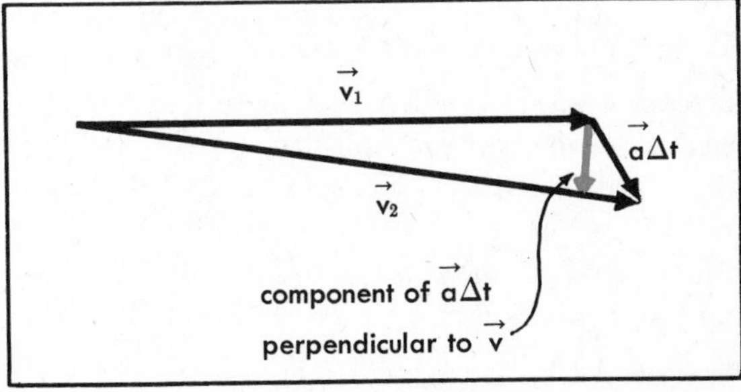

6–31. The component of $\vec{a}\Delta t$ perpendicular to $\vec{v}$ changes the direction of $\vec{v}$. When the component is zero there is no change in direction.

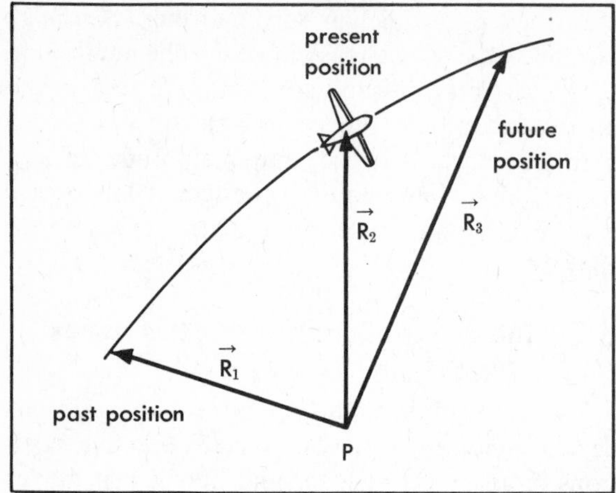

6–32. The positions of an airplane with respect to a point may be shown by position vectors giving distance and direction.

not find it necessary to distinguish, either because we cannot observe them or because they remain fixed relative to one another. A planet, such as Jupiter, moves in the sky. We can represent its position at each instant of time by a vector which we imagine drawn from the earth to the planet Jupiter. An airplane drones on its course for some destination; its positions can also be represented by vectors (Fig. 6–32). Neither the planet nor the airplane is a tiny point; and, if we wish to know what happens within them, we would need much more information than is given by these position vectors. But for many of the needs of astronomy or of navigation, it is sufficient to think of each as a point at the tip of a vector. As the planet or airplane moves, the vector moves, changing in magnitude and direction.

In each of our examples the position vector extends from some identifiable point called the origin to the moving object, from the earth to Jupiter, from the control tower to the airplane. Furthermore, motion, as we noticed in Section 6–2, is always measured with respect to some frame of reference, and so are positions. The airplane's motion is described with respect to the earth's surface, for example, and so is the motion of the falling balls in Fig. 6–19.

The motion of the airplane with respect to another airplane may be very different from its motion with respect to the ground. The motion of the thrown ball in Fig. 6–19 is just motion with a constant velocity with respect to the other ball falling on the left of the figure. The motion of Jupiter with respect to the sun is simpler than its motion with respect to the earth. To the driver of a moving car a raindrop falling vertically with respect to the earth rushes almost horizontally toward him. Motion is described differently depending on the frame of reference with respect to which we give the description.

In general, we wish to view motion in such a way as to make it appear simple. We therefore place ourselves mentally in a frame of reference in which the motions are easy to describe, and draw the position vectors locating the object from the most convenient point. Another example will show what we mean. Suppose we stand on the earth again and look at the motion of a point on the edge of a slowly moving wheel of a car. The point moves through the curve illustrated in Fig. 6–33, a complicated curve known as a cycloid. A position vector from us as origin to a point on the wheel performs an extremely complicated motion. But a point on the earth is not always the most convenient origin for position vectors. We are far better off if we get in the car and hang out of the window to look at the wheel. The point on the wheel then moves steadily around a circle, and the motion of the position vector looks far simpler.

6–33. Path of a point on the rim of a rolling wheel. This curve, a cycloid, shows the path as it appears to an observer standing alongside. One small light was mounted on the rim of a wheel, and another light at the center. The camera shutter was held open while the wheel rolled.

In describing motion we try to put the origin in the most convenient place even though we are sometimes physically unable to go there. The motions of the planets, for example, look very complicated when we describe them with position vectors whose origin is in the earth. Copernicus pointed out that the planetary motions are much simpler to describe when we assume that the sun is the center of the solar system, and move the origin of the position vectors to the sun. Ever since Copernicus pointed out the importance of placing the origin in a convenient place, the proper choice of origin has been an important technique used by physicists to describe motion in simple terms.

6–8. Kinematics and Dynamics

What we have been discussing is the branch of physics called *kinematics* after the Greek word *kinema,* meaning motion. It is that part of our subject which treats of the description of motion, without taking into account what it is that moves or what causes the motion. The science of mechanics, indeed much of physics, is dominated by the study of motion; but that study is complete only when we extend it to what is called *dynamics* (after the Greek word *dynamis,* meaning power). In dynamics one discusses the causes of motion, what is moving, and how its nature affects the motion. In our study of kinematics, we needed to measure only positions and times; in dynamics, the pushes and pulls which cause and resist and determine motions must be taken into account as well.

Motion can be simple or complex. The method of physics is to analyze first the simpler cases, to extract what we can from them, and to go forward to more and more complicated cases. It would be a mistake to think that a quick elementary study of physics can explain the breaking of the surf on a shore, the path of a jet plane in the sky, or the intricate rhythms of a Diesel engine. But these motions and many more can be handled by pursuing the same methods of analysis that we have outlined here in simple cases. When, instead of a single separate object like a pebble or a car, a whole fluid like the air or the water is in motion, even the kinematics may become difficult. The eddies behind a spinning propeller and a flying baseball (Fig. 6–34) are complex indeed. Their study is a specialized kind of unraveling, requiring enormous "bookkeeping" operations to keep track of every small bit of the moving air. Powerful mathematical methods are needed, but the basic ideas used in solving such problems flow out of the discussion we have given; the underlying laws are not different. One may well be wary, though, of too simple an explanation of what is obviously kinematically complex. You cannot design airplanes or understand the weather without checking theories with experiments or without interpreting experimental results in terms of theories. We must go back and forth between theory and the experimental study of the real complex motions. Nevertheless, great progress has been and will be made with such a process. Nowhere in the whole domain of the motions of the natural world, here on earth or in the skies, in our large-scale machines or in our means of transport, have we yet found any case to which the analysis of mechanics does not apply. Where the kinematics is hard, progress is slow; where the kinematics is less demanding, progress is fast. In this course, where we are trying to learn fundamentals, we do not want to produce the false impression that there are no complex cases of interest; there are, especially in technology. In engineering and technology, the aim is to get something done for people to use; in a science such as physics, the aim is to understand and hence to predict and to control. In physics we seek out the simple and examine it, even if it is costly and difficult to attain. In engineering the orderly

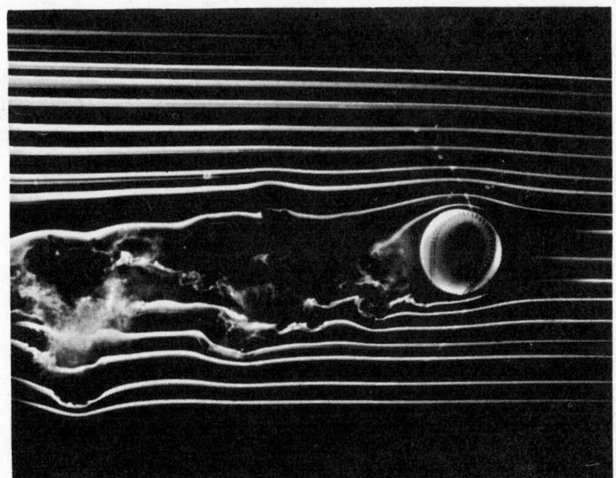

6–34. (Above) The motion imparted to air particles by a rapidly spinning ball, such as a pitcher throws for a curve, is an example of a very complex form of motion. (Below) Eddies formed behind a propeller spinning at 4080 rpm. This is another example of a highly complex motion. (Photos Courtesy: F. N. M. Brown.)

methods developed in this research are painstakingly and often brilliantly applied to more and more complex cases, which have clear usefulness for men. The complicated, trial-and-error extension always rests on the foundation of the simple and the well-understood.

6–9. The Speed of Light

We have pointed out earlier that from everyday experiences we can develop a wide extension or extrapolation. This is the kind of thing we have just been doing, basing our study of motion on the ideas of space and time we have built up from experience. But if such schemes are pushed too far, they may go wrong. They need to be tested. For fifty years now we have been finding that our usual notions of space and time, extremely reliable for most of the motions that we notice daily, do not work for extremely fast motions. For speeds which begin to be of the order of magnitude of that of light, the kinematics we have just discussed begins to go wrong. It turns out that the speed scale cannot be extended indefinitely; if you add velocities that are too big, you reach a region where the rules of addition go wrong. There arises a natural limit to speed, which cannot be surpassed. This universal speed limit is the speed of light in free space, which is known to be very close to 3×10^8 m/sec. The speed of the fastest rockets does not exceed about 2×10^4 m/sec. Speeds up to 10^5 m/sec span the whole range of speeds of every large object in the solar system, from planets and meteors to the engineering devices of man. Only small particles, electrons and their kin, move appreciably faster. These closely approach the speed of light. For their study, the ideas of relativity kinematics are needed. But for everything else — solar-system astronomy, engineering, or any large-scale laboratory physics, the kinematics we have studied, that of Newton, is accurate enough. This whole topic is an example of how you can begin with familiar ideas, which hold well over a wide range, and reform them entirely when you reach another order of magnitude. The fact that familiar ideas may be modified to fit extreme conditions does not end their meaning and use in the domain for which they were originally built up and in which they have been amply tested. Newtonian kinematics is a good approximation to relativity kinematics whenever the speeds are small compared with the speed of light.

FOR HOME, DESK, AND LAB

In doing the following problems, you should always draw an accurate diagram using ruler and compass, either on plain paper or on paper ruled in squares. Many of the problems can be solved by the construction and measurement of such a diagram, without numerical calculations.

1. Draw diagrams to represent the following displacements:

(a) 5.00 cm to the east followed by 3.00 cm north followed by 6.00 cm west.

(b) 5.00 cm to the east followed by 6.00 cm west followed by 3.00 cm north.

(c) 6.00 cm to the west followed by 3.00 cm north followed by 5.00 cm east.

(d) Compare the diagrams of parts (a), (b), and (c) and state a general rule about adding three displacements.

2. A man follows this route: From his house he travels four blocks east, three blocks north, three blocks east, six blocks south, three blocks west, three blocks south, two blocks east, two blocks south, eight blocks west, six blocks north, and two blocks east. How far and in what direction will he be from home?

3. A man walks along a path which is in the shape of a regular hexagon; each side is 10 ft long. Two of the sides run east and west.

(a) Describe his successive displacements.

(b) What is his total displacement?

4. The minute hand of a watch is 2.2 cm long.

(a) What is the displacement of the tip of the minute hand between noon and 12:15?

(b) What is the displacement of the tip of the minute hand between noon and 12:30?

(c) What is the displacement of the tip of the minute hand between noon and 1:00?

5. For the watch of Problem 4 the hour hand is 1.5 cm long. What is the displacement of the tip of the minute hand from the tip of the hour hand:
   (a) at noon? (c) at 6:00?
   (b) at 3:00? (d) at 12:30?

6. A horizontal vector 10.00 cm long is added to another vector 10.00 cm long pointing 70.0° up from the horizontal. Make as accurate a scale drawing as possible to determine the magnitude and direction of their sum. In your answer try for 0.1-mm precision in length and 0.1° precision in angle.

7. (a) Find the result of adding a vector 2 cm east to one 3 cm northwest.
   (b) Find the result of adding a vector 8 cm east to one 12 cm northwest.
   (c) Compare the results of parts (a) and (b), and state a theorem about adding a pair of vectors which are multiples of another pair. Can you prove the theorem in general?

8. A plane flies southeast at 600 mi/hr. Draw a diagram of its displacement from its starting point after 0.50 hr, 1.00 hr, 1.50 hr, and 2.00 hr.

9. The air speed of a plane is 480 km/hr. What is the ground speed of the plane
   (a) with a 32 km/hr head wind?
   (b) with a 32 km/hr tail wind?

10. A group of hikers walking at an average rate of 5.0 km/hr walk the following path:

Compass Heading (Clockwise from north)	Time During Which Heading Is Maintained
45°	1.50 hr
130°	0.75 hr
60°	1.00 hr
180°	1.00 hr
225°	1.00 hr
325°	0.50 hr
240°	1.00 hr

   (a) In order to return directly to their starting point, in what direction must they walk?
   (b) How long will it take them to return?

11. An airplane maintains a heading of due south at an airspeed of 540 mi/hr. It is flying through a jet stream which is moving east at 250 mi/hr.
   (a) What direction is the plane moving with respect to the ground?
   (b) What is the plane's speed with respect to the ground?
   (c) What distance over the ground does the plane travel in 15 min?

12. The pilot of an airplane which flies at an air speed of 300 mi/hr wishes to travel to a city 600 miles due north. There is a 40 mi/hr wind from the west.
   (a) What heading should the plane fly?
   (b) How long does it take to make the trip?

13. An airplane is flying toward a destination 200 miles due east of its starting point, and the wind is from the northwest at 30 mi/hr. The pilot wishes to make the trip in 40 min.
   (a) What should be the heading?
   (b) What air speed should he fly?

14. A steamer is sailing directly south at 25 km/hr in an area where the wind is from the southwest at 18 km/hr. What is the angle from true north of the smoke trail from the stack?

15. The small winged seed of a tall evergreen reaches a constant vertical component of velocity of 1 ft/sec almost immediately after it is blown from the cone. About how far from the base of a 180-ft tree on level ground would seeds from the top of the tree be carried by 40 mi/hr winds?

16. A man rows a boat "across" a river at 4.0 mi/hr (i.e., the boat is always kept headed at right angles to the stream). The river is flowing at 6.0 mi/hr and is 0.20 mi across.
   (a) What direction does his boat actually go relative to the shore?
   (b) How long does it take him to cross the river?
   (c) How far is his landing point downstream from his starting point?
   (d) How long would it take him to cross the river if there were no current?

17. The weather bureau determines the height of cloud layers by measuring the angle of elevation to the point where the light of a vertical beam is reflected by clouds. The angle is measured at an observation station separated from the foot of the light beam by a base line.
   (a) If the base line is 300 meters in length, what is the altitude of the layers which are observed at 18°, 43°, and 77°?
   (b) For observations at angles greater than 84°, the heights are classed as estimations. Why should they differ from readings at lesser angles?
   (c) What is the height of a layer which reflects light at this 84° angle to the 300-meter base line?

18. What is the magnitude of a displacement whose components along the perpendicular X, Y, and Z axes are respectively 4.00 m, 2.50 m, and 8.50 m?

19. At what range will a radar set show a plane flying at 10 km above the ground and at a distance on the map of 18 km from the radar station?

20. An airplane takes off due south from an airport and maintains a ground speed of 4.0 km/min while climbing at a rate of 0.30 km/min. After 0.50 min, it turns due east, maintaining the same ground speed and the same rate of climb. At the end of 1.0 min after taking off:

(a) How high is the airplane?

(b) What is its direction from the airport?

(c) How far is the point on the ground directly under the airplane from the point of take-off?

(d) How far is the airplane from the take-off point?

21. A plane flying north at 320 km/hr passes directly under another plane flying east at 260 km/hr.

(a) What is the horizontal component of the displacement of the second plane relative to the first 20 minutes after they pass each other? 50 minutes after they pass?

(b) What is the horizontal component of the velocity of the plane flying east relative to the plane flying north?

(c) Does the direction of this velocity vector (relative to the earth) change?

22. An ocean liner is traveling at 18 km/hr. A passenger on deck walks toward the rear of the ship at a rate of 4.0 m/sec. After walking 30 meters he turns right and walks at the same rate to the rail which is 12 meters from his turning point.

(a) What is his velocity relative to the water surface while walking to the rear? While walking toward the rail?

(b) Draw the displacement vectors relative to the water surface for his stroll. What was the total displacement from his starting point?

23. A navy pilot, in plotting his trip to rendezvous with his carrier, learns that he is 600 nautical miles due south of the carrier at the time his position is determined. The carrier is on a course 15° east of north and is making 25 knots (nautical miles per hour). The wind at his flight altitude is from 70° west of north at 40 knots. What must be his heading and air speed to make his rendezvous in just two hours' time?

24. A screw has 24 threads to the inch and a diameter of 0.25 in. (See Fig. 6–35.)

(a) Find the resultant displacement of a point, *P*, shown on the screw, when the screw "advances" one turn, in terms of displacement up, down, right, left, into and out of the paper.

(b) Do the same for $\frac{1}{2}$ turn.

(c) Do the same for $\frac{1}{4}$ turn.

25. An object moving in a circular path with a constant speed of 2.0 m/sec changes direction by 30° in 3.0 seconds.

(a) What is its change in velocity?

(b) What is its average acceleration during the 3.0 seconds?

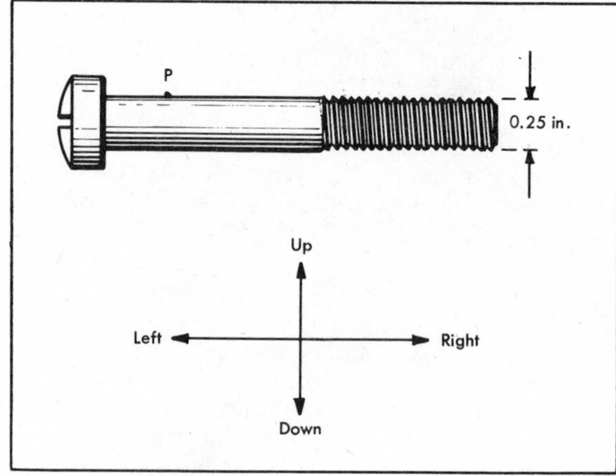

6–35. For Problem 24.

26. A watch has a second hand 2.0 cm long.

(a) Compute the speed of the tip of the second hand.

(b) What is the velocity of the tip of the second hand at 0.0 seconds? at 15 seconds?

(c) Compute its change in velocity between 0.0 and 15 seconds.

(d) Compute its average vector acceleration between 0.0 and 15 seconds.

27. Indicate on Fig. 6–36, the components of $\vec{A}$ and $\vec{B}$ along each axis. Show that the sum of the component of $\vec{A}$ and the component of $\vec{B}$ along each axis is the component of $\vec{C}$ along that axis. Then notice that you can get $\vec{C}$ either by adding $\vec{A}$ and $\vec{B}$ directly or by adding the components of $\vec{A} + \vec{B}$.

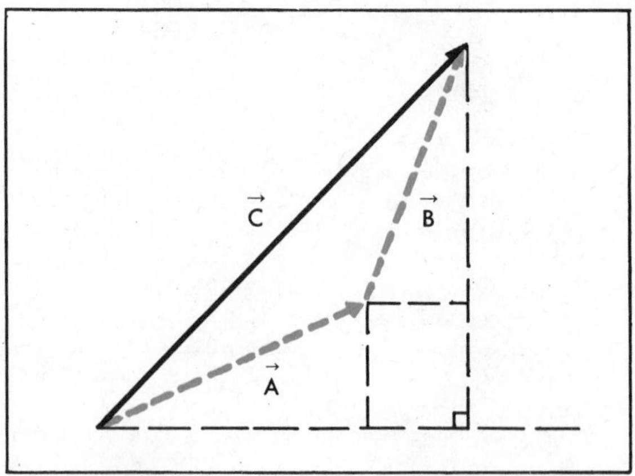

6–36. For Problem 27.

MASS, ELEMENTS, AND ATOMS

CHAPTER 7

A. MATTER AND MASS

7–1. Matter and Its Measure

We have set the stage of the physical world. The stage, the framework within which all the events that we study take place, is spanned by time and by space. It is made lifelike by their combination — motion. But so far we have not really introduced the actors. The stage of the world is occupied by matter. The actors are matter of every kind, in bewildering variety, moving and changing before us — the sun and the stars; the earth itself with its soil, rock, air, and sea; and the living world of plants and animals, even you.

Contrast this picture with the view of time and space we have already taken. To be sure, time and space revealed much novelty as we expanded or contracted our view to include the very slow and the incredibly fast, the tiny and the vast. But there is a kind of sameness to time and space which we do not see in matter. One second is like another, and its million microseconds are much more alike than so many peas. But in the panorama of matter, there appears no such unity.

In all this variety, can we find some sort of universal measure for matter as we have for time and space? We can compare any length with the meter, and any time interval with the second, and such techniques have opened up for us the whole of our science. Can we find such a single general means of measurement for matter, something in terms of which we can compare a grain of sand with a planet, a breath of air with a bite of bread? Is there a measure for matter, not of this or of that special feature, not of color or texture or hardness, but of something shared by all the objects we can find? Let us look at some of the possibilities.

A common clay brick contains a certain amount of matter. We expect two similar bricks together to contain twice as much matter as either one alone. However, no two bricks are exactly alike; they are crudely constructed. Let us think of new silver dimes, all closely identical shiny pieces of the same stuff. It seems reasonable to suppose that the simple count of the number of dimes defines the total quantity of matter in the dimes.

Of course, we could cut some of the dimes in half and get a different count of the number of pieces, without changing the amount of matter present. The volume occupied by the metal is not changed when we cut some of the pieces in half, and it may therefore seem that volume is a better measure for matter than the count of pieces.

But volume by itself is surely a dangerous guide for measuring matter. We can pump more and more air into an inflated tire; yet air, thin though it is, cannot be left out of our list of material things! Thus, more and more matter — air — is being placed within the tire, which does not change appreciably in volume. Expansion and contraction of metal shapes is also familiar; is there more steel in a railroad rail when the summer

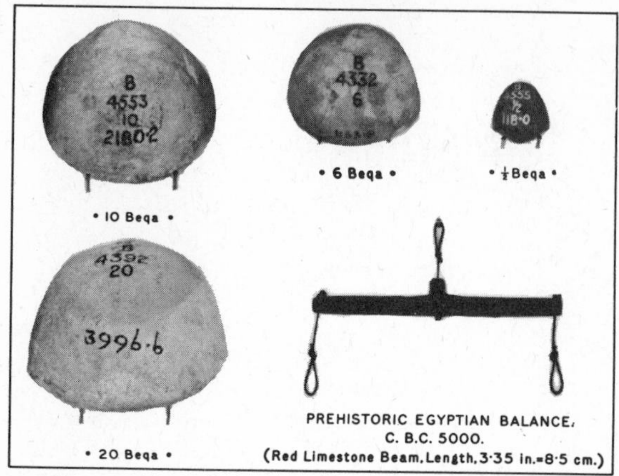

7–1 (a). This balance, the earliest one known, comes from a prehistoric grave at Naqada, Egypt. It may be 7000 years old. The arm and weights are made of limestone. Other limestone masses of different numbers of beqa were also found in these prehistoric graves. Is there any reason why you should not use the beqa as your unit of mass? (Photo courtesy: Science Museum, London)

7–1 (b). This wooden balance with its bronze weights was made in Egypt almost 3500 years ago, somewhat more recently than the one mentioned in the text. The main features of the design are still used today. This balance could handle a load of a kilogram or so, and detect differences of a few parts in a thousand. (From "A History of Technology," Singer, Holmyard, and Hall; Oxford University Press.)

heat lengthens it? We would find no evidence for the answer "yes," for the rail will return to its original size on a cooler day. In a heaping bowl of whipped cream, there is plainly no more cream than once filled the bottom of the whipping bowl. The rest is air — pleasant enough, but not nutritious nor expensive!

Neither counting pieces nor measuring volume is a sure guide to quantity of matter, but the fact that we can often pick out identical pieces and find that number and volume go together indicates that we may be able to find a measure. Many other common experiences indicate the same thing. For example, burning two logs will give, roughly, twice as much heat, twice as much ash, twice as much crackle as burning one log. Evidently, some sign of this simple fact must remain in the gases that rise up the chimney. Somehow two times as much matter is involved. This familiar experience suggests to us that there is a quantitative measure of matter and that, although this measure is not to be gauged by shape or by bulk, it has a determining effect on what happens in the world.

7–2. Mass in the Balance

The simple balance — the apparatus Justice traditionally carries — has for a long time given men the power to measure the quantity of matter even more simply and precisely than they could measure space or time. From Egyptian tombs several thousand years old the archaeologists have recovered a little balance arm of carved stone, with its carefully made stone weights (Fig. 7–1). It was almost surely used then, in the very dawn of history, for the careful measurement of gold dust. The goldsmiths knew even then that the balance was the best way to estimate the amount of solid gold they could cast from any heap of dust or from irregular nuggets.

When an object on one side of a balance is in equilibrium with some standard pieces of matter on the other side, it will remain in equilibrium even though there may be severe changes in the form of the object. Sawing apart a piece of iron, or filing it to a pile of small grains, will not affect the equilibrium of the balance. Let an ice cube melt away to water: the equilibrium remains. A balance responds to something quite independent of the apparent form of the object tested. This is gravitational *mass*. The use of gravitational mass will enable us to give as clear a meaning to the idea of the quantity of matter as does volume to the notion of the amount of three-dimensional space. This measure of the quantity of matter is the third of the great, simple, physical magnitudes: to time and to distance we now add mass.

Note that if a certain quantity of gold just balances a standard piece of matter, and a piece of brass or a piece of wood also balances against

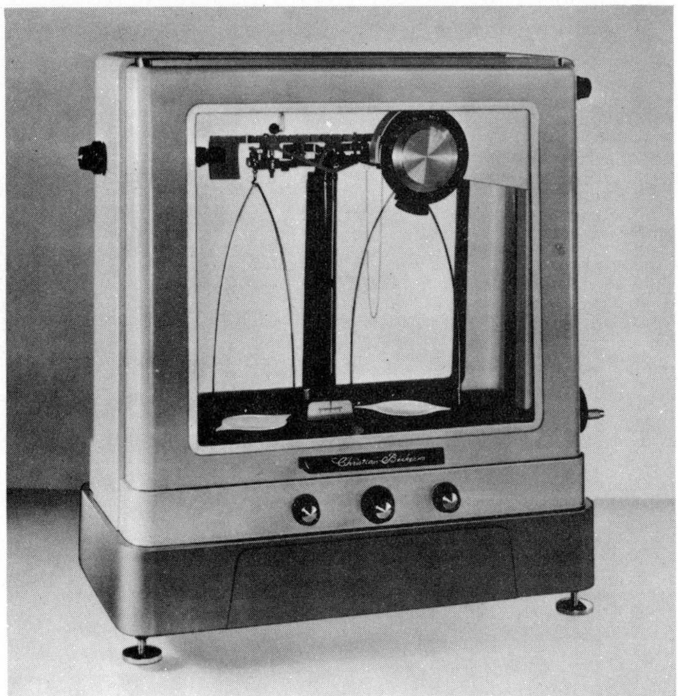

7–2. This is a modern analytical balance. It is a very much refined version of the old Egyptian apparatus. Such a balance is part of the basic equipment of almost every laboratory. It is capable of indicating the mass of a sample of a few hundred grams to about a part in a million. The balance is so sensitive that it is mounted in a case to protect it from the slightest air current. A knife-edge firmly mounted on a beam rests on a polished plane surface on top of the center column. The two pans are supported on similar knife-edges mounted on each end of the beam. A vertical pointer, fastened to the center of the beam, indicates when the masses of the two pans plus their contents are balanced. In use, the object whose mass is to be determined is placed on the left-hand pan; while objects of known mass are placed on the right-hand pan until the pans balance. The final known masses that must be added are often so small that they are difficult to handle. This difficulty is overcome by using an additional micro-mass balancing device in the form of a small chain of identical links. One end of this chain is fastened to the right side of the beam and the other end is fastened to the case by means of a circular counting dial that indicates the amount of chain being used. Only one half of the weight of each link is supported by the beam. As the dial is turned, half the weight of the additional links is added to the right-hand beam. To obtain the total mass being measured, this weight must be added to the known weights in the right-hand pan.

the same standard, then each of these quantities of matter balances any of the others. This gives us a way of comparing gravitational masses of objects of any kind.

Just as we needed to choose a standard meter as the start of our measurement of length, so we need some standard masses to put on one side of the balance with which various other pieces of matter can be compared. The standard used in scientific work is the kilogram. The basic kilogram is a carefully made and guarded cylinder of a durable platinum alloy kept at Sevres, near Paris, along with the standard of length. Here we have a standard which is arbitrary, but reproducible and durable, like the standard meter.

The men who made the metric system originally took pure water as their standard rather than a platinum alloy. They defined the kilogram as the quantity of matter represented by the water which could just be contained in a cube one-tenth of a meter on each edge at a temperature of 4 degrees Celsius* and at atmospheric pressure. The original choice was made with the idea that the standard could be reproduced by anybody, anywhere, if it was destroyed or lost. Actually, however, it is not easy to be sure, for one thing, that one has an exact volume of pure water, all at the same exactly determined temperature. So eventually the standard was shifted to the platinum cylinder.

The brass sets of masses that are available in every laboratory have been compared, through a series of steps, with the standard kilogram. In order to provide flexibility, masses of 500 grams, 200 grams, etc., are included. For example, by 500-gram masses we mean identical masses, any two of which will balance the standard kilogram. With an assortment of these standards, one can find combinations which will balance against a wide variety of masses and so allow any mass to be measured.

The balance has for a long time been about the most accurate and at the same time the most versatile of instruments. The analytical balance (Fig. 7–2) in its glass case is well designed and beautifully made; it costs a few hundred dollars, but it is by no means uncommon. It will compare masses of a few hundred grams to as little as one

*The Celsius (for Anders Celsius) or centigrade temperature scale is the one on which the freezing temperature of water is 0° and its boiling temperature is 100°. See Chapter 9 for further discussion.

Table 1. Masses of Some Common Objects

A. Masses Found on the Balance

Object	Mass
A check mark written in pencil	≈ a microgram
A fly wing	50 micrograms
A postage stamp	20 milligrams
A dime	2.5 grams
A nickel	5.0 grams
A silver dollar	25 grams
A paperback book	200 grams
A pound	453.5924277 grams (legal definition)
A pint of water*	473 grams
A quart of water	≈950 grams
One liter of water	10^3 grams
A metric ton	10^3 kilograms, about one long ton

* "A pint's a pound, the world around" (to 5%)

B. Some Masses Found by Other Means

Object	Mass
A house	≈200 tons
S.S. Queen Elizabeth	several times 10^4 tons
Mt. Whitney	≈10^{12} tons
The moon	7.35×10^{22} kilograms
The earth	5.98×10^{24} kilograms
The sun	1.99×10^{30} kilograms
A red corpuscle	10^{-13} kilograms (10^{-4} micrograms)
A bacterial cell	5×10^{-12} kilograms (5×10^{-3} micrograms)
A molecule of egg-white protein	≈10^{-22} kilograms
A molecule of stearic acid	8.9×10^{-25} kilograms
A molecule of oxygen	5.3×10^{-26} kilograms
An electron	9.1×10^{-31} kilograms

part in a million. In Table 1 a list of a few common objects is presented to give you some idea of their masses. A simple form of balance which you can make yourself will easily measure a tenth of a milligram (or 10^{-7} kilogram), and the best laboratory microbalances will measure differences as little as 10^{-11} kilogram (Fig. 7–3), though only for postage-stamp loads. Large balances, rigidly built, sometimes using rather more complicated parts than the simple equal-arm device, will give excellent results for masses up to almost a metric ton. On such a balance we can see a person lose mass with every breath, as he "burns" his food and exhales the gases of combustion, and as water evaporates from the pores of his skin.

7–3. The Meaning of Mass

The balance is to the measurement of mass what the meter stick is to the measurement of length. It is the direct, defining form of instrument. Gravitational mass is what we measure on the balance; that is its definition. But the balance is not the only means of comparing masses with a standard. We are all able to judge the equality of masses when we "heft" them, one in each hand. Here our senses do not really perform a balance; we are in fact comparing the set and strain of the muscles of the two hands and arms. We are comparing masses by comparing the relative pull exerted on the two masses by the earth.

We know that the pull of the earth for any given object is not constant. This pull, which we call the weight, varies somewhat from place to place even on the earth's surface. On the moon, we all expect to find the pull toward the surface to be much less than it is on earth, for one and the same chunk of matter. But the shape, the bulk, the physical appearance, and the chemical behavior of that chunk would be unchanged. A hammer, for example, whether it is at home, in the orbiting satellite, or in a lunar station, is the same. It will drive nails into a wall equally well in all three places. Also its mass, defined by a balancing operation, does not change when the hammer is moved to a new location. Unlike the pull toward the ground, the mass remains the same along with the other properties that seem to belong to the hammer itself. Two masses that balance on the earth will also balance anywhere else.

Mass, then, is an unchanging property of a

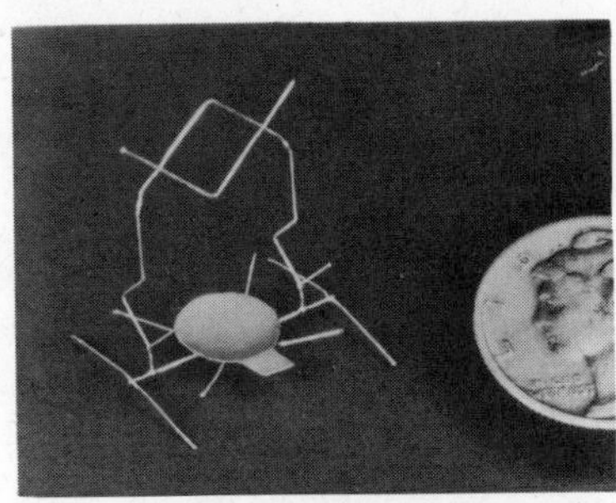

7–3 (b). Some idea of the small size of the quartz-fiber balance can be gained from this photograph, in which one of the pans and its gossamerlike supporting frame are compared with a dime. In use, the pans are suspended in the cylindrical chambers that project below the case as shown at the left. (Photos Courtesy: Microtech Services Co.)

7–3 (a). An ultra-microbalance. Even the delicate analytical balance is not sufficiently sensitive for some purposes. The balance pictured above, however, is capable of measuring a mass to within 5×10^{-11} kg, although its load is limited to 2×10^{-4} kg. Balances of this type have been made for measuring within 10^{-12} kg, but the maximum load is then decreased to 4×10^{-6} kg. Like a conventional balance, the microbalance consists of a beam supported at the middle with a pan suspended from each end. In this case, however, the beam (the group of fine lines near the center of the picture) is made of light quartz and is supported by a quartz fiber that extends the length of the case. The pans are suspended in the cylindrical chambers projecting below the main case. The mass to be determined is placed on one of the pans. This causes the beam to rotate about its point of support. The beam is then restored to its original position by applying a small amount of twist to the supporting quartz fiber. The amount that the fiber is twisted is recorded on a dial and the mass is then calculated by multiplying the amount of the twist by a constant, known as the calibration factor, that has been determined for the balance. The entire balance is about 40 cm long, 33 cm deep, and 30 cm high. The humidity inside the case is controlled by the device at the left.

body. The weight of a body — the pull of gravity on it — changes very much indeed when the body is moved from the earth to the moon, or to a satellite. Weight and mass are not the same, and we must be careful not to confuse the two terms. Their relationship will be a topic of Part III. Throughout physics we shall find mass more important than weight.

7–4. Density

The notion of density is a familiar one (Fig. 7–4). Lead is denser than wood. A small volume of lead can have more mass than a larger volume of wood. *Density* is defined as the mass of a sample divided by its volume:

$$\text{Density} = \frac{\text{Mass of sample}}{\text{Volume of sample}} = \frac{m}{v}.$$

The density of water, for example, is very close to 1 gm/cm^3 or to 1 metric ton (10^3 kg) per cubic meter.

7–4. These two mineral specimens — pumice (left) and obsidian, or volcanic glass (right) — are of the same chemical composition and the same mass. Their relative densities are inversely related to their volumes. The obsidian has almost the same density as glass, while the pumice is of such low density that it floats with about 20 per cent of its volume above water. These two materials, which come from volcanic craters, have the same general composition as quartz. The rapidly cooled pumice solidified with spaces in it created by volcanic gases and steam. The obsidian has no spaces.

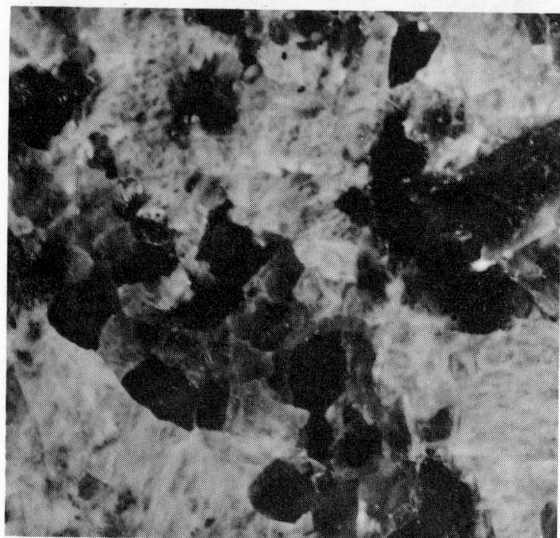

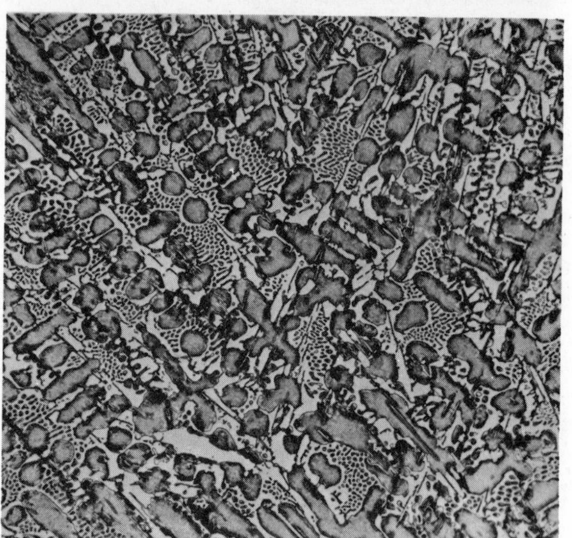

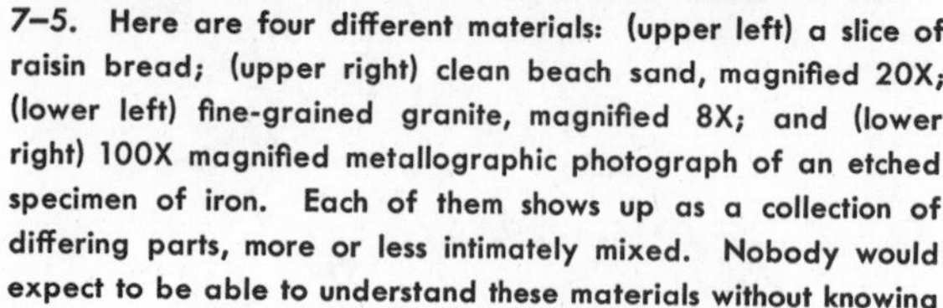

7–5. Here are four different materials: (upper left) a slice of raisin bread; (upper right) clean beach sand, magnified 20X; (lower left) fine-grained granite, magnified 8X; and (lower right) 100X magnified metallographic photograph of an etched specimen of iron. Each of them shows up as a collection of differing parts, more or less intimately mixed. Nobody would expect to be able to understand these materials without knowing about their patchy nature. The average density, for example, would tell only a small part of the story. How can we be sure that an apparently uniform substance such as clean sea water is not patchy like these at some small scale? Answering this question led physicists to the atom, and later inside it. (Photograph of iron: Courtesy British Cast Iron Research Association.)

For uniform substances the mass of each unit volume is the same and we can find the density from a sample of any size. But many substances are not uniform (Fig. 7–5). The density depends on the particular sample volume you choose. The density of a piece of concrete has one value for the whole chunk, which is called the average density. It has another value if you chip out a stone from the sample, and still another value if the volume you select includes only cement. In this way we can assign a local density to any small volume within an object.

For a uniform material such as water, the local density for any visible volume v is the same as that for any other visible volume and is equal to the average density. On the other hand, materials with non-uniformities do not give the same local densities everywhere unless the volume v is always chosen to be large compared with the size of the non-uniformities. Finally, if you choose a volume v of submicroscopic size, it is doubtful if even the local density has any clear meaning. The value we get may change radically if we choose another volume a short distance away or make it a little smaller or a little bigger. Indeed we shall find in Part IV, Chapter 32, that the atoms of which matter is made consist largely of empty space around some small cores of high density; and these cores do not stand still. What we really measure with gross, large-scale laboratory apparatus is some kind of average density. So we see that the idea of the density of a uniform substance, a single value good for any sample, must be greatly modified in order to apply to real substances. When we extend the idea to the atomic domain, we cannot take it for granted.

Table 2 is a brief table of densities. It is rather a surprise that the whole range of density of the solid or liquid substances we normally encounter does not span much more than a single order of magnitude. Only gases or vapors, like air or steam, have values outside this rather small range. As we shall see in Chapter 9, their low densities provide an important clue for unraveling the nature of all matter.

7–5. Indirect Measurements of Mass

Some objects are too large to put on any balance, but if we know the average density of an object and its volume, we can find its mass. Consider as one example the earth itself. We often regard it as a kind of neutral, unchanging, indefinite background to our life and work. But it is of course a large and complicated chunk of matter (Fig. 7–6). In some special places, such as the Grand Canyon of the Colorado River (Fig. 7–7), we can see down into it for a few kilometers and we discover it to be made of various rocks. If we rashly assume that the deep interior of the earth has the same density as the typical exposed rocks, it is not hard to estimate the mass of the earth, using the known volume. The answer we thus obtain is about 3×10^{24} kg. It is interesting to compare this estimate with the value of 6×10^{24} kg given in Table 1B. The tabulated value is very much more precise; it rests upon

Table 2

[*Some Densities of Substances Over a Wide Range*]

Substance	Density		Substance	Density	
	kg/m³	*gm/cm³*		*kg/m³*	*gm/cm³*
The core of the atom, nuclear matter itself	10^{17}	10^{14}	Aluminum	2.70×10^3	2.70
The compressed gases in the center of the densest stars	10^8	10^5	Lucite	$1.16–1.20 \times 10^3$	1.16–1.20
24-carat gold	1.93×10^4	19.3	The human body (average)	1.07×10^3	1.07
Mercury	1.36×10^4	13.6	Ice	0.917×10^3	0.917
The compressed iron core of the earth	$\approx 1.2 \times 10^4$	≈ 12	Butter	0.87×10^3	0.87
Lead	1.13×10^4	11.3	Cork	0.24×10^3	0.24
Steel	$7.6–7.8 \times 10^3$	7.6–7.8	Liquid hydrogen	7.1×10^1	0.07
Titanium	4.5×10^3	4.5	Room air	1.2	1.2×10^{-3}
Diamond	3.53×10^3	3.53	Air at 20 km altitude	9×10^{-2}	9×10^{-5}
Quartz	2.65×10^3	2.65	The gases of interstellar space	(poorly known) $\approx 10^{-18}$	$\approx 10^{-21}$
			The gases of the space between the galaxies	(poorly known) $\approx 10^{-21}$	$\approx 10^{-24}$

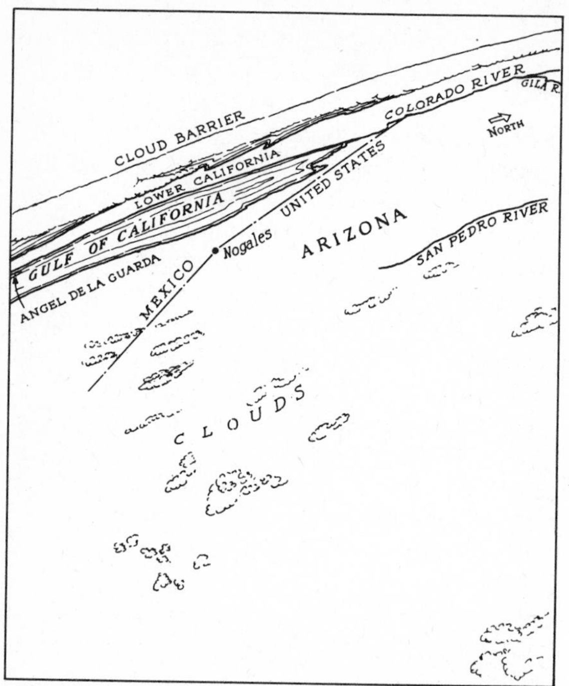

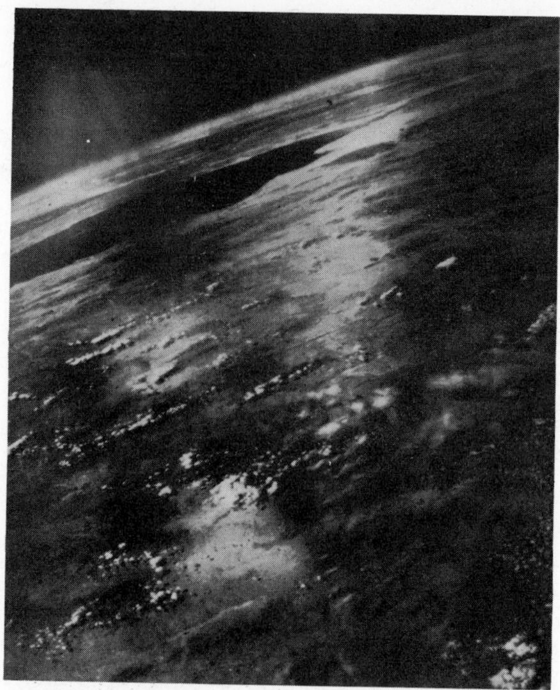

7–6. The earth from 160 km up. We get some idea of the mass of the earth from this photo (right) taken by a camera in a V-2 rocket soaring above White Sands, New Mexico. Several hundred thousand square miles of the United States and Mexico are visible. From the hills seen at the bottom of the photo to the horizon is about 1540 km. The width of the area shown is about 400 km. The Gulf of California, dark area in upper left, is about 100 km wide. Beyond this, the curvature of the earth is apparent. Notice how the earth's features are smoothed out at this distance. Such massive features as the mountains are barely visible and the earth takes on the appearance of a smooth globe. Huge cloud masses appear as small white spots. Evidences of man all but disappear. The diagram at the left indicates some of the features visible in the photograph. Compare the diagram with the photo to see how many features you can actually locate and identify. The presence of the earth, a sample of great mass, makes itself felt by its gravitational pull in every step and breath we take. The gravity which drives the balance also molds every part of life. (Courtesy: U. S. Navy.)

laboratory measurement of gravitation, which you will study in Part III. Comparison of the two values demonstrates that the unseen interior of our earth consists of rather denser stuff than the familiar rocks.

Whereas the earth is too big to be measured on a balance, an atom is too small. Just as there are gravitational means of measuring the mass of the earth or the sun, there are electromagnetic means of finding the mass of subatomic particles. (See Part IV.) Such methods of mass measurement are useful extensions of our mass measurements with the balance. In Table 1B we listed a few masses which were measured by methods different from the simple balance. Our knowledge extends from the tiniest subatomic masses to the mass of the sun itself.

Notice that we have defined the elements of our subject with simple, immediate means—heft here has been for mass what span was for distance or what pulse was in connection with time. Using the balance makes heft precise and extends our means of measurement much as the accurate meter stick refines and extends the span of our hands. Mass measurements go far beyond the reach of our senses. They go beyond the balance; yet they are still within the mind's grasp.

7–6. Conservation of Mass and Conservation of Matter

In the notion of mass, as found on the balance, we have arrived at a way of measuring and comparing every form of matter we encounter. There arises out of this measurement a simple and wonderful experimental result. Once we have established an equilibrium between pans, the equilibrium is not affected by changes such as cutting, chipping, shaving, grinding, melting, dissolving, fading, rusting, burning, flashing, exploding, *within* the matter on either balance pan. In none

7–7. Grand Canyon, Arizona. This view of the Grand Canyon taken from Cape Royal covers a length of about 10 km. A bend in the Colorado River is visible in the center of the picture. At this point, the river is about 220 m wide. From the camera position across to the opposite rim of the canyon is about 2.1×10^4 m. This is one of the widest points in the canyon, which averages about 1.6×10^3 m deep. A good idea of the mass of earth and rock that have been eroded and washed away to form the Grand Canyon can be gained if we picture how dwarfed New York's Empire State Building (about 400 m high) would appear if it were transplanted into the canyon floor. In this spectacular place, as in the more commonplace scenery everywhere, geologists have demonstrated the earth, at least near its surface, to be a great block of familiar material. (Courtesy: The Tozier Collection.)

of these events, each of which can modify the appearance of a sample of matter beyond recognition by the senses, can we detect a change in the mass. The mass of the initial material is just that of the final material.

Of course, account must be taken of the mass of air or steam or other invisible vapors or gases which may enter or leave the balance pan during the changes that involve evaporation or chemical reaction. The simplest way to avoid such complications is to perform the changes within a tightly sealed container. We all know that a sealed aquarium may be made to sustain a variety of living forms. The organisms grow, die, decay, and rebuild life anew; light and heat enter and leave. But the mass of the sealed system remains the same so far as we can measure it. Indeed, the earth is just such a system. A photographer's flash bulb retains its mass though it has sent out much brilliant light, and the fine silvery wire has burst into a smoky white deposit on the glass. You can check for yourself the conservation of mass in a flash of that kind to quite satisfying accuracy.

The conservation of mass holds to really high precision in all ordinary processes. Its validity has been checked to a part in a billion, to about one microgram in a kilogram, both for simple chemical and mechanical processes, and for more complex ones, like the growth of plants. No balance is more accurate than that.

In this work on the balance, we measure the quantity of matter on the balance before and after a chemical or mechanical change and find that it is essentially the same. However, the balance is only accurate to within the limits we

7–8. Albert Einstein at 26. When this photo was taken, he was working as a clerk in the Swiss Patent Office. It was around this time that he published some of his greatest work, such as that establishing the relation between mass and energy. (Courtesy: Lotte Jacobi.)

have indicated. No balances are precise enough to show directly what we now know. During this century we have learned that the loss of light, heat, or sound actually does modify the mass. But this modification does not mean that the *total* mass changes; as far as we can tell, the conservation of mass is precise. The total mass is always the same, but a slight amount of it may escape or enter the matter on the balance, going in or out in radiant form.

These losses or gains of radiant mass are real, but in ordinary processes they are so small that they can be neglected. Only in changes that are far more violent and deep-seated than ordinary chemical ones (as an atomic-bomb explosion is more violent than a chemical one) do these effects become noticeable. The rise of nuclear physics has brought us into contact with processes in which the masses released in radiant form are unusually large. As a result the prediction of Einstein that radiant energy is mass has been clearly verified. We know even of fascinating processes (on the atomic scale) in which 100 per cent of the mass changes from particles of matter into radiation. Then, unless we trap the radiation it will escape from the balance. But only in nuclear laboratories and in the great natural nuclear engines in the centers of stars, do changes go on in which mass is noticeably converted into radiant form. For everything else we can ignore the minute changes in the mass on the balance. This means that the observed conservation of mass is normally equivalent to the conservation of quantity of matter. In chemical changes the quantity of matter stays essentially the same.

The observation that chemical changes leave the quantity of matter unchanged strongly suggests that the chemical change is a process of rearranging component parts. No parts are lost and none gained, so there is no loss or gain of matter. Thus interpreted, the observation that the masses of ordinary substances are precisely conserved to the billionth part in every mechanical and chemical change is the cornerstone of chemistry. On this cornerstone, set by such men as the French chemist Lavoisier at about the time of the founding of the United States, the modern chemist's view of the atom was built.

In the next sections we shall look at some of the chemical ideas about matter. We shall examine the idea of elements which are the basic substances from which everything is combined. Then we shall take up the idea of atoms. These are little individual units of which everything is built. In the early nineteenth century the ideas of elements and atoms were combined. This led to a single view of all material structure: little individual units of a number of different elementary types act as the basic pieces from which everything is built. These units are the atoms of the elements. Paint and mountains, hair, skin, and steel beams, carrots and planets — all the wide variety of solids, liquids, and gases — are different collections of atoms of elements. We shall look first at elements; then at some evidence that everything comes in small particles; and finally we find that the idea of individual particles and the idea of elements are combined in the chemist's idea of an atom of an element. The chemist got there somewhat differently. We shall see how in the next chapter.

FOR HOME, DESK, AND LAB

1. When shelling peas you may find that 12 full pea pods yield 12 empty pods and 91 peas, that is 103 pieces in place of the original 12.

(a) Has the quantity of matter changed?

(b) Has the volume changed?

(c) Has the mass — as determined by weighing on a balance — changed?

2. Assume you are sent on a South American jungle expedition to analyze ore deposits. On arrival you find the laboratory equipment complete except for the standard masses. You do have a nugget of pure gold of unknown mass that you estimate to be about one kilogram.

(a) Could you use the nugget as a standard mass for the duration of your work?

(b) It is impractical to have masses sent to you and you are determined to complete the work. How would you improvise a set of masses that would give dependable results?

(c) Your quantitative results are to be mailed to the main laboratory in London. Obviously, the data in terms of your own standard mass would have limited meaning to them. How would you solve the problem of making the data completely useful for them?

3. The apparent pull of gravity varies with the altitude and the latitude. The relative amount of this pull at various places is indicated in the following table:

A standard station (sea level at 45° latitude)	1.000000
Canal Zone	0.997530
Denver, Colo.	0.998923
Worcester, Mass.	0.999652
Greenland	1.001906

(a) At which place would an object weigh the most? The least?

(b) By what per cent would each of these weights differ from the weight at the standard station? In general, what would you say about the variation in weight from place to place?

(c) Does the mass of the object change from place to place?

4. The crewmen in a spaceship are discussing whether they could crack a walnut with a hammer. Man A says that hitting the walnut with the hammer would be no more effective than hitting it with a feather because the hammer is weightless out in space. B states that he found the mass of the hammer to be about one kilogram by comparing it with known masses on an equal arm balance; therefore, he could break the walnut as easily as back on earth. C maintains that the comparison with other masses proved nothing because out in space they too are weightless.

Comment on the statements of the crewmen. Can they crack the walnut?

5. The mass of the earth has been calculated to be 5.98×10^{24} kg. The radius of the earth is 6.38×10^6 m.

(a) What is the average density of the earth?

(b) Would you expect the average density of the material near the surface to be the same as the average density near the center of the earth? State your reasons.

6. Cork is only one fourth as dense as water. Could you lift a sphere of cork one meter in diameter?

7. During World War I a number of cargo vessels were made of concrete. It is known that any object which floats must have an average density less than that of water. How can you account for the fact that these vessels floated?

8. A quantity of confectioner's sugar fills a package 16 cm × 8.0 cm × 5.0 cm.

(a) How many packages can be placed in a freight car 22 m × 2.4 m × 2.4 m?

(b) If the mass of sugar in one of the small packages is 450 grams, what is the mass of sugar in the freight car?

(c) What is the density of the sugar?

9. A student knows that dense objects sink in water and that less dense objects float. He undertakes to find out something about the relations involved. He carefully measures the mass, volume, and submerged volume of several floating objects with the following results:

	Volume	Mass	Submerged fraction
Cork	60 cm³	10 gm	0.17
Wood	36 cm³	27 gm	0.75
Sponge rubber	40 cm³	20 gm	0.50

(a) What is the density of each material?

(b) What is the mass of the water displaced by each object?

(c) What general conclusions can you draw by comparing your computations with the original data? Your conclusions should be the same as those of Archimedes when he leaped from the bath shouting, "Eureka!"

10. (a) How would you use a sensitive balance to determine whether the *local density* varies in a sheet of notebook paper?

(b) What assumption would you have to make about the paper?

(c) How could you check the correctness of this assumption? Could you use the optical micrometer to check?

11. One kg of water is decomposed into the elements hydrogen and oxygen. The mass of hydrogen released is 111 grams.

(a) What mass of oxygen do you expect to be released?

When hydrogen is burned in air, water is formed. When 10 grams of hydrogen are burned, 350 grams of air must be used.

(b) What mass of water is formed? (Water always has the same proportions of hydrogen and oxygen.)

(c) What is the mass of the unburned air?

Note: If you do these experiments, the numbers computed from the conservation of mass agree with the numbers observed.

B. THE CHEMICAL ELEMENTS

7–7. Chemical Analysis and Synthesis

If you "burn" sugar, you will get black char and some steam, which is of course only water vapor. The wonderful conclusion which every cook can reach from his or her own experience is that no matter what foodstuff he "burns," from beef to pie crust, he is almost sure to get the same black, charry product — carbon. Apparently the black matter, which we call carbon, is contained somehow in all the variety of things from which it can be produced by sufficient heating. In "burnt" sugar, for example, the carbon formed accounts for about two-fifths of the mass of the original sugar; the other three-fifths is accounted for by water. This ratio is the same for every sample of cane sugar.

Of course, the sugar has to be pure. Sugar adulterated with sand will not all go to black carbon and water when heated in the kitchen oven. The sand will remain nearly unchanged. Wood, rocks, raisin bread — plainly these are not pure substances. The last example serves as a model for them all. There are regions of raisin, and regions of bread. Most of the complex substances of which the natural world is made contain regions of one character interspersed with those of another (Fig. 7–5).

Sometimes the eye, or the eye aided by the microscope, can reveal the presence of an impurity, as in the case of sugar mixed with sand. Sometimes visual observation does not work so well, as demonstrated by sugar mixed with salt. In this case we can find out that there are two components mixed and we can separate them by immersing the sample in a liquid such as carbon tetrachloride; there the sugar will float and the salt sink to the bottom. There are as many means for separation of mixtures as there are kinds of mixtures.

Chemists usually find it most convenient to work with pure substances, those of uniform properties which have passed through many processes of purification, of which the above separation of salt and sugar is a simple example. Pure substances are certainly simpler than mixtures. Once the chemist has purified some of the common substances, he can ask whether they are the simplest possible kinds of matter or whether they are combinations of a still simpler set of substances. For example, he uses heat to break sugar into carbon and water. He can break down the carbon no further, but the passage of an electric current through the water (or extreme heat) decomposes it into two gases, oxygen and hydrogen, which he cannot decompose further.

This breakdown of a material into several others is an example of a chemical reaction, a decomposition. Another example which can be demonstrated easily in the laboratory is the breakdown of a heavy, red powder called mercuric oxide. After heating the powder strongly, we find a silvery, heavy liquid which we can identify as mercury. Obviously, the mercury has come from the red powder. But was this red powder only another form of mercury? If we insert a glowing splint into the container during the heating, the splint bursts into flame. This indicates that, in addition to mercury, the red powder also contained another substance, one which is highly reactive. The reactive substance is oxygen.

Not all chemical reactions are decompositions. Some are just the reverse, the formation of a new material from two or more others. Another simple experiment will serve to illustrate this type of reaction. If we mix some iron powder or filings thoroughly with about twice its volume of powdered sulfur, we shall have a mixture which can be separated because iron is attracted to a magnet while sulfur is not. We can also separate the two with a liquid called carbon disulfide, in which the sulfur will dissolve but the iron will not. If, however, we heat our mixture of iron and sulfur, we shall soon see it glow. If we then let it cool and test it with a magnet and with carbon disulfide, we find no separation.

Obviously, a change has occurred in which the original substances have been put together into something new. We call this chemical reaction a synthesis. In addition to decomposition and simple synthesis of single substances, there are many more complicated reactions. The reaction of sodium hydroxide (lye) and hydrochloric (muriatic) acid to give common salt and water is a simple example of a somewhat different type.

7–8. The Elements

So far we have used the term *pure substance* to indicate any material of uniform properties. Mercuric oxide, iron, sulfur, water, carbon, and cane sugar are all examples. We can break down, or decompose, mercuric oxide into mercury and oxygen; cane sugar into carbon and water. Some pure substances are, therefore, decomposable. But if the chemist tries to resolve carbon, iron, sulfur, mercury, or oxygen into anything else, he fails. Pure substances are of two kinds, those which are decomposable and those which are not.

Until the time of Robert Boyle (1627–1691), the word *element* had been quite generally used with no specific meaning. In his book, "The Sceptical Chymist," Boyle introduced the modern definition. He said, "I mean by elements, . . . certain primitive and simple, or perfectly unmingled bodies; which not being made of any other bodies, or of one another, are the ingredients of which all those called perfectly mixt bodies are immediately compounded, and into which they are ultimately resolved." In other words, elements are those substances that are not made up of other substances. Pure substances that are not elements are compounded from elements and can be decomposed into elements. They are *compounds.* These definitions are fine. But there remain the problems of seeing whether there really are elements and of finding out which substances are elements. At the time of Boyle, chemical knowledge was so primitive that Boyle's idea of an element was not immediately useful. It was not until a century later that Lavoisier proposed that any substance not known to be decomposable should be regarded as an element, and lists of elements were made. As one would expect, the list of elements had to be revised frequently at first. Not every product of decomposition is an element, and compounds which were hard to decompose were mistaken for elements; but it was not long before the list of elements took very much the form it has today.

By 1800 about twenty-five or thirty substances had been recognized as elements. We now know that there are approximately ninety which occur naturally, as well as about ten more that we can make in small quantities by the most modern methods of nuclear physics. The number of elements is large enough to create a real problem of sorting and identification, but small enough so that the job has been done.

In the examples we have used, it turns out, iron and sulfur are elements. So also are carbon, hydrogen, oxygen, and mercury. On the other hand, the iron sulfide formed from iron and sulfur is a compound; it cannot be an element because it is formed of two things. Similarly, cane sugar is a compound, as we know because it decomposes into carbon and water; water is a compound of hydrogen and oxygen; and mercuric oxide is made of mercury and oxygen.

Most of the material of the earth is in the form of compounds of elements. Almost all the matter in living things — even the most complex compounds of which we are made — consists of only about two dozen elements. Of these the most abundant ones are carbon, hydrogen, oxygen, nitrogen, sulfur, phosphorus, magnesium, potassium, calcium, iron, sodium, chlorine. The same two dozen elements make up all but a tiny fraction of sea water. The air contains about half a dozen more.

All the rest of the elements are found in rocks and ores. Here are tremendous amounts of silicon and aluminum, as well as oxygen and the other elements found in living things. Here, also, are the ores from which we get the familiar elements iron, gold, silver, tungsten, lead, chromium,

Table 3

Abundance of Elements in the Earth's Crust

Element	Per Cent of Total Mass	Relative Abundance (Number of atoms per 100 atoms of oxygen)
Oxygen	46.6	100.0
Silicon	27.7	33.9
Aluminum	8.1	10.3
Iron	5.0	3.1
Calcium	3.6	3.1
Sodium	2.8	4.2
Potassium	2.6	2.3
Magnesium	2.1	3.0
Titanium	0.4	0.3
Hydrogen	0.1	3.4

Table 4

Abundance of Elements in the Human Body

Element	Per Cent of Total Body Weight	Relative Abundance (Number of atoms per 100 atoms of hydrogen)
Oxygen	60.0	37.9
Carbon	20.2	17.0
Hydrogen	10.0	100.0
Nitrogen	2.5	1.8
Calcium	2.5	0.6
Phosphorus	1.14	0.4
Chlorine	0.16	0.05
Sulfur	0.14	0.04
Potassium	0.11	0.03
Sodium	0.10	0.04
Magnesium	0.07	0.03
Iron	0.01	0.002

copper, zinc, and nickel. Add to these a large number of elements found in special ores and very rarely elsewhere, and finally a few which only chemists and physicists know very well, and the list mounts to about a hundred. These hundred substances appear to be pure and resist the efforts of chemists to decompose them.

The importance of an element in economic use may make it familiar to us. Yet many familiar elements, like the gold used by jeweler and dentist, the tungsten in the incandescent bulb and radio tube, and the chromium on flashy cars, are only rarely found among the elements of which the earth is made. It is interesting to take a census of the make-up of the earth as a whole. Since no chemist has put the whole earth into his test tubes, the result depends on many indirect arguments about whether the rocks and soils have been properly sampled. Table 3 is to be regarded as a good approximation and nothing more; its improvement and then its explanation is one task of the sciences of the earth — geochemistry, geophysics, and geology. In a similar but more accurate way, the census of the human body has been taken. The relative abundance of the most common elements which form the living human body is shown in Table 4. In Tables 3 and 4 we have taken the census both in terms of the masses of the elements present and in terms of the atomic population. Later in this chapter and in the next we shall learn how these numbers of atoms of the different elements can be determined.

7–9. Spectrum Analysis

If you hold a piece of iron wire in a gas flame, the flame will flare yellow for an instant. Scatter some crystals of common salt into the flame and the same yellow flare will appear much more strongly. The salt itself is not necessary; a chemist can analyze salt into two elements, sodium and chlorine, the first of which is a soft, whitish metal. A small speck of sodium makes the flame flare even more yellow. The highway lamps which give off yellow light also contain sodium. Many other substances give the same yellow light; all of them contain sodium. Why, then, did the iron wire give this light? A chemist can show, by making sure that he has cleaned the iron wire surface well, that it is not the iron that gives this yellow flame color; the color comes from the small amount of salt accumulated on the surface which people have handled with their salty fingers. (Taste yours.) The visible yellow flame color is a very sensitive test for sodium. The eye can pick up the coloring of the flame which comes from adding much less than a microgram of the element. To detect such a small amount is not easy for chemists without the flame method.

Sodium is not the only substance which gives off a characteristic color when heated. Every element — heated by flame or by the passage of the intense current of an electric arc — radiates a characteristic color. In fireworks a red flare is made with strontium, a green one with barium or copper, and so on. But for most elements, the

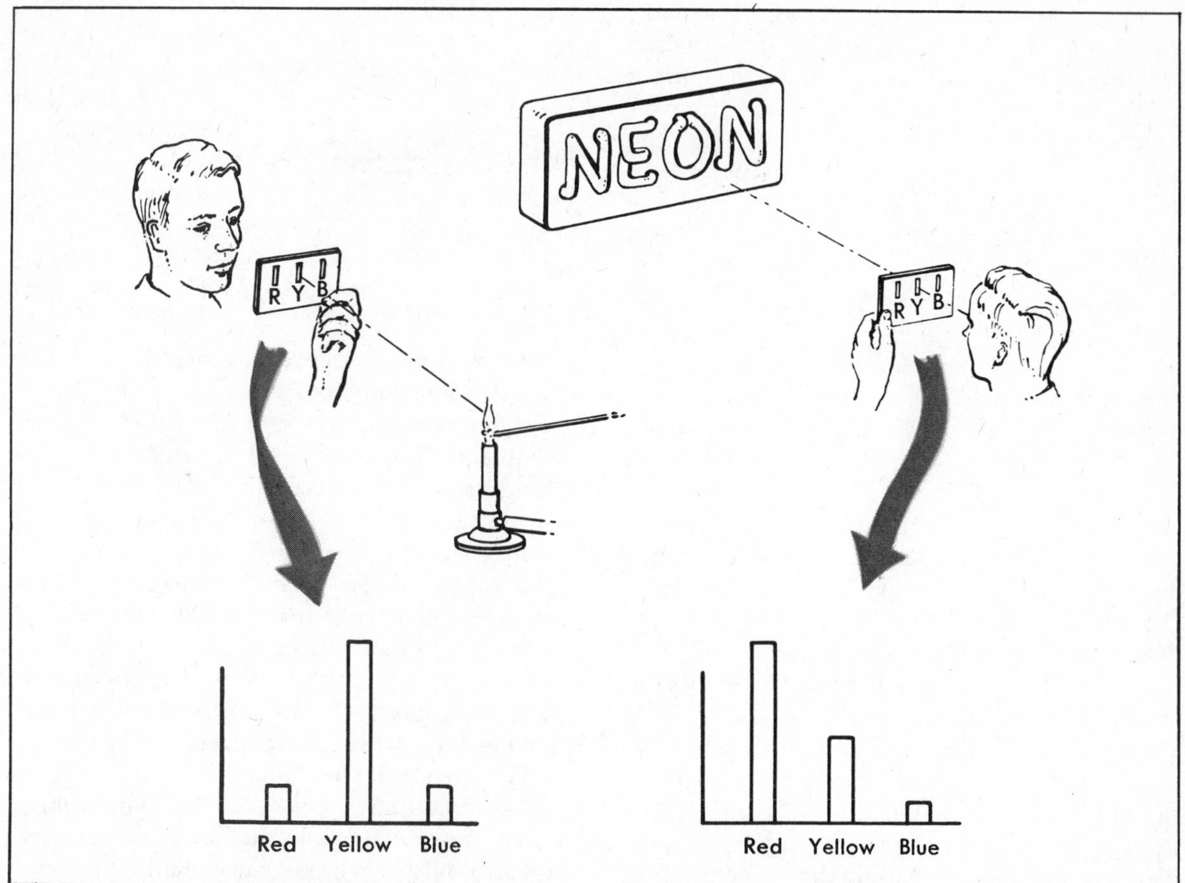

7–9. The basic idea of spectroscopy. Complex light from a source is broken down into several components of differing colors by using slits covered with dyed Cellophane filters. The brightness of the light seen through each of the filters is graphed at the bottom of the figure for the two sources shown — a neon light and a flame containing a compound of sodium. The graphs represent, in a crude fashion, the spectra of the light sources.

radiated light combines many colors and the eye alone is unable to recognize anything so characteristic as the yellow of sodium or the red of strontium.

There is a simple principle which can be applied with great success to turn the simple judgment of a color into a much more powerful and versatile measurement. Suppose you prepared a cardboard screen with three parallel slits cut into it and then pasted over each slit a piece of Cellophane, a piece of a different color for each slit. For example, one of the slits might be red, one yellow, and the third blue. Now if you held this set of color filters against any source of light, you would note differences in the brightness of the light coming through the three filters. In sunlight you would see all three colored slits passing considerable light; the exact brightness of each would depend very much on just what dyes were in your filters, but all three would be conspicuous. But if you looked at a sodium flame through your filters, the yellow slit would appear much brighter than the others. With a simple visual matching of the brightness of each slit against any standard you might choose, or with the help of photographic film or of an exposure meter, you could describe the color of the light source numerically by giving three numbers, one for each of the slits of your filter. (See Fig. 7–9.)

With only three filters, a number of different sources might still look the same; they might give the same relative brightness through the slits. But it is easy to see how to improve this device so that it will distinguish smaller differences in the light from different sources. You would use not three slits, but a dozen or two and find color filters with much less marked differences in color. You would have a few filters shading from deep red through orange into yellow, some going from yellow into green, and so on. Your group of filters would give you a whole set of numbers, one for each slit, to describe the source of light you were looking at. Such a plot of the relative amount of light found in each of a series of colors is said to be the *spectrum* of the light source.

With a device of this sort you could distinguish the combinations of colors in the radiation of most elements. For example, the red glow of a neon sign would be seen to contain fainter but unmistakable light which would come through a yellow and a green filter. The greenish-blue glare of a mercury lamp contains orange, green, and yellow light. The multiple filters act to sort out the constituent colors and allow at least a rough measurement of the amount of each present in the source.

Colors can be sorted out in other ways. It is not necessary to use dyed filters chosen somewhat arbitrarily and arranged in arbitrary order. Optical instruments called spectroscopes act to sort out the constituent colors of a beam of light by shunting or dispersing one color into one path, a neighboring color into a neighboring but slightly different path, and so on, for the whole range of colors.

Take a long-playing phonograph record and look at the reflection in the record of a small or distant light. When the angles between the light and the surface of the disc and between your eye and the surface are both small, the reflection is colored like a rainbow. The reflected red light and reflected blue light are actually seen at slightly different positions. Colors are also separated when a light is viewed through a prism from an old glass chandelier. Either the record or the prism gives you a crude spectroscope. In such instruments the order of the colors is no longer whimsical. As we shall find in Part II, the order depends on the nature of the light. It follows the color order of the rainbow.

Now place a piece of cardboard with a narrow slit cut in it between a mercury or neon lamp and the record or prism so that the only light reaching the record or prism from the source comes through the slit (see Fig. 7–10). When the long dimension of the slit is perpendicular to the direction in which the colors are spread out, you will see a number of narrow, colored lines. Each of these is a separate projection of the slit formed in a different color and at a different position from the others. They are called *spectral lines.* The arrangement of lines typical of any light source is again called the *spectrum* of the source (plural: *spectra*). Even in a spectroscope that is not very elaborate the number of distinct slit images which can appear, the number of possible colors, is not the few dozen that could be obtained with filters, but typically a thousand or two, and it can be made many more. How these devices work will be studied in Part II. Here they serve us as would a very large set of dyed filters.

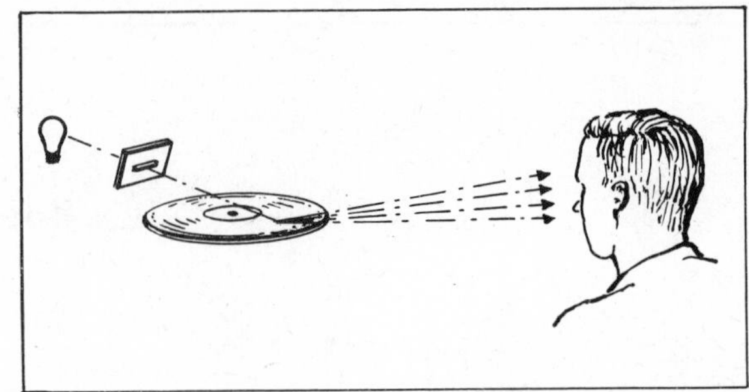

7–10. Using an LP record as a crude spectroscope.

If all colors are present in the light from a source, the eye observing the output of the spectroscope will see the complete rainbow pattern. If some color is missing, the picture shows a dark line at the position of the missing color. If some color is present in unusual quantity, a bright line is seen at the proper place.

With this instrument, the sodium yellow looks like Fig. 7–11. The detail can be great. Now we see the yellow of the sodium flame is not just any yellow. It is a very specific color indeed, made by no other element. This particular pair of lines, appearing in the same location as in Fig. 7–11 (b), always means that sodium is present. Even if the yellow color is masked to the unaided eye by many other colors, the spectroscope will show the presence of sodium.

In Fig. 7–12 the top line is the spectrum of calcium metal. Below are the spectra of three different compounds of calcium, all taken with the same spectroscope. Notice the strong similarity of the spectra when the same element is present. Also notice the complete difference between the spectra of calcium and sodium. The regions of color of the spectra shown in Figs. 7–11 (a) and 7–12 overlap considerably, but this

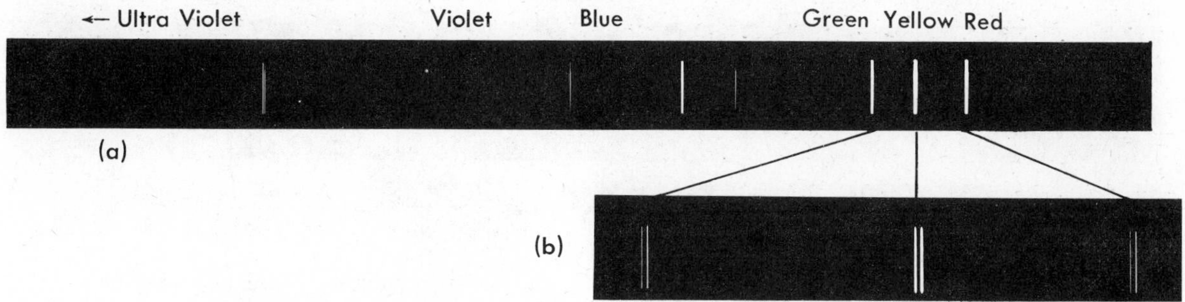

7–11. (a) The spectrum of sodium as photographed in a spectrograph. The line in the yellow is extremely intense. It has been photographed through an absorbing filter, because otherwise the line would be so strong that we could not photograph it and the other lines well at the same time. The close pair of almost invisible violet lines arise from a potassium impurity. (b) A part of the sodium spectrum has been photographed using a spectrograph that spreads out the light more, enabling us to see more detail. The yellow sodium line is really two neighboring lines known as the sodium *D* lines.

whole region from ultraviolet through green looks completely different in the light of calcium, where there are many spectral lines, and in that of sodium, where there are practically no lines.

Each element gives out its own spectrum, different from that of any other. A particular set of spectral lines means that a particular element is present. Look at the spectra of iron at different high temperatures (Fig. 7–13). Although these spectra are not exactly alike, many of the lines are present in all of the spectra. At each temperature there are enough characteristic lines to identify iron.

Spectra are not always simple. The spectra of flames sometimes show very complicated patterns of many closely spaced lines. These groups of lines occur much more often in flames than in arcs and sparks, which are much hotter than flames. They are never found in very hot sources. This behavior suggests that they may result from something that is destroyed by high temperature, and such is indeed the case. They are produced by groups of atoms which are closely combined and not by single atoms. At high temperatures these compounds decompose and only the line spectra of the elements are produced.

A glowing source of light may be such that the characteristic lines do not appear in the spectroscope, even though the element is present. But if the telltale lines are seen, the material must be there, for no two elements give the same pattern of lines. Sometimes a part of the pattern of one element can resemble or obliterate that of another, but the differences are there, if hard to unravel. Every substance that can be made to give glowing gas — and that means all substances, though for some the temperatures are so high that special means like big electric sparks are needed — can

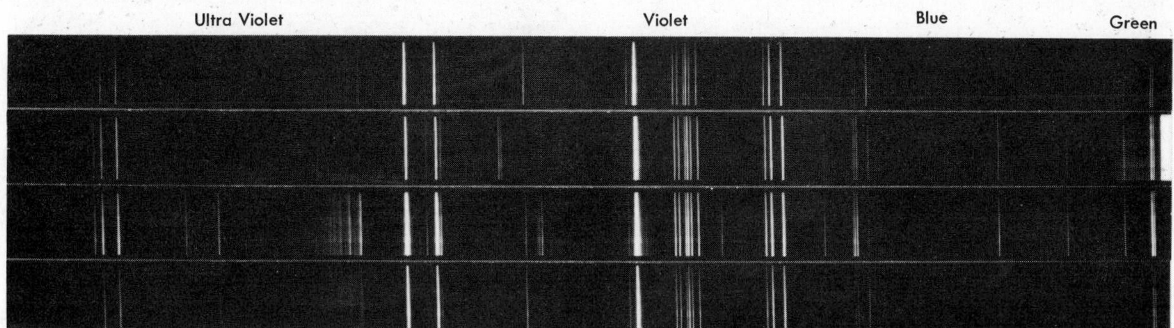

7–12. The spectrum of calcium appears whenever calcium is present. The top line was photographed with calcium metal in an arc in the spectroscope; the second line with the salt calcium fluoride, CaF_2; the third with calcium carbonate, $CaCO_3$; and the bottom with calcium hydroxide $Ca(OH)_2$. A spectrum was taken with the arc alone to be sure that the pattern of lines belongs only to calcium. Note the same pair of violet lines as in Fig. 7–11, again arising from a potassium impurity.

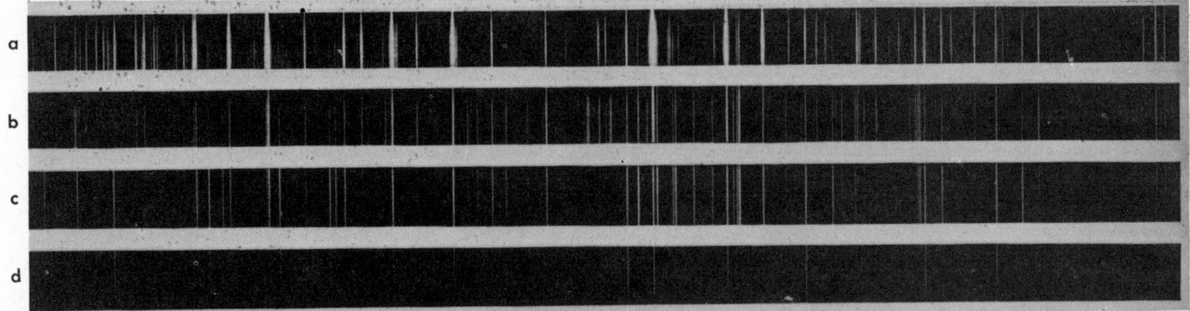

7–13. The spectra of iron in the violet and the blue at different temperatures. From the bottom up, the spectra show the effect of increasing temperature. The three lower spectra are from iron in furnaces, the upper one from an arc. Note that new lines appear at higher temperatures, but the lines seen at lower temperatures are still present, in some cases becoming more intense. (Courtesy: Arthur S. King, in *The Astrophysical Journal*, November 1922.)

be analyzed by its spectral lines. Now we come to the important point: these analyses of the spectroscopist agree in every cross-check with the results of the chemist. We find that the same near-hundred elements account for the observed spectra. Thus light becomes a tool for the chemical analyst, more sensitive than usual chemical methods.

Spectroscopy is not restricted to visible light. Beyond the violet end of the spectrum, the normal eye sees nothing, but photographic plates or fluorescent dyes show the existence of many ultraviolet lines. All kinds of radiation, X rays and even radio waves, have a kind of spectroscopy. These spectra tell us much more about matter than we could learn using visible light alone.

Spectroscopic analysis is a powerful and delicate tool, forged through decades of hard work. In the visible-light region alone, we have identified nearly a quarter of a million distinct lines and we know the exact position in the spectrum of more than a hundred thousand of them. Besides this careful collection of data, and the use of these data in quick chemical analyses, spectroscopy has meant more. During the decades from 1910 to 1940, it became the testing ground for theories dealing with the deepest nature of matter. Regularities in spectral lines exist; the patterns that they reveal can be unraveled into much simpler form, and the story of that unraveling is much of the story of our present physics, to which we shall return in Part IV.

Finally, spectroscopy opens a path to chemical analysis, at least in rough terms, of objects like sun and stars which cannot be brought into the laboratory. Nearly a hundred years ago this was first done and physicists were able to determine the key spectral lines of the elements present. Everywhere in the visible universe, out to the galaxies of remote space, the same spectra are found. Everywhere the same elements must be present.

In the 1860's a spectral pattern was seen which had never before been found. It was seen in a spectrum taken from the edge of the sun, from which only a small fraction of sunlight comes. Because no element was known on earth which gave the pattern, it was attributed to a new element. Finally the element was found in some rare minerals here on earth. It is the gas helium, named from the Greek word for "sun."

To see if there were still other elements that had not yet been found, every region of the sky was examined spectroscopically. Curious spectral patterns were found in nebulae, in the sun, and in the glow of the northern lights, but it has always turned out that these patterns could be made by known elements under appropriate conditions here on earth. Only in helium, the first example, did we recognize a new element before we had any sample of it in the laboratory.

We have seen that chemist and spectroscopist agree; complex as a sample may appear, it will yield in the end to the attack of the chemist with reagent and furnace, or to the spectroscopist with flame, arc, and spark. The sample will be resolved by the chemist into some of a hundred or so unresolvable substances: the elements. It will present to the spectroscopist a superposition of some of the hundred or so typical spectral patterns which go with these elements.

The invariable agreement of the analyses made by two such different means — one with light and the spectroscope, one with crucible, balance, and acid — confirms our idea that all matter is put together out of the same set of elements.

FOR HOME, DESK, AND LAB

1. Three white crystalline substances — silicon dioxide (quartz), calcium chlorate, and sodium carbonate (washing soda) — are mixed together. It is desired to separate each of these substances from the others. Using the properties listed in the table, describe how you could do this.

2. Hydrochloric acid vapor — a pure substance — can be decomposed into two different gases each of which acts as a pure substance. On the basis of this evidence alone

   (a) Can the original vapor be an element?

   (b) Can either of the other two gases be an element?

   (c) Can you be sure that any of the pure substances mentioned is an element?

3. When zinc metal is put into hydrochloric acid, the metal is "eaten," a gas bubbles off and a "salt" is left behind.

   (a) On the basis of this information alone can you be sure which of the pure substances mentioned are compounds and which are elements?

   (b) We then find that the gas acts just like hydrogen gas — it has the same chemical and physical properties. Also we find that hydrochloric acid can be decomposed (see Problem 2) into hydrogen and chlorine. Can the "salt" be an element?

   (c) Using the table of known elements (Chapter 32), which substances mentioned are elements and which are compounds?

4. By studying the information given in Table 3 can you decide

   (a) Why hydrogen makes up only 0.1 per cent of the total mass of the earth's crust, although in relative abundance it ranks fifth on the list?

   (b) Whether the mass of a silicon atom is greater or less than that of an iron atom?

   (c) Whether silicon is more or less dense than iron?

5. Table 4 suggests that a particular compound makes up the major portion of the human body. What is this compound?

6. * Project — Construct the three-color transparent screen described in the text, Section 7–9. Use your screen to examine the light from various sources such as an incandescent bulb, a neon sign, a sodium vapor lamp, a mercury vapor lamp, etc. What conclusions do you reach?

Table for Problem 1.

Substance	Density (gm/cm^3)	Melting Point	Solubility (gm/liter) Cold Water	Hot Water	Alcohol
Silicon dioxide	2.65	1400°C	Insoluble	Insoluble	Insoluble
Calcium chlorate	2.71	100°C	1777.	Very soluble	Soluble
Sodium carbonate	1.44	32.5°C	215.2	4210	Insoluble

C. THE ATOM

7–10. Spelling Out Matter — Atoms

In the time of Socrates, Greek thinkers like Democritus taught that all matter is made from very small distinct parts. These small parts were supposed to be identical and to be arranged in many different ways to display to our senses the marvelous differences and variety of the material world. No one brought forward very convincing arguments for these ideas, but through the ages the tradition continued. Finally, in the nineteenth century, physicists and chemists found convincing but indirect evidence for these ideas.

When Lewis and Clark made their way west in 1805, the chemists of Europe were beginning to explore the inner nature of matter. They were learning, very largely by use of the balance, that the changes they could study left the total mass unchanged and occurred according to some other rather complicated, but quite definite, rules as well. These regularities brought the chemists back to the old Greek ideas.

As indicated at the end of Section 7–6, the conservation of matter on the balance allows us to suppose that all the changes we see in the nature of matter simply amount to the reorganization of the same unchanging fundamental units. In any rearrangement, the number of blocks does not change, and so the balance remains unaffected by dissolving or rusting or even explosion of the sample. Also, because we are combining units of only a few types, our combinations should exhibit some rules of regularity. Many of these chemist's rules, as we shall see in the next chapter, can thus be attributed to the existence of small blocks of matter. There are, in short, natural units for matter, something which we have never found for space and time. These natural units are the atoms.

Out of these atoms the world of matter is built. They occur in great numbers, but there are only a few hundred kinds of them. All the diversity of matter arises from the combination, in intricate but repetitive patterns, of these little component particles. That is the essence of the idea of the atom, the ancient idea.

Whoever knows how to read has before his eyes an almost perfect analogy: the way in which the enormous variety of printed material in English, from "Hamlet" to this physics book, from "The Star-Spangled Banner" to the telephone directory, are but combinations of a few dozen letters, figures, and signs assembled in a vast variety of ways. What is the alphabet of matter, how are the words spelled, and what do they mean for the properties and origin of all the matter of the world? To answer these questions has been the main task of modern science — of physics, chemistry, astronomy, and biology.

7–11. Seeing Atoms

While the nineteenth-century chemists were finding cogent evidence for atoms, physicists like Maxwell and Boltzmann, who studied the behavior of gases, also found evidence for small units of matter. In their own way, they too approached the atom. In this century new methods of research have made the existence of atoms even more evident. Today the units of the chemical elements are as real as bricks or chairs. They are as much a part of scientific thought as are rocks or stars — and they are often easier to manipulate.

The most direct way to see that matter has a fundamental structure is to look at its fine detail through an instrument of high magnification. The microscope using light can magnify linear dimensions a few thousand times. An electron microscope uses a beam of electrons in place of light and displays its images on a screen exactly like a TV screen. It can magnify linear dimensions by a million times or more. Its full field of view, however, is only about 10^{-6} meter across. To survey fully the area of a single postage stamp at such magnifications would require so many photographs that, printed two to a page, they would bind into half a million standard volumes and crowd a good-sized library building! But careful analysis of a few of these tiny magnified portions of matter and space can reveal new and wonderful things.

It is true, of course, that before we use such instruments intelligently we must learn how to interpret what we see. We must discover each instrument's limitations and how to correct for the errors which the instrument itself may introduce. Sometimes decades of constant research and interpretation are required before an instrument is fully understood and accepted. A few centuries ago the telescope was distrusted. It was thought to give a distorted and false picture. As recently as twenty-five years ago the electron microscope had a similar history. Today, these instruments are fully accepted, and we use them as readily as we use ordinary eyeglasses. Careful study, cross-checking, and analysis have made the images of the telescope, of the optical microscope, and of the electron microscope meaningful.

Fig. 7–14 shows a study of a sample of a certain green pigment known to have a somewhat larger fundamental structure than most substances. In the last photo, we see layer after layer of atoms lying with the great regularity so characteristic of the arrangement of the fundamental units in solid matter. This may be compared with Fig. 7–15 taken at a lower magnification, which shows a kind of halfway house to the atom. Here the regular array, like a stack of many cannon balls, is a crystal made from virus particles. These virus particles are little assemblies themselves, each with a complex substructure containing some millions of atoms. Similar regular piles of atoms, much smaller than these virus particles, make up the crystals of salt or sugar or metals. It is not hard to believe that the regularity of such small structures is responsible for the regularities we see in crystals.

We can see individual atoms, too, not simply

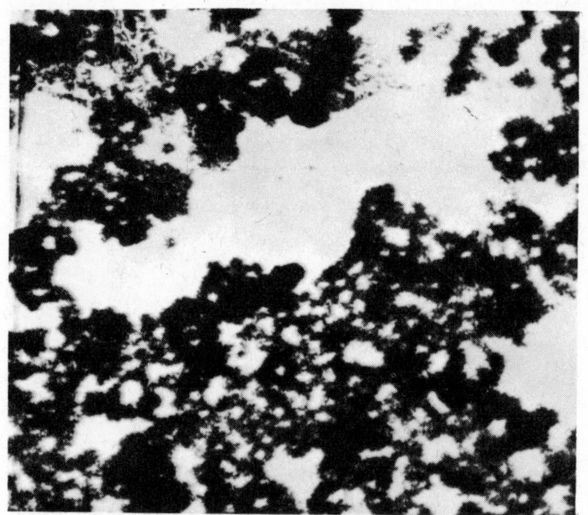

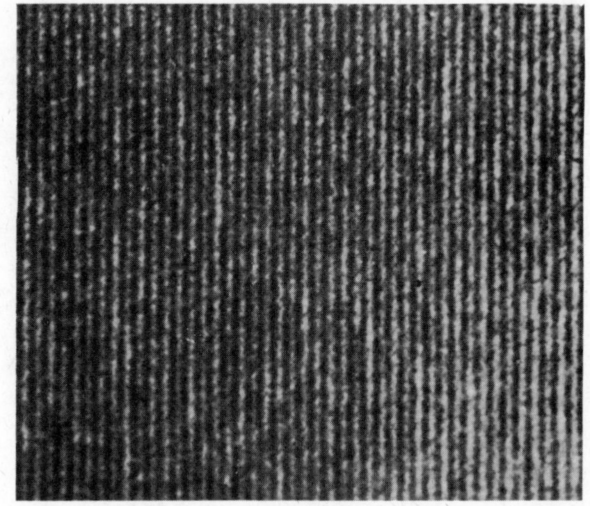

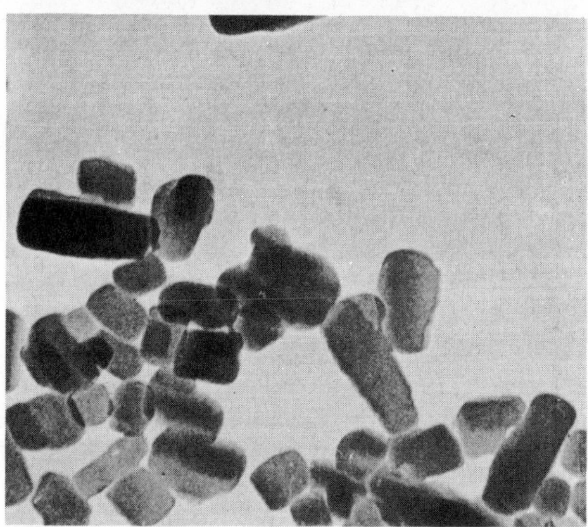

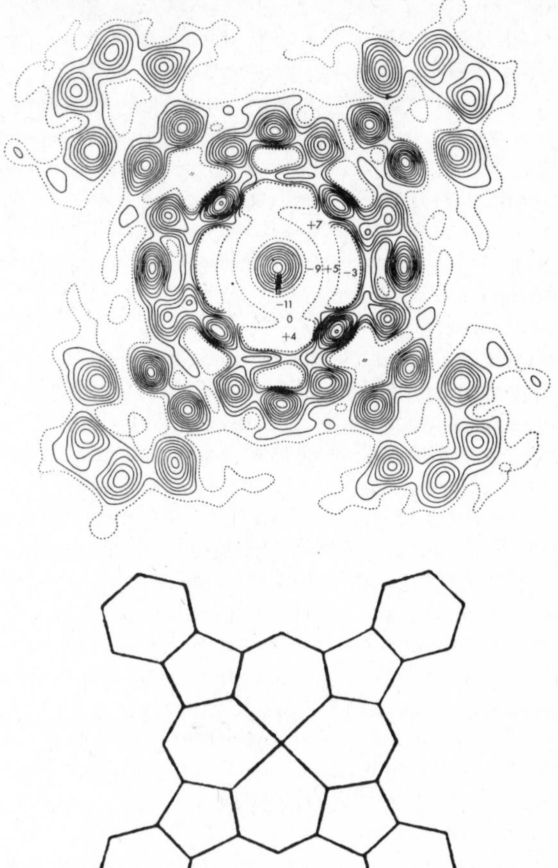

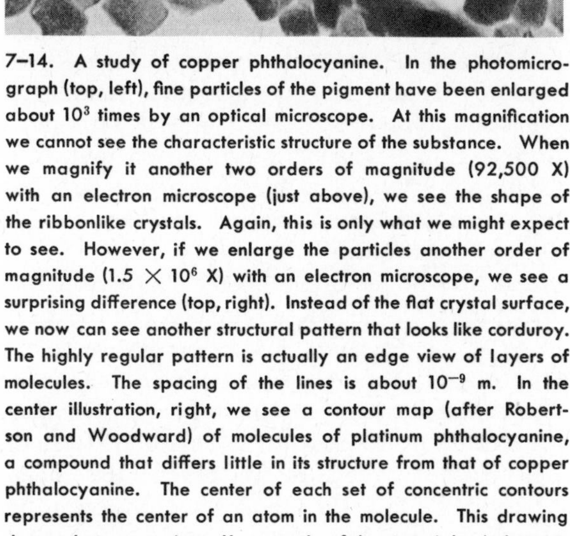

7–14. A study of copper phthalocyanine. In the photomicrograph (top, left), fine particles of the pigment have been enlarged about 10^3 times by an optical microscope. At this magnification we cannot see the characteristic structure of the substance. When we magnify it another two orders of magnitude (92,500 X) with an electron microscope (just above), we see the shape of the ribbonlike crystals. Again, this is only what we might expect to see. However, if we enlarge the particles another order of magnitude (1.5×10^6 X) with an electron microscope, we see a surprising difference (top, right). Instead of the flat crystal surface, we now can see another structural pattern that looks like corduroy. The highly regular pattern is actually an edge view of layers of molecules. The spacing of the lines is about 10^{-9} m. In the center illustration, right, we see a contour map (after Robertson and Woodward) of molecules of platinum phthalocyanine, a compound that differs little in its structure from that of copper phthalocyanine. The center of each set of concentric contours represents the center of an atom in the molecule. This drawing shows what we see in an X-ray study of the material. At bottom, right, we see the simple geometric arrangement of the atoms in the molecule corresponding to the contours. These molecules are arranged as they would appear in a group in a crystal (after Robertson and Woodward). These last two illustrations represent cross sections of the long, rodlike structures in the illustration at top, right. (Photos Courtesy: W. Kay, Jackson Laboratory, Du Pont; J. W. Menter.)

7–15. Crystal of necrosis virus protein. This electron-micrograph of a portion of a protein crystal shows the molecules to be arranged in a very orderly way. At this magnification (about 8×10^4 times), the molecules look like so many neatly stacked oranges. The actual size of the entire crystal is about 1.7×10^{-6} m. (Courtesy: Ralph Wyckoff.)

crowds of them. The Müller field-ion microscope can show the location and even the motions of atoms, or perhaps groups of a few atoms, in the tip of a very fine needle of hard metal. As in the electron microscope, the image is displayed on a fluorescent screen. In Fig. 7–16 compare the image of the atomic array in the tip of the tungsten needle with the model of the same array.

Neither the moons of Jupiter nor the germs of pneumonia can be seen by the unaided eye. To make the distant moons visible, we need a telescope, and only a microscope can show us directly the tiny germs. So with the atom: man-made instruments, whose functioning we can understand, help our eyes to see the very tiny building blocks of matter.

Let us use our instruments to find the dimensions of some atoms. Look again at Fig. 7–14, the study of the green pigment. The corduroy pattern repeats every 10^{-9} m. This pattern is formed by groups of atoms, identical groups repeated over and over again. These groups have been studied with X rays, another indirect means of seeing atoms; and the result of the X-ray analysis is shown in the contour diagram. Where the contours form dark globs, we "see" the atoms. There are between 40 and 50 of them in an area about 10^{-9} m on a side. In other words, it takes about 7 atoms to span each layer of the corduroy structure. Thus each atom has a linear dimension of about 2×10^{-10} m. It is common to give a special name, an angstrom unit, to a length of 10^{-10} m. In this language we say that the atoms in the green pigment have diameters of about 2 angstroms.

The size of the atoms in the tungsten needle examined with the field-ion microscope turns out to be about the same. From the picture on the lower right in Fig. 7–16 and the known magnification of the microscope, we can tell how far apart the corners of the atomic planes are in the tungsten needle. Then, if we believe the model which shows how the atoms are arranged in the needle, we can estimate an atomic dimension. You will find that it is again an angstrom or two. The agreement between the atomic dimensions

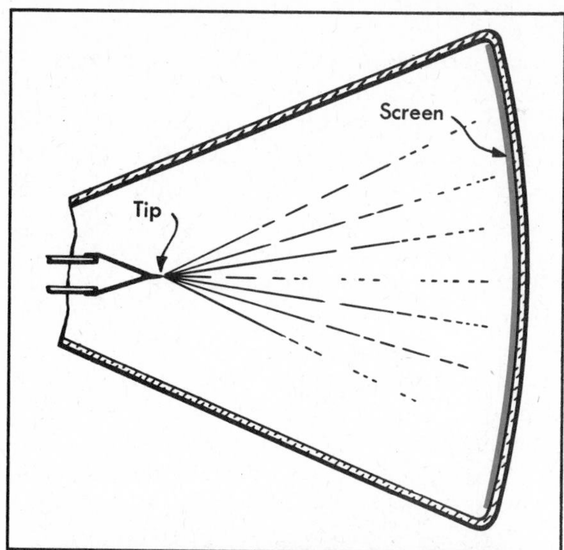

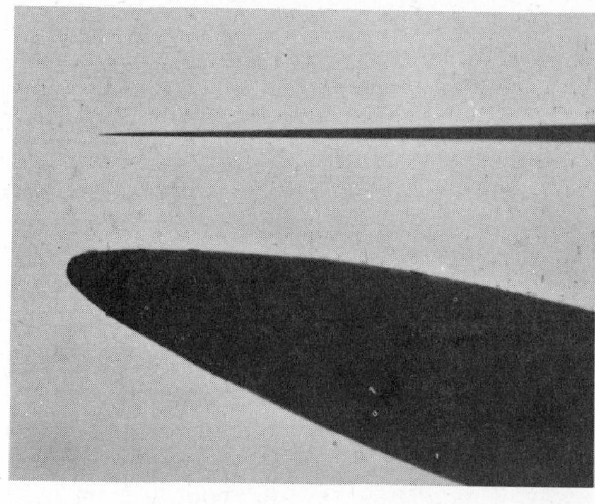

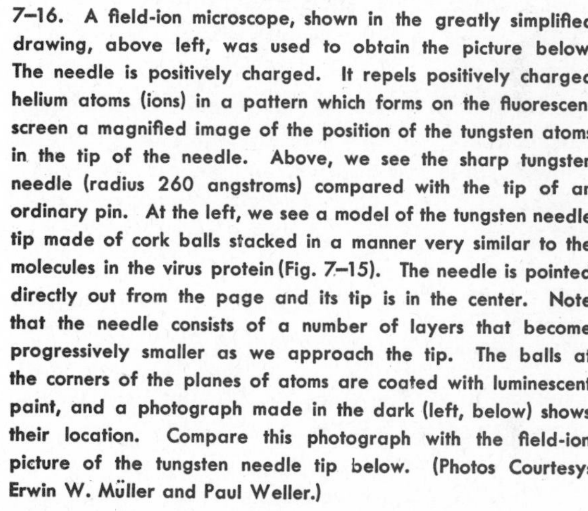

7–16. A field-ion microscope, shown in the greatly simplified drawing, above left, was used to obtain the picture below. The needle is positively charged. It repels positively charged helium atoms (ions) in a pattern which forms on the fluorescent screen a magnified image of the position of the tungsten atoms in the tip of the needle. Above, we see the sharp tungsten needle (radius 260 angstroms) compared with the tip of an ordinary pin. At the left, we see a model of the tungsten needle tip made of cork balls stacked in a manner very similar to the molecules in the virus protein (Fig. 7–15). The needle is pointed directly out from the page and its tip is in the center. Note that the needle consists of a number of layers that become progressively smaller as we approach the tip. The balls at the corners of the planes of atoms are coated with luminescent paint, and a photograph made in the dark (left, below) shows their location. Compare this photograph with the field-ion picture of the tungsten needle tip below. (Photos Courtesy: Erwin W. Müller and Paul Weller.)

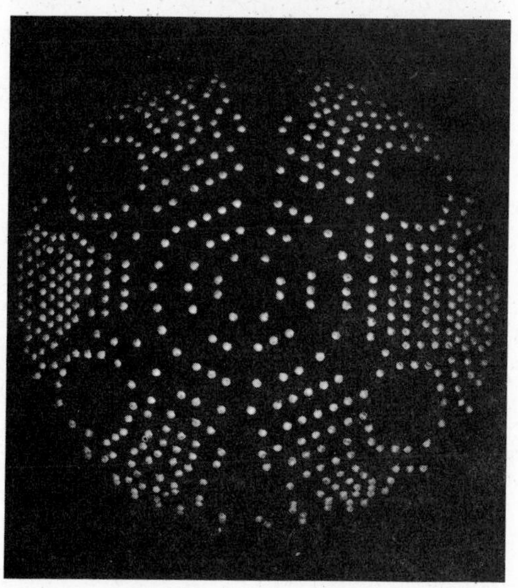

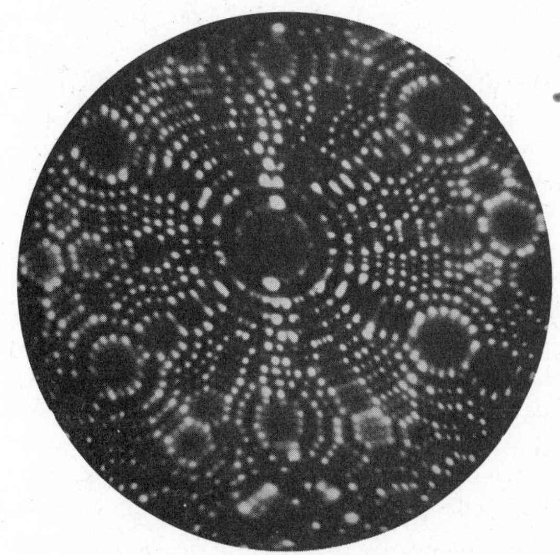

obtained in this way and the atomic dimensions obtained by the X-ray study of the green pigment makes us far more confident that both methods are giving us the right answer.

Neither of these measurements alone would really convince us that there are atoms. Even the two taken together are not enough, but in fact there are now so many different measurements of atomic dimensions — all of them giving a few angstroms — that the whole body of evidence appears overwhelming. We shall see more of this evidence before the end of this chapter, but it would take impossibly long to list all the evidence that physicists can marshal. The atoms are really there, and they are all about the same size.

7–12. More Evidence of Atoms

The virus particles seen in the electron microscope are much larger than atoms, and even the corduroy-like layers seen in Fig. 7–14 are many atoms apart, but these photographs do show that there is some sort of repeating pattern deep within apparently uniform matter — a structure which reflects the orderly stacking of natural units.

We can approach the problem of revealing this structure in quite a different way. Suppose we were to try to cut a sample of material into smaller and smaller pieces until we got to its natural unit. When we approached the size of the unit, we would expect the ease of cutting to change. Unfortunately, the sizes of the units we expect are so small (10^{-9} meter or less) that any such chopping process will soon fail. We cannot get down to the natural unit with this method. We have no knives sharp enough, and we could neither hold nor see the small pieces.

There are less obvious ways to break matter down into its natural units. For instance, we can try to flatten out a sample of matter, hammering it as thin as possible to see if a limit is set by the natural unit. Unfortunately, however, hammering is a crude process. Even the most skillful gold beater, making thin gold leaves for the glittering letters on a store window, must stop when the leaf is about 2000 angstroms thick. This thickness is determined not by the fundamental units of gold but by the difficulty of handling such a thin sheet.

There are ways to spread out far thinner layers of matter. Here is one which you can do in your school laboratory. A sample of a tallowy substance called stearic acid is dissolved in a volatile solvent like benzene. By repeatedly diluting the solution with more solvent, one can make sure that there is only a very small, but accurately known, amount of the solid substance dissolved in each cubic centimeter of solvent. If a very small drop of this solution is placed on the surface of clean water, it spreads quickly, after which the solvent evaporates and the stearic acid remains. A remarkable thing happens. A thin layer of stearic acid floats on the water surface, but it spreads out only so far and no farther. There is a maximum area; and this means that there must be a minimum thickness. Furthermore, when we use a different number of drops we find that this thickness stays the same. It is naturally determined — determined by the dimension of the natural units of stearic acid.

The natural minimum thickness of a stearic acid layer must be at least as great as one dimension of the natural units of stearic acid. How small is it? If we dissolve a tenth of a cubic centimeter of stearic acid in a liter of benzene, we should have only 10^{-4} of the original amount, or 10^{-5} cm^3 of stearic acid in each drop of the solution. (There are about ten drops per cm^3.) One drop of this solution on water forms a layer with an area about 50 cm^2. Dividing this area into the volume of stearic acid dropped on the water, we get a thickness of about 20 angstroms or 2×10^{-9} meter. This is the natural limiting thickness.

Let us imagine a model of the layer. Perhaps it is made up of small cubes, each one of which is a natural unit of stearic acid, 20 angstroms on an edge. It turns out that such a picture is only approximate. In a better approximation, the layer is a collection of cylinders, each about 5 angstroms across and a little more than 20 angstroms long. All these cylinders stand up obliquely on the water surface. This more precise picture is based on detailed studies of the mechanical behavior of the layer, chemical studies, X-ray studies, electron-microscope pictures, and the like.

Stearic acid can be decomposed into carbon, hydrogen, and oxygen. The natural unit of stearic acid, then, is not itself an atom of a chemical element. It is a group of atoms of three different elements. Such a group, which forms the natural unit of a complex chemical substance, we usually call a *molecule*. Also, the film of stearic acid molecules one layer thick is appropriately called a monomolecular layer or *monolayer*.

We have been measuring the dimensions of the molecules of stearic acid. Can we also use monolayers to find the dimensions of the atoms? The chemist can take the molecule apart, and the X-ray expert can look inside it in much the way that he looks inside the green copper phthalocyanine dye studied in Fig. 7–14. In this way we learn that the stearic acid molecule is a long chain of carbon atoms surrounded by hydrogen atoms. Each carbon atom occupies about $1\frac{1}{2}$ angstroms along the chain. Actually, there are 18 carbon atoms in the whole molecule; but, because the chain is not stretched taut, and because it slants a little rather than being exactly perpendicular to the surface of the water, the length of 18 carbon atoms in a line is a bit greater than the thickness of the monolayer.

Stearic acid is not the only acid formed in this same general way. The chemist can make similar acids of many different lengths. By studying the monolayers of these different acids, we get still another piece of evidence on the size of an atom. Any molecule of a whole series of these acids will occupy the same area on the surface of water, almost exactly 22 square angstroms. The thickness of the monomolecular layers, however, changes in a regular progression. There is a whole sequence of thicknesses increasing in steps of almost exactly 1.43 angstroms. The layers of different thickness correspond to chains of carbon atoms, each 1 carbon atom longer than the one before. The chain length has been varied from 14 to 34 carbon atoms without appreciable change in the area of the molecule, while we can see the length increasing atom by atom. Here again we have more of the evidence indicating that atoms have dimensions of about 2 angstroms.

The formation of visible monolayers suggests that others, less easy to detect, are likely to be present on every surface around us. What we call a clean steel surface often contains monolayer areas of various sorts, some formed by the gases of the atmosphere. The tendency for surfaces to collect such thin layers is quite general, and is largely responsible for the somewhat erratic behavior of surface friction and electrical contacts, for the wetting of solids, and for the properties of lubricants. A "smooth" and "clean" surface is rarely either smooth or clean on the scale of monolayer thicknesses, so that, unless rigid precautions are taken, the very placing in contact of two "smooth" surfaces is a somewhat haphazard thing. Most surfaces are covered with a patchy monolayer of air, just as a person getting out of water is for a while covered with a much thicker film of water.

The mechanics and the chemical nature of monolayers have been a subject of very detailed study for fifty years. It represents one of the subjects on the borderline between physics and chemistry. The people who study such topics are sometimes spoken of as physical chemists. Their detailed studies of monolayers add certainty to our belief that when we measure the thickness of a monolayer we are measuring a natural unit of the substance. We are finding the dimensions of molecules and even of atoms.

7–13. Counting Atomic Particles

Atoms are so small — about 2 angstroms or so in dimensions — that there must be tremendous numbers of them in a small piece of solid matter. Your thumb is probably about 5 cm long, 2 cm across, and 1 cm thick. With atoms of about 2×10^{-10} m diameter, this is $\frac{5}{2} \times 10^{8}$ (that is, $\left.\frac{5 \times 10^{-2}}{2 \times 10^{-10}}\right)$ atoms long, $\frac{2}{2} \times 10^{8}$ atoms across, and $\frac{1}{2} \times 10^{8}$ atoms thick. Your thumb, therefore, contains about 10^{24} atoms. Suppose we turn this reasoning around: if we could count these atoms directly and measure the volume of your thumb, we could find out the volume occupied per atom. In this way we would get still another evaluation of an atomic dimension. Although we cannot count atoms in your thumb, there are ways of making direct counts of atoms. In this section we shall describe one.

You have probably seen in the sky the vapor trail left behind by a jet plane that is itself invisible. Fast-moving atomic particles also leave behind them trails that can be made visible in many ways. The particle sets off a change in the material through which it passes, and the change can be amplified into a visible mark. The bubble chamber is a device which shows such changes. In it a liquid is ready to boil, but no bubbles have yet grown. When a fast particle goes through the liquid, it disturbs the atoms of the liquid, and bubbles of vapor begin to form

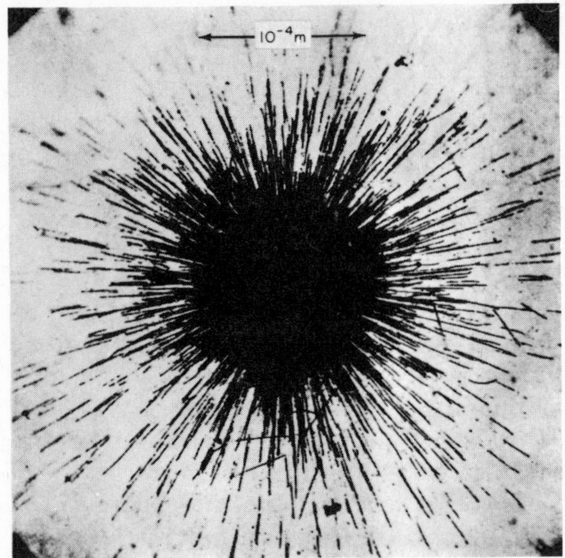

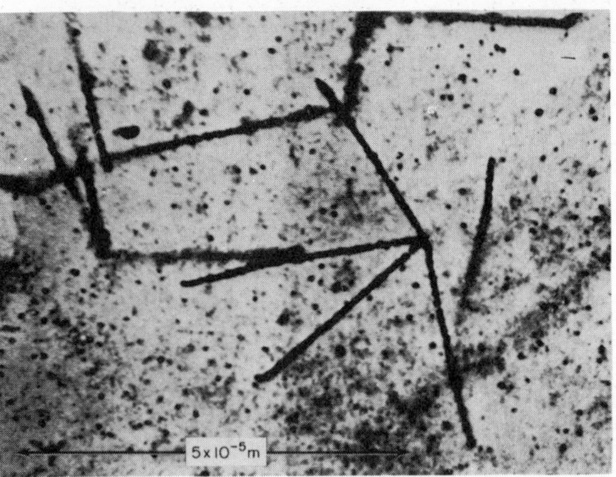

7–17. At left are particle tracks on a photographic plate. A small quantity of radium, too small to be seen under a microscope, was placed on a plate and after a few days the plate was developed. The tracks that we see are those of the alpha particles (charged helium atoms) like those from polonium. If a tiny amount of radioactive material is incorporated throughout the photographic emulsion on the plate, alpha-particle tracks like those shown in the print at right will result. Note the approximate scales of distance. (Courtesy: C. F. Powell and G. P. S. Occhialini, "Nuclear Physics in Photographs," Oxford University Press.)

along its path. In a short time the bubbles grow to visible size; and the wake of the particle (its track through the liquid) can be photographed even though, long before the camera has clicked, the particle has either come to rest or passed completely through the device. Still another method depends upon the fact that the material in a photographic plate changes along the path of a fast-moving particle. When the plate is developed, the track can be seen. The tracks of many fast particles are seen in Fig. 7–17; they originated in a speck of matter so small that no balance of the chemist could begin to weigh it.

The effect of a single fast-moving atom is easy to see for yourself. It can be seen in the luminous dial of a watch or clock which glows in the middle of the night because the paint contains a small amount of radioactive material. The dial paint also contains a substance much like that on a TV screen. In a TV picture tube a stream of particles strikes the screen and each impact causes a momentary glow. In the watch dial the glow arises from the atoms ejected from the radioactive material that has been mixed into the paint.

Examine the luminous dial of a watch in complete darkness, holding the dial only an inch or so from your unaided eye. As your eyes become dark-adapted, you will see no steady glow, but a continual random succession of individual flashes of light, scintillations, like so many tiny fireflies. A magnifying glass will make the flashes appear sharper and clearer. Each flash signals the passage of a single fast particle which originated in the radioactive material. Each fast particle comes from the breakup of the very heart of a single atom — the nucleus — of the radioactive material. With patience and simple apparatus, physicists were able by 1905 to detect, identify, and measure radioactivity by counting scintillation flashes one by one with the eye. In the years just before World War I, the physicists working with Ernest Rutherford in Manchester, England, counted hundreds of thousands of such individual flashes in the famous experiments that led to the discovery of the existence and the nature of the atomic nucleus.*

There are good reasons for suspecting that each flash signals the breakup of one atom. Here is one persuasive reason. To get the same count of fast-moving particles, over and over again, there is only one essential condition. We must have the same amount of the radioactive substance. It makes no difference, for instance, if

*The eye is a fine detecting device, but is reliable only for brief periods of time at low counting rates. Scintillation counting is now done by using a phototube, which creates a tiny pulse of electricity every time it sees a flash of light. The electric pulse is very weak and must be amplified by electronic circuits; but, unlike the eye, the phototube with its circuits can count 10^6 flashes a second, day after day.

we hammer the substance, if we put it into intimate chemical combinations with other atoms, or if we vaporize it, spreading its atoms apart. The environment and the physical treatment are not relevant. The emission of fast-moving particles does not depend on anything external to the individual radioactive atoms themselves. It must reflect some profound change that takes place in those atoms and is controlled by their nature. In a little while we shall see further evidence showing that counting ejected particles is equivalent to counting atoms. This evidence will again emphasize the smallness of the atom and the large number of atoms found in a small sample of matter.

Now let us describe an experiment in which we count the number of atoms in a sample of radioactive material. Suppose we have a mass of 10^{-7} kg, a tiny speck of the radioactive element polonium. (Polonium was first obtained by the Curies during the same experiments in which they discovered radium. Nowadays it is synthesized in the reactors at Oak Ridge, Tennessee, and has many uses both in the laboratory and in industry.) This little speck is a source of particles which shoot out in straight lines in every direction. Suppose we make a tiny square screen (Fig. 7–18) one-tenth millimeter on an edge; cover it with a thin layer of luminescent material like that in a TV picture tube; and hold it one meter from the source. It would take 10^9 such screens to cover a sphere of this radius surrounding the source. Consequently, on the one screen we then count about one particle for every 10^9 the source sends out. (Since air slows down the particles, preventing them from striking the screen, we must remove the air between the source and the screen.)

It is characteristic of radioactive substances that they emit particles at a steadily decreasing rate (see Fig. 7–19). In two years the activity of the polonium sample will have decreased greatly. By that time it will send out its particles at only a few per cent of the original rate. If we stop the count after two years' time, we shall have counted more than 95 per cent of all the particles it will ever emit. In those two years we get 3×10^8 scintillations on our screen. This from a mere speck of material barely visible to the eye, on a screen that catches only one-billionth of the total number of ejected particles!

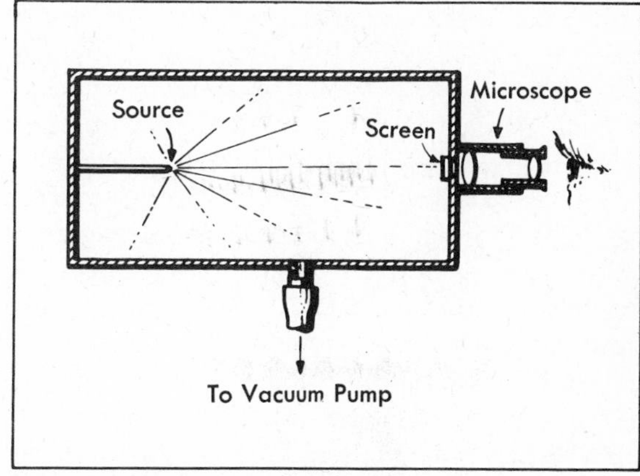

7–18. Scintillation counting. A tiny radioactive source is placed in a chamber from which most of the air has been exhausted. As particles are emitted in all directions, a certain fraction of them hit the fluorescent screen. By observing the screen, we can count the flashes or scintillations and compute the number of particles emitted.

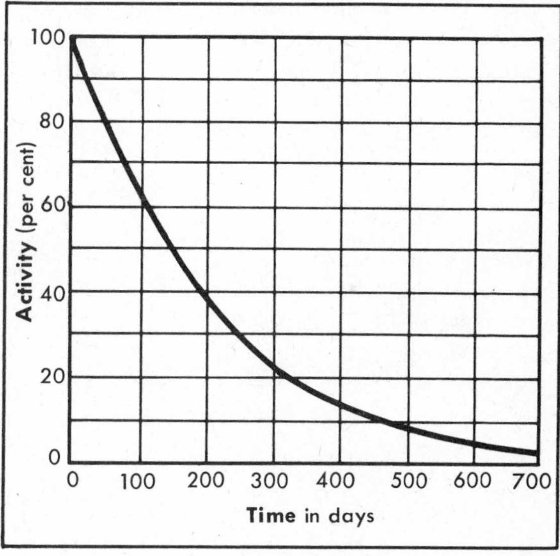

7–19. Disintegration curve of polonium. After about 138 days, a sample of polonium emits only half as many particles a minute as at the start. After another 138 days, its activity is again halved so that it is only one fourth as active. After another 138 days, its activity is again halved, and so on. We call this time interval the half-life of the element. Will its activity ever reach zero?

From this experiment we can draw a striking result. We counted 3×10^8 flashes; and because we only stopped the particles traveling within a small cone of directions, this number of flashes represented only 10^{-9} of the fast particles emitted by the sample. Somehow, within 10^{-7} kg (only a tenth of a milligram) of a soft metal called polonium, there are processes which cause the ejection of $3 \times 10^8 \times 10^9 = 3 \times 10^{17}$ individual particles.

Each process in which an individual particle is ejected is called a radioactive disintegration. We have sketched above some of the reasons for believing that one radioactive disintegration is associated with one individual atom. Now we are in a position to check up. We can find out how great a volume of polonium is associated with a disintegration. If this volume is the same as the volume associated with an atom, we can take this as additional evidence that the radioactive disintegration of polonium is indeed counting atoms.

In order to find the volume associated with each disintegration, we shall divide the volume occupied by our sample of polonium metal by the number of disintegrations that go on in the sample. How large a volume does the sample occupy? Recently the density of polonium has been measured. It is 9400 kg/m³. Therefore, our 10^{-7}-kg sample occupies

$$\text{Volume of sample} = \frac{10^{-7}\ \text{kg}}{9.4 \times 10^3\ \text{kg/m}^3} = 1.06 \times 10^{-11}\ \text{m}^3.$$

To find the volume associated with one disintegration, we divide the volume of the sample by the 3×10^{17} disintegrations.

$$\text{Volume per disintegration} = \frac{1.06 \times 10^{-11}\ \text{m}^3}{3 \times 10^{17}\ \text{disint}} = 35 \times 10^{-30}\ \text{m}^3/\text{disint}.$$

As a crude model, we may think of each disintegration volume as a little cube. The length of the edges of these cubes is then given by the cube root of their volume. Thus each edge is about 3×10^{-10} m long. In other words, our count has given us 3 angstroms for the linear dimension associated with an individual disintegration. This length is in excellent agreement with the atomic dimensions of about 2 angstroms that we obtained by other methods. Counting radioactive disintegrations is equivalent to counting polonium atoms; and these atoms, like all others, have dimensions of a few angstroms.

7–14. The Crowds of Atoms

Let us reflect a bit on the tremendous numbers we have been counting — 3×10^{17} atoms in a tenth of a milligram of polonium; 10^{24} atoms in your thumb. We have seen large numbers before, but they were less striking. Furthermore, they involved an arbitrary unit (meter, kilogram, etc.), while now we are concerned with the count of a natural unit, an individual, identifiable thing, like a single scintillation. These counts are counts of a real population.

Large numbers are hard to count. If you were to make a career of counting, working at full speed, all day, every workday, and you had begun to do this when you first learned to count, retiring on a well-earned pension at 65, you would be judged a star at counting if you had reached 2×10^9. That is about the human population of the whole world. Now, if every man, woman, and child in the whole world's population spent a lifetime in just such counting, doing nothing else, they could all together just about count off, one by one, the atoms in a pinhead. Such a human team of counters would, on the other hand, be able to count all the leaves on all the trees of the world within a few months.

It is this smallness of an atom, this extravagant number in a pinhead, that makes atoms so difficult to detect with the unaided senses. On the other hand, it is this very smallness of size and massiveness of number which enable us to use the atom to explain all the wonders of matter. It is not easy to conceive of these numbers, but we can understand how only atoms so small and so numerous can make up in their individual motions the apparently uniform, smooth, and featureless air, water, or glass. On a completely different scale, the uniformity is like that of a sandy beach which appears to be smooth when viewed from a slight distance away, showing little or no trace of the individual grains of sand. It is also not hard to believe that the atoms can combine in a myriad of ways to give all the materials of the world with all their different properties. Our example of the English alphabet showed this.

The spread of the odor of ether through a room, which means in the end the emptying of the bottle by slow, invisible evaporation, is accomplished by small clusters of atoms flying out of the liquid and moving through the air. The combination of hydrogen and oxygen to form water is a regrouping of atoms. These, and many another such process, are but cases of the mutual shuffling of so many small particles. Such homely affairs as dissolving sugar have an atomic explanation, as do the strange phenomena of radioactivity, magnetism, and the actions of the living cell itself. All these processes appear to go on smoothly because they involve tremendous numbers, the all-but-unbelievable swarms of the tiny atoms.

7–15. A Glance at the Chapter

The structure of matter, its regular patterns, the limiting thickness of monolayers, counts of matter as it changes form in radioactive decay — all imply that there are basic units of matter. The electron-microscope pictures, the field-emission pictures, and the scintillation count are some of the most direct ways to count these units. All of them agree in their count; all indicate that the smallest units we thus see are a few angstroms in diameter. The chemical and spectroscopic evidence, on the other hand, tells us that the material things of our world are made up of some 100 elements. The notion that we have basic units, atoms of these elements, is immediate: we must have 100 different kinds of units of matter — 100 different species of atoms. In the next chapter we shall examine chemical evidence for these atoms. We can already be pretty sure that all the atoms of any single element are highly similar, for neither chemist nor spectroscopist can coax any new results from a sample of an element. But this is not a guarantee that there are no differences among atoms of a given element. All we can say is that any differences do not affect the work of chemist or spectroscopist. In that sense the differences must be small.

Matter in bulk is made up of myriads of atoms of 100 different species. Combined in various ways, they produce the almost infinite variety of the world. Nevertheless, all matter can be subject to a common measure. Mass, as established by comparison on a balance, is independent of physical and chemical conditions like temperature, position in space, or aggregation of the atoms in different molecules. It usually agrees with our intuitive notions of quantity of matter. Only when large amounts of radiant mass are involved does the measure of mass diverge from our expectations about a measure of matter. The conservation of mass (or matter) is basic to the idea that chemical reactions are rearrangements of atoms. It underlies the whole of the discussion of this chapter.

FOR HOME, DESK, AND LAB

1. Why are you sure there are more than 200 atoms in a spoonful of water? Use the evidence of your senses — not some numbers or sizes someone else tells you.

2. * A moist project (with a sensitive balance).

After estimating the diameter of several equal-sized soap bubbles, try to catch the material of the bubbles on a sheet of lightweight plastic such as Saran wrap. Weigh it and determine the average amount of material per bubble. Can you determine the order of magnitude of the thickness of the bubble wall? Compare this with the thickness of a monolayer.

Note: You will find the solution easier if you use the fact that the inside and outside areas of a bubble are very nearly equal and therefore the volume of bubble material is approximately given by either area times the thickness.

3. A cube of aluminum 4.30×10^{-2} m on an edge has a mass of 2.14×10^{-1} kg and contains 4.78×10^{24} atoms.

(a) What is the volume of the cube occupied by each atom?

(b) If the atoms are spherical and just fit inside the cube, what is the diameter of the atom in angstroms?

(c) What is the mass of each atom?

4. A student performs an experiment with monolayers. He mixes 5.0 cm^3 of oleic acid with 95 cm^3 of alcohol. He dilutes 5.0 cm^3 of this solution with 50 cm^3 more of alcohol.

(a) What is the per cent of oleic acid in the solution?

(b) What is the mass of oleic acid in one cm^3 of solution? The density of oleic acid is 0.90 gm/cm^3.

He now finds that 1.0 cm^3 of solution in his laboratory dropper gives 50 drops. One drop of the solution on a water surface forms a monolayer film with an average diameter of 32 cm after the alcohol has dissolved into the water.

(c) What is the mass of the oleic acid in the film?

(d) What is the volume of the film?

(e) What is the thickness of the film?

(f) Can the thickness be obtained without knowing the density?

5. The natural unit of oleic acid (a molecule of it) has a cross-sectional area of about 4.6×10^{-19} m^2 and a length of about 1.12×10^{-9} m. The density of oleic acid is 0.90 gm/cm^3.

(a) How many molecules are there in one milligram of oleic acid?

(b) What is the mass of one oleic acid molecule?

(c) This molecule is made of 54 atoms of different kinds. What is the average mass of these atoms?

(d) Give an upper limit for the mass of the lightest atom in oleic acid. (Make this limit as small as you can.)

6. Fig. 7–15 shows a crystal of necrosis virus protein magnified about 8×10^4 times. Measure the diameters of several individual protein molecules and find the volume of one molecule. Use the known radius of a carbon atom, about 10^{-10} m, to find the order of magnitude of the number of atoms in the virus molecule.

7. In the description of scintillation counting it was stated that only one particle in every 10^9 sent out from the source reaches a square screen 10^{-4} meters on an edge at a distance of one meter. Prove that this statement is true if the source radiates equally in all directions.

8. From scintillation counting we know that about 3×10^{18} particles are emitted by a milligram of polonium in the course of complete decay.

(a) Assuming that one particle is given off by each atom, what is the mass of a polonium atom?

(b) Now, using the approximate density of polonium, 10 gm/cm^3, find the volume occupied by a polonium atom. Check with the number computed in Section 7–13.

9. The rate of decay of a sample of radon gas is timed by counting its activity. On the first day, 0.1 milligram of radon emits 4.3×10^{16} particles. The following readings of per cent of original activity were found for successive days:

Days Elapsed	Per cent of Original Activity	Days Elapsed	Per cent of Original Activity
0	100	6	34
1	84	7	27
2	70	8	24
3	59	9	20
4	49	10	17
5	41		

(a) Plot the activity as a function of time.

(b) What fraction of the original quantity of gas would remain after twelve days have elapsed?

(c) What fraction of the radon changes in a day?

(d) How many days elapse before only half of the radon is left?

(e) What is the total number of particles that a 0.1-milligram sample of radon gives off? Compare this with the polonium count.

Note: The total number can be obtained by using this geometric series:

$$1 + f + f^2 + f^3 + \cdots = \frac{1}{1-f}$$

Here f is the ratio of the second day's activity to that of the first day. You can also approximate the total by using the area under the curve of activity vs. time.

FURTHER READING

BOYS, C. V., *Soap Bubbles.* Doubleday, 1959. A Science Study Series paperback.

GAMOW, GEORGE, *One, Two, Three . . . Infinity.* Mentor Books, 1957 (pp. 115–128). An entertaining and authoritative description of the nature of atoms.

HOLTON, GERALD, *Introduction to Concepts and Theories in Physical Science.* Addison-Wesley, 1952.

MÜLLER, E. W., "A New Microscope." *Scientific American*, May, 1952 (p. 58). How the field-emission microscope resolves individual atoms and molecules.

MÜLLER, E. W., "Atoms Visualized." *Scientific American*, June, 1957 (p. 113). A further refinement of the microscope that projects pictures of atoms on a screen.

PAULING, LINUS, *General Chemistry.* W. H. Freeman & Co., 1956. An outstanding and thorough college-level first course.

ATOMS AND MOLECULES

CHAPTER 8

8–1. The Laws of Chemical Composition

Chemists have prepared a couple of hundred thousand distinct compounds containing carbon, a few thousand without that element. Every day, more are being found in living material and in soil and rock; still others are being synthesized. Analyses of all these substances are repeatedly made, and from these analyses very important general conclusions have been drawn. They came first from John Dalton, around 1800, when the body of information was far less convincing than it has become today.

The first of these general conclusions is the *law of constant chemical composition.* It asserts that every sample of a given substance, judged sufficiently pure by various criteria, always contains the same proportions by mass of all the elements into which it can be analyzed. The recipes do not change. Water is always one gram of hydrogen to eight of oxygen, common salt always one gram of sodium to each 1.5 grams of chlorine, and common sugar 1.0 gram of hydrogen to 6.5 grams of carbon and 8.0 grams of oxygen, whenever it is resolved into its three elements. Every source of table sugar (the chemist calls it *sucrose*) gives the same analysis; if a sample deviates, it is always possible to find that it is impure sugar, for its taste or its crystal shapes or its color or some other property will distinguish it from samples of the expected constant composition. Some process will in the end separate the other components and yield whatever sucrose is there in normal composition.

The law of constant composition holds to high accuracy for just about all the organic carbon-containing substances, and for thousands of others. For example, suppose that we wish to make some sodium chloride — common salt. We find that 39 grams of sodium will combine with 61 grams of chlorine to give 100 grams of salt. Now suppose we try to combine 50 grams of sodium with 61 grams of chlorine: we will get just 100 grams of salt as before. There will be 11 grams of sodium left over; the 61 grams of chlorine can combine with only 39 grams of sodium. Moreover, when we decompose any sample of pure sodium chloride, we always get 39 per cent sodium and 61 per cent chlorine.

The law of constant composition, however, does not hold for every material of unmistakable uniformity. A pail of salt water, for example, can be uniform in composition. Every sample taken from it may prove to contain exactly the same proportions of water and salt. Stir in a handful of salt. After thorough mixing the salt water is again uniform in composition, but the proportions of salt and water are now different. Unlike water or sugar, salt water does not have a fixed composition. Salt water is a solution, best described in terms of two distinct compounds — salt and water — of which it is made. The same sort of description applies to many alloys like brass, bronze, steel, dural, coin and sterling silver, jeweler's gold, and so on. Brass has a wide range of color and other properties, depending on the composition, just as does salted water.

Many plastics also share this property of variable composition, even though they may appear homogeneous under every test.

The behavior of the substances of constant composition is the principal subject matter of traditional chemistry; but other substances are so interesting and important that they have become the domains of specialists such as metallurgists and polymer chemists. We shall see that our picture of a world made up of a limited number of kinds of atoms is broad enough to include both. Let us for the moment try to learn what we can from those substances which do show the remarkable property of constant composition.

We can sum up by saying that there are many uniform materials in which chemists and spectroscopists find the constituent elements always combined according to the same definite "recipes." These materials are the compounds. In a compound, for each gram of one elementary ingredient, there is always present a definite number of grams of each other ingredient.

So far these results — which were new in Dalton's time — fit well enough with the idea of atoms. If the elements are each a collection of identical atoms which link together in small groups to form the compounds, we would expect large-scale samples to exhibit constant proportions of the elements. For example, we found that water is always composed of one gram of hydrogen to eight grams of oxygen. If the natural unit of water — the water molecule — were made of one atom of hydrogen and one atom of oxygen, then any sample of water should contain equal numbers of hydrogen and oxygen atoms. Also, the masses of hydrogen and oxygen should always occur in the same ratio as the masses of their atoms. On the other hand, if the molecule of water consists of two hydrogen atoms and one oxygen atom (as we now know it does), then every sample of water must contain hydrogen and oxygen atoms in the ratio two to one. Again the ratio of the masses of the elements will be constant, this time in the ratio of the mass of two hydrogen atoms to that of one oxygen atom. As long as atoms of one kind combine in any definite way with those of another kind, we get the law of constant chemical composition.

Perhaps there are several different kinds of molecules containing only hydrogen and oxygen. For example, if the water molecule is made of

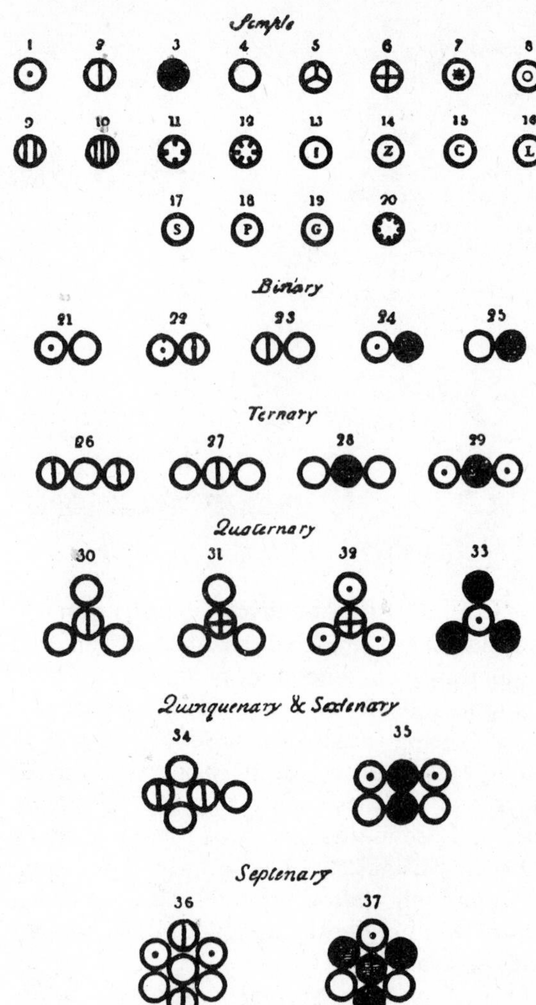

8–1. Dalton's symbols. Early in the nineteenth century (between 1802 and 1808), John Dalton tried to discover the number and kind of atoms in molecules of compounds. These are some of the symbols he used: (1) hydrogen, (2) azote (nitrogen), (3) carbon, (4) oxygen, (5) phosphorus, (6) sulfur, (7) magnesia, (8) lime, (9) soda, (10) potash, (11) strontia, (12) baryta, (13) iron, (14) zinc, (15) copper, (16) lead, (17) silver, (18) platinum, (19) gold, (20) mercury. Note (21), Dalton's formula for water. He gave it as HO, although we now know it to be H_2O. Data from combining masses alone are not enough to determine a molecular formula. His formulas for carbon monoxide (25) and carbon dioxide (28) are correct.

two hydrogen atoms and one oxygen — which we then write H_2O — a molecule with only one hydrogen and one oxygen atom would be a molecule of a different compound. There is another simple compound of hydrogen and oxygen. This is the substance we call hydrogen peroxide.

How would we decide how many atoms of hydrogen and how many of oxygen form one hydrogen peroxide molecule? We can make one relevant test by decomposing some of the peroxide and finding the ratio of the masses of hydrogen and oxygen. The result is that in the peroxide as compared with water only one-half as much hydrogen is combined with a given amount of oxygen. In water there are 2 grams of hydrogen for every 16 grams of oxygen, and in hydrogen peroxide there is only one gram of hydrogen for 16 grams of oxygen. This result is consistent with the idea that hydrogen peroxide molecules are HO and water molecules H_2O; but it does not prove it. Water molecules might be HO, as Dalton thought (Fig. 8–1), and hydrogen peroxide molecules HO_2. Or, if we know that water is H_2O, the hydrogen peroxide molecule might be H_2O_2. (This means two hydrogen and two oxygen atoms combining to form the natural unit of the compound.)

Water and hydrogen peroxide are only examples. In the course of this chapter we shall see many more. For all compounds, the combinations of definite numbers of atoms of various kinds lead to constant proportions of the elements. What is more, as we have seen with our simple example, whenever two elements combine in more than one way into different molecules, the ratio of the different masses of one element which combine with a given mass of the other comes out as a ratio of small whole numbers. It is not always one-to-two as it was for the amount of hydrogen that will combine with the same amount of oxygen in hydrogen peroxide and in water. But it is always some ratio of small whole numbers. This law, based on observation, is just what we would expect if it is atoms that are combining. If only whole numbers of atoms can combine to form a molecule, only ratios of small whole numbers are possible. This law of ratios is known as the *law of multiple proportions;* it is one of the other major pieces of evidence for the atomic composition of matter that Dalton brought forward.

Probably the most striking example of multiple proportions occurs for the combinations of nitrogen and oxygen. With one gram of nitrogen $\frac{4}{7}$ of a gram of oxygen will combine to make laughing gas. Exactly twice as much oxygen ($\frac{8}{7}$ gram) will combine to make nitric oxide. In other nitrogen and oxygen compounds there are just three times, four times, and five times the original amount of oxygen per gram of nitrogen. In other words, with 1 gram of nitrogen we find in different compounds $1 \times \frac{4}{7}$ gram, $2 \times \frac{4}{7}$ gram, $3 \times \frac{4}{7}$ gram, $4 \times \frac{4}{7}$ gram, and $5 \times \frac{4}{7}$ gram of oxygen. These whole numbers (and the similar whole numbers for other combinations of elements) are a direct reflection of the atomic nature of matter.

The constant proportions and in particular the multiple proportions which are observed in the chemical composition of compounds are strong evidence for the existence of atoms. But unlike Dalton, who brought this evidence forward at the beginning of the nineteenth century, we have seen other evidence of atoms. We have seen the evidence of the existence of natural units in monolayers and other microstructures. We have counted atoms by counting their radioactive emissions. Now we can add the chemical evidence to all these other indications of the existence of atoms.

8–2. The Problem of Determining Molecular Formulas

How many atoms of each different kind combine to form the molecules of pure substances? If we look back at the last section we see that the laws of chemical composition do not uniquely determine the chemical formulas for molecules. We could not be sure that the molecule of water was H_2O (2 atoms of hydrogen and 1 of oxygen) or that hydrogen peroxide was HO. (In fact, it is H_2O_2.) How to determine exact molecular formulas will be the subject of the next sections.

As often happens, there are many ways of determining chemical formulas, and many lines of evidence have contributed to the practical determination of a large number of them. The problem of making a table of chemical formulas is something like that of assembling one of those Chinese puzzles in which a set of separate wooden pieces lock together to form a compact solid. Where you place a particular piece in the puzzle, or a compound in the table, depends on where you have placed the others. By comparing the ratios of masses found in a wide variety of compounds and by using many other pieces of evidence, chemists have gradually arrived at formulas of which they can be certain.

In the story of ascertaining molecular formulas, the chemical reactions of gases play a large part.

Here we shall not follow the historical development of the story; but by using some information gained with modern techniques of counting radioactive disintegrations and some information from the traditional methods of gas chemistry, we shall illustrate how chemical formulas can be pinned down. The formulas so established agree with those worked out from the huge mass of evidence accumulated during the past century. They are checked by other modern techniques, for instance by measuring the masses of individual atoms and molecules with the mass spectroscope which we shall study in Part IV. In order to illustrate the determination of molecular formulas we shall discuss gases briefly in the next section, and then in Section 8–4 we shall determine a few complete formulas.

8–3. The Number of Particles in Gases

In Section 7–13 we described an experiment counting polonium atoms by their radioactive disintegrations. As we saw there, each polonium atom sooner or later "explodes," sending out a fast-moving particle which we can detect and count. From 10^{-7} kg of polonium 3×10^{17} of these particles are eventually ejected — corresponding to 3×10^{17} atoms of polonium originally present. But the story does not stop there. The ejected particles are themselves matter. When the polonium ejects a particle it loses mass. By weighing the sample after the experiment we find that the particles take away about 2 per cent of the original mass. Also, by performing the experiment again, this time in a sealed glass tube, we can prevent the escape of the particles. At the end of this new experiment the tube contains not only a metal but also another substance, the gas helium. Weighing now shows that this helium, formed from the emitted particles, accounts for almost all the change in mass of the material. Moreover, in either experiment the metal sample remaining at the end is no longer polonium. It has turned into a more common nonradioactive metal, lead.

Apparently, when an atom of polonium explodes, it fires out a particle of helium, and what is left behind is a particle of lead. The helium can be collected, as was first done by Rutherford; and we can thus obtain a sample of helium containing a known number of helium particles. From 10^{-7} kg of polonium we get 3×10^{17} particles; from 1 g we get 3×10^{21} particles. By weighing this amount of helium, we find that the mass is .02 gram, or about 6.7×10^{-24} gram per particle of helium.

Now, using this information, we can learn something about the behavior of a gas. We can find out how many separate helium particles occupy a certain volume at a particular temperature and pressure. We can take a very light plastic balloon, a bag which when inflated has a definite volume, say 5 liters, and find out at room temperature how many particles must be put in the bag to fill it out so that it just barely maintains its shape against the pressure of the atmosphere outside squeezing it in. Of course, accurate experiments are not done in just this way; but with experiments which are entirely similar in principle and which are closely approximated by the experiment described, we find that 0.89 gram of helium gas occupies a volume of 5 liters (5×10^{-3} m^3) at atmospheric pressure and the temperature of melting ice (that is at 0° C). This 0.89 gram consists of

$$\frac{.89 \text{ gram}}{6.7 \times 10^{-24} \text{ gram/particle}} = 1.34 \times 10^{23} \text{ particles of helium.}$$

So we conclude that 1.34×10^{23} particles occupy 5 liters under these conditions.

Notice that the volume occupied by one particle in the gas is

$$\frac{5 \times 10^{-3} \text{ m}^3}{1.34 \times 10^{23} \text{ helium particles}} = 4 \times 10^{-26} \text{ m}^3\text{/helium particle.}$$

As we saw in the last chapter, this is about a thousand times greater than the typical volume, some 30×10^{-30} m^3, occupied by an atom in a molecule. Can a helium particle really be so large? To answer this question, let us think of the properties of gases. We shall look at them in more detail later, but all of us have certainly observed the compression of gases. For instance, with some extra pressure, we can force more gas to occupy the same volume in an auto tire. Also we see that gases are mobile; they get out of our way; they mix easily with one another — one gas interpenetrating the other; and they move about in a volume until they fill it, no matter what its shape. These common observations indicate that gases may consist of many molecules which take up only a small part of the space occupied by the gas as a whole. Between the molecules there are empty regions larger than the molecules themselves, and it is through these spaces that the molecules of one gas move as it penetrates into another.

A model of a gas with separate molecules flying about and spaced widely compared to their own size will explain the common properties of gases. This model makes it reasonable that each helium particle is much smaller than the 40,000 cubic angstrom* volume which it seems to occupy at normal temperature and pressure. But what then determines the number of gas particles that occupy a given volume? Do all gases have the same number of particles in identical volumes? Does the number depend on the mass of the individual molecules, or does it perhaps depend on some other property? To start answering these questions we now turn to a different gas.

The gas radon is the product of the radioactive disintegration of radium, and we can determine the number of particles in a sample of radon.† By using radon gas we find that 1.34×10^{23} particles of radon would occupy a volume of 5 liters at atmospheric pressure and 0° C. In other words, at the same temperature and pressure, the same numbers of particles of helium and of radon occupy exactly the same volumes. The mass of radon in this sample, however, instead of being 0.89 gram, which we found for the mass of helium, would be 49.5 grams. The mass of each particle of radon is therefore about 55 times the mass of a helium particle; but as a gas the particles act the same way. The same number of particles of either kind give the same pressure when contained in identical volumes at a given temperature.

Since the same number of particles of two entirely different gases act the same, we would certainly like to know whether equal numbers of particles of all gases occupy identical volumes at the same temperature and at the same pressure. Unfortunately, it is not so easy to count the particles in samples of most gases. We shall have to use a somewhat less direct method of investigation. This indirect method will show that the numbers of particles are the same. It will also allow us to determine molecular formulas.

8–4. The Determination of Molecular Formulas

Let us start out by collecting samples of different gases which contain hydrogen. Some of the common hydrogen-containing compounds are hydrochloric acid, hydrogen gas, water, and ammonia. Suppose that we take equal volumes of the gases of each of these compounds at the same temperature and pressure. Now we tentatively assume that the number of molecules — that is, the number of particles of gas — in each sample is the same. This assumption is known as *Avogadro's hypothesis*, after the Italian physicist who proposed it in 1811. What consequences — what observable behavior — can we expect on the basis of this hypothesis?

According to our ideas of atoms and molecules, all the molecules of a particular gas should be the same. If the molecules contain hydrogen, each molecule should contain the same number of hydrogen atoms. Furthermore that number must be one hydrogen atom per molecule, or two hydrogen atoms per molecule, or three per molecule, etc. It can only be a whole number. Now if there are the same number of molecules in each of our different gas samples, we can conclude that there should be the same mass of hydrogen in every sample in which the molecules contain only one atom of hydrogen. There should be exactly twice this mass of hydrogen in every gas with two atoms of hydrogen per molecule and there should be three times the mass of hydrogen in every gas with three atoms of hydrogen per molecule. If we decompose the compounds and measure the masses of hydrogen in our various samples, these masses should be the same or else their ratio should be a ratio of small whole numbers.

Here is a consequence of Avogadro's hypothesis that can be tested experimentally. By the middle of the nineteenth century the masses of various elements contained in standard samples

*One angstrom $= 10^{-10}$ m; one cubic angstrom $= 10^{-30}$ m^3; 4×10^{-26} m$^3 \div 10^{-30}$ m^3/A^3 = 40,000 A^3.

†We take a sample of radium and pump away the radon formed from its disintegration. Then from the rate at which the radium disintegrates, we find how many radon particles are made in any short interval of time. This gives us a known number. But in this case we must go further. The radon itself disintegrates. One-half of its atoms change, each firing out a particle of helium, in a little under 4 days. From the rate at which it is steadily formed from the disintegration of radium and the rate at which it disintegrates itself, we can know exactly how many radon particles we have in a sample at any time.

of gases had been measured. At that time Stanislao Cannizzaro made a collection of the results. Many such experiments have been performed since. For instance, we find the following experimentally: (1) the mass of hydrogen in a particular volume of hydrogen gas is just two times the mass in the same volume of hydrochloric acid vapor under the same conditions; (2) the mass of hydrogen in water vapor is also just two times that in hydrochloric acid vapor; and (3) the mass of hydrogen in ammonia vapor is three times that in hydrochloric acid. Table 1 contains these results and several others. Notice the whole-number ratios. Their appearance strongly supports our hypothesis that at the same temperature and pressure equal volumes of any gas contain the same number of molecules. In addition, it makes it appear likely that each molecule of hydrochloric acid contains one hydrogen atom; the molecules of hydrogen gas and those of water vapor contain two hydrogen atoms apiece, and each molecule of ammonia vapor contains three hydrogen atoms.

Table 1

Masses of Hydrogen from Gas Samples of Equal Volume at the Same Temperature and Pressure

Gas	Mass of hydrogen (in grams)
Hydrochloric acid vapor	0.1
Hydrogen	0.2
Water vapor	0.2
Ammonia vapor	0.3
Methane	0.4
Nitric acid vapor	0.1
Acetylene	0.2
Propane	0.8
Ethylene	0.4
Ammonium chloride	0.4
Ethane	0.6

Of course, the molecules of hydrochloric acid might contain two hydrogen atoms apiece, those of hydrogen gas and of water vapor four hydrogen atoms, and those of ammonia six hydrogen atoms, but this possibility seems extremely unlikely. Even after years and years of searching, chemists have not found any compounds in which the amount of hydrogen is less per molecule than that contained in hydrochloric acid. They have found no compound in which the amount of hydrogen is intermediate between the amount found in hydrochloric acid and the amount found in water vapor, and none intermediate between that in water vapor and that in ammonia vapor. If there were really two atoms of hydrogen in a hydrochloric acid molecule, we would expect to find other compounds with only one atom per molecule. These would give us a mass of hydrogen half that found in hydrochloric acid. We should also find molecules with three atoms of hydrogen. They would have a mass of hydrogen between that of hydrochloric acid and water vapor. The absence of any such compounds is strong evidence in support of the idea that the molecules we have discussed contain exactly one, two, and three atoms of hydrogen per molecule rather than two, four, and six, or any other number. The idea that the samples with the smallest amount of hydrogen are made of molecules with only one hydrogen atom follows almost directly from the definition of an atom as the basic unit or smallest amount of an element. It is bolstered by the fact that all the other masses are whole-number multiples. Consequently we reason that those whole numbers of the same basic units are present in the molecules. We have, therefore, found concrete evidence from which we can get detailed molecular composition.

Other evidence (some of which we shall discuss in Part IV) agrees perfectly with our conclusions. For example, a molecule of hydrogen gas is about twice as long as it is wide. It seems to be made of two units, in agreement with our earlier conclusion that each molecule of hydrogen contains two hydrogen atoms. Furthermore, at sufficiently high temperatures we can decompose the molecules of ordinary hydrogen gas into two atoms of hydrogen. The evidence is that molecules of hydrogen gas are definitely H_2 molecules. Furthermore, we can now see that water vapor does contain exactly two hydrogen atoms per molecule; hydrochloric acid has one and ammonia has three. We have exactly determined one part of the formulas for these molecules.

We have now learned the numbers of hydrogen atoms per molecule in certain compounds, but what is the number of chlorine atoms in a molecule of hydrochloric acid vapor, or the number of oxygen atoms in a molecule of water vapor? There are several ways to answer these questions. One way is to use exactly the same method we

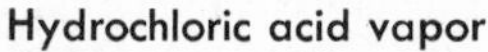
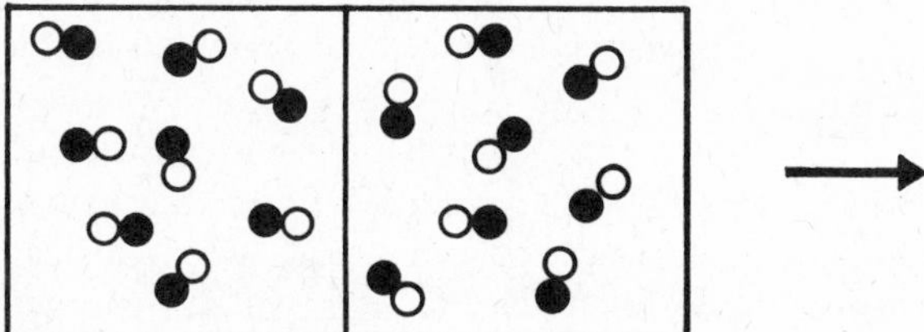

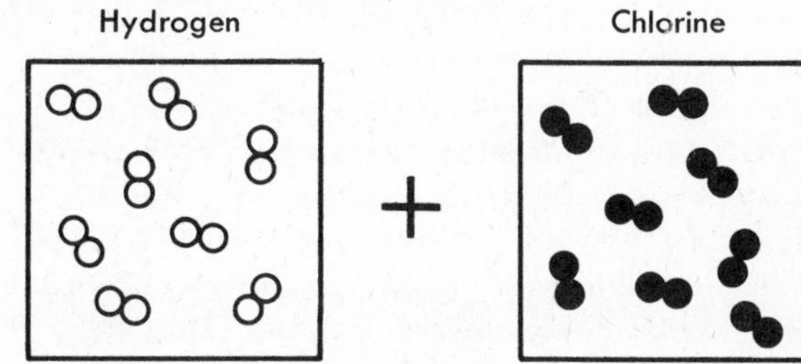

8–2. Two volumes of HCl vapor yield one volume of hydrogen gas and one volume of chlorine gas at the original temperature and pressure.

employed to determine the number of hydrogen atoms in a molecule. For instance, to learn the complete formula of hydrochloric acid molecules, we can take a series of gaseous compounds of chlorine. In addition to hydrochloric acid we take chlorine itself, which exists as a poisonous greenish gas. We also use two other gases containing chlorine, the vapors of chloroform and of carbon tetrachloride (the first used by criminals in detective stories and the second a common poisonous cleaning fluid). We collect equal volumes of these gases at a definite temperature and pressure, and then measure the masses of chlorine contained in our samples. We find that the mass of chlorine in the chlorine gas is exactly twice that of the chlorine in hydrochloric acid. The mass of chlorine in chloroform vapor is three times the mass in the hydrochloric acid, and the mass of chlorine in carbon tetrachloride is just four times the amount in the acid. We therefore conclude that there is one atom of chlorine per molecule of hydrochloric acid, two atoms per molecule of chlorine gas, three per molecule of chloroform, and four per molecule of carbon tetrachloride. We have now completely determined the molecular composition of hydrochloric acid. Molecules of hydrochloric acid contain one atom of hydrogen and one atom of chlorine, and the molecular formula of hydrochloric acid is HCl. Incidentally we also have found that, like hydrogen gas, the molecules of chlorine gas each contain two atoms. These gas molecules are Cl_2 just as those of hydrogen gas are H_2.

We can extend this kind of analysis to many compounds. For example, by studying the gases which contain nitrogen and oxygen we find that the molecule of ammonia is NH_3, water is H_2O, nitrous oxide is N_2O, oxygen gas O_2, nitrogen is N_2, and so on. Eventually by using such evidence we obtain a reasonably complete set of chemical formulas for the molecules.

8–5. The Law of Combining Volumes

Everything seems to be in order, and the consistency of our results lends strong support to Avogadro's hypothesis that equal numbers of gaseous molecules occupy the same volume at a given temperature and pressure. Further evidence for this hypothesis can be found by studying the *volumes* of the gases into which various compounds are decomposed. Suppose we decompose hydrochloric acid. We start with the hydrochloric acid vapor occupying a known volume at a certain temperature and pressure. We decompose the hydrochloric acid into hydrogen and chlorine (Fig. 8–2). The hydrogen and chlorine are also gaseous, and we can collect the hydrogen and chlorine gases separately. At the original temperature and pressure each gas occupies exactly half of the volume originally occupied by the hydrochloric acid vapor.

This result is exactly what we should expect. Each molecule of hydrochloric acid vapor is HCl. Each contains only one atom of hydrogen and one of chlorine according to our earlier conclusion (Fig. 8–2). On the other hand, each molecule of hydrogen contains two atoms of hydrogen, and each molecule of chlorine gas also contains two atoms. Consequently, there should be only half as many hydrogen and half as many chlorine gas molecules as there were originally hydrochloric acid vapor molecules. According to Avogadro's hypothesis, half as many molecules of any kind should occupy half the volume. Under the same conditions of temperature and pressure, therefore, the hydrogen gas should occupy only half the volume originally occupied by HCl vapor, and the chlorine gas should also occupy half the volume. This is just what we find.

Let us consider one more example. Suppose we decompose water. We believe that the formula of a water vapor molecule is H_2O. When we decompose water, therefore, each molecule should provide one atom of oxygen and two atoms of hydrogen. In the decomposition of water vapor, therefore, we should obtain the same number of molecules of hydrogen that we originally had of water. (Remember, hydrogen gas is H_2; each of its molecules has two H atoms.) Therefore, at the same temperature and pressure the hydrogen gas should occupy the same volume as was originally occupied by water vapor. This is exactly what is found experimentally.

Since we know that oxygen molecules contain two atoms apiece, and each molecule of water vapor supplies only one atom of oxygen, we now expect that under the same conditions of temperature and pressure, the volume of oxygen released will be only half as big as the original volume of water vapor. This too is exactly what happens.

In general, we expect that when substances are decomposed the volumes of gases produced under the same conditions of temperature and pressure should bear simple whole-number relations to each other. Also, when compounds are made in a chemical reaction between gases, the volumes of gases used up should exhibit simple whole-number relations. This expectation about combining volumes is generally borne out.

We have put history out of order — almost reversed it — in our discussion. The *law of combining volumes* at which we have just arrived was actually formulated by the French chemist Gay-Lussac in 1808. Then in 1811 the Italian physicist Avogadro showed that the law of combining volumes made sense in an atomic picture of matter. He introduced the assumption that equal volumes of gases at the same temperature and pressure contain the same number of molecules. The work of Cannizzaro about 1858 convinced many that Avogadro was right. As we have seen, Avogadro's hypothesis is now amply justified — it has become *Avogadro's law*. With modern methods we can even count the number of molecules in a gas sample.

8–6. Molecular and Atomic Masses

Because we know the number of molecules in a gas sample and can measure the mass of the sample, we can easily find the mass of a molecule. The mass of a molecule of hydrogen gas measured this way is about 3.34×10^{-24} grams. The mass of an oxygen molecule is 16 times this much — that is, 5.3×10^{-23} grams. We could write down a long list of molecular masses determined in this way.

From the masses of the molecules we can go on to the masses of atoms. We know that hydrogen molecules are each made of two hydrogen atoms. Consequently the mass of a hydrogen atom is

$$\frac{3.34 \times 10^{-24} \text{ grams}}{2} = 1.67 \times 10^{-24} \text{ grams.}$$

In the same way we find the masses of the atoms listed in Table 2.

Table 2

Atom	Mass (10^{-24} grams)
Chlorine	58.9
Fluorine	31.5
Helium	6.64
Hydrogen	1.67
Nitrogen	23.2
Oxygen	26.6
Sodium	38.1

Not every element can conveniently be made into a gas. We obtain pure carbon, for example, as graphite or diamond, neither of which vaporizes easily. But we can find the mass of a carbon atom by measuring the mass of a gaseous carbon dioxide molecule. The formula for carbon dioxide (as the name implies) is CO_2. We know that formula by applying the method of Section 8–3 to many gaseous carbon compounds (and from other evidence). Now we find the mass of a CO_2 molecule by measuring the mass in a standard volume of CO_2 at standard temperature and pressure. We find that it is 7.3×10^{-23} grams per molecule. Since we already know that the mass of O_2 is 5.3×10^{-23} grams, this leaves 2.0×10^{-23} grams for the mass of one carbon atom. Using similar chemical methods we can find the masses of all the different kinds of atoms. The masses in grams and amu of some of the more common atoms are shown in Table 3. From various methods the masses of some 100 elements are known with considerable precision.

When we are dealing with the masses of atoms and molecules, it is sometimes inconvenient to express them in grams or kilograms. We are

Table 3

Atom	Mass (10^{-24} grams)	Mass (amu)
Aluminum	44.8	26.98
Carbon	19.9	12.01
Chlorine	58.9	35.46
Copper	105.	63.54
Fluorine	31.5	19.00
Gold	327.	197.0
Helium	6.64	4.003
Hydrogen	1.67	1.008
Iron	92.8	55.85
Lead	344.	207.2
Mercury	333.	200.6
Neon	33.5	20.18
Nitrogen	23.2	14.01
Oxygen	26.6	16.
Silicon	46.6	28.09
Silver	179.	107.9
Sodium	38.1	22.99
Sulfur	53.2	32.07
Zinc	109.	65.38

always dividing by a large factor (about 10^{24}) which scales us down from the size of our thumb to the size of an atom. Long before this scale factor was accurately known, atomic and molecular masses were put on a convenient relative scale. John Dalton himself chose the lightest element, hydrogen, as the basis for the system of relative atomic masses. In the latter part of the last century, it became standard. On this scale oxygen was 16. But fifty years ago it had become clear that the ratios were not so simple; careful measurement of the masses in compounds of hydrogen with oxygen shows that the ratio of the masses of the atoms is about 1 per cent less than 16. As so often happens, the basis for the unit was shifted. It was decided to keep oxygen as 16, defining 16.000 atomic mass units as the atomic mass of oxygen, and letting hydrogen move to 1.008 atomic mass units. In the third column of Table 3 we have entered the masses of the atoms in these atomic mass units.

Once we know the table of atomic masses, or even just the table of their relative masses, we can easily find the combining masses in various compounds. For example, nitrous oxide is N_2O, and 28 grams of nitrogen do combine with 16 of oxygen to give the 7-to-4 ratio mentioned earlier. Ammonia is NH_3, and 14 grams of nitrogen combine with 3 of hydrogen. Nitric acid is HNO_3, and 1 gram of hydrogen is combined with 14 of nitrogen and 48 of oxygen in that compound.

These examples are of limited interest. The combining masses are well known, and they contributed to setting up the table. From Table 3, however, we can get the combining masses of all sorts of compounds without having to determine each one separately by experiment. Such computations are employed in estimating the amounts of various chemicals needed for all the chemical processes used in industry.

A much more exciting application of our knowledge of relative atomic masses arises when we investigate an unknown compound. From the observed combining masses and the known relative masses of the atoms, we can then learn about the unknown chemical formula. Pretend, for example, that we don't know the formula of a compound in which oxygen and hydrogen combine with the relative *masses* 16 to 1. We then learn from the table that in this compound oxygen and hydrogen *atoms* combine in 1-to-1 ratio. The example is trivial — we undoubtedly have hydrogen peroxide — but the principle is clear. In the same way the chemist has found out about more complex compounds.

8–7. Moles and Avogadro's Number

We started the last section by finding the mass in grams of a hydrogen atom. This gives us a way of determining how many atoms there are in a sample of ordinary size. How many hydrogen atoms are there in one gram of hydrogen? Since each hydrogen atom weighs 1.67×10^{-24} grams, one gram of hydrogen contains

$$\frac{1}{1.67 \times 10^{-24}} = 6 \times 10^{23} \text{ hydrogen atoms.}$$

This number of hydrogen atoms we call a *mole* of hydrogen atoms. Furthermore, we call this number of identical objects of any kind a mole of those objects, and the number 6×10^{23} we call *Avogadro's number*. From the relative masses of molecules we can foresee what a mole of a given kind of molecules must weigh. A mole of hydrogen molecules (each containing two atoms of hydrogen) has a mass of 2 grams. A mole of oxygen molecules has a mass of 32 grams, and so on. The number of grams in a mole is the same as the number of atomic mass units in the mass of the molecule.

By measuring the masses of moles of different objects, we learn the relative molecular masses. This gives us a simple way of measuring molecular masses on the scale of atomic mass units. In Section 8–3 and the following sections we learned that every mole of sufficiently small particles occupies the same volume when it is made into a gas at atmospheric pressure and the melting point of ice. As we saw there, 1.34×10^{23} particles occupies 5 liters under these conditions. Consequently, a mole occupies

$$5 \text{ liters} \times \frac{6 \times 10^{23}}{1.34 \times 10^{23}} = 22.4 \text{ liters.}$$

By measuring the mass in grams of a gas which occupies 22.4 liters at this temperature and pressure, we therefore determine the number of atomic mass units of the particles of that gas.

Although a mole of any gas made of sufficiently small particles occupies the same volume, when the gases are condensed into a solid or liquid, the volumes they occupy differ. They depend on the size of the particles themselves. For molecules which contain only a few atoms the volume of a mole is of the same order of magnitude as your thumb. But if the particles themselves are large, each containing many atoms, a mole may occupy a far greater volume. A mole of pins, for example, would cover the surface of the earth with a layer about twenty meters deep.

To get the idea of a mole and of Avogadro's number, we have crudely defined it as the number of hydrogen atoms in a gram. More accurately a mole is the number of identical particles whose mass in grams is equal to the mass in atomic mass units of one of the particles. Avogadro's number is then the number of atomic mass units per gram. Because we set the scale of atomic mass units so that the mass of a hydrogen atom is about 1.01 atomic mass units, Avogadro's number is about 1 per cent more according to this definition. In any case it is 6×10^{23} to within less than 1 per cent. The most precise modern value of Avogadro's number is 6.025×10^{23}. That is the number of objects in a mole.*

*In the next section we shall see that physicists now define the physical atomic mass unit so as to make the mass of the most abundant isotope of oxygen exactly 16 atomic mass units. (An isotope is an atom of a particular mass as well as a particular chemical type.) Avogadro's number is then precisely defined as the number of these isotopes in 16 grams. This number is 6.025×10^{23}.

This way of getting to a mole is long-winded — and even so we have omitted a lot of history in giving our account. If we were to reorganize physics now on a rational basis we would undoubtedly go a different way. We would begin by choosing a nice round number like 10^{24} to define a mole of identical objects. Then we would introduce a unit of mass $\frac{1}{16}$ that of a mole of oxygen. In this way nature would supply a unit of mass to replace the gram, and the scale factor between atoms and ordinary objects would be a power of ten. Unfortunately such a change would now confront a world-wide set of gram masses. Many of our units like those for force and energy depend on the present units of mass. A change is impractical, and we shall continue to use the kilogram at Sèvres and moles of 6×10^{23} objects.

8–8. Atomic Masses and Integers; Isotopes

The scale of atomic mass units was originally set by choosing the mass of a hydrogen atom as the unit. Why was the scale shifted to make the mass of an oxygen atom 16 units?

The basis for the decision was partly one of convenience; many compounds containing oxygen had been studied directly. In addition, a new argument favored the choice of the oxygen atomic mass as exactly 16.000 atomic mass units; with that choice, many of the elements heavier than oxygen have values for the atomic mass which are within about one part in a thousand of being integers. Thus, bismuth is 209.00; manganese, 54.94; chromium, 52.01; iodine, 126.91, and so on. Such a result is very suggestive; it might be the sign that some still more fundamental unit combines to make the elements themselves. Indeed, the British physician and chemist, William Prout, had boldly suggested that all the elements were in fact somehow made by the union of hydrogen atoms. He had done this anonymously in 1816. Far ahead of his time, he found little support for his view. As the data grew better, it became clearer and clearer that some elements had atomic masses which were not near integers. It is hard to find anything farther off from an integer than the atomic mass of chlorine, which is 35.457, and that of copper, which is 63.54. Prout's hypothesis seemed dead.

Yet the atomic masses were near-integers far too often for it to be sheer chance. Once more the physicist's hope for a simple and orderly fundamental structure for the whole of matter was realized. The answer to the problem of the fractional values came from the study of radioactive decay, and almost at the same time in other ways.

Consider the polonium sample we described in the last chapter. Polonium is an element; its compounds, spectra, and so on are pretty well known. It is unstable, to be sure, and decays into lead. From the decaying polonium, a good chemist who can handle very small amounts of material is able to extract lead, by any of a number of chemical processes. It is real lead; its appearance, its melting point, its chemistry, even its spectrum are like those of any other sample of lead. But it is not exactly like ordinary lead. The density of lead that results from the decay of polonium is less than that of ordinary lead by about half a per cent; its atomic mass is only 206.04, while that of normal lead is 207.21.

The conclusion is not hard to draw. Lead atoms come in more than one distinct variety. Every atom of lead has the same chemistry, and very nearly the same spectrum, quite different from the chemistry and spectra of other kinds of atoms. These identify it as lead, the element. But lead atoms may have different masses, all integers or very nearly so. The elements as we find them in nature are not really unresolvable; they can be resolved, generally not by chemical means but rather by means depending on the atomic masses. An element may be a mixture of several of these atoms, all of similar chemical nature but differing in mass. The measured atomic mass is simply the average. Chlorine, for example, is a mixture of two different types of atoms. Three out of four chlorine atoms have the near-integer mass 34.98; the rest have the near-integer mass 36.98. Atoms of the same element which differ in mass we call different *isotopes* of the element. An isotope is an atom of a specific mass as well as a specific chemical character. The units of matter as we find it on earth are isotopes.

In the early work the average value often concealed the integer nature of the individual atomic masses. But some elements have only a single stable — that is, nonradioactive — isotope; an example is iodine. Iodine always showed its integer atomic mass, 127 amu, because there was no need to unravel a mixture of isotopes. Oxygen itself, the standard of mass, is a mixture of three isotopes, with masses near 16, 17, and 18. Fortunately for our units, the heavier isotopes of oxygen occur rarely; in any natural oxygen sample more than 99.7 per cent is oxygen of mass near 16. For precision work, physicists nowadays take the standard atomic mass not to be just oxygen, but the particular oxygen isotope which is most common, and give it an atomic mass of exactly 16.0000 atomic mass units. This requires a small increase in the values of the atomic masses of the other isotopes, but only by about three parts in ten thousand. The new standard is sometimes called the physical scale of atomic masses.

As Prout guessed, the isotopes are built up of hydrogen units, and very likely they were formed in this way. The physicists and chemists whose work deals with the differences among isotopes indicate an isotope by writing the symbol of the chemical element to which it belongs, with a superscript giving the number of hydrogen units closest to the atomic mass of the isotope in question. Thus we write for the chlorine isotopes, Cl^{35} and Cl^{37}; or for oxygen isotopes, O^{16}, O^{17}, and O^{18}. The superscript used is called the *mass number* of the isotope. It tells what Prout foresaw — how many hydrogen atoms need be combined to form the atom in question.

Once isotopes were found, it became possible to see that there are small differences in chemical behavior and in spectra among isotopes of the same element. These differences had earlier been missed. It has even been found that two samples of an element from different sources may differ a little in atomic mass, depending on the exact mixture of isotopes present. Carbon obtained from petroleum is a little lighter than carbon from natural graphite. This demonstrates that the natural processes which form such substances are capable of discriminating between the various isotopes of a single chemical element. But the effects are always small, and it appears that such geological or biological processes can separate isotopes only very slightly. We can separate isotopes artificially on a large scale. Such separations are an important part of the atomic-energy industry.

The element hydrogen has two stable isotopes, found in every sample of water, in a ratio of about 1 of the rarer one for every 6,500 of the common one. Their masses are 2.015 for the heavier, rarer one, and 1.008 for the common atom of hydrogen. Since these masses differ by such a large relative amount, the chemical and physical properties of compounds of heavy hydrogen show marked differences from the same compounds with ordinary hydrogen. Heavy hydrogen is produced commercially by distilling water — boiling it and condensing the steam in a separate container. The "heavy water" (it appears to be ordinary water; but it costs about $10/kg) distills less rapidly than "light water." "Heavy ice" looks, feels, and tastes just like ordinary ice; it floats on pure "heavy water" but in normal water it sinks. Hydrogen of mass 2 is often called deuterium (from the Greek word *deuteros*, "second"), and written with its own symbol, D.

Small discrepancies from integer values still remain in the atomic masses of the heavier isotopes; the values tend to be farther off from whole numbers as the mass number grows larger and larger. The mass number for the heaviest isotope found in nature, uranium U^{238}, is 238.12, large by about one part in two thousand. As we go down the scale to lighter elements, we find a fairly regular decrease in the discrepancy, but below elements like iron, with mass numbers in the 50's, the discrepancies begin to increase again, and become somewhat irregular. The biggest discrepancy known among the natural elements is that for hydrogen itself, which has the precisely known value of 1.008145, high by almost 1 per cent. These discrepancies, too, have a profound meaning. We know that they represent what Prout could not guess — that the elements must be built up out of hydrogen and another "constituent" called energy. These discrepancies are fully accounted for by the Einstein relation $E = mc^2$.

8–9. The Innermost Structure of Matter

Behind the diversity of compounds, chemists found the unity of the hundred elements. Today we have gone still further. Now the units of the elements can *themselves* be analyzed, the atoms transmuted, one turned into another, although this cannot be done with the traditional tools of the chemist. It can be done, according to various rules and regularities, by such devices as the cyclotron of the nuclear physicist.

Through a long chain of steps, in which we expend much energy (and see much energy turn into forms which we cannot stop or catch), we could finally resolve any sample of matter into one special form, the element hydrogen. Hydrogen itself consists of natural units — a proton and an electron, the pair assembled into a structure which is bound together. We know of no other permanent sub-units into which we can resolve these simplest of units. Moreover, matter as we find it always has very precisely just one proton for each electron in its fundamental analysis. From this point of view, mass is but the count of the number of these pairs (electron plus proton) into which any piece of matter can ultimately be resolved.

Once we fix the constant of proportionality, by counting how many of these pairs are found in the standard kilogram, we have the simplest measure of the quantity of matter of any sample. It is the number of protons and electrons into which it can be ultimately analyzed. The unity of matter flows in a sense from the fact that it can all be resolved into or built up out of such hydrogen units. All of these units are identical. Matter measurement is then reduced to the problem of counting the identical component parts.

It seems likely, too, though far from certain, that all the matter of the universe began as hydrogen, or perhaps as separated parts of protons and electrons. It evolved into its present complexity by combination in that long history of the galaxies, the stars, the planets, and of life, which we have by no means fully unraveled. The actual processes of element formation, which went on to make our sun and our earth and which go on in other stars today, appear to begin with the masses of hydrogen gas that astronomical observation finds filling the space within our galaxy and making up most of the mass of the stars. These processes proceed through the binding together of hydrogen units into atoms.

In the tiny nuclei of atoms, protons are accompanied by neutrons and are surrounded by far-flung electrons. The neutrons are made from hydrogen units in the process of condensation, but they are unstable. If pulled off from nuclei and isolated, they decay into protons and electrons. The nuclei are less than 10^{-14} m in diameter, while the electrons move about at distances up to 10^{-10} m, the size of an atom. These atoms are themselves quite stable units, and they are the building blocks for the next-bigger pieces of matter. They are the fundamental units seen by the chemist. The story of how we take apart the atoms of chemical elements, subdividing them into hydrogen units, is the subject of another field of physics — nuclear physics.

Prout has finally been vindicated. The elements can be built out of hydrogen units; moreover, each single atom was once upon a time condensed out of hydrogen as our galaxy evolved. The small discrepancies we find between the atomic masses of the isotopes and the integers represent the mass equivalent (found from the Einstein relation) of the total energy given out or taken up in all the many intermediate steps.

We could count the number of hydrogen units in any chunk of matter. This count would form an impractical but logically satisfactory basis for all chemical mass measurements. It and the mass measured on a balance agree to a part in a thousand. Count the hydrogen units in the sample, count the hydrogen units in the standard platinum kilogram; their ratio is just the sample mass in kilograms. But the practical balance does better; it responds even to the loss or gain of those small amounts of mass which radiate away or are supplied when the elements are formed from hydrogen units. Mass measured on the balance is more inclusive than the count of the number of mass units. The balance, or some wonderfully precise balance of the future, can measure the mass of light and of heat as well as that of hydrogen units. For this reason, we shall retain it as the defining method to fix the meaning of mass.

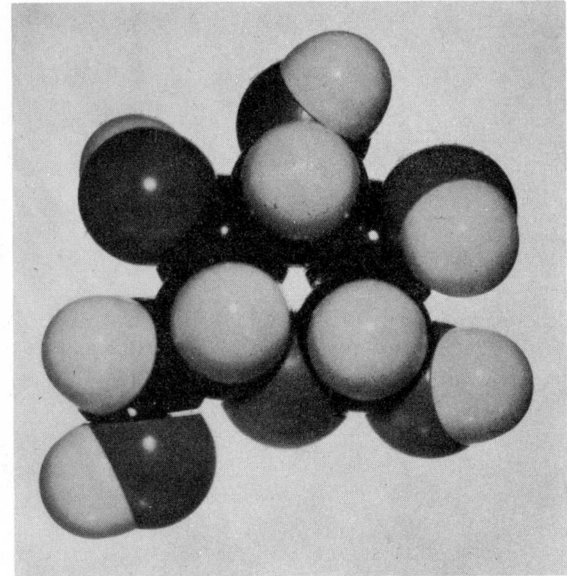

8–3. A model of a sugar molecule. One of the many different sugars is represented by this model. This particular sugar is $C_6H_{12}O_6$. Near the center we can see the dark carbon atoms. Attached to these are the light-colored hydrogen atoms and the somewhat larger oxygen atoms. The atoms represented in this model are of the order of 10^{-10} m in diameter. The colors are arbitrary.

8–10. Molecules – Structures and Properties

The chemist's skill and joy is in understanding molecules well enough to take them apart and put them together again. Simple ones, like H_2O or CO_2 (the carbon dioxide in the gas we exhale), are written in the primer of his science, but his range is far wider. We have used stearic acid to form a tallowy monolayer. The formula for stearic acid is a more complex one than those we commonly see. It may be written as $C_{18}H_{36}O_2$. Common table sugar is written as $C_{12}H_{22}O_{11}$. Fig. 8–3 shows a model of still a different sugar.

In the English language the same letters, in different proportions, spell different words, as you can see in *too, toot, to, tot.* Molecular "spelling" follows similar rules. Properties as different as those of sugar and of tallow arise from the differences between molecules all built of three kinds of atoms — C, H, and O. The molecules differ because the proportions of C, H, and O are different.

In addition, molecules may differ even when they contain the same proportions of the elements. Just as a different order of the same letters can spell different words, *arch* and *char*, for example, so molecules can differ if the same atoms are put together in different three-dimensional patterns. The molecular clump has a definite geometrical shape. Not only the number of atoms and their kind determine the properties of a substance, but even these differences in the arrangements of atoms in the molecule are important. Learning the structure of molecules is one of the main goals of the chemist.

A couple of examples will illustrate the differences in structure and in properties that can exist when we have not only the same proportions but even exactly the same numbers of atoms in different molecules. The butane molecule and the isobutane molecule are both described by the formula C_4H_{10}, but the atoms of carbon and hydrogen are put together differently in the two cases. The two different structures are illustrated

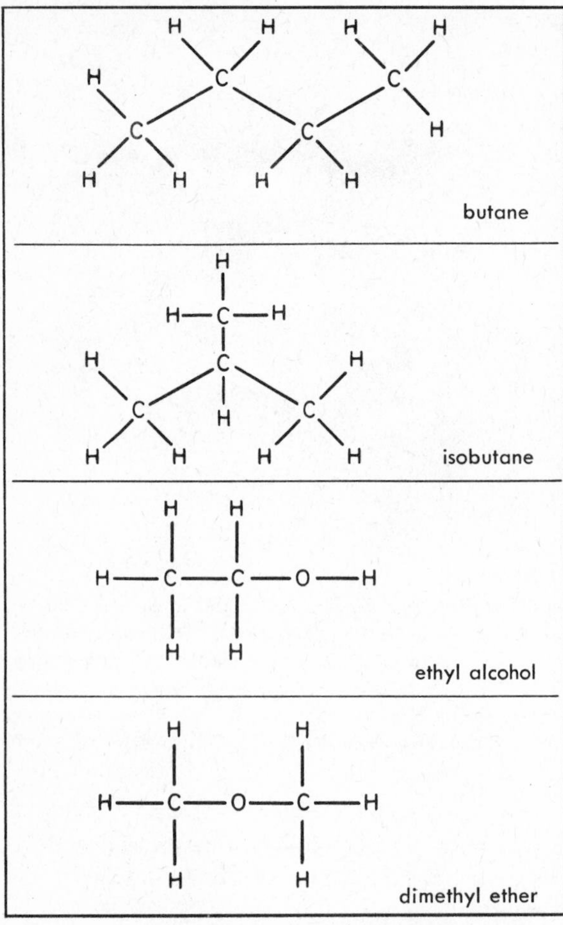

8–4. The molecules of butane and isobutane both have four carbon atoms and ten hydrogen atoms, but they have different structures, which makes them different compounds with different properties. Ethyl alcohol and dimethyl ether also have the same atoms in the same proportions, but are different compounds. Such pairs are called "isomers."

in Fig. 8–4. The properties of butane and isobutane are different. The boiling points, for example, are different. Butane boils very close to the freezing temperature of water while isobutane boils at $-10°$ C. The melting points are $-135°$ C and $-145°$ C, respectively; and butane is more soluble in water, alcohol, and ether than is isobutane. Another example is supplied by the molecules in which C, H, and O combine according to the formula C_2H_6O, ethyl alcohol and dimethyl ether. They are shown in Fig. 8–4. Some people drink the first, but the second is universally considered poisonous to drink. (It is not even used as an anesthetic; that is a different ether.) Ethyl alcohol melts at $-117.3°$ C and boils at $+78.5°$ C, while dimethyl ether melts at $-138.5°$ C and boils at $-23.65°$ C. (Here °C stands for degrees on the Celsius or centigrade scale of temperature which is discussed in Chapter 9. Recall that zero Celsius is the freezing temperature, and 100° C is the boiling temperature of water.)

8–11. The Study of Organic Molecules

The chemistry of the compounds of carbon is often called organic chemistry because such compounds were known long ago as products of living organisms. For more than a century carbon compounds have been made in the laboratory in enormous variety. The history of the chemistry of organic compounds can boast of ingenious reasoning which beats any detective story.

Analysis into atoms, which we have discussed, is the final result of chemical analysis. But the intermediate steps are just as important for unraveling molecular structure. The chemists found that they could prepare thousands of compounds of carbon, which had once been thought to be exclusively products of life. They found many examples of compounds with the same atomic proportions, the same atomic formula, that still have quite distinctly different properties. Such different compounds can all be broken down into the same elements. However, if the analyst proceeds carefully, he will not break down his compound all at once, but will go step by step. The kind of product he obtains at each intermediate step will depend on the specific compound he begins with. Similarly, compounds with the same atomic formula are distinguished by the way in which they can be synthesized. The different compounds can be synthesized only by quite a different series of steps. Consequently chemists inferred that atoms appear in molecules in certain definite groups and can be split off in similar groups. Finally, they decided that these groups must represent actual arrangements in space. In this way they mapped out many molecules, some even in their full three-dimensional shapes, without knowing any way to determine the size of a single atom or molecule.

It became possible to write out molecular formulas in ways which more and more closely suggested the molecular structure in space, such as these for stearic acid:

$C_{18}H_{36}O_2$	$CH_3(CH_2)_{16}COOH$
atomic formula	formula showing atomic grouping

or by the "stretched" formula, which follows.

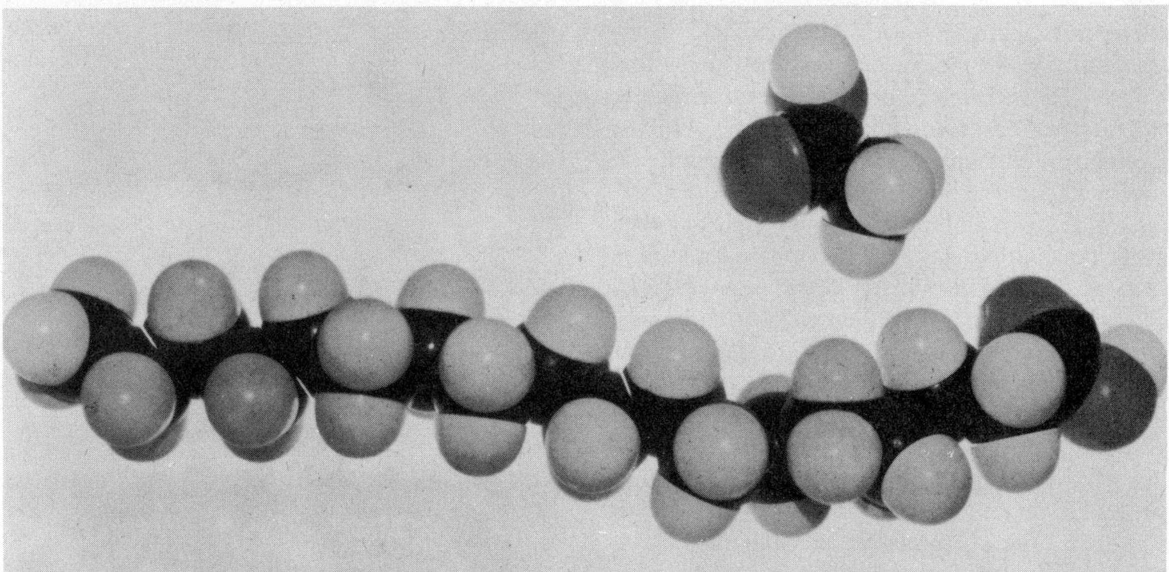

8–5. The structure of molecules of stearic acid (bottom) and acetic acid. In the stearic acid on the left-hand end a carbon atom (black) is surrounded by three H atoms (white). Extending to the right from this CH_3 group is a chain of CH_2 groups — carbon atoms surrounded by two H atoms apiece. At the right the chain ends in a COOH group. (The oxygens in the model are gray.) Acetic acid has the two end groups linked together directly.

```
  H H H H H H H H H H H H H H H H H
  | | | | | | | | | | | | | | | | |   O
H-C-C-C-C-C-C-C-C-C-C-C-C-C-C-C-C-C-C//
  | | | | | | | | | | | | | | | | |   \O
  H H H H H H H H H H H H H H H H H     \H
```

stretched formula

Nowadays chemists make small three-dimensional models showing how atoms fit together, and they find great order, but by no means any monotony, in the result. A conventional model of the stearic acid molecule is shown in Fig. 8–5. The atoms are represented as balls of definite size. X-ray evidence, for example, indicates that the spacing of atoms in molecules tends to be characteristic of just which atoms are present, and what neighbors they have. Although there are small deviations in actual spacing, balls of definite size make a good model.

For about a century, organic chemists studied manifold analyses and syntheses without any important aid from physicists. Physicists could not then point out the many paths now known to the direct study of molecular structure. Today, the purely chemical method (drawing inferences from the chemical reactions among molecules) and the physical ones (using X rays and electron beams to demonstrate the actual geometry of the molecule) are fused. In this domain of science, chemists and physicists are hard to tell apart.

8–6. Models of molecules: water (left), and oxygen.

With their combined techniques, estimates of the spacing of atoms can be made as precise as three significant figures. As a result, we know the actual spatial arrangement of some molecules more accurately than we can make the models like those of Fig. 8–6. Again the story is an extraordinary tale of creative thought, of inspired conjecture, and of hard, painstaking testing of ideas.

In some cases, when he knows the structure of the molecules, the chemist can understand their properties. In stearic acid, for example, he recognizes the group COOH on one end as carrying an acid property; it is highly soluble in water. The other long portion, a chain of seventeen carbon atoms, each bearing two hydrogens, plus one final hydrogen terminating the molecule at the other end, he recognizes as a relative of the main constituents of paraffin wax. The acid end is attracted by water molecules; the waxy end is repelled. He is therefore quite prepared to see the stearic acid form a monolayer on water. In the monolayer, all the molecules are standing on end, each with its acid head buried in the water surface and its waxy tail protruding a couple of dozen angstroms out into the air. More detailed studies show that the long chain of atoms in each molecule actually is joined to the neighboring chains. As a result of this coupling each chain stands tilted with respect to the water surface as we mentioned before. This sort of understanding is the aim of the chemist for each of the substances he can study. He still has much to do. He cannot yet tell us very clearly why an egg cooks hard, or a muscle fiber contracts, or penicillin kills bacterial cells. But the answers to more and more such questions come month by month.

8–12. The Chemistry of Life

The chemistry of life is the most complex and, for us who are living beings, the most interesting chemistry. In the last decade or so, real progress has been made in understanding and even in mapping out the structure of the complex substances of which our bodies are made. Fats and sugar are not very simple, but for the analyst of biochemical molecular structure they are warming-up exercises compared to substances like the simple protein insulin, the powerful drug which controls diabetes; or albumen, the material of egg white; or the serum of blood. For such substances, a model of a molecule does not show just a repetition of a lot of carbon atoms, each with two hydrogen side arms. Like many other molecules, these proteins are built of groups of atoms, groups which exist separately as well as in combination. The groups themselves are moderately complex combinations of a dozen or so atoms, and a dozen or two different groups are put together. When the groups join to make a protein, they string out into a long helix (Fig. 8–7), a coil perhaps thousands of turns long. Along the helix the order of the groups must follow a certain complex sequence, just as the words in a book must be properly arranged to make sense. In the very simple protein insulin, the first of the few so far analyzed (by Sanger and his co-workers at Cambridge University, England, in the years since World War II), the helix is made of two parallel strings of groups, each a couple of dozen groups long. Let one or two of these be misplaced, and the powerful action of insulin on living cells is lost.

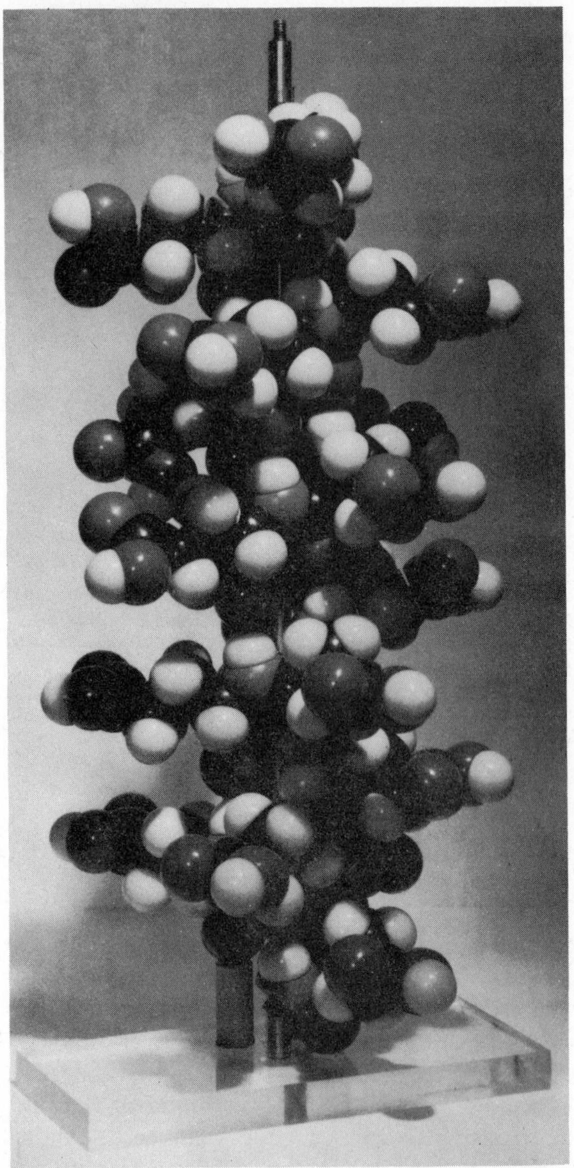

8–7 (a). The model shows a small section of a long protein molecule. In this model, almost a half meter tall, the light-colored hemispheres represent hydrogen atoms, which in reality are about an angstrom in diameter (10^{-10} m).

Here, we are at the border of our knowledge. Actually an alternative structure of insulin has been suggested, compatible with the present evidence. In many respects it must, of course, be the same, but the differences are significant. Settling the questions about just such structures carries us down near the basic mechanism of life.

The formula for CO_2 is a few letters long; that for stearic acid, something more like a long word; for insulin, something closer to a long sentence. For the wonderful molecules of the nucleus of the cell, those we believe carry the inherited traits that make one cell or one animal or one person differ from another, the formulas would fill a big book. Each such molecular "book" is no less than the recipe for the full inheritance of a living being.

Here is one of the most exciting branches of science today; the frontier beyond which physics, chemistry, and biology meet; the problem of the structure and the function of the molecular patterns of living things. For the men and women who have these interests this is a happy time in history. Earlier, the tools which made this kind of subtle study possible had still to be forged. Today, the puzzle remains to be solved. But in this generation or the next, this problem seems likely to find its solution.

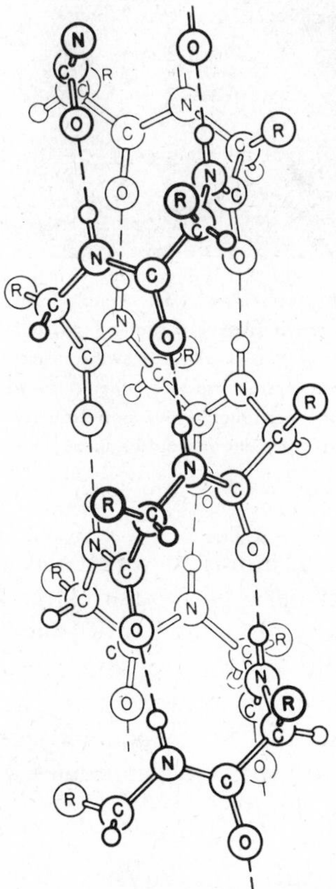

8–7 (b). The diagram shows the relative sizes, positions, and bondings of the atoms that make up a complicated protein molecule. The symbols C, N, and O represent atoms of carbon, nitrogen, and oxygen, while the small unlabeled circles represent hydrogen atoms which bond the structure into its helical shape. The symbol R represents other attached structures. In which direction does this helix wind? (Courtesy: Linus Pauling and R. B. Corey.)

8–13. Molecules and Solids

We have been discussing molecules, clumps of atoms in which definite numbers of atoms of specific kinds are held together in a definite structure. When these clumps are far apart as in a gas, we have no trouble recognizing the separate molecules. But sometimes, in some solids for example, the clumps are so closely tied together that it is hard or impossible to decide to which clump a given atom belongs. In a piece of common salt (sodium chloride), the formula for which is NaCl, each Na atom is surrounded by Cl atoms and each Cl atom by Na atoms (Fig. 8–8). Which way shall we break it mentally into molecules? In a diamond all the atoms are the same, and there are no clumps of definite size. Groups of only a few hundred carbon atoms in the right pattern may retain most of the diamond properties as well as groups of 10^{22} atoms (one-fifth gram). How many atoms make a diamond molecule? Clearly the word "molecule" is not so valuable as the word "atom" in describing all atomic arrangements. Because chemistry is the study of all possible atomic arrangements and how they come about, we must often consider ar-

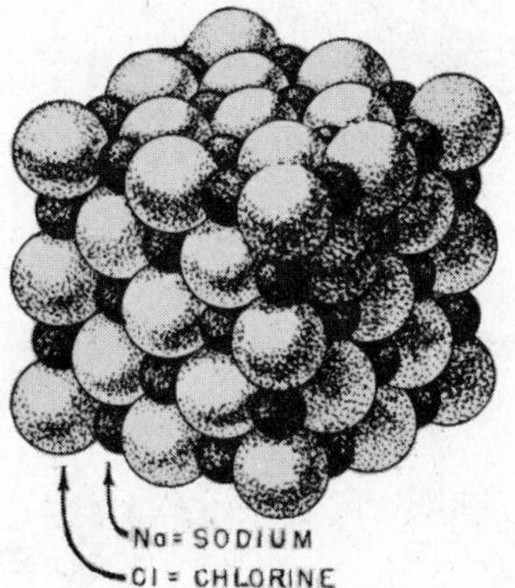

8–8. In sodium chloride, each sodium atom (smaller) is surrounded by chlorine atoms (larger) and each chlorine atom is surrounded by sodium atoms. Is it possible to decide which particular pair of atoms make up a sodium chloride molecule? (A portion of Fig. 4–10 from H. P. Knauss, "Discovering Physics," Addison-Wesley, 1951.)

8–9. A large group of gypsum crystals from a lead mine in Mexico. This group is over a meter high, but even the tiniest sample of gypsum that you may grow on a microscope slide will show the same crystal structure when viewed under a lens. Given the proper conditions and a sufficiently long period of time, comparable structures can be produced by man in the laboratory.

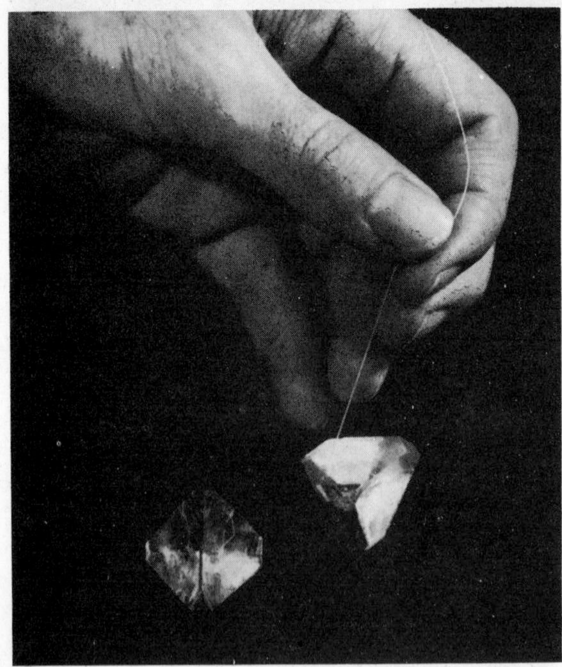

8–10. Crystals of sodium bromate. Similar, well-formed crystals may be grown in a few days' time in your basement or refrigerator. These are regular tetrahedrons grown on seed crystals tied to a length of string.

rangements of atoms to which the word "molecules" must be applied with caution. We now turn to a general discussion of solid structures of matter where we shall consider such questions as the distinction between soot, graphite, and diamond, all made of carbon and none described adequately in terms of molecules with definite numbers of atoms.

8–14. Crystals: The Physics of the Solid State

The hard, smooth faces of the natural crystal of quartz, like the little cubes of table salt, were not smoothed or shaped by tools in human hands. But the cool symmetry of crystals has always fascinated men; shining crystals have been found where cavemen collectors stored them.

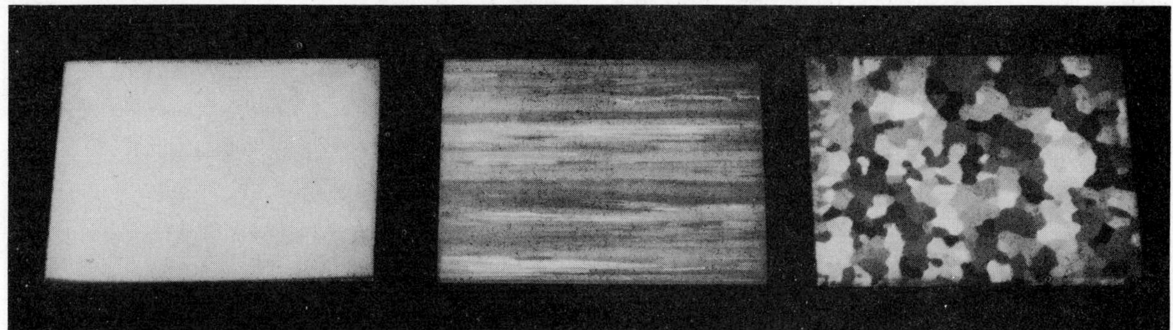

8–11. Crystals are hidden in many common substances. An aluminum plate (left) was treated with an etching solution to reveal lines of crystallization (center). This structure is the result of cold-rolling the aluminum stock, which stretches small crystal domains along the material. At the right is a similar sample that was heated to very near its melting point for a considerable length of time before etching. An intricate pattern of crystal domains can be seen to extend completely through the 3-mm thickness of the plate. The larger pattern segments are more than a centimeter in length. The etching process removes entire crystal filaments, leaving parallel crystal faces to reflect light. With some metals, the crystals will be large enough to be seen without aids; with others, the crystals must be viewed under a lens.

Their uniformity in the face of the apparent jumble of the inorganic world seems to carry meaning. How can matter take forms of such order and beauty?

If crystals were as rare as the fine specimens in the museum cases, or the cut gems of the jeweler, we might defer answering this question. The study of crystals would be a small corner of the study of matter, to be entered after we knew all the rest of the broad sweep. But this apparent rareness is an illusion. Nature has grown her beauties over the long span of geological time, out of materials like quartz which need the conditions of the hot, compressed layers beneath the earth. But anyone in his basement can grow a fine large crystal in a Mason jar out of a solution of commonplace chemicals such as sugar, alum, or sodium bromate (Fig. 8–10). Patience need be measured only in days, not eons. A wide variety of substances will form crystals, once the proper conditions have been established. So crystals, even large ones, are not simply the result of unknown geological action.

Small crystals are common. The microscope will show the crystallinity of salt or sugar or baking soda. More than that, every piece of metal, like almost every mineral substance down to the clay and sand of the soil, is simply a compacted mass of tiny crystals, whose regularities can be disclosed by the right sort of examination. In a sheet of aluminum the crystal structure can be brought out by treating with acid. The acid corrodes the various faces of the aluminum crystals at different rates. The resulting texture is visible in reflected light, and the crystals can be seen, distorted into long fibrous blocks by the rolling out of the sheet in the mill which reduced it from a thick ingot. If we heat a sheet of aluminum and allow it to remain very hot for some time, it will

8–12. A photograph (magnification 6.5X) of a piece of zinc. The fanlike group of crystals stands out clearly because, owing to the natural roughness of the specimen, it is on a plane slightly above the rest of the material. The basic crystalline form is not apparent in the darker regions because they are in different planes. This is but one possible illustration of the fact that metals do occur as crystals.

recrystallize into a jumble again, but now the slowly grown crystals are larger and clear to see. The beautiful patterns they make are displayed in Fig. 8–11. Under the microscope similar crystal patterns may be revealed by etching any sample of metal (Fig. 8–12). Metals, then, are really crystals, like the mineral specimens.

The symmetric natural crystals of quartz are large. They were grown slowly, and free from disturbing influences. The jumbled crystals of rock or of metals are not different, but have been forced to conform in their outlines to the neighboring crystals pressing in on all sides. The crystallinity is revealed in the local uniformities. Each little face maintains a kind of identity of its own.

The crystal state is so widespread we cannot put off an effort to understand it. It is easiest to work with crystals large enough to see and to handle, but the results we shall cite hold for crystal grains too.

8–15. The Geometry of Crystals

The smooth faces of crystals vary a great deal in size and in shape. The true simplicity of crystals was pointed out by contemporaries of Newton, like his English rival, Robert Hooke, and the Danish physician Nicolaus Steno. The angles between corresponding faces on every crystal of a given substance are always the same. Different substances have, in general, different sets of angles. For any one substance the angles are always characteristic. Of course, if you knock a chunk out of a crystal, you will not recognize the crystal faces on the irregular chunk. Microscopic measurements, however, show the characteristic angles between the many little facets along the break. Something internal fixes these angles.

Press the edge of a razor blade against the face of a soft crystal. There are some directions along which the crystal splits easily, displaying a smooth plane on each of the two new surfaces. Such planes of easy cleavage bear relative directions which again are characteristic of the substance. Mica is a good example. It splits into thin, smooth sheets. Even the hard diamond is usually split along such a cleavage plane by a single blow at an early stage of working it into a gem.

Today we have a theory for crystal structure. Two French crystallographers of the last decades of the eighteenth century put it forward in some-

8–13. Rhombohedral crystals of Iceland spar, a transparent variety of calcite, showing the planes of cleavage. (Courtesy: Ward's Natural Science Establishment.)

what different forms. Suppose a crystal to be a uniform stack of identical little blocks. These need not be shaped like bricks, with rectangular corners. They may have one of the shapes into which the crystal can be easily cleaved. For the familiar mineral crystal calcite, called Iceland spar for the region where it was first found, these cleavage shapes are rhombic (Fig. 8–13). From such "bricks" any shape can be built, its faces being either plane or stepped, but if the bricks are small enough, the steps will be too small to be seen. Any shape can be approximated by piling up these natural bricks, but wherever a plane face exists, it must bear one of a small number of angles to some other recognizable plane face. How plane faces large enough to be directly visible form out of so many tiny sub-units is of course far from obvious. The little sub-units must somehow tend to fill in gaps and irregularities in the process of slow crystal growth. But once the plane face is found, its relation to other such faces depends upon the nature of the units.

Moreover, not all angles are possible in such a structure. To see why, look at Fig. 8–14, reproduced from the drawing made by Rene Haüy and published in Paris in 1784. The face of the crystal is always made up of steps. The angles are determined by the number of blocks making up the "tread," compared with the number forming the "riser." On this model, therefore, the crystal angles should show a law of multiple proportions: for example, one riser unit, two riser units, or three riser units combining with a particular number of tread units to determine three possible angles. When we measure the angles on actual crystals, where of course the steps are not visible, we do find these multiple proportions in the riser to tread ratios.

Such whole-number ratios, concealed in the more complicated geometry of angles, are convincing clues. The analogy to chemistry is close. In chemistry, the atoms combine into molecules, with mass proportions which bear simple whole-number ratios. In crystals, the little units build up a crystal; the angles defined by the crystal faces bear relations which imply the same repetitive construction. Atoms are measured by their masses; the crystal faces, by their relations in space. Taking the two together, it is hard to doubt that the atoms pack together in space to form the building blocks out of which the crystals of solid matter are so elegantly constructed.

We know the size and the shapes of the building blocks well today. We have therefore modified somewhat the idea of Haüy. The building blocks are not little smooth-faced bricks, as he thought. Instead, they are the more or less complicated shapes of the atoms or molecules of the crystalline substance. But they pile up, by their mutual attractions, into a uniform pile, just like the virus particles of Fig. 7–14, which form a tiny crystal with its symmetry and its face angles easily visible. The individual virus protein molecules are little complex balls, rather like a ball of yarn. Each one is a long, wound-up molecular strand, made up of about a million atoms of carbon, hydrogen, oxygen, nitrogen, and sulfur. With less complex crystals, the units of which may be single atoms as in diamond, or groups of atoms as in salt, or molecules of modest size as in sugar, the story is the same. The geometrical grouping of the individual atoms determines the shape of the visible crystals. (See Fig. 8–15.)

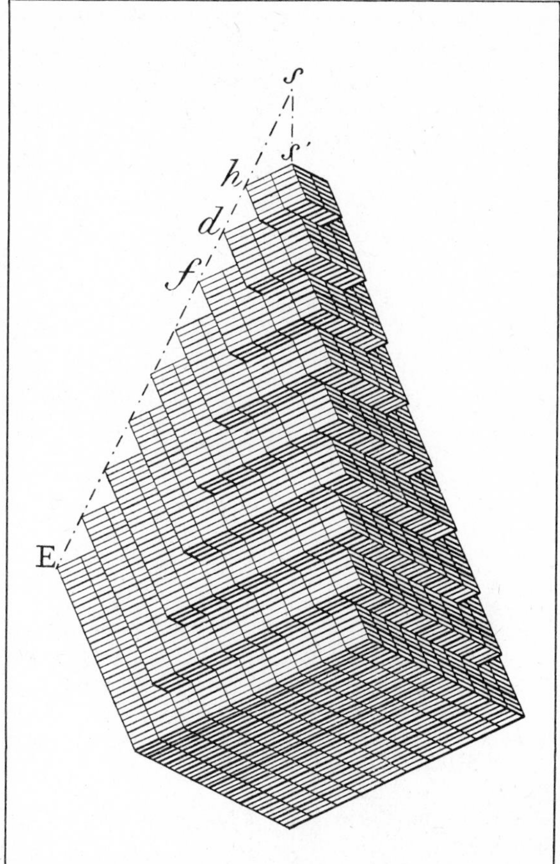

8–14. Haüy's diagram of crystal structure. Small identical geometric forms can be stacked to make a model of any crystal. This is possible because the only angles that occur in crystals are those that can be formed with whole blocks. In this diagram, we go two blocks over and up one for each step. For another crystal face, we may go three over and up one, or four over and up one. However, we never go π over and up one, or use any other such fractional combination. (From "A Short History of Science and Scientific Thought," F. S. Taylor. W. W. Norton.)

8–16. Order and Disorder

A crystal is a collection of its fundamental atomic or molecular units arranged in a pattern in space extending in all directions to its boundaries. Every point of space within a crystal has its indefinitely repeated images, the corresponding points within all the other little bricks. At any such point, the environment looks just the same. These repeated spatial units are called the unit cells of the crystal lattice. In every unit cell is a complete set of the right atoms in proper arrangement.

Somewhere the crystal has boundaries. Near them the internal conditions are a little different, for they lack layers of neighboring cells to surround them. So the surfaces of solid matter differ from its interior. Even in the interior, the assembly is not likely to be perfect. Sometimes a stray atom will be included in the lattice. In other places, a hole will be found; the needed atom is missing. Entire lines and planes will be missing here and there. At such points the forces are different, and the lattice adjusts and conforms to what is present.

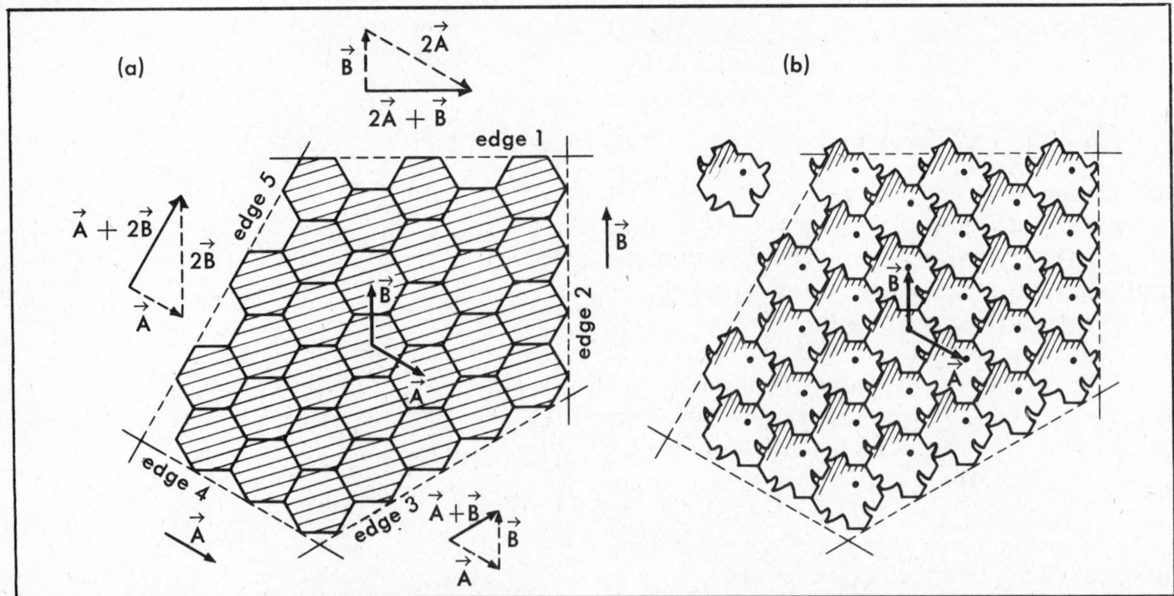

8–15. The shape of crystals is determined by the relative placement of the crystal units. In (a) we see a two-dimensional "crystal" made of hexagonal tiles. The figure shows how identical small unit "cells" fit together, forming definite angles between the boundary edges 1, 2, 3, 4, and 5 of the large crystal. Depending on the nature of the units they can fit together only at certain definite distances and directions from each other. The vectors $\vec{A}$ and $\vec{B}$ are the displacements between corresponding points in neighboring building blocks in the crystal. All the characteristic edge directions are made of some small whole number of $\vec{A}$ plus some small whole number of $\vec{B}$. Edge 1 is in the direction $2\vec{A} + \vec{B}$; edge 2 is in direction $\vec{B}$; 3 in direction $\vec{A} + \vec{B}$; 4, $\vec{A}$; 5, $\vec{A} + 2\vec{B}$. In (b) unit cells of different shapes will give the same angle between the boundary edges if the displacement vectors A and B between corresponding parts of neighboring cells are the same.

We can even see why the law of constant chemical composition does not apply to all substances. In brass, a substance formed by melting copper with zinc, the zinc atoms can fit into the same lattice frame as the copper, for they are quite similar in size and in the attractions they have for their neighbors. Although a less similar metal atom, say iron, could not be squeezed in without bulging and distorting the lattice, the zinc and copper atoms can fit more or less at random into the crystal. A sample of brass can have more or fewer copper atoms per zinc atom, depending on how it was prepared. Consequently, the law of constant chemical composition does not apply. As we remarked at the beginning of the chapter, alloys like brass frequently have variable composition.

Molecules with a long fibrous shape sometimes tend to form into bundles like yarn rather than into three-dimensional piles (Fig. 8–16). Such molecules form the muscles and the sinews, and the many fibrous structures of living organisms. In a way these are crystalline, for they exhibit an orderly arrangement within their fibrous bundles. With this extension of the idea of crystallinity from big single crystals, to the jumble of small crystals in polycrystalline material, to the partial ordering in fibrous matter, the study of crystals includes nearly all solid materials.

Some apparently solid substances do not show such a regular ordering. The forces which tend to produce the regular order of molecules are too weak to enforce it during the complicated processes in which the atoms group to form the solid. These substances are called *amorphous.* Lampblack is an example. Another common class is represented by glass. Unlike ice or any crystal, glass does not melt at a well-defined temperature. Instead it first softens, then flows. Some plastics, many parts of living matter, and a few other substances like tars fall into this class. The atoms of glass form a pattern rather like a distorted crystal. Plastics and similar substances are made of long molecules which tangle like a plate of spaghetti. These materials are sometimes regarded as not being solid. Even hard glass will flow, like tar, though only very slowly, over decades. But a swift blow will shatter both glass and tar.

8–16. Hair protein. Fibrous proteins, such as hair and muscle, are represented by the structure shown above. The molecules have the protein-molecule structure shown in Fig. 8–7. Each molecule is represented here as a single strand. The protein consists of a central helix with six others twisted around it in a right-hand direction. The spaces between "cables" are filled with other helixes. The diameter of a single "cable" is about 20 or 30 $\times 10^{-10}$ meter. Compare with Fig. 8–7. (From "General Chemistry," 2nd Ed., Linus Pauling. W. H. Freeman & Co.)

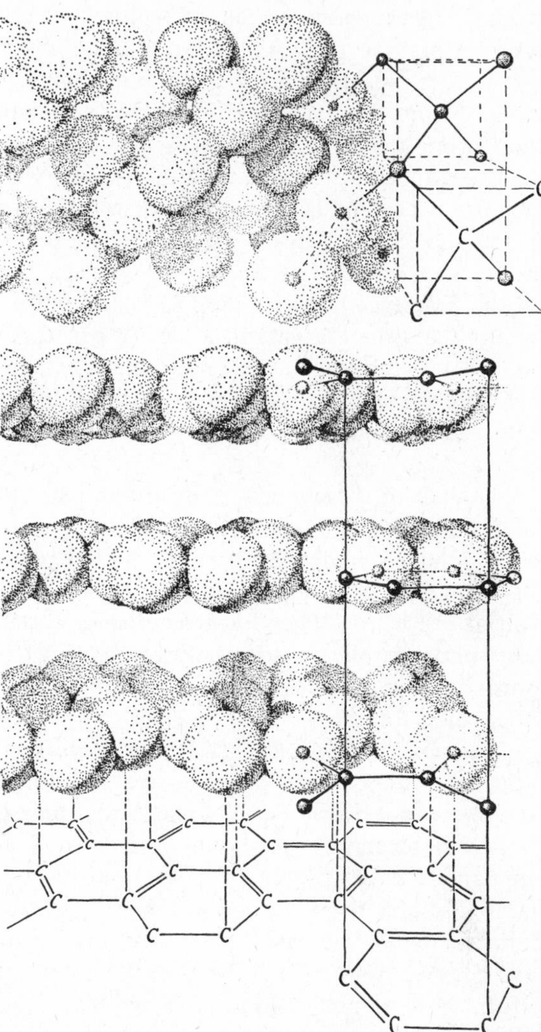

8–17. Above is the structure of diamond, the hardest substance known to man. Below we see the structure of graphite. Both of these substances consist of the same element, carbon. In diamond, the atoms are closely packed. In graphite, the atoms occur in spaced layers. From this we can see why graphite is useful as a lubricant — the layers can slide over one another easily. We would not expect this effect in the case of the diamond. The structures do not answer all questions, however. For instance, there is nothing in the structural pattern of graphite to indicate why it is dark in color or why pure white diamond is transparent and brilliant. The layers of carbon atoms in graphite are spaced 2 or 3 angstrom units apart. (From "General Chemistry," 2nd Ed., Linus Pauling. Copyright 1949, 1950, 1953, W. H. Freeman & Co.)

Liquids, like water, motor oil, or syrup, flow even more easily. Yet it is known from X-ray study that the molecules of these liquids have a crystalline order. Here, however, the order is local, extending over only a few atoms or molecules before it is lost. The liquid state is less fully understood than are the orderly crystals of the solid state of matter.

We can now understand the differences between soot (lampblack), graphite, and diamond. In each substance the atoms are arranged differently in space. Soot is the excess of carbon particles left when a substance is burned. In the residue, there are large and frequent spaces, and the tiny bits of carbon have no set shape or orientation. On the average, the carbon atoms are far apart; groups which are closely tied together contain few carbon atoms, and the weak structure is not ordered over any long distance even on the atomic scale of size.

Graphite, on the other hand, is a highly ordered array of carbon atoms lying in loosely coupled sheets (Fig. 8–17). Within the sheets the atoms lie in a close-spaced regular array, and each sheet stays together and in order despite considerable pushing. These sheets are farther apart than the atoms within a layer; and the forces tying layers together are weaker than those tying atoms together in one layer. It is difficult to push one layer through another, but it is easy to slide one layer over another or even off another. Graphite, therefore, feels (and is) slippery, and we use it to lubricate locks. It is also used in pencils because the black graphite slips easily onto paper. To feel the difference between lampblack and graphite, don't use the graphite in a "lead" pencil; it is mixed with too much clay. You can get reasonably pure graphite at hardware stores. Because of its industrial importance pure lampblack is also easily available.

A sample of diamond is more expensive, but small diamonds are more common than most people imagine. They are used as the hard cutting, grinding, or bearing surfaces in many industrial processes. They form the needle tips of some phonograph pickups. While graphite is approximately a collection of two-dimensional lattices tied together loosely in the third dimension, diamond is a close-packed three-dimensional lattice of carbon atoms (Fig. 8–17). While we can collect soot over a burning match and turn it into graphite quite easily under sufficient pressure and heat, we can produce only small diamonds, and these with difficulty. Over the immense span of geologic time, however, nature has occasionally provided the proper conditions to form both graphite and large diamonds.

We make graphite and diamonds by reproducing the conditions under which we believe these materials were made in nature. Our success is evidence for the accuracy of our ideas about the origin of these substances.

8–17. Summary

Let us conclude by looking back at the analogy between printing and the atomic picture of matter to which we have alluded more than once. It is pretty complete. In printing, the "elements" are the twenty-six letters, with the space and the punctuation marks. Every printed character is an "atom," and each atom belongs to just one of the elements. All the atoms of an element are very much alike, but not necessarily identical. A capital *A* and a lower-case *a* may be regarded as "isotopes" of the first element. Some methods of analysis — say reading out loud — would not find any difference between them, just as chemists can hardly manage to separate isotopes. Molecules of every size are found; words, sentences, even books, all spelled of letters in a particular and proper order. Crystals go a bit beyond the analogy, but it is not hard to imagine how it might be extended.

In a way, the chemist and the physicist have faced matter somewhat as though it were an extraordinary cryptogram, a coded message in print. They have cracked the code, cracked it so well that we can begin to use it ourselves. With more and deeper understanding of the rules of the atomic grammar, and of its logic, we shall be able to produce unheard-of combinations of elements to make drugs or fibers of a wholly new kind. Even now, we undertake the task of forming new elements and of modifying familiar substances like metals into new forms of enormous strength or hardness. The properties of these substances are the most stringent test of our understanding: We make them to order, and they will not turn out as we expected unless we have the right code.

FOR HOME, DESK, AND LAB

1. In sodium hydroxide, the combining masses are 23 grams of sodium to 16 grams of oxygen and 1 gram of hydrogen. In water, as you know, there are 8 grams of oxygen to 1 gram of hydrogen.

(a) If water were HO, as Dalton believed, could sodium hydroxide be NaOH?

(b) What possible pairs of chemical formulas for water and sodium hydroxide are suggested by these combining masses?

2. Dalton determined the ratios of the masses of carbon and oxygen in carbon monoxide to be as 3/4, of hydrogen and oxygen in water as 1/8, and of carbon and hydrogen in the compound methane as 3/1. Without firm knowledge to the contrary, he assumed water molecules to contain only one hydrogen atom for each atom of oxygen and he asserted correctly the 1/1 ratio of carbon and oxygen atoms in carbon monoxide. What is the ratio of numbers of carbon to hydrogen atoms in methane as determined by these ideas?

3. Copper and chlorine combine in different proportions to form two compounds, No. 1 and No. 2, with relative masses of copper to chlorine 0.895 to 1 and 1.79 to 1 respectively.

(a) How does this example illustrate the law of multiple proportions?

(b) Which of the following pairs of formulas may be correct on the basis of the information given?

Compound 1		Compound 2
Cu_1Cl_1	and	Cu_2Cl_1
Cu_1Cl_1	and	Cu_1Cl_2
Cu_1Cl_2	and	Cu_1Cl_1
Cu_1Cl_3	and	Cu_2Cl_3

4. In an experiment with polonium, over a two-year period a total of 9×10^{17} disintegrations occur, as measured by counting the flashes.

(a) What was the original mass of polonium?

(b) What mass of helium will be formed?

5. In a certain experiment you have samples of different gaseous compounds of oxygen and nitrogen; all have the same volume and the same temperature and pressure. The gases are decomposed and yield different masses of oxygen as shown in the following table:

	Mass of oxygen (grams)		Mass of oxygen (grams)
(1)	1.6	(4)	3.2
(2)	1.6	(5)	4.8
(3)	4.8		

(a) Give the most probable number of oxygen atoms in the molecule of each substance listed above.

To try to determine the complete formulas, you now measure the masses of nitrogen that result when equivalent samples are decomposed.

	Mass of nitrogen (grams)		Mass of nitrogen (grams)
(1)	2.8	(4)	1.4
(2)	1.4	(5)	1.4
(3)	2.8		

(b) What is the most likely number of nitrogen atoms in each molecule?

(c) Give the complete formula for each substance.

6. Nitric oxide (NO) will combine with oxygen from the air to form nitrogen dioxide (NO_2).

(a) Write the equation for this reaction.

(b) If one volume of NO is consumed, what volume of O_2 is consumed?

(c) What volume of NO_2 is obtained at the same pressure and temperature?

7. Forty grams of sodium hydroxide (NaOH) react to completion with 36.5 grams of hydrochloric acid (HCl) producing water (H_2O) and common salt (NaCl). After evaporating the water, we find 58.5 grams of salt are left.

(a) Using the law of conservation of mass, compute the number of grams of water that was formed.

(b) Whenever we decompose water we find that the ratio of the masses of hydrogen and oxygen in it is as 1 to 8. Compute the mass of oxygen that was contained in our original materials.

(c) We decompose some hydrochloric acid and find that the masses of hydrogen and chlorine are in the ratio of 2 to 71. How much chlorine was there in the hydrogen chloride that we used to make salt?

(d) How many grams of sodium were there in the sodium hydroxide we started with?

(e) How much hydrogen was contained in the sodium hydroxide?

8. A student carefully analyzes an organic acid and finds the following combining weights of the constituent elements: Carbon 6, Hydrogen 1, Oxygen 8.

(a) Knowing the atomic masses of these elements, indicate the relative numbers of atoms of each that occur in a molecule of the compound.

(b) Organic acids usually contain the carboxyl group COOH. Assuming that there is one such group per molecule, what is the formula of a molecule of this acid?

9. The relative atomic masses of copper and chlorine are 63.6 amu and 35.5 amu. Which of the pairs of formulas in problem 3 (b) are correct in the light of this information?

10. (a) Find the approximate mass in atomic mass units of a molecule of stearic acid ($C_{17}H_{35}$ COOH).

(b) Using Avogadro's number find the mass of the molecule in grams.

11. The results of a monolayer experiment show that there are 2.1×10^{21} particles per gram of stearic acid (molecular mass 284 amu). Calculate the value of Avogadro's number from this data.

12. Uranium undergoes radioactive disintegration forming an entirely different element which may be separated from the parent element by chemical means. This new element, thorium, has different chemical properties, and would exhibit a much lower density if sufficiently large amounts of it could be obtained. Its atomic mass is less by approximately 4 amu, the amount contributed to the other product of each disintegration — one helium atom.

Within a short time, and at a very predictable rate, this thorium undergoes two more disintegration reactions. No perceptible mass change accompanies these reactions, but the eventual product is a material having chemical properties which are indistinguishable from our first material, uranium. This newest element likewise exhibits the general physical properties of uranium, but we know it has lost 4 units of mass and has not, in either of the last two reactions, been able to recover any mass.

(a) In the light of this evidence, can uranium in nature consist of a single isotope?

(b) What is the mass, in amu, of natural uranium which consists of 0.72 per cent of U^{235} whose mass is 235.1156 amu, and 99.28 per cent of U^{238} whose mass is 238.1242 amu?

(c) Can these be the two isotopes involved in the radioactive process described above?

13. The atomic mass of copper is 63.54, and it is known to consist of a mixture of two stable isotopes. If the one of these which constitutes approximately 30 per cent of copper has a mass of approximately 65 amu, what is the atomic mass of the other isotope to the nearest whole number of amu?

14. The density of lead is 11.34 gm/cm³ and the mass of a lead atom is about 207 amu. Calculate the effective volume of each atom in this solid state.

15. When an oil film on water forms colored patterns, we know it must be at least 3 to 5×10^{-4} cm thick. The patterns of color are indicative of varying thicknesses.

(a) Assuming an average thickness throughout of 10^{-3} cm, what area will 1 cm³ of oil on the troubled waters cover?

(b) Oleic acid molecules are of the order of magnitude of 10^{-7} cm in length. What area of water could be covered by 1 cm³ of this material if it spreads to a monolayer?

16. (a) What is the mass in grams of a mole of water?

(b) What is the volume of this mass of water?

(c) Find the volume occupied by one water molecule.

(d) The atom of oxygen in this molecule occupies about half of the volume. What is the approximate diameter of an oxygen atom?

17. Pentane, which has the formula C_5H_{12}, consists of a chain of carbon atoms, with hydrogen atoms arranged in a manner similar to those of butane in Fig. 8–4. In this molecule each carbon is bonded with four atoms and each hydrogen with one atom.

(a) Show that there can be three compounds with the molecular formula C_5H_{12} in which these bonding relations exist. (The carbon atoms need not be extended in this chain order.) Diagram the three compounds. Do you think more than three compounds can exist?

(b) Do you expect these compounds to have the same properties?

18. Red corpuscles of the human blood stream are known to be flattened discs approximately 7×10^{-6} m in diameter and 10^{-6} m thick. Blood count shows on the order of 5×10^6 of these in each cubic millimeter of blood.

(a) If the adult body contains 5 liters of blood, what is the total number of red corpuscles it contains?

(b) The mass of a hemoglobin molecule is believed to be 6.8×10^4 amu. How many such molecules would there be in a red corpuscle if hemoglobin has a density of one gm/cm³, and if we assume a red corpuscle is made entirely of hemoglobin?

19. A single human nerve cell may extend 100 cm from the spinal column to the foot, and be as much as 10^{-4} cm in average diameter. If we assume that each of the constituent atoms of this structure occupies a volume of 3×10^{-23} cm³, what total number of atoms is required to build it?

FURTHER READING

BRAGG, SIR WILLIAM, *Concerning the Nature of Things.* Dover, 1954.

FOWLER, W. A., "The Origin of the Elements." *Scientific American*, September, 1956.

FULLMAN, R. L., "The Growth of Crystals." *Scientific American*, March, 1955 (p. 74).

"Giant Molecules." *Scientific American*, September, 1957 (entire issue).

HOLDEN, ALAN, and SINGER, P., *Crystals and Crystal Growing*, Doubleday, 1959. A Science Study Series paperback.

HOLTON, GERALD, *Introduction to Concepts and Theories in Physical Science*, Addison-Wesley, 1952.

JAFFE, B., *Crucibles: The Story of Chemistry.* Premier Books, 1957. Biographical sketches.

LE CORBEILLER, PHILIPPE, "Crystals and the Future of Physics." *Scientific American*, January, 1953.

WALD, GEORGE, "The Origin of Life." *Scientific American*, August, 1954.

THE NATURE OF A GAS

CHAPTER 9

EVERY solid or liquid can be made into a gas, and all gases can be made liquid or solid. At the surface of the earth, at ordinary pressures and temperatures, air is a gas. In other circumstances, however, it is liquid, and there is a considerable industry which liquefies air by cooling it. The familiar snow of carbon dioxide, called Dry Ice, turns into the gas as you watch. Upon boiling, water becomes steam, which is gaseous water or water vapor. (What we call vapors are gases whose liquid form is more familiar.) Out of the warm and humid air of summer, water vapor condenses to dew on colder surfaces. Even the most heat-resistant metals can be turned into gases by sufficient heating. Nearly all flames are hot gas, glowing and swirling. Such flames come out of every solid that can be burned.

From the study of the gaseous form of matter, using rather simple means, we can begin to understand the lines along which physics and chemistry have proceeded in solving the problems of the nature of matter. How can the grainy structure of matter, the arrangement of its atoms, determine the nature of the material world? It turns out that the atomic and molecular nature of a gas, which we cannot demonstrate by neat, orderly patterns as we can with crystals, goes a long way in helping us understand the nature of all matter. Here we shall begin the story. Its completion will demand more study of the physics of motion than we have yet made, and we shall take it up again in more detail in Chapter 26. The picture of a gas that we are about to describe was the first fruit of the atomic understanding of matter, and in its image science is trying to extend its still growing picture of the more complex forms of matter. Its success is one more piece of evidence for the depth and the range of the atomic picture.

9–1. Physical Models

In order to understand the behavior of gases, we are going to construct a model of a gas. What do we mean here when we say model?

By a model we do not mean simply a scaled-down replica of an object, like a ship model or an airplane model. We mean an idea, a picture, a system of concepts which creative intuition and hard work lead us to think describe the things we investigate. For example, when we talk about a model of a cloud, we don't mean that a small scale-model cloud might be made from cotton. We mean much more than this. Our model of a cloud is our description of what happens in clouds — the updrafts, the turbulence, the condensation, the rain and snow — all this in terms of what we can measure in the laboratory and in terms of the ideas and the tested physical laws which show the relations between such measurements. When we make such a model, we hope our model includes the essential features of the physical problems or systems we are investigating, but we are equally sure it cannot include all features. No model is perfect: this we know from history. Neither an abstract model made of ideas, nor a tangible one of plastic and wire is fully faithful. We therefore test all models to see how well they represent the real thing.

A model is tested first by examining it logically to find the properties that the physical system it represents ought to have. These properties are then sought out in the laboratory. A fair agreement between the properties expected on the basis of the model and those actually found is a good sign. Probably the model can be improved. With improvement the model grows more and more precise and more and more complete. Finally the models which have stood many tests, which predict many things well, and suggest new and unexpected experiments which in their turn agree and confirm or extend the model — such models are the content of physical theories.

It is no use to magnify a map and think it is the real thing, or to analyze the brass doorknobs of a doll house and expect the same number of atoms as in a life-size doorknob. Models must observe the proper scale. We cannot expect a model to be exact in a domain which is orders of magnitude beyond that for which it was constructed. Nevertheless, the successful models of the physicist are better than we might anticipate. We have kept those that have withstood close examination, those that withstand a push outside the range of magnitudes for which our original picture was formed. Even so, sooner or later, under scrutiny limitations appear. For example, we have given an atomic model of matter: all matter is described in terms of fundamental units — atoms. But we have not described the inner nature of the atoms, which requires a different theory, a different model which is an extension of the older one we have discussed.

Our models, the physical theories that we now have, describe much of our world. Tomorrow they will expand; they will become more complete and describe more and more of the natural world as we uncover it through experiment.

9–2. The Molecular Model of a Gas

When we invent any model to explain the behavior of the world about us, we are guided by the outstanding facts that we want to explain. In Chapter 8, we started to make a model for gases, and we mentioned some of their most striking properties: we noted that (1) gases are easily compressed as compared with solids and liquids; (2) they move about readily and one gas even penetrates easily through another; and (3) the densities of gases are low compared with the densities of the liquid and solid forms of the same substances.

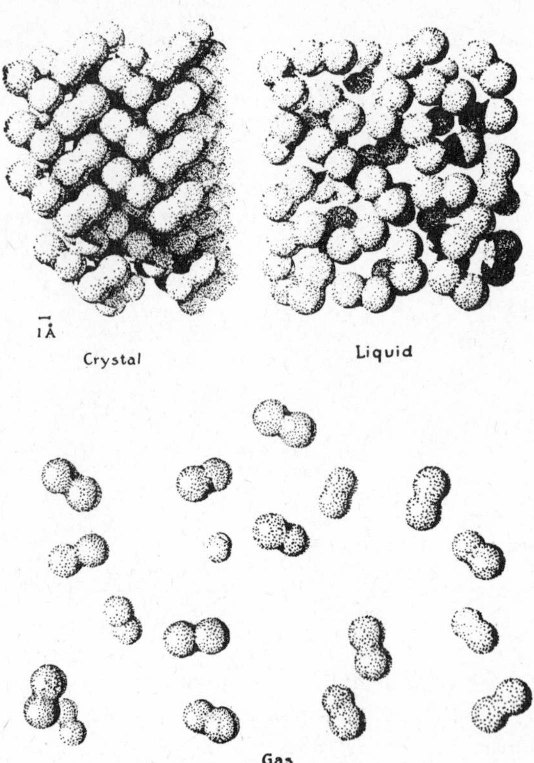

9–1. States of matter. Under the proper conditions any substance can exist as a solid, a liquid, or a gas. Iodine is represented above in each of these states. As a solid (crystal), the particles are rigidly and closely packed. As a liquid, the molecules are spaced apart a little and are capable of more motion. As a gas, the molecules are more widely spaced and capable of much motion. Notice that the molecules are of the same size (about 6×10^{-10} m) in all three states. In a change of state, the space between molecules changes, but their size remains the same. (From "General Chemistry," 2nd Ed., Linus Pauling. Copyright, 1949, 1950, 1953, W. H. Freeman & Co.)

We therefore inferred that a gas might consist of a large number of molecules spaced far apart, while solids and liquids consisted of the same atoms and molecules jammed close together (Fig. 9–1). Let us now reverse our procedure. We shall start with the molecular model and see

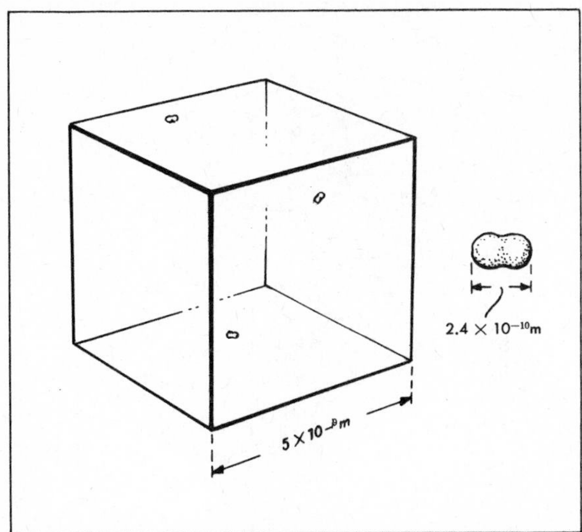

9–2. Molecules of oxygen in a room. A small cube of space shown has been enlarged millions of times to show what we might expect to find in such a space. It is possible that, selecting other identical volumes at random, we might find fewer or more molecules in the various cubes. However, it is most likely that we will find 3 molecules of oxygen as indicated. To the right is an enlargement of one of the molecules.

how it might account for the properties of gases. In order to account for these properties, we shall add one more essential feature to the model. We shall find that the molecules must be in motion.

The molecular model of a gas is simply described. The molecules of the gaseous substance are the units. If the gas is simple, the molecules may consist of only single atoms. Unlike the atoms or molecules in a crystal or liquid, they are not in contact. Instead, they are far apart as we saw in Section 8–3. Between them there is nothing: the void alone. If a solid or a liquid turns into a gas in a room, the same mass occupies 10^3 times its original volume, and takes on the observed density of an ordinary gas sample. Under ordinary conditions, then, the average spacing between molecules is about ten times the diameter of the molecules. This small density and large spacing accounts for the insubstantial nature of an ordinary gas sample (Fig. 9–2).

If you recall that the molecular diameter is only a few angstroms, a few times 10^{-10} meter, you will see that although the molecules are very widely spaced on their own scale, they are still closely spaced on ours. Indeed, there is no basic reason why the molecules should be spaced so closely. A gas can take on any density; the mean spacing of molecules becomes larger and larger as the density becomes less and less. What we call a good vacuum, like that in a radio or picture tube, may correspond to a spacing of only 5×10^{-6} meter, a distance barely the size of the smallest object visible in an ordinary optical microscope. How many times less dense is such a gas than the ordinary air?

The mobility of gases fits well with the wide spacing of molecules. If the molecules are spaced so that they cannot touch, they do not respond very much to one another's presence. (We shall assume that they do not push or pull on one another across long distances.) What then maintains their spacing? Indeed, it is not maintained. They do not stand still, but fly through space like a swarm of tiny bullets. Occasionally they collide with one another, changing direction, and sooner or later they collide with the walls of the container. So they spread until they are rebounding from containing walls on all sides. If they approach an opening in the wall, they fly on through it. If they encounter no wall, they keep going. So they move out through leaks on any side.

Can we now explain the mutual mixing of gases? If the gas molecules are so widely spaced, evidently one gas can interpenetrate another. Imagine a container divided into two parts by a tight partition separating two different gases. Remove the partition wall, or open a valve, and the flying molecules mingle, until finally the gas is uniformly mixed, every sub-volume of the container holding the same mixture of the two gases. Exactly this is observed.

When gas is allowed to flow out of a container directly into an empty space, the speed of the molecular motion is about that of sound; this speed must measure the typical speed of the molecules. In passing through long pipes, however, or mixing with another gas, the apparent speed is much less. Here many molecules are jostling one another, and the motion is rather like that of a crowd of people pushing out of a small gate. Because of the bumping back and forth, the speed of mixing is not a fair measure of the speed of individual motion. The mixing speed should be far slower, and it is.

Widely spaced molecules, moving every which way in empty space with speeds a bit faster than sound, colliding and rebounding as they move — that is our model for a gas. It satisfactorily

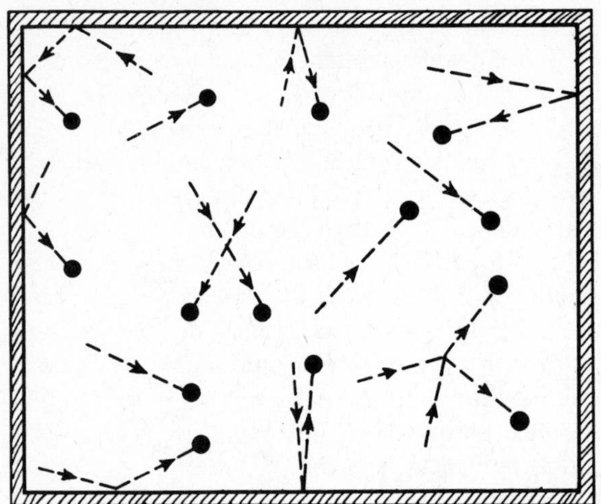

9–3. The continual motion of the molecules of a gas not only causes collisions between molecules, but also collisions between the molecules and the sides of the container. The push of these molecules upon the sides is the pressure of the gas.

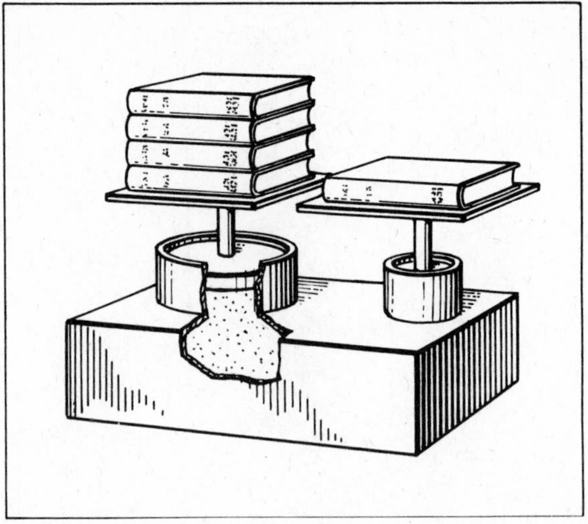

9–4. Pressure is the push per unit area. The piston on the left has four times the area of that on the right. The left-hand piston is subject to the same gas pressure, but it holds up four times the mass because it is struck by four times as many molecules each second. The same amount of mass is held up by each unit area.

accounts for the low density, the mobility, and the intermixing of gases.

That all matter can be vaporized also fits the model. Every solid or liquid can be taken apart into its constituent molecules or atoms. When the attractions which cause them to fit into more or less close-packed patterns are overcome, the freed atoms or molecules form a gas. Heating somehow frees the molecules from their neighbors and allows them to fly out in all directions. Under great heat, all solid or liquid compounds break up into gases. When hot enough, the molecules of the compounds break down into individual atoms of their constituent elements, forming an atomic gas, a mixture of all the atoms present in the sample. This is why the flame, the arc, and the spark produce the characteristic spectra of atoms. In even hotter regions atoms themselves break into their constituents.

Liquefying and freezing are the opposite process. If we compress a gas, we can decrease its volume until the molecules touch. When we remove heat, the newly packed atoms are frozen together. Attractions between the molecules again bind them close together.

9–3. Boyle's Law

The model we have described is plausible, even appealing. But it must be tested on a hard task before it is really acceptable. The description of gas pressure will serve to test the model, and to explain many of the familiar events of life, from breathing to the behavior of tires.

To decrease the volume of a gas sample requires an effort. The gas resists compression. On the other hand, any sample of gas increases in volume until it encounters resistance. Our model nicely accounts for this tendency to expand. The molecules fly against and rebound from walls like hail; they press momentarily against the walls (Fig. 9–3). This succession of momentary shoves is the pressure that pushes the walls away and resists compression.

The push exerted on a wall is perpendicular to the wall. The molecules fly at the wall from all directions, so any push of one molecule from right to left is countered by a push of another molecule from left to right. But all of the molecules press outward against the wall; and there is no counterforce pressing inward unless the wall supplies it.

Does the push on the wall vary from point to point? If the gas is uniform, the average number of molecules striking each unit area will be the same everywhere, and the gas will push impartially outward in all directions. Of course, if more molecules hit one area than another, this area is pushed harder, but there are so many molecules hitting any appreciable area that such effects smooth out in a very short time. Only the size of the area pushed should matter. In fact,

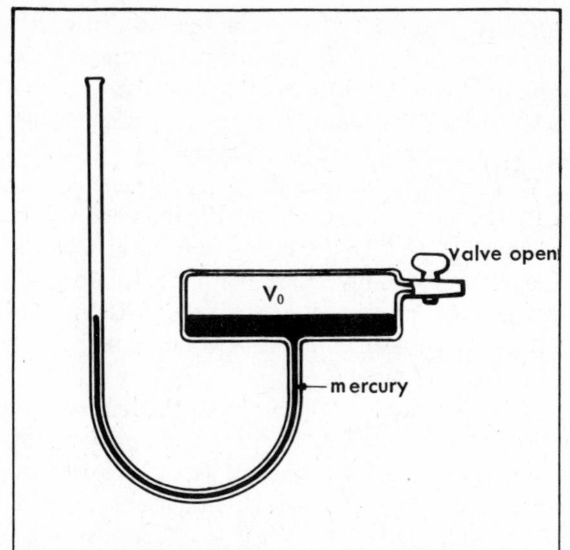

9–5. Apparatus for investigating the pressure of a gas. When the valve is open, the level of the mercury is the same on both sides of the tube. We can put an additional definite number of molecules in the space V_0 through the tube on the right.

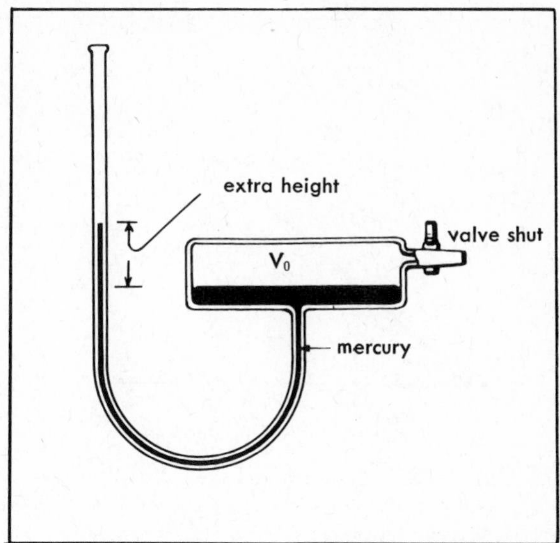

9–6. We have added additional molecules to the space V_0 and closed the valve. The mercury column rises on the left, measuring the extra pressure.

the amount of the push is proportional to the area receiving the molecular hail. The uniform perpendicular push per unit area is what we call the pressure of the gas (Fig. 9–4). It is an important quantity which we can measure by balancing it against the pull of gravity on some standard masses.

Experimentally we can investigate the pressure exerted by a confined gas in the following way: Mercury fills the bottom section of a tube which is open on both sides to the air (Fig. 9–5). The height of the mercury is then the same in both sides of the tube. The right-hand side of the tube opens into a gas space V_0 of a definite volume. A valve allows us to close this volume off from the air outside. Furthermore, through the tube with the valve in it, we can force additional amounts of gas into the space V_0.

Suppose we take a plastic bag of a definite volume, say for instance the volume V_b. When the plastic bag is full of air and opened to the atmosphere, it contains a definite number of molecules (actually V_b/V_0 times the number of molecules already present in V_0). We now attach the plastic bag to the end of the tube on the right (Fig. 9–5). We squeeze the gas out of the bag until it has all been forced into the volume V_0. By closing the valve, we can keep the gas compressed in that volume which now contains more molecules than before. The bombardment of the surface of the mercury in the right-hand vessel is increased because there are more molecules in the same volume. The extra pressure shoves the mercury down on that side; and therefore the mercury rises on the left (Fig. 9–6). The extra height of the mercury on the left measures the extra pressure, that is, the pressure resulting from the bombardment of the extra molecules we have squeezed in.

If we bring up another plastic-bag load of air and force it again into the volume on the right, we shall end up with two extra batches of molecules in V_0. According to our model we expect that the extra pressure on the mercury should now be doubled. Indeed we find that the height of the mercury on the left has risen again by the same amount that it did when we put in one plastic-bag load of molecules. We can continue adding known numbers of molecules to the right-hand volume V_0 and measuring the rise of the mercury on the left. With these measurements we find that the pressure rises in direct proportion to the number of molecules in a given volume (Fig. 9–7).

Suppose we do this experiment at the temperature of melting ice. At that temperature we know the number of molecules of any gas occupying a given volume at atmospheric pressure. In Chapter 8 we learned that a mole (6.025×10^{23} molecules) occupies 22.4 liters at this temperature;

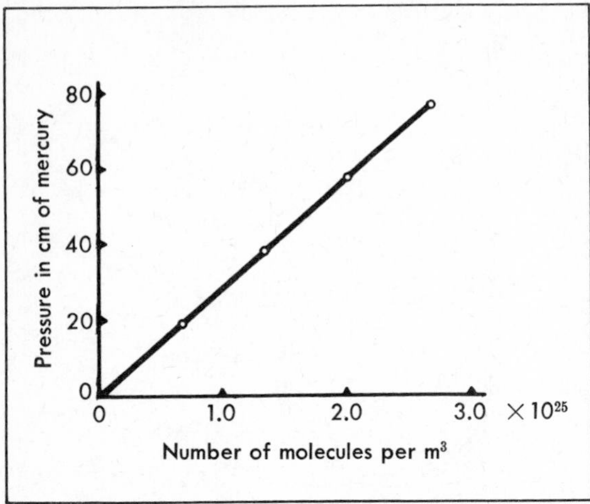

9–7. Additional pressure versus numbers of molecules per unit volume, as measured at the temperature of melting ice.

and so there are 2.70×10^{25} molecules/m^3. Consequently, we know how many molecules we have put into V_0. For example, if V_b, the volume of a bag, is 1 liter (that is, 10^{-3} m^3), each bag load is 2.70×10^{25} molecules/m^3 $\times$ 10^{-3} m^3 = 2.70×10^{22} molecules. We also know the pressure which they exert as measured by the height of the mercury column on the left. At the temperature of melting ice we find that when we have 2.70×10^{25} molecules/m^3 the gas pressure holds up a column of mercury 76 cm high. And in general, since the pressure is proportional to the number of molecules per unit volume, the pressure can be expressed by

$$\frac{\text{Pressure in cm height of mercury}}{\text{76 cm height of mercury}} = \frac{\text{No. of molecules/m}^3}{2.70 \times 10^{25}\ \text{molecules/m}^3}.$$

In symbols this is

$$\frac{P}{76} = \frac{N/V}{2.70 \times 10^{25}} \quad \text{or} \quad P = 2.81 \times 10^{-24}\,\frac{N}{V},$$

where N/V is the number N of molecules divided by the volume V they occupy, P has the units of cm height of mercury held up, and the volume V is in m^3.

In Chapter 8 we found that the volume occupied by a certain number of molecules at atmospheric pressure is independent of the kind of molecule. Now by using different gases we can see whether the pressure depends on the nature of the gas. With these experiments we find that in general the pressure depends on the number of molecules per unit volume but not on the nature of the molecules. All gases behave the same way as long as their densities are reasonably low, that is, as long as the average space between molecules is large compared to their dimensions.

We can repeat the whole set of experiments with a different enclosed volume V_1, in place of the volume V_0; we then get the same result in terms of the number of molecules per unit volume. In this way we are further assured that it is N/V, the number of molecules per unit volume, that determines the pressure.

So far we have worked only at the temperature of melting ice. We can repeat these experiments at the temperature of boiling water. Everything comes out the same except the proportionality factor, which is now $3.84 \times 10^{-24}\,\dfrac{\text{cm of mercury}}{(\text{molecules/m}^3)}$ instead of $2.81 \times 10^{-24}\,\dfrac{\text{cm of mercury}}{(\text{molecules/m}^3)}$ which we found at the ice point. Again at other temperatures the pressure is proportional to the number of molecules per unit volume but the proportionality factor differs, depending on the temperature.

In brief, then, from these experiments, we find that at a given temperature, the pressure exerted by a gas is proportional to the number of molecules divided by the volume they occupy:

$$P = \theta\,\frac{N}{V},$$

where θ is the proportionality factor. This is just what we should expect as long as the molecules do not get in one another's way too much. As long as they have enough space, the number of molecules bombarding the walls of the container depends on the number that are present in the region next to the wall; and consequently, the pressure should be proportional to N/V as we have found. If there are twice as many molecules per unit volume — twice as many in the region near the wall — then twice as many will hit the same area of wall in a given time, and the pressure will be twice as big. This law of the behavior of gases is known as Boyle's law, after Robert Boyle, brilliant contemporary of Newton, who first showed it experimentally.

You can also demonstrate Boyle's law by experimenting with a particular sample of gas in a container closed by a piston (Fig. 9–8). By placing more and more mass on the piston you can increase the pressure on the gas and watch the enclosed volume V decrease. If you make all changes slowly, the gas stays at room temperature. Then if you plot N/V versus the mass pressing down, as in Fig. 9–9, you see that the volume is inversely proportional to the pressure. (Remember, the container is closed so that only V, not N, changes.) Here you must remember to include the pressure of the atmosphere. The bombardment of the gas in the atmosphere shoves down on the piston about as hard as a column of mercury 76 cm high.

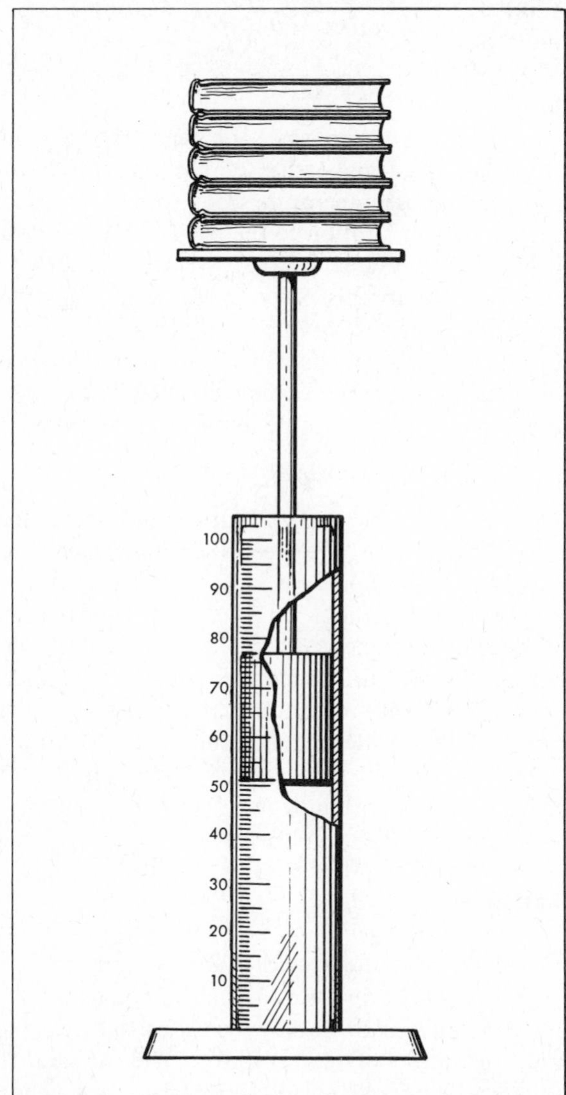

9–8. Apparatus to demonstrate Boyle's law. As additional books (masses) are placed on the platform, the air in the cylinder is compressed and the height of the air column becomes less. The number of books used serves as a measure of the pressure, and the height of the air column gauges the volume.

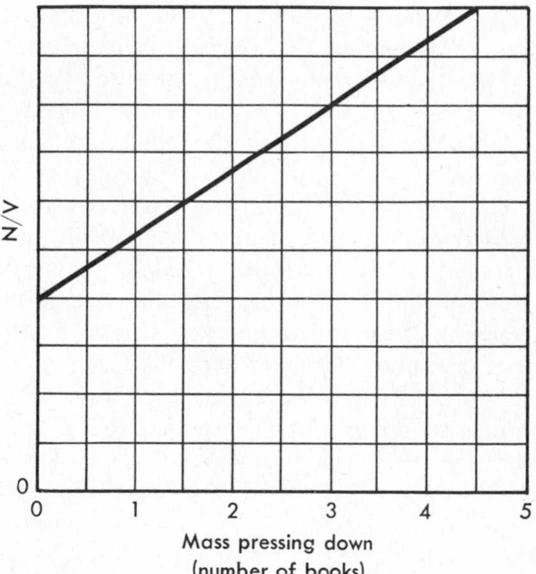

9–9. Boyle's-law curve. The data plotted in the above curve we obtain by using the apparatus of Fig. 9–8. Using the apparatus shown in Fig. 9–8, N/V does not become zero when there is no mass on the platform, because the pressure of the atmosphere is still pushing down.

The atmospheric pressure actually varies depending on the amount of air that happens to be above us, but 76 cm of mercury is about the value at sea level, and it is used to define a standard atmospheric pressure.

Boyle's law fits the molecular model of a gas beautifully. It is just what we should expect if a lot of wide-spaced molecules race around hitting the walls of a container. The model looks good. Let us seek its limitations. Suppose we increase the pressure on our sample greatly. We squeeze more and more gas into the same volume. The density goes up. Finally the molecules are no longer flying about freely. They must touch each other a great part of the time, and we are outside the range of our simple model in which it is assumed that the molecules are far apart. The model is therefore no longer valid. When the gas is so compressed, the pressure against the walls will no longer depend upon the collisions of the moving molecules. It has become the pressure required to squeeze the molecules themselves into a smaller volume. This is a property, not of the motion of molecules, but of their internal structure. Long before the molecules are so tightly jammed together, the model fails; and so does Boyle's law.

At pressures of thousands of atmospheres, gases show marked departures from the Boyle's law straight-line plot. As the pressure goes up, the volume decreases much less rapidly than before. Indeed the variation is not much different from the small variation of the volume of a solid or liquid with external pressure. The density of water or even of steel really does depend upon how hard the molecules are packed in. At a pressure of a thousand atmospheres, like that in the deepest abysses of the ocean, water has a density 4 per cent above what we normally observe. In the center of the earth, it is believed that iron is brought by pressure to a density like that of lead. Normally we do not specify the pressure when we give the density of liquid or solid because the single density we state is a good approximation even if we change the pressure by a large factor.

The gas law of Boyle holds for all gases at low-enough densities, when the molecules are far apart compared to their own dimensions. Indeed, it holds to higher densities for gases with simple molecules, like oxygen or hydrogen, than it does for those gases with large, complicated molecules, like alcohol vapor. The investigation of the deviations from Boyle's law is one path toward a more detailed but more complex study of molecules. Here we shall remain in the simple region of low densities.

9–4. Temperature and Gas Thermometers

Usually we measure changes in temperature by the changes in volume of a liquid, often mercury or alcohol. Each of these substances expands in its own pattern as temperature rises — and water even contracts a little just above the melting point of ice. But gases which behave in accord with Boyle's law (that is, all gases in which the molecules are sufficiently far apart) behave exactly alike. These Boyle's-law gases therefore measure temperature in a more fundamental way than does the expansion of other substances, and a rational definition of temperature can be made by using the behavior of these gases.

In the last section we found for gases that at the temperature of melting ice the pressure in cm of mercury is $P = 2.81 \times 10^{-24}\ N/V$. Here N is the number of molecules occupying the volume V. At the temperature of boiling water we found that $P = 3.84 \times 10^{-24}\ N/V$. In general, in the expression $P = \theta\,(N/V)$ the proportionality factor θ depends on the temperature and on nothing else. In other words, at a given temperature θ, the value of PV/N is the same for all gases of low density, for all values of pressure and all numbers N of molecules present. The volume V they occupy always comes out so that θ is the same as long as the temperature is the same. Furthermore, θ for all these gases rises steadily with increasing temperature. Consequently, θ is the natural measure of temperature.

We could choose the values of θ — that is,

$$2.81 \times 10^{-24}\,\frac{\text{cm of mercury}}{(\text{molecules/m}^3)} \quad \text{at melting ice,}$$

$$3.84 \times 10^{-24}\,\frac{\text{cm of mercury}}{(\text{molecules/m}^3)} \quad \text{at boiling water,}$$

etc. — as our basic scale of temperature. In effect we shall make that choice. Historically, however, other temperature scales were introduced earlier. Their relation to the basic scale is shown in Fig. 9–10. As we see there, the Kelvin scale is proportional to this basic scale; it is the same scale with more convenient units called degrees Kelvin and written °K. The centigrade scale has units of the same size as the Kelvin scale, but zero is arbitrarily shifted to the temperature of melting ice which is 273° K or $2.81 \times 10^{-24}\,\frac{\text{cm of mercury}}{(\text{molecules/m}^3)}$ on the basic gas scale. Notice that there are 100° C (or 100° K) between the temperatures of melting ice and boiling water.

The units on these scales were chosen in this way for convenience. Thermometers for scientific use are usually calibrated to read the centigrade temperature, but we should remember that the zero on that scale is the result of an arbitrary choice. It might as well have been set at the temperature of melting gold. The Kelvin and the gas scales, on the other hand, have a natural zero — the absolute zero which we shall discuss briefly in the next section.

9–5. Temperature and the Gas Model

In the last section, we saw that the proportionality factor θ in Boyle's law leads us to a reasonable definition of temperature. The factor θ is independent of the nature of the gas. It depends only on the temperature as defined by the melting point of ice, or the boiling point of water, or some other physical indicator. We can learn more about the nature of temperature if we now examine

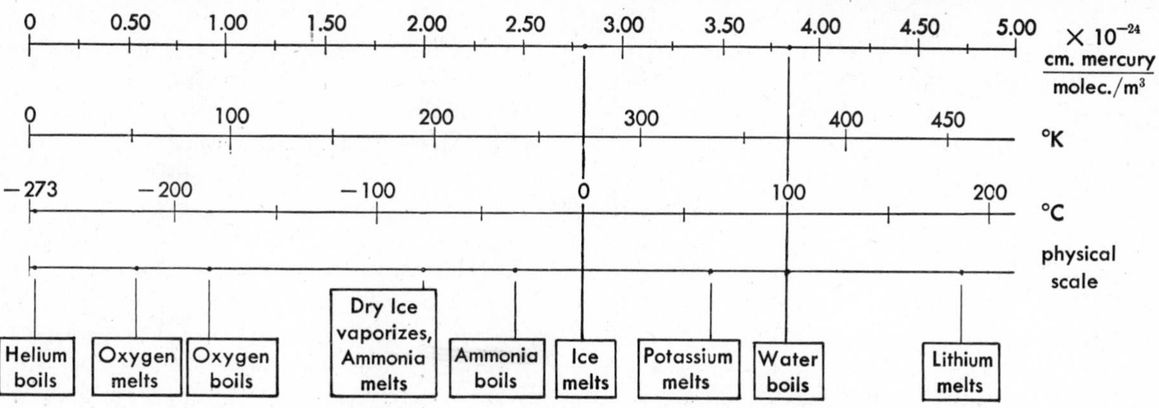

9–10. The relationship between the basic scale of temperature, the Kelvin scale, and the centigrade (or Celsius) scale.

what θ is according to our molecular model of gases. Boyle's law is

$$P = \theta \frac{N}{V}.$$

We have already seen why it is reasonable that the pressure is proportional to the number of molecules per unit volume. Whatever else affects the pressure is summarized in θ. What then on a molecular model should be contained in θ? Now with a given number of molecules in a region near a wall, the pressure on the wall must depend on how fast the molecules move. If they move very slowly, only a few molecules will bump into the wall in a second and they will not hit it very hard. If, on the other hand, the molecules are moving fast, many molecules will reach the wall and each molecule that gets there will hit the wall harder — just as a fast-moving baseball jolts you harder when you try to catch it than does a slow-moving one. The pressure on the wall, therefore, must rise if the speed of molecular motion rises, and fall if the speed of molecular motion falls. The proportionality factor θ in Boyle's law contains this dependence on the speed of molecular motion.

At least one more thing enters the proportionality constant θ: A cannon ball and a table-tennis ball moving at the same speed do not hit a stationary object equally hard. The more massive cannon ball hits far harder than the less massive table-tennis ball. The molecular mass is also contained in the proportionality constant θ. But when we increase the temperature we do not change the molecular mass. A bottle of gas at a high temperature has the same mass on a balance as that of the same bottle of gas at low temperature. On the molecular picture of gases, therefore, increasing the temperature must mean increasing molecular speeds.

We must extend the molecular model to include the idea that higher temperature means higher molecular speed. A good deal of common experience fits in with this conclusion. For instance, raising the temperature usually speeds up chemical reactions. This agrees with the idea that the molecules are then moving faster. At the higher speeds they should hit one another harder and more frequently. The collisions should break apart the molecules and rearrange the atoms more often; and the reactions should therefore take place faster.

Furthermore, the idea that increasing molecular motion goes with increasing temperature should not be restricted to gases. A hot gas will communicate its temperature to cold surroundings, increasing the speed and vigor of the small motions of the molecules in liquids or solids and of the atoms in molecules.

Suppose the walls of the container are made of metal with its atoms neatly arranged in each of the little crystal grains. The atoms cannot in general leave their lattice sites; but they vibrate to and fro in place like so many little balls mounted on springs. This incessant motion is measured by the temperature, no less than the motion of the free-flying molecules of a gas. The flying molecules also vibrate internally, one atom against another, and spin end over end, tumbling as they fly. Sometimes a gas molecule strikes an atom of a crystal in the wall, and sets it into more rapid vibration. The molecule rebounds, a little slowed. Sometimes a slow molecule drifts near the rapidly vibrating atom of the crystal lattice, receives a kick from the vibrating atom, and goes away faster than it came in. This constant exchange of the vigor of atomic and molecular motion is the means by which temperatures are equalized, and motion continued.

When they heat up, solids change by melting or even by vaporizing, if the temperature is high enough. The molecular motion increases as the temperature rises until it becomes so great that the atoms and molecules can change places or even fly apart. At the higher temperatures, the molecular motion is so intense that the flying gas molecules knock each other apart. The gas is reduced to atoms. That is why only the spectra of the elements, spectra of single atoms, are seen in the glow of really hot sources of light.

When we shove the plunger of a bicycle pump down, the moving plunger hits the molecules of gas in the pump and increases the molecular speeds. Higher speed means higher temperature just as much as higher temperature means higher speed. The gas should become hotter. In fact, it does; the temperature of the gas may rise so much that the outside of the cylinder feels hot. Our connection between molecular speed and temperature makes sense again. Higher temperature, higher speed.

Lower the temperature, and the molecules slow down. They fly slowly about. Finally they move so slowly that the molecular attractions may cause them to hold together, and not to rebound after collisions with each other or with the walls. As the temperature falls below 100°K, air, for instance, first becomes liquid and then solid, its two main components, nitrogen and oxygen, undergoing the changes at somewhat different temperatures. At 5°K and ordinary atmospheric pressure, there are no gases, and only helium does not solidify; it becomes an extraordinary new sort of stuff, rather like a liquid, but with properties not found in any other known substance. It is called a super-fluid.

Low temperatures favor orderliness, regularity, the careful fitting together of atoms and molecules. This is the deep reason behind the crystal and the snowflake. Order is cold. At high temperatures, we have the reverse. Everything is in rapid motion, all is disorder, chaos. Within all of this chaotic motion, the averages of density, pressure, and other properties remain predictable. In fact, the wonderful regularities of gases depend on disorder. Gas is all motion and disorder; there are no regular patterns, no specific shapes or necessary densities. Heat is disorder.

Life seems to require just the right mixture of each: it cannot function in a frozen state of complete and rigid order, though it can survive. On the other hand, it cannot even survive too great disorder. For the development of life, the temperature must be just right. As far as we now know, life is restricted to the special environment we live in, to the range of temperatures from about 200°K to 400°K. This is a narrow range in a universe where temperatures vary from a couple of degrees Kelvin in some parts of space to tens of millions of degrees in the centers of stars.

When we consider atoms and molecules, speeds increase with temperature; order decreases. No molecular motion is the least we can have, and no more perfect order is possible than a completely frozen crystal pattern. The natural zero of temperature, $\theta = 0$, which we get by extrapolating the behavior of gases in the Boyle's-law region down to low temperatures, appears to correspond to zero molecular speed. As there is no lower speed, the zero appears to have an absolute significance. Zero on the Kelvin scale (which is the same as $\theta = 0$) is often called absolute zero.

Lord Kelvin, the great English physicist and electrical engineer, gave different arguments for the Kelvin temperature scale and the idea of absolute zero. His reasoning was based on the general laws found to describe the operation of heat engines. These laws do not depend on the molecular picture. Consequently Kelvin's work established the temperature scale and the significance of absolute zero independent of the molecular interpretation of the gas laws. On the other hand, the idea that there is no molecular motion at absolute zero is not so sure. It is attractive because of our interpretation of the gas laws, but in going to 0°K we extrapolate far outside the realm of gas behavior. The motions all become motions of molecules or atoms close together. We now believe that for such motions there is a least amount, and the coldest state is not quite so motionless as extrapolation from the gas laws indicates. Extrapolation to absolute zero turns out to mean something different from extrapolation to absolute rest.

One unexpected result has turned up in the gas laws. A sample of a given number of massive molecules and one of the same number of light molecules exert the same pressure on the walls of a given volume at a given temperature. The pressure depends neither on the molecular mass nor on the molecular nature; it depends only on the number of molecules present. This is strange, for we expect a barrage of baseballs to push harder than one of hailstones. There seems to be only one way out: for a particular value of temperature heavy molecules must move more slowly than light ones. By measuring the speeds with which molecules of gases at the same temperature fly through a hole from a gas into vacuum (Fig. 9–11), we find that heavy molecules actually move with lower average speeds than light molecules. Indeed the experiments indicate that mv^2, the average value of the molecular mass times the square of the molecular speed, is proportional to the temperature.

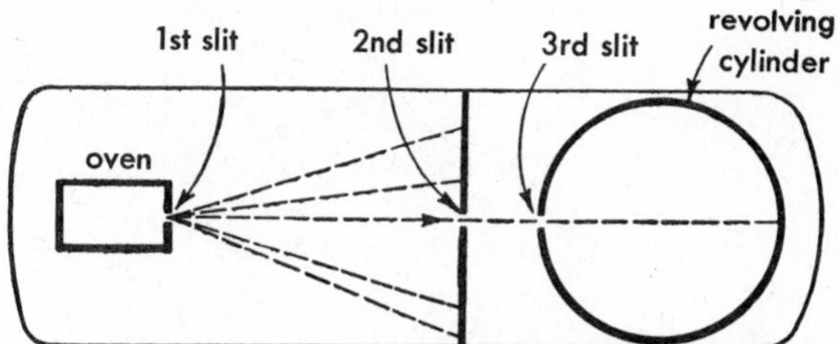

9–11. Measuring the speed of molecules. Molecules emerge from the gas in the oven into a vacuum and are formed into a narrow beam by the second slit. The third slit permits a short burst to enter the revolving cylinder. Because the cylinder is revolving, the molecules do not land directly opposite the slit. Using the position where they do hit and the cylinder's rate of rotation, the speed of the molecules can be computed. (From "Introduction to Atomic Physics," by O. Oldenberg, McGraw-Hill Book Company.)

It is easy to see approximately how these differences in speed come about. Molecular motion is not achieved by magic. Molecules move because they are struck by other moving molecules. Massive ones are harder to set in motion, and the same blows will set lighter molecules into faster motion. This suggests, though it does not prove, the observed result.

The nature of heat and of temperature is far too rich a tale to dismiss with these paragraphs; later chapters will go a bit beyond. (Chapter 26.) When we come to the study of mechanics, we shall give more detailed reasons showing that the temperature of a gas is proportional to mv^2. Further study, which we cannot go into in this book, indicates that if we wait, the average values of mv^2 for different kinds of molecules which hit each other should become the same. The temperature does tend to equalize in just this way. In the bicycle pump, after compression the motions of the molecules in the hot gas slow down while the other molecules around speed up. After a while the temperatures of the pump and that of its surroundings equalize near the original temperature of the larger collection of molecules.

9–6. Brownian Motion and Noise

On a sufficiently small scale, the density of a gas depends on what little volume you choose to consider. Here and there a molecule flies along; the rest of the space is empty. The constant density we usually observe must be an average one: the number of molecules in a small cube if we count them at different times and average the results. (See Fig. 9–2.) The same is true for pressure. The pressure we detect by weight or with a gauge is also an average pressure, averaged over space and over time. A quick-reading tiny gauge would fluctuate wildly, reading high when a molecule struck, low when no molecule was present. With such a gauge we would obtain direct evidence of the chaotic motions of gas molecules, but our normal gauges read only averages.

Is there no sign of this chaos that we can directly perceive? Because it is all on a very small scale, we do not usually see the wild fluctuations. Nevertheless, the chaos of the molecules can be directly seen in a fascinating group of experiments. The botanist Robert Brown was skilled in the use of a simple microscope such as you might well build in the laboratory. In 1827, using a single lens, a bead of glass, "the focal length of which is about $\frac{1}{32}$ of an inch," he was excited to see that tiny particles from the pollen grains of flowers constantly moved about in the water in which they were immersed. "These motions were such as to satisfy me," he wrote, "that they belonged to the particle itself," and were not due, for example, to currents in the water. He thought that these particles moved because they were alive, that he had discovered a new characteristic of life; but then he found that even boiled particles continued to move. Finally, he found, as we now know well, that any very small particle never stands still. This motion is called *Brownian motion.*

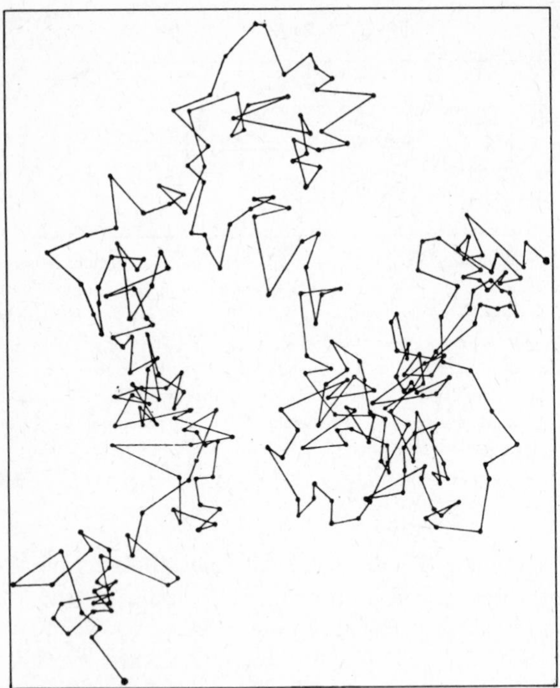

9–12. Brownian motion. Pictured is the erratic motion of a particle as photographed once every 20 seconds. In each time interval, the particle moved from one point to the next. Between photographic exposures, the particle may well have traveled an erratic path similar to the entire path shown.

9–13. Early in this century Jean Perrin carefully observed the numbers of small particles suspended at various depths in a liquid. He found the distribution of suspended particles illustrated here on an enlarged scale. It resembles the distribution of molecules in a gas. The upper particles in the suspension (or the upper molecules in the gas) push down on those below and crowd them together. Those nearest the bottom have the most particles above them and so are pushed closer together with the result that the density is greater near the bottom. This illustrates what happens in the earth's atmosphere, in which one half of the mass is in the first 5.5 km above the earth's surface. The higher we go, the less dense the air becomes.

We can record the Brownian motion of a small particle as in Fig. 9–12, where the randomness and chaos of its way are made plain. About fifty years ago, when the nature of this motion was understood, it became one of the most convincing pieces of evidence for the matter-of-fact reality of the molecule.

Such a small particle behaves like a huge molecule. If it is big enough to see in the microscope, it is big enough to contain some 10^{10} or 10^{11} atoms; it is really gigantic on the molecular scale. Whether it is in a liquid or in a gas, at any moment such a particle is being struck by swarms of moving molecules. They exert a fluctuating push on the little grain. Now it is pushed a little harder from one side, now from the other, and it moves accordingly. It spins, too, as the molecular chaos twists it about. From the fundamental laws of heat and from the mathematical theory of probability, it is possible to calculate just what the average motion of such a particle should be, and measurements of its path confirm these calculations. The path is different only in scale from the path of a single molecule as it passes from collision to collision. It is the same kind of path that molecules take as they slowly diffuse, carrying the odor of ammonia or cooking gas across a room.

In Fig. 9–13 we see little grains, heavier than the liquid in which they are immersed. They are kept up against gravity by the effect of Brownian motion. They behave like the molecules of the atmosphere, which are denser near the bottom, and more dilute near the top; but in this toy "atmosphere" the height extends only a fraction of a millimeter, while the air extends upward for a distance of many kilometers. The height of the suspension times the effective mass of the grains regarded as molecules is equal to the height of the air times the mass of its molecules. Iron filings or even nails would also have such an "atmospheric" height; but as molecules they are so heavy that this height would be quite without meaning — it is less than the size of the filings or nails themselves, in fact an extremely small fraction of the size of one atom.

Even large-scale objects show Brownian motion; but usually it is too small to detect. It is small because big objects don't respond fast and because so many molecules strike that their effects almost exactly balance in small time intervals. With sufficiently sensitive apparatus, however, we may see the fluctuations even in moderately large objects. In Fig. 9–14 a small mirror, free to turn, is shown mounted in a chamber which is

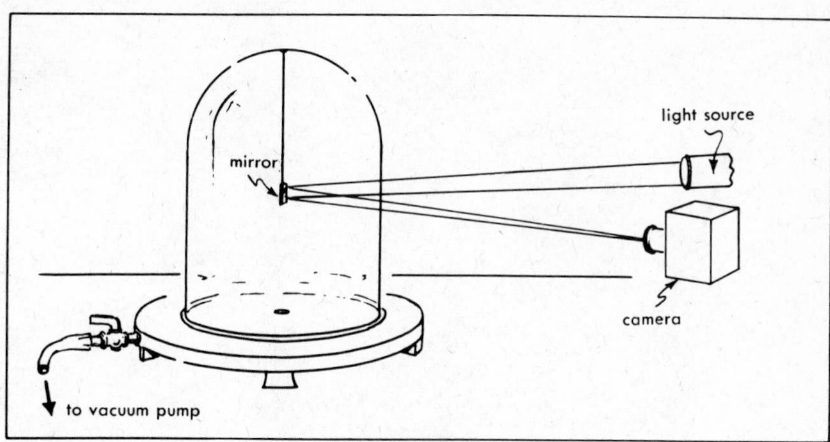

9–14 (a). Demonstrating another case of Brownian motion. Light from the source is focused on the freely suspended mirror in a protective chamber. Any motion of the mirror causes the spot of light reflected to the camera to move on the film. As the film moves through the camera, the reflected spot of light creates a wavy track showing that the mirror turns slowly to and fro. Typical tracks are shown below.

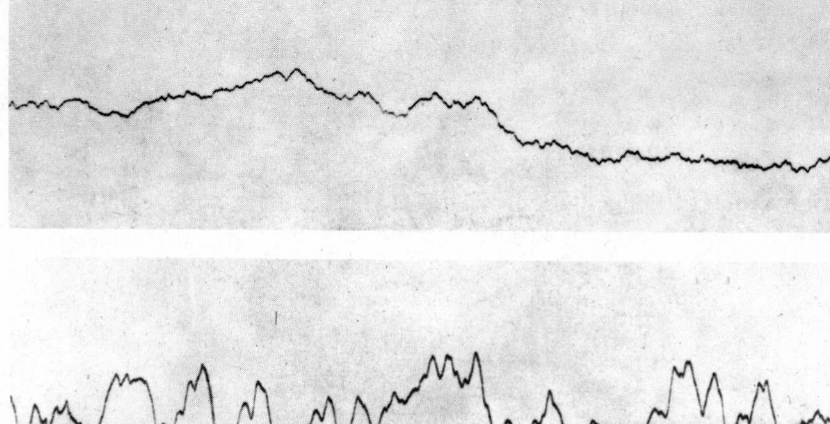

9–14 (b). During this exposure, the pressure in the chamber was equal to atmospheric pressure.

9–14 (c). This track was prepared under conditions similar to (b) except that the pressure in the chamber was reduced to about 1×10^{-5} of atmospheric pressure (enough to support a mercury column 4×10^{-3} mm high). The effect of the molecular collisions is now much more apparent.

carefully protected from all vibration, air currents, and other disturbances. It turns to and fro in a random way — another example of Brownian motion. Because a small change in the angle of the mirror can make a large displacement in the position of a reflected light beam, we can detect these fluctuations.

The Brownian motion plainly sets a limit to the use of small instruments to measure small quantities. The beam of a balance undergoes Brownian motion, and this sets a limit on the precision with which two masses can be compared. Every pointer on every instrument feels this same gentle but irresistible trembling. It sets a general limit to the precision of measurement. In electrical measurements, it puts a random fluctuating signal into every circuit. This signal can be heard as noise, called *Johnson noise* after its first observer. It is simply another manifestation of the Brownian motion of the materials of the circuit, and it cannot be eliminated. A TV receiver in a quiet location shows between channels a random pattern called "snow," much of which is simply the effect of the random electrical signals of the Johnson noise. It seems probable, too, that the human ear is just on the borderline of being able to hear the Brownian motion of the air as a constant noise in the quietest of rooms, where only the random molecular motion exists. Only one way is known to reduce Brownian motion: cold. At low temperatures, Brownian motion and Johnson noise diminish. A thermometer has been made which works by measuring the noise.

The size of the Brownian fluctuations can be used to measure Avogadro's number N_0. If N_0 were small so that molecules were as big as

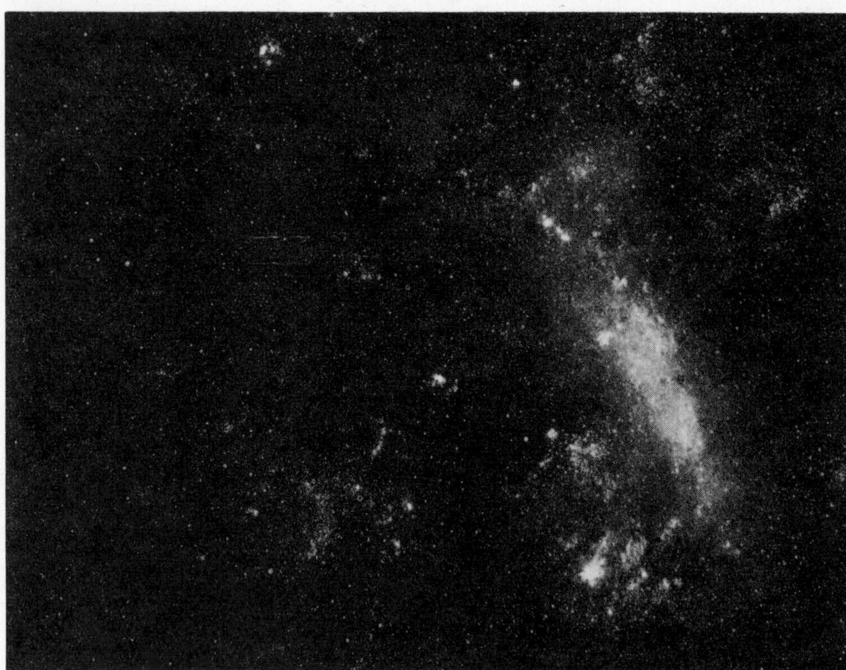

9–15. The Large Cloud of Magellan. This is a satellite galaxy of the Milky Way at a distance of 1.75×10^5 light-years from the earth. It is similar in nature to a gas that is not confined by walls. The stars represent the atoms in the "gas," although actually there are also atoms of ordinary gas among the stars.

sand grains, the fluctuations we observe in the motion of pollen or of little mirrors would be large — that is, assuming the pollen and the mirrors do not change in size. If N_0 were even larger than it is, the observed fluctuations would be balanced out more completely than they are. From the size of the fluctuations, the numbers of molecules causing the motion can be calculated. From detailed theory and observation of Brownian effects, Perrin and others in the first decades of this century made several measurements of N_0 (Section 8–7). The Brownian motions are thus connected directly with the molecular scale, and we know quantitatively that they reflect the thermal motion of the submicroscopic world.

These fluctuation effects go far to confirm the kinetic model of gases, and indeed the kinetic model of all gross matter. Here is evidence that molecules in liquids and solids are in motion. They have this property in common with gases, whose behavior is so much simpler. The incessant molecular chaos is all but visible.

9–7. Gases Without Walls

It seems a paradox to speak of a gas without walls. Surely such a gas would spread out rapidly and dissipate. In fact, however, we live immersed in one. The atmosphere is a gas with only an inner wall, the surface of the earth. Above the earth there is no second wall. Gravity holds the molecules of the atmosphere in place. In the relatively dense air near sea level, a molecule flies only a micron (10^{-6} m) or less before hitting another molecule. At the upper fringe of the atmosphere, hundreds of kilometers high, the density is low; the molecules fly many kilometers between collisions. There the molecules act like so many little bullets; they fly in curved paths, arcing up when hit from below and returning downwards under the pull of the earth. There is no sharp edge to our atmosphere, only a gradual fading out of the density of the air.

The star cluster of Fig. 9–15 is another sort of gas without walls. Its "molecules" are great stars; they fly about but rarely escape their mutual gravitational attractions. Thus it is with the galaxies. In a galaxy like ours there is a "gas" of stars and also a gas of atoms filling the spaces between the stars. The motions and the attractions which rule these structures are the subject matter of astrophysics. The idea of a system without walls and without solidity is one which we shall meet over and over again; the atom itself is such a structure and the nucleus another. It is worth while recalling that the atmosphere gives us an example of how such things may be.

FOR HOME, DESK, AND LAB

1. Consider the idea that all matter is made up of atoms. Does the idea that matter is constructed from 100 different types of atoms lead to a physical model? Why?

2. (a) Outline the atomic model of solids that was discussed briefly in the last chapter.

(b) How is the volume of a solid related to the volumes of the individual atoms? For instance, is the volume of a solid about the same as the total volume of the individual atoms? Much greater? Much less?

(c) On an atomic model how would you expect the compressibilities of solids and gases to differ?

3. In Section 9–2 we pointed out that motion is an essential feature of the molecular model of gases. Use the idea (discussed in Chapter 4) that gravitational effects become less important at small scale to explain that "molecules" of a gas may be in motion, although wooden molecules like those in Fig. 8–6 would just sit still on a table.

4. (a) What will happen when you turn a glass upside down and shove it down into water?

(b) Can you use this effect to reconstruct the reasoning that Hero of Alexandria used to show that air is a material substance?

5. What evidence can you think of that shows the mobility, interpenetrability, and mixing of gases? As a start, answer the questions, "How do most odors reach you?" and "What happens to the air when you move around?"

6. Two students set out to determine the density of air. First they weigh an empty container and find its mass to be 20 gm. Next they inflate a limp plastic balloon to a diameter of 21 cm and squeeze its contents into the container. The container with the air from the balloon now is found to have a mass of 26 gm. What is the density of air from this measurement?

7. A tire is inflated to three times atmospheric pressure. What is the density of the air in the tire?

8. At sea level a mercury barometer reads a pressure of 76 cm of mercury, and at an elevation of 1500 meters it reads 63 cm. What is the relative density of the air at this altitude compared to that at sea level? Assume that the temperature is the same at both levels. (Note: 1500 meters is about 4500 feet.)

9. To the apparatus shown in Fig. 9–5 we attach a plastic bag of volume V_0 full of gas. We squeeze this gas into the gas space V_0 on the right side of the apparatus. The height of the mercury on the left rises about 76 cm. We close the valve on the right; then we attach another bag of gas of volume V_0 at atmospheric pressure. Finally we open the valve and squeeze the gas out of this bag into the volume V_0.

(a) By what additional height does the column of mercury rise?

(b) With the plastic bag still attached we open the valve. By what height does the column of mercury fall?

(c) Why does the column fall farther than 76 cm?

10. In a mercury barometer (Fig. 9–16), at sea level the normal pressure of the air (one atmosphere), acting on the mercury in the dish, supports a column of mercury in a closed tube.

(a) What height h would you expect for the column of mercury in the barometer?

(b) If you go up in the air until the density has fallen to half its sea-level value, what height h would you now expect?

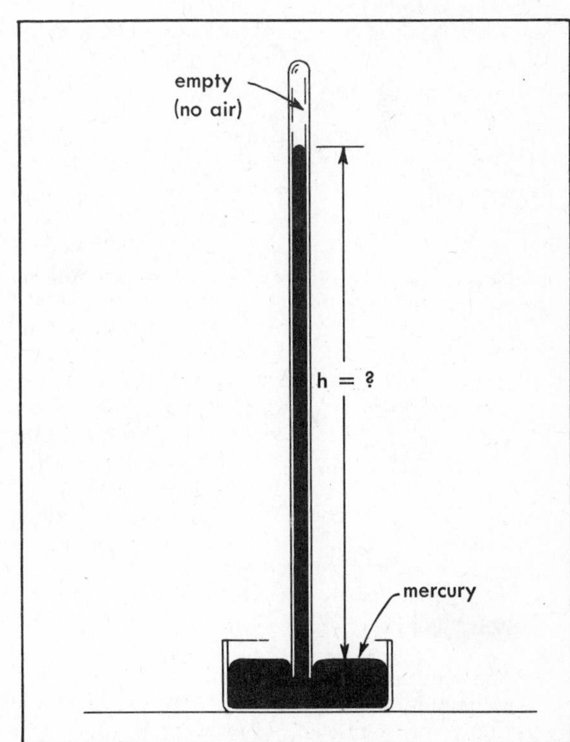

9–16. For Problem 10.

11. Every column of water 10 m high exerts a pressure approximately equal to that of the atmosphere. A diving bell (a cylinder open at the bottom) with a diameter of 2 meters and a length of 3 meters is sunk in 100 meters of water.

(a) Assuming that the temperature of the water is the same at all depths, how far in the diving bell will the water rise?

(b) What must be the pressure of the compressed air pumped into the diving bell to keep it entirely free of water?

(c) Have you ever made a Cartesian diver? (Your teacher is not to grade you on your answer to this question!)

12. A log or boat will float in water if its mass is less than the mass of water it displaces; a balloon will rise as long as the mass of the container and the enclosed gas is less than that of an equal volume of the air around it. If a soap bubble 20 cm in diameter with walls 10^{-3} cm thick is filled with neon gas, will it rise or sink through air (density 1.2×10^{-3} g/cm^3) of the same temperature? Consider the density of the bubble material to be 1.1 gm/cm^3, and the density of neon gas to be 8.4×10^{-4} g/cm^3.

13. A balloon with a mass of 10.3 gm is filled with helium to a diameter of 32.0 cm. It rises in the air and lifts, in addition to the balloon, 9.2 meters of string before it comes to equilibrium. The string is found to have a mass of 0.78 gm/m.

(a) What is the density of the helium in the balloon?

(b) What is the ratio of the pressures inside and outside the balloon?

Note: The density of air is 1.20 gm/liter; the density of helium at room temperature is 0.165 gm/liter.

14. (a) A gas thermometer containing helium is at the temperature of melting ammonia in which it has been immersed for some time. The volume of He at standard atmospheric pressure is read. Then the thermometer is moved into a bath of boiling water. The pressure on the He gas volume is still atmospheric pressure. By what factor does the volume of He change? (Use Fig. 9–10 to estimate the temperature of melting ammonia.)

(b) If the thermometer had a constant volume, by what factor would the pressure of the He gas change?

(c) If we used oxygen gas instead of He in the thermometer, how would that affect the answers to (a) and (b)?

15. The pressure in a tube of volume 1.00×10^{-3} m^3 containing helium has been reduced to 1.00×10^{-2} cm height of mercury at 0°C.

(a) What is the number of molecules per unit volume? What is the total number of molecules in the tube?

(b) The tube is immersed in liquid nitrogen. After waiting for a while, the pressure gauge connected to it settles down to 2.68×10^{-3} cm of mercury. What is the temperature on the basic gas scale (θ)? What is the temperature on the Kelvin scale?

(c) If the helium were replaced by air, how would your answers to (a) and (b) be affected? (Look at Fig. 9–10.)

16. Is air containing water vapor denser or less dense than dry air at the same temperature and pressure?

17. When a car is driven for an extended period, particularly in summer, the tires and their inflating air are heated both from the flexing and friction on the tires and from the warmth of the road surface. When the daytime temperature is 27°C, by what factor would you expect the pressure to increase with a 30°C temperature rise in the tire and air?

18. *Note:* In this problem you will probably find it an advantage to use ratios to find the answers at different temperatures and pressures. For this purpose, recall that at 273°K and one atmosphere pressure there are 2.70×10^{25} molecules/m^3 (Section 9–3).

A certain tire contains (10/81) m^3 of air. It is normally inflated to a total pressure of 3 atmospheres (3 times the standard atmospheric pressure).

(a) If this pressure was measured at a temperature of 27°C, how many molecules of air are in the tire?

(b) After a few hours driving the temperature within the tire rises to 47°C. What is the pressure now?

(c) How many air molecules would you have to release from the heated tire to reduce the pressure back to 3 atmospheres at 47°C?

19. A gas is made up of molecules of hydrogen and oxygen.

(a) Which molecules move faster?

(b) About what is the ratio of the speeds?

20. There is good reason to believe that for monatomic gases, the speed of sound is always a definite fraction of the speed of molecular motion. (Crudely, it is molecular motion that carries sound; consequently the two speeds must be related.)

(a) Using the following table compute the products of mass times the square of the speed of sound for each of the monatomic gases listed.

Gas	(273°K) Mass (amu)	Speed of Sound (m/sec)
He	4.00	970
Ne	20.2	435
A	39.9	308.5

(b) Explain the relationship of your results to the statements about thermal speeds of molecules near the end of Section 9–5.

21.

Temp. (°K)	Speed of Sound v_s (m/sec)	v_s^2 (m²/sec²)
273	308.5	9.55×10^4
573	446.5	19.9
873	551.1	30.0
1273	665.5	44.3

This table for argon gas shows the measured speed of sound and the square of the speed of sound at different temperatures on the Kelvin scale.

(a) Plot the square of the speed of sound vertically against absolute temperature horizontally.

(b) Assuming that the speed of sound is always the same fraction of the molecular speed, check your result against the statement near the end of Section 9–5 that temperature and the square of the molecular speed are proportional.

22. * Brownian motion occurs because in a short interval of time a particle is hit by more molecules from one side than the other. In this way the particle moves at random to the right or the left.

(a) As a rough model of this Brownian motion, flip a coin and move one pace to the right if it comes up heads, or one pace to the left if it comes up tails. Flip the coin 10 times over, following the directions it gives you each time. Then write down how far away you are from your starting point and whether you are to the right or to the left. Go through this whole procedure several times. After 10 flips do you always come out at the same place?

(b) Pool your results with those of your classmates and make a plot showing (vertically) the total number of times that any of you came to a given final position against (horizontally) the final position measured from the starting point. For example, if in all the various tries you or any one of your classmates landed 3 paces to the left 18 different times, you will plot a point on the graph 3 units to the left of center and 18 units high. If you and your classmates landed back at the start 27 times, you will plot a point at the center of the horizontal axis 27 units high, etc.

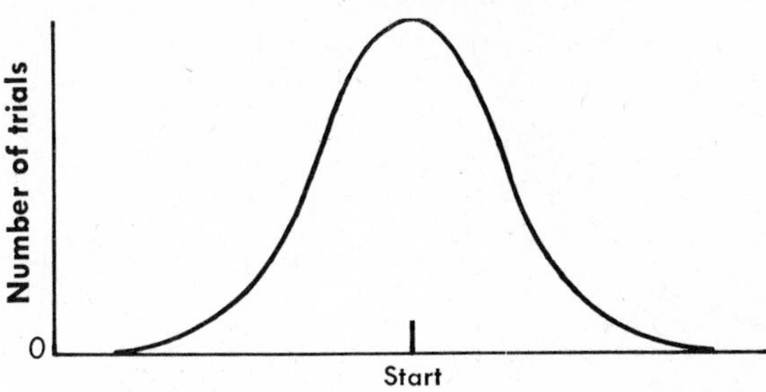

9–17. For Problem 22.

(c) Examine this plot to see where you (or a particle in Brownian motion) are most likely to end up. Should the curve be symmetric about the starting point? Is it?

(d) If you measure the distances moved without regard to direction away from the starting point, about what is the average distance in paces gone in 10 flips? Would you expect this average to be zero?

(e) Compare the kind of motion you have just studied with observations of real Brownian motion. See Fig. 9–17 or take your own observations of Brownian motion. Remember that the coin flipping, telling you which way to go, represents chance bombardment of molecules hitting a Brownian particle.

FURTHER READING

BORN, MAX, *The Restless Universe.* Second Revised Edition, Dover, 1957.

BOYLE, ROBERT, *The Sceptical Chymist.* Everyman's Library.

BRAGG, SIR WILLIAM, *Concerning the Nature of Things.* Dover, 1954.

EINSTEIN, A., and INFELD, L., *The Evolution of Physics.* Simon & Schuster, 1938 (pp. 59–67).

GAMOW, GEORGE, *One, Two, Three . . . Infinity.* Mentor Books, 1957 (pp. 184–219). An entertaining and informal description of the ideal gas model and the concepts of disorder.

HOLTON, GERALD, *Introduction to Concepts and Theories in Physical Science.* Addison-Wesley, 1952. Chapters 18 and 20 are a review of the ideas and the historical development of the ideal gas model.

JEANS, SIR JAMES, *An Introduction to the Kinetic Theory of Gases.* Cambridge University Press, 1952.

MORE, L. T., *Life and Works of Honorable Robert Boyle.* Oxford University Press, 1944.

PAULING, LINUS, *General Chemistry.* W. H. Freeman & Co., 1956.

MEASUREMENT

CHAPTER 10

THE delicacy of a quartz-fiber microbalance (Fig. 7–3) shows how painstaking the precision methods of physical measurement can become. But the notion that measurement is always something finicky and precise is foreign to physics. Gauging a length of wire at a glance or measuring a stellar distance so roughly that it may be in error by several powers of ten can be valuable measurements indeed. Measurement is the means by which we make progress, by which we test and refine our concepts of how the world works. By measurement, whether the roughest estimate or the most precise determination, we confront our ideas with a quantitative test. The lesson that such a test is necessary has been learned by generations of physicists in the dearest of schools: hard experience.

In the present brief chapter we consider measurement itself as a branch of physics. What is measurement, and how does it work? What limitations does it encounter, and why? These questions are not easy ones; they are reconsidered by generation after generation of physicists as the things they measure and the methods of measurement change with the growth of skill and possibility. The understanding of measurement has been greatly clarified even within the last few years.

10–1. Decision — the Unit of Measurement

The study of measurement has found a natural unit: the decision or choice between two alternatives. Any photograph reproduced in this book shows some sort of pattern, appearing in various shades of gray, ranging from near-black to near-white. But an enlargement shows that what is printed on the page is nothing but black ink, one uniform strength of black, on the white paper (Fig. 10–1). Many such dots, around 2,700 per square centimeter, form the picture. The dots vary greatly in size, but not at all in the shade of black. If you divide up the photograph (which is called a half-tone whenever reproduced in this way) by a rectangular coordinate mesh so small that several squares of the mesh are found in even the smallest printed half-tone dot, you can describe the whole picture in full detail by giving the successive coordinates of the squares, and saying *black* or *white* as the color of each square. Your long list of simple decisions, black or white, represents the half-tone. You can symbolize black as *yes* for ink and white as *no* for no ink, or write 1 for an inked and 0 for a blank square. A reproduction made according to your numbers would do justice to the picture. The most complicated scene can be represented by a series of such alternatives, of such simple choices.

We can do the same with measurement. The most rudimentary measurement of the length of a table, say, would be made by bringing up a meter stick and making just one decision, one choice. You ask the question, "Is the table longer than the meter stick, or not?" The answer is simply *yes* or *no*. This answer tells you very little; it is only the beginning of measurement. Suppose

10–1. The half-tone. The enlargement (upper right) made of a small section (center) of the black-and-white illustration shows that the printed picture consists of black dots. The larger the dots, the more nearly black the picture appears. The smaller the dots, the more nearly white the illustration appears. The actual enlargement above is about 10 times.

10–2. Decision in measurement. The drawings below illustrate the first few decisions that are made in the simplest measurement. The longer the series, the more accurate will be the measurement that you are making.

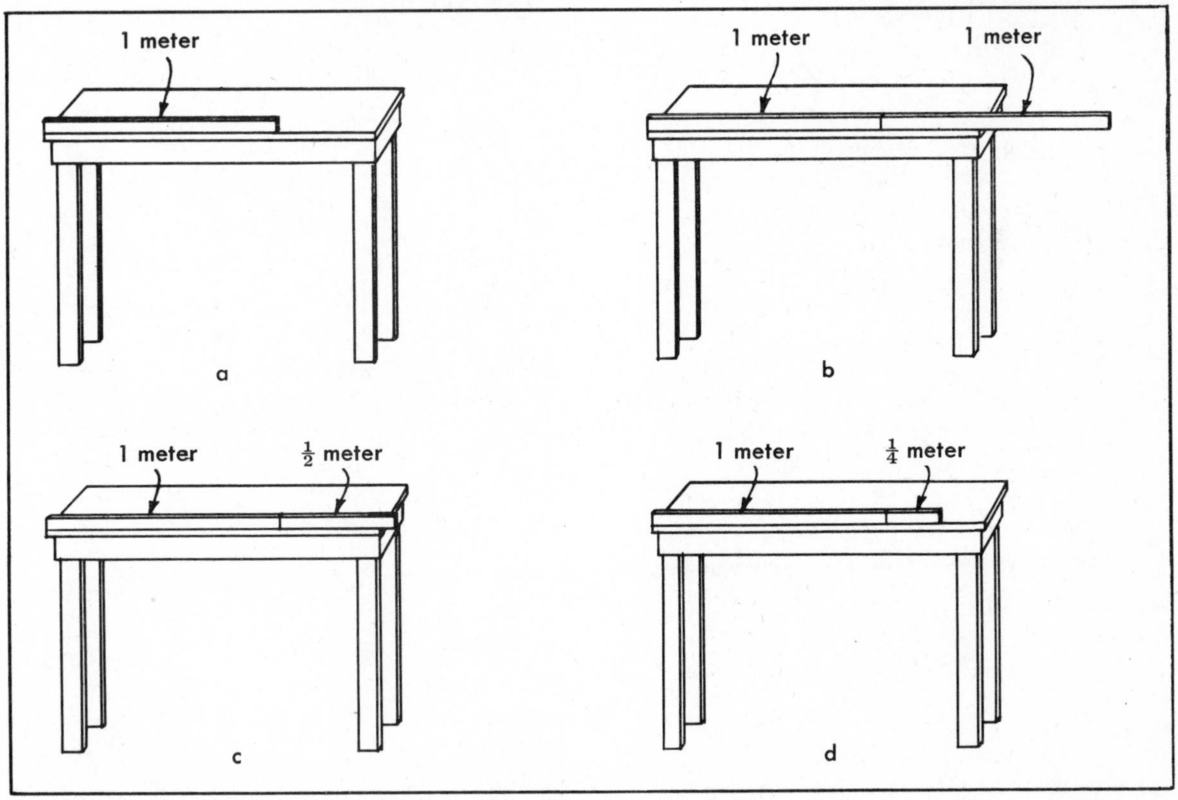

the answer is *yes*. Then you bring up two meter sticks end to end, or lay yours out twice, and ask the next question: "Is the table longer than the two sticks together?" Say the answer is *no;* then the true length must lie between one and two meters. Now you must subdivide the meter, and bring up half-sticks, quarter-sticks, and so on. With a long series of such questions, you can cite the length to a large number of significant figures. The more precise a measurement, the greater the number of choices needed; you can check for yourself, if you like arithmetical games, that it takes three or four choices for each significant figure. If, instead of measuring a simple length, you wish to measure a more complex quantity (e.g., a displacement vector), you must make more choices because you need to specify more numbers (e.g., the three components of the vector).

Even in counting, you make decisions. Is the object one you want to count, or not? When we count the number of particles emitted by a radioactive source, we look at a developed photographic plate or at a cloud chamber and decide whether or not various patterns of silver or of water drops mean that a particle passed. We must decide *yes* or *no*. Or perhaps an electrical counter collecting the light from a scintillating plastic says *yes*, there is a big-enough fluctuation in the light to mean the passage of a particle, or *no*, it is not big enough.

Any count whatever, any measurement whatever can be put into these *yes* or *no* terms. We can reduce all measurements to a common basis, and we can thus begin to measure measurement itself. It seems very reasonable to say that the unit of all measurement is the decision, and the number of decisions required measures what is contained in the measurement.

10–2. Amplification and Display

Somehow the final result of all measurements must be communicated to us. Sometimes we make the measurements directly with our own senses, as when we count scintillations. Sometimes automatic equipment presents us with numbers on a dial; all we need to do is distinguish the digits. Sometimes we make a kind of measurement on the measuring instrument itself, for example, when we carefully read a pointer on a scale with the aid of a magnifying glass. In all of these cases, sooner or later we make some decisions. That is really our role in the measurement. The instrument, be it eye or meter or complex rack of electronic chassis, must display something to us or to some other observer so that we may make at least one decision.

Just how we display the result of measurement is a question of the state of the art. Once the unaided senses would do; they display their readings within the body. Often some aid is needed, most frequently amplification: some small or weak physical event is made to cause a much larger one, and the larger one is eventually displayed directly to the senses of the observer. Amplifiers act as a means of extending our natural instruments. They are not in any important way different from the senses except that instead of being born with them, men make them. From our point of view all means of studying the physical world stand on an equal footing: all must be used with care, all have some limitations. A measurement starts in some original physical event and ends in some decisions by an observer. Whether it passes directly to the eye or first through a complicated radar system may be all-important for its usefulness and meaning, but it does not affect the general concept of the measurement.

10–3. Signals and Noise

It is not always possible to make a decision. That is the origin of the limitations of measurement, of error. The edge of the table may be so roughly sawn that some of the wood fibers go past the mark, some do not. Each mark on a scale always has some width, so that there are times when you cannot say whether a pointer is past the mark or not. If the mark were infinitely sharp, further decisions would always clear up which side you were on. Since it is not, there is a limit to what you can do without subdividing the mark itself. Finally, you come down to the scale on which molecular chaos, the Brownian motion, becomes limiting. The radio operator cannot always distinguish dot from dash; even on the quietest nights, the Johnson noise, Brownian motion within his own circuits, will cause him confusion. Brownian motion creates "noise" in all measurements and results in a constant danger of false decisions, especially when the measurement is a sensitive or delicate one. The true basis for decision, called the signal-to-noise ratio, is a quantity which expresses how accurately any measurement can be made. If the signal is weaker than the noise, not many measurements are reliable.

Amplifiers increase the signal until it can be displayed to the observer; but they amplify the noise too. A perfect amplifier cannot improve the signal-to-noise ratio; any imperfect one — no perfect one has yet been designed — will add

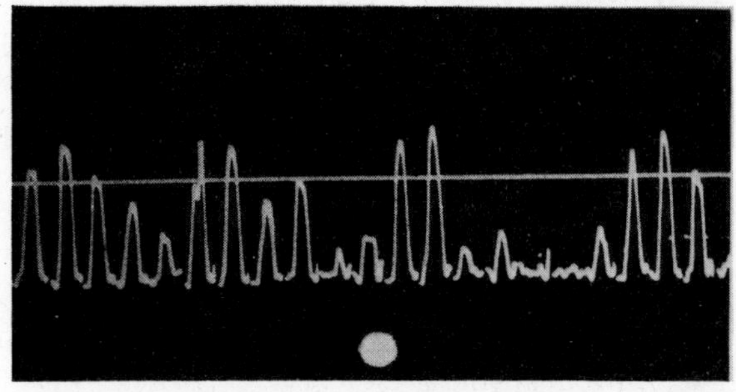

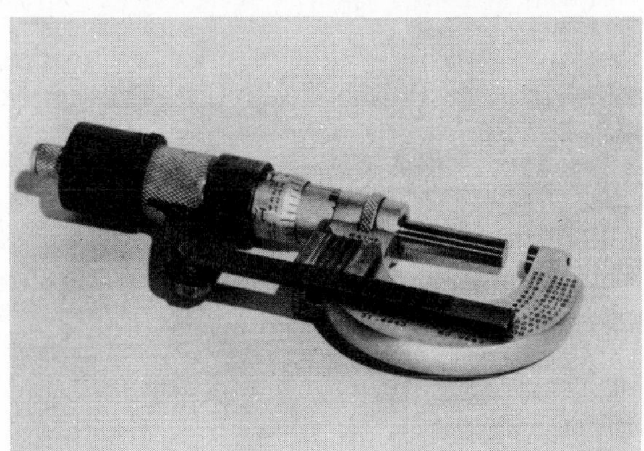

Decimal	Binary	Scaler 1 2 4 8
0	0	● ● ● ●
1	1	○ ● ● ●
2	10	● ○ ● ●
3	11	○ ○ ● ●
4	100	● ● ○ ●
5	101	○ ● ○ ●
⋮	⋮	
9	1001	○ ● ● ○
⋮	⋮	
13	1101	○ ● ○ ○
⋮	⋮	

○ = on ● = off

10–3. Display devices. A few of the many ways to display to our senses the information derived from inanimate objects are shown above. A pointer over a scale, as on a pressure gauge (above, top), is used to transmit information to the eye. The micrometer caliper (above, center), developed by C. M. Witcher, has ridges to present information to a blind man through his sense of touch. Information can be amplified and displayed to the sense of hearing by electronic devices and earphones (above). A fluorescent screen, such as the radarscope (also above), is used to transmit to the eye information such as the radar lunar echoes (top, right). Information for use in computers often is displayed on punched cards or tape. Above, center, is a machine for preparing these. Many electronic devices display their results in lights, turned *on* or *off* in a binary number system. Shown above are decimal numbers, corresponding binary numbers, and combinations of lights representing those numbers on an electronic scaler.

a little noise of its own, and so make the measurement a little less reliable.

In high-fidelity sound reproduction the signal is the music; the noise comes from the texture of the record or tape, from the amplifier, or from a passing truck outside. The display is to the ear of the listener. The number of choices we make each second as we listen to the music is in the tens of thousands. Measurement is similar, but it usually involves something new, not the reproduction of something old.

10–4. Black Boxes and Calibration

Look at an auto radio or, better yet, at the radio rack of an airlines plane. You will see one or a collection of black metal boxes. Various wires go in and out of the boxes, interconnecting them, or going to the outside world, to antenna or ground, to electric lines, or to a point of display like a loudspeaker or a dial. Open a box lid, and inside you will see a maze of colored wires and of little bits and pieces of electronic equipment. You do not grasp the purpose of each wire; but you can use the black box or radio well enough.

Such experience has given us a useful and expressive phrase: we speak of a physical system of any kind as a "black box" when we make use of it without analyzing how it functions, without lifting the lid. Sooner or later we hope to lift the lid on all the black boxes, but we have not done so yet. The point is that real progress can be made by the use of black boxes. With some care we can successfully use an instrument whose operation we do not understand.

The eye is a fine example. It is a real black box. But we know from innumerable cross-checks how to use it, how to judge light and dark, or large and small, or fast and slow. We know its limitations, too. So far in this book the microscope is a black box. Yet it is not likely that the use of the microscope is deceptive. To measure the size of a hair with it, we simply look at the hair against a finely ruled grating. The experience of ordinary viewing convinces us that when we see the hair beside the rule we can measure its size pretty well, even if we are looking through a microscope at the two of them. We are using the microscope as a black box; but we gain confidence in it by use.

Quite generally we find out how to use black boxes by using them to study known objects, objects like the little ruler which we feel we can understand from earlier experience. For example, we can use the split-field range finder of a camera even when we don't know how it works. We learn by use that when we fit both parts of an object together in the viewer, the reading on the range-finder scale gives the distance to the object. If the range finder has no scale, we can make a scale for it by using it on known distances. Then we can use the range finder to measure unknown distances. The use of a black box in known physical situations allows us to learn how it performs even if we don't find out why. When its performance is known we can use it to make new measurements. On the basis of use we can decide what display of the instrument (black box or not) corresponds to the value of the quantity we want to measure. This process, learning the performance of an instrument by measuring what we already know, is called *calibration.* Usually we calibrate measuring instruments, as you may have done for your microbalance or your range finder.

Physics is a great enterprise of human beings. No one knows it all or can do it all. All of us use some black boxes, and instruments are at least partly black box to everyone. The principle of the equal-arm balance is clear, but generations of design and experiment lie behind the shape of the beams made so that they will not bend, the support of the pans made so that they hang vertically, and a thousand other points. For every user but a skilled and experienced designer of the balance, some of this remains as a black box. Even the designer probably regards as black box the agate bearing on which his knife edge rests. He knows agate is hard and durable, but he does not know why. The properties of the agate depend on its molecular structure; that remains in a black box for the designer.

Although we have used the microscope as a black box, it cannot be all black box to everyone. Most man-made things cannot be complete black boxes, for someone has to make them. They are partly black box because we are aware of so much that we have yet to understand.

Curiosity to open the black boxes is needed for the understanding of physics. But also one needs the judgment to know when and where black boxes may be safely used. Confidence in the black box comes with calibration, use, cross-check, ultimately with opening the lid and tracing out the method of operation. What remains a black

10–4. "Black Boxes." The mobile rack (below) uses numerous electronic black boxes. Notice the meters, lights, oscilloscope, and recording graph that display information to the user. The operation of the black box (right) may involve only the use of the meter, controls, and input jacks in the front. The maintenance of it would involve the checking and replacing of tubes, etc. (below, right) or of the maze of wires, resistors, capacitors, etc., under the chassis. Both use and maintenance can be accomplished without an understanding of why it works as it does.

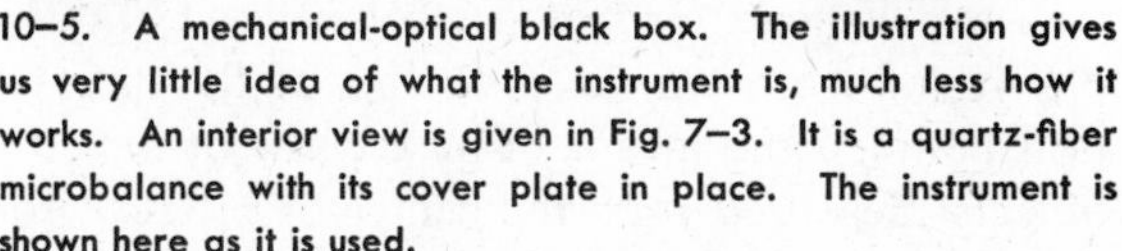
10–5. A mechanical-optical black box. The illustration gives us very little idea of what the instrument is, much less how it works. An interior view is given in Fig. 7–3. It is a quartz-fiber microbalance with its cover plate in place. The instrument is shown here as it is used.

10–6. Calibration. An object with known dimensions can be used to calibrate a black box. The diffraction grating (enlarged at left) has been ruled with 15,000 lines to the inch by advancing a screw $\frac{1}{15,000}$ inch at a time as the surface is ruled. We can use this grating to calibrate the electron microscope with which this enlarged photograph was made.

10–7. Interaction. Whatever measurement we attempt, the operation has some interaction with the thing being measured. The smaller the thing being measured, the more noticeable is the effect of interaction. In checking the air pressure in a bicycle tire, the interaction is not negligible. Each time we place the gauge on the valve stem a little air is removed from the tire. After a few times, the pressure of the air in the tire has been lowered quite a bit.

box today will be opened in a generation; but its opening is likely to involve the skillful use of all sorts of black boxes, black boxes which we have never seen.

10–5. Interaction

No measurement can be made without some interaction with the object or the event measured. You can measure a table with a meter stick in a dark room, but you must touch the table. If you have light in the room, you can line up the end of the stick with the table edge by sighting, but the light must strike the table and return to your eye. Even the planets cannot be measured without disturbing them, if ever so little. The sunlight pushes them a little out of the paths they would otherwise take. No sunlight, no measurements. Radar too could be used, but its signal must strike and return. All this seems trivial; but consider a single atom. No meter stick can fail to disturb it; even light may push it or distort it badly.

We must be careful to see that our measurements do not modify unduly the quantity we want to measure. Guarding against too much disturbance is an easy thing in large-scale physics, for we have delicate probes, such as light. In the physics of the atom the problems of the interaction between the means of measurement and the objects measured take the center of interest, for we have no probes that will not disturb these tiny structures. We must try to allow for the disturbance as best we can.

10–6. Light

Most of the decisions we make, most of the information we get about the world, we take in through the eyes. In the brain of man, the area called the visual cortex, which receives the signals from the eye, is larger than that for all other senses taken together. The eye is a black box, one we use with daring and precision. We are all experts in its use. But in a dark room, the eye is useless. It depends on light signals.

What is light? We have used it in many of the measurements described in this part of the book. We have made assumptions about its behavior. Light actuates our most important instruments. It is everywhere in our world. We depend on it so much that we cannot really allow it to remain unexamined.

Light is not matter, but sometimes it issues from matter. It is something different from all that we have studied. In the second part of this book it will be the central topic.

FOR HOME, DESK, AND LAB

1. Analyze the series of decisions you make in discovering that your watch reads 37 minutes and 23 seconds past eleven o'clock. How will the set of decisions change if the watch is turned 90 degrees from its normal position? If you read the face in a mirror what decisions would you make?

2. Which measurement is more complex and why: measuring a table approximately 2.5 feet long to the nearest sixteenth inch, or measuring the diameter of a hair to the nearest hundredth of a millimeter under the microscope? Discuss the decisions required.

3. Make a table showing all possible combinations of on-off conditions of a set of five lights. Use these to make an on-off code representing the alphabet.

4. In the game of "gossip," a leader composes a message which he then whispers to the next player, who writes down what he thinks he heard and repeats it to the next person. Each person (amplifier) in the path of the message is apt to introduce his own ideas (noise) into the original statement (signal). Try this game, comparing the final written version with the original. What kind of "noise" does any particular amplifier introduce?

5. * Try an experiment on signal-to-noise ratio by seating two people 4 feet apart and then turning up the volume of a radio or record player until they have difficulty understanding one another. They should keep their voices at about the same level all along. Place them 6 feet apart and repeat the experiment, then 8 feet, then 10 feet.

6. A camera is a "black box" to many people — to all in some degree, because we do not know how every part of the photographic action works. How much of a camera is "black box" to you?

FURTHER READING

BERKELEY, EDMUND C., *Giant Brains: Machines That Think.* Wiley, 1949.

BOWDEN, BERTRAM V., *Faster Than Thought.* Pitman & Sons, London, 1953.

GORN, SAUL, and MANHEIMER, WALLACE, *The Electronic Brain and What It Can Do.* Science Research Associates, Chicago, 1956.

WIENER, NORBERT, *The Human Use of Human Beings: Cybernetics and Society.* Doubleday Anchor Books, 1955.

PART II OPTICS AND WAVES

Reflection of water waves. Water waves strike a barrier and reflect, much as light is reflected from a mirror. This similarity suggests that a wave model may be useful in describing light. We shall use waves on ropes and springs, too, in our study of wave behavior. And we shall find that what we learn gives us a major key to understanding the structure of atoms.

HOW LIGHT BEHAVES

CHAPTER 11

MOST of the information that reaches us comes to us through the sense of sight. From the very beginning of history, men have puzzled about the nature of the light that affects our eyes. The questions they asked were probably the same that have occurred to you. What is light? How does it travel, and how fast? Is seeing always believing? Why are some objects colored, some white, and some black?

11–1. Sources of Light

Anyone who has spent a moonless night in the country, in a forest, or at sea knows how very dark it can be when the sun is on the other side of the earth. At early dawn, objects that we could not see a few minutes earlier begin to take shape. Then details sharpen, colors appear and brighten, and daylight begins. It is the sun, seen to rise above the horizon in the east, that brings with it the light that gives shape, detail, and color to our world.

The sun, the stars, lamps, even lightning bugs, give off light. They are called luminous bodies (from the Latin word *lumen,* meaning light). All other objects — trees, grass, the pages of this book, for example — are nonluminous. They are visible only when they receive light from some luminous source and reflect it to our eyes.

Whether a body is luminous or nonluminous depends as much on its condition as on the material of which it is made. By changing the conditions we can make many familiar substances luminous or nonluminous at will. The filament, or fine wire, inside an electric light bulb is nonluminous unless it is heated by an electric current passing through it. We can take a cold piece of iron and make it glow with a red, yellow, or white light by heating it in a bed of burning coals or over a gas flame. When solids and such liquids as melted metals are heated to temperatures above 800 degrees Celsius (about 1400 degrees Fahrenheit), they become sources of light. Such heated materials are known as *incandescent* bodies.

Careful observation shows that the light from candle flames comes from many small, hot particles of carbon that are burning within the flame. When hot they give off the candle light. Thus the flame is another incandescent source of light. Many of the carbon particles are not completely burned in an ordinary flame. They cool off as they are carried by the air above the flame, become nonluminous, and make up the main part of the rising smoke.

Not all light sources are incandescent. Neon tubes and fluorescent lamps, like electric light bulbs, give off a bright light as long as an electric current passes through them; touching each of them, however, convinces us at once that there must be a difference in the way the light is produced. The neon and fluorescent tubes remain quite cool, whereas the incandescent bulb soon becomes too hot to touch. Pursuing this difference further, we find that by gradually increasing the current in the filament of the incandescent bulb we can increase its brightness, but that there is also an accompanying change in color. At first we see a dull red glow which changes to a bright yellow and, with sufficient current, can become what we call "white hot" like the heated iron. On the other hand, if we increase the current through a neon tube to increase the brightness, we observe no change in color. Thus we have discovered a basic difference between incandescent sources and other sources. In the former, changes in brightness, temperature, and color seem to be closely linked, while in the latter the color of the source depends mainly on the nature of the material and does not vary with brightness.

A great deal of light reaches our eyes from nonluminous surfaces. To convince ourselves, we need only to imagine how the average room would appear if the walls and other surfaces were covered with a paint so black that it reflected none of the light reaching it. The lights would appear as bright glares against dark backgrounds. If the earth had no atmosphere to reflect or scatter sunlight, the sun and the stars could be seen at the same time against a dead black sky. White ceilings or bright walls reflect and diffuse much of the light they receive and so increase the brightness within the room. In fact, when we use indirect lighting we hide the lamps from sight, and all of the light reaches us after being diffused from the walls and ceiling. On a larger scale the moon, which we often think of as a source of light at night, is really an indirect-lighting device that reflects sunlight. Considering this fact, can you explain the phases of the moon, that is, the changing appearance of the moon in the course of a month? Can you see why a full moon rises approximately at sunset and why a new moon rises approximately at sunrise?

11–2. Transparent, Colored, and Opaque Materials

When you look through a clean window at a brightly illuminated scene outside, you are hardly conscious of the fact that the glass is there. Substances that transmit light in this way are said to be transparent. Later in the day, when dusk has come, look out through the same window from inside a lighted room. In addition to the world outside, you now see in the glass a reflection of yourself and of the room. The light by which you see yourself must have started from within the room. Instead of going through the glass to the outside, this light was returned to you. It was reflected.

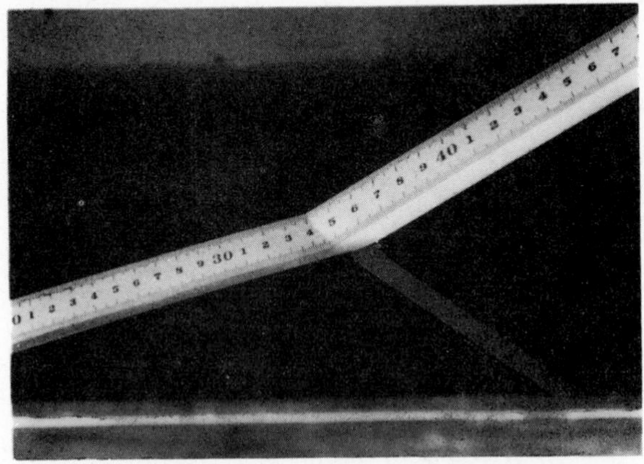

11–1. This photograph shows the apparent bending of a meter stick at the point where it enters water. The gray shape sloping down from the stick is a reflection.

Does the thickness of a transparent body have any effect on the amount of light it transmits? A single piece of the glass seems to transmit light almost perfectly, but if you pile up a thick stack of ten or twenty pieces of clear glass, some light is *absorbed* and the light passing through it dims and appears somewhat colored. Evidently we become aware of clear materials like plastics, glass, and water partly because they reflect as well as transmit light, and partly because some of the light is absorbed.

Such materials have another important effect on light. When light enters or leaves them, the direction of its motion changes in an interesting way. Fig. 11–1 shows a straight stick extending into a tank of clean water. The apparent bending of the stick at the point at which it enters the water certainly indicates that something happens to the light which passes from the stick to the camera. Another illustration of the same effect is shown in Fig. 11–2 (a). The coin on the right is in an empty container, and an identical coin is in a water-filled container on the left. The coins were photographed simultaneously with the apparatus shown in Fig. 11–2 (b). The coin in the water looks nearer to the camera and bigger than the other one. This "floating" coin effect and the illusion of the "bent" stick occur because light changes direction when it goes from one material, such as glass or water, into another material, such

11–2 (a). The "floating" coin.

11–2 (b). The position of camera and containers used in photographing the "floating" coin in Fig. 11–2 (a).

as air. This bending of a light path is called *refraction.* A detailed study of refraction contributes greatly to our understanding of what light is. We shall return to it several times.

Thus far, we have dealt only with colorless, almost perfectly transparent bodies. We all know that there are many transparent materials which are colored. We can see objects through them, but the objects appear in different colors. These materials clearly do something to the light passing through them. Do they add something to it, or do they take something away? At first glance this may seem like a very difficult question, yet a few simple experiments can give us an answer.

First of all, look through a piece of red glass at a sheet of white paper, illuminated by sunlight or by electric light. The paper now appears red. White light left the paper, but the red glass did something to the light to make it appear red. Suppose a second piece of red glass is placed between the first piece and your eye, so that the light must pass through both pieces. If the glass adds something to the light, the paper should appear a more brilliant red than before. If the glass subtracts something, we might expect that most of this "something" would be removed by the first piece of glass. The second piece should then have very little effect on the appearance of the paper. In fact, if we actually try two pieces of red glass this way, we find that the second has little effect.

We can account for the little change in color by arguing that one piece does not subtract quite all of the non-red parts of the light; there is something left for the second red glass to take away, and the red color we see through the two pieces may appear somewhat redder. We can do the same experiment with two pieces of green glass just as we did with the two pieces of red glass. As might be expected, the second green plate has little effect; at most, the paper appears a bit more green. Now what will happen if we try red and green together? After subtracting *everything but green* with the green glass, and *everything but red* with the red glass, we can certainly expect that what is left will be neither red nor green. At this stage of our investigation, we have not yet enough knowledge of the process of subtraction to predict what the color will be, but we can certainly say that much less light should reach us through the two pieces of glass than through either alone. When we try the experiment, we find, surely enough, that the brightness of the paper is tremendously reduced and that the little color left is neither red nor green but is rather a weak yellow or amber. This result convinces us of the correctness of the subtraction idea.

What is the "something" that is subtracted from white light to give color? This is a question whose answer we must postpone until we have learned a good deal more about light. Perhaps we can be satisfied for the moment with the recognition that white light is something more complex than light of a single color. We shall

11–3. Regular and diffuse reflection. The white cardboard (far left) sends more of the light from the lamp toward the camera than does the mirror.

not, in fact, come anywhere near to complete answers to many of the questions about color in this book. As any artist will tell you, the color you see is determined by the nature of the illuminated object, the nature of the light that is illuminating it, and the condition of your eye at the time that the color is seen. It also depends on the other objects you see at the same time.

Red and green glass together subtract almost everything from white light. Most common materials go further and either reflect or absorb everything in white light, allowing no light to be transmitted. We cannot see through even quite thin pieces of metals, wood, cardboard, or heavy cloth. Such materials are opaque. Opaque materials reflect some of the light that falls on them and absorb the rest, so that no light passes through them.

11–3. Reflection

All bodies, whether transparent or opaque, reflect some of the light that falls upon them. That is, they send some of the light back to the same side of the body as that from which it came. Most surfaces give a *diffuse reflection.* They send light off in many directions. It is by the help of this diffused light that we see illuminated bodies, observe their texture and color, and distinguish them from their surroundings.

A few materials, such as highly polished sheets of silver, aluminum, or steel, absorb little from white light and also reflect in a much more regular manner than do rougher surfaces. An ordinary mirror consists of a thin film of silver placed on the back of a plate of glass. In Fig 11–3, light from the same source shines on both a mirror and a piece of white paper. The paper appears well illuminated and is white against the dark background. On the other hand, the mirror appears quite dark. The same amount of light is reaching the two, and we know that this mirror reflects light very well, as is indicated by the reflection of the white candle. Why, then, is the paper brighter than the mirror in the photograph? The mirror sends all the light reflected from the lamp away from the camera, while the paper sends reflected light in all directions so that some of it reaches the camera.

It is the regularity of reflection from smooth surfaces that allows the formation of images. Fig. 11–4 shows a lake surrounded by trees and mountains. Is the picture printed right-side up? Turn the book over and examine it again. There is at least one clue in the picture that tells you whether it is right-side up or upside down.

What can you learn about images by simple observation? Look at yourself in a mirror. Is

11–4. Nearly perfect reflection. Is the picture right-side up? Which are the actual hills? Which are their reflections?

the view that you get of your image exactly like the view that other people get of you? Move your right hand. Does your image move a right or a left hand in response? Place an object such as a pencil against the mirror, then hold a similar one in your hand and observe the images. Does the image of the object in your hand seem to be on the mirror beside the other pencil, or behind the mirror? How do they compare in apparent size? How does the distance of the image behind the mirror compare with the distance between your hand and the mirror?

In Chapter 12 we shall try to see if we can find something about the laws of reflection that will allow us to discuss "why," as well as "what" happens when images are formed by mirrors or other smooth reflecting surfaces.

11–4. Light-Sensitive Devices

We have not yet mentioned how we know that light is present or what its color may be. We have taken for granted that marvelous instrument, the human eye. A thorough study of the eye would include discussions of how light is refracted to fall on the nerve cells of the retina at the back of the eyeball, how the eye adjusts itself to see clearly objects at different distances or of different brightnesses, how the effects of color are produced, and also a discussion of the things that can go wrong with our vision. Such a study could easily occupy us for a full year or more. Here we shall have to be content with the observation that in passing through structures in the front of the eye light is refracted in such a way that an image is formed on the retina. Chemical changes take place at the retina, and as a result electrical impulses are sent along the nerves to the brain.

There are many instruments, other than the eye, that respond chemically or electrically to the action of light. These instruments are often used in the laboratory to study light by methods that are more convenient or more satisfactory than is visual observation. The best-known substances that are *photosensitive* are some of the chemical compounds containing silver. Such compounds are used in photographic films. The full process involved in the exposure and development of the film is complex, but the essential thing is that those portions of the film on which light has fallen are left, after chemical treatment, with a deposit of finely divided silver. In this state the silver does not appear as bright, shiny metal, but as dull, opaque particles, the familiar black portions of a film negative. The portions not exposed to light become clear and transparent. Color film, sensitive to different colors of light, is made by the addition of various dyes and by changes in composition.

There are also a number of devices that give an electric current when light falls on them, without any chemical changes taking place. Chief among these are photoelectric cells, or photocells, which we shall discuss later. (Chapter 33.) The electric current that flows through a photocell is proportional to the light intensity.

11–5. Invisible Light

Photocells, photographic films, or other detectors of light sometimes show the presence of light when none is visible to the eye. For example, Fig. 11–5 shows a photograph of an ordinary flatiron, taken in a totally dark room using a special kind of photographic film. Apparently the flatiron is giving off "light" of some sort, although we cannot see it as a luminous object. We might guess that the light given off is the same thing as the heat which we feel when we hold a hand a few inches away from a heated iron.

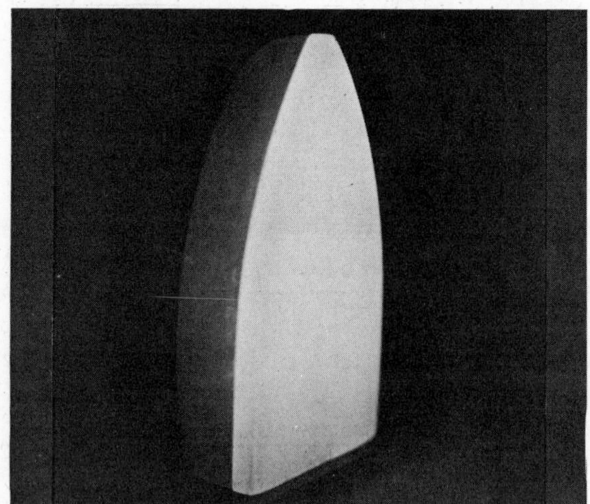

11–5. Photograph of a flatiron taken by its own invisible "light." What is the name of this invisible "light"?

As we shall see later, this guess is correct: *heat* radiation is indeed a form of light known as *infrared* radiation. About one-third of the radiation that reaches us from the sun is heat radiation; most of the rest is visible light.

Like the eye's retina, an ordinary photocell cannot detect heat radiation. This may be shown by placing a photocell near a heated flatiron in a dark room. We know from the photographic evidence that the iron gives off heat radiation, yet the photocell shows no response. A different result is obtained, however, if we use a mercury-arc lamp as a source of light. A good lamp for this purpose is one of the small sterilizing lamps sometimes used in refrigerators. (These lamps are constructed with a special kind of glass, known as Corex.) When a photocell is placed near such a lamp, the electric current passing through the cell increases with the intensity of the light striking it. If a piece of ordinary window glass, which is almost perfectly transparent to visible light, is placed between the lamp and the photocell, the current in the photocell decreases appreciably. From this simple procedure we learn several things. We observe no difference in the light from the lamp when looking through the window glass, but the photocell obviously does. There must be some part of the radiation from the lamp which is invisible to the eye, and which is not transmitted by window glass. It is evident, too, that Corex must be transparent to this invisible light; otherwise it would not reach the photocell. As we shall see, the mercury lamp emits *ultraviolet* light in addition to visible light. This radiation is not only invisible — it is harmful to the human eye. One should therefore avoid looking at sources of ultraviolet light.

In Section 7–9 we saw that a ruled surface like a phonograph record reflects light of different colors in different directions. Spectra are formed in which the red goes in one direction followed by orange, yellow, green, blue, and violet in order as the directions change. By using the appropriate detectors, we can show that the invisible light from the mercury lamp is always deviated into the region beyond the violet, and the light from the hot iron goes at the other end of the spectrum, "below" the red. The names ultraviolet and infrared mean "extreme violet" and "beneath the red," respectively. Where visible light ends and invisible infrared and ultraviolet begin depends on the detector. We see one part of the spectrum; other animals seem to see slightly different parts; and photographic films and other instruments see much further into the regions of the spectrum that we find invisible.

11–6. How Light Travels

The sun and the stars are so familiar that we seldom think of the vast stretches of almost empty space that separate them from us. Yet we know that the sun is about 1.5×10^{11} meters away from the earth, that the nearest star is about three hundred thousand times as far, and that countless stars have been seen at distances so remote that comprehension almost fails us. All the information from which we have learned about this vast universe has come to us "riding swiftly astride beams of light." It must therefore be true that light can travel over very great distances and that it can travel freely in empty space. Light is very different from sound in this respect, for sound can be transmitted from a source to our ears only through substances such as steel, water, or air. The difference between the two can be illustrated by a simple laboratory experiment. An electric bell and a small lamp are hung by wires inside a glass jar, which can be evacuated by a pump. As we pump the air from the jar the sound of the bell becomes fainter until finally it is scarcely heard. If light were equally affected, we should see the jar slowly darken and its contents fade into empty blackness. Instead, everything inside is just as brightly visible as it was before we pumped the air out.

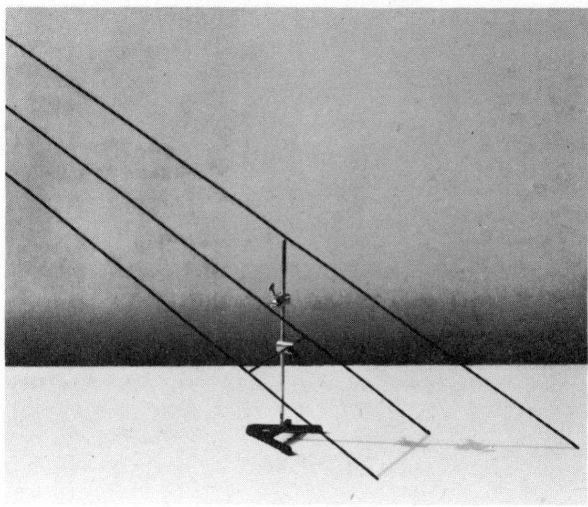

11–6. The formation of shadows. Lines connecting points on the shadow to points on the object casting the shadow are nearly parallel; all point to the light source.

As familiar as the sun itself are the shadows it casts. What can we learn from them about light? As we walk or run along on a sunny day, our shadows keep pace with us. This simple experience shows that light must travel much faster than we can run, for the shadows of our heads must lag behind us by the distance we move while light goes from our heads to the ground. Shadow shapes, too, reveal information about the nature of light. In Fig. 11–6 a set of lines connects various points on a shadow to the corresponding points on the object which casts the shadow. The lines are almost parallel and they all point to the source of the light. Evidently light travels in straight lines.

To learn more about how light travels, let us examine the behavior of light beams within a darkened room or box. Fig. 11–7 shows a light

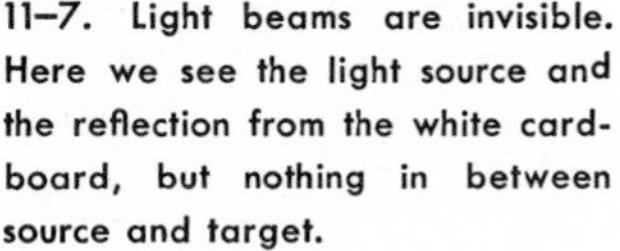

11–7. Light beams are invisible. Here we see the light source and the reflection from the white cardboard, but nothing in between source and target.

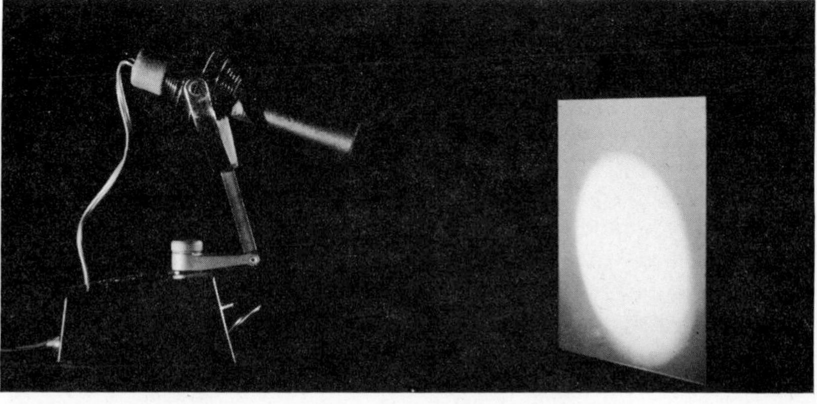

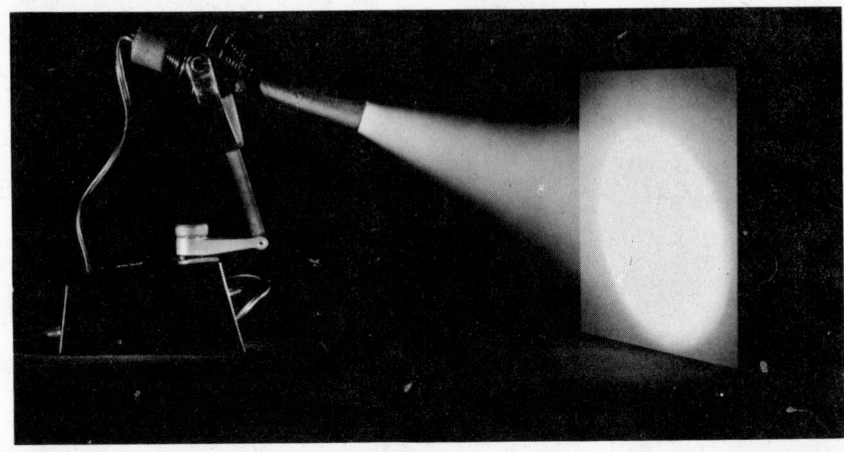

11–8. If fine particles are introduced into the air, as at the left, the light beam shows clearly all the way from the source to the cardboard target. Compare with Fig. 11–7.

source which is pointed at a piece of paper. We know that the light comes from the source and we see it reflected from the paper, but we do not see it between the two objects. Common sense suggests, however, that the light must travel between the two. In Fig. 11–8 fine smoke particles have been introduced into the air and now the beam shows clearly all the way. The straight edges of the beam connect the source with the edges of the illuminated spot, confirming our belief that light travels in straight lines. The fact that we saw nothing of the beam until the smoke was introduced tells us that light enters our eyes only when we are looking directly toward a source or when there are illuminated bodies that can reflect light directly to our eyes. In this case the light was reflected from the paper and from smoke particles, making them act like new sources to send the light on new straight-line paths toward our eyes.

11–7. Diffraction

We have seen evidence that light generally travels in straight lines, yet it is easy to find some exceptions to this rule. You have probably had the experience of looking at a distant light, such as a street lamp, through a window screen. You probably noticed that you saw not only the distant light but also two lines of color, at right angles to each other. A related effect may be observed if you hold two fingers in front of your eye in such a way that you look at a light through the very fine slit between them when they are not quite pressed tightly together [Fig. 11–9 (a)]. This experiment is most effective if the light comes from a long, thin source, such as a neon tube or a fluorescent lamp, and you hold your fingers parallel to the source. The narrow, alternating bands of dark and light that appear are certainly something different from what you ordinarily see in the light coming through a large opening [Fig. 11–9 (b)].

These happenings can be partially explained if we suppose that light bends slightly as it passes the edge of an obstacle. We would then expect the edges of *all* shadows to be slightly fuzzy, rather than perfectly sharp. When the sources of light are large and the openings through which light passes are large, this fuzziness is insignificant in comparison with the whole pattern of light and we do not notice it. When the source is far away and the openings are small, as are those in a piece of window screen, or between two fingers, the effect of the bending becomes important. This explanation, however, is not complete. We shall have to add more to it before it accounts for the dark and light bands.

The thought processes you have just gone through are a good example of the way in which scientists approach truth in a step-by-step fashion. For most purposes, the statement that light travels in straight lines accounts for many observations very well. A closer look at things shows us that it cannot always be accepted as completely true and that light does bend very slightly around obstacles. The bending is, however, so slight that we can neglect it for most purposes. We say that the assumption of straight-line travel is a first approximation to the description of the behavior of light. The second approximation to the behavior of light is more complicated and more troublesome to use, so we shall employ it

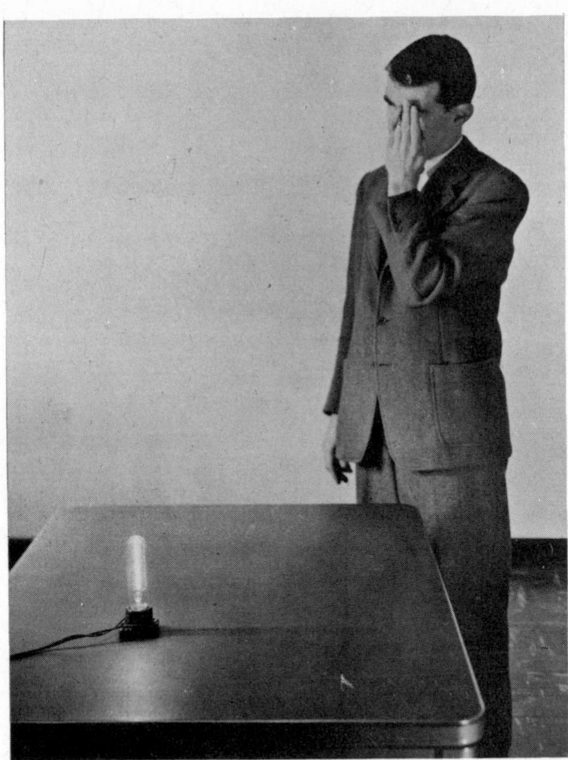

11–9 (a). A simple way to observe diffraction.

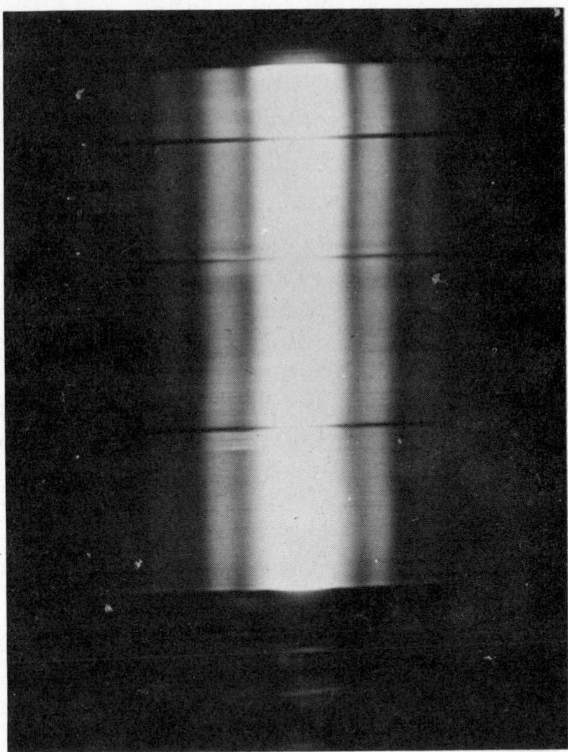

11–9 (b). A diffraction pattern similar to one seen through a slit formed by two fingers. This picture of a blue light source was taken with blue-sensitive film. The black lines are supports holding the filament.

only when the phenomena that we are studying demand that we do so. We shall find, for example, certain light effects that seem to be completely unrelated until we consider their explanation in terms of this bending of light around obstacles.

The pattern shown in Fig. 11–9 (b) is but one of the many odd shadow pictures that can be obtained as a result of the fact that light does bend around opaque bodies in its path. This bending is known as *diffraction.*

Diffraction accounts in part for the fact that the images of stars in telescopes appear as small blurs of light instead of sharp points. The blurs arise from the bending of light as it goes through the smallest "hole" in the telescope. Fig. 11–10 shows the shadow of a small hole.

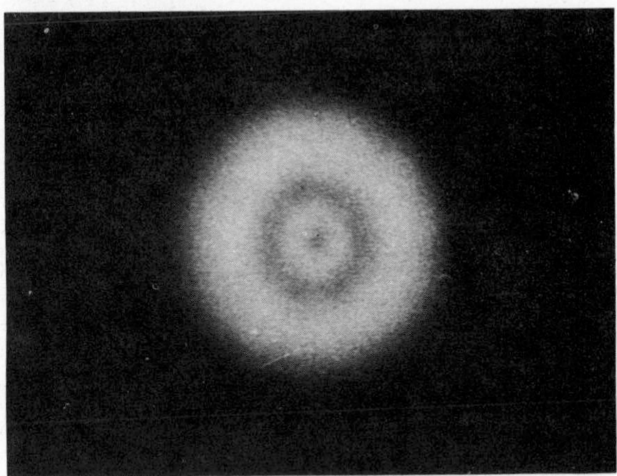

11–10. Shadow of a small hole. The lack of sharply defined edges and the presence of the light and dark bands are caused by the diffraction of light.

11–8. The Speed of Light

All of us have, at one time or another, heard the roar of a jet plane high in the sky and instinctively looked for it in the direction of the sound. We finally saw it far ahead of the sound. Then in deciding where the airplane actually was, we believed our eyes rather than our ears. Why did we trust our eyes? We know that sound takes some time to travel so great a distance and that light travels far faster than sound. We did not assume that the plane was beyond the point where we saw it, because we believe that light travels fast indeed!

Galileo suggested a method for finding the speed of light, similar to the method he used to measure the speed of sound. Two men with lanterns were placed at a measured distance apart. The first uncovered his lantern and started a clock, and the second uncovered his lantern when he saw the light from the first. When the first man saw the second's light, he stopped the clock, thus measuring the time for light to travel from the first man to the second and back — or so Galileo hoped. This experiment failed to give the speed of light because light travels so fast. But it was not a complete failure. It showed that the speed of light was too great to allow its passage to be measured over short distances with the crude timing mechanisms then available.

A satisfactory method of measuring the speed of light was first proposed by Roemer in 1676. This method does not need a highly precise measurement of a very short time interval. Longer time intervals are easier to measure. Roemer increased the time interval by increasing the distance the light travels. He used astronomical measurements to find the time taken for light to cross the diameter of the earth's orbit. What Roemer did was to observe the times at which some of the moons of Jupiter went into eclipse as they passed into that planet's shadow. These eclipses occur at regular intervals. For example, the brightest of the satellites revolves in its orbit about Jupiter in just a little over seven days and it is eclipsed once during every revolution. Using the average time between eclipses as the time of rotation of the satellite, he found that the eclipses occurred about 11 minutes early when the earth was nearest Jupiter and 11 minutes late when it was farthest away, because the light had to travel across the earth's orbit. Roemer could not find a good value of the speed of light from these observations. His measurements were inaccurate and also, at that time, the size of the earth's orbit was not accurately known. The great contribution of Roemer's work was the demonstration that light took a measurable time to cross the earth's orbit and that it therefore travels at a finite speed.

Later measurements of the delays in eclipse times showed that the interval required to cross the orbit is 16 min 20 sec rather than 22 min as Roemer found. The average distance of the earth from the sun is now known to be 1.47×10^{11} meters; hence the speed of light is

$$c = \frac{2 \times 1.47 \times 10^{11}\ \text{m}}{980\ \text{sec}} = 3.00 \times 10^{8}\ \text{m/sec}.$$

The first determination of the speed of light over a distance short enough to be practical on the surface of the earth was made by Armand Fizeau in 1848. It required the invention of a timing device that could measure very short intervals with accuracy. We shall discuss Fizeau's method in Chapter 15.

FOR HOME, DESK, AND LAB

1. * Take a flashlight with a rather old battery, turn it on and observe what happens to the brightness and to the color of the light that it gives off as the battery grows weaker. Does only the brightness change, or do the brightness and color change together? Is the bulb in a flashlight an incandescent source or not?

2. Remembering that we see the moon by reflected light, can you show that:

   (a) A moon rising in the east at midnight cannot be a full moon.

   (b) A new moon cannot be seen for long after dark.

   Hint: Make diagrams showing the positions of the sun, earth, and moon at different phases of the moon.

3. The moon, unlike the earth, has no atmosphere.

   (a) If you were standing on the moon, at a place where the earth appeared to be directly overhead, what would you see in the sky, assuming that the moon is seen as full from the earth at the time?

   (b) Answer the same question for the time when the moon is seen as a new moon from the earth.

4. We have seen that glass, although transparent, does not transmit all of the light that enters it, some of the light being absorbed. Is this also true of clear water? Be prepared to discuss what evidence you would look for to support your answer.

5. Occasionally one sees an airplane in the sky shortly after sunset or shortly before sunrise and is

surprised to see it appear to be very bright, more like a star or planet than like a plane as seen in daylight. Can you explain why this happens? Hint: Draw a diagram showing the earth, the sun, and the airplane.

6. Fig. 11–8 shows clearly that smoke scatters light toward our eyes, even though the light was originally traveling in such a direction that it would not reach us. In view of this, why does a dense cloud of smoke overhead appear dark, rather than light? Write briefly. Be prepared to discuss.

7. We have seen that when light from a white object falls on a photographic film it produces a deposit of black silver after development. This results in the familiar *negative* image on the film. If you shine light through the negative onto another photographic film, after development what kind of an image will you have?

8. One of the remarkable properties of the eye is its ability to adjust so that objects at different distances are seen clearly. To demonstrate this, place yourself about 3 or 4 feet from a window and concentrate your attention on the window itself. You will find that the window is seen very clearly, that the lines where the glass meets the frame are seen sharply, and that even such details as spots on the glass are apparent. Still concentrating your attention on the window, note the appearance of objects in the distance, outside. Are they sharp or fuzzy? Can you observe their details? Next, concentrate your attention on the far-away objects until you see them sharply. Can you now see the details of the window clearly?

9. Move this book toward you, with one eye closed or covered. When the book has just reached the point at which the print blurs, have someone measure the distance of the book from your eye. Repeat the experiment with the other eye. Are the two distances approximately equal? Try this with a few people of different ages, and record the results along with their ages.

(a) Is there a limit to the ability of the eye to adjust itself for clear vision?

(b) Is this limit the same for all persons, or for the two eyes of any one person?

(c) Does it vary, in general, with the age of the person? Compare your answers with those found by other people in the class.

10. * It was stated in Section 11–2 that color is a complicated phenomenon, depending on many factors, not just on the kind of light reaching a surface and on the nature of the surface. You can readily convince yourself of this. Cut a small square of light gray paper or cardboard, about 1 inch on a side, and place it in the center of a large piece of white paper. View it from a distance of about 2 feet and under bright illumination.

(a) Describe its color and brightness.

(b) Move the gray square to the center of a large piece of bright-red paper and view it under the same conditions as before. Again describe its color and brightness. Are they the same as before?

(c) Finally, move the gray square to a piece of black paper. What happens now?

11. (a) How long does it take light to reach the earth from the sun?

(b) If the light from the nearest star takes 4.3 years to reach us, how far away is the star?

(c) Why is it convenient to express distances to stars in terms of light-years, rather than in meters, kilometers, or miles?

12. Radio waves travel at the same speed as light in empty space or in air.

(a) How long does it take a radio signal to travel from New York to San Francisco, a distance of about 4.8×10^3 km?

(b) A radar transmitter, which sends out radio signals of a particular type, when pointed at the moon receives a reflection 2.7 sec after the signal is sent. What does this experiment give as the distance of the moon from the earth?

FURTHER READING

BRAGG, SIR WILLIAM, *The Universe of Light.* Macmillan, 1933.

MINNAERT, M., *Light and Color in the Open Air.* Dover, 1954. A classic, describing many light effects such as rainbows, mirages, sunset colors, blue sky, etc.

REFLECTION AND IMAGES

CHAPTER 12

12–1. Shadows

Examine your own shadow, cast by the sun on a smooth floor or pavement. Notice the difference in sharpness between the outline of the shadow of your feet and that of your head. This difference is even more noticeable in the shadow of a thin vertical stick or rod as shown in the left half of Fig. 12–1. Apparently the shadow becomes wider and less sharp as the distance from the object to the edge of its shadow increases. The fuzziness of shadows also depends on the source of light. The right half of Fig. 12–1 shows the shadow cast when the source is a lamp behind a screen in which a very small hole has been punched. This shadow is quite sharply defined over its entire length. The shadows cast by tiny light sources are generally quite sharp, indicating that light propagates in straight lines.

The sharp shadows cast by a source of light so small that it may be considered a point give us a hint about the reason for the less sharp appearance of shadows in sunlight. Every point on the surface of the sun sends out light, and the shadow as a whole is not really a single shadow but is the combination of a very large number of individual shadows cast by light from each point on the sun's surface. Fig. 12–2 indicates how the shadow is formed when the source of light has considerable extent, like the sun. Traveling in straight lines, light from no part of the source can reach the circular region between *c* and *d*; hence this region of the shadow is black. In the dotted region between the circle *ab* and the circle *cd*, light from some parts of the source gets past the object and onto the screen. Hence the shadow is less dark, and it finally fades off to an indistinct

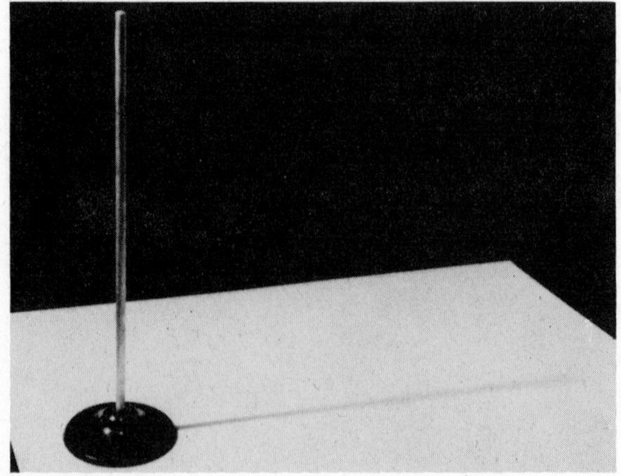

12–1. Shadows cast by an extended source of light (left) and by a point source of light (right). Notice the difference in their sharpness.

edge at the circle *ab*. Outside the shaded region between *a* and *b*, light arrives from all places on the source.

The dark part of a shadow, which no light from the source reaches, is called the umbra. The less black parts make up the penumbra. When we are in the umbra of the shadow of the moon, the sun is in total eclipse. When we are in the penumbra, we can see part of the sun, and we say the eclipse is partial.

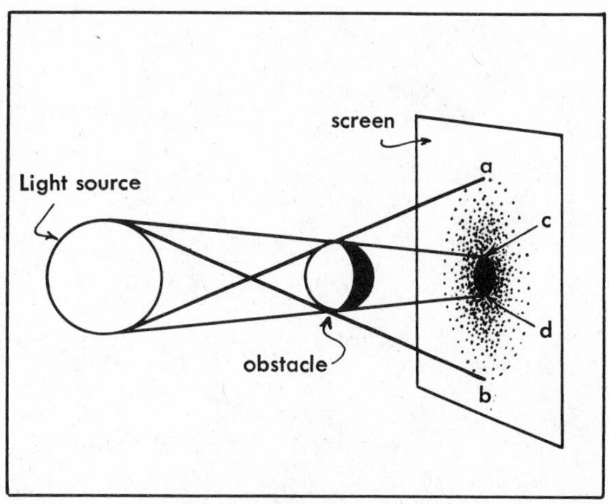

12–2. Formation of a shadow from an extended light source. Sketch is a cross section through the light source and obstacle in a plane perpendicular to the screen.

12–2. Light Beams, Pencils, and Rays

Point sources of light clearly give less complicated shadows than do extended sources. Fig. 12–3 (top) shows beams of light coming from a point source through a pinhole. In the upper picture, we see a cone marked out by the beam. Can you explain why it is a cone rather than a cylinder? The axis of the cone (the line joining the center of the pinhole to the center of the base of the cone) passes through the center of the source and the pinhole.

By putting two pinholes in line, as shown in Fig. 12–3 (bottom), we get a very narrow *pencil* of light. It is often convenient to imagine such a pencil of light that is smaller and finer than any pencil that we can produce in practice. The finest pencil that one can imagine is just a straight line. We call this extreme pencil a *ray* of light. Of course, we can never produce single light rays, but the idea of a ray is a very useful one. It

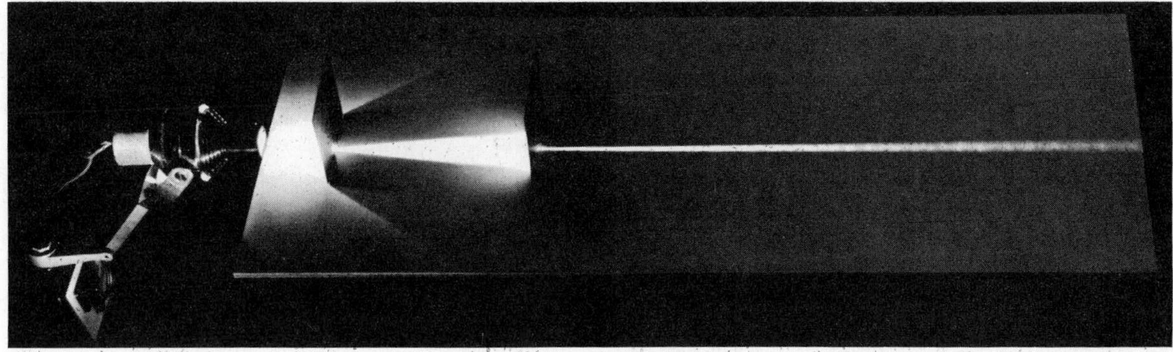

12–3. Beams and pencils of light. In the top picture, light coming from the source through a pinhole forms a cone-shaped beam. Below a second pinhole in line with the first produces a narrow pencil of light.

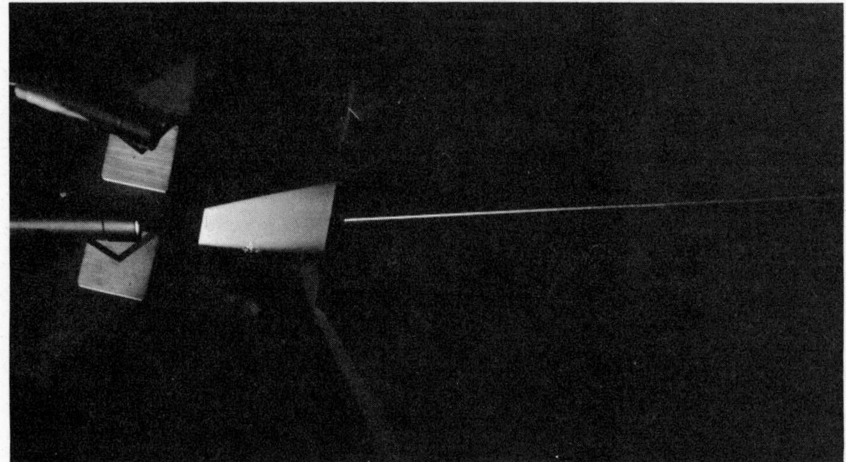

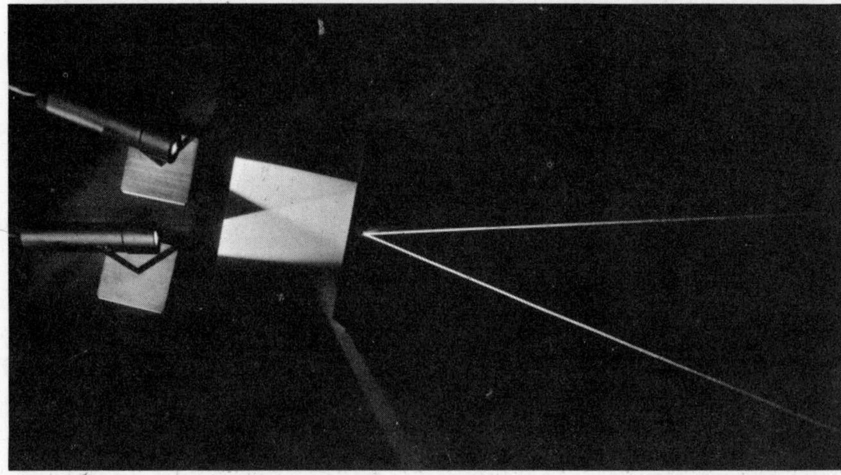

12–4. An experiment showing that two beams of light can pass through each other.

allows us to draw on paper lines that represent the directions in which light is traveling. A pencil of light can be found in nature; a ray of light is something we have invented to represent a very small pencil.

We often draw a few rays, for example, to indicate the limits of the illuminated region, the umbra and penumbra in Fig. 12–2. The rays we draw are not distinguishable in the light, which apparently goes in all directions from all points on the surface of the source. The rays we draw are useful like the lines on an architect's plan, but they are no more light than his lines are walls or windows. Light does not make rays; we do. They help us describe the way light behaves.

We know that light beams or pencils striking reflecting objects illuminate them so that they act as new sources. Light thus interacts with the material on which it falls, i.e., the light beam influences the material, and the material influences the behavior of the light beam. Can light beams also interact with each other? We can answer this question by letting the light beams from two different sources pass through a single pinhole, as is shown in Fig. 12–4. We find that each beam passes through the hole as if the other beam were not there.

In general, each light beam from two or more sources behaves as if the other beams were not present, and this independence of action is very important. The procedure of studying the pencils or rays from different sources or different parts of a source would otherwise be of little value. Tracing the rays that show the directions of two jets of water, for example, does not tell us much about where they go when they hit each other. It is because the light from each of two sources acts as if it were alone that we can trace rays to find the regions of light and shadow when both sources are present.

12–3. How We Locate Objects

We can always locate the position of a point source of light if we know the directions of several of the rays that come from this source. We simply draw two or more of these rays backward until they meet. The point of intersection is the location of the source. When a cone of rays comes to our eye from such a source, we automatically change the shape of the eye so that the diverging rays from the source are focused, and we can see an image of the source. This process of focusing our eyes gives us information equivalent to that of tracing back the rays, and in certain circumstances, without being aware of it, we use this information to estimate the distance to the source.

We can estimate distances more easily with two eyes than we can with one. To convince yourself of this, have a friend hold a thin piece of wire away from other objects (Fig. 12–5). With another similar wire in your hand try to touch the end of his wire when it is about as far away as you can reach. You will find that you can do this with considerable accuracy. Now try the same experiment with one eye closed. You will find it much more difficult to bring the two wires together.

One of the reasons you judge distances better with both eyes open is indicated by this experiment. Light coming from the end of an object

12–6. Binocular vision. We judge distance by the angle at which the eyes are converged on the subject, as well as by focusing them on the cones of rays.

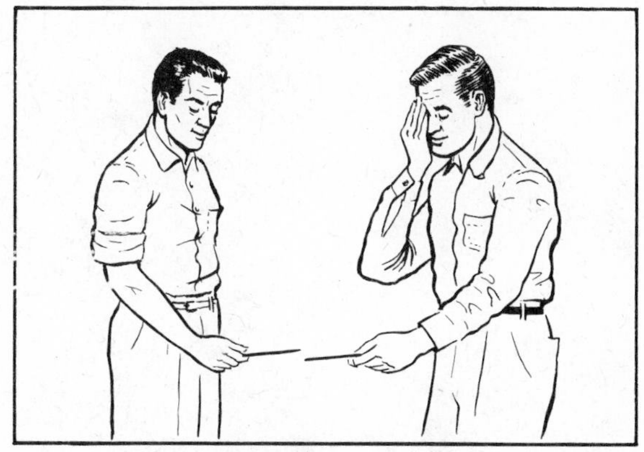

12–5. An experiment for testing your ability to judge distance with one eye.

must travel in different directions to reach the two eyes (Fig. 12–6). This is a simple case of triangulation (see Chapter 3). Here the base line is the distance between the eyes; and if the two eyes were independent persons, they could figure out the distance to the object by plotting the base line and the angles to the lines of sight or by doing trigonometric calculations. Of course our brain does not tell us the distance by such calculation. Instead the whole act of converging our eyes on the right sight lines and focusing them to the right cones of rays has been calibrated by our past experience. Our acquired knowledge of the distances associated with the particular act of converging and focusing tells us directly where the object is — and it tells us with more accuracy than just the act of focusing with one eye.

If you leave other objects around when you try to measure distance, or if you use blocks instead of thin wires, you will be able to touch one object to another still more easily. In such circumstances our brains take advantage of other clues, for example, the stereo effect that arises from the slightly different view of the faces of the blocks seen by each eye. These two views differ more as the object is moved closer. The size and position of near-by objects also help the brain to judge the distance of the wires.

There are many clues, such as size, shadows, and motion of familiar objects, that help us to estimate how far an object is from us. When these clues are present, the direct interpretation of the rays in the cones of light entering the eyes and of the angle between the cones becomes less important, but at short distances these obvious physical clues are definitely used.

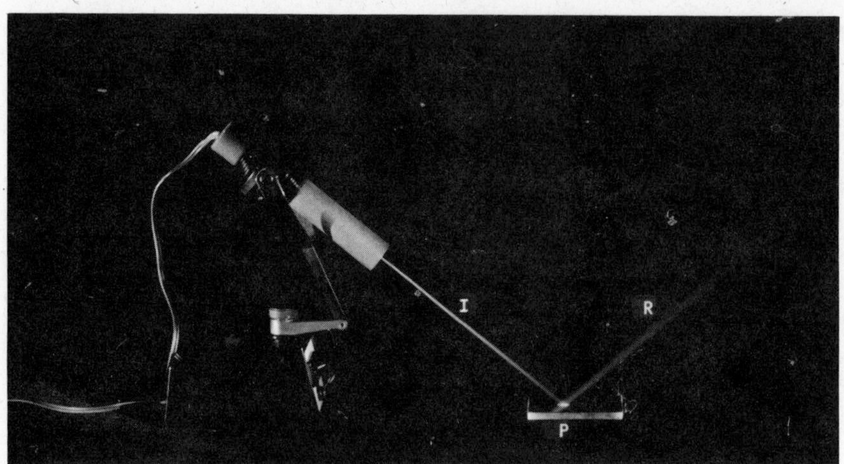

12–7 (a). Specular reflection. A beam of light striking a polished metal surface produces a sharply defined reflected beam.

12–4. The Laws of Reflection

All that we have said in the last section applies to finding the *apparent* position of a source of light. This position, however, need not be the actual position of the source. If the rays of light coming from the source have had their direction changed by reflection or refraction (see Chapter 11), when we trace the rays straight backward their point of intersection will not be the actual point from which the rays started. Nevertheless we shall see the source apparently located at the point of intersection. We are seeing an image of the source, not the source itself.

In Chapter 11 we briefly discussed the images seen in mirrors. We noted, for example, the fact that your image in a plane mirror appears to be a distance behind the mirror equal to your distance in front of it. Can we find laws of reflection that explain the position of such images? Figure 12–7 (a) shows a pencil of light falling on a polished metal plate; the pencil is made visible by smoke. We notice at once that the *reflected* pencil *PR* is as sharply defined as is the *incident* pencil *IP*. Polished metals, liquid surfaces, and mirrors that reflect in such a fashion that the reflected pencils are sharply defined are said to be *specular reflectors.* Materials such as white paper give *diffuse reflection.* [See Fig. 12–7 (b).]

To study specular reflection we place a sheet of white cardboard on the reflecting plate in such a way that the two pencils just skim along its surface as in Fig. 12–8. We find that the cardboard must be held perpendicular to the reflecting surface. If we do the experiment over and over again, changing the direction in which the incident pencil strikes the surface, we always

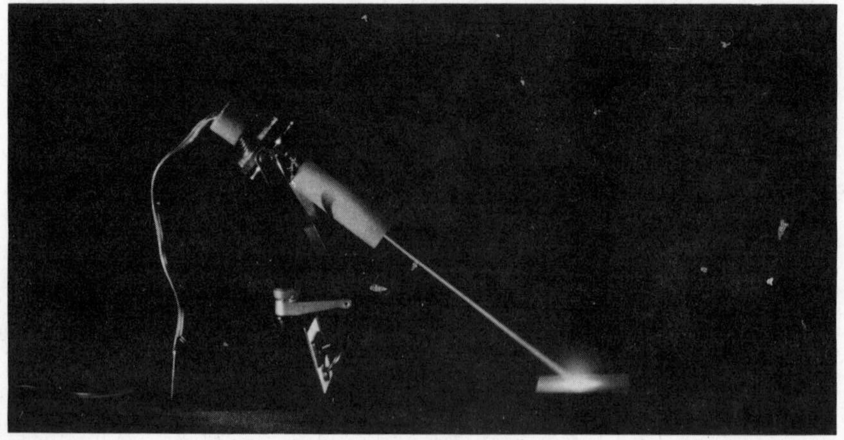

12–7 (b). Diffuse reflection. When a beam of light strikes a piece of white paper, light is reflected in all directions.

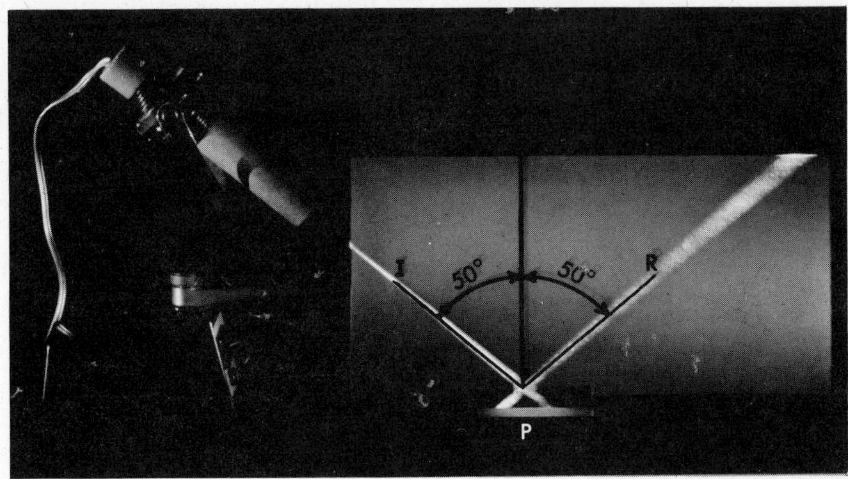

12–8. An experiment that demonstrates the first and second laws of specular reflection. The beams seem to cross because you see in the mirror the reflections of the lighted regions on the cardboard.

get the same result— the cardboard (and therefore the plane of the two pencils) is always perpendicular to the reflecting surface.

As a further step draw a line through the middle of the cardboard at right angles to one edge. Then place the cardboard in a position perpendicular to the reflecting surface as before, with the end of the line just touching the point at which the incident pencil strikes. Since the line is on the cardboard, it is in the same plane as the two pencils of light and also perpendicular to the reflecting surface. This observation gives us the first law of specular reflection:

When light is reflected from a plane specular surface, the incident ray, the reflected ray, and the normal to the surface (the perpendicular) at the point of contact all lie in the same plane.

Now suppose that we measure the angles between the normal and the two rays, as indicated in Fig. 12–8. We find that the angle between the reflected ray and the normal, called the *angle of reflection*, is equal to the angle between the incident ray and the normal, called the *angle of incidence*. This result is confirmed whenever we compare these two angles; hence we can state the second law of specular reflection:

The angle of reflection is equal to the angle of incidence.

12–5. Images in Plane Mirrors

Can these two laws of reflection help us locate and explain the nature of the images in ordinary mirrors? In Fig. 12–9 an arrow, *HT*, is placed near a mirror. We now ask whether light rays starting from any point, such as the head of the arrow *H*, and reflected from the mirror to the eye, seem to come from a common point. The reflected rays were accurately drawn according to the laws of reflection. As the figure shows, the two rays from *H* reach the eye as if they came from the common point *H'*. This suggests that the head of the arrow appears to be at *H'*. Similarly, the green rays in the figure indicate that the tail of the arrow *T* appears to us as if it were at *T'*.

If we were to draw a third ray originating from *H*, would it also appear to come from *H'*? What about a fourth ray? We shall use the laws of reflection to prove that all the rays originating from *H* and reflected from the mirror appear to come from *H'*.

Consider a ray from *H*. In accord with the laws of reflection, this ray, the perpendicular to the mirror's surface, and the reflected ray are in a

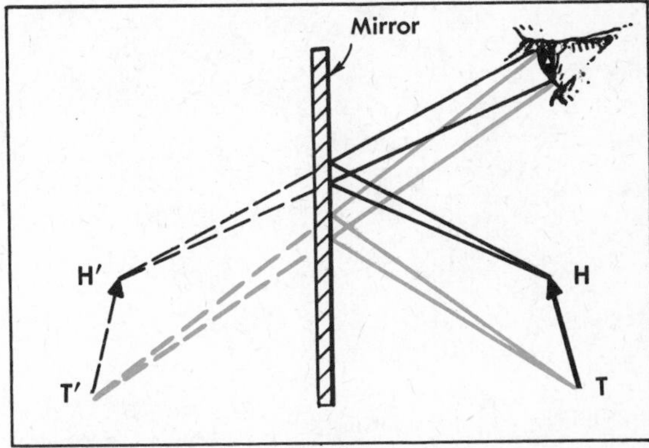

12–9. The formation of an image in a plane mirror.

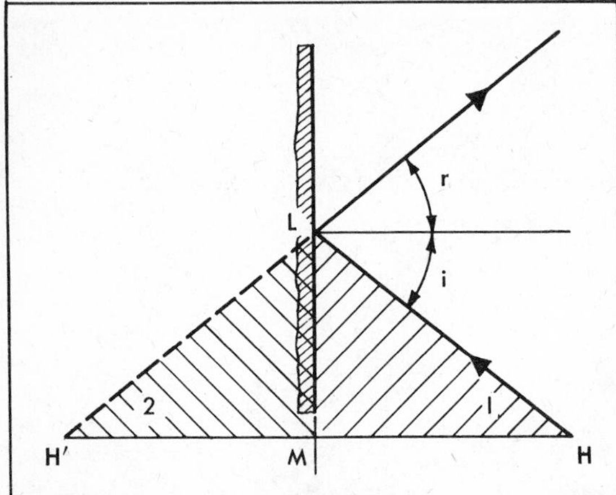

12–10. The geometry of a single ray reflected from a plane mirror.

plane. Fig. 12–10 is drawn in this plane and in it the angles of incidence *i* and reflection *r* are equal. The plane itself is perpendicular to the surface of the mirror. Consequently the perpendicular to the mirror from *H* is also included in the same plane. This perpendicular is the line *HM* in the figure. The dotted extension of the reflected ray cuts this perpendicular at some point *H′* (still in the same plane).

Now the angles marked *1* and *2* in the figure are equal because angles *1* and *i* are equal and angles *r* and *2* are equal. Therefore, the two right triangles have all their corresponding angles equal and they have a common side *LM* between corresponding angles. When folded about *LM* (the surface of the mirror) the triangles therefore fall on top of each other and, in particular, the points *H′* and *H* fall together. *H′* is therefore as far behind the mirror (on the perpendicular through *H*) as *H* is in front of the mirror.

We can repeat this reasoning, using another ray leaving *H* in a different direction. The point *L* on the mirror will be different, but the points *H* and *M* are the same. Consequently the triangle *HML* will still fall on the triangle *H′ML* when folded along the line *ML*. Hence the point *H′* will be the same as before. We can apply the argument to a third ray and so on. Therefore all the rays which originated from *H* and were reflected by the mirror appear to diverge from *H′*. The point *H′* is the image of *H*. *H′* is on the perpendicular to the mirror through *H* and is the same distance behind the mirror as *H* is in front of the mirror.

Summing up our findings, we have shown that those rays which start originally at the point *H* and are reflected by the mirror appear to diverge from the point *H′* located on the extended perpendicular from *H* to the mirror. *H′* is as far behind the mirror as *H* is in front of it. As far as the eye is concerned, then, there appears to be a point source of light at *H′*. We speak of this point as the image of *H*.

By the same reasoning we can locate the image of any point on the arrow, and thus find the complete image of the arrow. Every point on the image is exactly opposite the corresponding point on the object and equally far from the mirror

12–11. Location of the virtual image. This experiment verifies our calculations based on the laws of reflection.

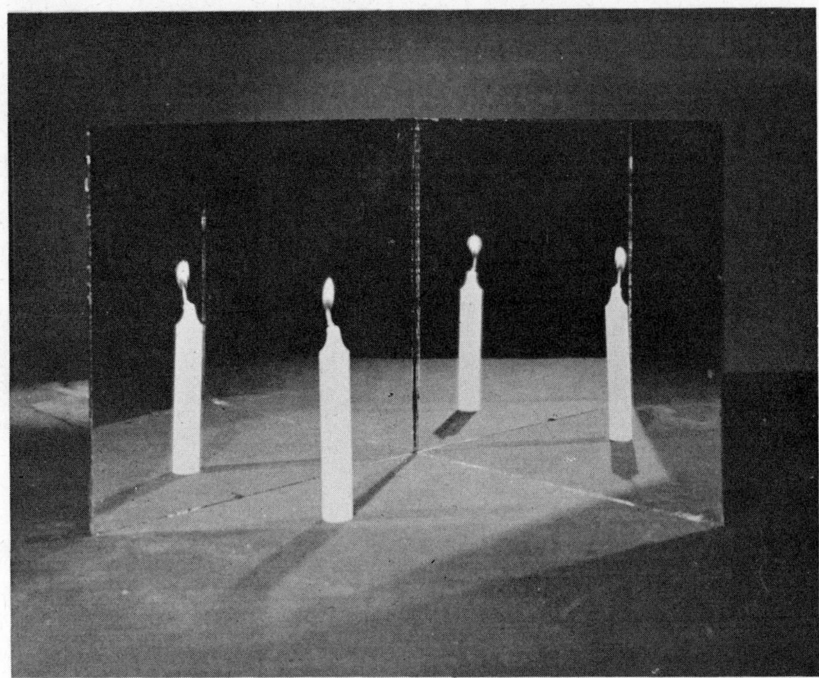

12–12. Multiple reflections in two mirrors. One candle produces three reflected images. Can you explain why?

surface. The image and object are exactly similar and of the same size.

In our construction we have extended the reflected rays behind the mirror, but it is quite clear that we could not find the light from the arrow by going behind the mirror. Because the mirror causes the rays to appear as if they come from the points of the image, although they actually do not, we say that a *virtual image* is formed. We use this term to distinguish it from a *real image*, which we shall meet later.

We have obtained the location of the virtual image by a calculation based on the two laws of reflection. It is easy to verify the results of this calculation by a simple experiment. A small mirror is mounted perpendicular to a table top, and an object having a height somewhat greater than the mirror is placed in front of it, as shown in Fig. 12–11. An identical object is then placed behind the mirror and is moved about until its top portion (seen over the top of the mirror) appears as a continuation of the image when it and the image are viewed *from any possible position.* The real object behind the mirror then is in the same position as the virtual image. Measurements show that this is the position given by our calculation.

Now that we have found a way to locate images in one mirror, we can easily locate all the images where there are several mirrors as in Fig. 12–12. For example, in Fig. 12–12 we see a candle and its three images formed in the mirrors which are set at right angles to each other. The location of the only image difficult to understand is illustrated in Fig. 12–13. By tracing back the "rays" entering the eye, using only the laws of specular reflection, we do find that they diverge from the candle.

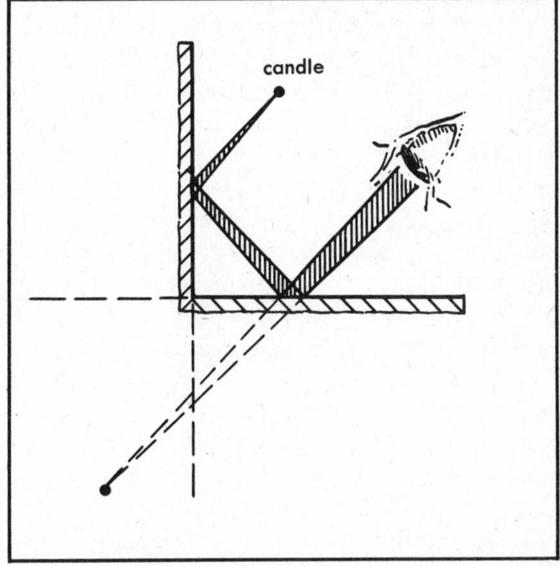

12–13. Formation of an image by double reflection.

12–14. Construction of an approximately parabolic mirror from plane mirrors.

12–6. Parabolic Mirrors

On the top of the Pic du Midi in the French Pyrenees research workers curious about the effects of ultra-high temperatures are cooking steel in the sunlight concentrated by a mirror. In India, with less expensive mirrors, housewives are cooking dinner. To make a photographic image of a star, we must gather the light that hits the large surface of the mirror of an astronomical telescope and concentrate it on a small spot on a sensitive photographic plate. In this way we can gather enough light to see stars in the otherwise blank spaces of the night sky.

We cannot concentrate light with a plane mirror, for the light always diverges, appearing to come from the virtual image behind the mirror. But by using several plane mirrors, we can cause several pencils of light from the same source to cross each other in a small region of space. To be specific let us assume that the source is far away — a star, perhaps — and therefore the pencils of light that come from it to our mirrors are almost parallel. The farther the source, the smaller the angles between the pencils of light, until for a star all the pencils reaching the earth are practically parallel. In Fig. 12–14 twenty-five mirrors cocked at slightly different angles are arranged to reflect parallel light so that it passes through a single small region. We see the region because the smoke there scatters some of the light in the many crossing pencils. Other regions are equally smoke-filled but appear darker because few pencils of light cross there. The pencils of light pass through the small region of overlap and then diverge from one another, each going on just as it does when the others do not cut across it.

We can concentrate the light further if we use more and smaller mirrors. Cut each one of our twenty-five mirrors into four pieces, for example. Then each pencil has only one-fourth of the previous cross-sectional area, and we can make them converge into a smaller region. Now cut the mirrors again, making them still smaller. The region of overlap is cut down still more. Do it all over, time after time. Eventually the mirrors are infinitely small, or at least as small as we can make them; but they intercept the same amount of light that our original twenty-five mirrors did. They reflect the same amount and send it all through a single tiny spot.

To carry out the construction of a mirror which focuses a large amount of light at a single spot by successively dividing and adjusting the orientation of plane mirrors hung up in space is easy in concept but difficult in practice. We can illustrate the procedure, however, with the somewhat easier job of concentrating parallel light on a line instead of a spot. Two stages in this process which you can carry out without too much difficulty are shown in Fig. 12–15. It is easy to imagine the similar processes carried out in space to produce the single spot.

As we subdivide and reorient plane mirrors in space, we construct closer and closer approxima-

12–15. The converging of light by five plane mirrors (above). As the number of mirrors is increased to ten, as shown at the right, the light is converged into a smaller region.

tions to a mirror with a continuously curved surface; and we can imagine the indefinite continuation of the process which results in a smooth mirror which focuses the parallel light. The shape of the smooth surface (called a paraboloid of revolution or parabolic mirror) is determined exactly by our imaginary procedure. The spot F to which all the reflected light converges is called the *principal focus* of the parabolic mirror. In Fig. 12–16 a cross section is shown through the principal focus parallel to the direction of the incident light. Each of the rays we draw indicates how the light is reflected. It stays in the plane of the figure according to the laws of reflection; and the angle of reflection of each ray equals the angle of incidence. If we choose one point on the mirror and the focal point to which we wish to bring the light, only one smooth surface can be constructed which will do the job. The curve cut by this surface on the plane in Fig. 12–16 is a parabola, and the whole surface is called a paraboloid of revolution because by revolving the figure about the ray through F the parabola would be moved around over the whole surface of the mirror.

When we make parabolic mirrors, we usually start by making a smooth surface that is approximately parabolic; then, if necessary, we improve it by distorting, grinding, and polishing until light sent in parallel to the axis of revolution is brought to an accurate focus.

12–7. Searchlights

We have seen that all of the light that falls on a parabolic mirror in a direction parallel to the axis

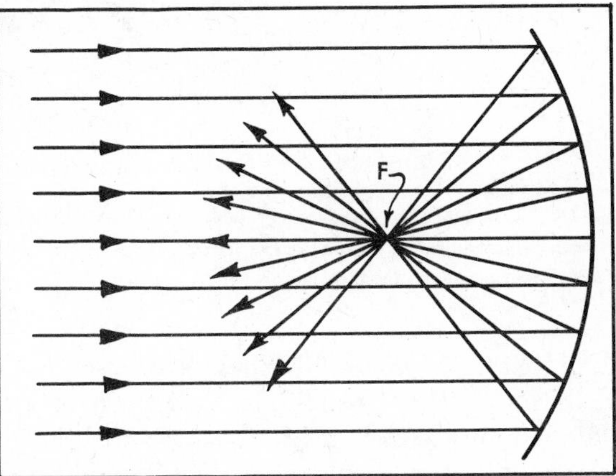

12–16. The converging of light by a curved mirror.

is reflected in such a way that it passes through the principal focus. Since light can travel in either direction over a given path, by putting a tiny intense source of light at the principal focus of a parabolic mirror we can interchange the incident and reflected rays. It follows, then, that any light starting from the principal focus will, after reflection, be traveling parallel to the axis of the mirror. Many searchlights are constructed on this principle as shown in Fig. 12–17. All light from the source that strikes the parabola travels outward in parallel paths to form a narrow, intense beam that penetrates to great distances through space. The light emitted from the source within the cone AFB, however, never strikes the mirror, and it therefore spreads out. But even this light can be used if a small spherical mirror, shown gray in the figure, is mounted in front of the source in such a location that the center of the sphere is at the source. Such a spherical mirror will reflect all

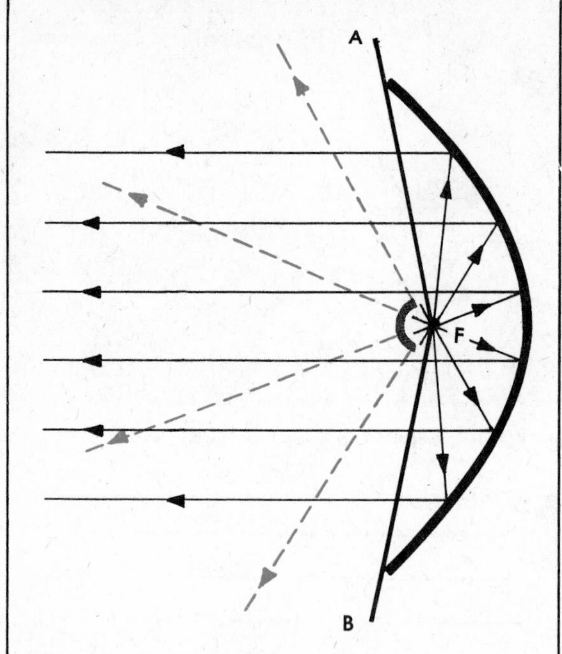

12–17. A searchlight. The "black" rays from the source are reflected parallel; the "green" rays spread out unless the small "gray" mirror reflects them to the parabolic mirror.

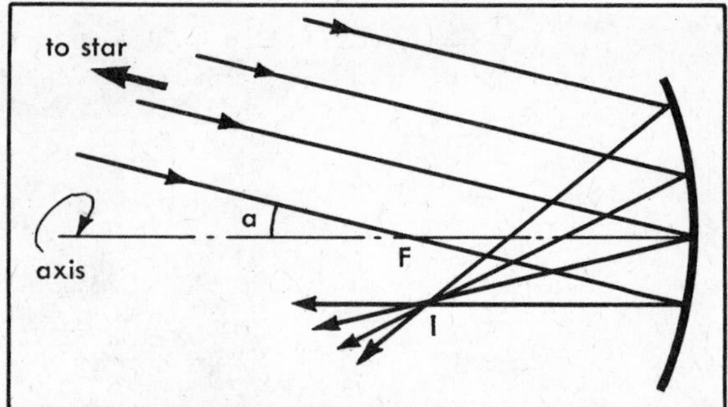

12–18. Formation of the image of a star that is not on the axis of the telescope.

rays back through the principal focus because the rays will all hit perpendicular to the mirror and will be reflected back along the same path to the parabolic mirror (see also the end of Section 12–9). Of course the small mirror will block off the light reflected from the central section of the big one, but this loss is not very important if the little mirror is made very small and is mounted close to the source at F.

How narrow is the parallel beam of light sent out by a searchlight? That depends on the opening of the parabolic mirror. Furthermore, the construction of the mirror also depends on the distance between the principal focus and the central point on the surface of the parabolic mirror. Once this distance is chosen, the shape of the parabola is fixed. The distance from the focus to the center of the mirror is therefore very important. It is given a special name and called the *focal distance* or the *focal length* of the parabola. We shall use the letter f for the focal length of any parabolic mirror.

12–8. Astronomical Telescopes

We know that a parabolic mirror brings to a focus all the light that arrives parallel to the axis of revolution; also when we place a tiny source at the focus of such a mirror it sends out a parallel beam. What happens to light that does not come in parallel to the axis or to light that diverges from a source which is not at the principal focus? The answers to these questions will lead us to understand such varied devices as astronomical telescopes and shaving mirrors.

Two ways are open to answer our questions. We can do experiments with parabolic mirrors, or we can decide logically what should happen according to the two laws of reflection. Indeed, no one will stop us from using both or mixing the two methods; and we certainly must check our logical conclusions by appropriate measurements.

Let us start again with the light from a star hitting a parabolic mirror. Suppose this time that the parallel pencils of light do not come in along the axis of the mirror; instead the direction of the rays is at an angle a to the axis. In Fig. 12–18 a plane is shown which includes the axis of the mirror and some of the rays representing the propagation of light from a star. By carefully constructing the reflected rays so that the angle of reflection in each case equals the angle of incidence, we can find out crudely how we expect the mirror to work. As we see in the figure, the various reflected rays pass through a small region located near the principal focus on the side of the axis opposite the star. They do not pass through a single point because to make them do so we would have to have the axis parallel to the incident rays; but very careful construction (or calculation based on geometry) shows that they do come close to one point even when we include those rays that are not in the plane of the figure. The mirror should therefore form a blurred spot of light at the position I where the light almost focuses.

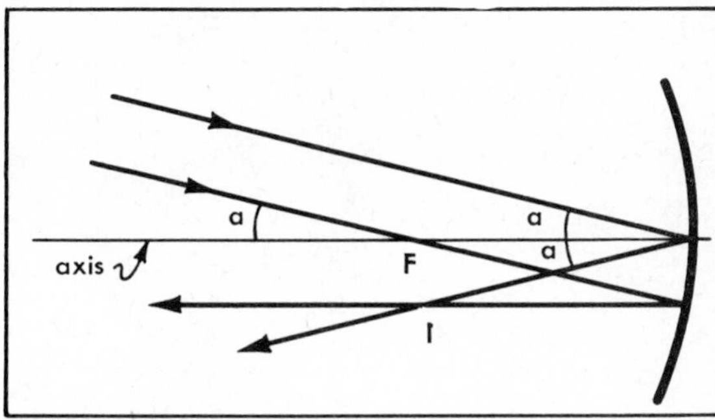

12–19. Simplified version of Fig. 12–18, showing how to find the position of the image.

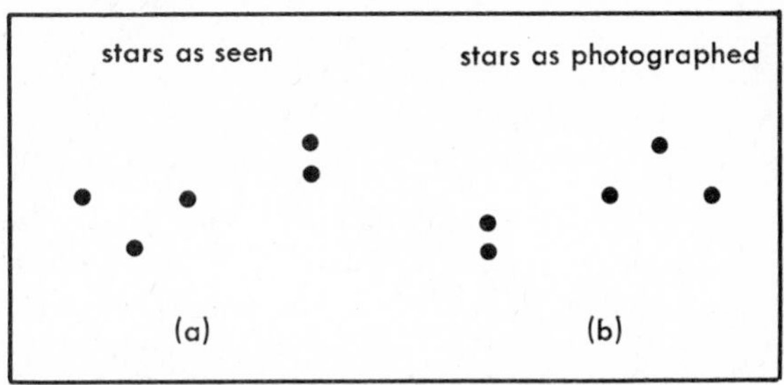

12–20. A sketch of stars as seen in the sky and photographed with a telescope. Try looking at the page turned upside down.

We can find the approximate position of *I* by tracing just two rays. These we choose so as to make the job of ray tracing as easy as possible. In particular we know that a ray through the principal focus will go out parallel to the axis. Also a ray that comes in parallel to the axis will go out through the focus. And finally a ray that hits the center of the symmetric mirror will leave it on the other side of the axis going out on a symmetrie path. Two of these rays will always allow us to find the image *I*. In Fig. 12–19 we locate *I* by tracing the ray that comes in through *F* (and therefore must go out parallel to the axis) and the ray that hits the mirror just at the center point. *I* lies at approximately the same distance from the center of the mirror as *F*, but it is at the same angle on one side of the axis that the star is on the other. Consequently, the images of several stars as seen from the center of the mirror form the same pattern as the stars themselves do in the sky; they are just turned top for bottom and right for left. Also, a photograph taken on a photographic plate placed perpendicular to the axis at *F* shows the spacing of the stars correctly (Fig. 12–20). The parabolic mirror therefore makes an astronomical telescope. It gathers light from the stars and concentrates it on near-by spots in positions corresponding to the positions of the stars on the celestial sphere. Nearly all modern large telescopes use parabolic mirrors.

The heart of the Hale telescope at Mt. Palomar is a parabolic mirror 5 meters in diameter. A metal framework which supports the parabolic mirror is mounted on axles and bearings in such a way that it can be pointed at various spots in the heavens. Fig. 12–21 shows the actual reflecting telescope and gives an idea of the mounting required. This mounting can be controlled so that it follows the apparent motion of a star from east to west while a picture is being taken. With such

12–21. The Hale telescope at Mt. Palomar Observatory. The arrow (bottom, center) points to the mirror.

telescopes photographs of the sky are taken, and every detail of our predictions and of the more careful calculations that predict the extent of blurring is borne out.

A photographic film, exposed for a long time, will gather more light and record a fainter image than can our eyes. It also gives a permanent record of the relative intensity and positions of star images. Large astronomical telescopes are seldom used to produce images directly visible to the eye, for the eye is too insensitive and unreliable as a recording instrument.

Even with long exposure times, we need as much light as we can get to record images of faint stars and galaxies on a photographic plate; and so telescopes with large-diameter mirrors are used to increase the amount of light collected. The largest telescopes gather enough light so that, with very sensitive photographic plates and long exposure times, faint galaxies as far away as 10^{22} km have been recorded. The light-gathering power of large telescopes is even great enough so that the light from stars can be photographed through a spectroscope attached to the telescope. Thus we observe the characteristic spectra of the elements in stars and learn that they are made of the same elements we find in our own sun and on earth (Section 7–9).

12–9. Images and Illusions

You can shoot bullets through the light bulb of Fig. 12–22 without marring its surface or causing the light to flicker. You can pass your hand right through the bulb without feeling a thing. It's the little lamp that isn't there. The light is there, all right; and it was perfectly visible to someone near the camera when the picture was taken. The ruler in the picture was there too, made of genuine wood. If your bullets hit it, it would splinter; your hand could not pass through it.

The little bulb is an image, the image of an honest light bulb located well out of sight about 17 meters in front of the image. The image was formed by a parabolic mirror almost 2 meters behind the illusory bulb.

Thus we see that parabolic mirrors do form images of extended near-by objects. Indeed, this experiment can tell us more. We know that the genuine light bulb stood upright on its base while its image was suspended in space upside down. If we change the distance to the light bulb, the image moves, and it changes size. When we move the genuine bulb toward the mirror, the image moves away from the mirror toward the incoming source. It also grows bigger.

12–22. Real image formed by a parabolic mirror. Notice the size measured by the meter stick.

From a series of such experiments, using parabolic mirrors of different focal lengths and moving the source through a whole set of distances in front of each mirror, we can discover simple systematic relations between the distances and between the size of the image and of the object, as the source is usually called in this kind of work. To discover these relations from the results of such experiments without using the laws of reflection is possible, but it requires lots of experiment and a good guess about how to represent the results simply and accurately.

On the other hand, once we know from experiment that images are actually formed, tracing a few rays in accord with the laws of reflection will lead us to the relations between object and image with very little work. A few checks with experimental results will then show that the laws of reflection are not leading us astray, and we can predict confidently what will happen with any parabolic mirror and an object at any distance in front of it.

Suppose that an object is located in front of a parabolic mirror a distance S_o beyond the principal focus (Fig. 12–23). The height of the object above the axis is H_o. Let us consider the light, coming from the top of the object, that hits the

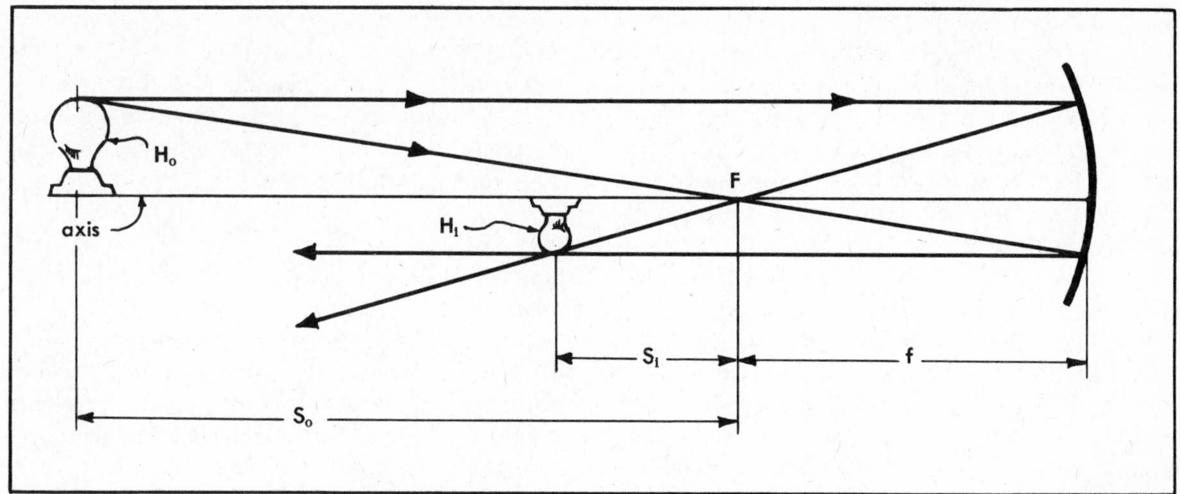

12–23. Finding the size and location of an image of an object at finite distance. The image is located by tracing two rays.

mirror. In particular follow the two rays drawn in the figure. One represents light passing through the focus, F, to the mirror and back out parallel to the axis. The other starts parallel to the axis and therefore must be reflected through the focus. These rays are all we need. Where they intersect after reflection must be the place where the light comes together again to form the image of the top of the object.

We see an image of the top of the object because the light moving along various paths is sent through an image point and diverges from there to our eye or camera just as if a small version of the object were located there. The intersection of the two rays tells not only how far away from F the image of the top is but also determines the length H_i of the whole image as it extends down from the axis. Any time we want to draw such a two-ray picture to scale, we can find out what the laws of reflection predict about the image. For example, consider the first experiment we discussed in this section. We used the following set-up to obtain the photograph in Fig. 12–22. The genuine light bulb was placed 17.50 m in front of the principal focus of the mirror. The focal length of the mirror, determined by using parallel light from the sun, was 1.75 m. So the distance between source and mirror was 19.25 m. The image is seen 0.175 m in front of the focal point or 1.925 m from the mirror. Furthermore an ordinary large electric light bulb 19 cm high was the source; and the image, as measured on the centimeter ruler beside it, is only 1.9 cm high as well as upside down. Tracing our two rays on a scale drawing of this set-up shows that the image should lie 17.5 cm in front of F, and that it should be only $\frac{1}{10}$ as tall as the object in agreement with the experimental facts. With similar drawings you can predict the size and position of the image for other arrangements of object and mirror, or for mirrors of different focal length.

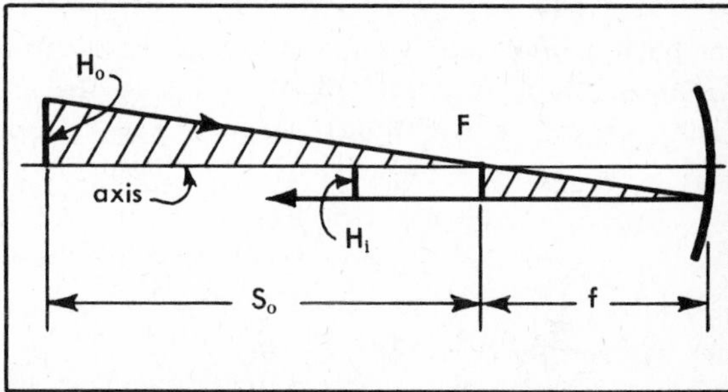

12–24. Finding the ratio of image size to object size by similar triangles. The ray from the top of the object through the principal focus is used to relate the ratio of the sizes to the ratio of the focal length and object distance.

The geometry of these two-ray drawings is so simple that it hardly seems necessary to go further in specifying the relations. But it is a nuisance to draw diagrams all the time, and the simplicity of the geometry suggests that we can express our results in extremely simple forms for numerical computation. Let's start with the relation of image to object size.

In Fig. 12–24 we have left out everything but the ray from the top of the object going through the principal focus. Because this ray is reflected parallel to the axis and passes through the image, the "top" of the image must lie the same distance away from the axis as the reflected portion of this ray. H_i therefore has the same height as the perpendicular from F to the reflected ray. Now we can get the ratio of H_i and H_o immediately from the shaded similar triangles. Because f and S_o are the bases and H_i and H_o the corresponding altitudes, we get

$$\frac{H_i}{H_o} = \frac{f}{S_o}.$$

In fact, the base of the little triangle is a bit shorter than f because of the curvature of the mirror; but, as long as the object isn't too big, the ray will cut the axis at a small angle; and the point where it hits the mirror will be almost exactly the distance f away from the principal focus. In this excellent approximation, then, to determine the ratio of image size to object size all we need to know is the ratio of focal length to the distance of the object from the principal focus. Using the example of Fig. 12–22 with $f = 1.75$ m and $S_o = 17.5$ m, we get

$$\frac{H_i}{H_o} = \frac{1.75}{17.5} = \frac{1}{10}.$$

In the experiment it was also $\frac{1}{10}$.

Now let's see what additional information we can obtain from the ray which comes in parallel to the axis and is reflected through the principal focus. We can use it to construct the shaded similar triangles in Fig. 12–25. From these triangles we find

$$\frac{H_i}{H_o} = \frac{S_i}{f}$$

again with a small error because in place of f we should use f minus the small distance pointed out in the figure. When this relation is combined with $\frac{H_i}{H_o} = \frac{f}{S_o}$, we get $\frac{S_i}{f} = \frac{f}{S_o}$

$$\text{or} \quad S_i S_o = f^2.$$

The distances of image and object from the focus are in inverse proportion. As the object comes toward the mirror, the image must move out so that the product $S_o S_i$ stays equal to f^2. This, of course, is just what we found when we moved the light bulb at the beginning of this section. Originally S_o was 17.5 m and $S_i = 0.175$ m, giving the product $S_o S_i = (17.5)(0.175) = (1.75)^2$, which is the square of the focal length. You should work out what S_o and S_i were after we moved the light in 8.75 m. Use the new S_o and the equation $S_i = f^2/S_o$ to find S_i. Experimentally the illusory little bulb moves 17.5 cm and doubles in height. Does your calculation agree?

Using $S_i = \frac{f^2}{S_o}$ and $H_i = \frac{f}{S_o} H_o$, we can quickly predict the positions and sizes of images in any parabolic mirror.

One example of the application of $S_o S_i = f^2$ is too attractive to resist. Let us ask: at what distance from the principal focus must the object be placed so that the image will be at the same place? That is, when are S_o and S_i equal? Clearly the answer is when both S_o and S_i are equal to f; that is, when object and image are both located at a distance $2f$ from the central point of the mirror surface. Furthermore, image and object are the same size, for $H_i = \frac{f}{S_o} H_o$ gives $H_i = H_o$. When the object is a tiny light source located on the axis at this point, the mirror must reflect the light right back on top of the object.

The idea that a parabolic mirror can bounce all the light striking it right back where it came from might be surprising. As we saw when we discussed the searchlight, the way to bounce light back at a small object is to put a spherical mirror around it with the center of the sphere at the object. Nevertheless, the parabolic mirror works the same way.

Apparently the effective portion of a parabolic mirror must closely resemble a portion of a sphere. In particular, a parabolic mirror of focal length f must be almost the same as a section of a sphere of radius $2f$.

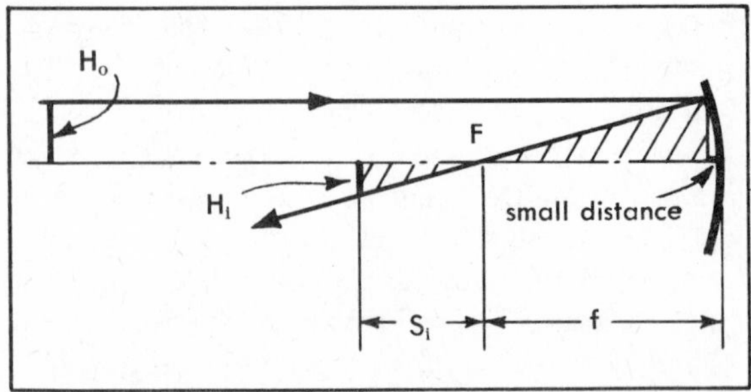

12–25. Finding another relation between image and object size. The ray from the top of the object parallel to the axis is used to relate the ratio of the sizes to the ratio of focal length and image distance.

The relation is shown in Fig. 12–26 where a circle with center at C and a parabola with focus at F are both drawn through the central point on the mirror surface. It is only far from the axis that we find appreciable difference as the sphere closes around in front and the paraboloid opens up. As long as we use only the central portion, we can just as well use a spherical mirror in place of a parabolic one. In fact, because it is usually cheaper to build part of a sphere than part of a paraboloid, we often use spherical mirrors of radius $2f$ when we want to obtain a mirror of focal length f.

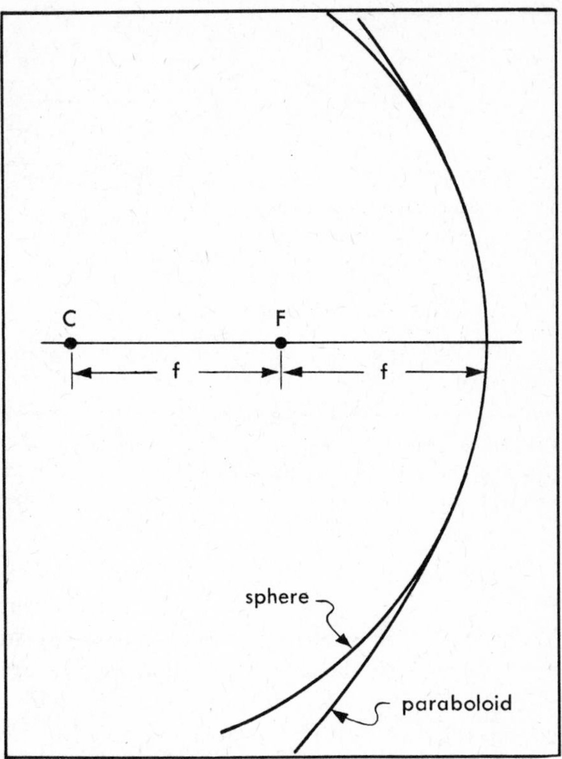

12–26. The relation of spherical and parabolic mirrors. The common principal focus is at F, and the center of the sphere is at C.

12–10. Real and Virtual Images

The illusory light bulb of Section 12–9 is a real image. The pencils of light that we see really converge to it and diverge from it to our eyes. It is thus distinguished from the virtual image seen in a plane mirror. There may be no light passing through a virtual image, but the light is sure to pass through a real image, and a photograph can be made by putting the film at the image as we noted in the case of the astronomical telescope. It would hardly help to put a film behind a plane mirror at an image position.

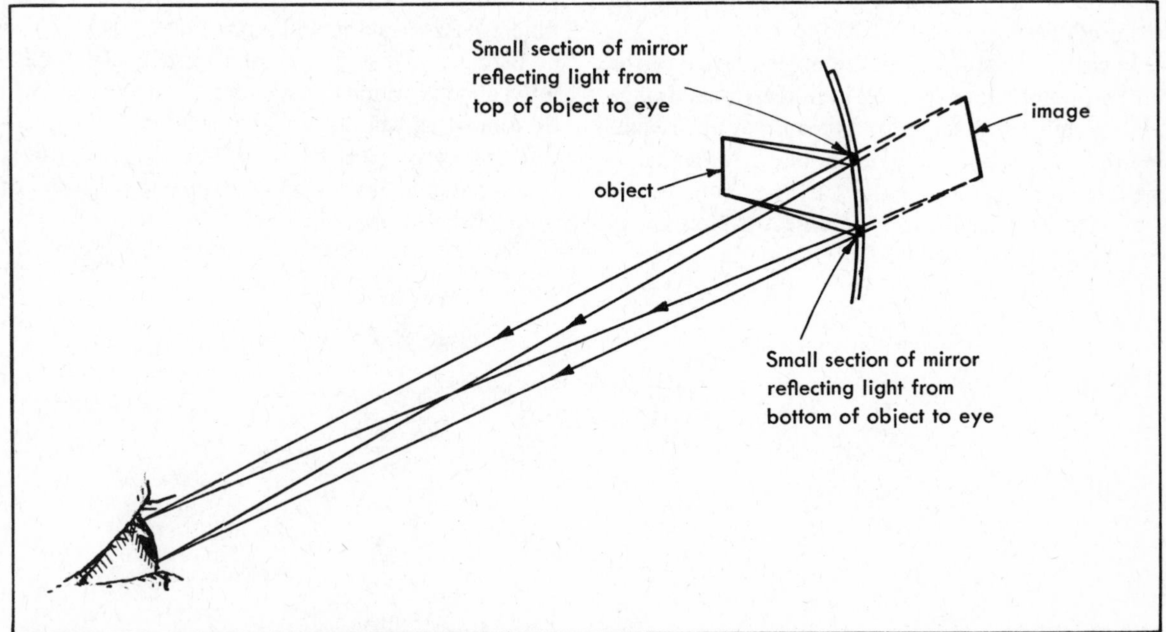

12–27. The formation of a virtual image in a concave mirror. The rays entering the eye from a point on the object are reflected by a very small section of the mirror, which can be treated approximately as a piece of plane mirror. Two such small sections are indicated. Note that they are oriented slightly differently. These differences in orientation result in a magnified virtual image.

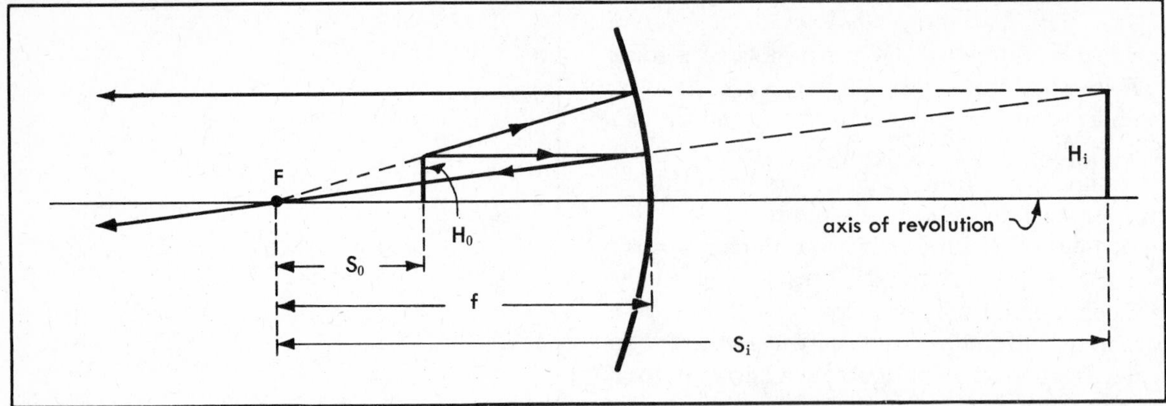

12–28. Formation of a virtual image in a concave mirror. The object lies between the principal focus F and the mirror. The principal rays are used to find the expected location of the image.

By studying parabolic mirrors (or their approximate spherical equivalents), we can learn a bit about the circumstances in which mirrors form real images and those in which the images are virtual. The clue is provided by our previous conclusions. From the relation $S_i = f^2/S_o$ we find that as we bring the object nearer to the focal point, the image runs away. When S_o gets very small, S_i, the image distance, becomes huge; and as the object passes through the principal focus, the real image disappears at infinite distance in front of the mirror.

If we continue to move the object closer to the mirror, we are not surprised to find a virtual image approaching from far behind the mirror and reaching the surface when the object does. After all, a small-enough section of the mirror is hard to tell from a plane; and when the object is close, only a small section of the mirror reflects light from the object to us. The small effective section of the mirror then acts like a plane mirror and forms a virtual image. (See Fig. 12–27.)

A two-ray diagram (Fig. 12–28) now makes it easy to see that whenever the object is between the focus and the mirror we get a virtual image. We use the same two rays — the principal rays, they are called — the one parallel to the axis, which must reflect through the focus, and the one coming from the focus to the mirror and then going out parallel to the axis. As Fig. 12–28 shows, after reflection these rays appear to come from an intersection behind the mirror, and the image is always magnified compared to the object. Ray tracing will work out the details just as before; and if you want to check experimentally, a metal soup tureen or even a large spoon will do almost as well as a shaving mirror. An accurate sphere or parabola will help to get accurate measurements, but won't change the nature of your observations.

FOR HOME, DESK, AND LAB

1. Fig. 12–2 shows how a fuzzy shadow is produced. How could you produce a sharper shadow of the same obstacle?

2. We sometimes see total eclipses of the sun by the moon, and sometimes annular eclipses. In the latter, a ring of light from the sun is seen around the edge of the moon.
   (a) By drawing a diagram of the earth, moon, and sun, explain why two different kinds of solar eclipses occur. Do the distances of the moon from the earth and of the earth from the sun remain the same?
   (b) The moon is about a quarter of a million miles from the earth, and the sun is about 93 million miles away. If the moon has a diameter of two thousand miles, what is the approximate diameter of the sun?

3. When we drive down a road that runs squarely into a valley, we frequently get the impression that the other side of the valley is getting farther away, instead of closer. Fig. 12–29 shows the light rays that reach the eye from the top and bottom of one side of the valley when the viewer is near the top of the other side. Draw the rays that reach his eyes when he is halfway down; when he nears the bottom.
   (a) What happens to the angle between these rays as he gets closer to the bottom of the valley?
   (b) How does this help to explain the illusion that the other side of the valley is retreating from him as he gets closer to it?

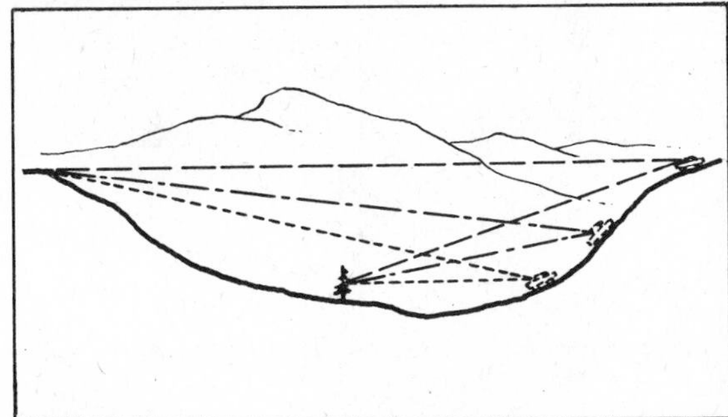

12–29. For Problem 3. Light rays crossing a valley.

4. In studying Brownian motion a pencil of light was used to amplify the twisting motion of a small mirror bombarded by air molecules (Fig. 9–14). When used in this way, to amplify small motions, a combination of light source and mirror is called an optical lever or amplifier.
   (a) If the mirror twists through an angle of .06°, through what angle does the reflected pencil move?
   (b) If the distance from mirror to camera is 2 m, about how far does the reflected pencil move across the camera lens? What fraction is it of the circumference of a circle of 2 m radius?
   (c) What effect does the position of the light source have on the amplification?

5. * Place a plane mirror (one about 30–40 cm high is convenient) with its center approximately at eye level. Hold a meter stick vertically just in front of your face, with the middle of the stick at eye level; stand in front of and facing the mirror.
   (a) Move toward and away from the mirror. Does your motion change the amount of the stick that you can see?
   (b) Formulate a general rule connecting the length of the stick that can be seen with the height of the mirror. By making a ray diagram, show that this rule holds for all distances from the mirror.
   (c) Clothing stores often have mirrors that extend all the way to the floor, designed to allow a customer to see his or her full length. Is it necessary for this purpose for the mirror to be as long as it is?
   (d) If the shortest customer has eyes at a height of 5 ft. 0 in., what is the maximum allowable height of the bottom of the mirror from the floor if the customer's feet are to be visible?

6. * Construct a diagram similar to the one in Fig. 12–13 for two mirrors at 90° to each other.
   (a) How does the light reach the eye when it is placed as in Fig. 12–30?
   (b) Set up two such mirrors and see if the experimental observation checks your diagram.

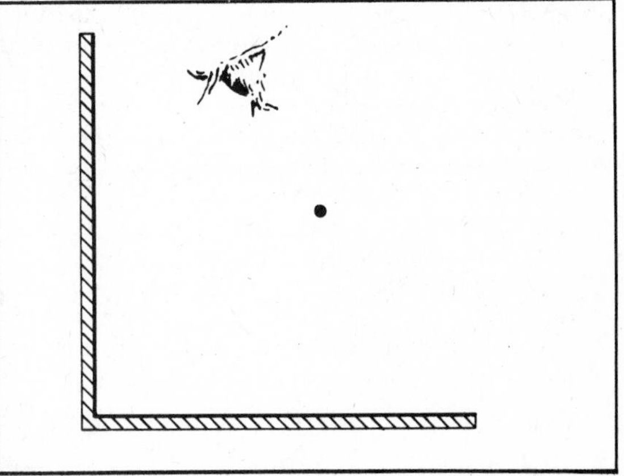

12–30. For Problem 6. The black dot is the object and the eye is looking at one of its images in the two mirrors. Where is the image?

How can you tell if the light goes the way your diagram indicates? Try first with an object midway between the mirrors, and then with it close to one of the mirrors.

7. A mirror 3 ft. wide is placed in the corner of a square room, 20 ft. on a side. Its surface makes an angle of 45° with each wall. You are standing in an adjacent corner. Show by construction what sections of the walls are visible in the mirror and where the images of these sections are located.

8. Two persons, A and B, and two mirrors are located in a room as shown in Fig. 12–31. By construction to scale, investigate the following:
   (a) Can A see his own image in either mirror?
   (b) If B raises his right hand, will his image as seen by A in M_2 raise the right or the left hand?
   (c) A can see two different images of B in M_1.
      (1) Where are they located?
      (2) Do they appear to be of the same size? *Are* they of the same size?
      (3) Are they both reversed as to left and right?
      (4) What is the distance of each image from A?

9. The rear-view mirror of a car is so placed that its upper and lower edges are horizontal and its center is at the same level as the center of the rear window. The driver's eye is also at this level, and the line of sight from his eye to the center of the mirror makes an angle of 30° with the line joining the centers of the mirror and the window. (See Fig. 12–32.) The distance from his eye to the mirror is 2.0 ft., and that from the mirror to the window is 8.0 ft. What is the least width of the mirror that is needed if the entire width (3.0 ft.) of the rear window is to be seen?

10. A *periscope* can be made by mounting two plane mirrors at the ends of a tube. (Fig. 12–33.) The mirrors face each other, are parallel, and each makes an angle of 45° with the axis of the tube. An eye hole is cut in the tube opposite the center of one mirror, and a larger hole is cut in the other end of the tube, opposite the other mirror. Suppose that the distance between the two mirrors is 4 ft. 0 in., and that you are using the periscope to look over a fence at a man 6 ft. 0 in. tall who is 50 ft. away.
    (a) What is the smallest possible height of the hole in the top of the periscope?
    (b) What is the smallest possible size of the top mirror?
    Hint: Draw rays from the man to the eye, and remember the properties of similar triangles.

11. What is the focal length of a plane mirror?

12. What will happen if, in Fig. 12–23, the real light bulb is placed at the position where the real image was previously formed?
    (a) Can you state a general rule about moving

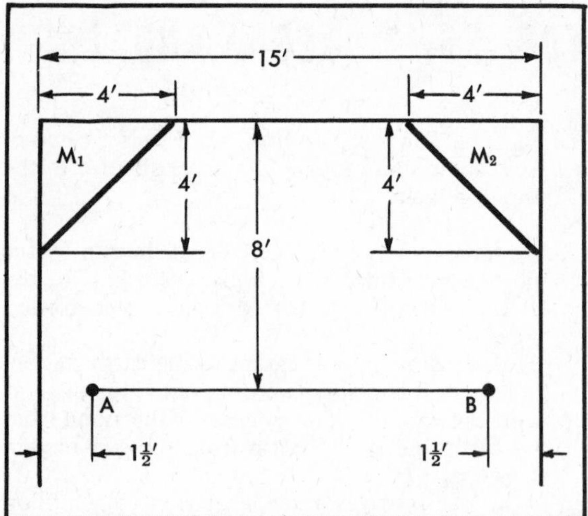

12–31. The arrangement of mirrors for Problem 8.

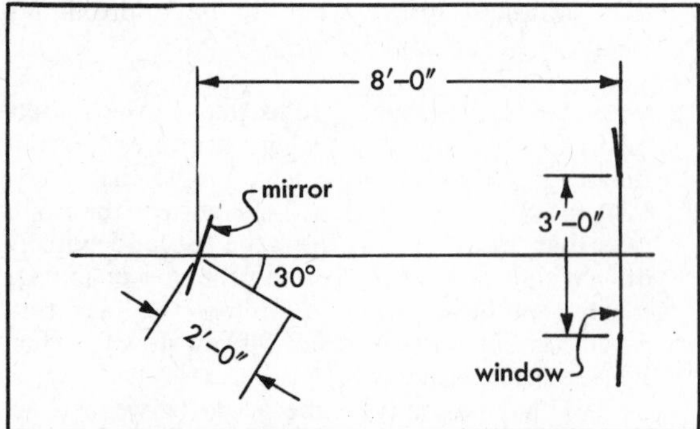

12–32. For Problem 9.

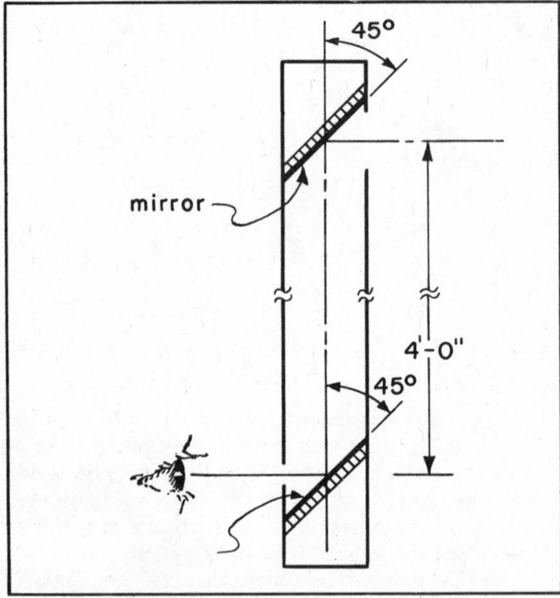

12–33. The periscope of Problem 10.

an object to the position of its real image?

(b) What happens if an object is placed at the position of its virtual image?

13. How large an image of the sun will be formed by the Palomar telescope, whose focal length is 18 m? The sun's diameter is about 1.4×10^9 m, and it is 1.5×10^{11} m away.

14. Show that the size of the image of the sun formed by a concave mirror is proportional to the focal length of the mirror.

15. A nail 4.0 cm high stands in front of a concave mirror at a distance of 15 cm from the principal focus. The focal length of the mirror is 20 cm. What is the size of the image?

16. The image of a candle is 30 cm from the center of a concave mirror. The candle is 10 cm long and its image is 5.0 cm long. What is the focal length of the mirror?

17. How far from a parabolic mirror of 1 m focal length must an object be placed to give an image (a) magnified 4 times (b) reduced to $\frac{1}{3}$ its size? Will the images be real or virtual?

18. * In Section 12–5 we used parallax to locate the virtual image of a candle. We adjusted the position of an object near the image until we could see no parallax (no relative motion).

(a) Can you locate a real image this way?

(b) Use a parabolic mirror to form a real image. Then locate this image by catching it on a piece of paper and by parallax.

19. The distances of an object and its image in a concave mirror are often measured from the center of the mirror, instead of from the principal focus. We call these distances D_o and D_i respectively. We have $S_o = D_o - f$ and $S_i = D_i - f$ where f is the focal length. Using these relations, show that from $S_o S_i = f^2$ follows $\frac{1}{D_o} + \frac{1}{D_i} = \frac{1}{f}$.

20. Our discussion of curved mirrors has been limited to the inner, or *concave*, surface. The outer, or convex, surfaces of these curves will also produce images. Such mirrors are called *convex mirrors* and are often used as side mirrors on a car or as ornamental mirrors in a room. Using the laws of reflection and assuming the surface to be parabolic, demonstrate the following facts by suitable constructions.

(a) The area reflected to the eye by a convex circular mirror is larger than that reflected by a plane mirror of the same diameter in the same position.

(b) Light rays parallel to the axis reflect as though they were coming from a point *behind* the mirror. This is the principal focus of the mirror. It is called a *virtual* focus. Why?

(c) Rays starting from a fixed point on the axis are reflected in such a way that they seem to come from a point on the axis behind the mirror. The image is therefore virtual.

(d) The image formed is smaller than the object and is not inverted.

(e) As the object moves in from a great distance, the image moves toward the mirror.

(f) There is a limit to the distance of the image from the mirror — that is, this distance can never be greater than a certain value. What is this value? Try drawing ray diagrams.

21. * As a project you can make a pinhole camera that is excellent for photographing the sun. Paint the inside of a cardboard mailing tube flat black (to prevent reflection of light). Cover one end with a piece of heavy black paper, in the center of which a hole has been punched with a fine needle. To the other end of the tube fit a piece of wood or metal that allows the tube to be mounted onto the front of a camera, in place of the lens. The connection, of course, must be light-tight. Insert a photographic film in the camera in the usual way, and point the tube toward the sun with the pinhole covered. When the tube is correctly placed, take a time exposure of a few seconds.

(a) If the film in a pinhole camera has a vertical height of 6 in. and is 9 in. from the pinhole, how far must the pinhole be from a man 5 ft. 6 in. tall if his image is to extend the full height of the film?

(b) In the same pinhole camera, if the image of the sun is $\frac{1}{10}$ in. in diameter, what is the diameter of the sun? The sun is 93 million miles away.

22. In Section 12–9 the question is asked: At what distance from the principal focus must the object be placed so that the image will be at the same place? Show that this question has two answers and explain the second answer, which was not discussed in the chapter.

FURTHER READING

BLACK, N. H., and LITTLE, E. P., *An Introductory Course in College Physics.* Macmillan, Fourth Edition, 1956. (Chapter 42.)

EDSER, EDWIN M., *Light for Students.* St. Martin's Press, 1952.

MINNAERT, M., *Light and Color in the Open Air.* Dover, 1954.

ROBERTSON, J. K., *Introduction to Optics, Geometrical and Physical.* Van Nostrand, Fourth Edition, 1954.

THOMPSON, ALLYN J., *Making Your Own Telescope.* Sky Publishing Co., Cambridge, Mass., 1947. Simple instructions for making a 6-inch reflecting telescope.

REFRACTION

CHAPTER 13

13–1. Refraction

In order to make an experimental study of reflection we set up apparatus to observe single pencils and beams of light being reflected from surfaces. By systematic observations we arrived at two simple laws of specular reflection. These laws, in turn, make it possible to explain the formation of images in both plane and curved mirrors. We thus see that the reduction of a wide range of phenomena to a couple of straightforward laws is a great gain in simplicity and gives us a powerful tool for prediction. It would be difficult to remember the characteristics of all the images we can produce with different mirrors and a wide variety of positions for the object. If, however, we know how to use these two laws we can arrive at a detailed description of the image formed by any combination of mirrors. Further, we can predict what kinds of images will be formed by mirrors of types that we have not studied experimentally.

Let us see if a similar study will give us simple explanations of the second group of optical phenomena we discussed in Chapter 11. There we noted that light penetrates the surface of certain materials and in doing so often changes its direction. This bending of a light beam as it passes from one material into another we called *refraction.* We saw some examples of refraction in the floating-coin illusion (Fig. 11–2) and in the bent-stick illusion (Fig. 11–1). Although the effect of the bending of light is clearly shown by such observations, they tell us little about what happens to individual pencils of light. We can simplify our study by isolating a single refracted pencil of light as shown in Fig. 13–1. This photograph shows a rather broad pencil of light passing through air, and entering the water in an aquarium. Notice that the direction of the pencil changes abruptly at the water surface and some of the light is reflected from the surface, back into the air.

We may call the incoming pencil of light the *incident* pencil, as we did in our study of reflection. In Fig. 13–1 the angle between this pencil and the normal to the surface is the *angle of incidence.* The light pencil after bending at the water surface is called the *refracted* pencil, and the angle that it

13–1. Light passing from air into water.

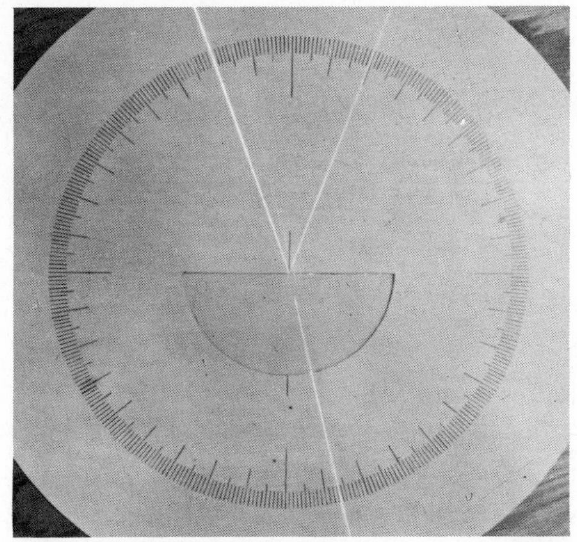

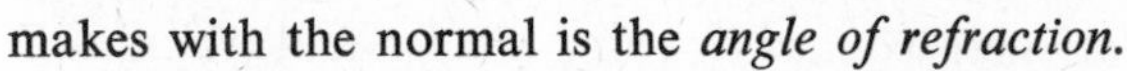

13–2. The refraction of light entering glass at different angles of incidence.

makes with the normal is the *angle of refraction.*

By inserting a plane sheet of white plastic into the aquarium, as in the figure, we can learn more about the direction taken by these rays. When we place the plastic perpendicular to the water surface so that the incident rays just glance along the sheet, the refracted rays just glance along the sheet also. We may repeat this experiment with different angles of incidence and different pairs of materials. For most materials we find the same result. It is summarized in the first law of refraction:

*The incident ray, the refracted ray, and the normal to the surface are all in the same plane.**

Notice the similarity between the first law of refraction and the first law of reflection (Section 12–4).

13–2. Experiments on the Angles in Refraction

The second law of reflection tells us that the angles of incidence and reflection are equal. Will experimental observation help us to arrive at some similar relationship between the angles of incidence and refraction?

*In some crystalline substances the incident ray, the normal to the surface, and the refracted ray are not in the same plane.

If we wish to make reasonably accurate measurements of the angles of incidence and refraction, we need narrower pencils of light than those shown in Fig. 13–1, so that we can approximate single rays. We must change the angle of incidence through a wide range and measure the various angles of refraction. Finally we must do all this for various pairs of materials to find a general law.

Using air and glass we carried out the experiment indicated in Fig. 13–2. We constructed a light source that is moved easily through an angle of nearly 90 degrees and is adjustable so that the narrow pencil of light coming from it can just glance along the surface of a piece of white paper to make the pencil visible. A semicircle of glass, placed in the path of the pencil of light as shown, served as the second material. The back of this plate was ground until slightly rough and then painted white so that the pencil is visible as it traverses the glass. The glass semicircle is mounted on a circular scale with both centers at the same point, and the normal to the diameter of the semicircle passes through zero on the scale indicating the number of degrees. The incoming narrow ray is directed exactly at the common center. We can therefore measure the angle of incidence and the angle of refraction associated with it. The reflected ray is also visible in the pictures, and we can use the measured angle of reflection to check the accuracy of alignment.

Pictures were made with this experimental arrangement with the pencil of light adjusted to angles of incidence of 0°, 10°, 20°, 30°, 40°, 50°, 60°, 70°, and 80°. Some of the pictures are shown in Fig. 13–2, and all the data appear in Table 1. Study this series of pictures carefully. Do you agree that the following conclusions can be reached?

(1) The angle of refraction for light passing from air to glass is always less than the angle of incidence, except when the latter is 0°.

(2) The behavior of the reflected pencil is described by the ordinary laws of specular reflection.

(3) The light passing through the glass travels along a radius and therefore hits the curved surface perpendicularly. It is not refracted at this boundary but goes straight out as it passes again into the air.

Each of these observations will be important to us eventually. For the moment, let us concentrate on the first, studying the relation of the angles more closely. Table 1 shows the values of the angle of incidence i and refraction r which we measured.

Table 1

Angle of Incidence i in Degrees	Angle of Refraction r in Degrees	Ratio i/r
0	0	Indeterminate
10	6.7	1.5
20	13.3	1.50
30	19.6	1.53
40	25.2	1.59
50	30.7	1.63
60	35.1	1.71
70	38.6	1.81
80	40.6	1.97

Relation between the angle of incidence i *and the angle of refraction* r *for the passage of light from air to glass.*

Certainly, angle r is always smaller than the corresponding angle i. We might try to investigate the ratio i/r to see whether it is constant, but we find, as shown in the last column of Table 1, that when we calculate the ratios they vary from about 1.5 at small angles i to more than 1.9 when $i = 80°$. The ratio is not a constant, but the angles of refraction do vary in a regular way with the angles of incidence. This regular relation becomes clear when we plot the graph shown in Fig. 13–3. This is the graph of the angle r versus angle i. It was made by plotting the experimental points, which are marked, and drawing a smooth curve through the points.

We can use the graph to predict what the angle of refraction would be for any given angle of incidence. For example, we can be quite sure what angle of refraction we shall find when the angle of incidence is 45°. From the graph we get 27.8°. A measurement taken with the same apparatus with which we got our original data gave the value 27.6°, in close agreement with our expectation.

Now a question naturally arises. Is the graph we have drawn correct for all pairs of materials that we might use, or is it true only for the passage of light from air into glass? To answer this ques-

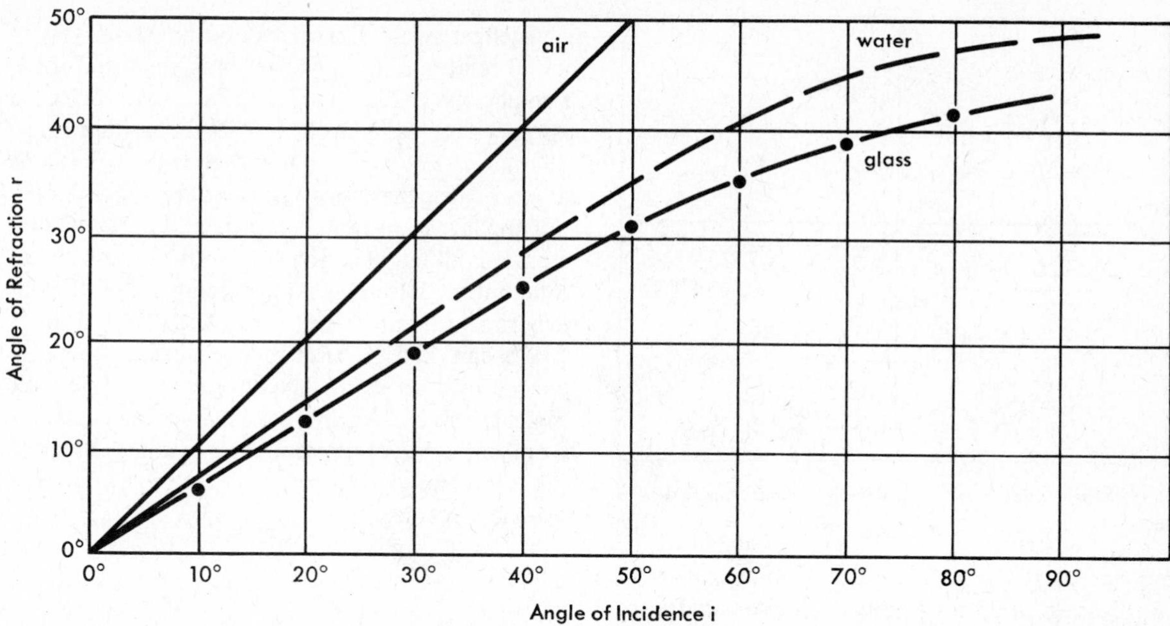

13–3. Graph of r versus i.

tion we may try a new experiment with a different pair of materials. The dashed line in Fig. 13–3 shows the graph obtained from a series of measurements made with light passing from air into water. Notice that for a given angle of incidence the angle of refraction is always greater in water than it is in glass. Furthermore, when light just passes from air into more air of the same density, the pencil of light is not bent and therefore $r = i$. This gives a straight-line graph at 45° slope instead of a curve that bends over. Evidently different pairs of materials lead to different graphs of r versus i.

13–3. The Index of Refraction: Snell's Law

It is possible to perform a series of similar experiments, using many different materials, and to plot a whole series of graphs of the type shown in Fig. 13–3. A book full of these graphs could be very useful in describing just how light is refracted in any pair of substances that have been studied. But it is less convenient than having a single law.

We have already tried the relation i/r = constant and found that it does not hold for all angles. But, as Fig. 13–4 shows, for small angles of in-

13–4. Graph of i/r versus i.

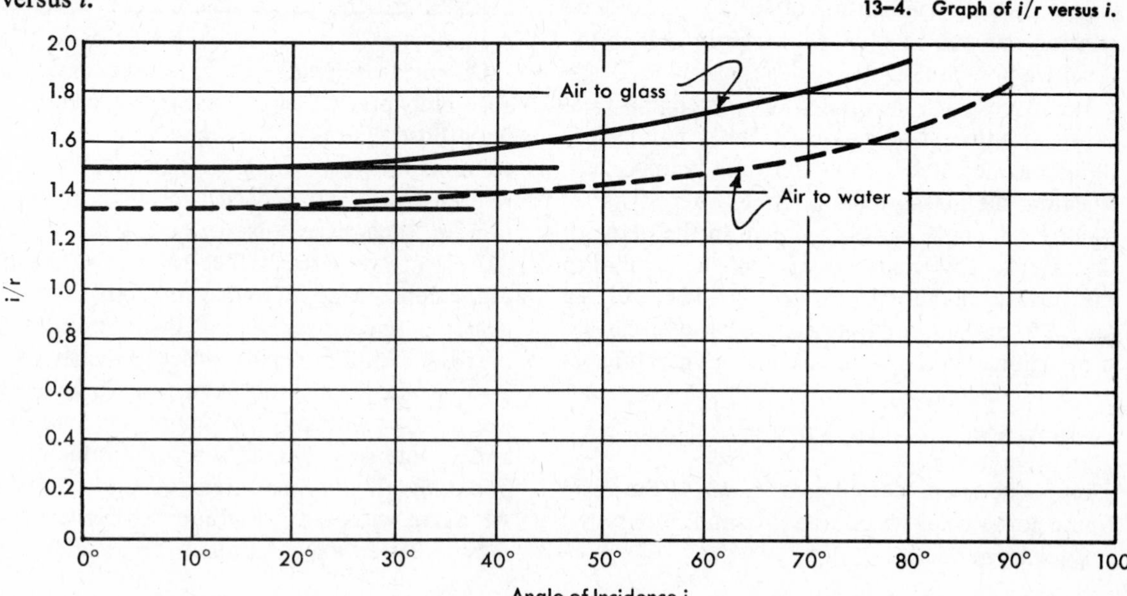

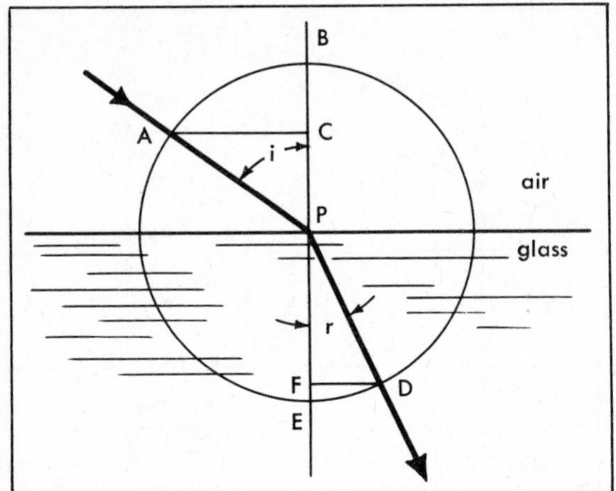

13–5. The geometry of refraction from which Snell's law is found.

cidence the law is that i/r is constant, about 1.5 for glass and 1.33 for water. At larger angles the constancy fails, and i/r rises.

One way to look for a convenient representation of the relation of r to i is to try to extend the constancy of the ratio i/r by finding simple functions of i and r that maintain the constant ratio at all angles. Following this program we would look for functions which are proportional to the angles when they are small and which compensate for the rise in i/r when the angles get large. That we shall find such functions is not clear before we start; in fact, data on refraction were known to Ptolemy and used for a thousand years before an adequate simple law of refraction was stated. Finally in 1621 Willebrord Snell found a beautiful way to describe the relation of i and r. The same relation was published by Descartes in 1638 in the form we now use.

We can explain the discovery of Snell and Descartes with the aid of Fig. 13–5. In the figure a ray of light is indicated coming in from the upper left. It enters the glass at the point P where it is refracted. A circle has been drawn in the plane of the rays with its center at P; and the normal to the surface of the glass is shown. The arcs AB and ED on the circumference of the circle are proportional to the angles i and r. Therefore

$$\frac{i}{r} = \frac{AB}{ED}.$$

This is the ratio plotted in Fig. 13–4, the ratio found to be nearly constant for small angles but not for large ones.

In effect, what Descartes and Snell did was to try to relate i and r by examining the ratio of the semichords AC and FD. That is, in place of AB/ED they calculated AC/FD for a wide range of angles. For small angles, their ratio is the same as i/r because the chords and arcs are almost equal, but for large angles the chords and arcs are substantially different so that the chord ratio behaves differently. Let us look at this chord ratio for our experimental data taken with glass (Table 1).

We can find AC/FD by measuring the semichords in a series of figures like Fig. 13–5. We make the figures with the measured angles i and r from our table of experimental results. Measuring the semi-chords and calculating their ratio gives the results shown in Table 2.

Table 2

i in deg.	AC in cm	r in deg.	FD in cm	$\frac{AC}{FD}$
10	3.47	6.7	2.3	1.5
20	6.84	13.3	4.60	1.49
30	10.00	19.6	6.71	1.49
40	12.83	25.2	8.52	1.51
50	15.32	30.7	10.2	1.50
60	17.32	35.1	11.5	1.51
70	18.79	38.6	12.5	1.50
80	19.69	40.6	13.02	1.51

The ratio of the semi-chords for the refraction of light in glass (see Fig. 13–5). The constancy of the ratio of the semi-chords (last column) illustrates Snell's law.

Our measurements of i, r, AC, and FD are not absolutely precise, as we have indicated by writing only those figures in the second, third, and fourth columns which we think are significant. Our last written figures are indeed subject to slight question in each case. Nevertheless the values of AC/FD are very nearly the same for all the angles of incidence; and it seems very likely that AC/FD is a constant. The value of this constant for the particular kind of glass we used is clearly between 1.49 and 1.51, probably very close to 1.50. If we assume that we really are dealing with a constant and in line with our data try the value 1.50, we find that all our measurements are compatible. All agree with 1.50 to within experimental accuracy. Better experiments with smaller experimental uncertainties confirm the conclusion that we have a constant whose value is close to 1.50.

We can also get the same ratio by using what are known as the sines of the angles. In a right triangle (Fig. 13–6) we define the sine of one of the acute angles as the ratio of the side opposite this angle to the hypotenuse:

$$\sin A = \frac{a}{c}.$$

The sines of all angles have been tabulated, and a table is included in the Appendix. Looking back at Fig. 13–5, we see that

$$\sin i = \frac{AC}{AP} \quad \text{and} \quad \sin r = \frac{FD}{PD}.$$

Because AP and PD are both radii of the same circle we can express $\sin r$ as FD/AP; and consequently

$$\frac{\sin i}{\sin r} = \frac{AC/AP}{FD/AP} = \frac{AC}{FD}.$$

The ratio of the sines of the angles of incidence and refraction is the same as the ratio of the semi-chords. It is equal to the same constant that we found experimentally for their ratio. In going from air to glass, therefore,

$$\frac{\sin i}{\sin r} = 1.50$$

according to our experiments. Because the sines of all angles have been tabulated, this form of our result is often more convenient than the expression in terms of the ratio AC/FD. We do not need to construct and measure the semi-chords on a set of drawings; we only look up the values of sines in the tables. (See Appendix.)

The use of the sines of i and r in place of the angles has allowed us to carry through our idea of trying to find a function that gives a constant ratio at all angles, large angles as well as small. We have thus found a simple law of refraction describing the passage of light from air to glass at any angle.

The next question is obvious: when the light passes from air into some other substance, is the ratio $\sin i/\sin r$ also independent of the angle of incidence? For many substances the experimental answer is "yes." For water, for example, $\sin i/\sin r$ is constant, and the value of the con-

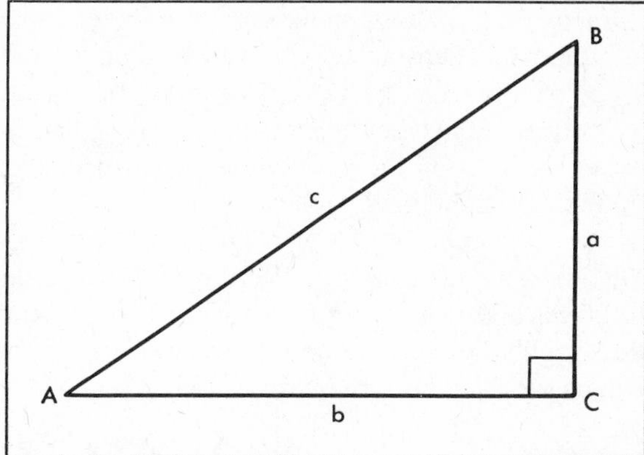

13–6. The sine of angle A is a/c.

stant is 1.33. We might even have expected this value since we already know that i/r for water is about 1.33 for small angles where the ratio of the sines and the ratio of the angles is nearly the same. (See Fig. 13–4.) For other substances the constant ratio $\sin i/\sin r$ has different values. The value for a particular substance is a property of the substance like its boiling or melting temperature. It may even help to identify the substance. The constant is called the *index of refraction* of the substance or, if you want to be more careful, the index of refraction for light going from air into the substance. Some of these indices are listed in Table 3.

Table 3

Substance	Index of Refraction
Glass*	1.5–1.9
Diamond	2.42
Fused quartz	1.46
Quartz crystal	1.54
Glycerin	1.47
Ethyl alcohol	1.36
Oleic acid	1.46
Water	1.33

*The index of glass depends on its composition. Most ordinary glasses have indices slightly above 1.5.

The law that $\sin i/\sin r$ is constant for all angles of incidence is Snell's law. It tremendously simplifies our description of refraction. If we wish to know how light will be bent on entering any material from air, we need have available only the index of refraction of the material. A collection of these indices, sufficient to include nearly all important substances, can be placed on a single page of a book and can replace many books full of graphs of the type shown in Fig. 13–3. Further, when we start on the development of a theory, or model, of light in Chapter 15, we now have a simple and general law of behavior of light that our theory must explain. We can test any model that we invent by seeing whether it can account for Snell's law, the second law of refraction for which we have been searching.

13–4. The Absolute Index of Refraction

We should note that all our photographs of the refraction of light have been for cases of light passing from *air* into glass, or water, etc. What would we find for the index of refraction when the light travels from a *vacuum* into glass? As a matter of fact, with the limited accuracy of our experimental equipment, we would notice no difference; the same value for the index would result. This we might expect because of the very low density of air. But measurements made with great precision actually show a slightly greater index for light passing from a vacuum into glass than for air to glass. For a sample of glass with index 1.50000 in air, the index in a vacuum is 1.50044.

The index of refraction of any substance in vacuum is called its absolute index of refraction. The value of the index from air to the substance is so close to the value of the absolute index that we rarely need to distinguish between them.

13–5. The Passage of Light from Glass (or Water) to Air: Reversibility

Thus far we have concentrated our attention on what happens to light as it enters glass or some other substance from air. Suppose that we now investigate what happens when light goes in the opposite direction, from glass into air. We have already found out that when light reaches the surface along the normal, the part that goes out enters the air without being bent. To find out what happens when the light approaches the glass-air surface at other angles we may make use of a glass block with parallel surfaces. As we see in Fig. 13–7, a pencil of light that is incident on one side of the glass leaves the glass on the other side traveling parallel to the incident direction. The refraction in going from glass to air, therefore, is exactly the opposite of the refraction in going from air to glass.

13–7. Light passing through a block of glass with parallel faces.

This situation is illustrated in the ray diagram of Fig. 13–8. Here the light is traveling in the direction shown by the arrows. As it passes from air to glass, the angle of incidence is θ_{air} and the angle of refraction is θ_{glass}. The two are related according to Snell's law by the equation:

$$\frac{\sin\theta_{\text{air}}}{\sin\theta_{\text{glass}}} = n_{\text{glass}},$$

where n_{glass} is the index of refraction of light passing from air into glass (very nearly the absolute index of glass). When the light approaches the second surface on its way from glass to air, it is incident on the surface at the angle θ_{glass} because the two surfaces are parallel. Furthermore we

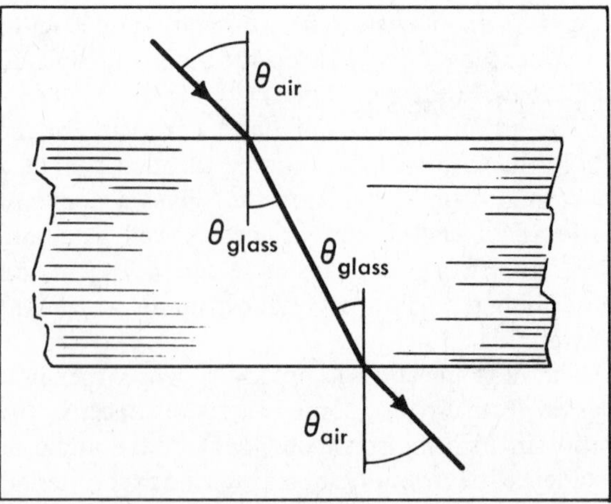

13–8. The angles and their relations for light passing through a block of glass with parallel faces.

found experimentally that the rays entering and leaving the glass are parallel; and since the two normals are parallel, the two angles in air are equal. Therefore the rays leave the glass at the angle θ_{air}. We can therefore conclude that in leaving the glass the angles of incidence and of refraction are related as

$$\frac{\sin i}{\sin r} = \frac{\sin \theta_{\text{glass}}}{\sin \theta_{\text{air}}} = \frac{1}{n_{\text{glass}}}.$$

This is Snell's law again, the ratio of sin i to sin r is a constant; and the index of refraction for light going from glass to air is just the inverse of the index for light going the other way. Because one index is the inverse of the other, we do not need two indices of refraction, one from air to glass and another from glass to air. We can use the single air-to-glass index, and write the relation of the angles in passing either from air to glass or from glass to air as

$$\sin \theta_{\text{air}} = n_{\text{glass}} \sin \theta_{\text{glass}}.$$

From experiments in which light goes from other substances into air we conclude that Snell's law applies equally well to light entering or leaving a substance. It is therefore convenient to write the law in the general form

$$\sin \theta_{\text{air}} = n_{\text{m}} \sin \theta_{\text{m}},$$

where n_{m} is the index for light going from air into the material m, and θ_{m} is the angle between the normal to the surface and the rays in that material. The letter m stands for the name of the material. For example, for light traveling from air to diamond or diamond to air, we will have

$$\sin \theta_{\text{air}} = n_{\text{diamond}} \sin \theta_{\text{diamond}}$$
$$= 2.42 \sin \theta_{\text{diamond}}.$$

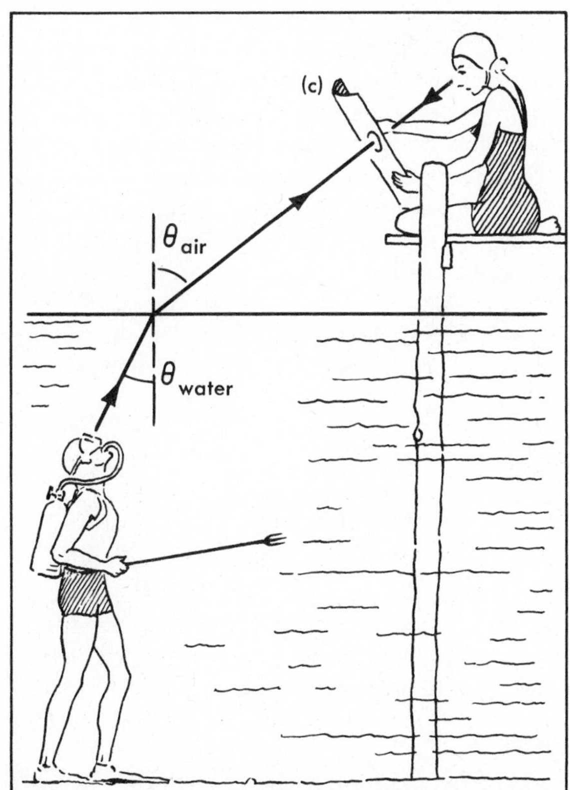

13–9. The reversibility of light paths.

The general relation, $\sin \theta_{\text{air}} = n_{\text{m}} \sin \theta_{\text{m}}$ implies that light paths described by Snell's law are reversible. In this respect they are just like light paths in which specular reflection takes place (Section 12–7). You can easily convince yourself of this reversibility with experiments like this: Suppose one of us is under water and the other is above. As in Fig. 13–9, we are looking each other in the eye. From the general form of Snell's law, the path of the rays of light going through the water's surface is described by

$$\sin \theta_{\text{a}} = 1.33 \sin \theta_{\text{w}}$$

regardless of whether θ_{a} or θ_{w} is the angle of incidence; thus the light rays from your eye to mine should follow the same path as those from my eye to yours. Now comes the test. We arrange a barrier (c in Fig. 13–9) with a small hole in it so that you can just see my eye through it. I then find that this is just the position of the barrier that also allows me to see your eye. Many experiments with many different substances confirm the prediction of Snell's law and the laws of reflection that such light paths are reversible.

13–6. The Passage of Light from Water to Glass: the Relative Index

We can now predict what happens when light goes from glass to water. Suppose for a moment there is a layer of air between two parallel surfaces of glass and water as in Fig. 13–10. Then as the light leaves the glass, it goes into the air at angle θ_{air} such that

$$\sin \theta_{\text{air}} = n_{\text{glass}} \sin \theta_{\text{glass}}.$$

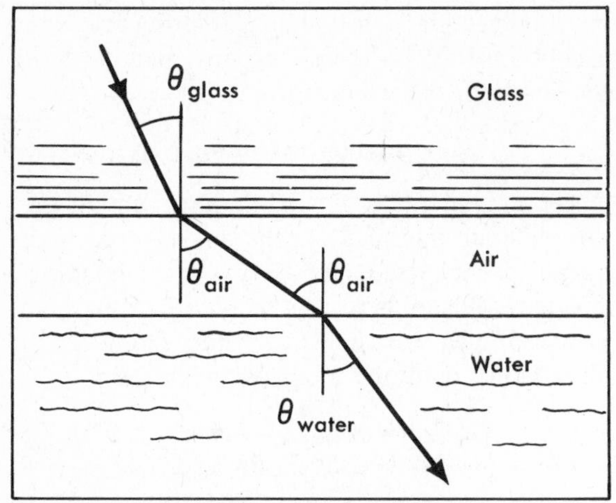

13–10. Light passing from glass to water through a layer of air.

It next enters the water and proceeds through the water at angle θ_{water} such that

$$\sin \theta_{air} = n_{water} \sin \theta_{water}.$$

Therefore

$$n_{glass} \sin \theta_{glass} = n_{water} \sin \theta_{water}.$$

This expression relates θ_{water} to θ_{glass}, and is independent of the thickness of air between the glass and the water. Consequently we may hope that it relates θ_{glass} to θ_{water} in the special case when the thickness of the air layer is zero; that is, when the water and glass are touching. Indeed, if you try it, you will find that this relation holds. Further, it is not restricted to glass and water. In general, for two materials, 1 and 2, for which Snell's law holds

$$n_1 \sin \theta_1 = n_2 \sin \theta_2$$

no matter which way the light is going. The symmetry of this form of Snell's law shows the reversibility of light paths as they pass any surface for which the law is valid.

It may seem that in going from the form $\sin i/\sin r = const$ to $n_1 \sin \theta_1 = n_2 \sin \theta_2$, we have substantially modified Snell's law. That this is not the case, we can see by a slight rearrangement of the above equation. In going from material 1 to material 2, θ_1 is the angle of incidence, and θ_2 is the angle of refraction. Our general statement can then be read

$$\frac{\sin i}{\sin r} = \frac{\sin \theta_1}{\sin \theta_2} = \frac{n_2}{n_1}.$$

It still says that the ratio of the sines of the angle of incidence and refraction is a constant since n_2/n_1 is constant. This constant is called the *relative index* of the two materials or the index of refraction of light passing from material 1 into material 2. It is often written n_{12} (read $n_{\text{one two}}$).

The statement

$$\frac{\sin \theta_1}{\sin \theta_2} = n_{12},$$

therefore, takes us back to the basic statement of the law.

Moreover, since

$$n_{12} = \frac{n_2}{n_1},$$

we can find the relative indices for any pairs of materials in terms of their absolute indices. From the relatively few absolute indices, all the relative indices can be computed. For example, the relative index for light going from water to glass is

$$n_{wg} = \frac{n_g}{n_w} = \frac{1.50}{1.33} = 1.13.$$

13–7. Total Internal Reflection

If we apply Snell's law blindly to all possible cases, we soon get into trouble. A difficulty arises when we try to compute the direction of the refracted ray for light traveling from a medium with a higher absolute index of refraction to a medium with a lower index. For example, consider light passing from glass, with $n = 1.50$, to air, at the particular angle of incidence of 41.8°. The sine of this angle is 0.667. The sine of the angle of refraction is given by Snell's law as

$$\sin \theta_{air} = n_{glass} \sin \theta_{glass}.$$

Hence

$$\sin \theta_{air} = 1.50(0.667) = 1.00.$$

When $\sin \theta = 1$, θ is 90°; therefore θ_{air} is 90°. In other words, the refracted light emerges from the glass in a direction parallel to the surface; it just glances along the surface. This angle of refraction is the largest one possible. What if a beam strikes the surface at an angle of incidence greater than 41.8°?

Let us try to set up an experiment that will tell us what actually happens. We can do this with

13–11. Pencils of light passing through a prism. Total reflection occurs for the two pencils incident near the bottom corner.

the arrangement shown in Fig. 13–11, in which several pencils of light, diverging from one another, enter the left side of a glass prism. After refraction at the first surface, they meet the surface at the top of the prism at different angles. Notice that the pencils in the right-hand part of the beam do not result in any refracted pencils; instead, they are totally reflected back into the glass. This phenomenon is known as *total internal reflection.* The smallest angle of incidence for which total internal reflection occurs is called the *critical angle.* If you measure the angle of incidence for the last two pencils on the right you will find that they are larger than 41.8°.

In general for light going from medium 1 into medium 2 as in Fig. 13–11, the critical angle in medium 1 occurs when $\theta_2 = 90°$, then from Snell's law,

$$n_1 \sin \theta_1 = n_2 \sin \theta_2,$$

we get

$$n_1 \sin \theta_c = n_2;$$

or

$$\sin \theta_c = \frac{n_2}{n_1}.$$

Clearly, total reflection can occur only when n_1 is greater than n_2.

It may seem strange that light suddenly stops being refracted and is totally reflected when the critical angle is reached. In fact there is no sudden change. As you see in Fig. 13–11, when the angle of incidence increases, more light (a brighter beam) is reflected and less light (a dimmer beam) is refracted; and as the critical angle is approached, we arrive at the point where all the light is reflected and none transmitted.

Sometimes light is piped around corners by means of total internal reflections. The "light pipe" consists of a cylindrical rod of transparent plastic. Light enters at one end of the rod nearly

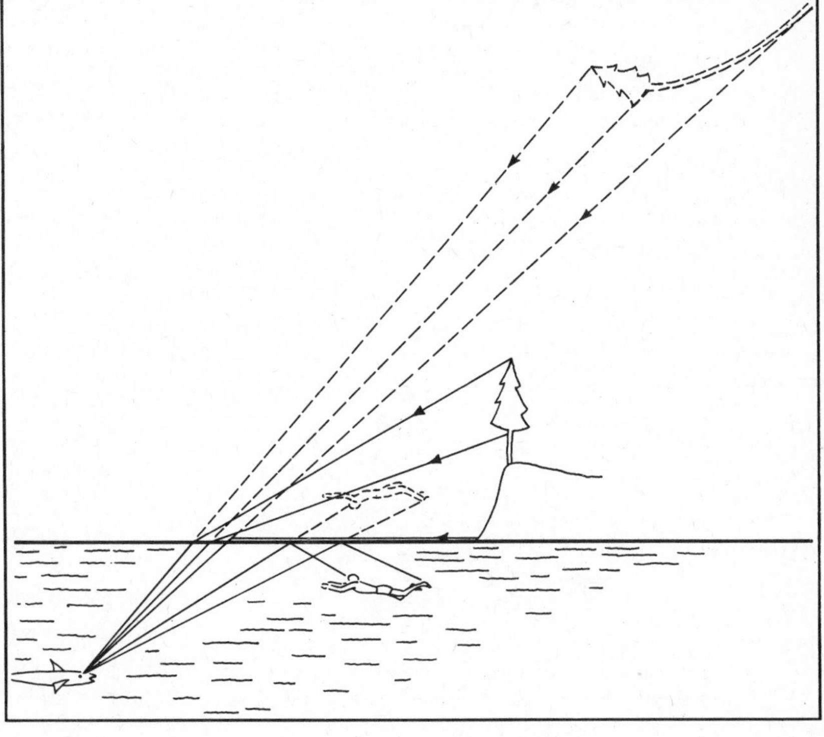

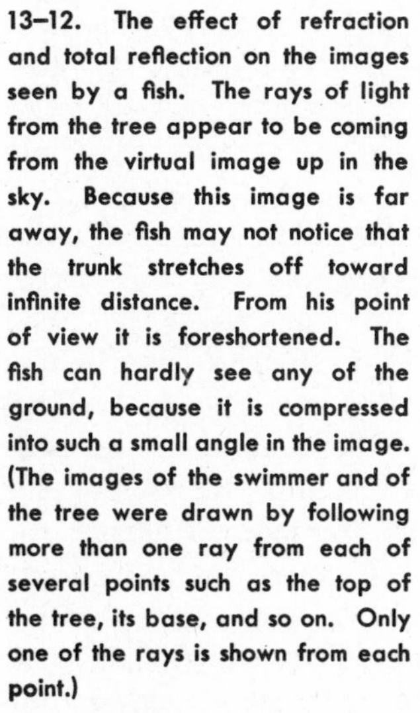

13–12. The effect of refraction and total reflection on the images seen by a fish. The rays of light from the tree appear to be coming from the virtual image up in the sky. Because this image is far away, the fish may not notice that the trunk stretches off toward infinite distance. From his point of view it is foreshortened. The fish can hardly see any of the ground, because it is compressed into such a small angle in the image. (The images of the swimmer and of the tree were drawn by following more than one ray from each of several points such as the top of the tree, its base, and so on. Only one of the rays is shown from each point.)

normal to the end surface. Any part of this light which reaches the side walls will have an incident angle greater than the critical angle and therefore will not escape into the surrounding air. Instead, a succession of total reflections will carry it around in the rod and it will finally emerge at the far end.

An interesting example of total internal reflection may be seen by a fish that looks upward through the surface of a large, smooth pond or lake. (Fig. 13–12.) He sees the trees around the pond hanging overhead in a small circle. They are surrounded by a mirror that reflects a man swimming near the bottom so that he appears to be swimming somewhere above the surface.

13–8. Refraction by Prisms; Dispersion

When we send light through a slab of glass having parallel faces, the rays emerging are parallel to the incident rays. We can, however, change the direction of a light beam by using a piece of glass with two non-parallel faces (Fig. 13–13). In fact, whenever the two faces are not parallel, the light will emerge in a new direction.

A careful examination shows that the beam or pencil of light that emerges from a prism diverges or spreads out more than the beam or pencil that is incident. (Fig. 13–14.) To investigate this spreading, which does not seem to be quite consistent with the laws of refraction, we shall allow the light to travel a considerable distance from the prism and then examine it. We shall use a very narrow incident pencil so that the spreading will be large compared to the pencil width. A simple arrangement for doing this is shown in Fig. 13–15 (a). Light from a distant white source, such as the sun or an incandescent light bulb, is allowed to pass through a narrow aperture in an opaque barrier. This aperture produces a narrow beam of light. A screen is set up at some distance from the prism. It is found that the light falling on the screen is no longer "white." Instead, a brilliant spectrum of colors — violet, blue, green, yellow, orange, and red — is spread across the screen. The colors are like those that we see in a rainbow, with red at one end and violet at the other. The red deviates least from its original direction, and the violet most.

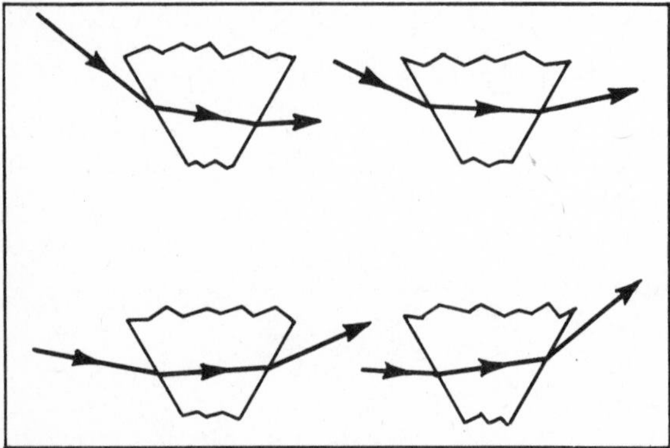

13–13. Light bent by passing through a glass block with non-parallel faces.

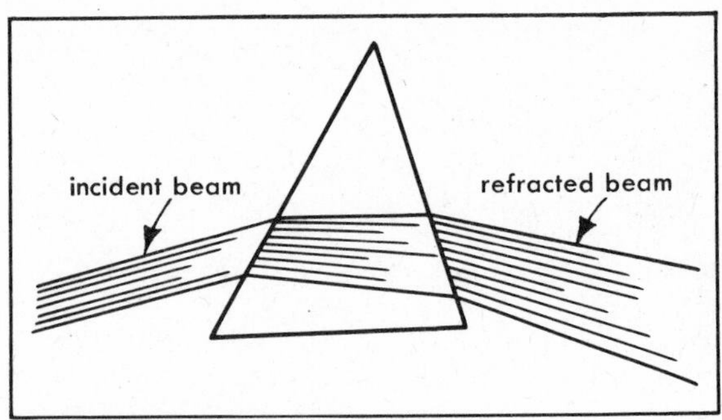

13–14. A beam of light diverging as a result of passing through a prism. The divergence is exaggerated.

The deviation produced by a prism is determined by the angle between the surfaces through which the light passes, by the direction of incidence on the first face, and by the index of refraction of the prism. Of these, the only quantity that can differ for the different colors of light is the index of refraction. We are thus forced to conclude that we must give up some of the simplicity achieved in our earlier experiments. Having decided that we could describe the refractive properties of any substance in terms of a single number, its refractive index, we now find that the refractive index appears to depend on the color of the light! Apparently white light is made up of light of different colors; and a material such as glass has different refractive indices for the different colors.

When a beam of white light strikes the prism as illustrated in Fig. 13–15 (b), the violet light is deviated most, while the red light is deviated least. Now no matter which way light passes between air and another medium, Snell's law tells us that the bending of the light is greater the greater the index of refraction of the medium. Consequently we learn that the index of refraction of the glass is greater for violet light than it is for red. The variation with color of the

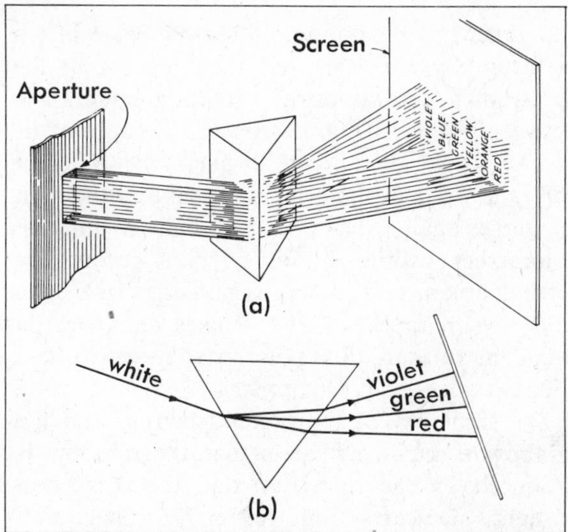

13–15. The dispersion of white light by a prism into a colored spectrum.

index of refraction for a glass that is used in many lenses is given in Table 4.

The difference between the index of refraction for violet and for red light is seen from the table to be only 0.019, just over one per cent of the average index of 1.52. It is not surprising that in our first experiments we did not detect this small variation, and that one can often calculate results that are in close agreement with experiment

Table 4

Index of refraction of "crown" glass

Color:	**Violet**	**Blue**	**Green**	**Yellow**	**Orange**	**Red**
Index:	1.532	1.528	1.519	1.517	1.514	1.513

by supposing that glass has a single index of refraction for all colors.

The spreading out of light into a spectrum is called *dispersion.* It was first studied in the seventeenth century by René Descartes and Sir Isaac Newton. Newton performed the additional experiment of trying to break up one portion of the spectrum by inserting a prism in light of a particular color, say red. All that happens is that the red is slightly further spread out but it remains red [Fig. 13–16 (a)]. Unlike the original white light, it does not split into a complete colored spectrum.

You will recall from Section 7–9 that not all sources emit light of all colors. What will we see on the screen if we send the yellow light from sodium through a narrow slit and then a prism? Only a yellow image of the slit will appear on the screen. By sufficient spreading out of the spec-

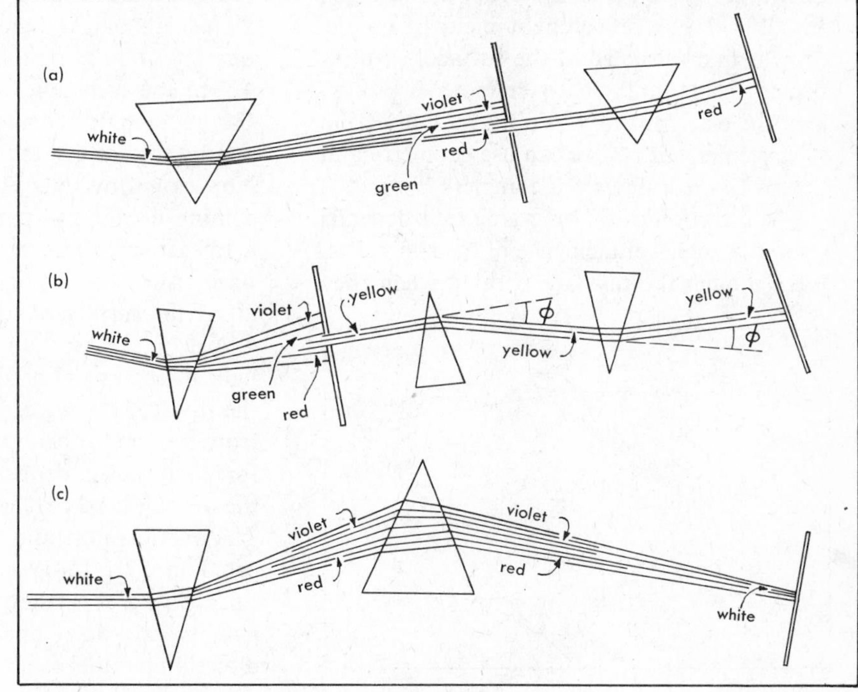

13–16. Experiments with a prism. (a) Light of one spectral color remains the same color on further analysis with a prism. (b) Light of one spectral color is always deviated through the same angle when passing on similar paths through identical prisms. (c) The spectral colors combine to make white light.

trum, we can see greater detail. For example, if the dispersion is great enough, this yellow image proves to be made up of two bright lines. (See Fig. 7–11.) But no matter how much we spread the yellow lines we do not change their color or analyze them into anything except finer detail. The individual colors of the spectrum cannot be decomposed; they are simple and basic in a way that white light is not. Yellow light from a spectrum will always deviate the same way through a prism. It will deviate less than green and more than red [Fig. 13–16 (b)], no matter how many prisms we use. A color-blind man can use the deviation to identify the kind of light.

Our conclusions are supported by a further experiment of Newton's proving that white light is a combination of many colors. He recombined the spectrum to make white light. We can do the experiment by breaking up a narrow beam into a spectrum by a prism, and then placing in the spectrum a second prism with a greater angle between its faces [Fig. 13–16 (c)]. Because of its greater angle this prism deviates the different colors more than the original prism and the light converges again. The pencils of light of different colors then overlap in some region beyond the second prism, and in this region the light on a screen again appears white. This is what Newton found, as you can too if you repeat his experiment with two glass or plastic prisms.

The similarity of the prism spectrum and the rainbow spectrum suggests that the rainbow is produced by the refraction and the dispersion of light. Descartes followed up this suggestion and thus found an explanation of the appearance of rainbows. This explanation is discussed below.

The Rainbow

We see a rainbow only when facing away from the sun when water drops are in the air somewhere ahead of us. Hence the sunlight must be reflected from the raindrops. Reflection from the outside of the drops will not do, for the light is scattered equally in all directions. The reflection that gives the rainbow takes place inside the drop, as shown in Fig. 13–17. A ray of light incident on the drop is first refracted at the surface, then reflected inside, and finally refracted again to give the emergent ray. To find the direction of this emergent ray we can use geometry and Snell's law to calculate the angles.

The direction of the emerging rays depends upon the angles of incidence of the sun's rays. Even though the rays are parallel when they reach the drop, they are striking a curved surface and therefore the angles of incidence spread over a wide range. We might guess that after reflection and refraction, the emerging rays would spread over a similar range and no rainbow would be visible. But when we trace a number of rays passing through a drop, we arrive at a very interesting result: almost all of the light that re-emerges after one reflection comes off at an angle of about 42° to the direction of the sun (Fig. 13–18). Far more reflected rays should come out at nearly this angle than at any other angle. You can show this effect experimentally by shining an intense parallel beam of light at a refractive sphere and seeing that the light once reflected inside comes out concentrated along the surface of a backward cone.

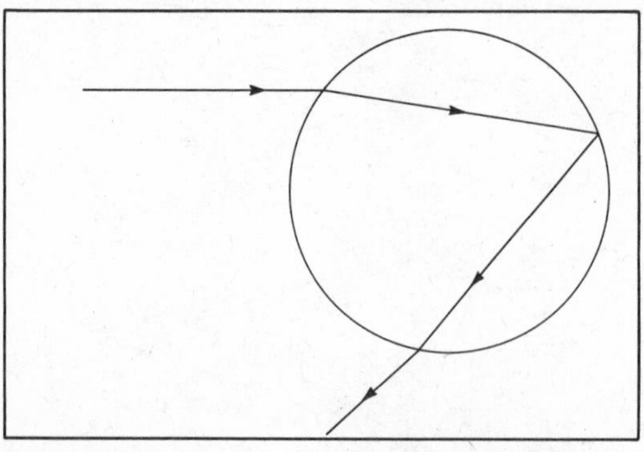

13–17. Cross section through a magnified raindrop.

A drop can send an appreciable amount of light to the eye only when the angle between the ray from the drop to the eye and the ray from the sun to the drop is about 42°. Therefore, only those drops in certain positions in the air can take part in forming the rainbow. The possible positions of such drops are indicated in Fig. 13–19. They all lie near the surface of a cone that has its apex at the eye and its axis on a line through the eye in a direction parallel to the sun's rays. Note also that the light rays reaching the eye from any

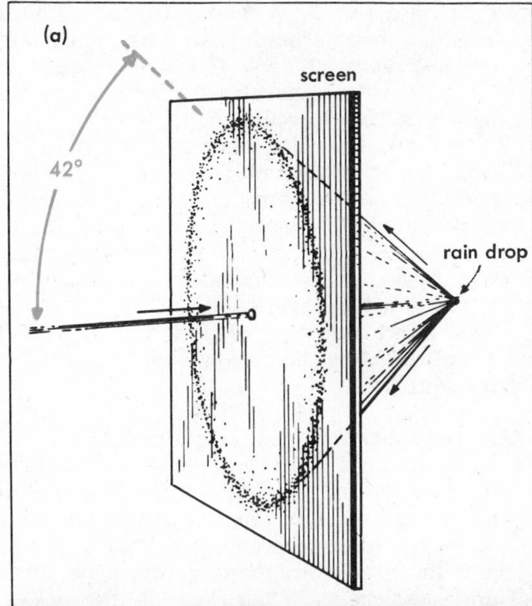

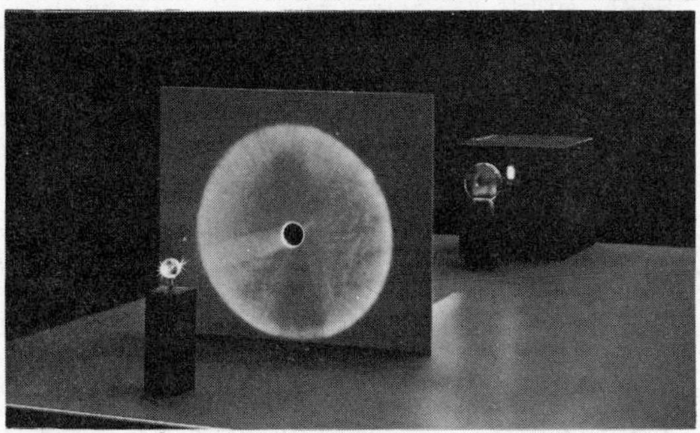

13–18. (a) Most of the light reflected once inside a raindrop comes out on the surface of a cone. (b) Experiment to show light re-emerging from a glass "raindrop."

single drop are parallel, so the light appears to be coming from a very distant source. Hence one sees a ring of light which appears to come from far away. The lines drawn from the ends of a diameter of this circle to the eye should make an angle of 2 × 42° = 84°. This, indeed, is found to be true for all primary rainbows.

Now what of the varied colors, the most striking thing about the rainbow? If the index of refraction of water were independent of color — that is, if there were no dispersion — the rainbow would appear as a bright band of white light. However, the index of refraction of water is not constant. It is about 1.333 for red light and 1.346 for violet light. Consequently, the once-reflected cone of violet light makes an angle of about 41°

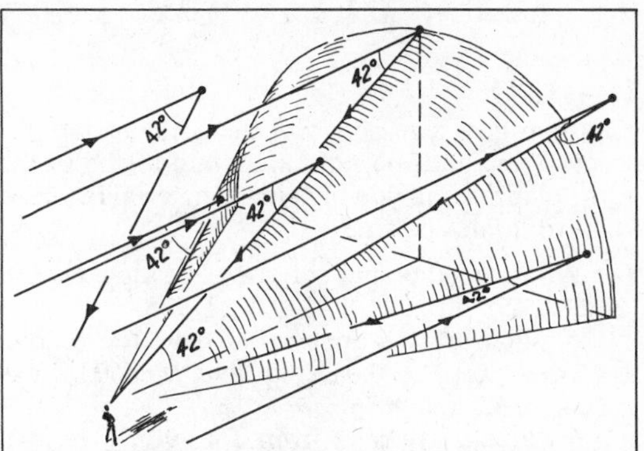

13–19. Location of drops that form the rainbow.

with the line joining the drop and the sun, while that of red light makes an angle of about 43° with this line (see Fig. 13–20). The position of each drop determines not only whether or not it will contribute light to the rainbow but also the color of its contribution. The drops returning red light to our eye lie on a cone with a bigger angle than those returning violet. Thus the primary rainbow can be expected to show violet light at the inside of the arc and red light at the outside. The other colors should occur in between in the order of decreasing refractive index — blue, green, yellow, and orange — and so they do.

The secondary rainbow, sometimes seen just outside the primary one, has red on the inside and violet on the outside. It is produced by light that has been reflected twice inside the raindrop before it emerges. Other less frequently seen bows are produced when the light is reflected three or four times within the drop. Because much of the light is refracted out of the drop, instead of being reflected several times, these rainbows are weak.

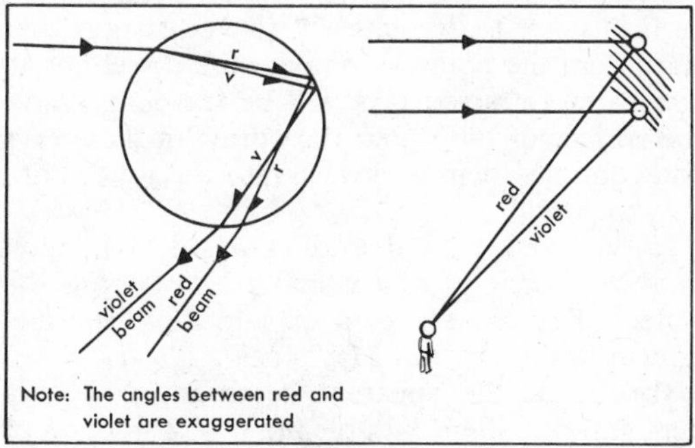

13–20. Formation of colors in the rainbow.

FOR HOME, DESK, AND LAB

1. Can you give a reason why the incident ray, refracted ray, and the normal should all be in the same plane? Can you imagine a material in which this would not be true?

2. (a) What are the sines of the following angles: 4°, 30°, 45°, 60°, 73°, 17.8°, 37.3°, 90°?
(b) What are the angles that have the following sines: 0.1045, 0.0000, 0.3090, 0.8660, 1.000, 0.5000, 0.5225, 0.9636?
(c) Plot sin *i* versus *i* from 0° to 90°.

3. A rectangular tank 8 cm deep is filled with water. A light ray enters the top surface of the water at a point just touching the side of the tank. After refraction it falls on a point on the bottom of the tank 3 cm from the same side of the tank.
(a) What is the sine of the angle of refraction? What is the angle of refraction?
(b) What is the sine of the angle of incidence? What is the angle of incidence of the entering ray?
(c) Suppose that the same tank were filled with a liquid other than water and you found that in order to fall on the same point 3 cm from the side the angle of incidence of the entering ray had to be 31 degrees. What is the index of refraction of the liquid?

4. A narrow pencil of light enters the top surface of the water in a rectangular aquarium at an angle of incidence of 40°. The refracted pencil continues to the bottom of the tank, striking a horizontally placed plane mirror which reflects it back again to the surface, and it is again refracted as it emerges into the air.
(a) What is the angle between the incident ray entering the water and the refracted ray emerging from it?
(b) If the water in the tank is 10 cm deep, what is the distance between the points on the water surface where the ray enters and where it emerges?

5. Make a drawing (to scale) of the side view of an aquarium in which the water is 12 cm deep. From a single point on the bottom draw two lines upward, one vertical and the other 5° from the vertical. Let these represent two light rays that start from the point. Compute the directions in which the refracted rays will be traveling above the surface of the water, then draw in these rays and continue them backward into the water until they intersect.
(a) At what depth does the bottom of the tank appear to be if you look straight down into the water? Does this help to explain the phenomenon shown in Fig. 11–2 (a)?
(b) Divide the apparent depth into the true depth and compare with the index of refraction of water.

6. A person looking into the aquarium described in Problem 5 sees light coming from the bottom. The light that reaches his eye is traveling along a line that makes an angle of 45° with the vertical.
(a) At what angle with the vertical must the light have been traveling in the water?
(b) Make a drawing, like that called for in Problem 5, showing the path of the ray. Then draw another light ray from the point on the bottom at which the first ray started, making its path in the water about 5° closer to the vertical than was the first ray. Compute and draw in the path of this ray above the water.
(c) At what depth does the bottom appear to be when viewed by the person who is looking into the aquarium?

7. A meter stick is dipping into a tank of water. It makes an angle of 30° with the horizontal surface of the water and its mid-point is just at the surface. Suppose that your eye is located directly above the submerged end of the stick. To find how the stick will appear to you, make a scale drawing showing a side view of the stick and the water. Draw two rays upward from the submerged end of the stick, each being 3° from the vertical. Compute the direction of the refracted rays above the water, draw in these rays, and continue them backward into the water until they intersect. The end of the stick will appear to be at this point. Draw a line connecting the point just determined with the mid-point of the stick and compare your drawing with Fig. 11–1. How do you account for the bent-stick illusion?

8. In the instructions given in Problem 7 it was assumed that the portion of the stick that was under water would appear to be straight and that the apparent position of the stick could therefore be determined by drawing a straight line connecting the apparent position of the end with the place at which the stick entered the water. Supposing that your eye was 60 cm above the water surface and vertically above the submerged end, can you invent a way of finding out where a point on the stick 20 cm from the submerged end would appear to be? If so, you could check on the accuracy of the assumption. Do not bother to make a scale drawing for this purpose. Instead make a rough sketch and describe the process that you would use.

9. Light from the setting sun comes through the earth's atmosphere along a curved path to your eye, so that the sun looks higher in the sky than it really is. How do you explain this? Illustrate your answer with a diagram.

10. Be prepared to discuss why turning Fig. 13–8 upside down shows you a way to prove the reversibility of light paths.

11. If the *relative* index for light going from glass into diamond is 1.61 and the *absolute* index of glass is 1.50, what is the *absolute* index of diamond?

12. If the relative index for light going from oleic acid into water is 0.91 and the index of water is 1.33, what is that of oleic acid?

13. With a square block of glass it is impossible, when looking into a side, to see out of an adjacent side. It appears to be a mirror. Using your knowledge of geometry and the critical angle, prove that this must be true.

14. Carbon disulfide (refractive index 1.63) is poured into a large jar to a depth of 10.0 cm. There is a very small light source at the center of the bottom of the jar.

(a) Calculate the area of the surface of carbon disulfide through which the light passes.

(b) What is the greatest distance in the carbon disulfide traveled by a ray that emerges from the surface?

15. * As a home project use a plastic cheese box (see Experiment II–3 in the Laboratory Guide) to measure the critical angle in water.

16. The absolute index of refraction of sodium chloride is 1.54 and the relative index of refraction for light going from sodium fluoride to sodium chloride is 1.15. What is

(a) the absolute index of sodium fluoride?

(b) the critical angle of sodium chloride?

(c) the critical angle between the two salts?

17. What will you see when you look at a piece of fused quartz submerged in oleic acid (refer to Table 3)?

18. To the jar in Problem 14 we add 5 cm of water. (The water will not mix with the carbon disulfide but will float on top.)

(a) Does this increase or decrease the area of the cone of light as it emerges from the carbon disulfide into the water?

(b) Calculate the critical angle at the surface between the carbon disulfide and the water.

19. A light source in a cylindrical glass container of carbon dichloride (C_2Cl_4; $n = 1.50$) sends a pencil of light from a point on the circumference. The pencil is parallel to the bottom and makes an angle of 45° with the radius. (See Fig. 13–21.) What will be the path of the light?

20. Show that the angle of the cone of rays reaching the fish from above the water is about 98°. (See Fig. 13–12.)

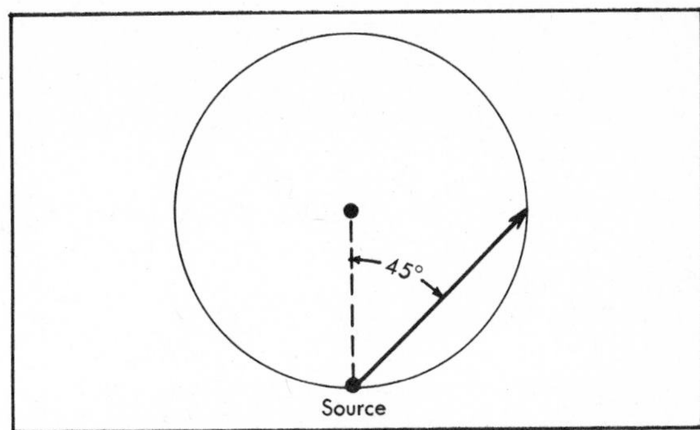

13–21. For Problem 19.

21. It is possible to place carbon disulfide, water, and kerosene in separate layers in that order, since they do not mix. A container having these three liquids in layers of equal depth has on its bottom a light source which projects a pencil of light upward through the liquids at an initial angle of 5° from the vertical.

(a) Calculate the angle of refraction of the ray as it finally emerges from the kerosene.

(b) Would a pencil of light travel over the same path in the reverse direction from kerosene through water into carbon disulfide?

(c) Suppose the cylinder had been filled with water only. How would the angle of refraction of the emerging ray compare with the angle calculated above?

22. A ray of light enters a triangular prism perpendicular to one face and emerges from the opposite face. The prism faces make an angle of 30° and the prism has an index of refraction of 1.50. Through what angle will the light be deviated in passing through the prism?

23. If the prism in Problem 22 were equilateral, through what angle would the light be deviated?

FURTHER READING

CROMBIE, A. C., "Descartes." *Scientific American*, October, 1959. The life and work of the French philosopher whose study of the behavior of light was only a part of his contribution to science.

NEWTON, SIR ISAAC, *Moments of Discovery*. Edited by G. Schwartz and P. Bishop, Basic Books, 1958. Newton's own account of his demonstration of the composite nature of white light by the use of prisms (p. 303).

NEWTON, SIR ISAAC, *Opticks, or a Treatise of the Reflections, Refractions, Inflections & Colours of Light*. Based on the Fourth Edition of 1730; Dover, 1952.

LENSES AND OPTICAL INSTRUMENTS

CHAPTER 14

OPTICAL instruments — cameras, projectors, telescopes, and microscopes — usually are built with lenses; that is, with pieces of refractive materials to converge or diverge light according to our design. A whole industry is devoted to the design and production of such instruments or their components. All these instruments are understood and designed in terms of Snell's law. The whole field of applications rests on the simple summary of refraction that we reached in the last chapter, $n_1 \sin \theta_1 = n_2 \sin \theta_2$. Most optical technology stems from this little bit of physics.

In this chapter, we want to learn how the laws of refraction are related to the construction of lenses and optical systems. An extensive treatment of the design of optical systems is, however, beyond the purpose of this chapter.

14–1. The Convergence of Light by a Set of Prisms

We found in Chapter 12 that we could control and redirect light beams by the use of curved mirrors. Devices that can accomplish similar purposes through refraction, instead of reflection, are called lenses. To understand how a lens operates, let us examine the behavior of light in passing through the combination of a plate of glass with parallel sides and the two triangular prisms shown in Fig. 14–1 (a). If a parallel beam of light falls on this system from the left, so that it is normally incident on the plate of glass, it will behave as indicated by the rays shown in the figure. The light that passes through the plate in the center will continue along its original direction, since the angle of incidence is 0°. Light striking the upper prism will be deviated downward by an amount depending on the opening angle of the prism and on its index of refrac-

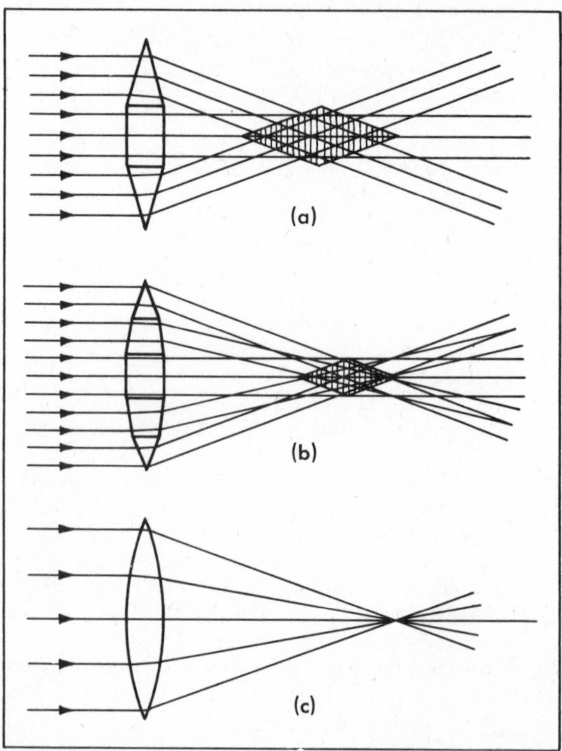

14–1. Construction of a lens by the process of subdividing prismatic sections.

tion. Similarly, light striking the lower prism will be deviated upward. As a result, there is a region, shown shaded in the figure, through which passes almost all of the light that falls on the plate and the prisms.

The convergence of a parallel beam of light into a limited region by this system resembles the convergence of a similar beam by a set of mirrors. (See Section 12–6.) While working with mirrors, we decreased the size of the region into which the light was converged by using an increased number of mirrors, each smaller than the original one. Let us try the same scheme here. Fig. 14–1 (b) shows parts of the central plate and of the two prisms cut away and replaced by pieces of new prisms. The size of the shaded region is clearly smaller than it was before.

If we continue the process of removing parts of the prisms and replacing them by sections having smaller opening angles, we come closer and closer to a piece of glass with the smoothly curved surface shown in Fig. 14–1 (c). This device is the limit that is approached as we increase the number of prisms indefinitely, just as the parabolic mirror of Fig. 12–16 was the limit approached as we used more and more plane mirrors to converge parallel light. In Fig. 14–2 we have actually carried out the construction indicated in Fig. 14–1. The lens produced by the process that we have outlined converges all of the parallel light that strikes it to a line as shown in Fig. 14–3.

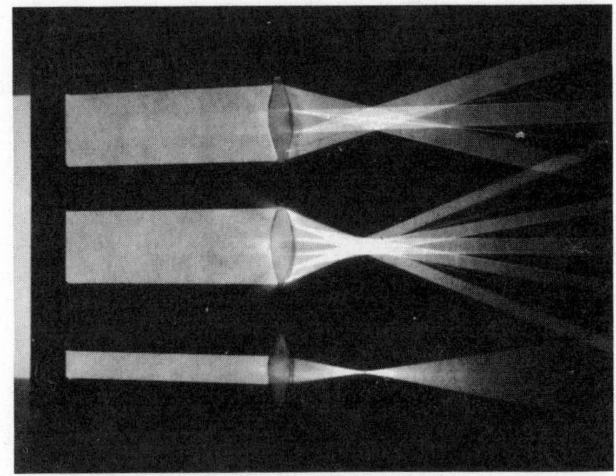

14–2. The experiments diagramed in Fig. 14–1.

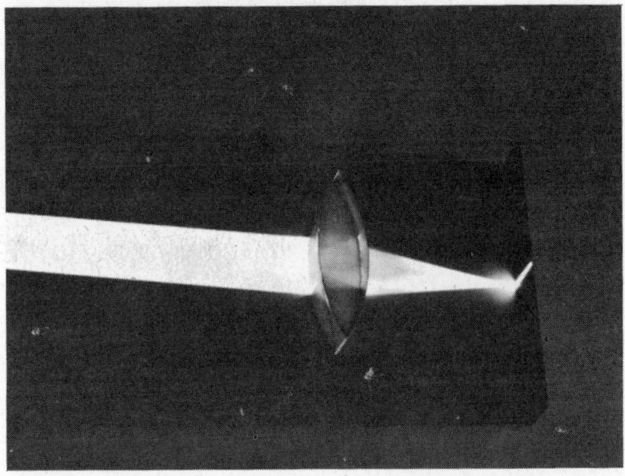

14–3. Convergence of light by a cylindrical lens like the one shown in Fig. 14–1. Note that the light is brought to a focus along a line.

14–2. Lenses

The device we have just constructed is called a cylindrical lens. Notice that we have not given any definition of the surfaces of the lens, except that they are obtained by increasing indefinitely the number of sections of prisms that are used to converge the light. It is possible to show that these surfaces are approximated very closely by circular cylinders. In other words, the lines representing the surfaces in Fig. 14–1 (c) are arcs of circles. The differences between the ideal surfaces and those of circular cylinders are very slight whenever both the width of the lens and its maximum thickness are considerably smaller than the distance from the lens to the line at which parallel light is converged.

Cylindrical lenses bring the light from a distant point source of light to a focus along a line. For most purposes we prefer that the light from a point source should be focused at a point. This focusing can be accomplished by constructing a lens whose surfaces curve equally in all directions. Such surfaces are portions of spheres. Almost all lenses are bounded by two spherical surfaces.

The line passing through the center of the lens and on which the centers of the two spheres are located is called the *axis* of the lens. The point on this axis at which incident parallel rays focus or converge is the *principal focus*, *F*. The distance of the principal focus from the center of the lens is known as the *focal length*, *f*.

The two surfaces of a lens do not always have the same radius. For example, the lens shown in Fig. 14–4 has a spherical surface of much larger

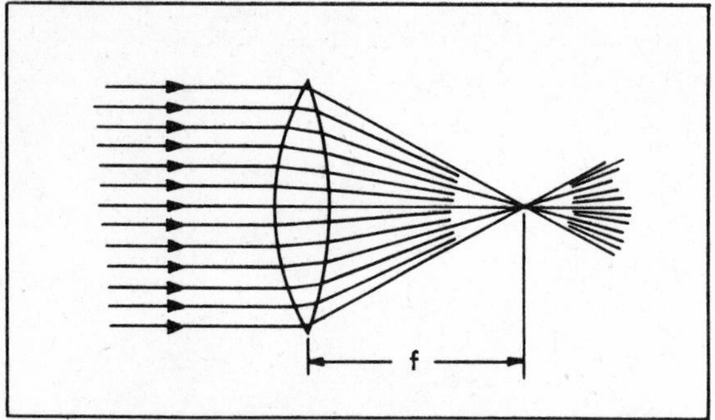

14–4. A lens with surfaces of unequal radii.

radius at its right-hand boundary than it has at the left.

If a lens is thin compared to its focal length, it makes no difference which side of the lens the light enters, the focal length is always the same. This symmetry is obvious if the lens is itself symmetric. That it is true for all thin lenses can easily be shown by an experiment in which a lens is used to focus the parallel rays of the sun to a point on a piece of paper or cardboard. If the lens is then flipped over, the focus occurs at the same distance from the lens (Fig. 14–5).

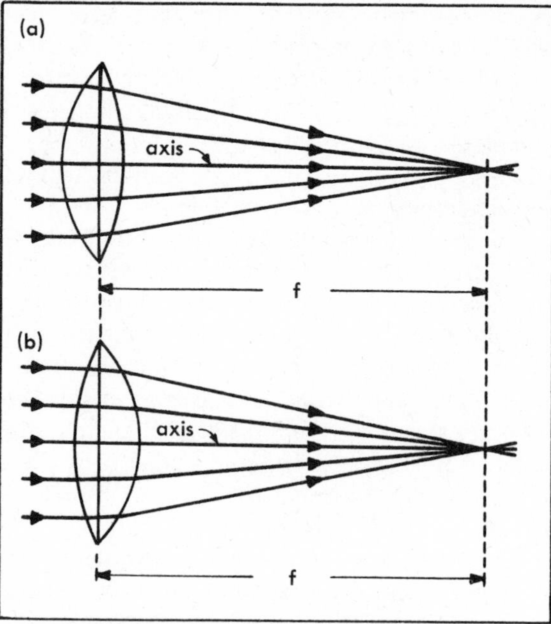

14–5. The principal foci of a lens. For thin lenses the focal distance is the same for parallel light entering either the side with a small radius (a) or the side with a larger radius (b).

This result is also predicted by a detailed application of Snell's law from which we find

$$\frac{1}{f} = (n - 1)\left(\frac{1}{R_1} + \frac{1}{R_2}\right),$$

where R_1 and R_2 are the radii of the opposing spherical surfaces.* We see that interchanging R_1 and R_2, which is equivalent to turning the lens over, does not change the calculated value of f.

From this equation, we can also see that when R_1 and R_2 are small, the lens will have a short focal length. This is illustrated in Fig. 14–6 where we see that the paths of light rays through the lens in (b) are bent more sharply, so that the focal length is shorter than in (a).

14–3. Real Images Formed by Lenses

We have thus far concentrated our attention on the focusing of light by a lens when the light comes from a very distant object. In the practical use of lenses, we are commonly interested in the light coming from near-by objects and we all know that lenses do form images of such objects. We can locate the images with the help of the knowledge that we have gained about the behavior of initially parallel rays.

Fig. 14–7 shows a lens, an object H_o, and its image H_i. To find the location of this image, we draw the two principal rays from the top of the object, one ray parallel to the axis and the other through the principal focus F_2. The ray parallel to the axis is bent by the lens so as to pass through the principal focus F_1. We also know that rays coming from the right and parallel to the axis would be deviated to pass through the other principal focus F_2. It follows from the reversibility of light paths that the ray from the top of H_o that passes through F_2 from the left must travel parallel to the axis after it has passed through the lens. All rays starting from the top of H_o will converge very close to the point at which these two bent rays intersect. This point is therefore the real image of the top of H_o.

We could have chosen any other point on the object and located its image in the same way. Had we done so for a number of points, we would have found that the image, H_i, falls along the line that is shown in the figure.

*We shall not give the proof of this "lens maker's" formula here. Although no new physics is involved, the proof is a long-winded application of trigonometry and Snell's law. Later, however, we can use the results of further study to get the formula more easily. It is therefore discussed at the end of Part II (see pages 302–303).

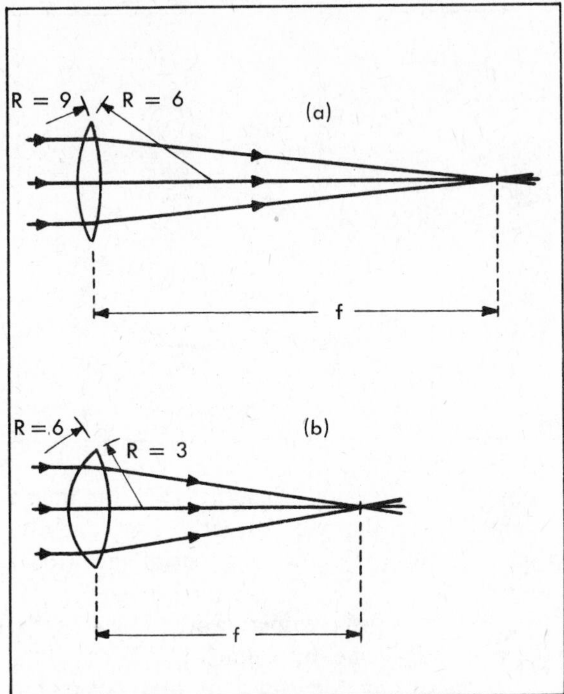

14–6. The shorter the radius of the surface of a lens, the shorter the focal length.

You probably have noticed that, in constructing the two principal rays, we have not considered the exact path of the ray within the lens, but have broken it sharply. This approximate construction is good enough for our present purposes because our location of the two principal foci is accurate only if the lens thickness (at its center) is small compared with the focal length. The only lenses to which our construction accurately applies are therefore *thin lenses.* For the purposes of ray diagrams, we may consider such lenses to be circular plates perpendicular to the axis.

Convex lenses, like parabolic mirrors, focus parallel rays to a point. Lenses, therefore, obey the same equation relating image distance, focal length, and object distance as do mirrors:

$$S_i S_o = f^2.$$

The proof of this equation in the case of convex lenses is the same as for mirrors (Section 12–9). As there, we use the shaded similar triangles formed by the principal rays shown in Fig. 14–7. Considering first the shaded similar triangles to the left of the lens, we see that $H_i/H_o = f/S_o$. The shaded triangles to the right of the lens give $H_i/H_o = S_i/f$. Combining the two equations, we have

$$S_o S_i = f^2.$$

14–4. Camera, Projector, and Eye

Produce an image of the sun with a convex lens. Since the sun is far away, the image is formed practically at the principal focus and you can see it there on a piece of paper. Images of closer objects lie beyond the principal focus; and, in order to capture them on paper or on a photographic film, we have to change the distance between lens and film. To make a photographic camera, then, we usually make a light-tight box with a bellows that allows us to move the lens. By adjusting the length of the bellows, we can place a sharp image on the photographic film. With some cameras we can place a piece of ground glass where the film is later inserted.

14–7. The formation of a real image by a converging lens.

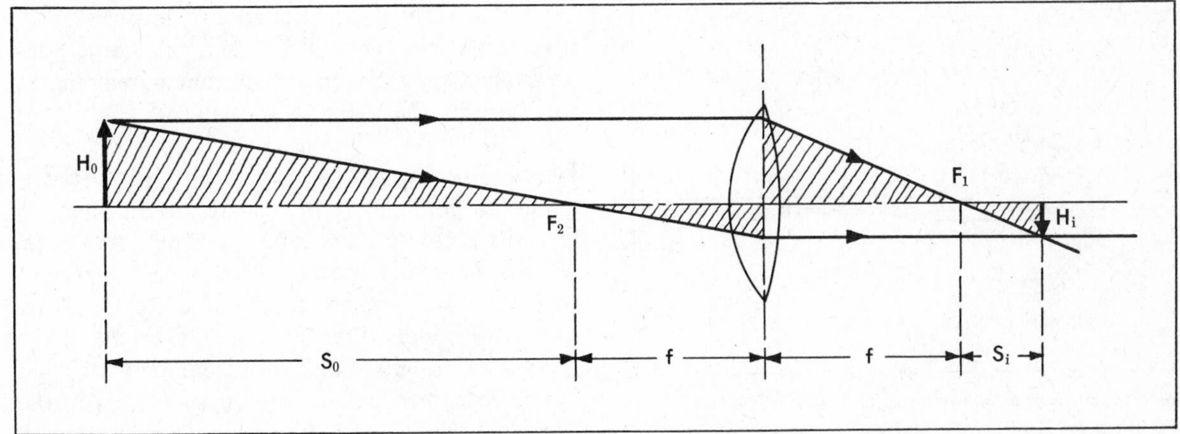

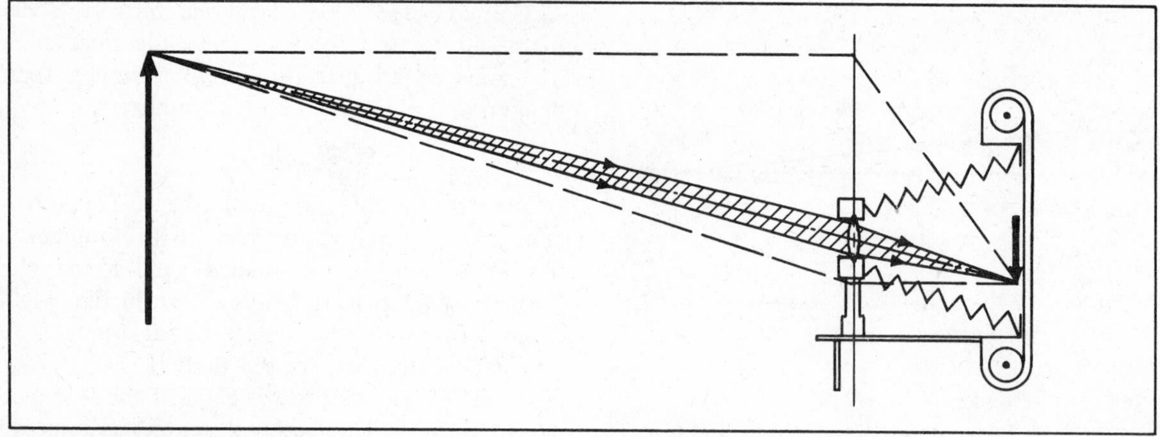

14–8. A camera. The rays of light that form the image of the head of the arrow are indicated.

We can then view the image directly and focus sharply on the particular object we want to photograph (Fig. 14–8).

As long as the object is more than twice the focal distance from the lens, so that S_o is longer than f, the image size is smaller than the object, as $H_i/H_o = f/S_o$ shows. When a small object is brought closer to the principal focus, the image moves to distances behind the lens that are large compared with the focal length; also, the image becomes bigger than the object. Consequently, to photograph small objects, a lens of short focal length is useful.

A projector is just a camera worked backwards. You can make one by taking the back off a camera, mounting the slides or film where the film usually goes, and shining a bright light through the film and out through the lens. The lens then forms an enlarged image well in front of the camera, where you can place a screen.

In cameras, projectors, and other man-made optical instruments, images are always brought into focus by changing the position of a lens with respect to the object. The eye, on the other hand, is unusual: it focuses images on the retina by changing its curvature and hence the focal length of its lens. When an object is at a very large distance from the eye, the rays entering the eye are nearly parallel and an image is formed at the principal focus as shown in Fig. 14–9 (a). When a close-by object is viewed, the image is formed beyond the focal point, and eye muscles form the elastic eye lens into a sharper curve, decreasing its focal length so that a real image will form on the retina [Fig. 14–9 (b)].

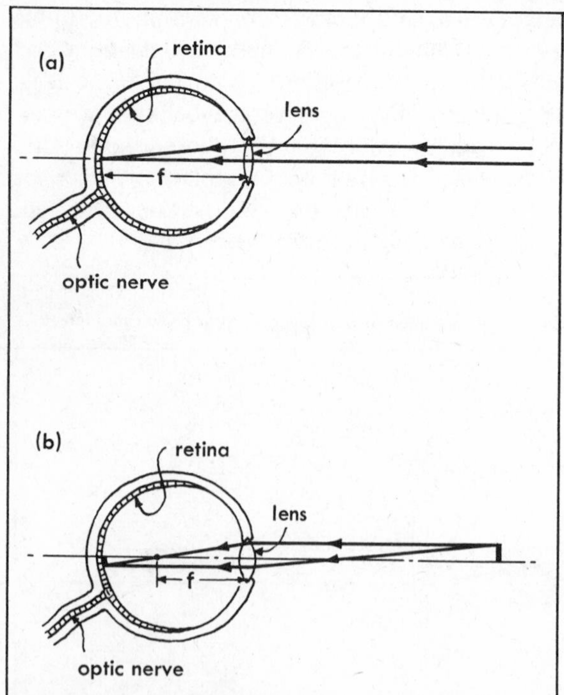

14–9. The lens of an eye adjusted to focus the light from a distant object (a) and from one near by.

14–5. The Magnifier or Simple Microscope

Let us go back to the small object that we brought close to the principal focus of a lens. As the object is moved through the principal focus the real image moves infinitely far away on the other side of the lens; and when the object is between the lens and the principal focus a virtual image is formed behind the object just as in the case of a concave mirror that we discussed in

Section 12–10. The situation is illustrated in Fig. 14–10. As in the case of the concave mirror, the convex lens always forms an enlarged virtual image.

What is the maximum magnification that we can obtain in this way? If we wish to see the greatest possible detail in an object, we get it as close to the eye as possible, thus giving a large real image on the retina of the eye. But there is a limit to how close we can view an object. As the object gets closer to the eye, the eye muscles must change the shape of the eye lens so that its radius of curvature becomes smaller and smaller in order to form a sharply focused real image on the retina. Soon a limit is reached; the adult eye cannot accommodate to an object closer than about 25 cm. This object distance is called the distance of most distinct vision. Try bringing a pencil closer and closer to your eye. You will see more and more detail until finally, with a great straining of your eye muscles, you can no longer keep a sharp image. Is your distance of most distinct vision greater or less than the average of 25 cm?

A convex lens helps us to see more detail by forming an enlarged virtual image which we can place at a comfortable distance from the eye. We notice in Fig. 14–10 that no matter where the object is placed between the lens and F_2, the top of the image always lies on the line F_1D, and $H_i = \frac{H_o}{f} S_i$ as usual.

Consequently, to make the image look as large as possible we should bring our eye right up to the lens as in Fig. 14–11; and in addition we should move the object (or the lens and our eye) until the image gets as close as we can clearly accommodate. This is the way to get the largest angle between the rays entering our eye from the top and from the bottom of the object; and since this light is what the eye works with, it is the way to make the object (or its virtual image) look largest.

Now for our own comfort we place the image at the distance of most distinct vision d, so the image distance S_i (measured from F_1) is approximately given by $S_i = d + f$. Therefore

$$H_i = \frac{H_o}{f} S_i = \frac{H_o}{f}(d+f) = H_o\left(\frac{d}{f}+1\right).$$

Furthermore, since we are looking at this image

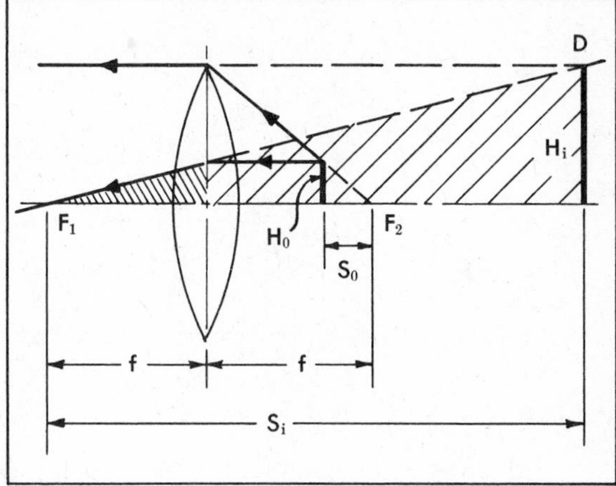

14–10. Formation of a virtual image by a converging lens.

from the distance of most distinct vision just as we could best look at the object without the aid of the lens, the magnification of the image we see is H_i/H_o. That is, maximum magnification is

$$\frac{H_i}{H_o} = \frac{d}{f} + 1.$$

This equation tells us the greatest magnification of a simple microscope. What, then, determines how great a magnification we can get? The focal length, f, of the convex lens is the determining factor; the smaller it is, the greater the magnification. In order to get a small f we use glass of high refractive index to produce sharper bending of the light for a given curvature of the lens surfaces. Also we need surfaces of small radius (sharp curvature). But a small radius of curvature means a small lens size, since the lens diameter cannot

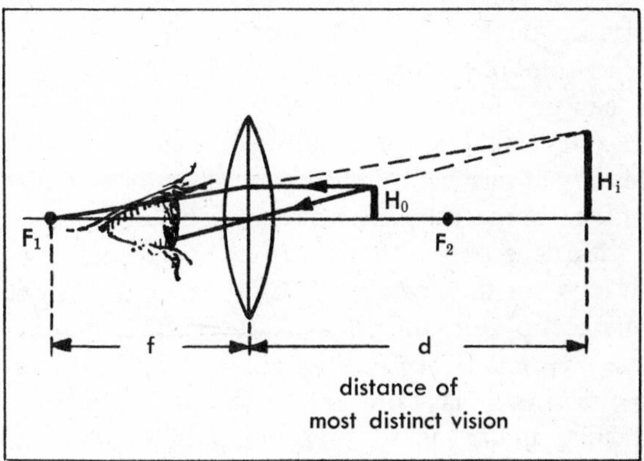

14–11. A converging lens used as a magnifier. The image is placed at the distance of closest distinct vision. Since the eye is very close to the lens, the distance from the image to the lens is about the same as that to the eye.

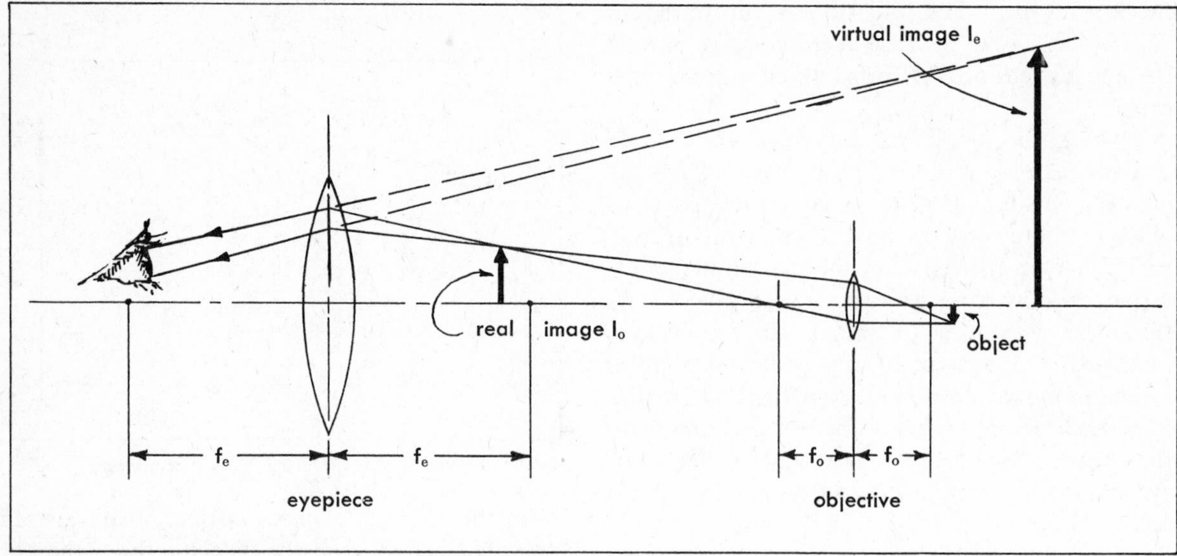

14–12. Compound microscope. The eyepiece and objective are located at the two ends of a tube. The diagram illustrates the formation of the images.

be greater than twice the radius of curvature. So we see that a high magnification means a small lens such as a jeweler wears over his eye while examining the works of your watch. (A big magnifying glass gives a large field of view but little magnification.)

As with all instruments, a simple microscope has its limitations. A small lens means little light is intercepted and even with strong illumination of the object, at high magnifying powers, the image is too dim to see. The compound microscope, described in the next section, circumvents this difficulty and gives sharper and brighter images, but it, too, has its limitations.

In spite of the limits of the simple microscope, it can give magnifications of 100 or so times; and in one of the most exciting discoveries in the history of science, Leeuwenhoek, a Dutch scientist of the seventeenth century, used such a microscope with a lens only a millimeter or two in diameter to look for the first time upon the teeming life of microscopic organisms invisible to the unaided eye. He made his lens, as you can make yours, by heating a glass rod until soft and then pulling it, like taffy, into a long, threadlike filament. He then slowly fed a piece of the filament into a flame until a spherical, molten globule of the right size formed on its end. This sphere he then used as his microscope.

14–6. The Compound Microscope; Telescopes

The most common and the most useful type of optical microscope today is the compound microscope. Perhaps you have used one in a biology course. It consists of a long tube fitted with converging lenses at each end (Fig. 14–12). The bottom lens, called the objective lens, is of short focal length and the microscope is adjusted until the object is just beyond the principal focus of the objective lens so that it forms an enlarged real image, I_o. This image is at such a distance from the eyepiece (slightly nearer the eyepiece than its principal focus) that a virtual image, I_e, is formed at the distance of most distinct vision. The eyepiece is thus used as a simple microscope to examine the enlarged real image formed by the objective.

You can make a crude compound microscope with two cheap, short-focal-length lenses mounted in a cardboard tube. Of course, to take full advantage of the potential of such an instrument, very carefully ground multiple lenses must be used for both eyepiece and objective.

Refracting telescopes are much like microscopes, but to increase the magnification and to gather more light, they have a large objective lens of long focal length. (Recall that $H_i/H_o = f/S_o$ and note that S_o is now large.) As in the compound microscope, the real image can be examined through an eyepiece.

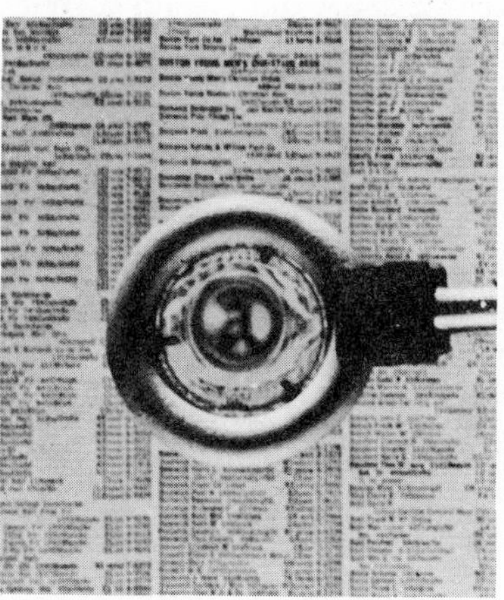

14–13. Distortion by a lens. These three photographs were made by looking through the same lens. At left, the lens was held so that the page of the telephone book is slightly below the focal region; in the middle picture, the page is in the focal region; at right, the focal region lies below the page. Note the geometrical distortions.

14–7. Limitations of Optical Instruments

If you hold a magnifying glass close to this page, you can see a clear, undistorted and slightly magnified image of the print. Now slowly raise the glass from the paper and at the same time increase the distance between your eyes and the lens. At some positions the image appears distorted. If your eyes are far enough from the glass, you may also detect some rainbow colors when looking at a corner of the page. In Figure 14–13 we see three pictures. They were made by looking through the same lens. In the first picture the lens was held so that the page of the telephone book lies entirely (but slightly) below the focal region; in the second picture the page is in the focal region; and in the last the focal region lies below the page. Clearly, in each case the image of the page looks quite different from the page itself. Part of the game of designing really good optical instruments is to minimize the geometrical distortions so apparent in these pictures.

What are the origins of these defects in images? First, we know even for mirrors (Chapter 12) that a surface designed to bring light from one small object to a sharp focus is not the correct surface to bring light to an exact focus from an object at a different place. The same is true for lens surfaces. Some blurring of the image therefore results. In addition, when we look through different parts of a lens the images are at different positions (and the magnification is different). The image therefore is distorted. In photography distortion and blurring are often cut down by using a "stop," a barrier with a small hole in it so that we use only a selected portion of the lens.

The colored edges of images usually arise because of the dispersion of the light that passes through a lens. The focal length of a lens is slightly longer for red light than it is for blue light, because the blue light is refracted more strongly than the red. This undesirable effect is called *chromatic aberration*. It can be greatly reduced by using a weakly diverging lens made of glass for which the index of refraction changes greatly with color, in conjunction with a strongly

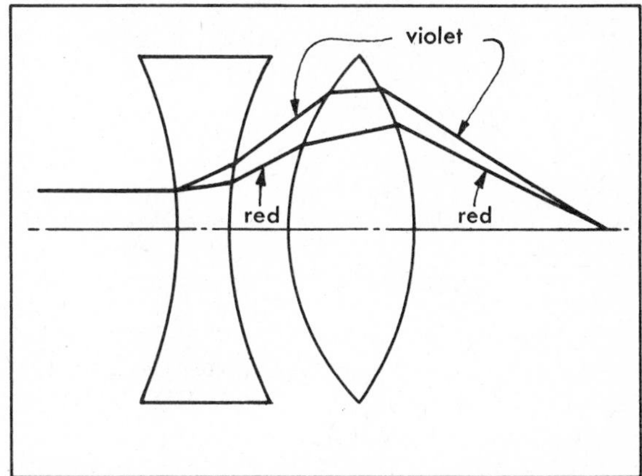

14–14. A lens built of two pieces to minimize the different focal properties of different colors. Such doublets are often made with one common surface and glued together. They are called achromatic lenses.

converging lens of glass for which the index of refraction changes less with color (Fig. 14–14). This trick makes the focal properties of the whole system of lenses nearly the same for all colors.

The problem of designing a system of lenses with the smallest amount of distortions and aberrations is a very complicated one. But the complications arise only in the detailed applications of the laws of refraction; they involve no new principle. Disentangling these complications will not enrich our understanding of basic optical phenomena, and therefore we shall not do it here.

There is one limiting factor affecting optical magnifiers which causes a blur in the image and is of a fundamental nature. This is the inevitable diffraction which results from the limited size of the objective lens through which the light must pass. At high magnification it is this blurring that prevents us from seeing finer and finer detail. We shall learn more about diffraction in Chapter 19.

FOR HOME, DESK, AND LAB

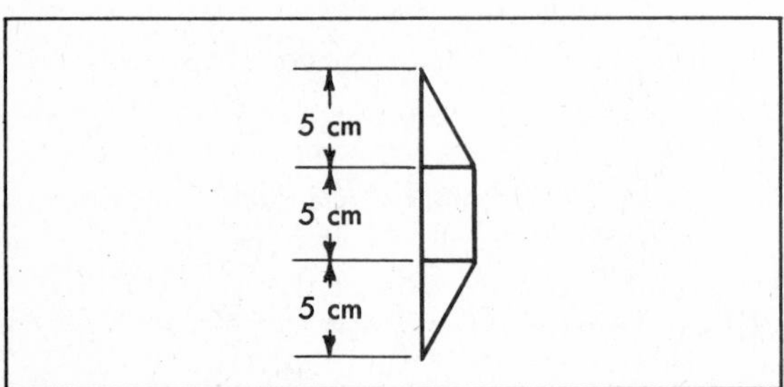

14–15. For Problem 1.

1. A crude converging lens can be constructed by placing two 30°–60°–90° glass prisms together with a glass block as shown in Fig. 14–15.
   (a) What is the focal length of this "lens" to one significant figure?
   (b) Would such a lens form a clear image? Explain.

2. If two 45° prisms of glass (index = 1.50) are arranged as in Fig. 14–16 they will not converge parallel light. Why not? What will happen to the light?

3. Some lighthouses and light buoys mark the positions of dangerous rocks and shoals. The light must be concentrated at a low angle with respect to the horizon (light directed upward is wasted) and must be equally visible from all points of the compass.
   (a) Can you design a "lens" which will do this?
   (b) Instead of using a continuous curved surface, such lights often use a lens made of sections of prisms. Can you draw a diagram of such a lens? It is called a *Fresnel lens* after the French physicist who first devised such a lens.
   (c) Automobile headlights are constructed to give a wide, flat, horizontal beam. Parabolic reflectors are made to give a narrow beam which passes through a Fresnel lens in the front of the headlight. Examine an automobile headlight and see if you can understand how it gives broad, horizontal beams.

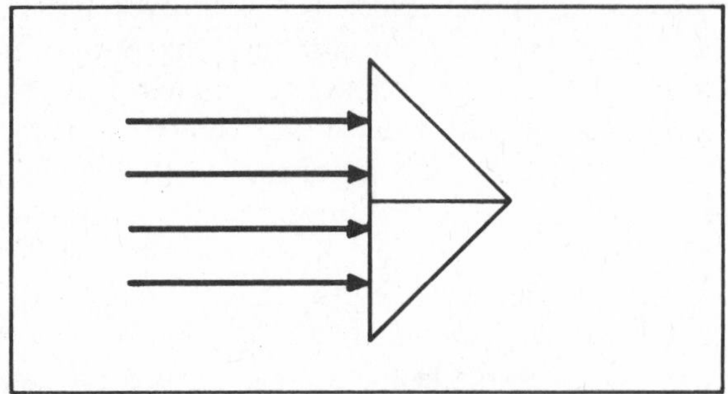

14–16. For Problem 2.

4. Use the Lens Maker's Formula
$$\frac{1}{f} = (n - 1)\left(\frac{1}{R_1} + \frac{1}{R_2}\right)$$
to find the focal length of a glass lens ($n = 1.50$) with one flat surface and one with a radius of 10 cm. (Such a lens is called a *plano-convex lens.*)

5. (a) What are the focal lengths of the two lenses shown in Fig. 14–17? (Index of glass = 1.50.)
   (b) How does the focal length of (b) compare with a flat block of glass?

6. A lens (index = 1.50) has a focal length in air of 20.0 cm.
   (a) Is its focal length in water greater or less than in air?
   (b) What is its focal length in water?
   Hint: Notice that every individual refraction depends on the relative index of refraction.

7. A lens whose focal length is 10 cm is used in a slide projector to give a real image on a screen at a distance of 6.0 meters.
(a) What will be the magnification?
(b) How far is the lens placed from the slide?

8. Prove that if two identical converging lenses of focal length 10 cm are placed 40 cm apart, the combination will form an upright image of an object that is 20 cm away from the first lens and the magnification will be 1.

9. (a) Prove that the size of the image of the sun produced by a convex lens is proportional to the focal length. What is the constant of proportionality?
(b) How large an image of the sun (diameter 1.4×10^9 m) will be formed by a lens of focal length 1.0 meter?
(c) What will be the ratio of the size of the images of the sun formed by a lens of 10 cm focal length and a lens of 10 m focal length?

10. How large an image will be formed of an artificial satellite (53 cm in diameter) passing at an altitude of 500 miles, if it is photographed with a camera whose focal length is 10 cm? Would you expect an actual photograph to show a larger or smaller image than the size you have calculated?

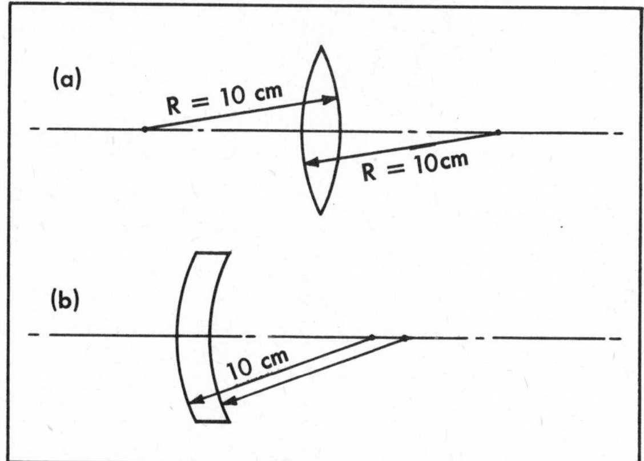

14–17. For Problem 5.

11. (a) What is the focal length of the lens in Fig. 14–18? (Index of the glass is 1.50.)
(b) By sketching the paths of some light rays, show what the lens does to incident light parallel to its axis.
(c) From the ray diagram of Fig. 14–18 (b), show that $S_oS_i = f^2$. Notice from which focal points S_o and S_i are measured.
(d) What happens as you move the object toward the lens? Can S_i ever get bigger than S_o? Is the image ever bigger than the object?
(e) How would you find (experimentally) the focal length of a diverging lens?

12. Assume your distance of most distinct vision is 15 cm. What is the maximum magnification that can be obtained with each of the following convex lenses when used as a magnifying glass or simple microscope?
(a) f = 30 cm,
(b) f = 10 cm,
(c) f = 1 cm,
(d) f = 1 mm.
(e) Graph the maximum magnification as a function of "f."

13. Assume your distance of most distinct vision is 25 cm. A compound microscope has an eyepiece of 2.0 cm focal length and an objective of 4.0 mm focal length. The distance between objective and eyepiece is 22.3 cm. What is its magnification to two significant figures?

14. Using the microscope of Problem 13, with the same adjustment, we see an amoeba. With a ruler, we measure the size of the virtual image by looking at it with one eye and at the ruler with the other. On the ruler the amoeba appears to be about 10 cm long. About how big is it really?

15. For the maximum magnification of an eyepiece, we found $\frac{d}{f} + 1$ where d is taken as the distance of most distinct (or closest distinct) vision. If your eyes can accommodate to see distinctly at 15 cm, we should write $\frac{15\text{ cm}}{f} + 1$ as the magnification of a simple magnifier for you. Also, if you can

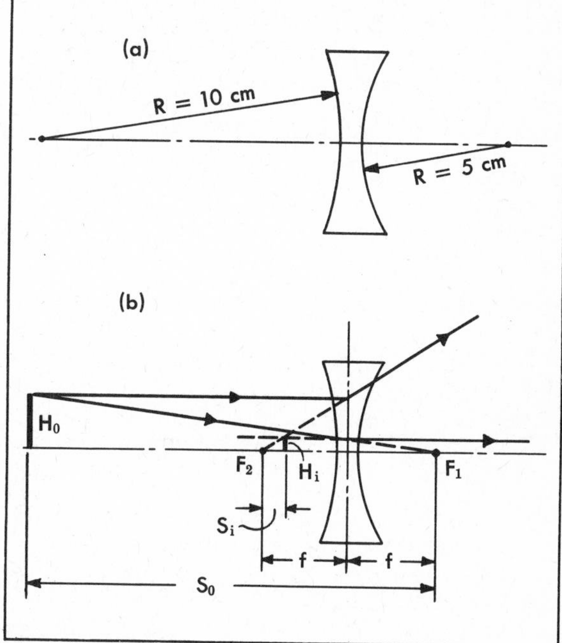

14–18. For Problem 11.

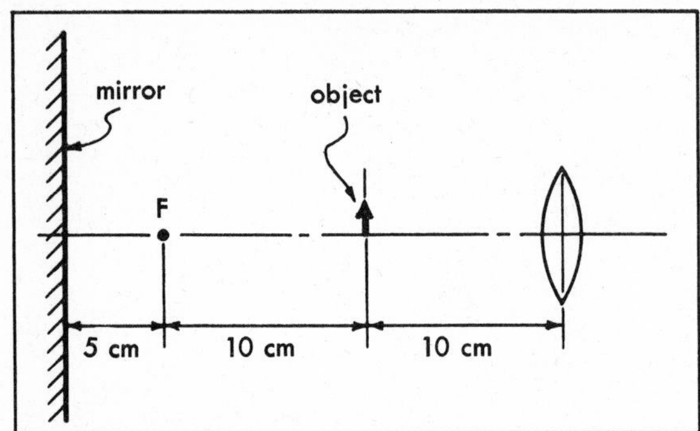

14–19. For Problem 19.

accommodate to images no closer than 35 cm, $\frac{35\text{ cm}}{f} + 1$ would apply. Why does the magnification go up for someone who accommodates poorly at small distances? Does he see more detail than someone who can accommodate closer? Be prepared to discuss this question in class.

16. Two lenses both have a focal length of 20 cm, but one has a diameter four times that of the other. Draw sketches of the two lenses and tell how the images they form differ.

17. (a) What is the ratio of the focal lengths of a crown-glass lens for violet light and for red light? (The index of refraction for various colors is given in Table 4, Chapter 13.)
(b) Is the ratio the same for all kinds of glass?

18. A lens of focal length 20 cm is placed 30 cm from a plane mirror and an object is placed on the axis 10 cm from the mirror. Where will the image of the object be found?

19. Where are the images of the object in Fig. 14–19? Can you see all the images if you look through the lens
(a) with your eye near the lens?
(b) with your eye far from the lens?

FURTHER READING

ROGERS, FRANCES, *Lens Magic.* Lippincott, 1957. A history of the development of lenses, and a description of their many applications.

TEXEREAU, JEAN, *How to Make a Telescope.* Interscience Publishing Co., 1957.

THOMPSON, ALLYN J., *Making Your Own Telescope.* Sky Publishing Co., Cambridge, Mass., 1947.

WALD, GEORGE, "Eye and Camera." *Scientific American*, August, 1950 (p. 32).

THE PARTICLE MODEL OF LIGHT

CHAPTER 15

IN CHAPTER 9 we built a molecular model of a gas. That model accounted for the fundamental properties of a gas and put them into a consistent picture. Let us try now to construct a model or theory of light, which will account for the properties of light we have thus far studied. Like the model of a gas this model will allow us to draw conclusions and make predictions which in turn can be checked by further experiments. In doing so, we shall retrace ideas that were developed over several centuries. The main architect of the model we shall study in this chapter was Sir Isaac Newton.

We have seen that light always has its source in some luminous body and that it travels in essentially straight lines. Any model of light must, then, include something that starts from the luminous body and moves along a straight path. The simplest thing that we can imagine traveling in this way is a *particle*, like a baseball. We might suppose that a luminous body gives off a stream of particles. You may object to this model on the grounds that baseballs or other particles do not travel in straight lines; they move in curved paths that bring them down to the earth. We do know, however, that the path of a baseball curves less and less as its speed is increased. We can expect that the paths of light particles which travel at a speed of 3×10^8 m/sec will hardly be curved by the earth's gravitational pull. With the particle model, therefore, we have no trouble in accounting for the propagation of light in straight lines.

Of course, light particles must be quite different from baseballs. In particular, unlike baseballs, they do not interact with each other, as we found out in Section 12–2. We can explain this lack of interaction by supposing that the particles are very small, so small that even for two intense light beams, the chance that particles in one beam will collide with those of the other is extremely small. In this way we can include the lack of interaction of light with light in our model. Our assumed light particles differ from baseballs, then, by their very high speeds and their very small size. If we keep these differences in mind, we can try to predict the properties of streams of light particles by studying the behavior of particles such as baseballs or marbles.

15–1. Reflection

We know that light is reflected when it strikes a surface. Do particles such as steel balls behave in the same way? To answer this question, we merely need to throw some ball bearings onto various surfaces. The balls thrown onto a clean, smooth steel plate bounce off regularly at an angle of reflection approximately the same as their angle of incidence (Fig. 15–1). The paths of incidence and reflection are in a plane normal to the surface; and also the speed after collision with the surface

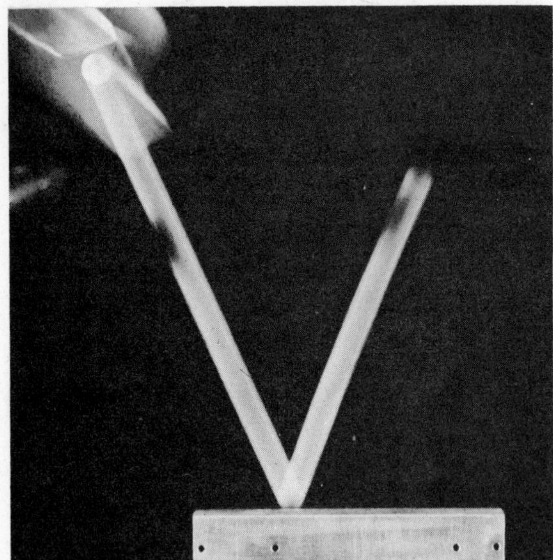

15–1. A time exposure of a ball being reflected from a steel plate. The angle of reflection equals the angle of incidence.

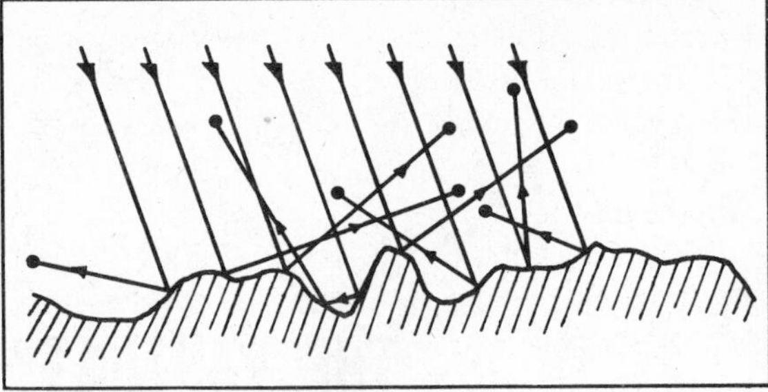

15–2. The diffuse reflection of particles. This occurs when a surface has irregularities larger than the size of the particles.

is about as great as before. If either the balls or the smooth surfaces are less resilient than steel, reflection does not take place with equal angles of incidence and reflection. Also, in such cases the speed of the balls after reflection is less than before — unlike light, which does not change its speed on reflection. To account for the specular reflection of light from smooth surfaces, therefore, we have to assume that light particles reflect like ideal ball bearings bouncing off resilient surfaces. By restricting our model to such elastic particles and using only surfaces which are elastic for the particles of light, we can explain specular reflection.

We have now seen that our particle model can account quite satisfactorily for the specular reflection of light. It can also account for the fact that light is sometimes reflected diffusely. Fig. 15–2 indicates how. Individual particles bounce off with equal angles of incidence and reflection; but if the surface is uneven, the reflected particles will be traveling in a variety of directions so that the surface as a whole scatters the light diffusely. We might ask just how smooth a "smooth" surface must be to show specular reflection on a large scale. The answer is that the bumps in it must be very small compared with the size of the particles that strike it. A surface that appears quite smooth when ball bearings are bounced from it may be very rough and uneven when the small light particles are reflected. We can therefore see why metals must be highly polished before they become good mirror surfaces.

15-2. Refraction

Can our particle model of light account for refraction as well as for reflection? In refraction the light particles are shoved off their path in air and onto a new path as they enter the refractive material. Can we design an experiment in which moving steel balls are shoved so as to change their path in the same way?

Suppose a ball rolls along a level surface and then down a steep slope onto a lower level surface. While the ball rolls on the upper level surface, it moves in a straight line at a constant speed. This upper surface, let us assume, corresponds to the region of air through which a particle of light moves in a straight line at a constant speed. When the ball comes to the steep slope, it is shoved in a direction perpendicular to the edge of the slope. The sloping region, therefore, can model the surface region of a refractive medium such as glass. In this surface region in the glass, the particles of light are supposed to be given a shove perpendicular to the boundary and toward the inside of the glass. To find out what happens to the particles of light as they pass through this region we need only look at the photograph in Fig. 15–3 which shows what happens to the balls as they roll down the slope. There we see that the ball is speeded up in the direction perpendicular to the edge, and the direction of its path is changed. If the ball rolling along the upper surface meets the slope at an angle, it rolls out from the slope along the lower surface in a different direction, closer to the normal. In the same way, light passing through a surface region in which it is shoved toward the inside of the refractive material should speed up and bend toward the normal as it enters the refractive material. The lower level surface on which the ball rolls corresponds to the inside of the refractive material. Here again the ball goes at a constant speed in a straight line like light inside of a piece of glass.

We can use the rolling-ball model to investigate the relation of the angles of refraction to the angles of incidence. The relation that we find in the rolling-ball model should be the same as the relation for light if refraction is caused by a shove that occurs when the light passes from the outside into the inside of a refractive medium. To carry out this investigation in the rolling-ball model, we always roll the balls across the upper plane at the same speed, because in a vacuum the light particles always travel at the same speed. Measurements of many pairs of angles show that the refraction of the balls agrees with Snell's law

$$\sin \theta_u / \sin \theta_l = \text{constant},$$

where θ_u is the angle between the path of the ball on the upper plane and the normal to the boundary and θ_l is the corresponding angle on the lower plane. What is more, the constant in Snell's law depends on the difference in height between the two plane regions and on the speed with which the balls move. The greater the difference in height, the greater is the index of refraction; the greater the original speed, the smaller the index. By always using the same original speed, we can model materials of different indices of refraction by planes of different heights. For example, to model the refraction of light going from air into water, the height of the sloping region must be smaller than the height needed to model the passage of light from air into glass. In each case we find that the rolling-ball model produces Snell's law; and by adjusting the heights, we can match any index of refraction.

In discussing the rolling-ball model we do not mean that light is made of rolling balls which fall down hills. The point of this model (which was devised by Sir Isaac Newton to explain the laws of refraction) is that refraction can be explained if at the surface of every refractive material light particles are given a shove. This idea is plausible. Far inside of a piece of glass or other refractive material, a light particle is surrounded by the same material on all sides. It is pushed in *no* direction; but at the surface the situation is obviously different, and a push or pull toward the inside might well occur. Then if the push acts like that in the rolling-ball model, refraction is successfully explained.

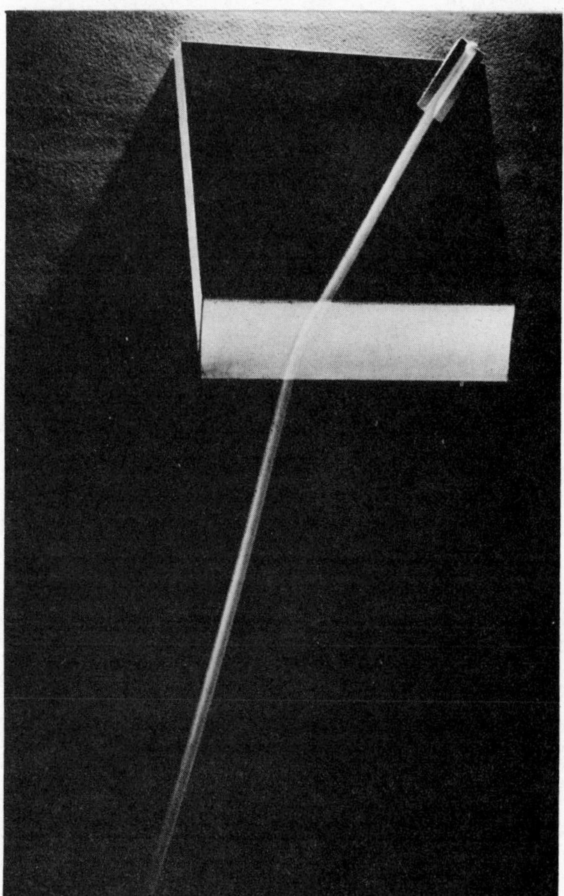

15–3. A time exposure of a ball bearing rolling from a higher to a lower surface. The change in direction of the ball shows "refraction."

So far this model is successful. We therefore examine it further. By taking stroboscopic pictures we can find the relation between the speeds of a ball on the upper and lower levels (Fig. 15–4). Analyzing many paths of many balls hitting the slope at different angles shows that, for the same v_u on the upper plane, the ball always attains a definite speed v_l on the lower plane. The angle of incidence on the boundary does not influence v_l. Furthermore, just as in the elastic specular reflection of balls, the component of the velocity along the boundary does not change in the refraction. Only the perpendicular component of the velocity is changed; it is increased in going into the lower level, which is the refractive region in our model.

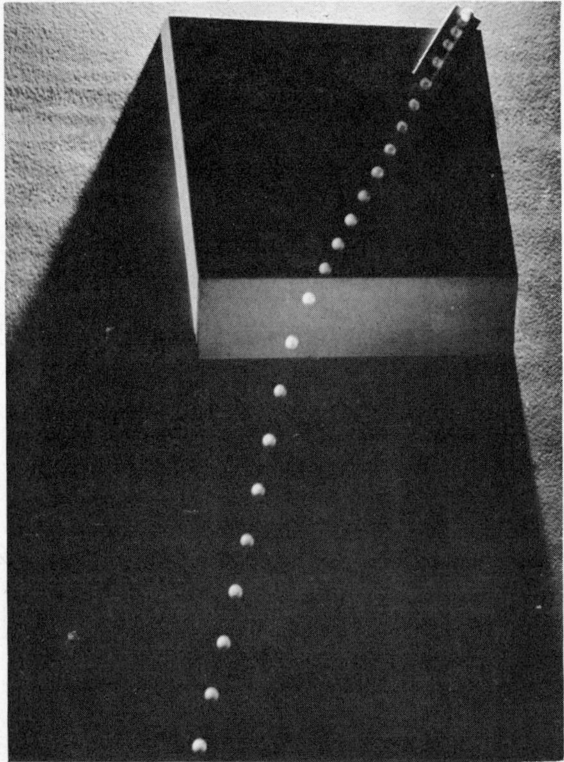

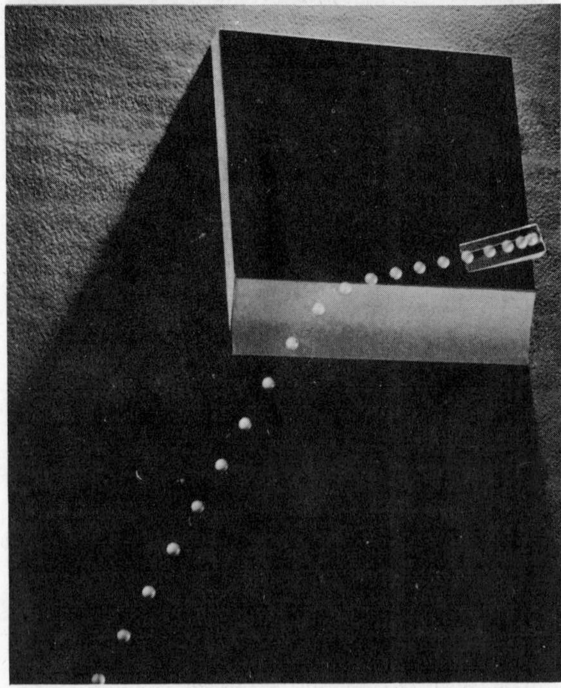

15–4. Two stroboscopic pictures of the ball bearing shown in Fig. 15–3. The speed on the upper level is the same in both pictures, since the ball bearing is released from the same height each time. Notice that the speeds on the lower level are also the same, although the angles of incidence are different in the two pictures.

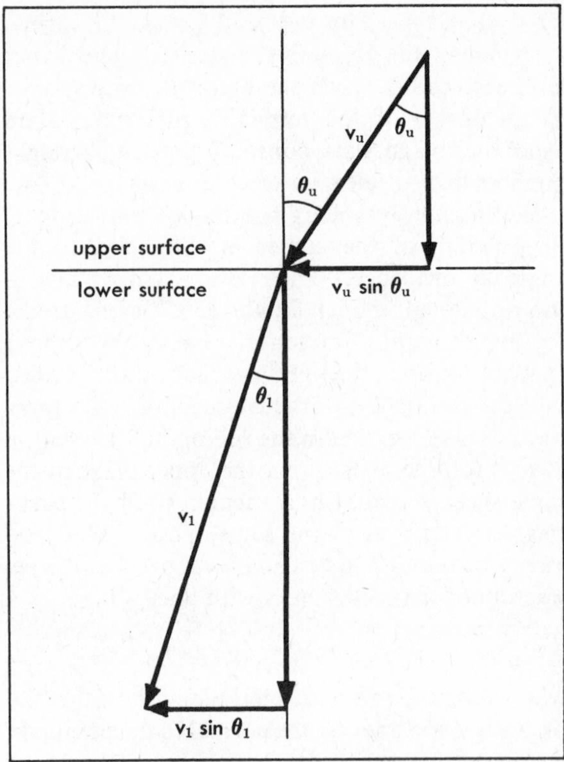

15–5. A vector diagram illustrating what happens in Figs. 15–3 and 15–4. The two velocity components $v_u \sin \theta_u$ and $v_l \sin \theta_l$, parallel to the boundary, are equal.

These observations of the speeds in the two materials are related to Snell's law. In fact, from them we can show that Snell's law follows logically. The component of the velocity along the boundary is $v_u \sin \theta_u$ in the upper region and $v_l \sin \theta_l$ in the lower region (Fig. 15–5). Because this component does not change when a ball passes from one region to the other, we have $v_u \sin \theta_u = v_l \sin \theta_l$ or

$$\frac{\sin \theta_u}{\sin \theta_l} = v_l/v_u.$$

Snell's law therefore holds, and the index of refraction must be v_l/v_u. From the speeds v_u and v_l measured with the stroboscope, and the measured angles, we then get a successful cross-check on the model.

We can also roll balls on the lower plane toward the hill starting at the speed v_l. Then we find, as we should expect, that everything is reversed. The balls arrive on the upper surface with v_u, and Snell's law holds in reverse just as it does for light.

We now have a particle model of refraction, and — as usually happens when we have a model — it suggests many experiments. For example our model says that the speed of light in a refractive material is independent of the angle of incidence and greater than the speed of light in vacuum. We should make measurements of the speeds of light in refractive materials and in particular find out if they agree with

$$\frac{v_m}{c} = n_m,$$

where v_m is the speed in the refractive material, c the speed of light in vacuum, and n_m the index of refraction. We shall discuss such measurements in Section 15–6. Also we should check to see that the speed of light in vacuum does not depend on the prior history of the light. According to our model a light particle slows down in going from a refractive material into vacuum by just as much as it speeds up in going from vacuum into the material. The constancy of the speed of light in vacuum — regardless of where the light comes from — is a check on this particle model of refraction.

15–3. Source Strength and Intensity of Illumination

In order to find the ratio of the distances to two similar stars in Chapter 4, we used the inverse-square law relating the intensity of illumination to the distance by $I = k/r^2$, where r is the distance of the source of light and k must have something to do with the strength of the source. Now, let us investigate the intensity of illumination and the strength of sources a bit more closely.

In order to measure the intensity of illumination, we can make use of a photoelectric cell or other light meter such as those used by photographers. These light meters come with a display in which a pointer moves over a scale. Higher scale readings on the meter correspond to greater illumination as we estimate it by eye, and lower scale readings are obtained in dimmer light. Our first job is to discover a sensible way to calibrate the meter with a scale of our own that we understand.

We start by finding a set of equal sources of light which we can identify by placing them, one after another, the same distance in front of the light meter in an otherwise dark room with dark walls to eliminate reflections. If we have a large-enough set of light bulbs which are made closely the same, we shall find several for which the light meter gives the same display. We try them over several times. The pointer goes to the same place each time, no matter in which order we examine them. These light bulbs are causing the same number of light particles to fall on the sensitive element of the light meter. They are giving the same illumination when placed at the same distance r.

The particle theory of light now suggests that if we place two of these equal sources at the same distance r, twice as many particles of light will illuminate the light meter. Indeed, using any of our standard light bulbs r away from the meter, we always get the same pointer reading on the meter; this reading indicates greater illumination than we get with only one standard source at the standard position.

Let us make our calibration of the scale for the light meter by marking the position of the pointer when one standard source is at the standard distance. We put the number 1 right on the scale at that point. We put the number 2 on our scale at the position of the pointer when two standard sources are at the standard distance. We can do the same thing with three standard sources at the standard distance in front of the meter, and so on. Our light meter is then calibrated to read illumination in multiples of the illumination given by one standard source placed at the distance r in front of the meter. When we use the meter to measure the illumination of an unknown source, our scale tells us how great that illumination is in terms of the number of our standard sources that would have to be placed the distance r in front of the meter to give the identical effect.

Suppose that we originally chose the distance r in front of the meter to be very long compared to the size of our light bulb and also long compared to the dimensions of the sensitive element of our light meter. We can now take one of our standard sources and move it to distances in front of the light meter which are smaller than r. Thus we can find out how the intensity of illumination at the sensitive element of the light meter changes as we change r. The results of such an experiment are shown in Table 1.

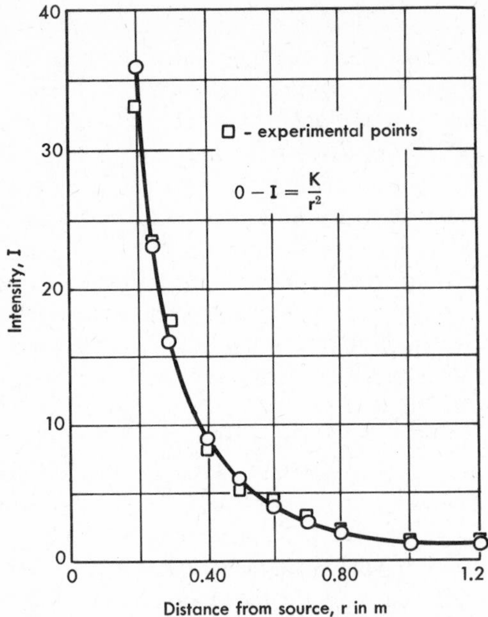

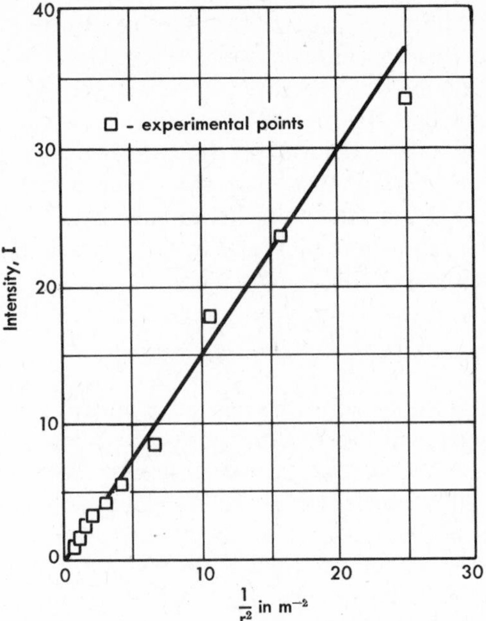

15–6. The graph on the left shows the intensity of illumination at different distances from a source. The experimental values agree closely with points computed, assuming an inverse-square relation. The graph on the right, where intensity is plotted against $1/r^2$, shows close agreement with a straight line.

Table 1

r (meters)	I	Ir^2
1.20	1.0	1.4
1.00	1.5	1.5
.80	2.3	1.5
.70	3.2	1.6
.60	4.3	1.5
.50	5.4	1.4
.40	8.5	1.4
.30	17.7	1.6
.25	23.5	1.5
.20	33.3	1.3

The intensity of illumination at different distances from a source.

The third column shows the product of the intensity and the square of the distance. This product is almost a constant, as we would expect if the inverse-square law is true.

The data from Table 1 are plotted in Fig. 15–6.

This result for the variation of illumination as a function of the distance of the source is just what we would expect according to the particle theory of light. The particles traveling away from the source in a straight line spread apart and the same numbers of particles pass through progressively greater and greater areas. The area through which a given number of particles pass increases as the square of the distance from the source, and the number of particles passing through unit area therefore decreases as the square of the distance.

This theoretical derivation of the inverse-square law is just that given in Chapter 4, but in place of a vague amount of light passing through greater and greater areas, we now have a certain number of individual light particles.

When the source and the receiver of light particles are close together compared to their sizes, the light particles can pass from one to the other at odd angles to the surface instead of along paths which are nearly parallel to each other and perpendicular to the sensitive surface of the light meter. We are, therefore, not surprised if we find greater deviations from the inverse-square law when the source and light meter are close together.

Like the standard units of distance or time, our standard lamp bulb is an arbitrary unit of source strength. Source strengths were systematically measured long ago, so long ago that the usual unit is the candle. You can imagine the prescription for making a standard candle. This candle is to be a $\frac{7}{8}$ in., No. 6 sperm candle burning at the rate of 120 grains per hour. When it is designed to burn just this way, it should then be just as bright in France as it would be in Alaska.

Of course, as has happened to other standards, the prescription has been replaced by a new one, but the basic ideas are no different. The standard candle now is defined in terms of the light that comes from a hole of 5 square millimeters area behind which you see the thorium oxide at the solidification temperature of platinum. The new candle is much more accurately reproducible than the old one, but there may be some question as to whether or not it is easier to set up your own standard source.

The standard unit of intensity of illumination is based in turn on the standard candle. It is the intensity given by one candle one foot away. This unit of intensity of illumination is known as the foot-candle.*

15–4. Light Pressure

Whenever a baseball or a stone hits us we feel a push. The pushes exerted by the tiny molecules of a gas bumping into the walls of a container or pounding on our skin give rise to gas pressure. So we found in Chapter 9. Do the particles of light bumping into a mirror similarly give rise to light pressure? The particle theory of light suggests that they do. Unfortunately, the particle theory we have developed so far is not specific enough to tell us how much light pressure to expect from a given stream of light particles. For example, we do not know what intensity is given by a mole of light particles passing each second through a square meter.

But even without this detailed knowledge we do know that if light exerts a pressure at all, it must be very small for an ordinary beam of light. We do not knock over a feather by switching on a bright light. Even experiments with delicate apparatus failed to reveal the existence of light pressure until the beginning of our own century, when Peter Lebedev in Russia and Nichols and Hull in the United States succeeded in finding and measuring this pressure. From their experimental results we know that the pressure of bright noon sunlight is just about the same as the pressure of a monolayer of oleic acid lying on a horizontal surface. This is a very small pressure, but not all light pressure is so small. Experiments verify the prediction of the particle theory that the pressure of light increases with the intensity of illumination. At the surface of the sun, for example, light pressure is several orders of magnitude larger than the pressure of sunlight here, and at the surfaces of some stars the light pressure is enormous.

15–5. Absorption and Heating

A good reflector of light does not warm up appreciably when placed in sunlight, whereas a dark, absorbing surface can become quite warm when exposed to the sun. Dirt, shoveled up from a sidewalk along with snow after a snowstorm, melts its way down through the snow when the sun comes out. The black dirt, a good absorber, gets warm and melts the snow beneath it faster than the white reflecting snow melts by itself.

Can the particle model account for this behavior? When particles are neither reflected from a material nor transmitted by it, they must come to rest. When a piece of matter is hit by particles that neither pass through it nor bounce off it, does the material heat up? We can easily show that heating really occurs with particles by substituting a hammer for the particles and using a block of lead for the absorbing material. If we strike the block a series of rapid blows (like a series of particles striking the lead), we find that the hammer does not bounce back (the particles do not reflect) and the lead gets warm. As a check to see that this heating is not an effect we get with every particle bombardment, let us repeat the experiment using a heavy steel block. The hammer now bounces back with every blow (it reflects), and the steel does not warm up. If light particles act like particles of ordinary matter, we expect them to heat any material in which they are stopped. The particle model therefore agrees with the observed heating of materials which absorb light and with the fact that materials which reflect or transmit all the light do not heat up.

Absorbing materials are not usually black. They reflect some of the light which strikes them, and they may transmit some of it. In order to make a model of a substance which reflects some particles specularly while it absorbs other particles from the same light beam, we may imagine that the material contains small regions that stop light particles, producing heat, intermingled with regions

*You must read this unit as a single word; it does *not* mean feet × candles. For example, at 1 ft, 3 candles give 3 foot-candles illumination; at 2 ft, they give (3 foot-candles) $(1\text{ ft}/2\text{ ft})^2 = \frac{3}{4}$ foot-candles.

that reflect light particles and produce no heat. Even the best reflectors, such as mirrors, warm up a little when placed in the sun, and we conclude that a mirror surface must contain a few scattered absorbing regions. A transparent substance such as a pane of glass must also contain some absorbing regions since we observe a slight decrease in the light intensity while the glass is inserted in a light beam. Furthermore, as expected, the glass does become slightly warm.

15–6. Some Difficulties with the Particle Theory

We have found that we can make a particle model which accounts for specular and diffuse reflection, which gives Snell's law of refraction, and which leads to the inverse-square law for the diminution of the intensity of illumination with distance. The model also suggests that light should exert a pressure and that heating should be associated with light absorption. Both of these effects, which we had not previously discussed, are found experimentally; and they may serve as examples of the value of a model in leading us to new investigations. The model is successful in describing coherently much that we already know by giving us a picture into which our knowledge fits. It also suggests that other things should take place about which we may have had no idea. It gives us the clue to what may otherwise be unexpected, because, like the pressure of light, the unexpected may exist in the model. We can then check the model by comparing nature with what the model says.

So far with our model of light, we have been very successful. Are there any respects in which the particle model is less successful? Are there aspects of the behavior of light which are poorly described by the model or even in conflict with it?

Let us take a closer look at what happens when light is refracted. Although we know how to account for refraction and reflection separately on the particle model, can we account for the fact that both take place when a light beam reaches the surface of a refractive material? To produce specular reflection the surface shoves the particles of light in one direction; to produce refraction on our model it shoves them the opposite way. How does it decide which way to shove? This question bothered Newton, and he attempted to explain the partial reflection and partial refraction of light by supposing that the particles of light had properties which changed periodically with time. What happens to the particle then depends upon the time at which it hits the surface.

Another attempt to explain the splitting up of light beams might be made by imagining that the surface is divided into little reflecting regions and little regions that refract. Either of these extensions of our model might account for a definite ratio of reflection and refraction. But they are in trouble because the ratio of refracted to reflected light decreases as the angle of incidence increases. Perhaps the difficulty can be overcome, but the model is getting complicated. When we have to fix it up too much, we look on it with suspicion.

More trouble arises when we try to account for diffraction. For example, there seems to be no simple particle explanation for the complicated diffraction pattern observed when light passes through a tiny hole (Fig. 11–10). In addition, as we shall see in the next section, there is trouble with the speed of light.

15–7. The Speed of Light and the Theory of Refraction

According to our particle theory, the speed v_m of light in a refractive material must be greater than the speed c in vacuum. In Section 15–2, we found $v_m = cn_m$ where n_m is the index of refraction. This is a quantitative result of the model which we can test if we can measure the speed of light over a short distance — in a tank of water, for example.

In Newton's time such a measurement was not possible. The first successful measurements of the speed of light over a measured path on earth were made by Fizeau (1849). His method of measurement is based on the same idea as that of the stroboscope. Think of directing a beam of light at the hole in the stroboscope. Little pulses of light are let through each time the opening in the whirling disc passes the beam. Now let these pulses strike a mirror so that they are reflected back to the stroboscope again (Fig. 15–7). On the return trip a pulse can pass through the stroboscope only if the opening in the disc is again in the right position.

For a stroboscope with a single opening in the disc, the disc must rotate at least one full turn in the same time that the light goes to the mirror and back. By measuring the speed of rotation when

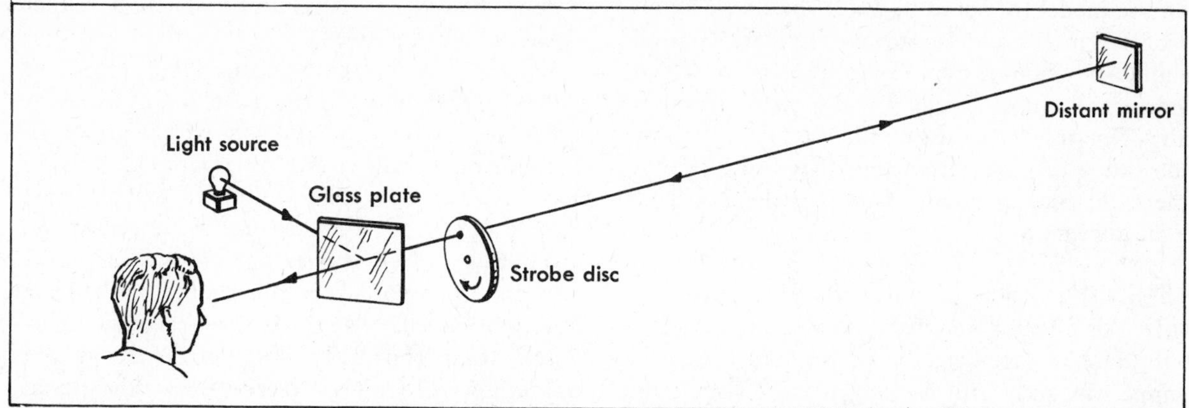

15–7. Timing a light pulse with a stroboscope. Light from the source reflects from the glass plate and goes through the hole in the strobe disc to a distant mirror. The returning pulse passes through the strobe disc and through the glass plate to the eye of an observer.

light can pass both ways, we can time the light as it goes the known distance from the stroboscope to the mirror and back again. Thus we determine the speed of light.

Of course no ordinary stroboscope will turn fast enough. But, by designing a special high-speed stroboscope with many holes, Fizeau succeeded in measuring the speed of light in air. Other physicists improved Fizeau's method, among them the French physicist Cornu. His stroboscope had 200 openings and could turn at 54,000 revolutions per minute. As he increased its speed from zero to the maximum he measured twenty-eight successive eclipses and brightenings of the light coming back through the disc from a mirror 23 km away. By using a rotating mirror to replace the rotating disc of the stroboscope, Foucault in France and later Michelson in the U. S. increased the accuracy of this method still further (Fig. 15–8). Michelson was able to determine the speed of light to an accuracy of about 3 km/sec (1 part in 10^5).

For this accurate measurement Michelson used a long path. But the same method can be used over short paths to find the speed of light in liquids, such as water, though with lower accuracy. In 1862, Foucault measured the speed of light in water and found it to be close to 2.23×10^8 m/sec. This is almost exactly three-fourths of its speed in air. Some years later, Michelson determined the speed of light in carbon disulfide, a liquid with an index of refraction of 1.64, and found it to be 1.71×10^8 m/sec.

When it encounters these results our particle theory of light really strikes a snag. In order to account for Snell's law, we were forced to assume that the speed of light is higher in refractive materials than in vacuum. Using Newton's particle model, we obtained $v_{\text{water}} = n_{\text{water}}c$; consequently

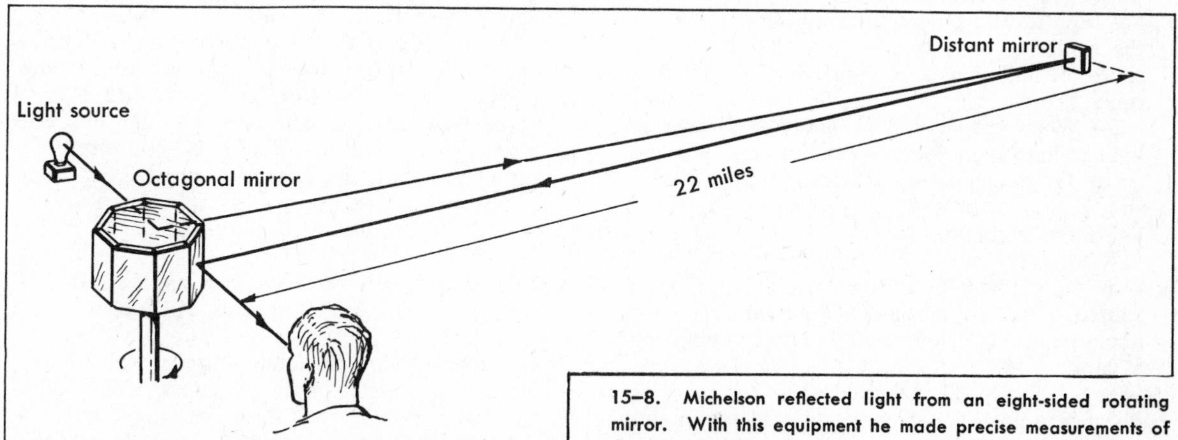

15–8. Michelson reflected light from an eight-sided rotating mirror. With this equipment he made precise measurements of the speed of light.

on the model the speed in water should be about $\frac{4}{3}$ of that in air; and in carbon disulfide the speed should be about $\frac{5}{3}$ of that in air. The observed values are almost exactly $\frac{3}{4}$ and $\frac{3}{5}$ of the speed in air. Not only have the experiments failed to show the ratios that we expected — they indicate that the ratios are inverted. Our particle model of light appears to fail.

15–8. The Status of the Particle Model

In this chapter we tried to develop a model of light based on the behavior of particles. This attempt was successful as long as we chose only *some* of the optical phenomena we know about and as long as we did not always demand precise and quantitative agreement between the predictions of the theory and results of experiments. When we included all of the phenomena and asked for quantitative checks, however, the model failed in several important respects. Since our particle theory of light failed it must be either abandoned or modified.

We are now in a situation in which physicists often find themselves. From time to time a theory, which successfully connects a whole group of experimental results and observations, fails to account for a new observation. Then we must modify the theory, or start over again and try to invent a new one. It is almost always true, however, that the efforts spent on the old model have not been wasted. The theory has served two purposes: it has shown that some of the things that were observed can be related to each other; and it has suggested new experiments. The particle picture of light, which here appears unsatisfactory, has played a very important part in the history of physics, and it still contributes to our understanding of light. We shall have more to say about it in Part IV. For the moment we learn to try a different model.

FOR HOME, DESK, AND LAB

1. The index of refraction of carbon disulfide is about 1.63. What should the speed of light be in this liquid, according to the particle model of refraction given in Section 15-2?

2. Occasionally there occurs in the heavens an explosion of a star, producing what is known as a super nova. The star suddenly becomes many times brighter than before. As you know, the stars are so far away that the light from them takes many years to reach us. An explosion that we observe must have occurred a long time ago, and the light has been traveling toward us ever since. We see the explosion as a bright white light, not as a series of different colors arriving at different times.
   (a) What does this show about the speed of light of different colors in vacuum?
   (b) Try to suggest a particle model for dispersion in prisms consistent with the single speed of light of all colors in vacuum.

3. Can you explain the different strengths of light sources in terms of particles of different size? How about the decrease in intensity caused by inserting a partially absorbing sheet of matter in a light beam? Can different intensities at varying distance from a source be accounted for in this way?

4. What assumptions do we make in using the inverse-square law to determine star distances? (See Section 4–3.)

5. * Make a simple photometer for comparing light sources. Place aluminum foil between two identical paraffin blocks and hold the blocks together with tape. When light falls on this photometer from one side the end of the block of paraffin on that side appears bright. When two light beams of equal intensity of illumination fall on the two sides, the ends of the paraffin blocks appear equally bright.
   (a) To check that the photometer functions properly we turn it over so as to interchange the positions of the two paraffin blocks. Why?
   (b) With such a photometer you can find out when two light beams are of equal intensity; but if the intensity of the light falling on the two sides differs, we cannot get a quantitative measure of the relative intensities of illumination. Why?

6. Devise a procedure for checking the inverse-square law with the photometer of Problem 5.

7. It is found that a 40-candle source placed 3.0 feet from a light meter gives the same scale reading as an unknown source 1.2 feet from the meter.
   (a) What is the strength of the unknown source?

(b) What is the light intensity in foot-candles read on the meter?

8. What does the particle theory predict about the intensity produced by an *extremely* weak light source — so weak that only a few particles are emitted per second? How might you test this prediction?

9. In the use of radar, a beam of radiation is sent out from a source. Some of this radiation falls on a distant object, such as an airplane, is reflected by the object, and is detected when it returns to its starting point. The radiation used behaves like light. Assuming that the source of the radiation is equivalent to a point source of light and that the object reflecting the radiation is a diffuse reflector, can you convince yourself that the intensity of the returning radiations varies inversely with the *fourth* power of the distance from the source to the reflecting object?

10. A light meter calibrated in foot candles and a mirror are 2.0 feet apart. A very small 25-candle-power source is placed midway between them. What is the reading of the meter if the mirror is

(a) a plane mirror?

(b) a concave mirror with a diameter of 6 inches and a focal length of one foot?

11. A sensitive thermometer placed in the different parts of the spectrum from a prism will show a rise in temperature. This shows that all colors of light produce heat when absorbed. But the thermometer also shows a rise in temperature when its bulb is in either of the two dark regions beyond the two ends of the spectrum. How can the particle theory account for this?

12. A thermometer is placed in the beam of light coming from a lamp. Its reading increases until it becomes steady at 26°C. When a piece of ordinary window glass is placed between the lamp and the thermometer, the reading drops to 23°C.

(a) What can you conclude about the nature of the light coming from the lamp?

(b) If the window glass is replaced by Corex glass (see Section 11–5), would you expect the thermometer reading to be above or below 23°C? Above or below 26°C?

(c) Can you be equally sure of each of your answers?

13. A calibrated light meter shows that one glass plate transmits 80% of the light from a fixed source.

(a) What fraction of the light will be transmitted by two, three, etc. up to ten such plates?

(b) Draw a graph of the fraction of light transmitted as a function of the number of plates.

(c) Plot the logarithm of the fraction of light transmitted as a function of the number of plates.

(d) How many plates are needed to absorb 90% of the light?

(e) Be prepared to discuss the effect of reflection on the accuracy of your results.

14. Using the data given in Section 15–7 about Cornu's application of the Fizeau method, compute the shortest distance from the rotating disc to the mirror that will permit the returning beam to pass through the opening immediately following the one through which it started.

15. It might be imagined that on each reflection the speed of light decreases slightly. Assuming that you can measure the speed of light (see Section 15–7) describe an experiment designed to test the assertion that reflection does not change the speed.

16. Can you modify your proposed experiment (Problem 15) to test the assertion that the speed of light in vacuum is independent of previous refractions?

17. In the Foucault-Michelson modification of the Fizeau method, rotating mirrors are used in place of the rotating wheel. (Fig. 15–8.) Assuming that mirrors are rotating 500 times per second and that the distance from them to the fixed mirror is 10.0 km, show that a mirror face rotates through an angle of 12° before it reflects the beam a second time and that the angle between this reflected beam and the original direction of the light is therefore 24°.

18. Suppose that someone were to propose to you that sound consists of small, rapidly moving particles that are emitted by a source and that affect your ear when they strike it. What evidence could you use to support or to refute it?

19. We have said that light particles must be very small. Suggest an experiment to show that they must also have an extremely small mass.

20. Is it possible that the slowing down of light as it goes from a vacuum into a transparent material is some kind of friction effect?

FURTHER READING

EINSTEIN, A., and INFELD, L., *The Evolution of Physics.* Simon & Schuster, 1938 (pp. 94–110).

HENRY, GEORGE E., "Radiation Pressure." *Scientific American*, June, 1957 (p. 99).

NEWTON, SIR ISAAC, *Opticks, or a Treatise of the Reflections, Refractions, Inflections & Colours of Light.* Based on the Fourth Edition of 1730; Dover, 1952.

ROBERTSON, J. K., *Introduction to Optics, Geometrical and Physical.* Van Nostrand, Fourth Edition, 1954.

WILSON, MITCHELL, *American Science and Invention.* Simon & Schuster, 1954. (Michelson: pp. 309–319).

INTRODUCTION TO WAVES

CHAPTER 16

16–1. A Wave: Something Else That Travels

In the last chapter we considered at some length a particle model of light, in which we supposed that light consisted of a stream of particles or corpuscles. We found that this model fails to provide completely satisfactory explanations for some of the behavior of light that we observed. We therefore find ourselves faced with a choice: we can try to construct a better particle model that will succeed where the earlier one failed, or we can look for a new model based on a completely different concept. Let us try the second approach.

The most basic thing to be accounted for in *any* model of light is the fact that light travels through space. In looking for a new theory, we first ask whether there is anything except a particle (or stream of particles) that can move from one point to another. The answer is "yes." Consider, for example, what happens when we drop a pebble into a quiet pond. A circular pattern spreads out from the point of impact. Such a disturbance is called a *wave,* and if you watch the water closely enough, as such a wave moves across the surface, you will find that although the water may be churned and jostled locally, it does not move forward with the wave. This is quite clear if you watch a bit of wood or a small patch of oil that may be floating on the pond. The wood or oil moves up and down as the wave passes; it does not travel along with the wave. In other words, a wave can travel for long distances, but once the disturbance has passed, every drop of water is left where it used to be.

If we look around us, we can find all sorts of examples of waves. For instance, we notice an American flag as it ripples in the breeze at the top of a flagpole. The ripples or waves travel out along the cloth. Individual spots on the cloth of the flag, however, hold their positions as the waves pass by. The fourth white star in the bottom line on the field of blue always remains the fourth star in the bottom line and its distances from the four edges of the flag remain unchanged. Just as the water does not travel with the water waves, so the cloth of the flag remains in place when the waves have passed through it.

Some waves are periodic or nearly so; the motion of the material repeats itself over and over. Not all waves, however, have this property. For example, when you slam the door of a room, the air in the doorway is suddenly compressed, and this single short compression passes as a disturbance across the room, where it gives a sudden push to a curtain hanging over the window. Such a wave of short duration is called a *pulse.*

Here is another example of a wave pulse. We place half a dozen pocket-billiard balls (plastic croquet balls will work, too) in a straight line so that each ball is touching the next one. We then roll another ball so that it strikes one end of the row head-on. The ball at the other end of the row moves away at a speed equal to that of the ball we rolled in. A pulse like that on the water surface or on the flag has traveled through the row of balls from one end to the other. Each ball has been disturbed; this disturbance has passed along the entire line of balls; but no ball has moved from one end of the line to the other.

You see another kind of wave — let's call it a "wave of starting" — if you watch a line of cars that has been stopped while waiting for a traffic signal to change from red to green. Shortly after the signal changes to green, the driver of the first car starts his car forward. A moment later, the driver of the second car, seeing that the car ahead of him is in motion, starts his car forward. Still later, the driver of the third car gets his car under way, and so on down the line away from the traffic signal. You can see a "pulse" move down the line of cars. It is interesting that this "starting pulse" travels in one direction while the cars travel in the other direction.

Just how fast the starting pulse travels back depends on how fast the various drivers react, and how their cars respond. If we were able to handpick a group of drivers with identical reaction times, and provide them with cars that accelerated in exactly the same way, the starting pulse would travel backward at a uniform speed.

What is alike in all of these examples? In each case the disturbance travels through some medium — through the water, the cloth of a flag, the billiard balls, or the line of cars; but the medium does not go along with the disturbance. Disturbances which travel through media are what we mean by waves. We can now answer the question we asked at the beginning of this section: is there anything except a particle that can move from one point to another? A wave, a thing which is not itself a particle of matter, can go from one place to another.

16–2. Waves on Coil Springs

Do waves really behave like light? To find out, we must know more about them. When we know how they act, we can compare their behavior with what we know about light and with other things that we can find out about it. The variety of examples we have mentioned also suggests that waves are worth studying for their own sake.

It is convenient to start our study of waves with a coil spring.* Fig. 16–1 shows pictures of a pulse traveling along such a spring. These pictures were taken by a movie camera at intervals of $\frac{1}{24}$ of a second.

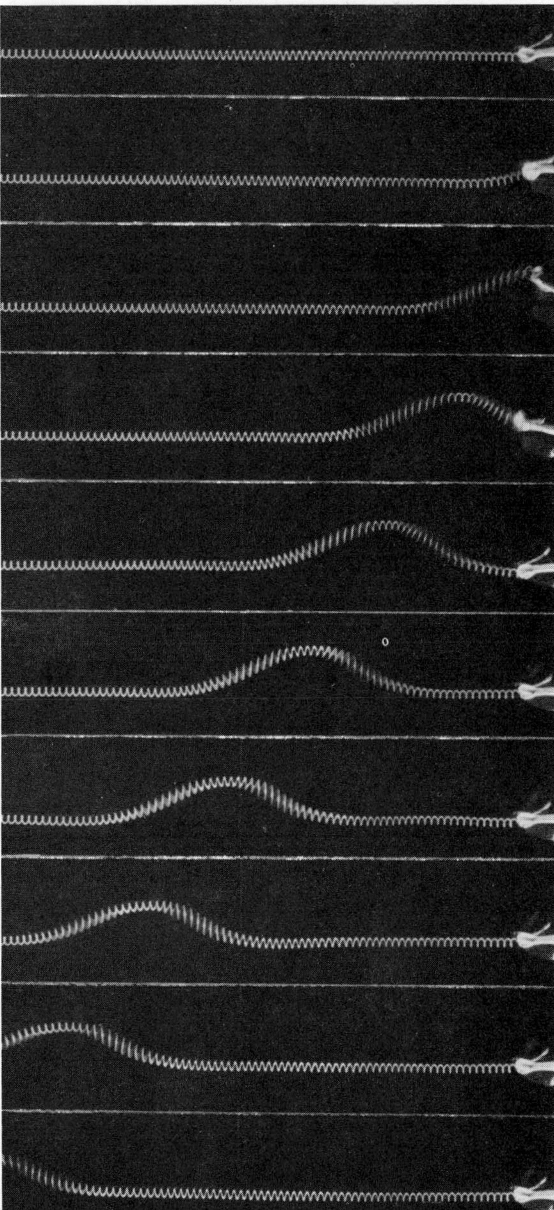

16–1. The generation and motion of a pulse along a spring shown by a series of pictures taken with a movie camera.

We see that the shape of the pulse does not change as it moves along. Except for the fact that the pulse moved, its picture at one moment is just like a later picture. Also we see that the pulse moves the same distance in each interval between pictures — it moves along the spring at constant speed.

*If you find it hard to get a coil spring, a flexible clothesline or a rubber tube will also do pretty well. Tie one end to a door knob and shake the other. If the tube is sufficiently heavy, you will get good pulses that travel slowly enough for easy observation.

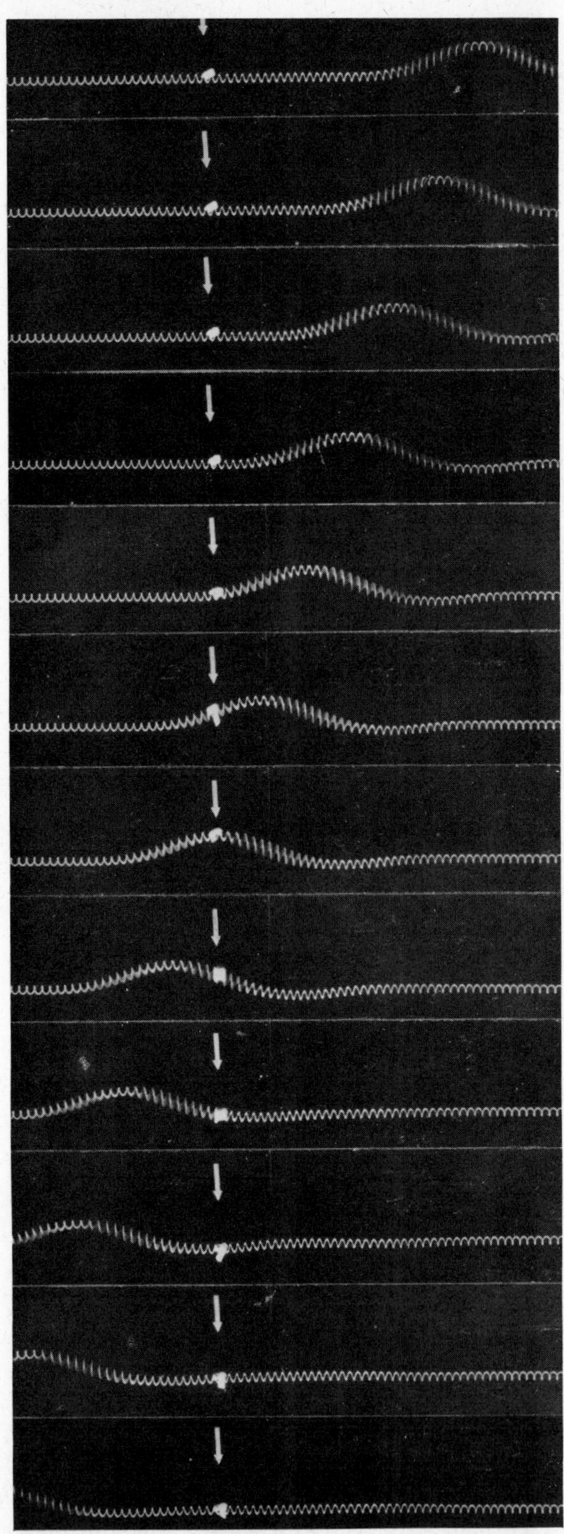
16–2. The motion of a pulse from right to left along a spring with a ribbon at the midpoint. The ribbon moves up and down as the pulse goes by, but does not move in the direction of motion of the pulse.

The spring as a whole is not permanently changed by the passage of the pulse. But what happens to each small piece of spring as the pulse goes by? To help us fix our attention on one piece, we can mark the spot by tying on a bit of white string or ribbon as shown in Fig. 16–2. If we then shake the spring to start a pulse moving along it, we can see how the marked spot is displaced. We find that it moves at right angles to the spring as the pulse passes it.

Other pieces of the spring, as well as the marked spot, also move. We can see which pieces are moving and which way they go if we look at two pictures, one of which is taken shortly after the other. Here we shall use two successive pictures taken from Fig. 16–2. We have printed these two pictures together in Fig. 16–3 so that we see the pulse in two successive positions just as we would see it in a rapid double exposure. Below the photo in Fig. 16–3 we have traced the pulse in its earlier position, and the green line shows the later position. As the arrows show, while the pulse moves from right to left, each piece of the coil in the right-hand half of the pulse moved up and each piece of coil in the left-hand half moved down.

If the pulse was moving from left to right, just the reverse would be true, as we show in Fig. 16–4. Here we use a schematic pulse because it is a little easier to work with and we can make the time interval between positions as short as we wish. In this way we can determine the instantaneous motion of the coil. Thus, if we know in which direction the pulse is moving, we can determine how each point of the spring moves at any particular stage in the passage of the pulse. On the other hand, if we know how the parts of the spring move, we can determine the direction in which the pulse is traveling.

We now have a good notion of how the pieces of spring move, even though there is no visible motion in any one of our pictures. Really, what we have done is to observe (1) that any pulse moves undistorted at constant speed along the spring and (2) that the spring itself moves only at right angles to the motion of the pulse. We can combine these two pieces of information to learn how each part of the spring moves at any time. Of course, we have looked only at the simplest waves, and the statement we have just made may not be true of all waves. Even in the cases we

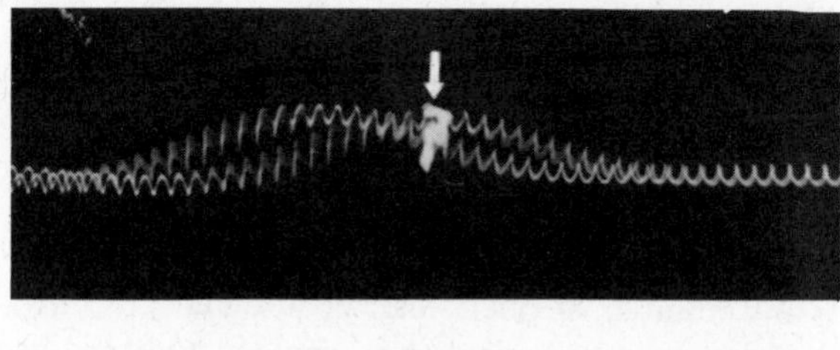

16–3. The relation between the motion of a pulse traveling from right to left and the motion of the coil. The photograph shows the pulse in two successive positions. The arrows in the diagram indicate how the coil moves as the pulse passes.

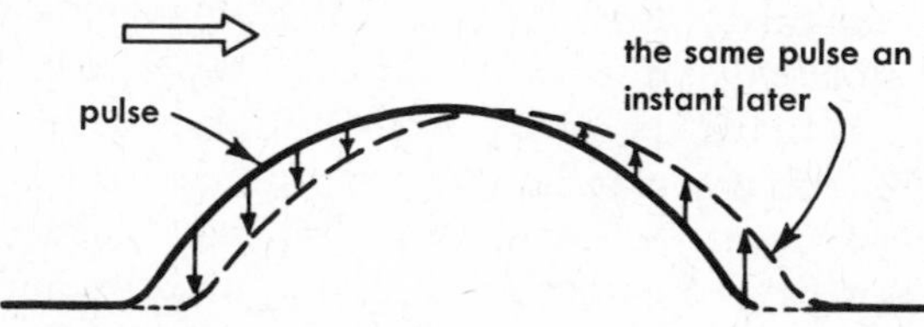

16–4. The relation between the motion of a pulse traveling from left to right and the motion of the spring.

have examined, a sharp eye may detect slight deviations from our description. Nevertheless we have formed a useful first picture. With slight changes it applies to many other waves.

16–3. Superposition: Pulses Crossing

So far we have discussed the behavior of a single pulse traveling in one direction. But what happens when one pulse moves from right to left at the same time that another moves from left to right? Particularly: what happens when the two pulses meet? Do they pass through each other, or do they somehow knock each other out?

The best way to find out is to try. The photographs in Fig. 16–5 show what happens when two pulses are started in the same spring at the same time, one traveling from left to right and one from right to left. The top pictures show the pulses approaching each other as if each had the spring to itself. As they cross each other, the two pulses combine to form complicated shapes. But after having crossed, they again assume their original shapes and travel along the tubing as if nothing had happened, as is indicated by the pictures at the bottom. The left-going pulse continues to travel to the left with its original shape. The right-going pulse continues to move on to the right with its earlier form. We can perform this experiment over and over with different pulses. We always get the same general result.

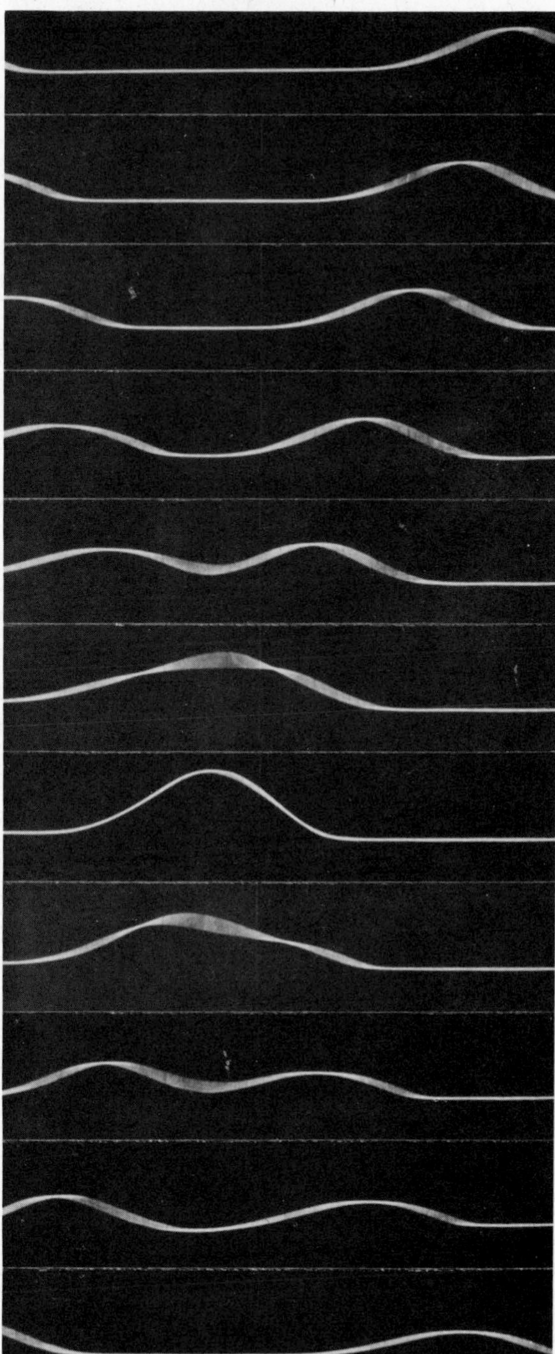

16–5. Two pulses crossing each other. Notice that the two pulses have different shapes. Thus we can see that the one which was on the left at the beginning is on the right after the crossing, and vice versa.

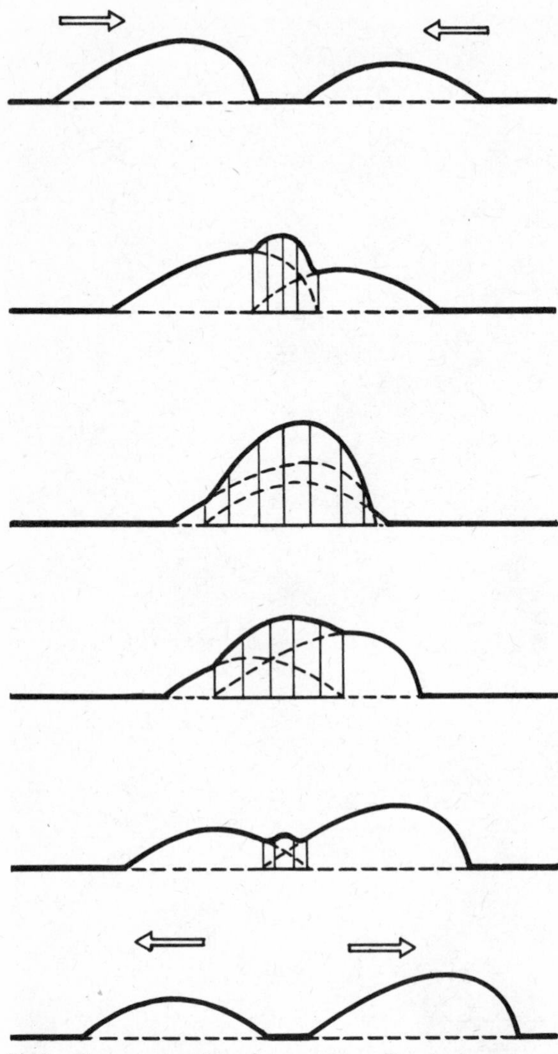

16–6. The superposition of two pulses. The displacement of the combined pulse is the sum of the separate displacements.

The fact that two pulses pass through each other without either being altered is a fundamental property of waves. If we throw two balls in opposite directions, and they hit each other, their motion is violently changed. The crossing of waves and the crossing of streams of balls made of solid matter are thus two very different processes.

Let us now take a closer look at the two pulses crossing each other (Fig. 16–5). Often the shape of the combined pulse does not resemble the shape of either of the original pulses. We can see its relation to them, however, if we visualize each of the original pulses at the position it would occupy if alone; then we add up the displacements of the original pulses to get a new pulse. We find that the total displacement of any point on the spring at any instant is exactly equal to the sum of the displacements that would have been produced by the two pulses independently. The method is illustrated in Fig. 16–6. It works for any two pulses. As a matter of fact, it also works for more than two pulses — the displacements due to any number of pulses can be added.

We can summarize the whole situation as follows. To find the form of the total wave disturbance at any time, we add at each point the displacements belonging to each pulse that is passing through the medium. That this simple addition gives the actual displacement of the medium is called the *Superposition Principle*.

Let us apply the Superposition Principle to two special cases. First, we consider the combination of a pulse that displaces the spring downward and travels along the spring from the left-hand end with one that displaces the spring upward and travels from the right. Suppose that the two pulses have exactly the same shape and size and that each is symmetrical. The experiment is shown in the sequence of pictures, Fig. 16–7. Notice that in one picture the addition of equal displacements upward (plus) and downward (minus) leaves us with a net displacement of zero. There is clearly a moment, as the pulses pass each other, when the whole spring appears undisplaced. (See also the drawing of Fig. 16–8.) Why does the picture not look exactly like a spring at rest? Let us consider the difference between an undisplaced spring carrying two equal and opposite wave pulses and an undisplaced spring carrying no wave at all. When the spring carries no wave, all the various pieces of spring stand still at all times. On the other hand, when two equal and opposite waves are passing, there is only one instant when the spring is passing through its rest position, and at that instant the spring is moving. The motion shows up as a blur in the pictures, just as a snapshot of a rapidly moving airplane appears blurred.

Our second special case is shown in Fig. 16–9. Here we have two similar pulses, one coming from the right and one from the left. In one the displacements are upward and in the other they are downward. These pulses differ from those of Fig. 16–7 in that neither is symmetrical, although the two are alike in shape and size.

Because neither of the pulses is symmetrically shaped, they never completely cancel each other.

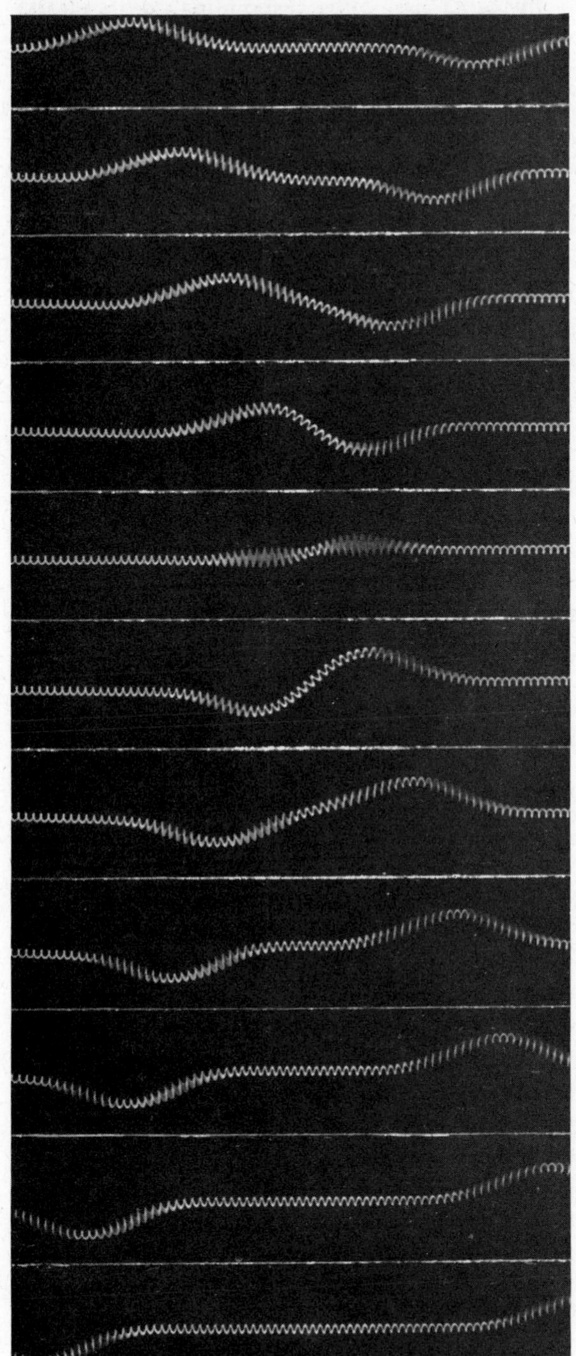

16–7. The superposition of two equal and opposite pulses on a white coil spring. In the fifth picture they almost cancel each other.

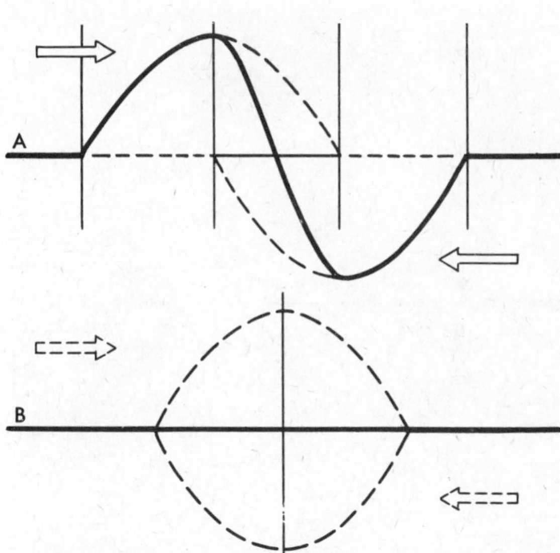

16–8. The superposition of two equal and opposite pulses. (A) Before complete cancellation. (B) At complete cancellation.

16–9. The superposition of two asymmetrical but similar pulses. Notice that the point midway between them remains at rest at all times.

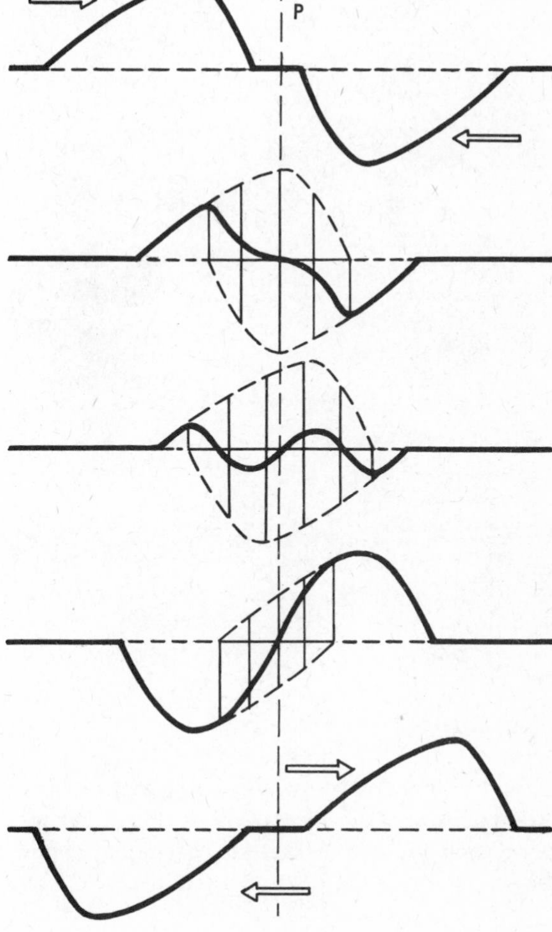

But there is always one point P on the spring which will stand still. That point is exactly half-way between the two pulses. As the pulses come together, they pass simultaneously through that

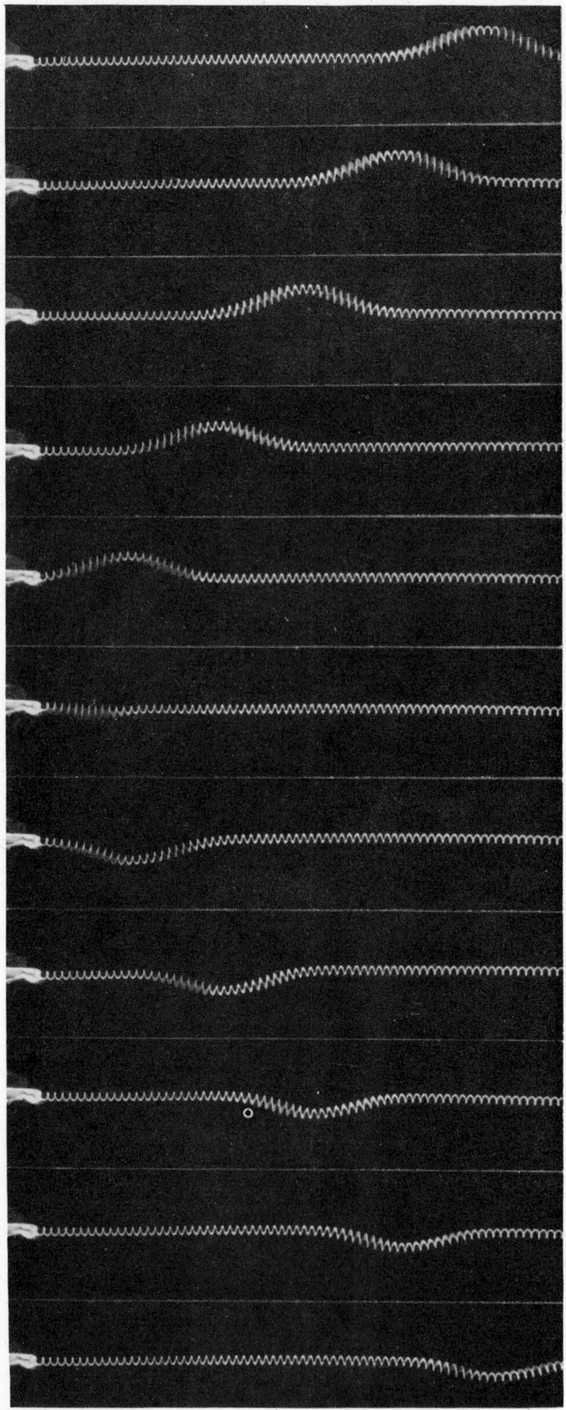

16–10. Reflection of a pulse from a fixed end. The reflected pulse is upside down.

halfway point in such a way that the highest point of one pulse and the lowest point of the other just cancel each other out. The same argument applies to any other pair of corresponding points on the pulses. They always arrive at the midpoint of the spring together, one on top and one at the bottom. Consequently, the midpoint stands still.

16–4. Reflection and Transmission

When a pulse moving on a spring comes to an end that is held fixed, it bounces back. This reversal of direction is called *reflection*, and the pulse that comes back is called the *reflected pulse.* In Fig. 16–10 the fixed end is on the left. In the original or *incident pulse*, which moves to the left, the displacement is upward. The returning pulse has its displacement downward. The pulse comes back upside down, but with the same shape that it had before it was reflected.

You may wonder why the reflected pulse is upside down. The reason for this behavior is that one point on the spring, in this case the end point held by the hand, does not move. We have already met a situation where a point on the spring remained at rest; this was the point P in Fig. 16–9. Cover the right-hand half of Fig. 16–9 and you will see an upward pulse moving to the right, "flattening out" as it approaches P, and finally being reflected upside down. Now, at the front of an upward pulse, the spring itself moves upward (Fig. 16–3). When the front of the pulse in Fig. 16–9 gets to P, the point P should move upward. But since P remains at rest, the upward motion of the spring must be canceled by a downward motion. The only difference between the situations shown in Figs. 16–9 and 16–10 is that in Fig. 16–9 we supply the necessary downward motion by sending a downward pulse from the right, whereas in Fig. 16–10 we supply the downward motion by simply holding the end point fixed. Forcing the end point to remain at rest is just another way of supplying the downward motion which cancels the motion of the spring due to the original pulse, and then propagates to the left in the form of an upside-down pulse.

Imagine now that instead of fixing our coil spring at one end, we connect it to another spring which is much heavier and therefore harder to move. Our new arrangement will be somewhere in between the two cases (a) the original spring tied down, and (b) the original spring just lengthened by an additional piece of the same material. In case (a) the whole pulse is reflected upside down; in case (b) the whole pulse goes straight on. We may, therefore, expect that under our new arrangement part of the pulse will be *reflected* upside down, and part of it will go on, or as we say, will be *transmitted.* This effect is shown in Fig. 16–11 where the original pulse comes from the right and the heavier spring is on the left. We see that at the junction or boundary between the two springs — which are the media in which the wave travels — the pulse splits into two parts, a reflected and a transmitted pulse. Like superposition, the splitting into a reflected and a transmitted part is a typical wave property.

What happens when a pulse goes the other way, traveling along the heavier spring and arriving at the junction between it and the light spring? This is not so easy to foresee. We no longer can bracket the behavior between two situations in which we know the answer. But experiment tells us what takes place. In Fig. 16–12 we see a pulse moving from the left, from a heavy toward a light spring. Here, as in the opposite case, illustrated in Fig. 16–11, part of the pulse is transmitted and part is reflected, but this time the reflected pulse is right-side up.

In summary, then, when a pulse is sent along a spring toward a junction with a second spring, we observe that the whole pulse is reflected upside down whenever the second spring is very much heavier than the first. As the second spring is replaced by lighter and lighter springs, the reflected pulse becomes small and a larger and larger transmitted pulse is observed to go on beyond the junction. When the second spring is only as massive as the first, no reflected pulse is left and the original pulse is completely transmitted. Then if the second spring is made still lighter, reflection sets in again, this time with the reflected pulse right-side up. The lighter the second spring, the larger is the reflected pulse. When the second spring is negligible the reflected pulse is nearly the same size as the pulse sent in. This can be demonstrated with a heavy spring tied to a thin nylon thread (Fig. 16–13).

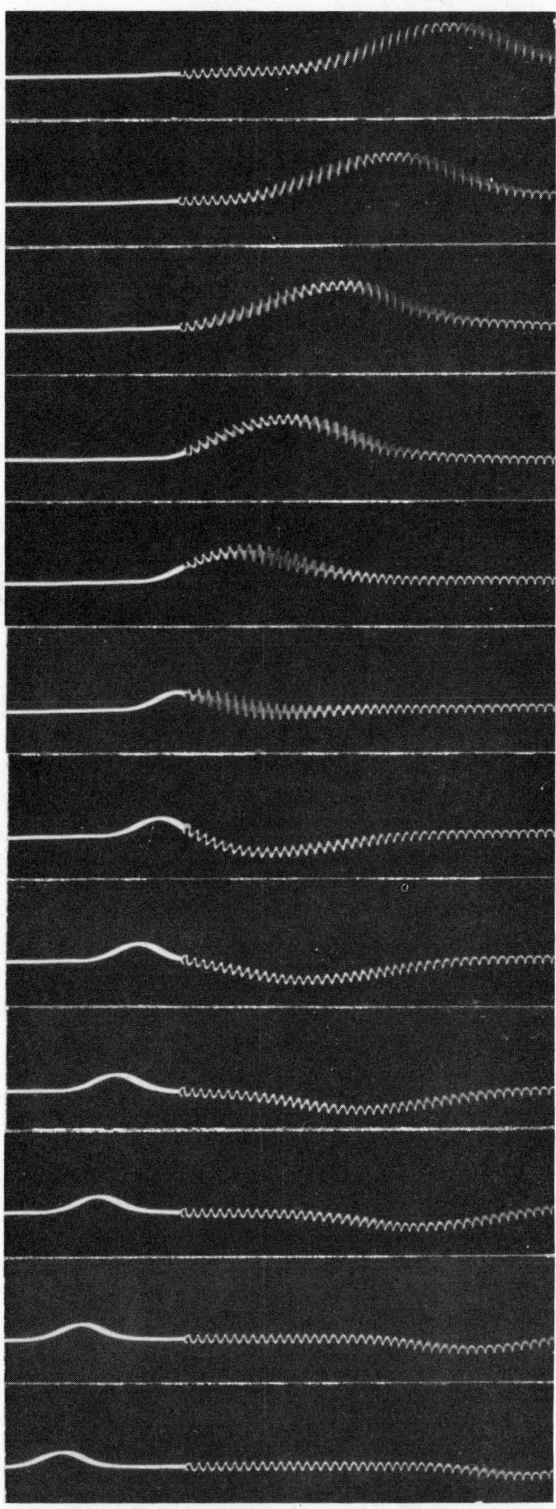

16–11. A pulse passing from a light spring (right) to a heavy spring. At the junction the pulse is partially transmitted and partially reflected. You will note that the reflected pulse is upside down.

16–5. Idealizations and Approximations

In discussing waves along a spring, we said that their shape or size remains unchanged during the motion. Indeed, if we look again at Fig. 16–1, we can notice hardly any change in the

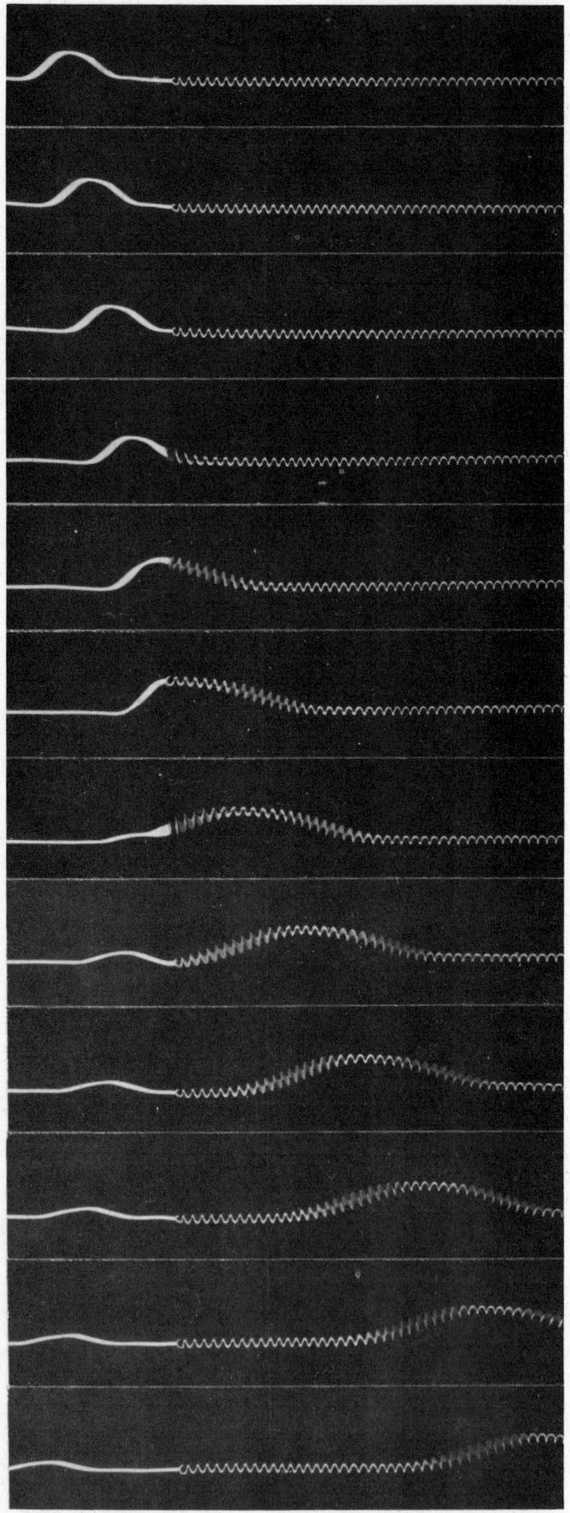

16–12. A pulse passing from a heavy spring (left) to a light spring. At the junction the pulse is partially transmitted and partially reflected. The reflected pulse is right side up.

size of the pulse as it travels along. Yet, as you have undoubtedly noticed, a pulse slowly diminishes and after several reflections it dies out completely. Is it reasonable for us to ignore the dying down of the pulse? Or has our description of wave behavior been wrong in some fundamental way?

To answer these questions, we start by observing that the time it takes a pulse to die out varies with circumstances. For example, if the spring is submerged in water, the pulse dies out more rapidly than it does in air. The water offers greater resistance to the motion of the spring than the air does. We may expect that in a vacuum the pulse will require a longer time to disappear than in air; experiments to test this, although not easy to perform, justify our expectation.

Even in a vacuum, the pulse eventually dies out because of internal resistance in the spring. The amount of this resistance depends on the material of the spring. For some materials it is very small and the pulse will keep moving for a long time.

We may imagine a spring with no internal resistance kept in vacuum. On such a spring a pulse would travel forever. By ignoring the dying out of the pulses, we have idealized our real springs and considered them as if they were free from both external and internal friction. We are entitled to do this so long as we consider the behavior of a pulse only for periods of time in which the size of the pulse changes so little that we hardly notice the change. For such times, the ideal resistance-free spring serves as a good *approximation* to the real one and can therefore be made the subject of our discussion. There is a clear advantage in this, since the behavior of the ideal spring is much simpler than that of the real one.

A similar idealization occurs in our discussion of the superposition of two pulses. We learned that the displacement produced by the combined pulse equals the sum of the displacements due to the separate pulses. But if we make the individual pulses too big, we find that the combined displacement is less than the sum of the two displacements. Again, when we ignore this deviation from the simple superposition, we are discussing an ideal spring instead of the real one. We are making an approximation rather than a complete description of the real situation. But as long as we keep our displacements small enough so that we hardly notice these deviations, the ideal spring will be a good approximation to the real one; and it has the advantage of simplicity.

These are not the first idealizations we have made. In Chapter 9, for example, we made an idealized model of a gas which leads to Boyle's gas law. The law is a good approximate description of the behavior of gases in which the molecules are far enough apart; but when the molecules are too close together, a real gas does not behave like an ideal one.

Idealizations and approximations are very frequently made unconsciously. Consider, for example, what we mean when we say that the area of a piece of land is 1000 acres. Usually we get the area by measuring length and width and then calculating the area *as if* the land were completely flat. That is, we ignore the fact that there are little hills and valleys and that the area under consideration is really part of the surface of a sphere. We replace a surface of complicated shape by a simple plane rectangle. This procedure is useful only as long as there are no big mountains and the dimensions of the land are small compared with the radius of the earth. Under those conditions an idealized flat land serves as a good approximation.

Most of the problems we attack in science are fairly complicated, and in order to make progress toward understanding them we have to separate the essential from the inessential: that is, we have to make idealizations. In this chapter we have been studying waves. This is a very complicated matter on a real spring, but by mentally replacing the real spring by the idealized one, we separate the essential from the inessential and simplify the problem to help our understanding. To make the right idealization is one of the secrets of the successful scientist.

16–6. A Wave Model for Light?

In this chapter we learned about two important properties of waves which clearly indicate the advantages of a wave model of light over the particle model. First, we found that waves can pass through one another undisturbed. If we shine two flashlight beams across each other, each proceeds after the point of crossing as if the other had not been there. (See Fig. 12–4.) Similarly,

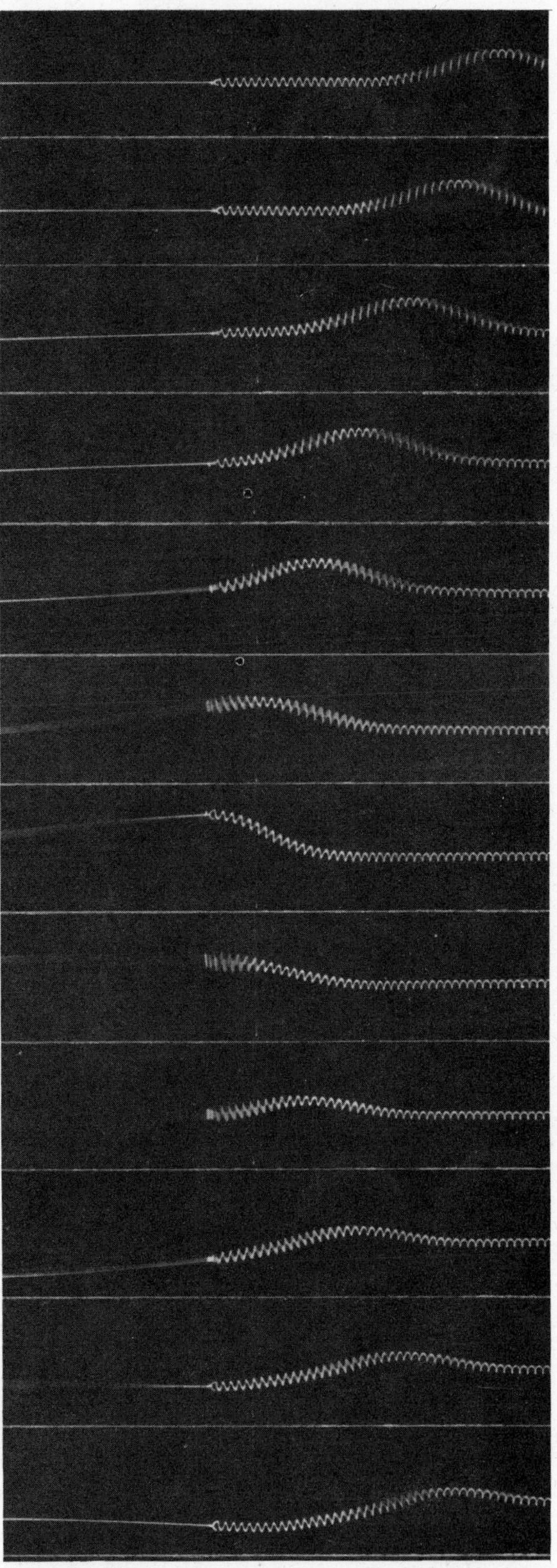

16–13. A pulse on a spring reflected from a junction with a very light thread. The whole pulse returns right side up.

we can see this page despite the light crossing in all directions between us and it. This means that the crossing of light beams resembles the crossing of waves much more than it does the intersection of streams of particles.

The second important wave property is that of partial reflection and partial transmission at a boundary. Recall now what happens when light passes from one medium to another — say, from air to glass. Part of the light is reflected and part of it is transmitted, as was shown by Fig. 13–2. This is just what waves do, but streams of particles do not split up this way.

These two wave properties which appear in light lead us to go on exploring a wave model for light; but they are far from demonstrating that a wave picture is an adequate model for light. For example, when a light beam hits a glass surface the angle of reflection equals the angle of incidence, and the direction of the refracted beam is described by Snell's law. On the basis of what we have studied so far, we cannot say whether a wave model accounts for the observed changes of direction. The waves on our spring are confined to move along one line or one dimension. Therefore there is no way of changing the direction of propagation except to reverse it. To find if waves can really account for the behavior of light we must have waves which move in space or at least in a plane, so that we can make a direct comparison. This we shall do in the next chapter, where we shall study waves on the surface of water.

FOR HOME, DESK, AND LAB

1. Suppose you look out your window and see your neighbor across the street sitting on his porch. In how many ways could you do something to attract his attention, make him move, or otherwise influence his actions? Which ways involve mass transmission and which ways wave motion?

2. What do you think are the important factors that determine the speed of a starting pulse? Will the speed be the same for a line of trucks and a line of passenger cars?

3. If an upward pulse is moving along a length of coil spring from the left to the right, how does a single point on the coil behave?

(a) Does it move up and then down, or does it move down and then up?

(b) Does it make any difference if the pulse moves from right to left?

4. Fig. 16–2 shows the displacement of a point on a spring as a pulse goes by. Make a graph showing the displacement of this point as a function of time. Plot displacement vertically and time horizontally with $\frac{1}{24}$-sec intervals (the interval between pictures of Fig. 16–2).

5. Sketch the motion of the spring for the pulse in Fig. 16–14.

6. Using the two pulses shown in Fig. 16–15, determine the size and shape of the combined pulse at this moment. Do the same thing for several other positions of the pulses.

16–14. For Problem 5. A pulse moving to the right.

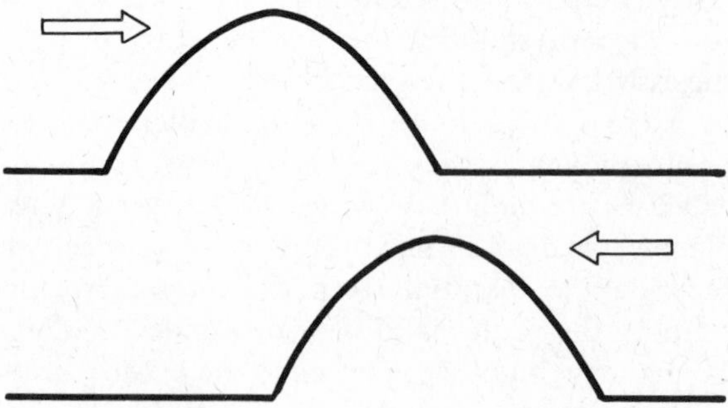

16–15. For Problem 6. Two equal pulses moving in opposite directions.

7. The seventh picture from the top in Fig. 16–5 shows two pulses at the moment of crossing. Specify the pieces of spring that are moving and their direction of motion.

8. In the fifth picture from the top of Fig. 16–7, which points are moving and in which direction do they move?

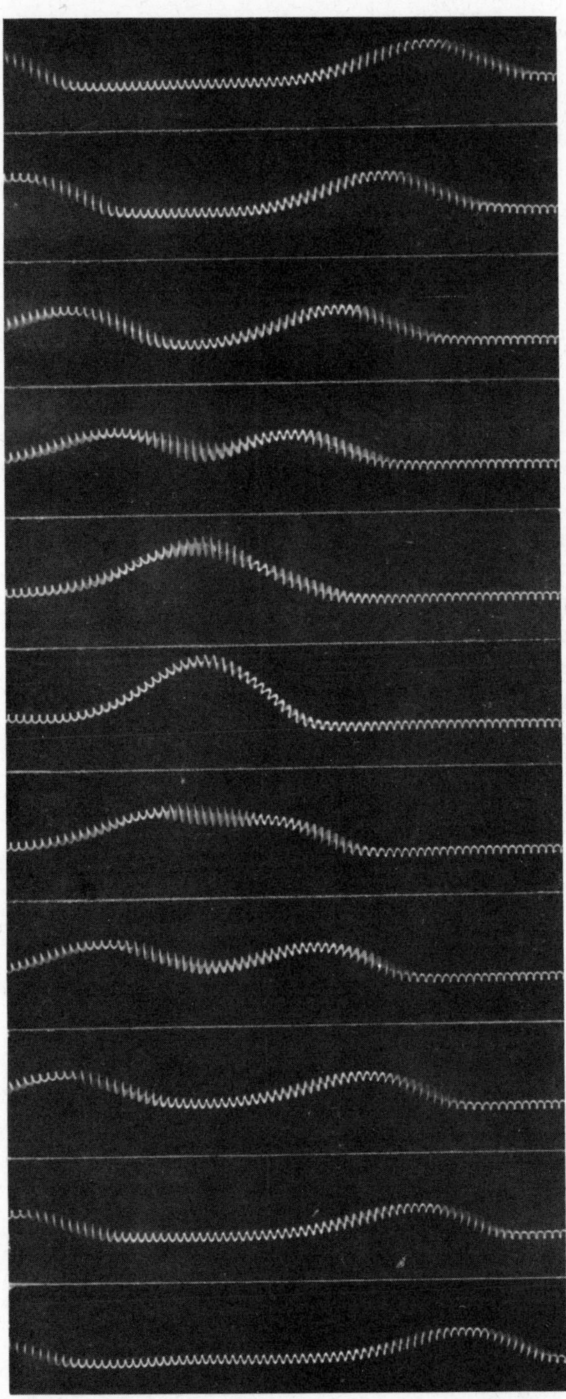

16–16. For Problem 9. Superposition of two equal and symmetric pulses.

9. In the sixth picture, Fig. 16–16, we see the superposition of two equal pulses, each of which is symmetrical about its center line.

(a) The absence of blur indicates that there is no motion at this instant. Show that this is true by using the principle of superposition.

(b) Assume you deform the coil spring in the same manner as shown in the sixth picture. What will happen when it is released?

10. The sixth picture of Fig. 16–10 shows the spring at an instant when the spring is almost straight. Explain why there is an instant when this happens.

11. Consider the asymmetric pulse coming from the *left* in Fig. 16–6. Draw the shape it will have after being reflected at a fixed end.

12. Imagine that you have a medium consisting of three sections of rope: light, heavy, and light. If you shake in a pulse, what will happen?

13. * Hold one end of a long rope with the other end tied to a rigid support. Stand looking along the rope and generate a wave by moving your hand through three fast clockwise circles.

(a) Describe the wave generated.

(b) Describe the reflected wave.

(c) Describe the motion of a particle of the rope as the wave passes forward and back.

14. * Investigate how a pulse on a rubber tube attenuates under various conditions such as on bare ground, grass, sidewalk, and in the air.

15. If the spring in Fig. 16–1 could be observed with very precise instruments, minute variations in speed would be found. In view of this, are we still justified in making use of the idea of a constant speed for a pulse?

FURTHER READING

GRIFFIN, DONALD R., *Echoes of Bats and Men.* Doubleday, 1959: A Science Study Series paperback.

WAVES AND LIGHT

CHAPTER 17

17–1. Water Waves

One of the first illustrations of waves mentioned in Chapter 16 was that of ripples on a pond. The spreading out of waves in the form of larger and larger circles is familiar to everyone. For example, a fish nibbling at a worm on a line gives away its presence to the angler who sees the circular waves produced by the up-and-down motion of the float attached to the line.

Because water waves move along the surface and do not extend downward to any appreciable depth, they are known as surface waves. If you have watched fish in an aquarium, perhaps you have noticed that they are undisturbed by the waves. A submarine commander does not fear a stormy sea as the captain of a surface ship might. He dives his submarine and travels along unaffected by the powerful waves above.

If we look at water waves through the side of an aquarium, we are able to see their shape. We notice that, while there are some variations, they are generally similar and look something like the illustration in Fig. 17–1. The upper portions are called crests and the lower portions, troughs. The waves produced by a boat as it moves through the water are a common example. We can also see waves in an ordinary tub of water, but in the laboratory we use a more convenient apparatus called a ripple tank. The ripple tank (Fig. 17–2) has a glass bottom which makes it possible to project images of the waves onto a screen. These images are produced because the crests of the waves act as converging lenses and tend to focus the light

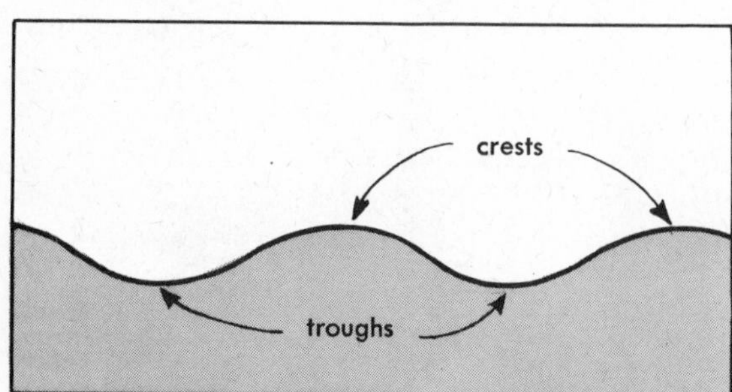

17–1. An illustration of water waves.

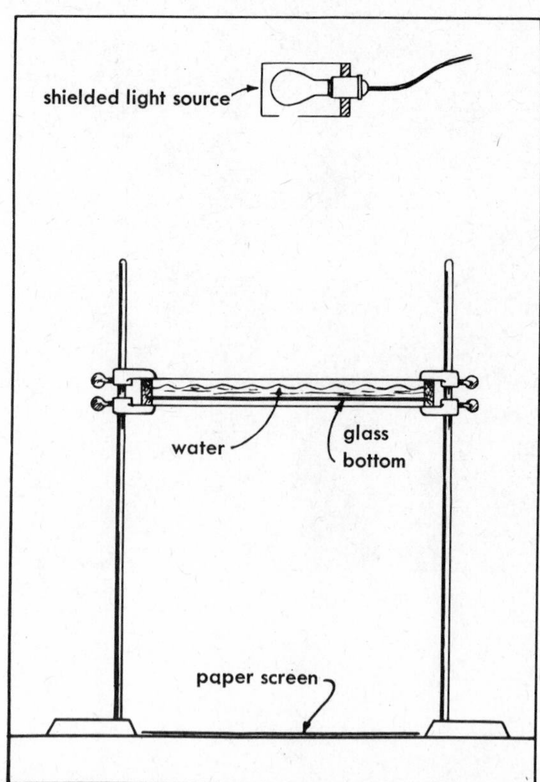

17–2. The ripple tank.

from the lamp while the troughs, acting as diverging lenses, tend to spread it out. Therefore the crests appear on the screen as bright bands while the troughs appear dark.

17–2. Straight and Circular Pulses

We can generate a straight pulse, like the long bow waves caused by a passing boat, by dipping a ruler into the surface of the water of the ripple tank. The motion of the pulse is such that its crest always remains parallel to a line marking its original position. The distance between parallel lines is measured along a perpendicular, thus the direction of motion of the pulse (also called the direction of propagation) is perpendicular to the wave crest. This direction is called the *normal* to the crest. In Fig. 17–3 the crest of a straight pulse is shown as a heavy black line. Its position at a later time is shown by the dashed line. The direction of propagation is shown by the arrow. Whenever we draw a straight pulse we shall indicate its direction of propagation by a small arrow.

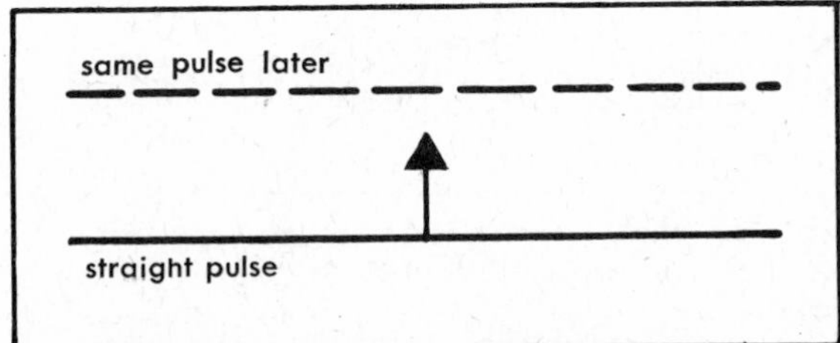

17–3. A straight pulse moves at right angles to its crest. The arrow indicates the direction.

We can also produce circular pulses in the ripple tank simply by dipping a finger into the water. Fig. 17–4 is a drawing of such a pulse at two different times. During the time interval, the pulse has expanded to form a larger circle. We cannot assign a direction to the whole circular pulse because it moves in all directions. Instead let us look at a segment of the circular pulse which is small enough to be considered straight (Fig. 17–5). The direction of propagation of such a segment is along the radius and away from the center of the circle. This direction is normal to the crest of the wave just as the direction of propagation of straight waves is normal to their crests.

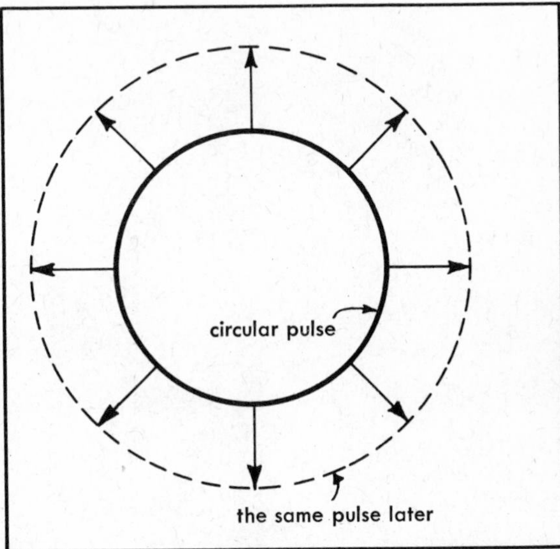

17–4. An expanding circular pulse.

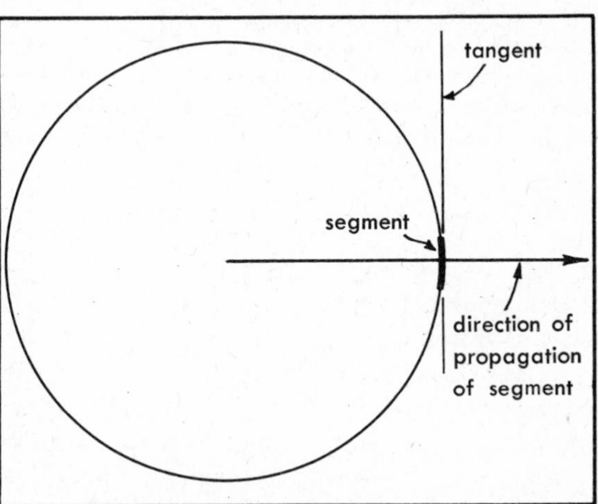

17–5. A tiny segment of a circular pulse. The segment acts as though it were straight and moves along a radius away from the center.

17–3. Reflection

We recall that a pulse on a spring can be reflected, and we may expect that water waves can also undergo reflection. Consider a straight pulse as it moves away from the ruler toward the opposite end of the tank. To reflect it we place a barrier in the middle of the tank parallel to the ruler. The pulse strikes the barrier and reflects back in the direction from which it came, just like a pulse on a spring.

Now let us change the position of the reflecting barrier so that the pulse is no longer parallel to it.

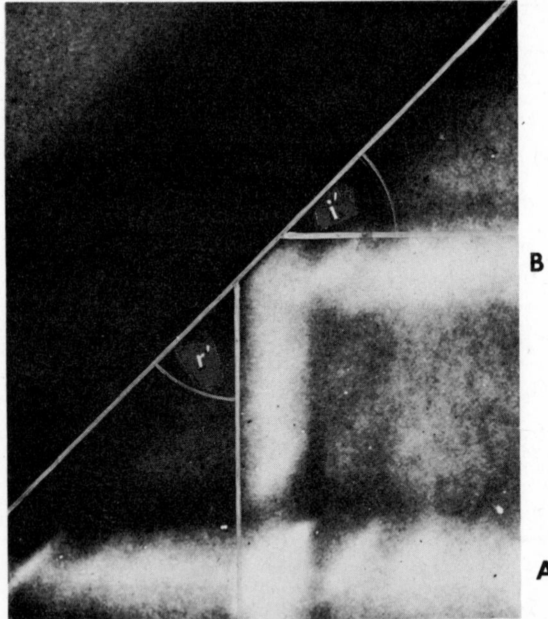

17–6. Two straight pulses. *A* is approaching the barrier, moving up the picture. While the upper part of *B* is still moving up the picture, the lower part of *B*, which appears as a vertical white wave crest, has been reflected, and it is moving to the right. The white diagonal line has been drawn in to show the position of the edge of the barrier.

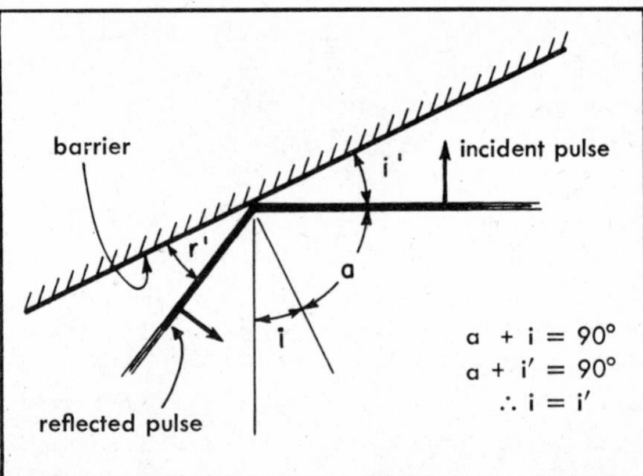

17–7. A straight pulse incident on a barrier. The angle of incidence *i* is equal to the angle the pulse makes with the barrier *i'*.

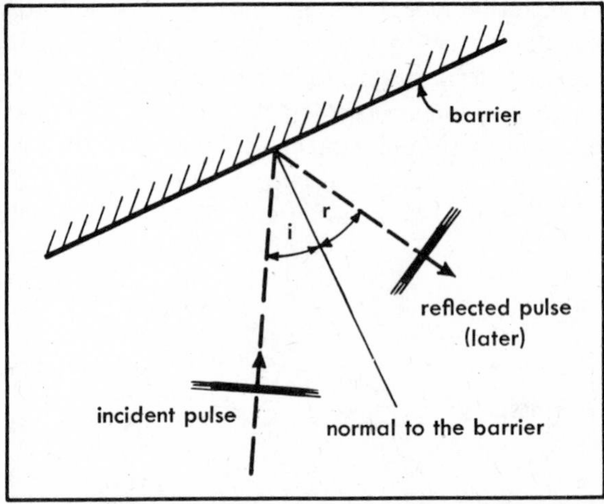

17–8. The reflection of a straight wave from a straight barrier. Just as in light, the angle of reflection *r* equals the angle of incidence *i*.

In Fig. 17–6 we see two straight pulses, one approaching and one being reflected from a barrier. The angle which the incident pulse makes with the reflecting barrier is labelled i' while the angle between the reflected pulse and the barrier is labelled r'. Measure the angles r' and i' on the photograph and you will find that $r' = i'$. If we repeated the experiment with different angles i', we would always find $r' = i'$.

This result resembles the law of reflection of light from mirrors, which we obtained in Section 12–4. There we found that the angle of reflection equals the angle of incidence. But in optics the angles were measured between the direction of propagation and the normal to the reflecting surface. We can define the angles of incidence i and reflection r for waves in the same way — that is, as the angle between the direction of propagation (which is normal to the wave crest) and the normal to the barrier.

The construction in Fig. 17–7 shows that the angle of incidence i is equal to the angle i'. A similar construction shows that $r = r'$. Our observed equality $r' = i'$ then becomes $r = i$, or in words, the angle of reflection equals the angle of incidence. We have shown, therefore, that waves and light follow the same law of reflection (Fig. 17–8).

An expanding circular pulse can also be reflected from a straight barrier. Fig. 17–9 shows the approach and reflection of such a pulse. We notice that the reflected part of the pulse is an arc of a circle. The center of this circle is at a point P' which is at the same distance behind the barrier as the source P is in front of it. The reflected pulse appears to come from P'. This corresponds to the situation in optics where we placed a point source in front of a mirror. The reflected light then appeared to come from the image point behind the mirror. (See Figs. 12–9

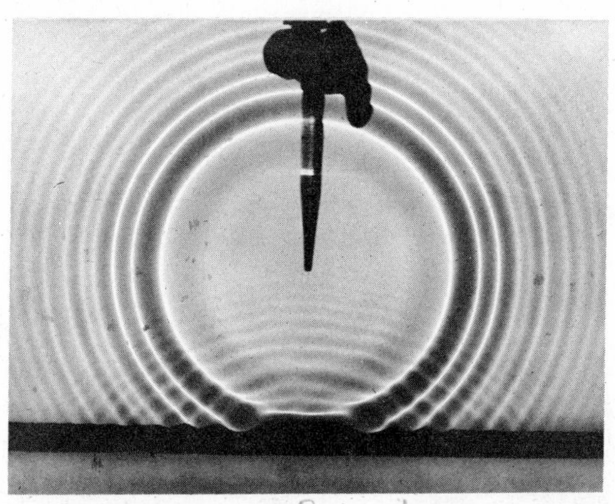

17–9. Reflection of a circular pulse from a straight barrier. In the photograph at the left, the pulse is approaching the barrier, while at the right a part of it has been reflected.

and 12–10.) By using curved barriers or combinations of two or more straight barriers, we can demonstrate with the ripple tank all of the phenomena of reflection that we studied in connection with light. Just as the formation of images by mirrors followed from the laws of reflection in optics, so does the corresponding formation of images by "mirrors" in the ripple tank.

17–4. Speed of Propagation and Periodic Waves

Waves in different media propagate with different speeds. For example, we can see the waves on a coil spring speed up when we stretch the coil, and we can see the waves in a rubber hose slow down when we fill it with water. In this section we shall learn how to make quantitative measurements of the speed of water waves in the ripple tank. There are several ways of going about such a measurement.

One way is to generate a straight pulse and measure with a stop watch the time t the pulse takes to travel a specified distance l. The speed v is then equal to the distance traveled divided by the time taken:

$$v = l/t\,.$$

Another way is to generate two pulses, one after the other. By the time the second pulse is generated (after a time t) the first pulse has traveled a distance l. From then on both pulses travel along, while the distance l between them remains the same. We can measure this distance with a ruler, and again $v = l/t$. These methods are simple in principle, but in practice it is rather difficult to follow the pulses and measure the distances and times required.

A third method is to generate pulses one after another at equal time intervals T. In doing this, the wave generator repeats its motion once every interval T. Such a motion is called *periodic*, and the time interval T is called the *period*. Another way of describing this periodic motion is to tell how often the motion repeats itself in a unit time interval; that is, by giving the *frequency* f of repetition. For example, if the motion repeats every 1/10 sec, the frequency is ten times per second. In general $f = 1/T$.

Let us now concentrate on some point in the tank. The pulses produced by the generator move toward this point, and they pass the point with the same frequency with which they leave the source. If ten are sent out each second, ten will pass each second. The frequency of the wave is therefore also given by $f = 1/T$, and T is the time between the passage of successive waves. Furthermore, as the waves move, the distance between any two adjacent pulses is always the same and is called the *wave length* λ (lambda). The wave pattern which we have been describing is called a periodic straight wave (Fig. 17–10).

We can obtain the speed of a periodic wave in a manner similar to that which we used for a pair of pulses. We know that the pulses are separated by a distance λ and that each pulse moves over this distance in a time T. Hence the speed of propagation is

$$v = \lambda/T.$$

17–10. Periodic straight waves moving across a ripple tank.

Using the relation $f = 1/T$, we find that

$$v = f\lambda,$$

or that the speed of propagation of a periodic wave is the product of the frequency and the wave length.

The relation that we have just obtained is by no means restricted to waves in a ripple tank. It is equally good for *any* periodic wave. Such things as the straightness of the wave, the nature of the ripple tank, and the properties of the water did not come into the argument from which we got our result. In particular, we could have followed the same procedure with circular periodic waves and would have found the relationship $v = f\lambda$ again. In this case the wave length is measured along the radius (Fig. 17–11); and we find it is equal to the wave length of a straight wave of the same frequency. The speed of circular waves is therefore equal to that of straight waves in the same medium. Furthermore, we could have applied the above arguments to any other kind of periodic waves — for example, periodic waves on coils — and we would have the same relation $v = f\lambda$.

Now we come to the advantage of the above relation for the measurement of v. Imagine that instead of watching the wave continuously we look at it through a shutter which is closed most of the time and opens periodically for short time intervals. The stroboscope described in Chapter 2 is such a device. The first time the shutter opens we will get a glimpse of the wave pattern in a certain position. During the time the shutter is closed, all of the pulses will move a distance equal to their speed times the time the shutter is closed (Fig. 17–12). If we look through the shutter while it is periodically opening and closing, the pattern will usually appear to move. Suppose, however, that the period of the shutter is just the same as that of the wave. Then, during the time the shutter is closed, every pulse just moves up to the position of the pulse ahead of it, and we see the same pattern every time the shutter opens. That is, we

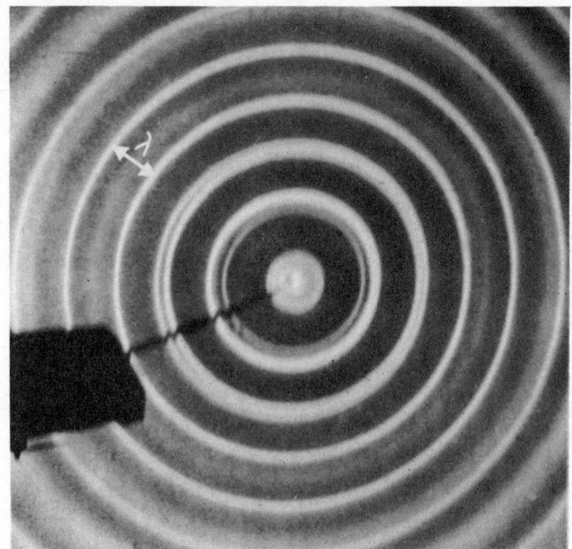

17–11. Periodic circular waves.

17–12. Crests of a periodic wave seen at successive openings *A* and *B* of a stroboscope shutter. In the top diagram the frequency of the stroboscope is greater than that of the waves. At the bottom, it is the same. The dashed lines, of course, are not visible.

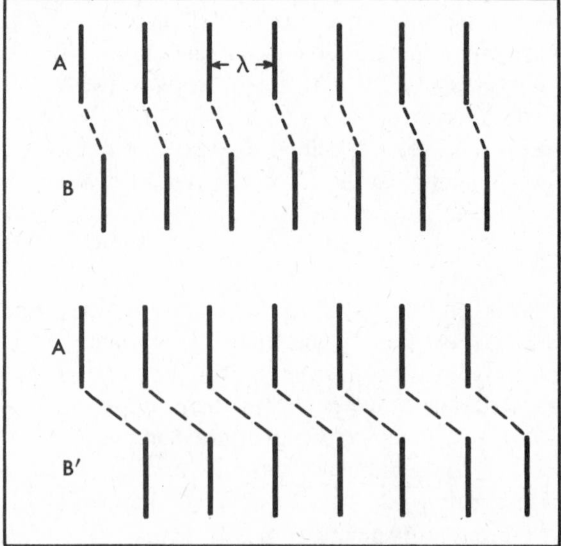

see a stationary pattern from which it is easy to measure the wave length. Moreover, as we have said, the period of the shutter is equal to the period of the wave and it can be measured by counting the number of times the shutter is opened in a given time interval, i.e., by measuring the frequency of the shutter. This gives us f. Now that we have both λ and f for the wave, we can make use of the general relation $v = f\lambda$ in order to determine the speed.

17–5. Refraction

We mentioned earlier that the speed of propagation of waves depends on the properties of the medium through which they move. In the case of waves on the surface of water, the speed depends on the depth of the water. Therefore water of two different depths can be considered to be two different media for wave propagation. This is a very useful property because by merely changing the depth of the water in part of the ripple tank we are able to study the behavior of waves when they pass from one medium to another. To see that the speed indeed depends on the depth, we now make half the tank shallow by placing a thick glass plate on the bottom of the back part of the tank, thereby dividing it into two sections of different depths with the dividing line parallel to the waves. Let us look at the waves through the stroboscope. By turning it at the right frequency we can stop the motion of the pattern in *both* sections of the tank simultaneously. Hence the frequency is the same in both sections; it is not affected by the change in depth. But Fig. 17–13 shows that the wave length λ_2 in the shallow part is shorter than λ_1, the wave length in the deep part.* Since the speed of propagation is the product of the same frequency and the appropriate wave length, we see that the speed in the shallow part (where the wave length is smaller) is less than in the deep part — that is, $v_2 < v_1$.

Now let us repeat the experiment with another glass plate inside the tank, cut in such a way that the boundary between the two sections will form an angle with the waves. We already know that

*You will notice that the waves tend to disappear toward the end of the shallow section. They die down only because we do not have an ideal state of affairs where we can isolate the phenomenon we wish to study. Here, as in the experiments with the coil spring, there is a certain amount of resistance present which reduces the motion and finally causes it to die out.

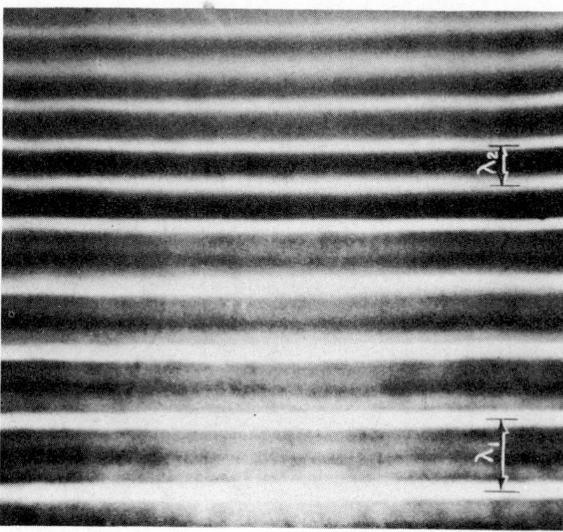

17–13. Passage of waves from deep to shallow water. The deep water is at the bottom and the shallow water at the top of the picture. Note that the wave length is shorter in the shallow water.

the wave length in the shallow section is less than in the deep one. But this is not the only change. Fig. 17–14 shows that when the straight waves hit the boundary, they remain straight but change their direction of propagation. The new direction is closer to the normal to the boundary than the original direction of propagation. We remember from our study of optics that this is what happens to light when it passes from one medium to another in which its speed is less (Sections 13–2 and 15–7). For light this refraction is quantitatively described by Snell's law. The following

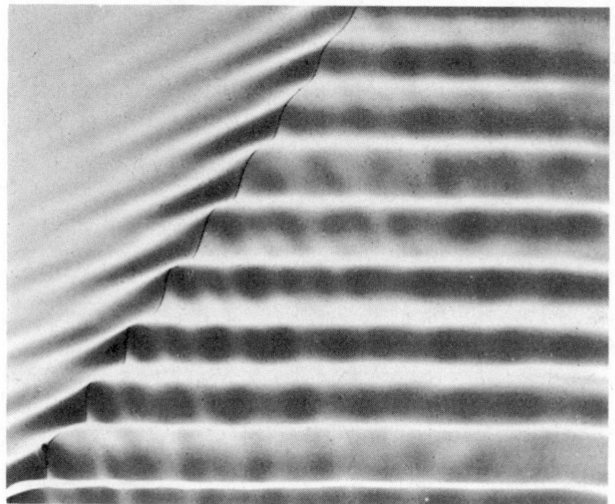

17–14. Refraction of waves at a boundary between deep and shallow sections of the ripple tank. Note the weak reflected waves.

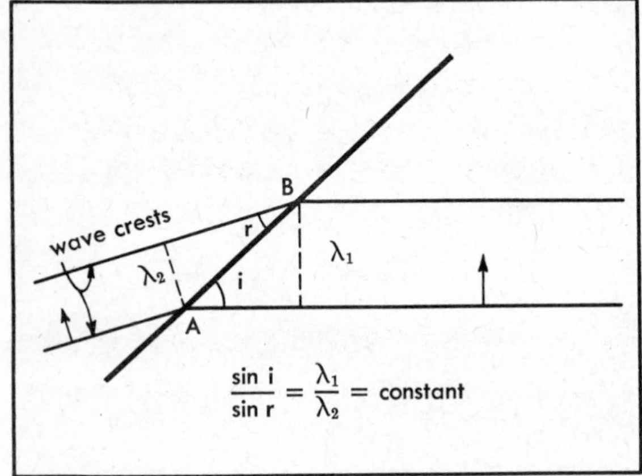

17–15. The geometry of the refraction of two consecutive wave fronts.

question now suggests itself. Does Snell's law also hold true for waves such as those in the ripple tank, when they pass from one medium to another?

There are two procedures open to us at this point. We can measure many angles of incidence and angles of refraction in the ripple tank, and thus find experimentally whether they are related by Snell's law; or we can find out whether Snell's law can be predicted theoretically from the properties of waves which we already know. We shall take the second course here.

In Section 17–3, we proved that the angle of incidence is equal to the angle between the incident wave crest and the barrier. Likewise, the angle of refraction is equal to the angle between the refracted wave crest and the barrier. Let us now draw two consecutive wave fronts as they are refracted at the barrier (Fig. 17–15). (There is no need to add the normals, since angles equal to i and r already appear in the drawing.) Then by definition

$$\sin i = \frac{\lambda_1}{AB}, \quad \sin r = \frac{\lambda_2}{AB}.$$

The values of $\sin i$ and $\sin r$ change from case to case, but their ratio is a constant independent of the angle of incidence, as we see by actually dividing $\sin i$ by $\sin r$:

$$\frac{\sin i}{\sin r} = \frac{\lambda_1}{AB}\frac{AB}{\lambda_2} = \frac{\lambda_1}{\lambda_2} = \text{constant}.$$

The relation $\sin i/\sin r$ = constant is Snell's law, this time for waves. We shall again call the constant the index of refraction and denote it as in optics by n_{12}. Thus

$$\frac{\sin i}{\sin r} = n_{12} \text{ and } n_{12} = \frac{\lambda_1}{\lambda_2}.$$

We can now express the value of n_{12} in terms of the speeds of propagation of the waves in the two media. In general the speed v is related to the wave length as $v = f\lambda$. In particular then, $\lambda_1 = v_1/f$ and $\lambda_2 = v_2/f$. Hence

$$n_{12} = \frac{\lambda_1}{\lambda_2} = \frac{v_1/f}{v_2/f} = \frac{v_1}{v_2}.$$

This equation says that the index of refraction is equal to the ratio of the speed of propagation in the first medium to that in the second medium.

We arrived at Snell's law and the relation of n_{12} to the speeds by theoretical analysis of our previous results. We could get the same conclusions by direct measurements. First we could measure many pairs of angles i and r and thus establish that $\sin i/\sin r$ = const. = n_{12}. Then we could measure the speeds of propagation in the two media and establish that $n_{12} = v_1/v_2$. Such measurements have often been carried out, and they do agree with our conclusions.

We now recall that the particle model of light as developed by Newton (1669) also explained the existence of a constant index of refraction for a given pair of substances but predicted its value to be $n_{12} = v_2/v_1$ (Sections 15–2 and 15–7). Our wave model, advocated by Huygens (1677) predicts $n_{12} = v_1/v_2$, just the inverse of Newton's result. The position of the wave model of light was strengthened by various experiments at the beginning of the nineteenth century. But this particular question was not settled for almost two hundred years. In 1862 Foucault actually measured the speed of light in air and in water and found that the speed in water was less. The exact ratio $v_1/v_2 = 1.33$ was measured by Michelson in 1883. This ratio agrees with the wave model because the index of refraction of water is 1.33 (Chapter 13).

One point still needs clarification: not all the light hitting the boundary between the two media is refracted. Part of it is reflected even if both media are transparent. The same holds for waves. In Fig. 17–14 the size of the reflected wave is rather small, but you can see it if you look closely. We conclude, therefore, that as far as refraction is concerned, waves have just the properties which we need in order to explain the behavior of light.

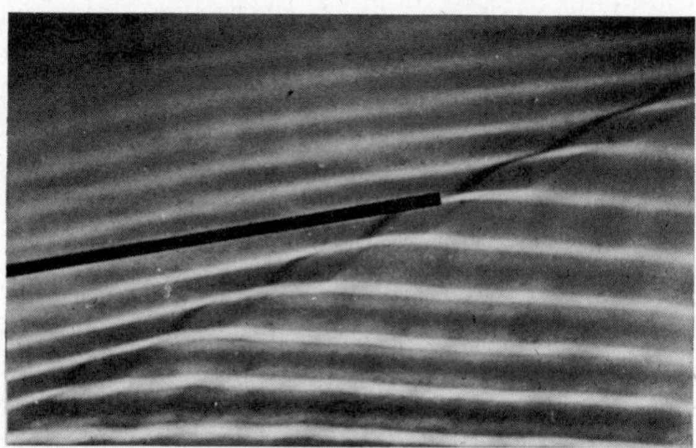

17–16. Refraction of low-frequency waves. The black marker is placed parallel to the refracted waves.

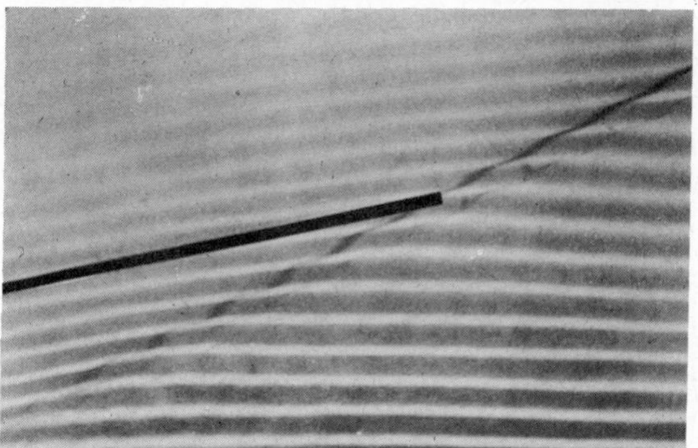

17–17. Refraction of high-frequency waves. The refracted waves are not parallel to the black marker.

17–6. Dispersion

In the last section we studied the refraction of periodic waves as they pass from one medium to another. We found the index of refraction to be equal to the ratio of the speeds of propagation in the two media: $n_{12} = v_1/v_2$. We did not state the frequency of the waves because we had previously learned that the speeds of propagation depend only on the media in which the waves travel. Accordingly we would expect to find the same index of refraction for waves of different frequency provided we repeat the experiment with the same two media, for example, water of the same two depths.

What we actually observe is shown in Figs. 17–16 and 17–17. In Fig. 17–16 we see the refraction of a wave of low frequency (long wave length). To indicate the direction of the refracted waves we placed a rod on the screen of the ripple tank. It is exactly parallel to the refracted wave fronts. We then increased the frequency (i.e., decreased the wave length), leaving the rod untouched. Notice that in Fig. 17–17 the rod is no longer parallel to the refracted wave crests. The wave with the higher frequency is clearly refracted in a direction slightly different from that taken by the low-frequency wave, although the angle of incidence is the same in both cases. The index of refraction for the two media therefore depends somewhat on the frequency of the wave. By analogy with the dependence of the index of refraction on the color of light, which we have discussed in Section 13–8, this phenomenon is called *dispersion.* Since the index of refraction equals the ratio of the speeds of propagation in the two media, we have to conclude that the speed must depend on frequency in at least one of the two media; otherwise the ratio could not show such a dependence. A medium in which the speed of waves depends on the frequency is called a *dispersive* medium.

In the ripple tank we can measure the speed of periodic waves of different frequencies (Section 17–4), and thus see directly that the speed changes with the frequency, provided we make our measurements accurately enough. The statement we so often make, that the speed of waves depends only on the medium, is therefore an idealization. To be sure, this idealization is a good approximation to the true state of affairs provided we are not concerned with small changes in the speed (Section 16–5).

We made a similar idealization in our study of the refraction of light in Chapter 13. You will recall that the index of refraction of light at first appeared to be dependent only on the two media through which the light was passing — for example, air and glass. Then a closer examination of refraction, using prisms, showed that the index changes slightly with color; it is a little larger for violet than for red.

The index of refraction of waves depends slightly on the frequency. That of light depends slightly on the color. Is there perhaps a relation between the dependence of the index of refraction of waves on the frequency and that of light on color? It is tempting to assume that light is a periodic wave and that different colors correspond to waves of different frequencies. At this point we cannot prove that our assumption is correct, but in the next chapter we shall learn how to measure the wave length of light of different colors. We can then find the corresponding

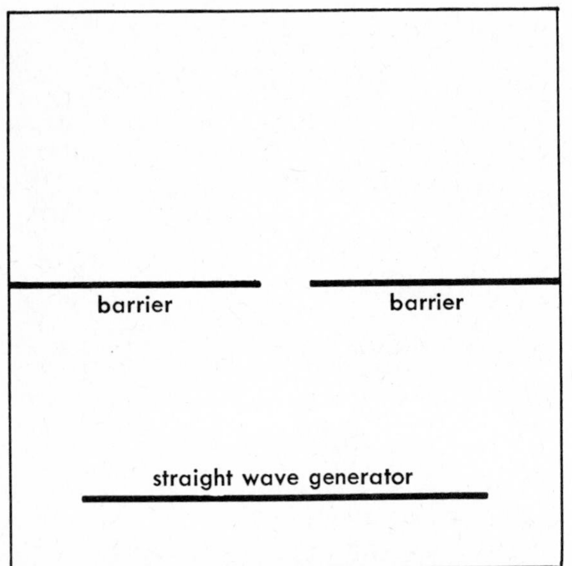

17–18. Ripple-tank arrangement for the experiment shown in Fig. 17–19.

frequencies, and we shall indeed establish that light waves of various frequencies appear to our eyes as light of various colors.*

17–7. Diffraction

Our study of refraction and dispersion clearly shows that the wave picture of light succeeds where the corpuscular picture fails. Yet the corpuscular picture predicts correctly that light should propagate in straight lines and cast sharp shadows. Can a wave model also account for these properties of light? Again, a good way to investigate these questions is to experiment with waves in the ripple tank. We use a straight-wave generator and two barriers parallel to it placed in line with an opening between them (Fig. 17–18). These barriers would cast sharp shadows if light were incident upon them from the direction of the generator. What happens when we send in a periodic straight wave of wave length λ is shown in Fig. 17–19. In the middle of the pattern beyond the opening the wave crests are almost straight, but at the sides they curve, giving the impression of circular waves originating from the edges of the opening. This means that after passing through the opening not all of the wave propagates in its original direction. Part of it is bent. This phenomenon is called *diffraction.*

The diffraction of waves makes it hard to understand how we can explain the straight-line propagation of light with a wave model. If light is a wave, when it passes through a small hole some of the light should bend instead of traveling straight ahead. In a wave model of light there must be at least one great difference between light waves and water waves.

What could this difference be? We know the wave length λ of the water waves. We do not know the wave length of light waves; it may be very different. Let us, therefore, examine the diffraction of water waves of different wave lengths. In Fig. 17–20 we see three pictures of periodic waves with different wave lengths, each passing through the same opening. We notice a definite trend. In the first picture the wave length is six-tenths of the width d of the opening. There the part of the straight wave which gets through the opening is almost entirely converted into a circular wave. Or, in other words, the opening acts like a source of circular waves when straight waves fall on it. In the second picture λ is three-tenths of d. In this case the wave which gets through is not so curved as in the first picture. It has a straight section in the middle but part of it still bends at the sides. In the third picture λ is one-tenth of d and here the bending fades away close to the forward direction and we obtain an almost sharp shadow. Provided we keep the

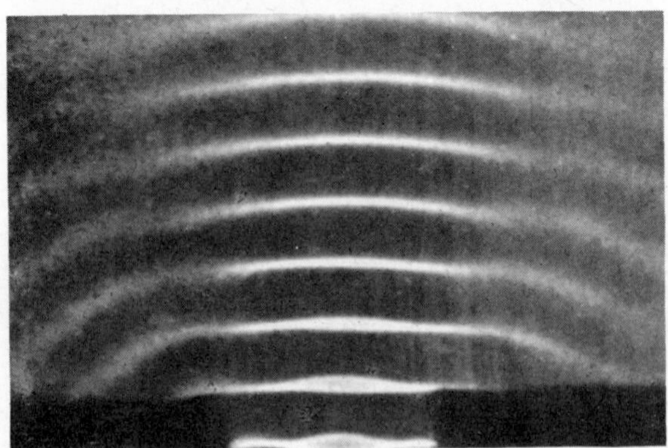

17–19. Straight waves passing through an opening. Note the curving of the waves around the ends of the barriers.

*By comparing the bending of waves in Figs. 17–16 and 17–17 with the dispersion of light by glass (see Fig. 13–15), we might come to the conclusion that the wave length of violet light is longer than that of red light. However, blue light does not refract more than red in all materials. In some materials it is the other way around. Therefore, studying the dispersion of water waves does not establish the relation between color and wave length of light.

width of the opening d fixed, a further decrease in λ makes the shadow still sharper. We can also keep λ fixed and change d; then we find that the amount of bending does not depend on λ and d separately but only on the fraction λ/d. To sum up, waves are strongly diffracted when they pass through an opening of size comparable to their wave length, and there is hardly any diffraction if the wave length is very small compared to the width of the opening.

We all know that light passing through a keyhole is not bent but seems to continue in its original direction. If light is a wave, this implies that its wave length must be much less than the size of a keyhole. But to be certain that light is a periodic wave we should be able to do an experiment which will show diffraction. Two such experiments were described in Section 11–7. Suppose that we repeat the experiment in which we examined a light source through a narrow slit between two fingers. When the slit is half a centimeter across, an electric light bulb viewed through it appears normal. As the slit is narrowed to a width of about a tenth of a millimeter, however, the bulb appears elongated in a direction perpendicular to your fingers. Moreover, you can hold your fingers in any direction and the elongation always appears perpendicular to them. This is a clear indication that the light is diffracted by the opening.

We can get a little more information from our experiments with light if we return for a minute to Fig. 17–20. Examination of Fig. 17–20 suggests an explanation of the fact, stated in Chapter 11, that all shadows, even those of large obstacles, are slightly blurred by diffraction. Even in the bottom picture, where λ/d is about 1/10, the wave crests near the edge of the shadow are slightly bent. If we observe these waves at a distance far from the slit, the effect of this bending will be to spread the region reached by the waves. Since, as in the experiment with our fingers, we only begin to see the diffraction of light when the aperture is about one-tenth of a millimeter, we can now conclude that the wave length of light is even smaller than this.

Briefly then, from our discussion in this chapter, light can be described as waves of very small wave lengths.

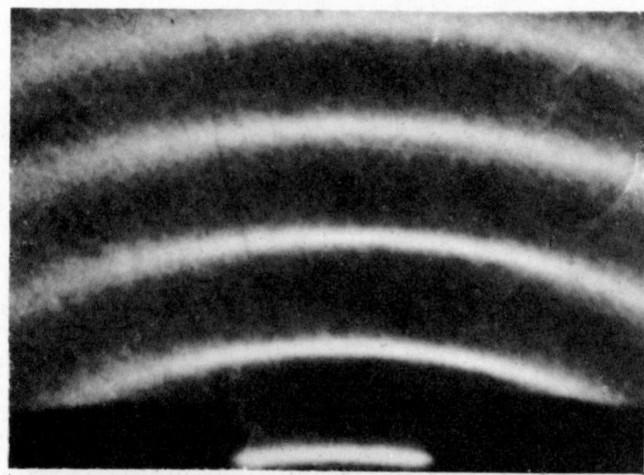

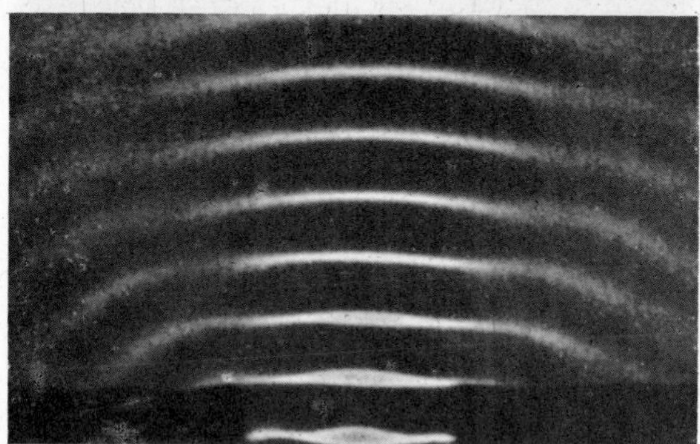

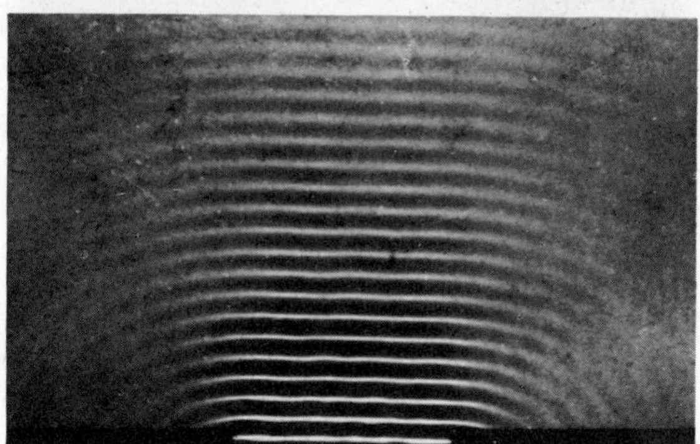

17–20. Three views of waves passing through the same opening. Note the decrease in bending at the shorter wave lengths.

FOR HOME, DESK, AND LAB

1. In Fig. 17–7 if $i = 25°$, what is the value of r'?

2. A straight pulse approaches a barrier at an angle of 30°. What is the direction of motion of the pulse after reflection? Indicate it on a diagram.

3. Describe the wave motion that results when you dip your finger into the center of a circular tank of water. What would be the motion under ideal conditions?

4. Suppose we place a barrier in a ripple tank in the shape of an ellipse as in Fig. 17–21. When a circular pulse is generated at point *A*, it reflects from the barrier and converges at point *B*.
   (a) From this experiment what can you say about the geometry of an ellipse? (Hint: Consider tiny segments of the circular pulse originating from *A* and see how the ellipse must be shaped so that all segments reach *B* at the same time.)
   (b) What will happen if we generate a pulse at point *B*?
   (c) Will such a convergence also happen when you dip your finger in at some point other than *A* or *B*?

5. In Fig. 17–22 a straight pulse approaches a right-angled barrier at an angle of 45°.
   (a) How does it reflect?
   (b) What happens if the wave is incident at some other angle?

6. Assume you are looking at a periodic wave of frequency $f = 4$ per sec through a two-slit stroboscope. What do you expect to see if you rotate the stroboscope with a frequency of 1, 2, and 4 revolutions per sec?

7. A point source in the ripple tank produces circular periodic waves. By using a stroboscope to stop the motion, we measure the difference in radius between the first and sixth circular crests and find it to be 10 cm.
   (a) What is the wave length?
   (b) Why didn't we calculate the wave length by using the radius, say, of the fifth pulse only?
   (c) Why do we use this method of measurement rather than take the difference between neighboring crests?

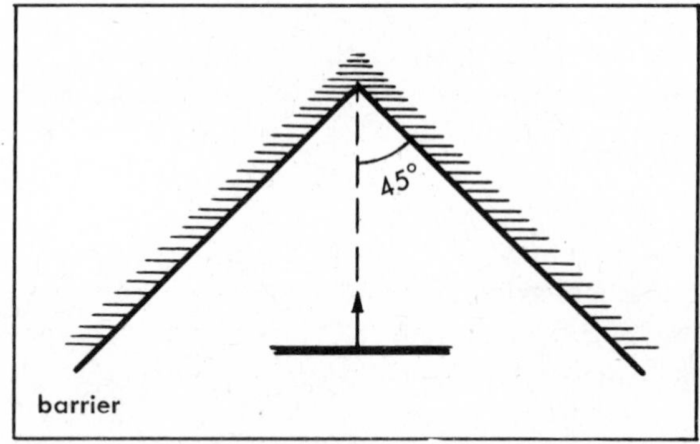

17–22. A straight pulse approaching a right-angled barrier.

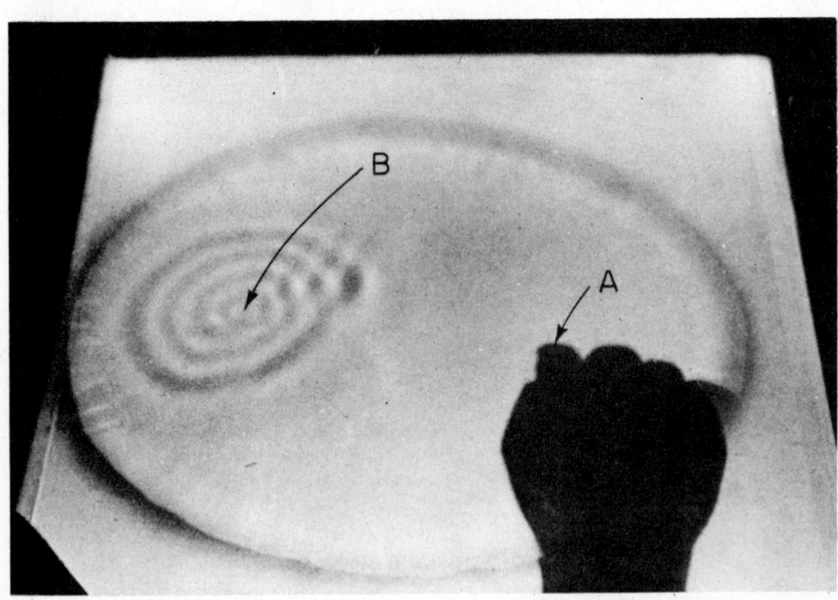

17–21. Reflection from an elliptical barrier. A pulse has been generated at *A* and is photographed as it converges on *B*.

17–23. Curving of a straight wave when the water becomes more and more shallow from one side to the other.

8. (a) In a ripple tank when one pulse is sent every $\frac{1}{10}$ sec, we find that λ is 3 cm. What is the speed of propagation?

(b) In the same medium we send two pulses, the second one $\frac{1}{2}$ sec after the first. How far apart are they?

9. What is the index of refraction in passing from the deep to the shallow water in Fig. 17–13?

10. Measure the index of refraction in Fig. 17–14 by the method you used in the previous problem, and by finding the ratio of the sines of the appropriate angles. Compare the results.

11. A ripple-tank wave passes from a shallow to a deep section with an incident angle of 45° and a refracted angle of 60°.

(a) What is the ratio of speeds in the two sections?

(b) If the wave speed is 25 cm per second in the deep section, what is it in the shallow one?

12. (a) A tire on an automobile wheel has a circumference of 7.0 feet. When the wheel is turning 200 times per minute, what is the speed of the automobile in feet per min?

(b) A light wave whose frequency is 6.0×10^{14} per sec is passed through a liquid. Within the liquid the wave length is measured and found to be 3.0×10^{-5} centimeters. What is the speed of light in this liquid?

(c) What is the wave length in vacuum (from which the frequency was calculated)?

(d) What is the index of refraction of the liquid for light of this frequency?

13. The ripple tank is arranged so that the water gradually becomes shallow from one side to the other. Because of this, on one side of the tank the speed of a wave crest is different from that on the other side. As a result, straight waves become curved (Fig. 17–23). In the picture the pulses are moving toward the top of the page.

(a) Which is the shallow side?

(b) Does a similar phenomenon occur with light? Be prepared to discuss this in class.

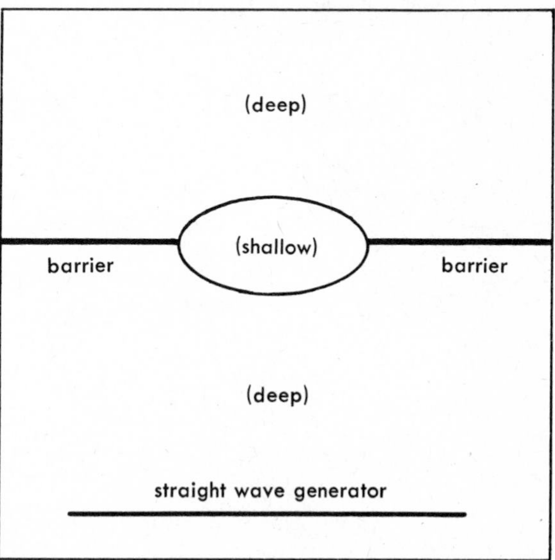

17–24. The ripple-tank arrangement used in making the picture in Fig. 17–25. The oval region between the barriers has shallow water, while water in the rest of the tank is deep.

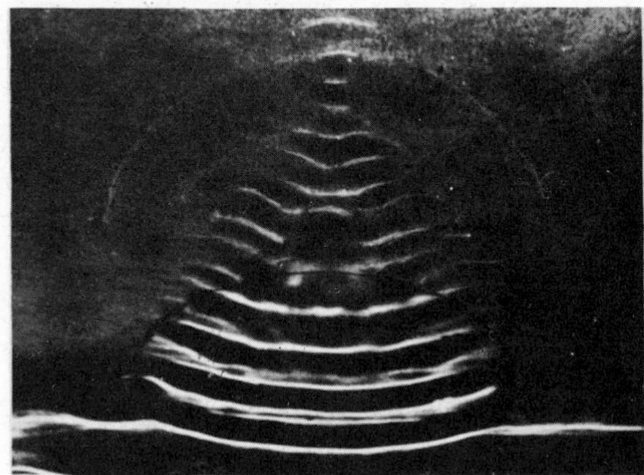

17–25. The wave pattern with periodic waves and an arrangement as in Fig. 17–24.

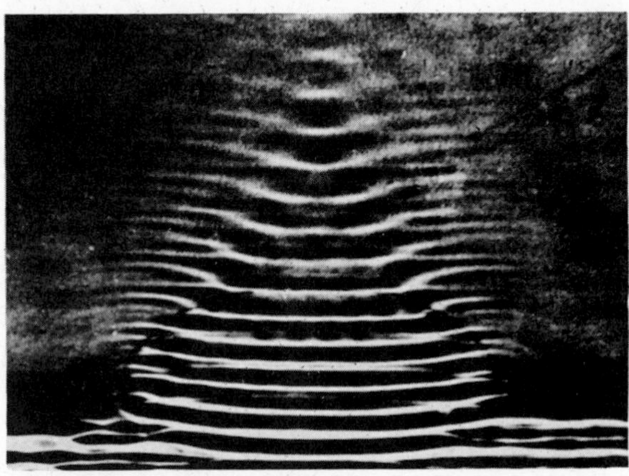

17–26. The same wave pattern as in Fig. 17–25 but with a shorter wave length.

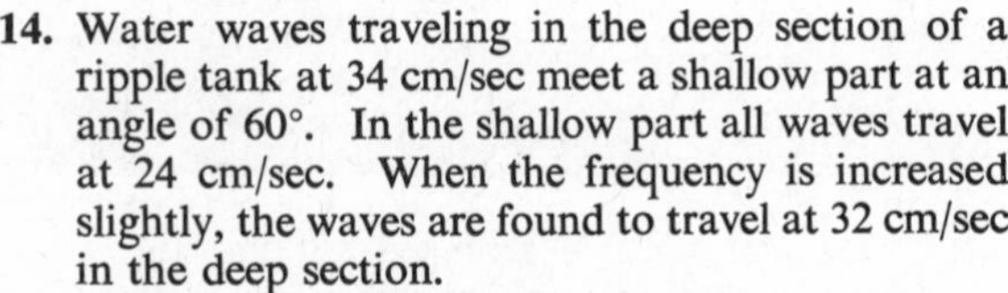

14. Water waves traveling in the deep section of a ripple tank at 34 cm/sec meet a shallow part at an angle of 60°. In the shallow part all waves travel at 24 cm/sec. When the frequency is increased slightly, the waves are found to travel at 32 cm/sec in the deep section.

(a) Compute the angle of refraction for each case.

(b) Considering the ripple-tank conditions, is it easier to measure the two speeds and find their difference directly or to measure it indirectly by the angular difference found in (a)?

(c) How can we detect small differences in the speed of light?

15. We set up the ripple tank as shown in Fig. 17–24 and generate a periodic straight wave. The resulting wave pattern is shown in the photograph in Fig. 17–25.

(a) Explain what is taking place.

(b) Of what optical arrangement is this a model?

16. In Fig. 17–26 we see a photograph taken under the same conditions as those in Problem 15 except that here the waves have a shorter wave length.

(a) How do the two photographs differ?

(b) What can you conclude from this difference?

17. Suppose the oval region in Fig. 17–24 is deep and the surrounding region is shallow.

(a) What will happen to the straight waves?

(b) Of what optical arrangement is this a model?

18. How do we know that the wave length of light must be very much less than a centimeter?

19. Imagine our eyes were sensitive only to light of wave length 0.1 mm. How would this affect our ability to see? Could you thread a needle?

20. If sound is a wave phenomenon, how would you explain the common experience of hearing sounds from around corners?

21. Sound waves in air usually travel at about 330 meters per second. Audible sounds have a frequency range of about 30 to 15,000 cycles per second. What is the range of wave lengths of these sound waves?

FURTHER READING

HUYGENS, CHRISTIAN, *Moments of Discovery*. Edited by G. Schwartz and P. Bishop, Basic Books, 1958. Huygens' original account setting forth the wave theory of light.

INTERFERENCE

CHAPTER 18

18–1. Introduction

In Chapter 17 we studied the properties of waves to see if they can account for the common properties of light. We had already learned how light is reflected from a mirror, and we found that waves obey the same law of reflection. We had also learned how light is refracted when it passes from one medium to another, and we found that the refraction of waves follows Snell's law just as light does.

In the last section of the preceding chapter we recalled that light propagates in straight lines and produces sharp shadows. We then experimented with waves in the ripple tank and found they were diffracted when they passed through an opening. We could reduce the amount of diffraction by decreasing the wave length but could not completely eliminate it. Therefore we changed our approach; we went back to light, and found that light is also diffracted when it passes through a very narrow slit. This was a rather convincing demonstration of the wave nature of light. In this chapter we shall follow the latter approach. That is, we shall continue to study in detail the properties of waves and in the next chapter do the corresponding experiments with light.

One of the most striking results of the experiments with waves on a spring described in Chapter 16 was that two pulses traveling in opposite directions passed right through each other. The shape of the displacement of the spring could be explained by adding the displacements of the individual pulses (the principle of superposition). For example, Fig. 16–9 shows the successive shapes of a spring as two opposite pulses pass through each other. The point P halfway between the two pulses remains undisturbed because adding the displacements of the individual pulses at this point produces a cancellation at every instant during the crossing. This behavior of two opposite pulses is somewhat difficult to see because you have to look at the pulses exactly at the moment they cross. However, if we use periodic waves, we can observe the cancellation more easily.

When a periodic wave travels along a spring which is tied down at one end, every individual pulse is reflected upside down. Now we know that a reflected pulse superposes with every oncoming pulse it meets. Thus, suppose we first consider only two of the pulses, a and b, a wave length λ apart as they travel toward the reflecting end (Fig. 18–1). Some time after the first pulse

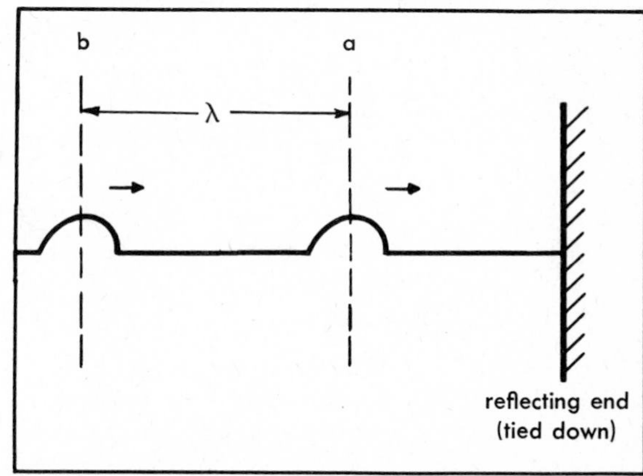

18–1. Two pulses travel toward the reflecting end of a spring.

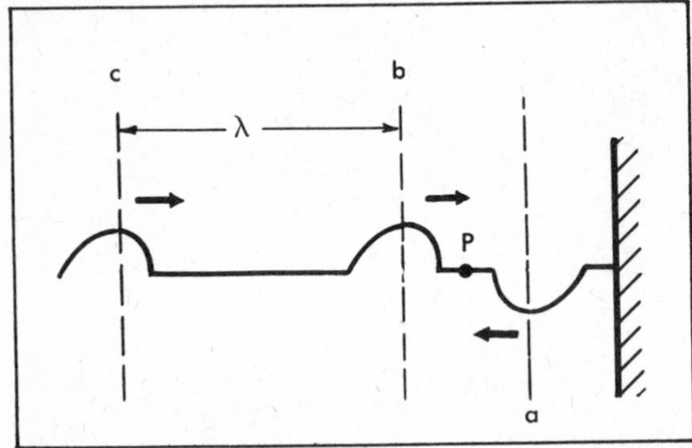

18–2. The spring after one of the pulses has been reflected. The reflected pulse *a* is upside down and traveling toward the incident pulse *b*. A third pulse *c* is approaching at a distance λ behind *b*.

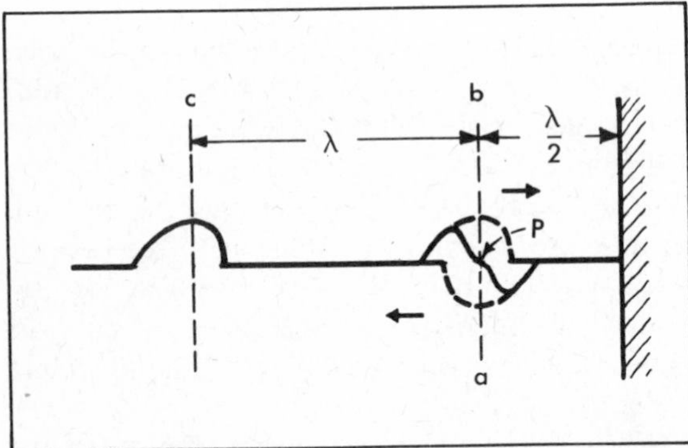

18–3. The pulses *a* and *b* of Figs. 18–1 and 18–2 meeting at point *P*.

is reflected it will meet the second pulse and there will be a cancellation at the midpoint *P* between them (Fig. 18–2). In Fig. 18–3 the pulses are shown as they meet. Because they were originally a distance λ apart we can see that the point *P* is a distance λ/2 from the reflecting end. The next pulse *c*, which reaches *P* later, will be superposed with the reflected pulse *b* so that the same cancellation occurs again. Because the wave is periodic this will happen every time a pulse passes *P*, and, although the motion of the spring as a whole is complicated, the point *P* always remains at rest. We call such a point a *node*. There are other nodes spaced λ/2 apart as you can see by working out where the next few must be (for example, the cancellation of *a* and *c*).

It is clear that we could have obtained nodes just as easily by sending appropriate periodic waves from opposite ends of a long spring. The use of the fixed end as a means of producing a

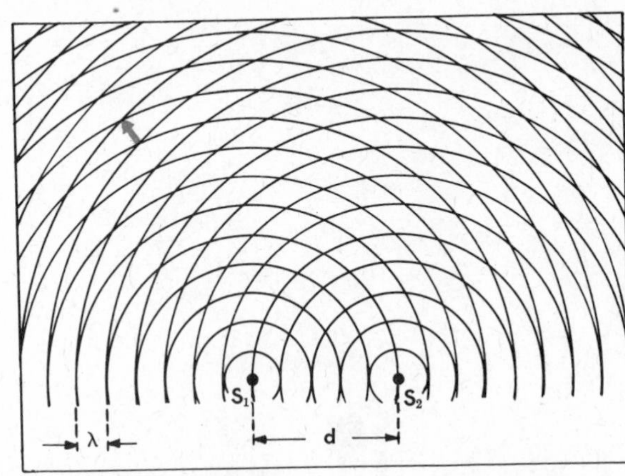

18–4. The circles represent the crests of waves from two sources S_1 and S_2 a distance *d* apart. The sources are periodic and are in phase. The green arrow points out a region we will examine more closely later (Fig. 18–7).

wave moving in the opposite direction is only a convenience.

The phenomenon we have just described — that is, the superposition of two periodic waves to produce a series of nodes, is called *interference*. Rather than try to find the corresponding effect in light at once, we shall first go on to make a systematic study of interference between water waves in a ripple tank. Then we shall look for interference in light.

18–2. Interference from Two Point Sources

For the purpose of studying interference in the ripple tank, we shall use point sources generating circular waves. Imagine two point sources side by side a distance *d* apart, each one generating pulses at the same frequency. Furthermore let them move so they dip into the water together — that is, so each source produces a crest at the same instant. When this is the case, we say that the sources are *in phase*. We can represent the waves the sources produce by drawing two sets of concentric circles side by side with centers a distance *d* apart (Fig. 18–4). The circles represent the crests of the waves expanding from each source. Since the sources are periodic, the crests are always the same distance apart — one wave length. The distance between crests is the same in both sets of circles because the wave lengths are the same for both sources. The radii of corresponding circular crests in each set are equal because the generators are in phase.

What will happen when the waves from the two

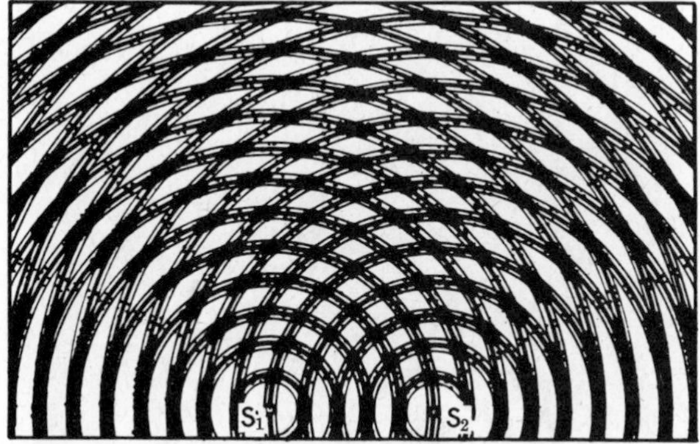

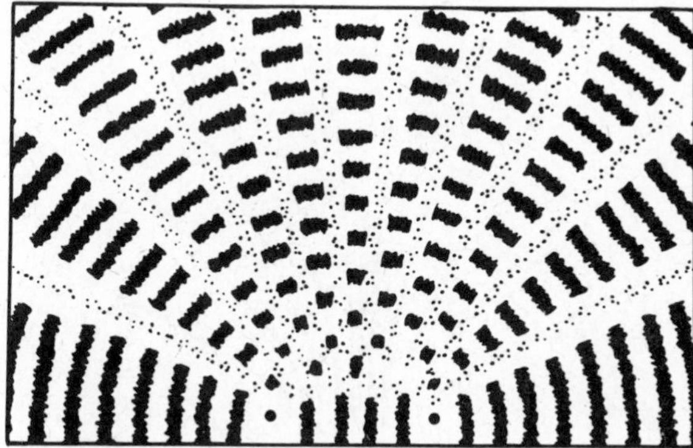

18–5. The pattern we predict by applying the principle of superposition to the waves from the two point sources shown in Fig. 18–4. Darkened areas show where crest meets crest; dotted areas represent undisturbed water, where crest meets trough; places where troughs meet are left blank. In (b) we have omitted the construction lines used in drawing (a).

sources overlap? Let us try to predict the resulting wave pattern by using the principle of superposition. Where two crests cross each other, a "double crest" will be formed. Such "double crests" will produce bright regions on the screen of a ripple tank. In Fig. 18–5 (a) we have emphasized these regions by blackening them. Where a crest from one source meets a trough from the other, the water will be practically undisturbed and there will be a gray image on the screen. In these regions we have used some dots in Fig. 18–5 (a) to give a gray appearance. Finally, where two troughs meet, a very dark image will be formed on the screen. In Fig. 18–5 (a) we have left these regions blank. In Fig. 18–5 (b) we have suppressed the construction lines, leaving only the pattern we expect to see. Therefore, the superposition of the waves in Fig. 18–4 should result in the pattern in Fig. 18–5 (b). An actual photograph of the waves from two point sources shows that this prediction is correct (Fig. 18–6).

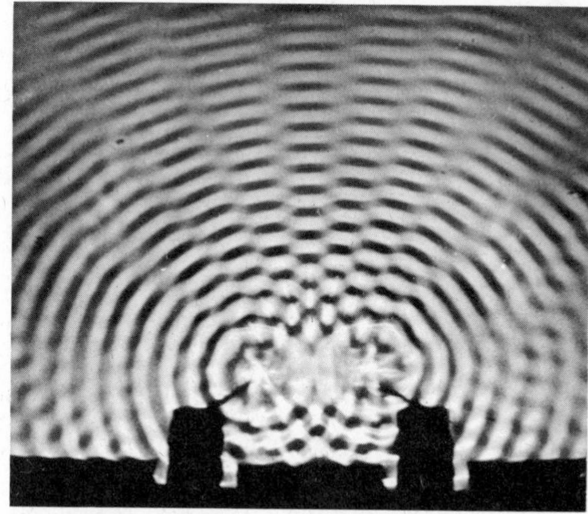

18–6. A photograph of the interference pattern from two point sources in phase. Notice the nodal lines radiating outward.

We have just constructed an interference pattern by superposing the waves from two sources. We have found that at one moment this predicted pattern agrees with what we see. Now let us consider how the waves in the pattern move. We shall start by finding out how one "double wave crest" moves. In Fig. 18–7 we show the two wave crests that cross to form the double crest at the tail of the arrow in Fig. 18–4. The green circles in Fig. 18–7 represent the same two crests a short time later. Each crest has expanded away from its source; and as a result the double crest moves away from the region of the sources in the direction of the arrow. If we wait for one whole period T, the wave crest from each source will have moved out a whole wave length λ and the double crest will have moved from the tail to

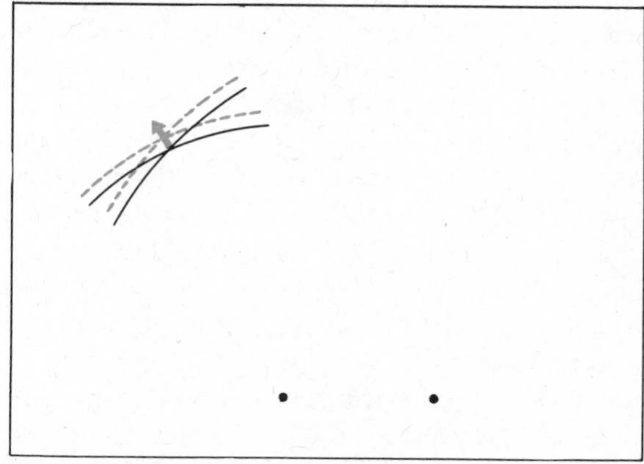

18–7. The black lines show the double crests at the tail of the green arrow in Fig. 18–4. The green circles show two crests a short time later. The two dots represent the sources.

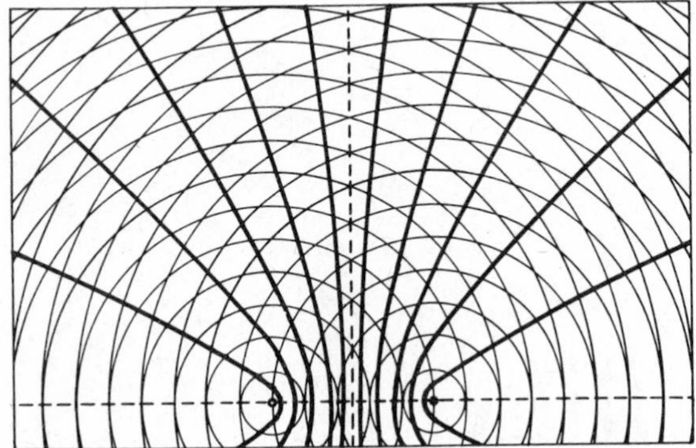

18–8. The nodal lines from two sources. Between the nodal lines are moving double crests and moving double troughs.

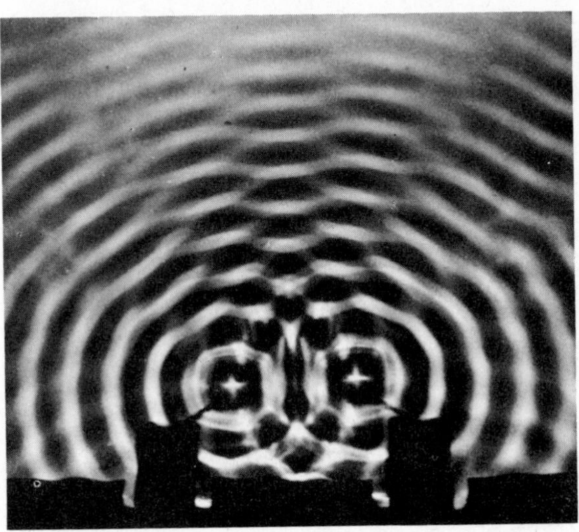

18–9. A two-source interference pattern like that in Fig. 18–6, but with a longer wave length.

the head of the arrow in Fig. 18–4. The double crests and double troughs all over the ripple tank have the same kind of outward motion. Consequently, each row of double crests and double troughs moves away from the source region while new double crests and troughs are formed near the sources. Each row is a moving train of waves.

What happens in the gray regions, the regions between the moving wave trains? Here crests lie on troughs at all times and the water surface is not wavy. To see why, let us examine the line between two wave trains at any given instant. In Fig. 18–5 (a) pick one of the dotted gray regions. Start at the crest of a wave from S_1. Because it lies on a trough from S_2, there is no net displacement of the water surface. It is practically undisturbed. Now let us move out from the sources along the gray line. As we do, we descend from the crest of the wave from S_1 and we go up from the trough of the wave from S_2. As long as the waves are nearly symmetrical — so that a trough looks like an inverted crest — the addition of the displacements of the two waves continues to give zero total displacement. As we look farther out, we come to a trough from S_1 at the same place that we reach a crest from S_2. The upward and downward displacements still cancel; and we can see that by continuing out along the line through the intersections of crests and troughs, we shall find practically undisturbed water. Looking at Fig. 18–6 (or, even better, at the surface of a ripple tank), we can see these lines of undisturbed water extending outward from the region of the sources and separating the moving wave trains of reinforced crests and troughs. By analogy with the nodes on a spring, we call these lines of zero disturbance nodal lines. In Fig. 18–8 we have drawn them as thick black lines.

With different wave length or different separation of the sources, the interference pattern changes in detail; but the general structure of such patterns is the same. Another pattern with a longer wave length is shown in Fig. 18–9. Again you can see the nodal lines, and the waves moving out between them. The waves are slightly blurred because the photograph was exposed $\frac{1}{50}$ of a second, and in that time the waves moved an appreciable fraction of a wave length.

Although we considered water waves in our investigation, we really have not used any special property of water waves to obtain our result. We used only the principle of superposition, which is common to all waves. The results of this entire chapter apply equally well to all waves.

18–3. The Shape of Nodal Lines

If we examine the pictures (Figs. 18–6 and 18–9) for a while we notice that, although the nodal lines are slightly curved near the sources, they soon become quite straight. Another striking fact is that the number of nodal lines decreases as the wave length increases.

In order to facilitate further discussion of these patterns, let us number the nodal lines so we will

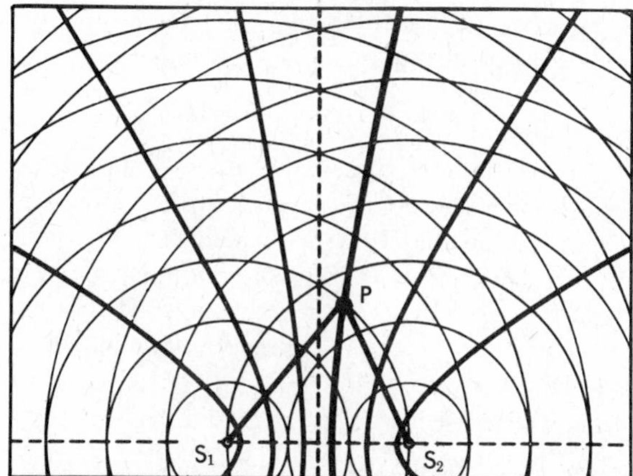

18–10. The first nodal line. For any point P on the line the difference in path length from P to S_1 and P to S_2 is half a wave length.

be able to refer to them conveniently. To do this we re-examine Fig. 18–8 and notice that the pattern is symmetrical — that is, it looks exactly the same to the left of the central line as it does to the right. This should not be too surprising as our sources also look exactly the same left and right. For this reason we need only count half the nodal lines, say those to the right. Thus we call the first one to the right of the central (dotted) line the first nodal line. The next one is called the second nodal line, and so on. When we want to talk about one of the nodal lines and we don't care which particular one it is, we usually say the nth nodal line, where n is an integer (1st, 2nd, 3rd, etc.).

Let us call a point on the first nodal line P, and connect it to the two sources by drawing the lines PS_1 and PS_2 (Fig. 18–10). We call these lines the path lengths from P to S_1 and from P to S_2. By counting the crests on the diagram it is easy to see that, for our particular point, $PS_1 = 3\lambda$ and $PS_2 = 2\frac{1}{2}\lambda$, so that the difference in path lengths is

$$PS_1 - PS_2 = \tfrac{1}{2}\lambda.$$

If we had taken any other point on the first nodal line, we would have found the same difference, $\frac{1}{2}\lambda$, between the path lengths. Indeed, we may say that the first nodal line is composed of those points P for which the difference in the path lengths is $\frac{1}{2}\lambda$, so that one crest and one trough always arrive there at the same time.

The second nodal line can be characterized in

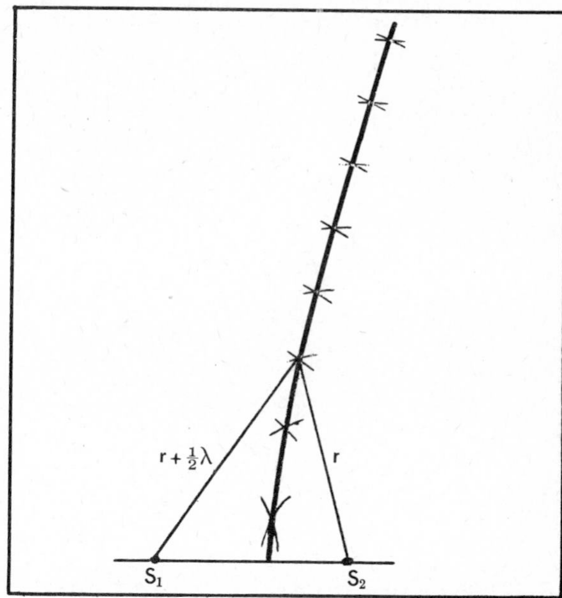

18–11. Construction of a nodal line. Arcs are swung around the two sources with radii r and $r + (n - \frac{1}{2})\lambda$ respectively. The nodal curve runs through the intersections. The curve shown is the first nodal line: $n = 1$.

a similar way. In this case, if P is any point on the second nodal line, the difference in path length is

$$PS_1 - PS_2 = \tfrac{3}{2}\lambda,$$

which can also be seen from Fig. 18–10. Continuing this procedure we arrive at an equation describing the nth nodal line:

$$PS_1 - PS_2 = (n - \tfrac{1}{2})\lambda.$$

According to this equation we can construct the nodal lines by finding the intersections of circles with radius r centered at S_2 with circles of radii $r + (n - \frac{1}{2})\lambda$ centered at S_1 (Fig. 18–11).

18–4. Wave Lengths, Source Separation, and Angles

In a ripple tank we can measure the path lengths to any point on a nodal line; and using

$$PS_1 - PS_2 = (n - \tfrac{1}{2})\lambda,$$

we can find the wave length λ. We do not need to stop the waves to make such a measurement. The nodal lines stand still while we take our time measuring PS_1 and PS_2.

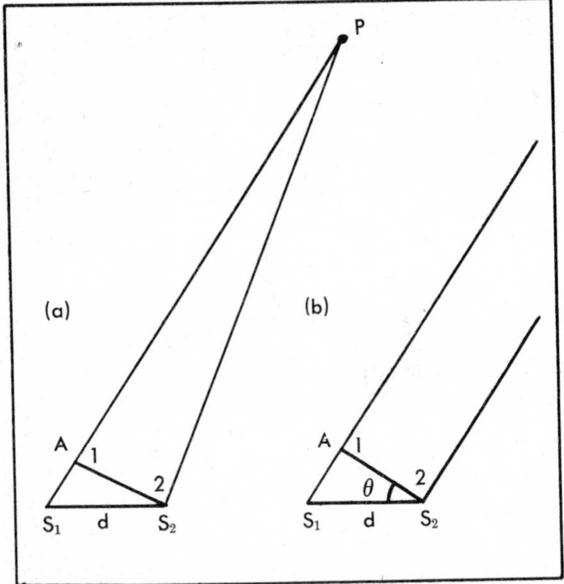

18–12. (a) The path difference AS_1 can be determined in terms of the source separation d and an angle. (b) When P is far from the sources, $AS_1 = d \sin \theta$.

It is often convenient or even necessary to make our measurements at a point P which is far away from S_1 and S_2. But if we then measure the two large lengths PS_1 and PS_2 directly and subtract to find the small difference between them, we shall have a hard time getting sufficient accuracy. We may subtract away most of our measurement, leaving only our errors (see Section 3–7). We therefore look for a more accurate way to measure the path difference.

For any point P far away from the sources, the difference in the path lengths $PS_1 - PS_2$ depends on the angle between PS_1 and d. Consider Fig. 18–12 (a), which shows the two sources S_1 and S_2, and a point P very far away compared to the source separation d. The distance PA is made the same as PS_2 so that the angles 1 and 2 are equal and $PS_1 - PS_2 = AS_1$. The farther away P is, the more nearly parallel the lines PS_1 and PS_2 become. We shall consider only points P that are far enough from S_1 and S_2 so that for all practical purposes PS_1 and PS_2 are parallel. Then we can draw Fig. 18–12 (b). Because angles 1 and 2 have become right angles, the triangle AS_1S_2 is a right triangle. Therefore from the definition of the sine of an angle (Section 13–3)

$$\frac{AS_1}{d} = \sin \theta,$$

where θ is shown in the figure. Recalling that AS_1 is the path difference, we then find

$$PS_1 - PS_2 = d \sin \theta.$$

This equation expresses the path difference in terms of source separation and angle. The angle θ tells us the direction of P with respect to the sources. When $\theta = 90°$, for example, P is to the right on the line passing through the sources; when $\theta = 0$, P is in the direction of the top of Fig. 18–12 (b).

Now when P is on the nth nodal line

$$PS_1 - PS_2 = (n - \tfrac{1}{2})\lambda.$$

Consequently,

$$(n - \tfrac{1}{2})\lambda = d \sin \theta_n$$

or

$$\sin \theta_n = (n - \tfrac{1}{2})\lambda/d$$

as long as P is far away from S_1 and S_2. Incidentally, this result tells us that far from the sources the direction of a nodal line does not change. It is given by the angle θ_n. Far from the sources, therefore, the nodal lines must be straight as we noticed in the last section. Actually, if these straight portions of the nodal lines are extended back toward the sources, they pass through the midpoint of the line between the sources.

In the last section we also noticed that the number of nodal lines increases as the wave length decreases. We can relate this observation to our equation for the direction of the nodal lines far from the sources. Sin θ_n cannot be greater than 1; therefore $(n - \frac{1}{2})\lambda/d$ cannot be greater than 1. The largest value of n which satisfies this condition is the number of nodal lines on each side of the center line. This number depends only on λ/d, and increases as λ decreases. We can make an approximate measurement of the wave length, merely by counting the number of nodal lines.

To make an accurate determination of λ, we can find the direction of the nth nodal line, that is, the angle θ_n, and calculate λ from the equation $\sin \theta_n \doteq (n - \frac{1}{2})\lambda/d$. In the ripple tank, θ_n is easily found; this is not always the case with other waves. Therefore we shall look for a way to determine $\sin \theta_n$ directly without first measuring the angle θ_n itself. Let the point P in Fig. 18–13 be on the nth nodal line far away from the two sources S_1 and S_2, so that the lines CP and S_1P are practically parallel to each other and both are perpendicular to AS_2. Since the center line is perpendicular to d, we see that $\theta_n' = \theta_n$. But, from the figure, $\sin \theta_n' = x_n/L$ where L is the distance PC and x_n is the distance from P to the center line. Therefore we have

$$(n - \tfrac{1}{2})\lambda/d = \sin \theta = \sin \theta' = x/L$$

or

$$\lambda = \frac{d(x/L)}{n - \frac{1}{2}},$$

where we have omitted the subscript $_n$ on θ and x, but you must remember that θ and x refer to the nth nodal line.

An example will show how simple the procedure is. Suppose we are working with sources 10 cm apart. We may pick a point P on the third nodal line, measure its distance L from the midpoint of d, and measure the distance x from the center line. Suppose we find that L is 80 cm long and x is 48 cm. x/L is therefore 0.6. We can now test the accuracy of our ratio by measuring other L's and the corresponding x's. If P is far enough away, x/L remains 0.6.

Now because we are working with the third nodal line we must use $n - \frac{1}{2} = 5/2$ and with $d = 10$ cm we find

$$\lambda = \frac{d(x/L)}{n - \frac{1}{2}} = \frac{10(0.6)}{\frac{5}{2}} = 2.4 \text{ cm}.$$

Using the various nodal lines we can get several evaluations of λ. Agreement between the values obtained gives us a check on our reasoning and on our measurements.

18–5. Phase

Two generators with the same period are *in phase* when they always dip into the water together, producing crests at the same instant. However, it is not necessary for two sources with the same period to be in phase. For example, one of the sources may always dip into the water somewhat later than the other, after a time delay t. Since the natural time unit for a particular periodic motion is its period T, it is convenient to measure the time delay between the dips of S_1 and S_2 in fractions p of the period. Thus we use $p = t/T$ to measure the delay. For example, if each source dips every $\frac{1}{6}$ second and S_2 always dips $\frac{1}{18}$ second after S_1, then the fraction p is one-third.

When two sources of the same frequency do not dip together we say that they are *out of phase.*

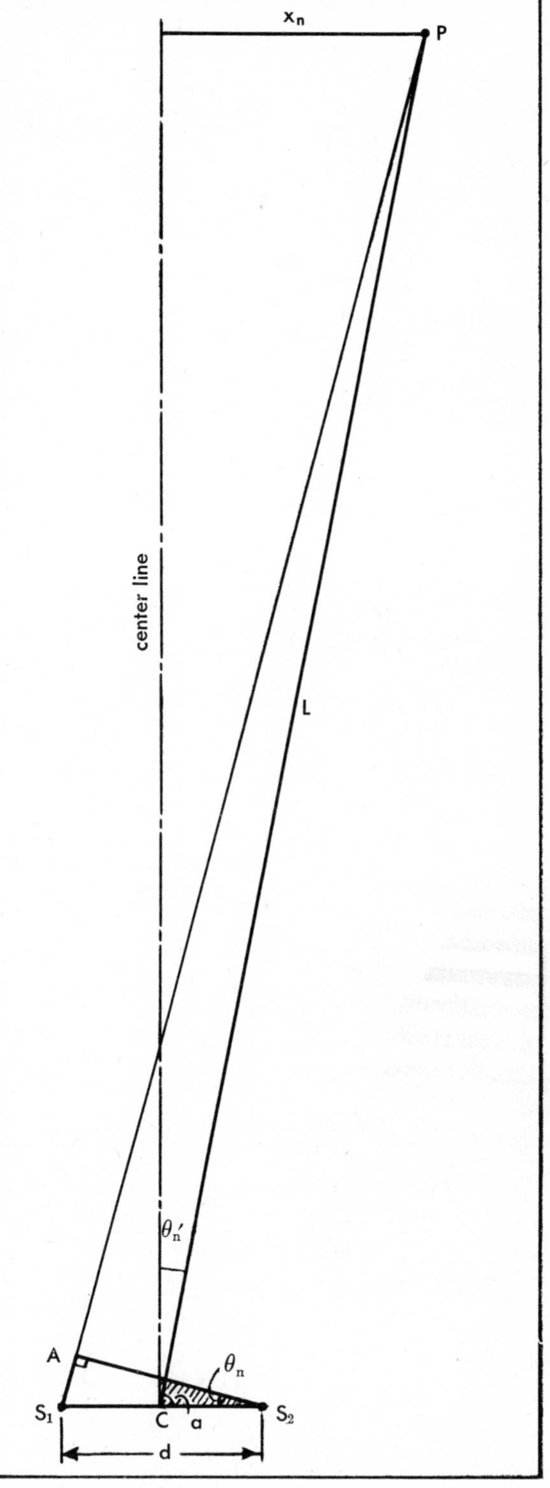

18–13. When P is far from the sources, $\theta_n + a = 90°$. Since $\theta_n' + a = 90°$, $\theta_n = \theta_n'$. Also, $\sin \theta_n' = x_n/L$, and so $\sin \theta_n = x_n/L$.

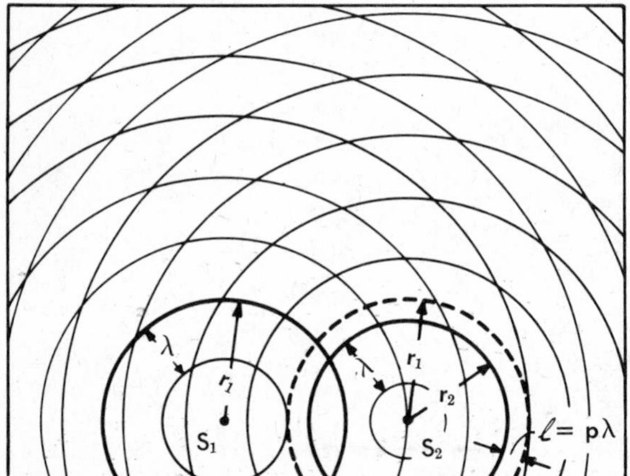

18–14. The waves from two point sources out of phase. S_2 has a phase delay p with respect to S_1. The difference in the radii to corresponding crests is the distance $l = r_1 - r_2 = p\lambda$.

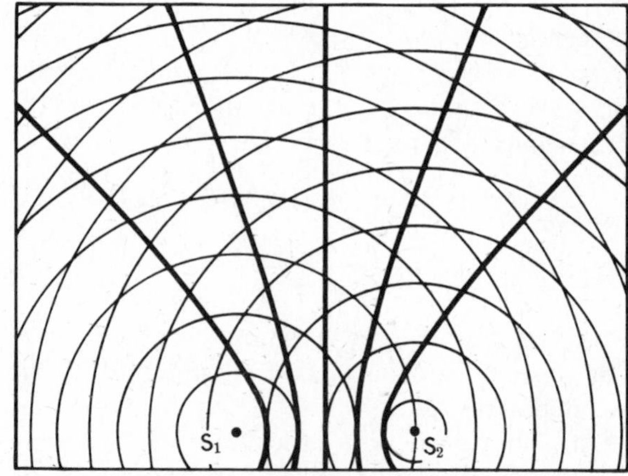

18–15. The pattern of nodal lines when there is a phase delay $p = \frac{1}{2}$.

The fraction p describes the *phase* delay of one source with respect to the other. There are no delays which are longer than the period T because we always measure the delay of the second source from the most recent dip of the first source, and its dips come a time interval T apart. Consequently there are no phase delays greater than 1. p is always between 0 and 1.

Let us now use two point generators of waves operating so that S_2 has a phase delay of p with respect to S_1. What will the interference pattern look like? We can again try to discover this graphically by drawing two sets of concentric circles representing the wave crests from each source. As in Fig. 18–4, the crests in each set are always one wave length λ apart; however, this time the sources are not in phase, and the radii r_1 and r_2 of corresponding crests from the two sources are not equal (Fig. 18–14). The radii of the delayed crests from S_2 are smaller than those of the corresponding crests from S_1 by a distance l equal to the fraction p of a wave length

$$l = p\lambda.$$

For example, if S_2 is delayed one-third of a period, the circles centered on S_2 are smaller than those around S_1 by one-third of a wave length.

As an example let us see what happens when one of the sources is half a period behind the other. Then the distance l is half a wave length, and the phase delay p is $\frac{1}{2}$. In Fig. 18–15 we have drawn the wave crests for such a situation and constructed the nodal lines by joining the points where a crest crosses a trough. We see that the pattern of nodal lines is different from the pattern for two sources in phase. For the same ratio λ/d the nodal lines are at the places where the reinforced crests used to be, and the reinforced crests are now where the nodal lines used to be. Compare Fig. 18–15 with Fig. 18–10. In each of these figures $\lambda = \frac{1}{3}d$, but in Fig. 18–10 the sources dip in phase while in Fig. 18–15 there is a phase delay $p = \frac{1}{2}$.

The photograph in Fig. 18–16 was taken with a phase delay $p = \frac{1}{2}$ between the sources. We can see, for instance, that there is now a nodal line along the center where in Fig. 18–6 (and Fig. 18–9) there are reinforced crests.

We have given examples of the interference pattern for two particular choices of the phase, $p = 0$ and $p = \frac{1}{2}$. Actually we could have chosen any phase from 0 to 1, and in each case the interference pattern would have been different. The series of pictures in Fig. 18–17 shows the interference patterns in the ripple tank for different phases of S_2. Changing the phase causes the whole pattern of nodal lines to shift in a definite direction. As the phase delay of S_2 increases, the radii of the crests from S_2 fall behind those from S_1 by an increasing distance $l = p\lambda$. Consequently the nodal lines bend more sharply around S_2, away from the center line. This is just what we see in the photographs. By including the distance $l = p\lambda$ in our computation of the difference in path lengths from any point on a nodal line to the sources S_1 and S_2, we can develop

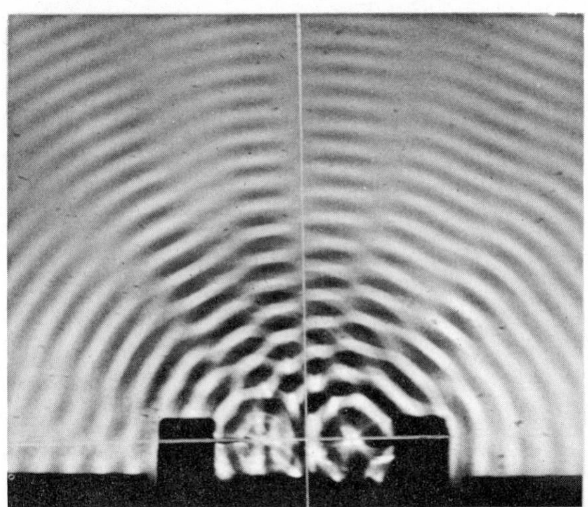

18–16. A photograph of the ripple-tank screen when two sources are operating with a phase $p = \frac{1}{2}$.

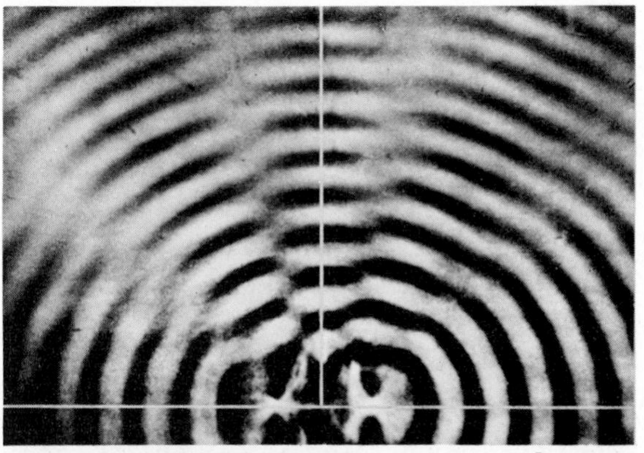

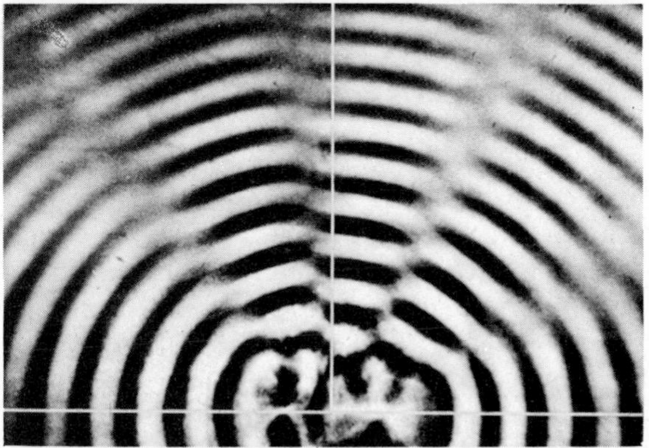

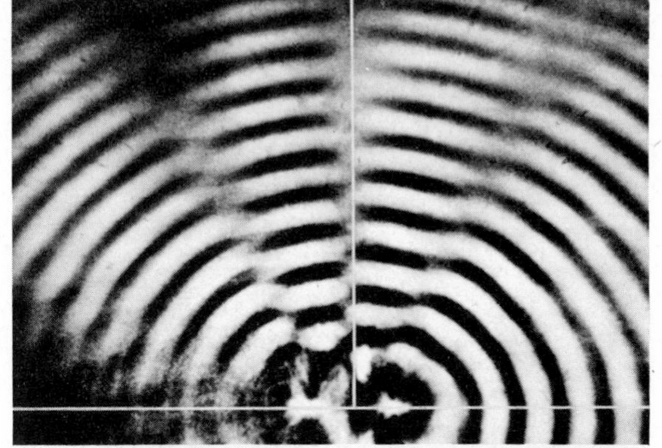

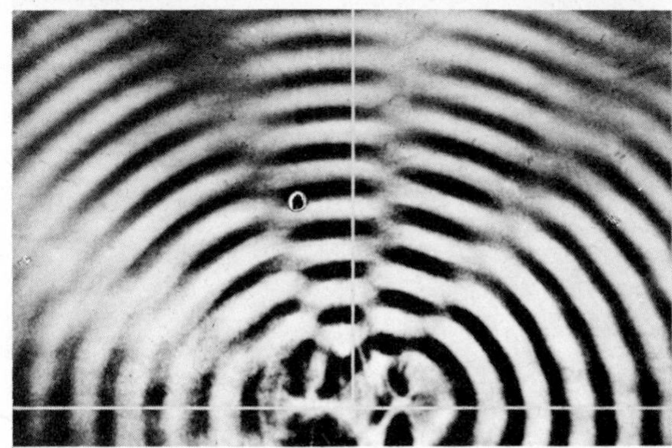

a general formula describing the nodal lines with any phase delay p. It is

$$PS_1 - PS_2 = (p + n - \tfrac{1}{2})\lambda,$$

and therefore (for the reasons given in Section 18–4) the angles at which the straight portions of the nodal lines are found are given by

$$\sin \theta_n = (p + n - \tfrac{1}{2})\lambda/d.$$

These equations can be understood by noticing that the nodal lines are determined by the intersections of arcs of radius $r + (n - \frac{1}{2})\lambda$ around S_1 with arcs of radius $r - p\lambda$ around S_2. At such points a crest from one source always arrives at the same time as a trough from the other. (See the end of Section 18–3.)

As the phase delay of S_2 changes, the wave trains of reinforced crests and troughs curl in the same way as the nodal lines. As the phase of S_2 is increased, any particular wave train bends away from S_1 and progressively curls around S_2. As an example, in Fig. 18–18 we have drawn the wave crests from two sources three wave lengths apart. The black circles from S_2 indicate waves generated when S_2 dips in phase with S_1. The dashed circles around S_2 indicate waves generated with a phase delay. Notice that the double crests bend around S_2 as the phase delay is intro-

18–17. The interference from two point sources with different phase delays p of the right-hand source. In the top picture the sources are in phase; $p = 0$. In the subsequent pictures p increases, passing through $p = \frac{1}{2}$ in the third photograph.

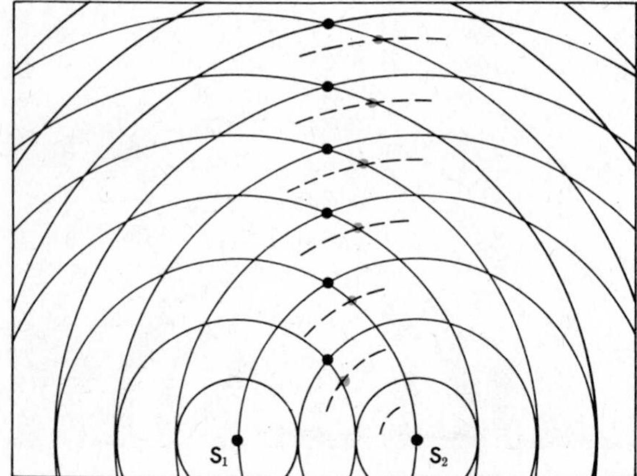

18–18. The row of black dots represents a line of double crests formed when S_1 and S_2 are in phase. The green dots represent a line of double crests which result when S_2 has a phase delay. The delayed waves from S_2 are represented by dashed circles.

duced. In particular, with no phase delay there is a wave train along the center line perpendicular to the line through the sources. When S_2 is delayed, this wave train moves off to the right around S_2. All the other wave trains have a similar shift.

18–6. Summary and Conclusion

The interference pattern from two point sources in the ripple tank is characterized by a set of lines where the water surface remains undisturbed — the nodal lines. When the sources are in phase these nodal lines are distributed symmetrically about the center line, the perpendicular bisector of the line S_1S_2 joining the sources. In the immediate neighborhood of the sources the nodal lines are curved, but not very far away from the sources they become nearly straight. If the straight portions are extended back toward the sources, they pass through the center point between the sources. The number of nodal lines and the angle between any of these lines and S_1S_2 is determined by λ/d, the ratio of wave length to source separation. This means that we can determine either d or λ if we know the other.

Even for the same wave length and source spacing, different interference patterns are obtained for different phase delays p between the two sources. When the sources are in phase there is an even number of nodal lines symmetrically arranged about the center line. When the source S_2 produces crests later than S_1 with a time delay $t = pT$, crests from S_2 are all at smaller radii than the corresponding crests from S_1. The corresponding radii differ by the distance $l = p\lambda$. As a result the points where crests from S_2 cross troughs from S_1 are closer to S_2. This means that the nodal lines are bent away from S_1 and swing in closer to S_2; and the pattern becomes asymmetrical. Only for $p = \frac{1}{2}$ do we again get a symmetrical pattern. Then one nodal line covers the center line and there is an odd number of nodal lines.

When the distance between the sources is fixed and we generate waves of one particular wave length, the interference pattern depends on the phase delay between the sources. Consequently, to maintain a fixed interference pattern, the phase delay must also remain constant. For two sources which run continuously at the same frequency, the phase delay will remain constant. But if each of the two sources is turned on and off in an irregular fashion, the phase delay will vary and with it the interference pattern. This shifting of the interference pattern will be of great importance in the next chapter, where we shall discuss the interference of light waves.

FURTHER READING

HUYGENS, CHRISTIAN, *Moments of Discovery*. Edited by G. Schwartz and P. Bishop, Basic Books, 1958.

FOR HOME, DESK, AND LAB

1. Summarize the evidence for the wave nature of light.

2. We showed in the text (Figs. 18–1, 18–2, and 18–3) that when pulses are incident periodically on the fixed end of a spring, the point P, a distance $\lambda/2$ from the end, never moves and is therefore a node. Extend the argument to show that

   (a) the point P_1, a distance λ in front of the end, is a node,

   (b) the point P_2, a distance $3\lambda/2$ in front of the end, is a node.

3. Draw the sets of concentric circles and the interference pattern from two sources with $d = 5\lambda$ at the time:

   (a) when the generators have just produced crests,

   (b) when they have just produced the following troughs.

   How have the reinforced crests moved during the time interval between these drawings?

4. * Fold two pieces of ruled paper into long strips about 2 cm wide and hold them as in Fig. 18–19. Imagine that the lines are wave crests. Your fingers then represent the sources of the waves. Notice how the crests from both sources add together. Now by sliding the free ends sidewise, locate nodal lines and moving wave regions.

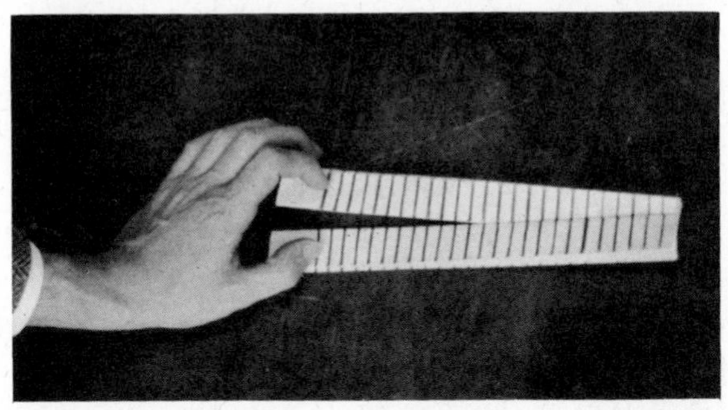

18–19. For Problem 4.

5. Draw the interference pattern for the case $d = 5\lambda$ on a piece of paper large enough so that you can see the nodal lines become straight at a great distance from the sources. Continue these straight lines back toward the sources and show that they all pass close to the midpoint of the line joining the sources.

6. Consider an interference pattern produced by two point generators. What happens at the positions of the nodal lines if we place a third source exactly like the others at the point midway between them?

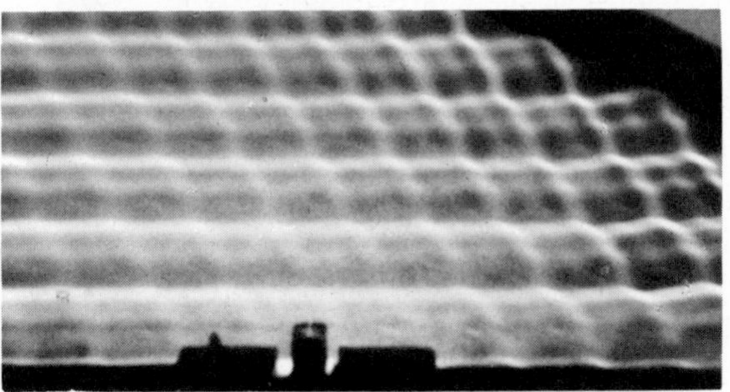

18–20. For Problem 7. Straight waves reflected from a straight barrier produce an interference pattern. The upper photograph is a short exposure, and the lower one is a time exposure and shows the stationary nodal lines. In the lower picture a shorter wave length was used.

7. Draw the crest lines of straight waves incident on a reflecting barrier at 45° and the crest lines of the reflected waves (Fig. 18–20). Indicate the incident direction of motion and the reflected direction. Shade the places where crests cross.

   (a) Which way do these shaded double crests move? Indicate with an arrow on your drawing.

   (b) Can you find nodal lines in the interference pattern?

8. You know the distances from a point on a nodal line to the two point sources in a ripple tank. What else do you have to know to calculate the wave length of the waves?

9. Construct the nodal lines for two point sources with $\lambda/d = \frac{1}{3}$ by the method of Fig. 18–11. Is this really a different method from that used in Problem 5?

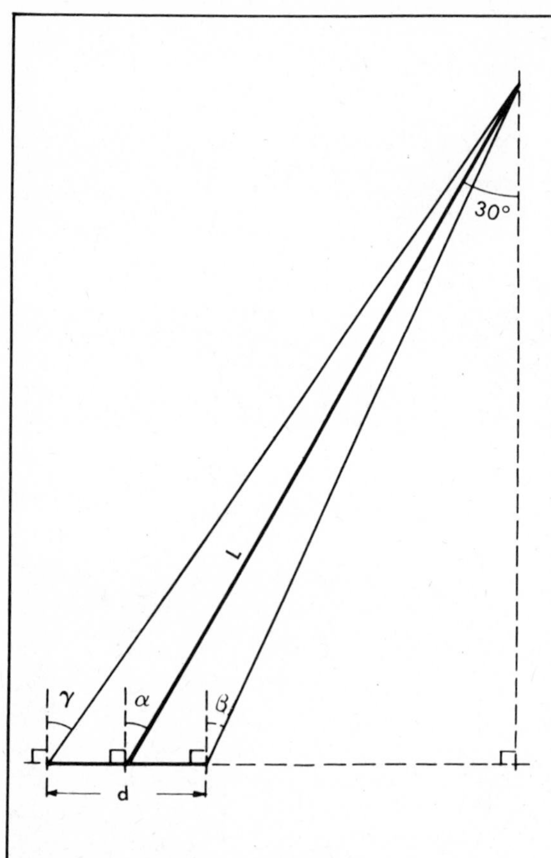

18–21. For Problem 14.

10. Two sources 6.0 cm apart operating in phase produce water waves with a wave length of 1.5 cm. Draw the nodal lines far from the sources. Determine the position of each line by means of intersecting arcs of circles drawn from the two sources. Measure the angle between the second nodal line and the center line of the pattern. Compare the sine of this angle with $(n - \frac{1}{2})\lambda/d$.

11. Suggest an interference experiment to prove that sound is a wave phenomenon. How could you use such an experiment to determine the wave length of sound?

12. (a) From Figs. 18–6 and 18–9 find the ratio λ/d by using the equation $\sin \theta_n = (n - \frac{1}{2})\lambda/d$.
(b) The dimensions of the photographs are one-fourth the actual size. By measuring d on the photographs estimate the actual value of λ.

13. Look up the definition of "hyperbola" and show that nodal lines are hyperbolas.

14. In Fig. 18–21, $L = 50$ cm, $d = 10$ cm, $\alpha = 30°$. What are γ and β? Find γ and β when $L = 500$ cm. Does this convince you that it is a good approximation to set $\gamma \approx \beta \approx \alpha$ when L is much greater than d?

15. One red and one blue car are going around a circular race track 5.0 km in circumference. They move at constant speed. Each car takes 2.5 minutes for each lap. The blue car always comes around 0.50 minutes behind the red.
(a) What is the phase delay p of the blue car with respect to the red car?
(b) What is the speed of each car?
(c) If the track were only 4.0 km long, would this change the answers to (a) and (b)?

16. Prove that for two sources with phase difference p, the first nodal line can be plotted from the equation: path length difference $= (p + \frac{1}{2})\lambda$.

17. Suppose we look at an interference pattern from a great distance L in front of the sources and find that the first nodal line is a distance x from the center line. If $x = .008L$ and $\lambda = .01d$, what is the phase of the sources? (See Fig. 18–13.) If $\lambda = .016\,d$, what is the phase?

18. Suppose that two point sources are generating waves with the same wave length λ. They are placed in the ripple tank a distance $d = 5\lambda$ apart.
(a) If the sources are in phase what angle θ does the straight part of the first nodal line make with the central line?
(b) If the sources have a phase $p = \frac{1}{2}$, what is θ?
(c) How many nodal lines will be produced?

19. A point source of periodic waves is placed a distance 3λ in front of a reflecting barrier. The superposition of the incident and reflected waves produces an interference pattern. (Fig. 18–22.) Describe this pattern. Examine such a pattern experimentally in a ripple tank. What is the phase of the image of the source?

18–22. For Problem 19.

20. Two sources in a ripple tank are operating at frequencies of 15 cycles per second and 16 cycles per second. Describe the resulting pattern of nodal lines.

LIGHT WAVES

CHAPTER 19

19–1. Can We See Interference in Light?

In the last chapter we studied the interference patterns produced in a ripple tank by two point generators. Now we wish to do similar experiments with light in order to see whether it has all the properties of periodic waves.

In designing an interference experiment with light we must keep in mind some important differences in the way we observe water waves and light waves. We can see water waves by standing at any place where light reflected from the waves reaches our eyes. We easily recognize a nodal line in the ripple tank because we can see where the water is undisturbed. Imagine now that we replace the two point generators by two light sources. How can we find out whether there are places where the light waves from the two sources cancel each other, places corresponding to the nodal lines in the ripple tank? In the ripple tank we could see the waves, but we cannot look across a light beam and see the light waves. Since we see only light that hits our eyes, we shall have to look directly along the path of the light, or place a reflecting object like a piece of paper in the path and observe the light that is reflected from it.

You can get an idea of the problem involved in detecting the interference of light if you imagine that you have to study the interference of water waves in a completely dark room, so that you cannot see the water. In this case you could locate the nodal lines by putting your finger in the water and moving it slowly across the tank. Most of the time you would feel the waves moving up and down; but when you came to a nodal line, you would not feel any motion. Similarly, when we observe light waves, we can either move our eyes or place a reflecting screen in the path of the light. Where light waves are reinforced on the screen, we can see light. Where a nodal line intersects the screen, we see a dark region.

At what angles do we expect to see these bright and dark bands? In the interference pattern generated by two point sources the angles between the nodal lines depend on λ/d. For a given wave length λ, these angles all increase as the source separation d decreases. We already know that the wave length of light waves is much less than a tenth of a millimeter; therefore to achieve an observable separation of the nodal lines at a reasonable distance from the sources we must place the sources close together. This means that they must be very small.

Also, to observe clear nodal lines we need sources which emit waves of a definite wave length or at most a small range of wave lengths; otherwise the nodal lines corresponding to one wave length will be buried in the crests resulting from the others. Imagine, for instance, that each

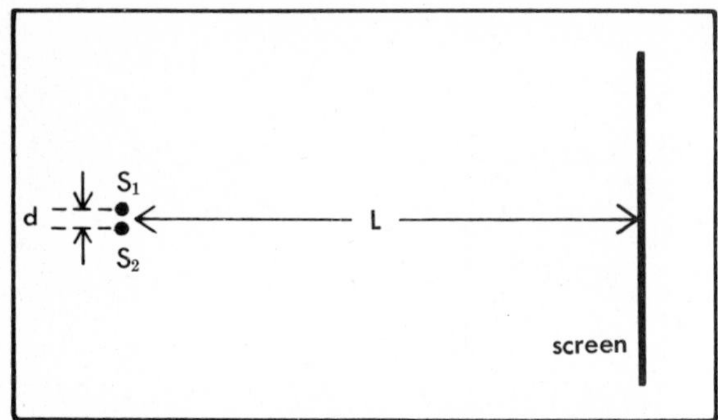

19–1. This apparatus resembles the setup for producing interference in a ripple tank. But with separate sources of light S_1 and S_2, we cannot find interference. No pattern appears on the screen.

source emits waves of the two different wave lengths which give the patterns shown in Figs. 18–6 and 18–9. The total pattern you would then observe would be a combination of the patterns shown in the two photographs, and there would be no places which remain undisturbed in the total pattern.

In the following discussion we shall assume that the light we observe contains a narrow-enough range of wave lengths so that the nodal lines, although they may become somewhat fuzzy, are not wiped out.

Imagine that we have two very small light sources placed a small distance d apart and that a screen is placed at a large distance L away from them, as shown in Fig. 19–1. This arrangement seems similar to that of a ripple tank in which there are two neighboring sources of circular waves. Consequently, from the results of Sections 18–4 and 18–5, we might expect to see a pattern of bright and dark bars on the screen. The bright bars should be the regions where light waves from the two sources reinforce, and the dark bars should occur where the waves cancel. Just as in the ripple tank, if the two sources emit waves in phase there should be a bright region (that is, a large wave) hitting the middle of the screen. On each side of this central bright region, there should be dark bars where the first nodal lines meet the screen; and as we go away from the center, bright and dark bars should alternate.

In this pattern of alternating bright and dark bars the nth dark bar on each side should be a distance $x_n = (n - \frac{1}{2})L\left(\frac{\lambda}{d}\right)$ from the center of the pattern. Consequently the spacing between neighboring dark bars should be $\Delta x = L\left(\frac{\lambda}{d}\right)$. Also, as in the ripple tank, if one source emits its waves with a phase delay p compared with the other, the pattern should shift off center. It should shift sidewise on the screen by the fraction p of the distance between the dark bars.

Can we observe these interference patterns? We already know that if light is a wave, its wave length must be much smaller than a tenth of a millimeter (Section 17–7). Consequently, $\left(\frac{\lambda}{d}\right)$ for any practical sources will be a very small fraction. However, we can choose a very large distance L to the screen; therefore, it should be possible to see the bright and dark bars.

In reality, if we use the arrangement we have just described we never see an interference pattern. No matter how we vary d or L, the screen is always uniformly illuminated.

Does our failure to observe an interference pattern prove that the wave model of light is a failure? Not necessarily. On the basis of the evidence we have discussed so far, the wave model may have failed, but another explanation is also possible. As we have just mentioned, the interference pattern produced by two sources depends on λ, on d, and also on the phase delay p. If the phase delay between the sources changes rapidly, the nodal lines and the dark bars on the screen must shift position rapidly. Our eyes cannot follow these rapid shifts; so the screen will appear uniformly bright. In other words, the interference patterns may possibly be produced, but we fail to see them because they move too rapidly.

We can show that the rapid shifting of phases is probably the explanation of our inability to observe interference in the last experiment. To do this we must modify the experiment so that the phase delay between the two light sources is forced to remain constant. When the phases of two sources are locked together in this way, we do observe the expected interference pattern.

19–2. Interference of Light Waves: Young's Experiment

In 1801 Thomas Young described some of the first interference experiments with light. He found a simple way to lock the phase of two light sources together. The trick is to use a single

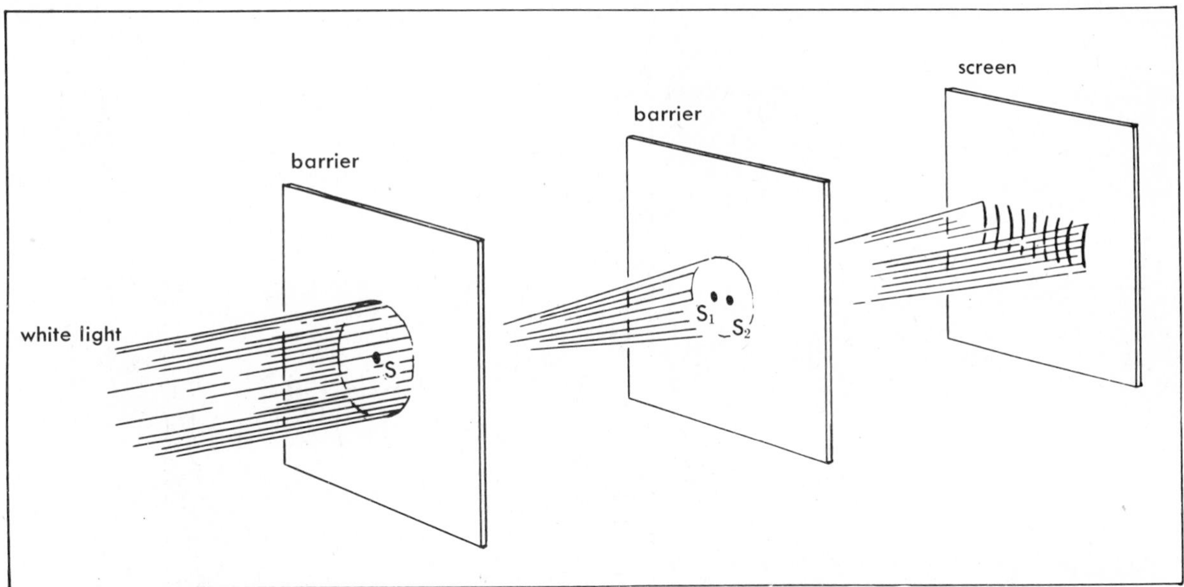

19–2. Young's experiment. The sunlight reaching the screen from the sources S_1 and S_2 all comes through the pinhole S. An interference pattern is visible on the screen.

light source and to split the light from it into two parts which will then interfere with each other. For instance, we can use an opaque screen containing two tiny pinholes. We place the screen in front of a point source of light so that the holes are equidistant from the source. The pinholes then strongly diffract the light and act as two point sources. Because light originating from the source at any moment passes through both pinholes at the same time, the waves from the two holes must always be in phase. With such an arrangement the interference pattern does not shift; it can be observed.

Young used sunlight passing through a distant pinhole (*S* in Fig. 19–2) to make the distant point source of light. He observed the resulting interference pattern on a white screen. Today we can easily do this experiment with an artificial source. Instead of using sunlight and a pinhole we use an incandescent bulb with a long, straight filament. This is called a *line source*. Such a source gives much more light than a pinhole. To create an interference pattern we allow the light to pass through two narrow slits in an opaque barrier (Fig. 19–3). The slits are parallel to the line source and very close together (about $\frac{1}{10}$ mm apart). If we then place a screen in front of the two slits in a darkened room, we see on the screen an interference pattern consisting of bright and dark bars of various colors. The bars are parallel to the slits, with a bright one in the center just as predicted by the wave model.

A permanent record of the interference pattern produced by this system can be made by placing a camera in front of the two slits to let the film record the result. Such a picture is reproduced in Fig. 19–4 opposite page 290.

19–3. The Phase of Light Sources: Atoms

We can couple two generators in a ripple tank with any desired phase delay, start them, and let them run as long as we wish. We do not have such control over light sources. That is shown by our inability to observe interference between light waves unless Young's method (or some similar method) is used to lock the phase of the two sources. We can also understand why the phase delay between two sources usually shifts rapidly. Consider two separate sources of light. The light from each source comes from a large number of individual atoms, each of which sends out a burst of light waves only during a very short time. When we turn on the sources we start the over-all process of the emission of light, but we do not control the individual atoms; they emit their light waves at random.

To see the significance of this situation for our interference experiments, let us consider a pair of atoms, one in each source. In all probability these atoms, considered as light sources, will be out of phase, say by a fraction p_1. The light

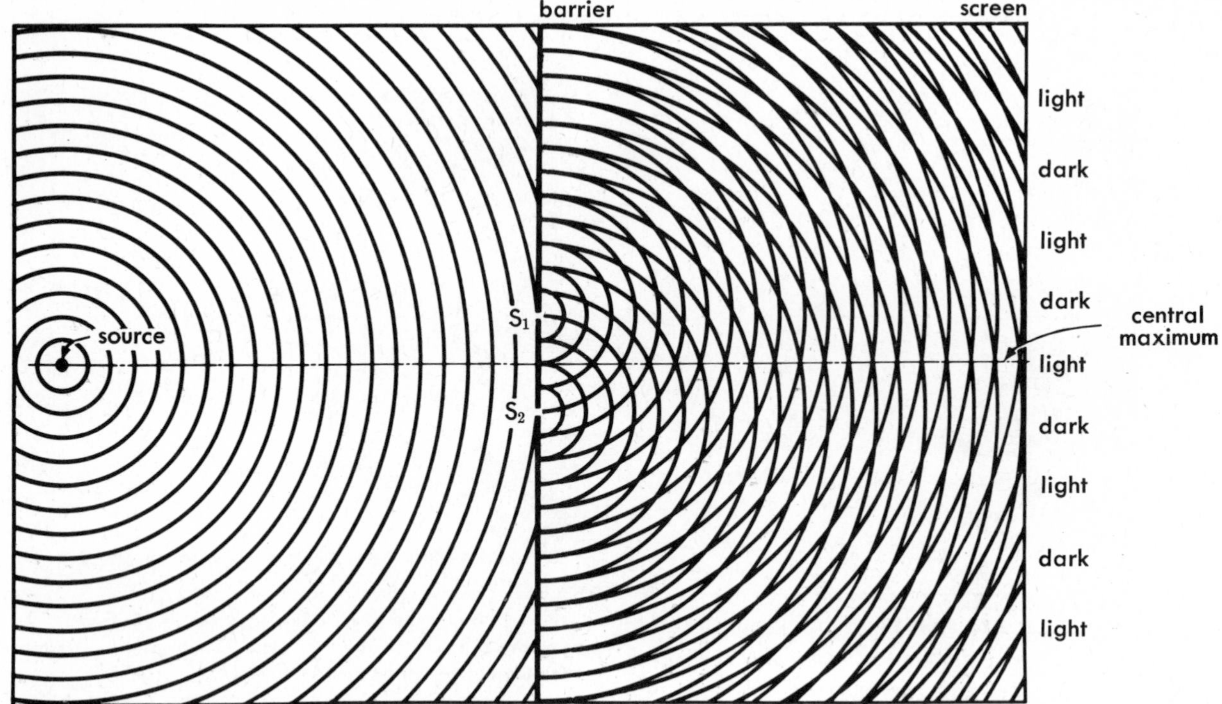

19–3. Waves from a line source of light passing through the slits S_1 and S_2 interfere to give alternate bright and dark bands on a screen.

waves from these two atoms will produce an interference pattern that depends on the value of p_1. A short time later these particular atoms will have stopped radiating, so we shift our attention to another pair of atoms which happen to be radiating at that moment. Since we have no way of influencing their behavior, these atoms will also be out of phase, but this time in all probability by a different fraction p_2. They will, therefore, produce a different interference pattern. Still later we consider a third pair of atoms, and so on. A typical time during which an atom emits light has been found to be about 10^{-9} sec. If we consider only one atom radiating at any moment in each source, we must change atoms every 10^{-9} sec to have the radiation continue. Then the interference pattern would also change in an irregular fashion every 10^{-9} sec. Since this is certainly much too fast for our eyes to follow, we would see no interference pattern at all.

In reality there are many atoms radiating at the same time. At each moment the interference pattern will be determined by the superposition of light waves from all the atoms. Now let's concentrate on all the atoms that are radiating in one source at a given moment. They will have finished radiating in about 10^{-9} sec. By that time a new set of atoms will be emitting the light from that source. Consequently, the phase of the source will have changed at random just as if we switched from one single atom to another. This shifting of phase therefore goes on in each source in about 10^{-9} sec and the interference pattern moves violently in this length of time. No wonder we cannot see any interference pattern.

When we use Young's method to obtain an interference pattern, the light wave emitted by each atom in a single source passes through two slits. These slits are so far away from the light source that the waves from any atom in the source travel the same distance to each slit (Fig. 19–5). As a result the light waves passing through the slits and going on beyond them always leave the slits in phase. The slits, therefore, act as sources of waves, and these sources are locked in phase. On the screen beyond them we see the interference pattern that we expect.

19–4. Color and the Wave Length of Light

The photograph in Fig. 19–4 (opposite page 290) was taken by letting white light from a small source pass through two closely spaced parallel slits and fall on a distant photographic film.

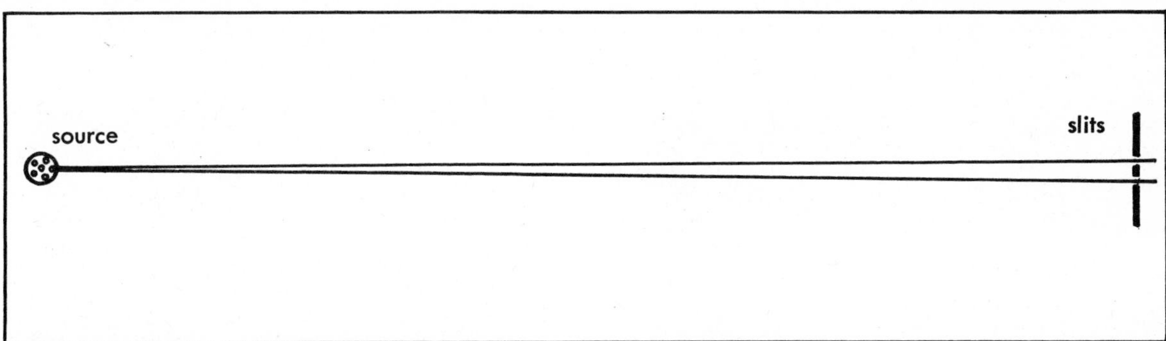

19–5. Because the source is far from the slits, the paths from any atoms in the source to the two slits are almost parallel and the distances almost equal.

Notice that the bright bar in the center (called the central maximum) is white, but the edges of the bright bars on the sides are colored.

We know that white light is a mixture of all colors, and the colored edges of the bars suggest that different colors are deflected at different angles in the interference pattern. The idea that different colors interfere at different angles implies that the wave length of light is associated with its color. We already had some reason to suspect an association of color and wave length when we studied dispersion. Now we can settle the question by further interference experiments. Let us, therefore, look at the interference pattern of light of one color. In Fig. 19–6 we see the interference pattern for red light alone. It is a series of alternating bright and dark bars. The spacing of the bars in the photograph depends on the separation d of the two slits, the distance L from the slits to the photographic plate, and the wave length of the light. Consequently, when we know the distances d and L, the separation of the bars in the photograph tells us the wave length of the light. As we saw in Section 19–1, the separation Δx of neighboring dark bars is given by

$$\Delta x = L\left(\frac{\lambda}{d}\right).$$

On re-arranging this equation we get the wave length as

$$\lambda = \left(\frac{d}{L}\right)\Delta x.$$

By measuring across a large number of bars we can get an accurate value of Δx to use in computing the wave length λ. For red light this turns out to be

$$\lambda_{\text{red}} = 6.5 \times 10^{-7}\ \text{m}.$$

We can go through the same procedure with light of any other color. If, for example, we use a blue-violet filter to select the light, we obtain a wave length

$$\lambda_{\text{b-v}} = 4.5 \times 10^{-7}\ \text{m}.$$

Other typical wave lengths, similarly measured, are given in Table 1. Our early conjecture that color is associated with wave length is borne out by experiment.

The colors associated with definite wave lengths are known as spectral colors. They are the same ones seen in the rainbow. Not all colors we see are of this kind. For example, purple is not a

Table 1. Wave Lengths of Light in Vacuum

A. *The wave lengths in angstrom units of the colors of the spectrum. The visible spectrum ranges from about* 4,000 *A in the deep violet to about* 7,500 *A in the deep red.* (1 *A* = 10^{-10} *m.*)

Violet	< 4,500 A
Blue	4,500–5,000
Green	5,000–5,700
Yellow	5,700–5,900
Orange	5,900–6,100
Red	> 6,100

B. *The wave length of some of the strongest visible lines in the spectra of a few common gases.*

Lithium	*Neon*	*Sodium*
6,103.6		5,890
6,707.8	5,400.6	5,896
Mercury	5,832.5	*Potassium*
4,358.4	5,852.5	4,044
5,460.7	6,402.2	4,047

19–6. Interference pattern produced with red light. This is shown in color in the upper part of Fig. 19–7, opposite page 290.

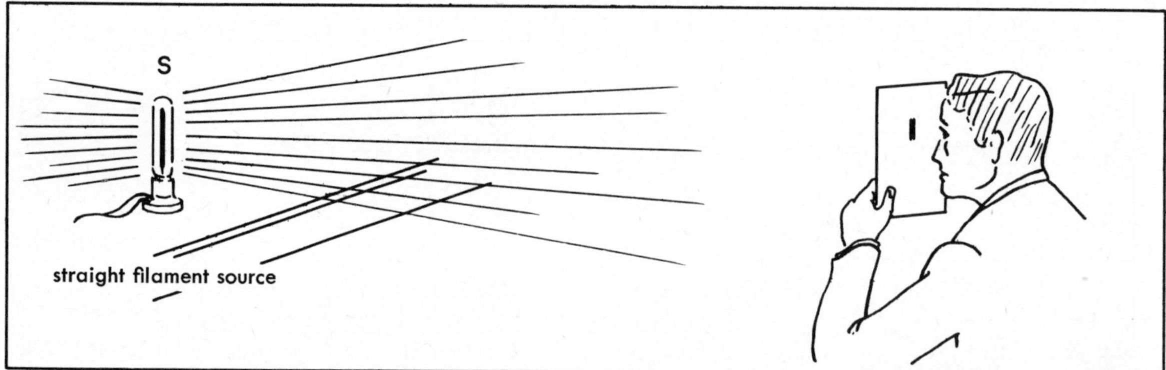

19–8. Observing a two-slit interference pattern.

spectral color. If we use an interference experiment to analyze the light that comes through a purple filter, we find that it is made of blue light and red light. Color vision is in fact very complicated. We sometimes see what appears to be a spectral color when only light of other wave lengths enters our eyes. The analysis of light by locating maxima and minima in an interference pattern makes it possible to characterize the light accurately in terms of wave length. Thus interference patterns extend our knowledge far beyond what we can learn with our unaided eyes.

The experiments we have been describing are ones that you can do yourself. Indeed, you can check up on our evaluation of the wave lengths of red and blue-violet light just by making some measurements of Fig. 19–7. This photograph was taken with a single source of white light and two slits. We made the different patterns that you see, one above the other, by placing a red-colored filter above a blue-violet-colored filter in the horizontal path of the light between the source and the photographic film. The ratio of the spacing of the bars in the two halves of the picture should correspond to the ratio of the wave lengths of red and of blue-violet light. By measuring the photograph we find that the separation of the bars in the red pattern is greater than that in the blue-violet by a factor of about 1.4. We can compare this to the ratio of the wave lengths measured independently. That ratio is

$$\frac{\lambda_{\text{red}}}{\lambda_{\text{b-v}}} = \frac{6.5 \times 10^{-7}\ \text{m}}{4.5 \times 10^{-7}\ \text{m}} \approx 1.4.$$

You can also carry out the complete set of experiments and measure the wave length of light. Use your eye in place of the camera, and make your own slits. You can cut them by pulling two razor blades side by side across a piece of glass covered with carbon. (See the Laboratory Guide.) The only other equipment you need is a strong narrow source of light, and some filters of colored plastic or glass. For the light source, a showcase lamp in which you can see the straight filament is a good choice (Fig. 19–8).

We have now succeeded in showing that the spectral colors of light are related directly to its wave length in vacuum. We have measured the wave length of light of one color by measuring the spacing of the bars in the interference pattern from two slits. We therefore have a primitive spectroscope (see Chapter 7) whose operation we understand.

A much more efficient spectroscope that sorts out the colors of light by interference can be made by using many equally spaced slits. With many slits, we get sharp, well-separated maxima for light of different colors. Such grating spectroscopes are commonly used to analyze light into its component wave lengths. For some purposes these spectroscopes are superior to those that use a prism to spread the light out into a spectrum.

19–5. Diffraction: An Interference Effect in Single Slits?

If you scratch one slit with a needle (instead of a razor blade) and look through it at a white light source, you will see something like the photograph in Fig. 19–9. There is a bright, broad central region surrounded by colored regions of lower intensity. In light of one color the pattern is similar. Fig. 19–10 shows what you find if you use a red light source — a bright center, then dark regions alternating with progressively less intense regions of light.

19–4. Interference pattern produced by white light passing through two narrow slits.

19–7. Interference patterns of red light and blue-violet light made with exactly the same set-up used to make the white light interference pattern above.

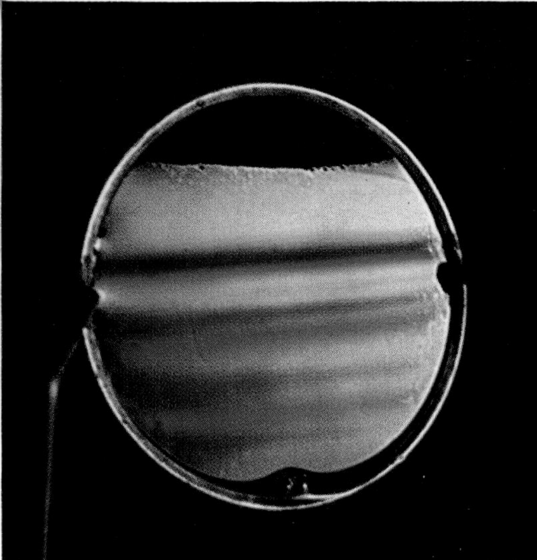

19–19. Interference seen in white light reflected by a thin soap film. The film fills a circular aperture. The picture was taken shortly after the film had drained enough so that the upper region is less than $\lambda/4$ thick for all wave lengths of visible light.

19–20. Right: interference seen in red light reflected from the same soap film. Above: at almost the same time that Fig. 19–19 was photographed. Below: at a later time. Because the film has drained more, the dark region extends farther down at the top.

19–9. White light passing through a single slit produced this pattern.

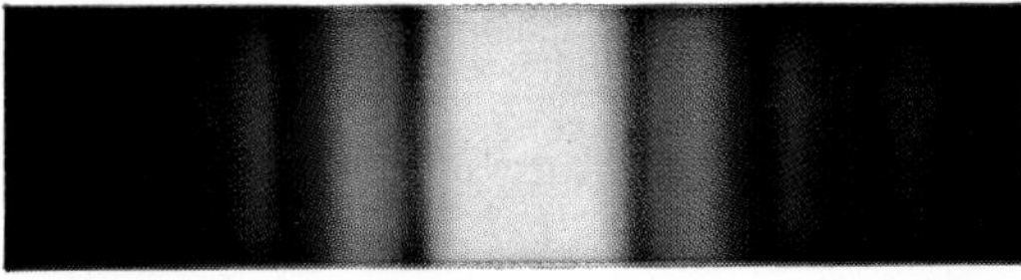

19–10. With the same set-up as in Fig. 19–9, red light produced this pattern. Both patterns are called diffraction patterns.

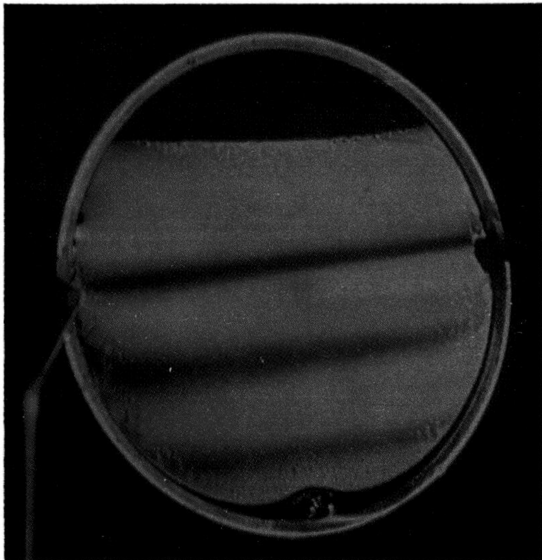

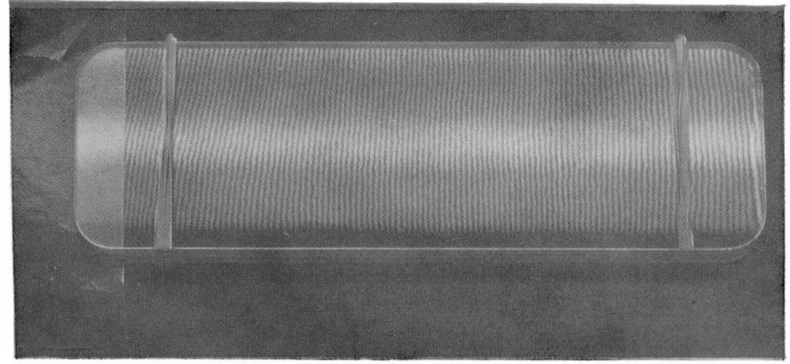

19–21. An interference pattern produced when light of one spectral color is reflected from the two sides of an air wedge made by separating two pieces of plate glass by a thin sheet inserted at the left end.

How a Colored Diffraction Pattern Is Formed by White Light

From top to bottom in Fig. 19–28 you see the diffraction patterns of the same slit in red light, green light, blue light, and white light. If you look down the center line, you see that light of every spectral color is at a maximum. Their combination in the pattern at the bottom looks white. Now look down the line AA. The red light is moderately intense; the green almost absent; and the blue completely gone. In the white light pattern we see red. A little bit to the left of the line AA in addition to red, there will be more yellow and green and there you see yellow. To the right of the line the red disappears but the intensity of blue rises. What do you see in the white light pattern?

Try the line BB a little further out on the same side of the center. Here the red light is almost absent, the green light is bright and the blue light has almost disappeared. The resulting yellowish color in the white light pattern arises from the yellow-green region of the spectrum. Run down any line of your own choosing and see how the white light pattern is formed.

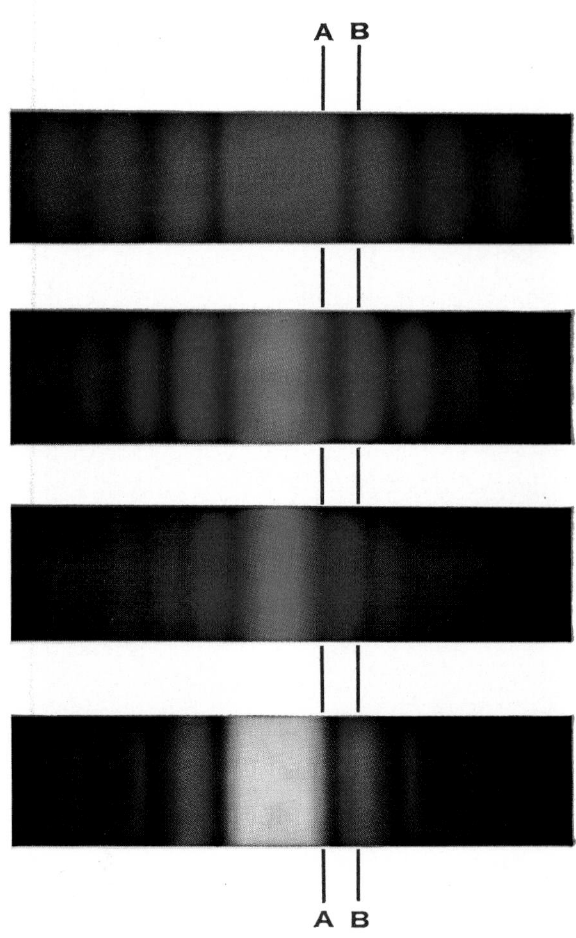

19–28. Formation of a white light diffraction pattern from the diffraction patterns of the spectral colors.

Although the pattern of light and dark differs from Young's pattern, it looks suspiciously like an interference pattern. There are nodes and maxima in light of one color, and color effects when white light is employed. Because this interference effect takes place with only one slit, it may seem to make our interpretation of Young's pattern questionable. To clarify the situation we shall study more carefully the behavior of light passing through a single slit.

If we look back at our earlier discussion of the diffraction of waves by a slit (Section 17–7), we notice that the single slit does not act like a point source of waves unless its width is less than a wave length. Normally, the slits we use in observing diffraction or interference in light are much wider than the wave length of light. (Both the narrower slits we scratch with a razor blade and the wider ones made with a needle are many wave lengths wide.) Perhaps they are 10^{-1} mm wide while the wave length of light is between 4 and 7×10^{-4} mm. The explanation of the interference patterns we see in light passing through single slits must be found by carefully examining the behavior of light as it passes through a narrow slit which is, nevertheless, many wave lengths wide.

In Fig. 17–19 we saw how straight waves traveling through a narrow slit in a ripple tank spread out or diffract. The waves on the far side of the barrier arise from the propagation of the parts of the crests and troughs that enter the slit. Instead of producing the crests and troughs in the slit by letting a straight wave fall on it, it seems possible that we might produce them by a line of point sources moving up and down together at the position of the slit. As a test of this idea let us replace the slit by a line of very small point sources, separated by a small fraction of a wave length. We shall use enough sources so that they just fill the space of the original slit. If we now run the sources in phase and at the same frequency as that of the original wave, we see (Fig. 19–11) that the pattern produced does look like the diffraction pattern of the slit.

It seems reasonable that the wave patterns formed when straight waves are diffracted by a slit are the same as the patterns formed by the waves from a large number of point sources evenly spread through the width of the slit. We shall now assume this equivalence, and try to explain the interference patterns we observe through single slits by superposing the waves from the effective point sources in the slit. This general procedure of predicting the further propagation of waves by replacing wave fronts by sources was applied by Huygens to a number of problems including reflection and refraction.

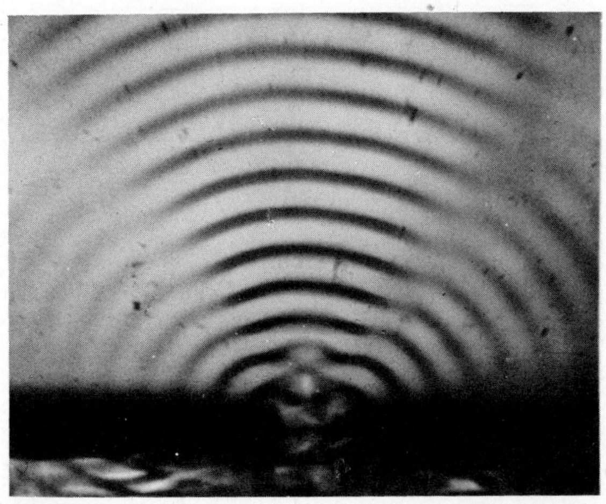

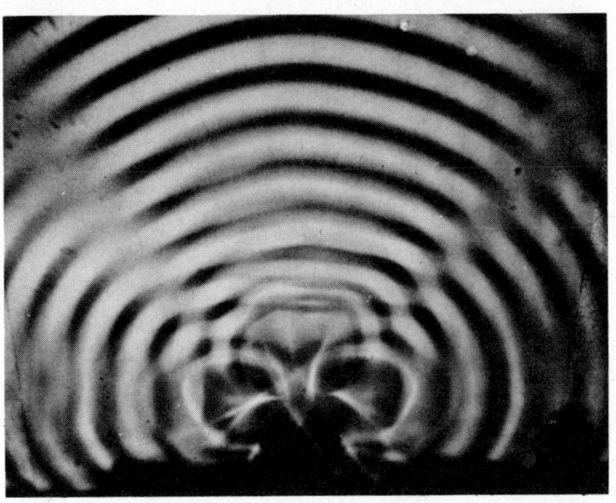

19–11. A diffraction pattern of straight waves passing through a slit and, below, an interference pattern of a line of equally spaced point sources extending across the slit. Near the sources the effect of source separation leads to some difference in the patterns. Far away the two patterns are the same.

19–6. A Theory of Diffraction by a Slit

In our study of the interference pattern from a line of close-spaced point sources occupying the width of a slit, we shall consider the pattern only at distances great compared to the slit width. We start with the total wave produced by the sources at a distant point directly in front of the slit. The path lengths from all the sources to that point are

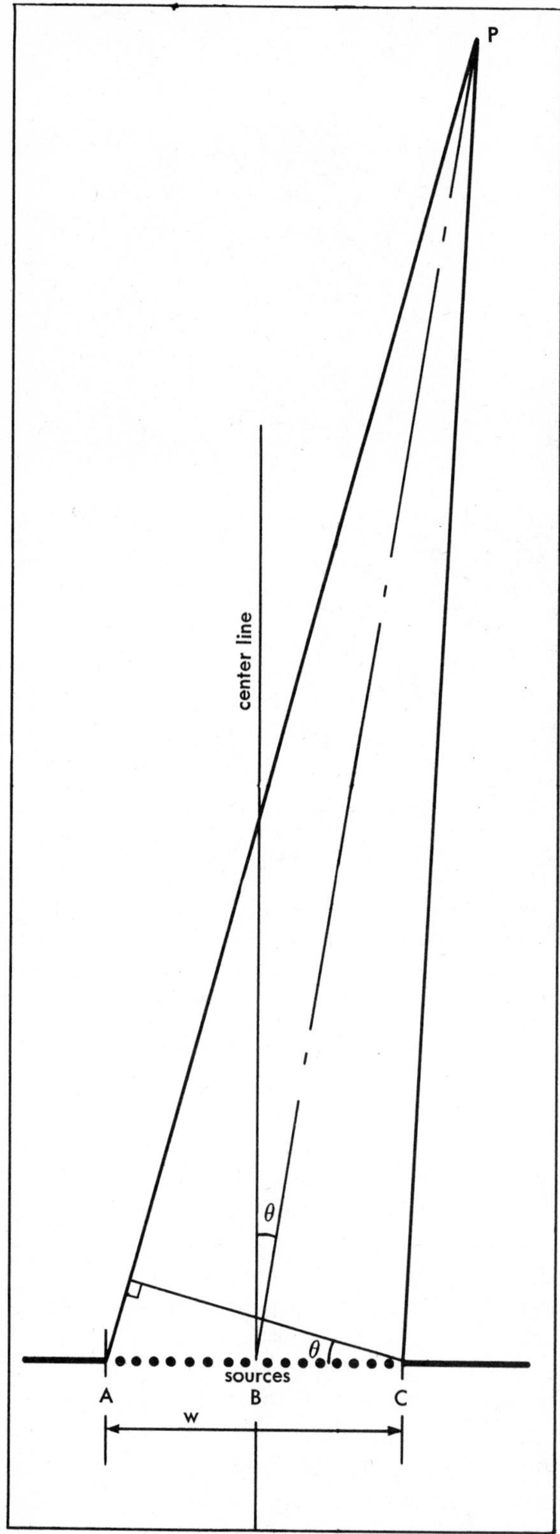

19–12. The intensity of light at *P* is less than that along the center line because the path lengths from the sources to *P* are not equal.

almost equal, and crests from all the sources arrive there together. This reinforcement of all the individual waves means that strong waves go out from the slit along the center line.

Next we examine a point P some distance off the center line so that the angle θ between BP and the center line in Fig. 19–12 is no longer zero. (B is at the center of the slit.) For such a point the path lengths from the various sources are no longer equal. In particular, for instance, PC is shorter than PA. The individual crests do not arrive at P at the same time, and the total wave is weaker than it is along the center line.

We now move P farther away from the center line so that the angle increases until the difference in the path lengths to the two ends of the slit becomes

$$PA - PC = \lambda.$$

At this point $\sin \theta = \lambda/w$ as we see in Fig. 19–13. Also, as the figure shows, $PB - PC = \lambda/2$. We can now show that the waves from the individual sources reaching any far-away point P at this angle cancel each other so that the total intensity far away in this direction is zero. To understand this cancellation we match the sources in pairs which cancel. Consider the sources just to the left of C and of B; they give crests at P which come $\frac{1}{2}$ wave length apart. In other words, at P a trough from one of these sources arrives with a crest from the other, and they cancel. Moving to the next pair of sources to the left, the second points to the left of C and B respectively, the same thing happens. Again we get the same result for the third pair, the fourth pair, and for all succeeding pairs. We have thus superposed the effects of all the sources; they all cancel in pairs; and no resultant disturbance takes place at P. It does not matter in what order we add up the effects of all the sources; we must always get the same result. The trick of adding them in pairs is just an easy way of seeing what the result is. Thus we have shown that there is complete cancellation of waves at the angle θ given by $\sin \theta = \lambda/w$.

As the angle θ becomes larger the cancellation is no longer perfect, and the intensity rises. It goes through a maximum and then falls to zero again when $\sin \theta = 2\lambda/w$. We can understand the cancellation at this angle by reference to Fig. 19–14. All the sources in interval 1 on the figure can be paired with those in interval 2 so that all

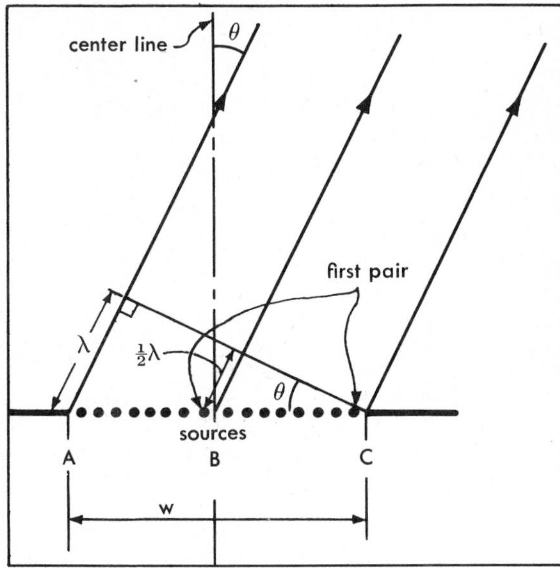

19–13. When $\sin\theta = \frac{\lambda}{w}$, waves from the sources cancel.

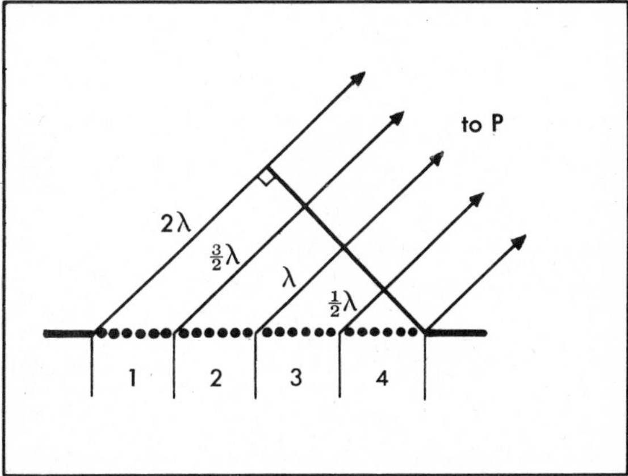

19–14. When $\sin\theta = \frac{2\lambda}{w}$, there is cancellation.

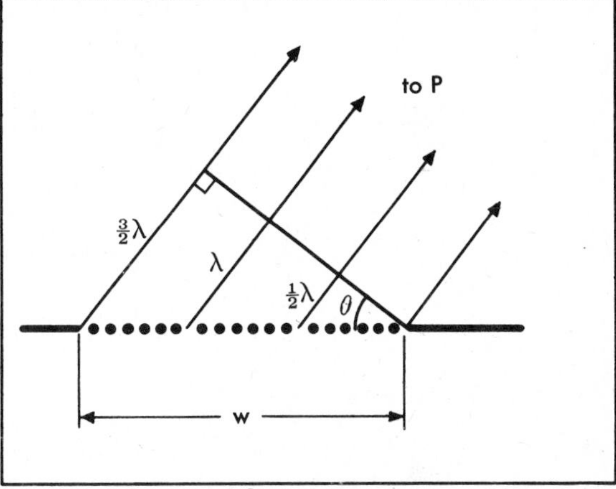

19–15. When $\sin\theta = \frac{3\lambda}{2w}$, partial reinforcement occurs.

pairs cancel; and the sources in interval 3 can be paired with those in interval 4 to produce complete cancellation. The intensity in this direction is therefore zero.

It is natural to expect a maximum intensity approximately halfway between $\sin\theta = \lambda/w$ and $\sin\theta = 2\,\lambda/w$, near $\sin\theta = \frac{3}{2}\,\lambda/w$. At this angle (Fig. 19–15) we can divide the sources into three intervals with path difference of $\frac{1}{2}\,\lambda$ between their ends. Pairing the sources in the two intervals on the right we find that they all cancel out as before. Only the third interval is left over. The effects of the sources at each end of the third interval cancel. But there are no other sources which can be paired off this way; consequently there will be at least partial reinforcement. We conclude that there is a net effect at $\sin\theta = \frac{3}{2}\,\lambda/w$; but the intensity is less than that which would be observed along the center line from one third of the sources in the slit. The light intensity in this maximum is therefore considerably less than it is in the maximum along the center line where all the sources in the slit contribute to a complete reinforcement.

Beyond the node at $\sin\theta = 2\,\lambda/w$, as $\sin\theta$ increases, the intensity rises to a still weaker maximum near $\frac{5}{2}\,\lambda/w$, and falls to zero again at $3\,\lambda/w$. It continues its rise and fall with increasing angle while the maxima get progressively weaker as shown in Fig. 19–16

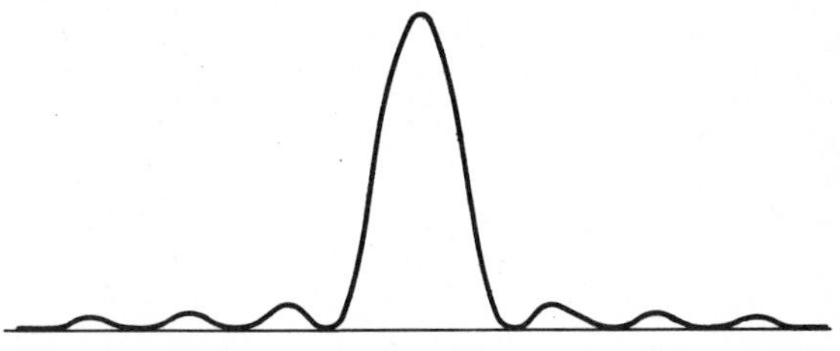

19–16. A single-slit diffraction pattern for light of one definite wave length. The intensity of the light is plotted vertically as a function of the distance from the center line.

19–7. Experimental Checks with Single and Double Slits

We now have a theory which connects the appearance of the diffraction pattern of a slit with the width of the slit and the wave length of light. Does the theory account for actual observations? To be sure, we must construct slits of accurately known width and measure the distances from the

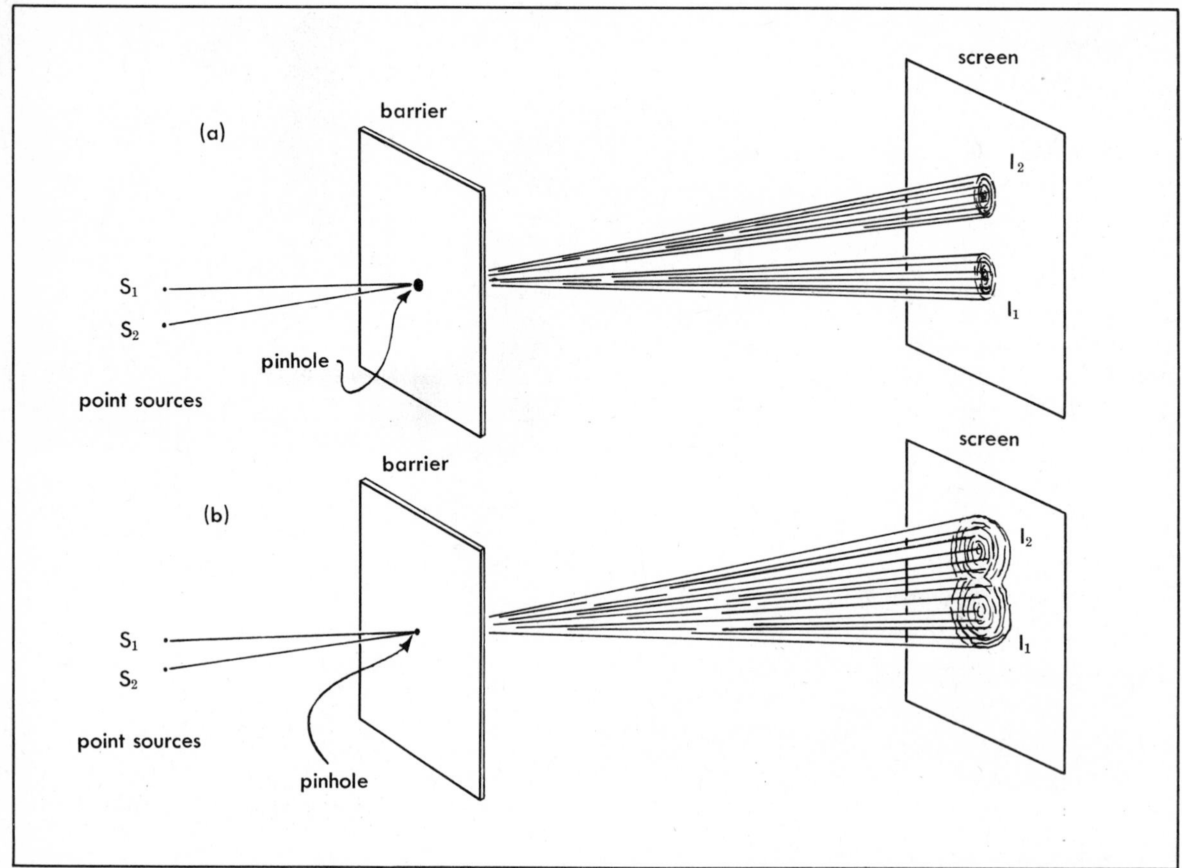

19–17. When light from two point sources S_1 and S_2 passes through a small hole, the images I_1 and I_2 are fuzzy but resolved. When the hole is very small, the images overlap and are unresolved.

center line to the dark regions which occur in the diffraction pattern of light of a single color. When we make such measurements, we find that the distance between the nodes at the sides of the pattern is constant. Also, as expected, the distance across the central bright band is twice the distance between the other nodes. (Measure it yourself on Fig. 19–10 opposite page 290.) Furthermore, the intensities of the maxima decrease with the distance from the center as predicted by the theory. We therefore have reason to believe that the theory is good.

Finally, we can find the wave length of the light by measuring the distance between the center of the pattern and the first node. Using

$$x/L = \sin\theta = \lambda/w,$$

we find values of λ for light of various colors. These values are the same as those found by using two slits or a many-slit spectroscope. Our interpretation of both Young's experiment and single-slit diffraction is probably correct.

We can now see why we did not need to worry about the diffraction pattern of single slits when we discussed Young's experiment. We performed Young's experiment with very narrow slits (cut with two razor blades). For such slits the central bright region of the diffraction pattern of each slit covers a rather large angle. Far enough away from the slits the central bright regions will largely overlap, and in this overlapping region we see the simple double-slit pattern. The other maxima of the single-slit diffraction pattern occur far out to the sides, and they are too weak to be seen. To see them, the slits have to be wider.

19–8. Resolution

We have learned from our study of single-slit diffraction that light from a point source passing through a small slit or pinhole spreads out to give an image larger than the size of the hole. We also learned that small holes spread the light more than large holes. This diffraction caused by a small hole is of great importance in designing microscopes and telescopes. It determines the ultimate limit of their magnification.

To see why diffraction limits magnification, let us consider what happens when two point sources, close together, send light through a pinhole onto a screen. In Fig. 19–17 (a), I_1 is the image of source S_1, and I_2 is the image of source S_2. These images are, in fact, diffraction patterns produced by the tiny pinhole, and they are large and fuzzy. In Fig. 19–17 (b) everything is the same but the hole is smaller. This spreads the light still more, and the images are now so large that they overlap. It is difficult to decide, from looking at the screen, whether the pattern is that of two separate sources or a single odd-shaped source. When the hole is so small, or the sources are so close that the images cannot be distinguished, we say the sources are unresolved. When we can separate them, we say they are resolved. The *resolution* of an optical instrument is a measure of its ability to give separated images of objects that are close together.

If we substitute a lens for the pinhole we can focus the light from two point sources and produce what appear to be sharp images. Careful examination of these images, however, shows that a lens cannot eliminate the spreading of light by diffraction because light in passing through a lens is passing through a hole of limited size. Fig. 19–18 shows a series of photographs of three point sources seen through lenses of the same focal length but different diameter. In the top picture the light passes through a small-diameter lens; in the second picture it passes through a larger lens, and in the last through a very large lens. In the top picture, the images are unresolved. As the lens becomes larger, diffraction decreases and resolution improves, until with a large lens the images are so clearly separated that even if the sources were closer together, we could still resolve them.

In a microscope, where the light passes through a small objective lens, we expect that diffraction will be important. We can usefully increase the magnification of a microscope until diffraction stops us from resolving near-by objects. A further increase in magnification makes everything look larger, but it does not enable us to see objects which are closer together. Increasing the magnifying power of microscopes with the best of lenses is futile beyond the point where detail fails to be resolved because of diffraction.

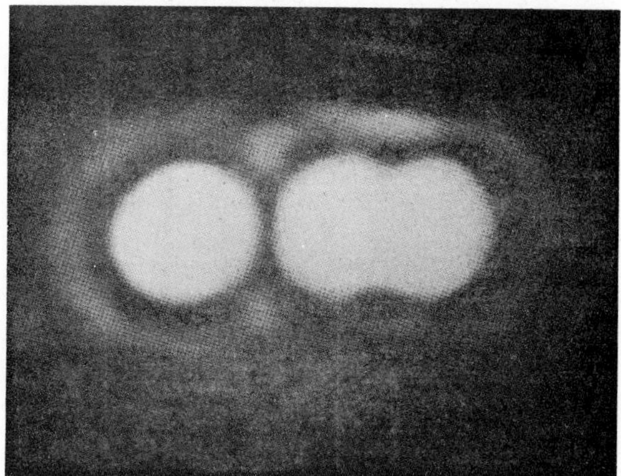

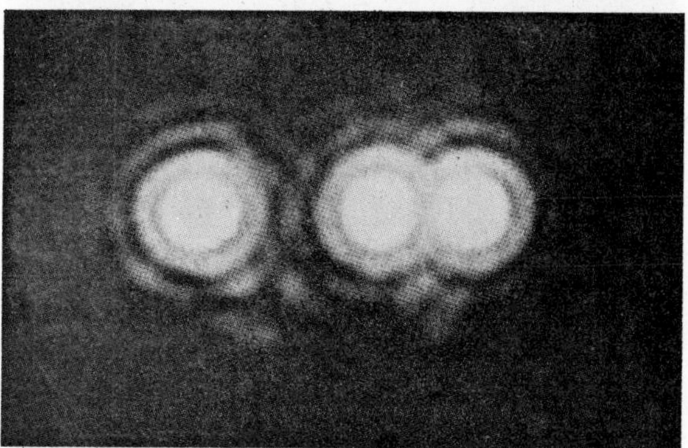

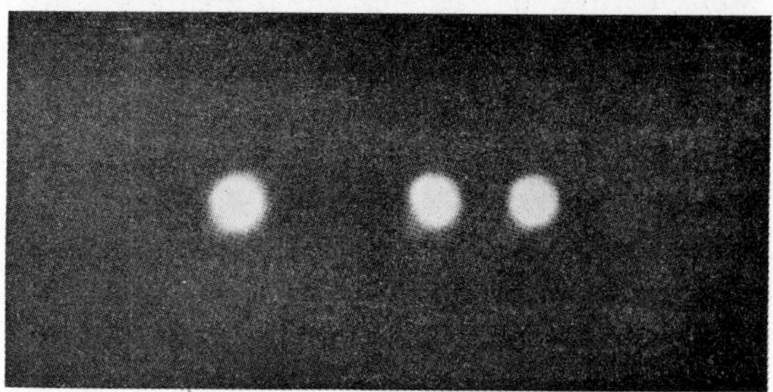

19–18. Diffraction patterns from three point sources produced by lenses of different diameters. As the diameter is increased (top to bottom), the resolution improves. (Courtesy: Francis Sears, "Principles of Physics, III," Addison-Wesley Publishing Co.)

Telescopes also are subject to diffraction. The greater the size of the objective, whether mirror or lens, the better is the resolution. The large Hale telescope on Mt. Palomar gives sufficiently good resolution to resolve individual stars in the Andromeda Nebula, a feat that smaller telescopes are unable to accomplish.

19–9. Interference in Thin Films

Of the many interference patterns we can see, among the most common are those we observe when light is incident on a thin soap film. When white light falls on a thin film it gives striking color effects. (Fig. 19–19 opposite page 290.)

To study this effect we shall examine the pattern obtained with a single color (Fig. 19–20 opposite page 290). In the reflected light from the film there is a wide dark region at the top. In this region the soap film is very thin because the water has drained down toward the bottom, leaving only a few clinging molecular layers behind. If we look farther down the film, the thickness increases, and eventually we come to a thickness at which reflected light is clearly visible. Still lower down, at greater thickness, a dark bar appears in the photograph; the reflection is absent. Then continuing farther, bright and dark bars succeed one another as the thickness gets greater.

That the observation of a bright or a dark bar really depends on the thickness of the film is borne out by watching the bars while a newly formed film is draining. When the top has drained to a certain thickness, a bright bar forms there. As the draining continues, the bar moves down the film, and a dark bar forms in the thinning region above. Bar after bar moves down the film, each staying with its appropriate thickness. Finally a dark region spreads down from the top when the film is very thin.

Experiments with wedges — air between plate glass, for instance — show the dependence on thickness even more clearly (Fig. 19–21 opposite page 291). As the angle of the wedge is reduced, the bars, which in this case are equally spaced, move apart so that each bar stays exactly at its own thickness in the wedge.

How can we explain these alternating bright and dark bars? They are very similar to the alternating bars in Young's interference pattern, and their explanation is almost the same. When light passes through a sheet of refractive material, some of the light is reflected at the first surface it meets, and some is reflected at the second surface. Take a look at Fig. 13–7, or think of your reflection in a glass window when you sit in a lighted room on a dark night. If the glass is thick, the two reflections are sufficiently far apart to be apparent. Of course, a small part of the light that has been reflected at the bottom of the glass will be reflected again at the top instead of passing out. (Fig. 19–22.) Some light may be partially reflected several times inside the glass, but for a weakly reflecting material like glass or a soap film, only the reflection as the light enters and the first reflection inside are usually appreciable.

Just like the light reflected from thick glass, the light reflected by a thin soap film is made up of two beams which have traveled over different paths. We shall call the beam which is reflected at the outside surface No. 1, and the beam which has passed through the film and has been reflected at the other side beam No. 2. (Fig. 19–22.) It is the interference between these two beams that produces the bright and dark bars in the reflected light of a single color and the color effects when white light is incident.

To understand the interference patterns in more detail, let us start with a very thin film like that at the top of the soap film in Fig. 19–20. As we know from experiments with monolayers (Section 7–12), even if the film in this region is many molecular layers thick, it is still very thin compared with the wave length of visible light. For yellow light the wave length is about 6×10^{-7} meter, while the thickness of a film 100 atoms thick is only 10^{-8} meter. Our thin film is illustrated in Fig. 19–23. Because its thickness is much less than the wave length of the light, the path difference between the two beams is very small compared to a wave length, and we might expect that the two reflected beams add together so that a reflected crest in one and a reflected crest in the other are almost superposed. The reflected light should then be appreciable. Instead, we see that no net reflection occurs. The whole top of the soap film is dark. Apparently the waves in the two reflected beams cancel each other instead of reinforcing.

This cancellation may seem puzzling; but when we recall the behavior of waves reflected on coil springs, it is less astonishing. When a pulse traveling along a spring is reflected from a heavier spring in which the speed of waves is smaller, it turns upside down. When a pulse is reflected from a lighter spring where the speed is greater, it stays right-side up (Section 16–4). Here in the light we have an analogous situation. The light beam reflected from the outside of a soap film is reflected from a more refractive material in which

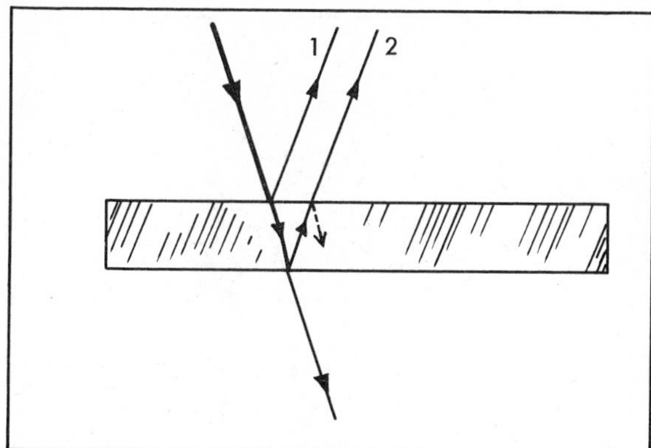

19–22. Rays 1 and 2 represent the two most important reflections from a thin film.

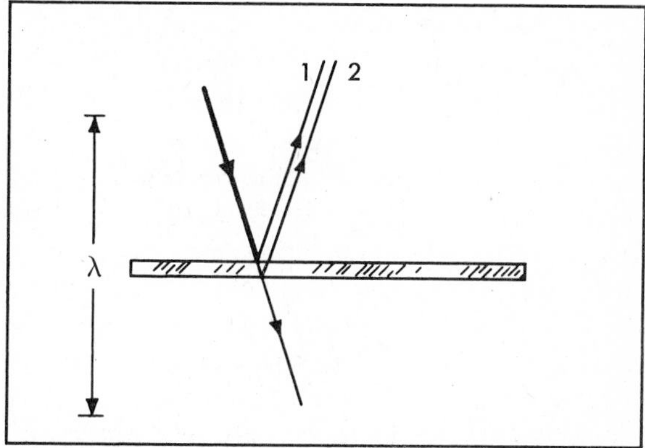

19–23. Although there is negligible path difference between beam No. 1 reflected from the top of a very thin film and beam No. 2 reflected from the bottom, the two reflected beams cancel.

the wave moves slowly, while the light beam reflected inside the thin film is reflected from air, a less refractive medium in which the wave moves fast. Perhaps we can picture the more refractive medium as acting like a heavy spring. Then light waves reflected from the outside of the film into beam No. 1 should turn upside down. An incident crest turns into a reflected trough. On the other hand, an incident crest reflected inside the film will be reflected into beam No. 2 as a crest. Because one wave is turned upside down and the other is not, the two waves cancel; and we see no reflected light.

Let us now consider what happens as the soap film becomes thicker. Beam No. 2, which penetrates back and forth through the soap film, has a longer path than the beam reflected from the top surface. In beam No. 2, therefore, the crests fall farther and farther behind as the thickness is increased. When the thickness becomes one-quarter of a wave length, the path in the soap film is a half wave length long; and the crests in this beam have dropped behind by a half wave length. (Fig. 19–24.) Instead of coinciding with troughs in beam No. 1 as they do for a very thin film, they have now been delayed until they coincide with crests. The crests in the two beams add together, and the total reflected light intensity is at a maximum.*

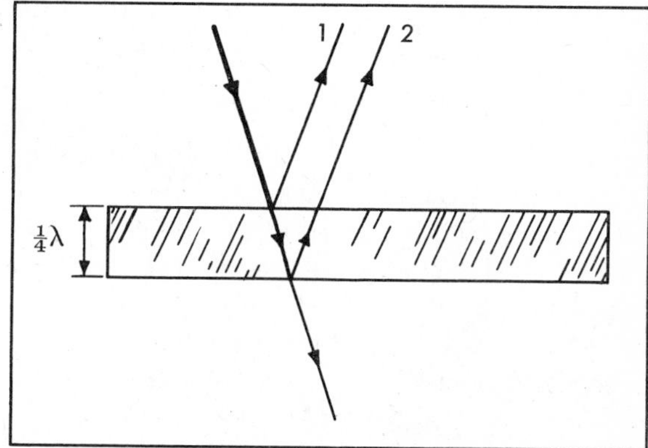

19–24. Light reflected from the top and bottom of a film that is $\lambda/4$ thick. Because of the extra path length $\lambda/2$ in beam No. 2, and because the waves in beam No. 1 are turned upside down on reflection, the two reflected rays reinforce.

As we increase the thickness of the soap film still further, the crests in the internally reflected beam fall still farther behind. When the film is half a wave length thick, the length of the path back and forth inside the film is a full wave length.

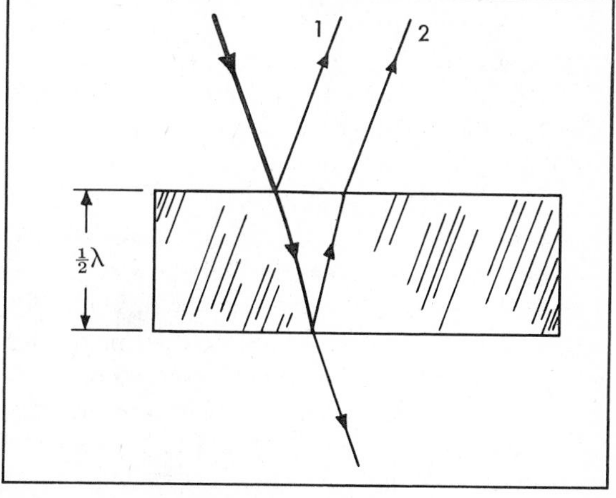

19–25. The two reflected rays when the film is half a wave length thick. The path difference is λ, and beam No. 1 is inverted on reflection. They cancel.

*Clearly, the wave length we are using is the wave length in the soap film.

Since the crests in beam No. 2 have fallen behind by a whole wave length, they now coincide with troughs in beam No. 1 just as they did when the film was extremely thin (Fig. 19–25). The crests and troughs in the two reflected beams cancel again, and we see a dark bar in the light reflected from the soap film at this thickness. As we continue to increase the thickness, every quarter wave length we shift from a region in which there is no reflection to a region of maximum reflection, or from a region of maximum reflection to a region of no reflection again. There is no reflection from the film when its thickness is $\frac{1}{2}\lambda$, λ, $\frac{3}{2}\lambda$, etc. Maximum reflection occurs when the film is $\frac{1}{4}\lambda$ thick, $\frac{3}{4}\lambda$, $\frac{5}{4}\lambda$, and so on. It is for this reason that the bright and dark bars seen in a thin wedge are equally spaced. The thickness of the wedge increases at a constant rate, so the bars alternate with constant spacing.

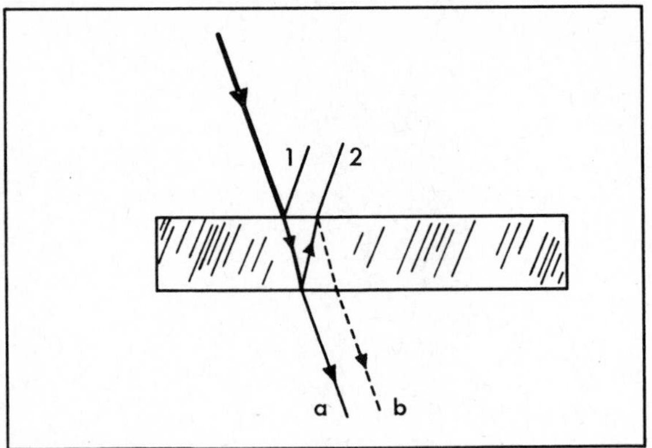

19–26. The unreflected ray *a* and the ray that is twice reflected, *b*, are superposed in the transmitted light.

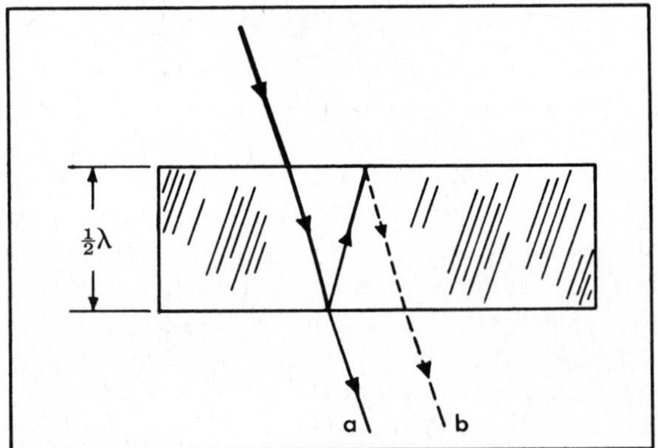

19–27. The transmitted ray and the twice-reflected ray reinforce when the film is $\lambda/2$ thick. The extra distance traveled by *b* is λ.

19–10. Interference in Light Transmitted Through Thin Films

When the intensity of reflected light changes as a function of thickness, what happens to the light transmitted by the film? When there is no reflected light we expect that the intensity of the transmitted light will be the same as that of the incident light. Experiments agree with our expectation. At thicknesses $\frac{1}{2}\lambda$, λ, $\frac{3}{2}\lambda$, etc., all the light is transmitted. Furthermore, at those thicknesses for which reflection takes place, the intensity of the transmitted light is less by just the intensity of the reflected light.

We can understand in terms of interference why the transmitted light decreases when the reflected light increases. Like the reflected light, the transmitted light is made of two interfering beams. They are the beam of light that passes straight through the film without any reflections and a beam made of the light which is internally reflected twice (Fig. 19–26). Other internal reflections give beams too weak to be important.

We now examine how the two beams *a* and *b* in Fig. 19–26 add up for two different thicknesses of the film, a thickness at which there is no reflection and a thickness at which there is maximum reflection. There is no reflection when the film is $\frac{1}{2}\lambda$ thick. In this case (Fig. 19–27) the twice-reflected wave *b* is delayed by a whole wave length with respect to the unreflected wave *a* because of its extra journey back and forth across the film. A crest in the twice-reflected wave, therefore, comes out of the bottom of the film along with a crest in the unreflected wave. The two crests must be added together, and the net effect is to produce crests in the transmitted light which are larger than those in the unreflected beam.

On the other hand, when there is a maximum reflection, at the thickness $\frac{1}{4}\lambda$ for example, the twice-reflected wave *b* travels an extra distance $\frac{1}{2}\lambda$ compared to the unreflected beam *a*. The crest in *b* therefore coincides with a trough in *a* and the superposition of *a* and *b* results in smaller troughs and smaller crests in the transmitted light. We thus see that when there is no reflected light from the film, the transmitted beam is more intense; and when there is a maximum in the reflection from the film, the transmitted light is less intense. If we work through the details quantitatively, we find that the sum of the intensity transmitted and the intensity reflected is, indeed, equal to the intensity of the incident light.

19–11. Color Effects in Interference

In explaining interference patterns we have concentrated on those produced by light of a single spectral color. We can now go back to the interference patterns of white light, shown opposite pages 290 and 291, and explain the many bright colors in those patterns. In each case the explanation is basically the same. We consider the interference pattern of each spectral color separately; then by noting which spectral colors are present and which are absent at a given place, we can predict the color that we shall see at that place in the white light pattern. For example, if at one place blue light is absent but red light is intense, we shall see a color at the red end of the spectrum — yellow or red. If at another place only blue and red light are present, we shall see purple. The procedure is illustrated in Fig. 19–28 and in the accompanying text opposite page 291. There it is applied to the white light diffraction pattern of a single slit. You can apply the same procedure to Young's interference pattern, to thin film interference patterns, and in fact to any other interference pattern.

19–12. Conclusion

In this part of the course, we have examined the behavior of light. We started with its simplest properties, propagation through vacuum, reflection, and refraction. These we tried to explain with a particle model. We have gone on to the characteristic wave behavior of light, examining diffraction and interference. With the aid of the ripple tank, we have seen this kind of wave behavior directly.

We now see that light behaves like waves. Not only does it reflect and refract like waves; it also exhibits interference effects. Reflection and refraction may be explained on a simple particle theory, but interference is the identifying characteristic of waves. Since the demonstration of interference in light, the wave nature of light has never been doubted.

Although light is an old interest, new aspects are still being discovered. Just in our century, we have shown that X rays are light waves, and we have measured their wave lengths by observing interference patterns. But we have also discovered that light exhibits some particle-like behavior. In certain circumstances we can even count these particles, as we shall see in Part IV. We now are beginning to understand how to describe both the wave and particle aspects of light in one theory.

You probably have many questions to ask about light. For example, just how is the measured intensity related to the height of the waves? We shall not answer this question here, but you can learn about it. Probably most of the questions you will ask have intrigued other people, and something is already known about them. A number of them have given rise to startling developments. Take one example: Through what medium is light propagated? Its propagation is influenced by various materials, but it does pass through vacuum. If we assume the existence of a medium for the propagation of light through vacuum (it has been named "the aether"), we later find that this aether is impossible to detect. The failure of measurements designed to show the presence of the aether was one of the important puzzles that led Einstein to formulate his theory of relativity.

We can study more about light, and we can also study more about waves in general. The relation of wave height to intensity is really a general question. So are many others. To illustrate we shall take a last example.

You may have noticed that some rooms (usually those with large, unbroken wall areas) have "dead spots" where it is very difficult to hear a note of a certain pitch. Near by, this same note may be clearly audible. You can easily demonstrate this effect with a high-pitched whistle. It occurs because of interference between direct waves from the source and waves reflected from the walls. At some frequencies the nodes and maxima form a fixed pattern in the room, commonly referred to as a standing wave pattern.

In the ripple tank you have undoubtedly seen waves hitting a reflecting barrier head on and traveling back in the opposite direction. If the incident and reflected waves are of about equal height, close to the barrier you can see regularly spaced regions of no motion alternating with zones where the water appears to move up and down. In this region we do not see the traveling waves propagating in either direction. Here again we have an example of a standing wave interference pattern. Standing wave patterns occur for all kinds of waves. We shall return to them briefly in Part IV when we study matter waves.

Where now do we stand? We have learned enough about waves to recognize their behavior. We know why we believe in the wave nature of light. But there is a great deal about waves and light that we can still study. In this concluding section we have mentioned further questions about light and waves to which answers (at least partial answers) are known. In addition to answered questions about light, there are always a few unanswered, and there are probably many questions about light and waves that we have not yet learned to ask. Asking the right new questions is often the key to new and interesting physics. Perhaps *you* will formulate a key question.

FOR HOME, DESK, AND LAB

1. Why can't we see interference from two independent light sources?

2. In an interference pattern produced by white light passing through two narrow slits, the distance between the black bars is 0.32 cm. The distance between slits is about .02 cm, and the distance to the screen on which the bars are observed is 130 cm. Find the average wave length of white light.

3. A source of red light produces interference through two narrow slits spaced a distance $d = .01$ cm apart. At what distance from the slits should we place a screen so that the first few interference bars are spaced one centimeter apart? What will be the spacing of the bars if we then use violet light?

4. What will happen to the interference pattern in Young's experiment if the source is not exactly on the center line between the slits?

5. When a source of light of wave length λ is used in a two-slit experiment with narrow slits separated a distance d, at what angles do you expect to find the *maxima* in the light intensity in the interference pattern?

6. Suggest an optical method for measuring the width of a narrow slit.

7. Calculate the period of yellow light. About how many wave lengths are included in a light wave during emission of a light burst by a single atom?

8. What happens to the diffraction of a single slit when you turn the slit as in Fig. 19–29 instead of holding the opening perpendicular to the path of the light? Why?

9. (a) When yellow light passes through a slit 1 mm wide, at what angles are the first three nodes in the diffraction pattern?
   (b) If the slit is 10 times as wide?
   (c) If it is $\frac{1}{10}$ as wide?

10. When two identical fairly wide slits are used to make an interference pattern and when they are separated by a distance comparable to their width, the resulting pattern combines the features of a single slit diffraction pattern and the pattern of interference between the two slits. A photograph of such a pattern is shown in Fig. 19–30. Identify the dark regions arising from the diffraction pattern of each slit and the dark bars arising from interference between the slits.

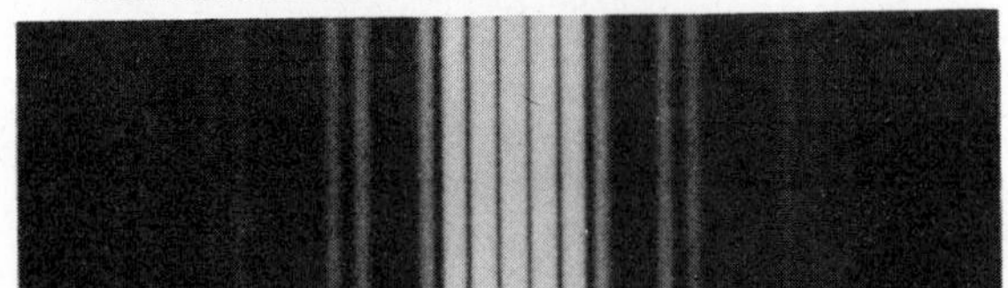

19–30. For Problem 10. Courtesy Bruno Rossi, "Optics," Addison-Wesley Pub. Co. 1957.

19–29. For Problem 8. The light rays pass obliquely through a single slit.

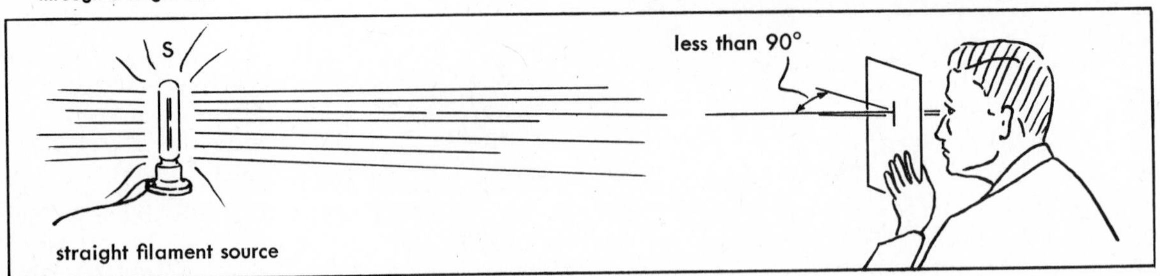

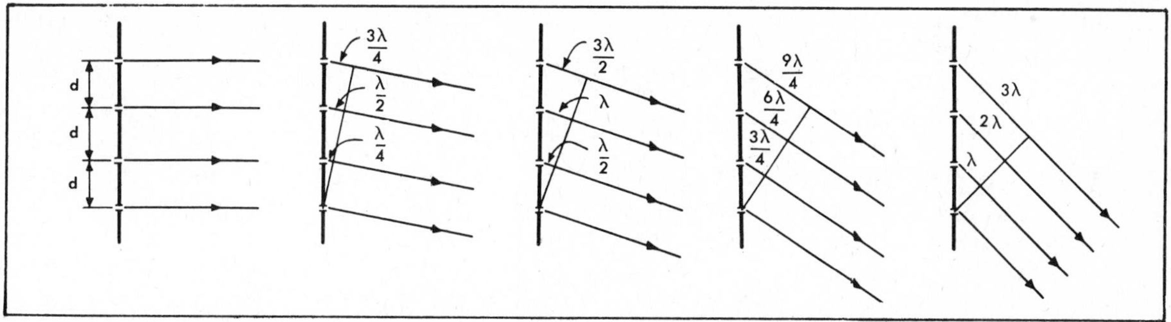

19–31. For Problem 12. Light emerging at different angles from four slits spaced a distance d apart.

11. When a source of wave length λ is used with three slits, each separated from its neighbor by the distance d, show that you get maximum intensity at the same angles as for two slits only.

12. (a) For four narrow slits spaced d apart, find out at which of the angles given by $\sin \theta = 0, \lambda/4d, \lambda/2d, 3\lambda/4d$, and λ/d you expect maxima and at which of the angles you expect nodes in the intensity of light in the interference pattern. The diagrams (Fig. 19–31) and the idea of pairing may help you.

(b) Which of these angles is a node of the two-slit pattern? Which a maximum?

13. Microscopes in which the object is illuminated by ultraviolet light can give higher magnifications than microscopes that use visible light.

(a) How do you explain this?

(b) How are the images seen if no visible light is used?

(c) Since glass is opaque to ultraviolet light how can such a microscope be made?

14. Two images can just be resolved when the central maximum of one falls on the first node of the other.

(a) Show that the resolution of a narrow slit depends upon λ/w where w is the slit width.

(b) About how close together can two line sources be placed and still be resolved if they are viewed through a .01-cm slit (about the smallest size you can make easily) 3 meters away from the sources?

15. Stars are often photographed through a blue filter. What is the advantage of this?

16. From the photograph of a soap film at the top in Fig. 19–20, plot a graph of film thickness against vertical distance down the film.

17. Two pieces of plate glass 10 cm long make an air wedge (Fig. 19–21). The plates are separated at one end by a human hair with a diameter of 0.09 mm. The reflected interference pattern is observed by looking in a direction perpendicular to the surfaces of the plates.

(a) What is the spacing of the bars if the incident light is blue?

(b) How many bright bars are seen per centimeter if the incident light is red?

(c) Is the light reflected from the end where the plates are in contact a maximum or a minimum?

(d) Can you tell from this experiment which reflected waves are turned upside down?

18. Lenses are often coated with a thin film to reduce the intensity of reflected light.

(a) If the index of refraction of the coating is 1.3, what is the smallest thickness that will give minimum reflection of yellow light?

(b) Such lenses often show a faint purple color by reflected light. Why?

19. Two 3-inch loudspeakers emit a steady pitch whose frequency is 1,000 vibrations per second. These sources are in phase and are 2 meters apart.

(a) At what angles would you expect to hear no sound? (The speed of sound is about 300 m/sec.)

(b) What do you think would happen if you tried this experiment in a room with hard-surfaced walls?

20. Can you suggest reasons why no interference is seen when light reflects from the two surfaces of a windowpane?

FURTHER READING

EINSTEIN, A., and INFELD, L., *The Evolution of Physics.* Simon & Schuster, 1938 (pp. 110–126).

LAND, EDWIN, "Experiments in Color Vision." *Scientific American*, May, 1959.

MAGIE, W. F., *A Source Book in Physics.* McGraw-Hill, 1935. (See especially Thomas Young.)

ROBERTSON, J. K., *Introduction to Optics, Geometrical and Physical.* Van Nostrand, Fourth Edition, 1954.

VAN BERGEIJK, W.; PIERCE, J.; DAVID, E. E., Jr., *Waves and the Ear.* Doubleday, 1959: A Science Study Series paperback.

Discussion of the Lensmaker's Formula

When light from a source is focused by a lens, the various portions of one wave crest must converge at the focal point at the same time. This is the way in which the light is concentrated there. Otherwise, as we know from our study of interference, the superposition of crests and troughs arriving at the same time will result in cancellation. Suppose that in the set up illustrated in Fig. (a) there is a distant source of light far out to the left. Then the crest of the wave from that source will arrive at the same moment all along the green line. As the wave goes on to the right, various portions of the crest move on different paths, and finally those portions of the crest that pass through the lens are concentrated at the focal point on the right. Since these portions arrive at the focal point at the same moment, they must take the same time to move from the green line to the focal point.

(a)

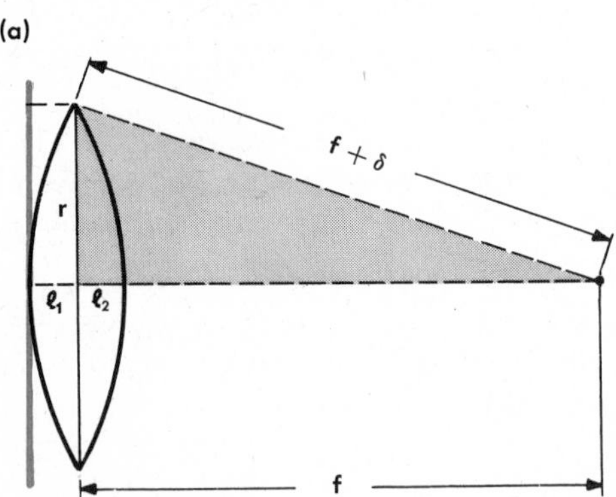

To find the relation between the shape of the lens and the focal distance f, we shall consider two paths. It is possible to trace the motion of the wave crest on all the paths through the lens, but two are enough to determine the relation for which we are looking. The paths we chose are indicated by the dashed lines in the figure. One passes through the center of the lens and the other through its outside edge. As you can see in Fig. (a), the portion of the crest that moves through the outside edge of the lens moves in air almost all the way. The distance it moves is $l_1 + f + \delta$ so the time it takes to get to the focal point is

$$\frac{l_1 + f + \delta}{v_a},$$

where v_a is the speed of the wave in air. On the other hand the portion of the wave moving through the center of the lens travels the distance $l_1 + l_2$ through glass and then reaches the focus after traveling the distance $f - l_2$ through air. The time it takes to go through the glass is

$$\frac{l_1 + l_2}{v_g},$$

where v_g is the speed of the wave in glass; and the time it takes to go the rest of the distance is

$$\frac{f - l_2}{v_a}.$$

The sum of these two times (the time to pass through the glass and through the air) must be the same as the time taken on the path through the edge of the lens, that is,

$$\frac{l_1 + f + \delta}{v_a} = \frac{l_1 + l_2}{v_g} + \frac{f - l_2}{v_a}.$$

On multiplying both sides of this equation by v_a and collecting similar terms, we obtain

$$\delta = \left(\frac{v_a}{v_g} - 1\right)(l_1 + l_2). \tag{1}$$

Since $f + \delta$ is the distance from the edge of the lens to the focal point, δ is the excess of this distance as compared with the focal length. The last equation, therefore, relates this extra distance to the thickness $l_1 + l_2$ of the lens.

The focal length itself can be determined from the radius r of the lens and the extra distance δ. The radius of the lens r and the focal length f are the sides of a right triangle with the hypotenuse $f + \delta$. This triangle has been shaded in the figure. The theorem of Pythagoras will allow us to find the relation between δ, the radius of the lens, and its focal length. Because the square of the hypotenuse is equal to the sum of the squares of the two sides, we have

$$(f+\delta)^2 = f^2 + r^2.$$

The left side of this equation can be written as

$$f^2 + 2f\delta + \delta^2.$$

And on subtracting f^2 from both sides of the equation we obtain

$$\delta(2f+\delta) = r^2.$$

As long as the radius of the lens is small compared to the focal length, δ will also be small compared to the focal length; and it can be neglected in the parentheses in the last equation. In this way we get a good approximate value for δ. It is

$$\delta = \frac{r^2}{2f}. \qquad (2)$$

We can also relate the thicknesses l_1 and l_2 at the center of the lens to the radius r of the lens and to the radii of R_1 and R_2 of the surfaces of the lens. l_1 is determined by the radius of the left-hand surface and l_2 by the radius of the right-hand surface. The relations are derived in almost the same way as we derived the relation between δ and the focal length f. Figure (b) shows how we carry out the procedure for the relation of l_1 and R_1. Here we see that R_1 is the hypotenuse of a right triangle one of whose sides is the radius of the lens r while the other side is of length $R_1 - l_1$. By applying the Pythagorian theorem we then get

$$R_1^2 - (R_1 - l_1)^2 = r^2.$$

Now for $(R_1 - l_1)^2$ we put in

$$R_1^2 - 2R_1 l_1 + l_1^2.$$

The result is

$$l_1(2R_1 - l_1) = r^2.$$

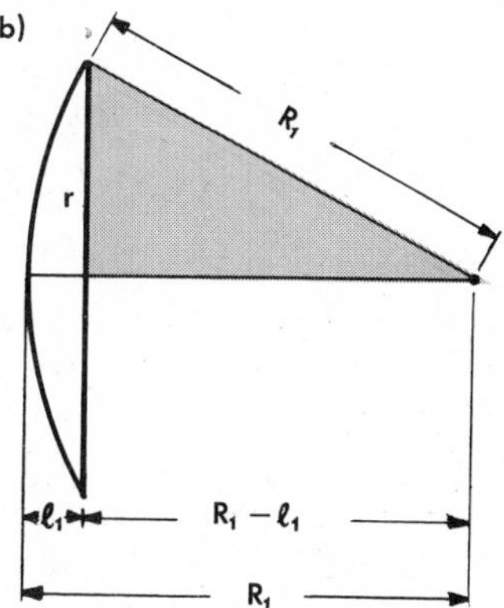

As long as l_1 is small compared to R_1 so that we have a thin lens we can neglect l_1 compared to $(2R_1)$ in the parentheses in the last equation. We, therefore, obtain a good approximate value for l_1 as

$$l_1 = \frac{r^2}{2R_1}. \qquad (3)$$

Exactly the same procedure gives us

$$l_2 = \frac{r^2}{2R_2}, \qquad (4)$$

where R_2 is the radius of the right-hand surface of the lens.

Now we can re-express Equation (1) by substituting the expression for δ given in equation (2) and those for l_1 and l_2 given in equations (3) and (4). We obtain

$$\frac{r^2}{2f} = \left(\frac{v_a}{v_g} - 1\right)\left(\frac{r^2}{2R_1} + \frac{r^2}{2R_2}\right).$$

On canceling $\frac{r^2}{2}$ from both sides of the equation we obtain

$$\frac{1}{f} = \left(\frac{v_a}{v_g} - 1\right)\left(\frac{1}{R_1} + \frac{1}{R_2}\right).$$

This is the lensmaker's equation relating the focal length of a lens to the radii of curvature of its surfaces.

We see that the index of refraction comes out automatically as the ratio of the speed of light in air to that of light in the lens.

PART III

MECHANICS

A multiple flash photograph of a bouncing ball. In our study of mechanics we shall study motions of bodies that range in size from enormous suns and planets, through things of ordinary size, like this ball, down to the minute particles in atoms.

Throughout this great range we shall find a few basic ideas, such as momentum and energy, that clarify our understanding at any scale.

NEWTON'S LAW OF MOTION

CHAPTER 20

AUTOMOBILES move down highways or wind in and out of traffic, passenger planes fly high above us; jet planes and artificial satellites streak across the sky; the stars perform their regular progression. What makes each of them go? What makes anything move? Is there a single cause common to all motion? Is any cause necessary?

So far in our study of physics we have been concerned almost entirely with building up a systematic way of describing and analyzing physical phenomena. We have measured the sizes of atoms, the distances to stars, and the lengths of time intervals; we have learned to recognize the angles in reflection and the patterns of interference of waves. In the study of motion this systematic description of observations is called *kinematics* (Chapter 5). It is the description of motion without regard to the causes of the motions. But description alone can never enable us to satisfy our desire to do something new, to control motions, to go beyond the mere description of what occurs. In this part of the book we shall take the next step: we shall examine the causes of motions or of changes in motion. This study is called *dynamics.*

Newton's law of motion, on which we now base our understanding of dynamics, does go beyond kinematic description. For example, we make use of it when we design rockets and launch man-made satellites. In this part of the book, once we have understood Newton's law, we shall apply it to the motions of the moon and planets. Like Newton, we shall find the connection between the time it takes a planet to move around the sun and the gravitational attraction between chunks of matter. In Part IV we shall use the same law of motion to study electrical forces and to enter the submicroscopic world. With this single law we shall investigate motion throughout all this range.

Amid the complex motions of complicated bodies, flying, tumbling, and vibrating, we shall find certain aspects of simplicity. With the aid of Newton's law we can find in all these various motions some properties which remain unchanged, new quantities which are conserved while all else changes. The conservation laws eventually carry us outside the range of mechanical behavior. We can change mechanical energy into electrical energy. But to understand energy we start with Newton's law.

20–1. Ideas About Force and Motion

Questions about the causes of motion arose in the mind of man more than twenty-five centuries ago, but our present answers were not found until the time of Galileo (1564–1642) and Newton (1642–1727).

Let us start in terms of our own personal experience. What sort of thing do we associate with the "cause of motion"? The answer is muscular pulls or pushes (Fig. 20–1). To move a piano across a room you have to do a lot of pushing. To move a sheet of paper off your desk takes very little push. These pulls or pushes we call *forces.* The notion of force as used in physics certainly started this way. Later, as understanding grew, the idea of force was extended to include all causes of motion. The pull of a magnet on a nail is a force; it can change the nail's motion in the same way that a muscular force can.

20–1. All pushes and pulls are called forces.

More specifically, what is the relation between force and motion? Suppose we move a desk across the floor. We must apply a force all the time to keep it moving steadily from one side of the room to the other. Similarly, a horse must keep pulling on a wagon to keep it rolling at constant speed. Everyday experience seems to indicate that it is necessary to exert a force constantly to maintain a steady motion such as motion in a straight line with constant speed (Fig. 20–2). Aristotle (384–322 B.C.) had noted this fact. He concluded that a constant force was required to produce a constant velocity. It then follows that in the absence of force bodies would come to rest.

The hypothesis that in the absence of outside forces bodies would come to rest and stay at rest helps us to understand a great many observed motions, but it does not explain *all* the motions which occur in nature. For example, the Greeks were aware that bodies fell with increasing speed without the application of any evident outside force. They were also acquainted with the motions of the sun, moon, and stars which seem to occur without pushes or pulls to maintain them. There seemed to be three kinds of motion. We must explain not only the motion of things we push around on the surface of the earth, but also the motion of bodies falling to earth and the unceasing motions of heavenly bodies. Aristotle explained that ordinary matter falls toward the earth because the earth is the center of the universe to which matter naturally moves. He proposed that celestial matter was fundamentally different in nature from matter on earth and that it therefore obeyed different laws. To Aristotle, celestial matter had the built-in property of supplying from within itself the force necessary to maintain the observed motions.

We need not think that these separate explanations for three different classes of observed motions are foolish. We often do the same thing. When we see a piece of metal that attracts iron nails, we say it is a magnet — a different kind of matter from wood; and we may investigate its magnetic behavior separately from its nonmagnetic behavior. When we see a comb that attracts our hair, we say it is electrified, and we may explain its electrical behavior separately from its usual mechanical behavior. Of course we try, as the Greeks tried, to explain all we observe, but there are other desirable objectives. Explaining as much as we can with as few assumptions as possible is preferable to making a separate model for each new observation. As far as we can, we describe wood, magnets, and electrified combs in a

20–2. Steady motion seems to require a steady force.

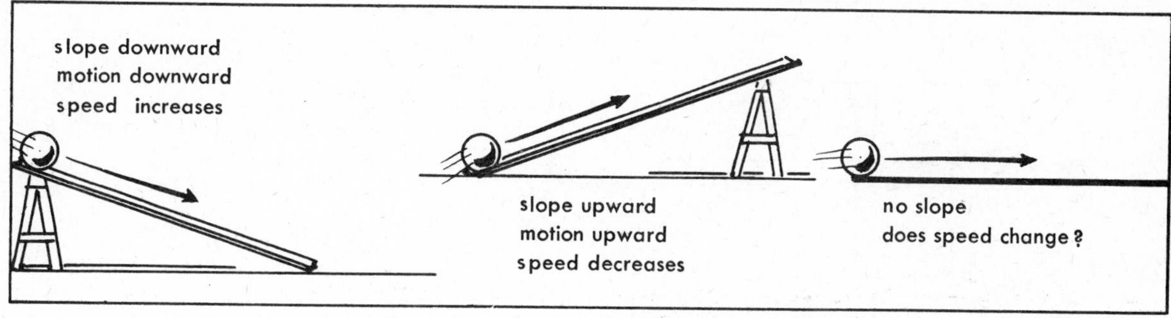

20–3. From observing motion on inclined planes, Galileo reasoned that motion along a horizontal plane is steady.

single model, as simple as we can make it. Likewise, we try to explain all motion on one theory rather than three.

A modern Aristotle would hardly explain the unceasing nature of celestial motion by invoking a distinct kind of matter. We can send our own earthly matter into the celestial realm. The world of motion on earth and the unceasing motions of the planets are now united. The artificial satellites offer us an excellent demonstration that we need assume no difference between earthly matter and celestial. Our understanding of the motion of falling bodies, of heavenly bodies, and of bodies which we ourselves push and pull along the surface of the earth is now described in a single fundamental law of motion. The satellites were designed, built, and fired according to this law. Their behavior is one of many pieces of evidence that Newton's law of motion encompasses the three types of motions described by Aristotle.

20–2. Motion Without Force

For two thousand years after the time of Aristotle, the apparent difference between celestial motions and motion on earth halted significant progress in dynamics. Then in the seventeenth century Galileo took the first big step toward creating a single explanation of both these types of motion. He asserted that . . . "any velocity once imparted to a body will be rigidly maintained as long as there are no causes of acceleration or retardation, a condition which is approached only on horizontal planes where the force of friction has been minimized." This statement embodies Galileo's law of inertia. Briefly it says: When no force is exerted on a body, it stays at rest or it moves in a straight line with constant speed.

How did Galileo reach the startling conclusion, so different from everyday experience, that constant motion requires no force? He was studying the motions of various objects on an inclined plane. He noted that "in the case of planes that slope downward there is already present a cause of acceleration, while on planes sloping upward there is retardation." (Fig. 20–3.) From this experience he reasoned that when the plane slopes neither upward nor downward there should be neither acceleration nor retardation. ". . . motion along a horizontal plane should be constant." Of course Galileo knew that such horizontal motions were not in fact constant, but he saw that when there was less friction, bodies moved for a longer time with nearly constant velocity. Because of his arguments he was convinced that friction provided the forces which stop bodies in horizontal motion, and in the absence of all forces the bodies would continue to move forever. He therefore stated his result for the idealized situation in which *no* forces act.

In a second series of experiments, Galileo showed that if he placed two of his inclined planes facing each other (as in Fig. 20–4, top), an object starting from rest would roll down one and up the other until it almost reached its original height. Friction prevented it from attaining this height, but Galileo saw that this height was the limit to the motion. He reasoned that if the slope of the upward plane is decreased, as in the middle of Fig. 20–4, the distance that the object will travel to reach its original height will increase. If, as in the bottom portion of Fig. 20–4, the slope is finally reduced to zero, so that the second plane is a horizontal surface, the object will never attain its initial height. It should travel on forever. "From this," Galileo again concluded, "it follows that motion along a horizontal plane is perpetual."

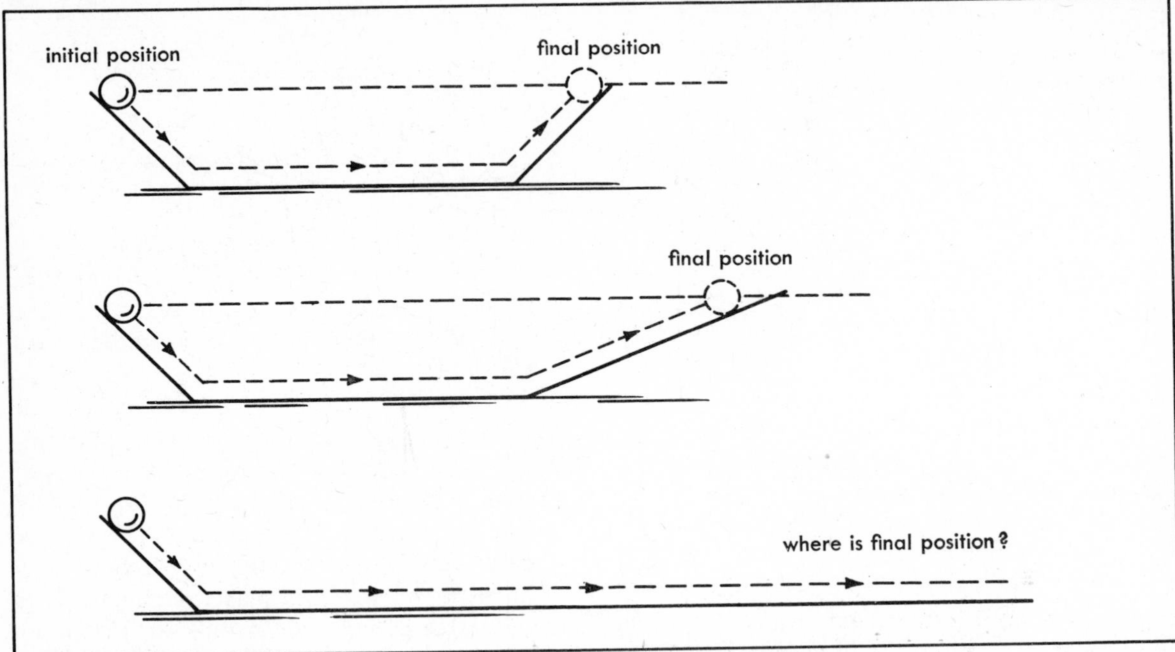

20–4. Galileo observed that a ball tends to rise to its original height regardless of the slope of the incline. With zero slope, the original height can never be reached. Therefore motion along a horizontal plane should be perpetual.

Galileo's experiments are not difficult, nor is there any evidence that he performed them with exceptional skill. Some, like the extension of the experiment at the bottom of Fig. 20–4 to the idealized case of perpetual motion, were not "real" experiments. They were experiments in thought alone. But they were based on solid fact. It is just this combination of thinking and fact that distinguishes Galileo's work. It was this combination which allowed him to pick out the useful idealization despite the great variety of observed motions. His principle of inertia was the great break-through which enabled Newton to build up our present understanding of dynamics.

Many of the motions Galileo analyzed, and those which Newton later studied, were so highly idealized that they seem to have very little to do with motions of real systems as we observe them. But it was only by careful consideration of these idealized situations that Galileo and Newton made their great contributions to mechanics. In the same way, we must look hard at very simple and idealized motions to obtain a real understanding of the basis of dynamics. Then, and only then, will we be ready to apply dynamics to the ordinary complex world.

With modern equipment we can do experiments that almost realize Galileo's idealized experiment on motion without force. To get the flash photograph of Fig. 20–5 (b), we used a disc sliding across a metal plate on a layer of gas. The gas bearing almost eliminates friction. In Fig. 20–5 (a), you can see a disc of the kind we used. The top of the disc is painted black and white to make it easy to locate the center. Underneath there is a white layer of Dry Ice. This frozen carbon dioxide changes slowly into gas; it continuously provides the gas bearing on which the disc rides. The photograph in Fig. 20–5 (b) was taken by flashing a light every $\frac{1}{10}$ sec as a disc coasted over the smooth aluminum plate. As you can see, the distance traveled between flashes is almost constant. The velocity hardly changes at all. From such experiments we can calculate that if this disc were set going at about 10 miles per hour on a long-enough horizontal plate, it would coast for about 2 miles.

20–3. Changes in Velocity When a Constant Force Acts

Galileo's law of inertia tells us that an object on which no force acts moves with unchanging ve-

20–5 (a). A disc, consisting of a layer of metal on a layer of Dry Ice, rests on a thick aluminum sheet. With such apparatus we can study almost frictionless motion.

20–5 (b). The motion of a disc with a Dry Ice bearing. The disc moved from left to right while the light was flashed every $\frac{1}{10}$ sec. The scale at the top is in centimeters. Here is a close approach to the ideal situation of motion without force. The disc moves nearly equal distances in equal time intervals.

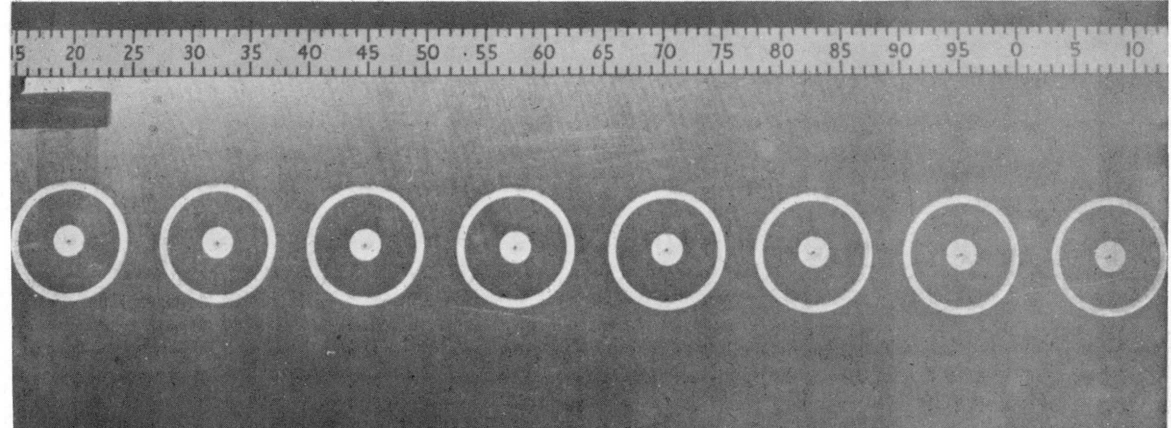

locity. If the velocity changes, we conclude that some force is acting on the object. What is the relation between force and change in velocity?

We shall begin our study of this question with the simplest experiment we can imagine. We shall apply a single force to a single object. To minimize other effects we use one of the same Dry Ice bearings on the same metal plate with which we examined motion with no force. The force we now apply is therefore the only force we need consider.

We need some way to recognize when the applied force is constant. For this purpose we employ a spring attached to the disc [Fig. 20–6 (a)]. It is common experience that the force exerted by a spring increases in some manner with the stretch of the spring. Also, whenever a particular spring is stretched a definite amount it seems to exert

20–6 (a). Unextended spring mounted on disc.

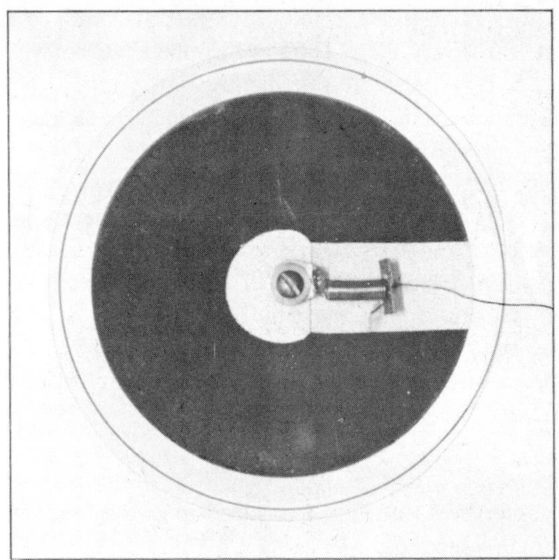

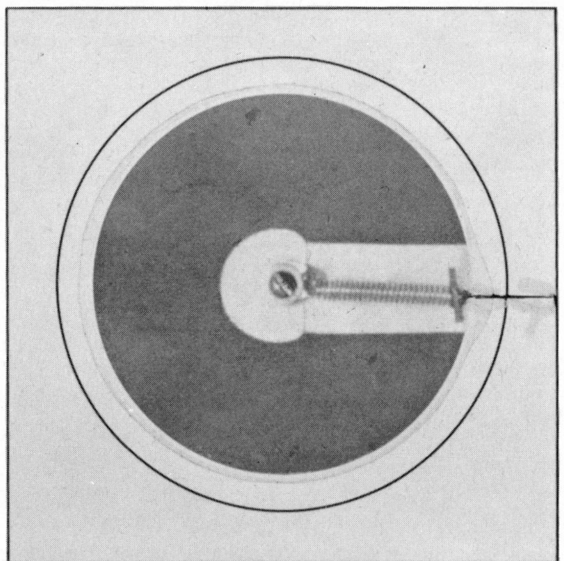

20–6 (b). The spring extended. Whenever this spring is stretched the same definite amount, we seem to get the same force.

the same force. We shall assume that the force exerted by our spring is the same whenever it is stretched the same amount [Fig. 20–6 (b)].

We now pull our disc in such a way that the spring is always stretched the same amount, and record the motion of the disc by flash photography. The result of such an experiment is shown in Fig. 20–7. In this experiment the light flashed at intervals of one-fifth of a second. We can see the successive positions of the disc, and we can see that the extension of the spring remained constant. The disc started from rest and moved in the direction of the force we applied. Clearly, in each time interval the distance traveled by the disc increased. Therefore the speed $v = \Delta x/\Delta t$ increased. By measuring the successive changes in position, we can establish quantitatively how the speed changed. As Table 1 shows, in each $\frac{1}{5}$ second after the motion started, the speed changed by almost exactly 20 cm/sec. Dividing the change of 20 cm/sec by the time interval of $\frac{1}{5}$ sec, we see that the speed changed at the constant rate of 100 cm/sec/sec. The change of v in any interval Δt of time is

$$\Delta v = 100\Delta t,$$

where the speeds are measured in cm/sec and the time in seconds.

Table 1

Data from Experiment Shown in Fig. 20–7

Interval No.	Interval Length Δx(cm)	Average Speed in Interval $\Delta x/\Delta t = v$(cm/sec)	Change in Speed Δv(cm/sec)
1	5.68	28.4	
			19.0
2	9.48	47.4	
			20.1
3	13.5	67.5	
			19.0
4	17.3	86.5	
			20.0
5	21.3	106.5	
			20.0
6	25.3	126.5	

We began our measurements with interval 1, *since it is doubtful that the light flashed at the instant the disc started moving. All time intervals were* $\frac{1}{5}$ *sec. The average-speed column was therefore made by dividing the second column by* $\frac{1}{5}$ *sec. The last column shows how the speed increased in* $\frac{1}{5}$*-sec intervals. It was made by finding the differences in speed during successive intervals. For example, the difference between the speed* 28.4 *cm/sec in interval* 1 *and the speed* 47.4 *cm/sec in interval* 2 *is* 19.0 *cm/sec. Within the limits of our experimental accuracy, the change in speed* Δv *is constant* ($\approx$ 20 *cm/sec*) *in equal time intervals* Δt *of* 0.20 *sec.*

The particular value 100 cm/sec² occurs in this experiment because we pulled with a particular force on a particular object. When we pull with other forces or pull on other objects, we usually obtain other values of the proportionality factor. But all experiments like the one just described show that under influence of a constant force the speed changes in direct proportion to the time the force acts.

In this example the disc moves in only one direction without reversing. But if the disc were slowed down and its direction of motion reversed, v would become negative. Consequently we see that v is the velocity, rather than just its magnitude, the speed.

20–4. Dependence of Change of Velocity on Magnitude of Force

What happens when we apply a different constant force to the same body? Let us apply twice

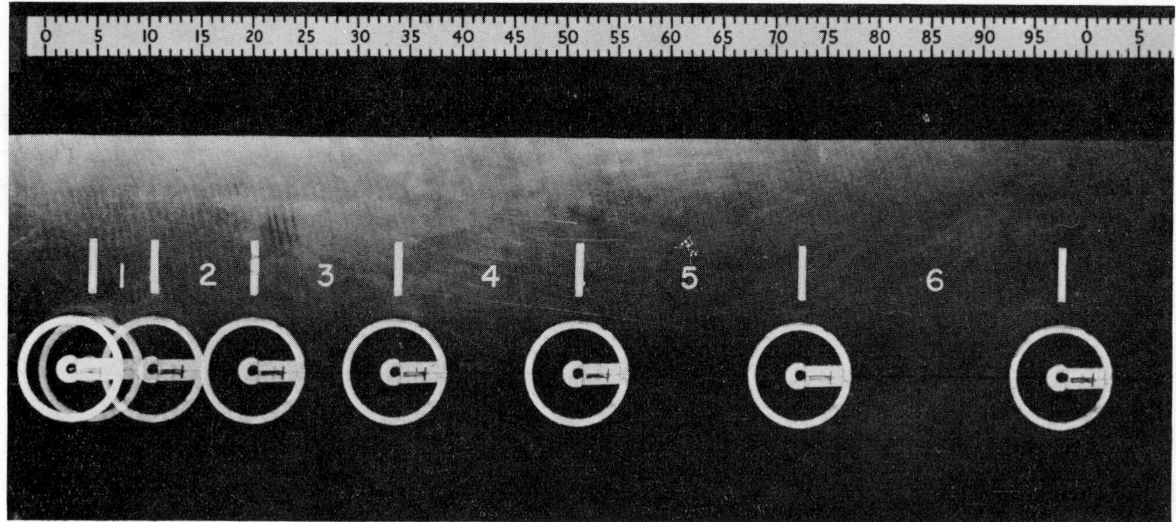

20–7. This flash photograph shows the disc being pulled to the right. The light flashes were separated by $\frac{1}{5}$ sec. A constant force was applied by keeping the spring extension constant. The distance the disc moves in each interval marked on the photograph has been measured and appears in Table 1.

the force and see what happens. This simple suggestion raises a new problem. We have seen that we could use a spring to remove the human element from the operation of applying a force of a particular size, giving us confidence that we applied the same force throughout our last experiment. But how can we use the spring to apply twice the force?

One simple way of getting twice the force is suggested by the familiar fact that two men can push harder than one. Thus two men may be needed to push a stalled car which one alone could not move. We can arrange two springs to give twice the force that one gives. Let us construct a second spring as nearly identical with the first as we can make it. When we stretch the second spring the same amount as the first, it should exert an equal force. We can assure ourselves that the forces are equal by doing our last experiment over again with the new spring. When the force is the same as before, the disc speeds up in just the same way as before. We thus show that the new spring gives the same force as the old one.

Now we can apply twice the old force to the disc. We hook both springs to the disc side by side and pull each of them in the same direction [Fig. 20–8 (a)]. We make sure that each spring is extended the same amount as in the original experiment with one spring, and we observe the motion in the same way as before. In this way we can double the force on the disc, leaving everything else the same.

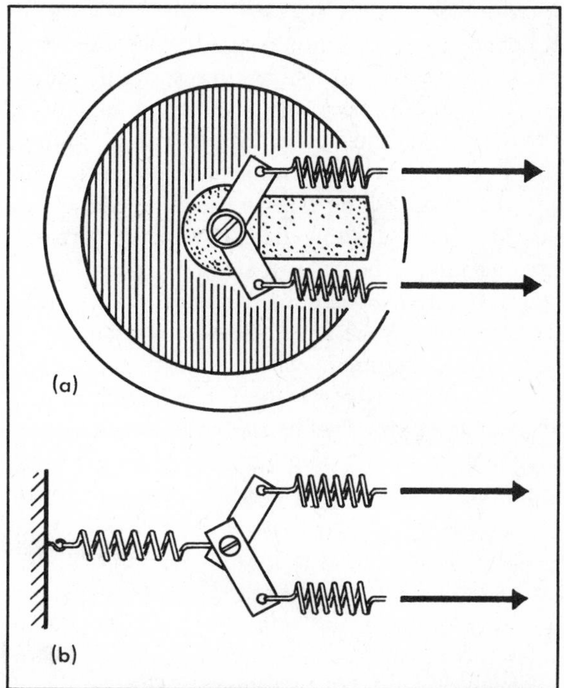

20–8. To apply twice the original force, we attach two identical springs to the disc (a). For convenience we may use a third spring that applies the same force as our two identical springs pulling together. The diagram in (b) shows how the springs could be arranged to establish the correct extension of the third spring.

Sometimes it is inconvenient to yoke two springs side by side on our test body. But we can easily apply a force of double strength to the disc by

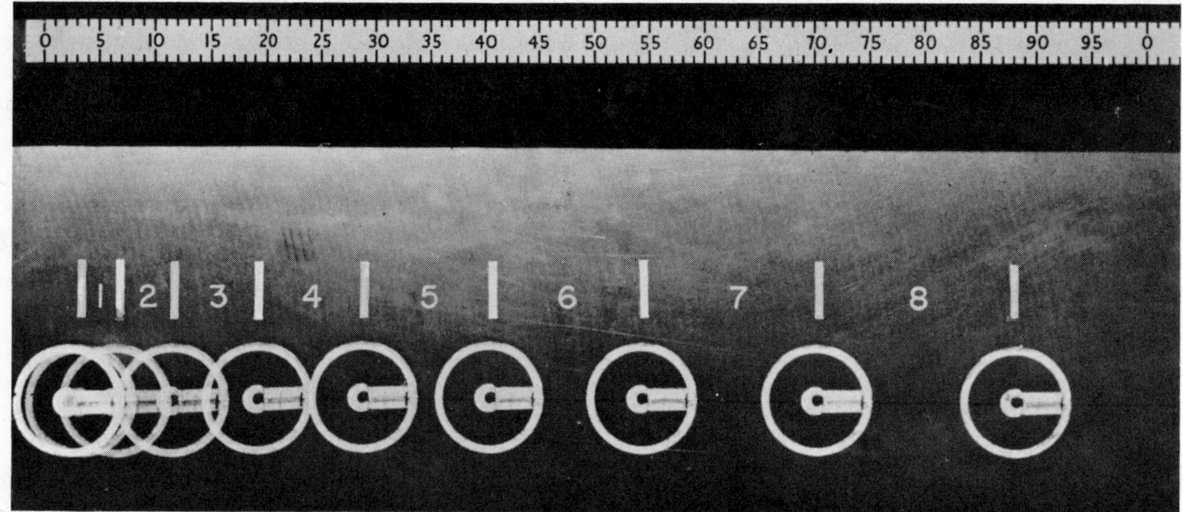

20–9. The disc used in the first experiment is accelerated by twice the force used before. The interval between flashes has been reduced to $\frac{1}{10}$ sec to catch the more rapid motion.

Table 2

Data from Experiment Shown in Fig. 20–9

Interval No.	Interval Length Δx(cm)	Average Speed in Interval $\Delta x/\Delta t = v$(cm/sec)	Change in Speed Δv(cm/sec)
3	7.7	77	
			19
4	9.6	96	
			19
5	11.5	115	
			21
6	13.6	136	
			20
7	15.6	156	
			21
8	17.7	177	

These are the results of an experiment in which the applied force was twice that used in the first experiment (Table 1). The pictures were taken every $\frac{1}{10}$ sec. Note, therefore, that the change in speed occurred in a time interval half as great as before. The rate of change of speed is therefore about 200 cm/sec/sec. (Intervals 1 and 2 were not used because the overlapping of the successive exposures made the picture too hard to measure in this region; interval 3 is still somewhat more dubious than the others used.)

stretching a third spring with our two identical ones yoked together and noting the stretch of this third spring which results when the double force is acting [Fig. 20–8 (b)]. Then we can always apply the doubled force by using the third spring stretched this new amount. We have used this procedure to put a doubled force on the same disc as before. The result is shown in Fig. 20–9.

What do we find? The data in Table 2, taken with exactly the same arrangement as before but with the light flashing every tenth of a second and the force doubled, show that the velocity increases twice as fast as before. Instead of $\Delta v = 100\Delta t$, we obtain $\Delta v = 200\Delta t$, where again we measure the speeds in cm/sec and the times in seconds.

Further experiments show that this result is general. Whenever we double the force on a given object, we double the rate at which its velocity changes. Moreover, if we make the force three times as large by putting three identical springs side by side, we triple the rate at which the velocity changes. From many measurements of this kind we conclude that the change in velocity of a body in a given time interval is proportional to the force F that acts on the body.

We have now found two things. The change in velocity Δv increases with the length of time interval Δt, and it is greater the greater the force. We can combine this information in one statement: Δv is proportional to $F\Delta t$.

20–5. Inertial Mass

The change Δv produced by a given force F acting for a given time Δt depends on the object on which the force acts. Applying equal forces for the same time to a baseball and to an elephant produces less change in the velocity of the elephant.

Because larger bodies are less easily accelerated by forces, it is convenient to write the proportionality between $F\Delta t$ and Δv in the form:

$$F\Delta t = m\Delta v.$$

The proportionality constant m depends on the object. Its value increases with the size of the body, at least for objects made of one uniform substance.

The constant m is called the *inertial mass* of the body. By rearranging the above equation, we define m as $F\Delta t/\Delta v$ for a given object. This ratio is experimentally constant and it tells how difficult it is to change the velocity of the body. As you already know, $\Delta v/\Delta t$ is the rate of change of velocity, or the acceleration a, in the direction of the force. The inertial mass can therefore be written $m = F/a$. The greater the force needed to produce a given acceleration, the greater the inertial mass of the object.

Naturally we wish to know whether inertial mass, this measure of the difficulty of accelerating a body, is a new property of a body. Is it unrelated to anything we know already, is it some familiar property in a different guise, or is it some combination of familiar properties? To answer these questions, we investigate the relation of the inertial mass to the shape, size, composition — in fact to any other known property of an object.

Of course, we do not look about at random. As the example of the elephant and baseball shows, our experience already indicates that size is a reasonable place to start. But volume alone will not do. A hollow elephant, on a float in the Mardi Gras parade, is not so hard to accelerate as a real elephant; so let us start with objects of uniform composition. Let us try the effect of doubling the size of an object while keeping its composition uniform. One easy method is to use two identical discs. We can decide whether two discs are identical by subjecting them to the same force for equal times. If each gains the same speed, they have identical inertial masses.

Let us pull the two identical discs side by side, applying the same force to each with identical springs. The two discs travel along together, each gaining the same Δv as they progress. Next we join the discs rigidly together and pull them with both springs yoked side by side. Again, we would expect them to gain speed in the same way. Experiments show that this is so. Now let us try pulling the connected discs with the force of only one spring. This is half the previous force; and from what we know already, we expect that the double disc will gain speed at only half the previous rate. Again experiment confirms our expectation. In other words, when we apply one standard force to two standard discs, the doubled disc speeds up just half as fast as a single disc does.

In all experiments with a double disc the ratio F/a is doubled. But this ratio is defined as the inertial mass of the body; so we have doubled the inertial mass by using two identical discs. These experiments indicate that mass is directly proportional to the size of bodies made from the same material. Further experiments, using various numbers of pieces of the same substance, all agree with this conclusion.

There is nothing magic about discs and Dry Ice bearings. We can investigate the dependence of inertial mass on the number of pieces by joining together numbers of identical well-loaded model railroad cars, with carefully made bearings so that there is little friction in the wheels. Such experiments are not quite so close to the ideal of eliminating all forces except those we apply on purpose, but the proportionality of the inertial mass to the number of cars is still clearly evident.

Our results for identical bodies are not astonishing. The real questions about inertial mass arise when we consider objects made of different materials. We cannot have a piece of silver identical with a piece of gold. But we can find pieces that have the same inertial mass, pieces for which F/a is the same. Such pieces are certainly not identical in size or composition. Inertial mass is, then, not entirely a matter of size.

What happens when we join together a piece of silver and a piece of gold of the same inertial mass? To find the inertial mass of the new body we pull it with various forces F for certain times Δt. We find that F/a, the inertial mass of the new body, is just twice the inertial mass of each original piece. Thus when we add the pieces together, we also add their inertial masses. In fact, we can take any piece of gold and any piece of silver and measure their individual inertial masses, m_1 and m_2. When we join these bodies together we find that the inertial mass, m, of the combination, again measured as F/a, is now equal to the sum of the two original inertial masses: $m = m_1 + m_2$. The same is true for bodies made of any other substances. Inertial masses are additive.

In concluding that inertial masses add, we have concluded that the inertial mass does not depend on the shape or the chemical nature of an object. We did not specify how we combined silver and gold pieces, nor do we need to. If we melt down any object and cast it again in any shape we choose, the ratio F/a will not be affected.

Let us go even further. Suppose we measure the inertial mass of a flashbulb, then flash it so that the magnesium and oxygen inside combine to form magnesium oxide. We find that the chemical combination has not affected the inertial mass. Or, we can place separate solutions of sodium carbonate (washing soda) and calcium chloride in a closed vessel (Fig. 20–10). We measure the inertial mass of this system, then upset the container so that the substances react to form calcium carbonate (an insoluble white solid) and a solution of table salt. When we measure the inertial mass again, we find no change.

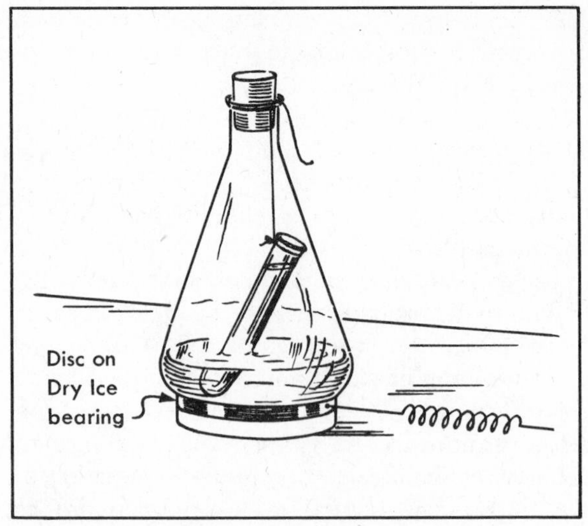

20–10. Apparatus used in an experiment to show that inertial mass does not change in chemical reactions.

What then do we know about inertial mass? It increases in proportion to the amount of a single substance in an object. When various pieces of matter are put together, the inertial masses add irrespective of the nature of the materials involved. Finally, inertial mass is conserved in chemical reactions.

20–6. Inertial and Gravitational Mass

The properties of inertial mass remind us of the properties of mass as measured on a balance (Chapter 7). When a balance is in equilibrium we say that we have equal masses on each side. The masses thus measured are called *gravitational* masses because at equilibrium the gravitational pull of the earth on each mass is the same. Actually the earth is not important; the property we measure is a property of the body alone. The balance works just as well at the top of a mountain where the pull of the earth on each object is weaker. It would work as well on the moon where the masses we compare would be pulled still more weakly. The only important thing in measuring gravitational mass is that we compare gravitational pulls on the objects when they are in the same place in relation to the other pieces of matter in the universe.

In terms of the measurements by which we determine them the gravitational mass and the inertial mass have no connection. To measure inertial mass we apply a force to an object and find its acceleration. Gravity is irrelevant. On the other hand, when we measure gravitational mass by using a balance in equilibrium under gravitational forces, we do not have any motion and we must have gravitational forces. Two measurements could hardly differ more completely. Nevertheless the properties of the gravitational mass are strikingly similar to those we have just found for inertial mass. The gravitational mass of one substance is proportional to the amount of the substance present. Gravitational masses of any substances add. Gravitational mass is conserved in chemical reactions.

The additivity of masses of each kind and the conservation of each kind of mass in chemical reactions suggest that the gravitational and inertial mass may be proportional for any object. This proportionality can be tested by measuring the inertial and gravitational masses of many different objects, objects of different compositions. In fact such experiments have been done many times over. To within our best experimental accuracy, the inertial masses of all objects are proportional to their gravitational masses.

The equivalence of inertial and gravitational mass — their experimentally revealed proportionality — makes it convenient to use the same standard of mass for both. The kilogram — that carefully protected cylinder of platinum alloy at Sèvres — is the standard unit of both gravitational and inertial mass. To find the inertial mass m of an object in kilograms, we accelerate the object and accelerate a standard kilogram mass m_s with the same force. Then we know that $m = F/a$ while $m_s = F/a_s$; therefore

$$\frac{m}{m_s} = \frac{a_s}{a}.$$

Because $m_s = 1$ kg, the mass m in kg is given by the ratio a_s/a. For example, if a certain force accelerates a kilogram mass at $\frac{1}{2}$ m/sec^2 and another object at 2 m/sec^2, the mass of the other object is $\frac{1}{4}$ kg.

It is often difficult to establish the idealized conditions in which we can attach a particular force to an object and can be sure that no unknown forces influence the resultant motion. But we need not measure the inertial mass of every object in which we are interested in this direct way. Because of the equivalence of inertial and gravitational mass, a measurement of gravitational mass tells us the inertial mass. We need not normally worry about the distinction between them, and we usually use the word "mass" alone to refer to either one.

20–7. Newton's Law: Dynamical Measurement of Force; Units

The relation $F\Delta t = m\Delta v$ tells us how the change in velocity Δv is related to the inertial mass m, to the cause of motion F, and to the time Δt that the force acts. This relation embodies Newton's law of motion.*

When we know the mass of an object, we can use Newton's law in either of two ways. We can predict the change in velocity of the object if we know the force F and the time Δt that it acts; or we can determine the force by observing the change in velocity it imparts to the object. When we observe the acceleration of a body and thus determine the force acting on it, it is convenient to write Newton's law as

$$F = m\frac{\Delta v}{\Delta t}$$

or

$$F = ma,$$

showing explicitly that the force is proportional to the acceleration. In this form the cause of the motion is on one side of the equation and the inertial mass of the body and its motion are on the other.

Suppose that we observe the same object in two different experiments. Perhaps we see that it speeds up three times as fast in the second experiment as in the first. We can then conclude that the force acting in the second experiment is three times as great as the force in the first experiment. In other words, we can use the acceleration $a = \Delta v/\Delta t$ of a given object as a measure of the force, just as we used it earlier to establish the equality of the forces exerted by two identical springs when they produced equal acceleration on the same object.

We now have a dynamical method to determine both inertial masses and forces. We start with a kilogram mass. We use the force which accelerates it at the rate of 1 m/sec^2 as our unit of force. It is called a *newton.* To measure another mass we determine its acceleration when acted on by our 1-newton force. By definition its inertial mass is F/a; and in this case where the force is 1 newton, the mass in kilograms is $m = (1 \text{ newton})/a$, where a is expressed in meters/sec^2. In this way we have used one standard mass to give us a standard force. Then we have used the standard force and the relation $m = F/a$ to measure the masses of other objects that interest us.

We can also use the same relation to find other forces. From $F = ma$ we can determine any force which acts on one of our known masses by measuring the acceleration it produces. The acceleration in meters/sec^2 times the mass in kg gives the force in newtons.

20–8. Forces That Change, and Newton's Law

We have discussed Newton's law of motion under what appear to be rather special conditions. For simplicity, we have accelerated masses from rest using a constant force. Does the connection that we have found between force and acceleration hold equally well if we change the magnitude of the force while a body is in motion?

Suppose we push some object, initially at rest, with a steady force for a definite time. It will gain speed as long as we push it. If we stop

*What we call Newton's law is often called his second law, and Galileo's principle of inertia, which is a special case of the general law, is sometimes called Newton's first law. The names of Newton's first and second laws don't change the content, but it may be important to know them so that you can understand what someone means when he says, "According to Newton's first law . . ."

pushing, acceleration ceases; the body moves on at constant velocity. If we begin pushing again, we again get acceleration. Suppose we apply a force in the direction opposite to the motion. Then we expect the acceleration to be in the direction of the force. Because it is opposite to the motion, the object should slow down instead of speeding up. Experiments show that the rate of slowing down is indeed F/m where F is the force and m the inertial mass.

Whether a body is standing still or sailing through outer space at 10^5 m/sec, a force will accelerate it: $a = F/m$. We need not consider what velocity the body now has, nor what process produced this velocity. No matter what the past history or the present motion of a body, a given force applied in the direction of motion will produce the same acceleration. The equation $F\Delta t = m\Delta v$ emphasizes that we can chop out any period of time, large or small, and during this Δt we will find a definite Δv depending only on inertial mass and applied force — no matter what comes before or after in the progress of the body.

What we have said in this section is observed experimentally to extremely high accuracy. But when we observe masses moving at increasingly greater speeds, slight discrepancies between the observed behavior and Newton's law become apparent. By the time the speed has increased to 10^8 m/sec, deviations of a few per cent occur. The equation $F\Delta t = m\Delta v$ is no longer an adequate description. By extending the range of observations, we thus learn that Newton's law must be modified. It must be extended so that in its new form it makes slightly different statements about objects moving at high-enough speeds. On the other hand, at lower speeds it must continue to say the same thing that we have stated here. Einstein and others have formulated the needed extension for ultra-high speeds. This modification does not overthrow Newton's law: it includes and extends it.

20–9. How Forces Add; the Net Force

So far we have studied the motion of an object acted on by a single force. What happens when two or more forces act on the same object? Recall, for example, the Dry Ice puck pulled by two identical springs yoked one next to the other. As we learned, with this arrangement the force on the puck is twice that of the single spring; and the acceleration that results is twice the acceleration imparted by one spring. The acceleration is proportional to the sum of the two individual spring forces.

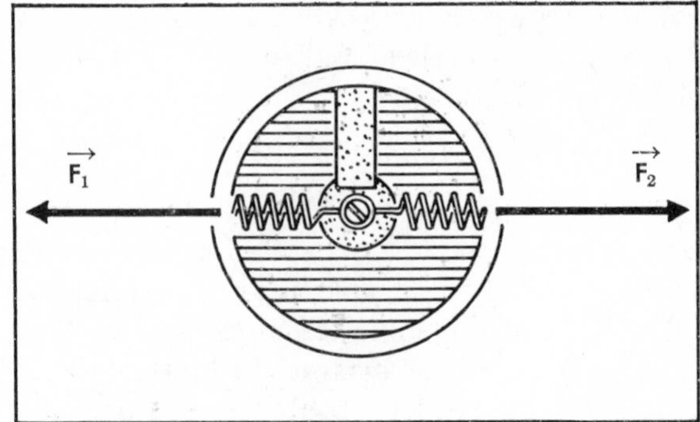

20–11. Two forces, equal in magnitude but opposite in direction, are acting on a Dry Ice disc. The net force is zero, and the observed acceleration is zero.

We can also make two identical springs, each stretched the same amount, pull in opposite directions (Fig. 20–11). Then no acceleration takes place. For example, if you and a friend pull equally hard on a book, but in opposite directions, the book does not accelerate. Because they are oppositely directed, the forces on the book add to zero. Apparently the net force, the force which changes the motion, is obtained by adding the forces in the same way that we added trips or vectors in Part I. As far as their effect on the motion is concerned, two forces of equal magnitude and opposite direction just cancel, and one of them can be considered to be the negative of the other.

In general, when we apply forces on an object in opposite directions, the acceleration of the object is found to be proportional to the sum of the forces taken with the direction included. When a force of 1 newton acts to the left, and a force of 3 newtons pulls to the right on a Dry Ice disc, the disc accelerates to the right in just the way it does when a single force of 2 newtons acts on it. The net force of 2 newtons is the sum of the individual forces taken as indicated in Fig. 20–12. Furthermore, when any number of individual forces act on an object, we find that Newton's law of motion holds and the observed acceleration arises from the net force.

Two forces need not pull in the same or in opposite directions; they may be pulling at an angle to each other. What is then the direction

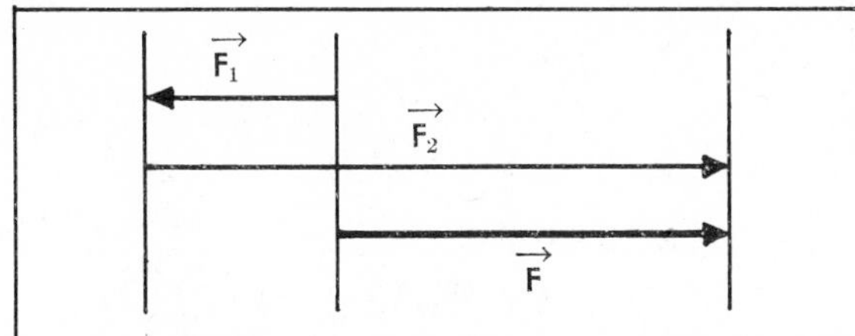

20–12. A force $\vec{F_2}$ of 3 newtons is acting to the right, and a force $\vec{F_1}$ of 1 newton is acting to the left. Adding them like trips, we obtain the sum $\vec{F}$ of 2 newtons acting to the right. This is the net force that appears in Newton's law.

and magnitude of the net force? Suppose we pull equally hard on an object, with each of two identical springs as in Fig. 20–13. We find that the object accelerates along the line bisecting the angle between the directions of the two forces, the line dotted in the figure. Apparently we have applied a net force along the dotted line. It is easy to jump to the conclusion that the net force is the vector sum of the two separate spring forces. Experiments show that this is indeed the case. The acceleration imparted by the two springs in Fig. 20–13 is given by $F = ma$ where F is the magnitude of the vector that we obtain by treating each individual force as a vector and adding them together to get the net force vector (Fig. 20–14). Also when the two forces are not equal or when there are more than two forces, the magnitude and direction of the net force is given by the vector sum of the individual forces. This net force determines the acceleration in accord with $a = F/m$.

Let us sum up what we have learned so far. We started out by studying the acceleration of bodies from rest under the influence of a single force. This led us to Newton's law of motion. We then investigated what happens to a body which is already moving when a force acts on it in the direction of motion or opposite to it. We found that Newton's law still holds. We then asked what happens if several forces act on a body. Again, Newton's law holds as if a single force, the net force, acts on the body. The net force is the vector sum of all the forces.

20–10. The Vector Nature of Newton's Law

Newton's law is even more general than we have yet indicated. So far we have applied a net force only along the direction of motion of an object or

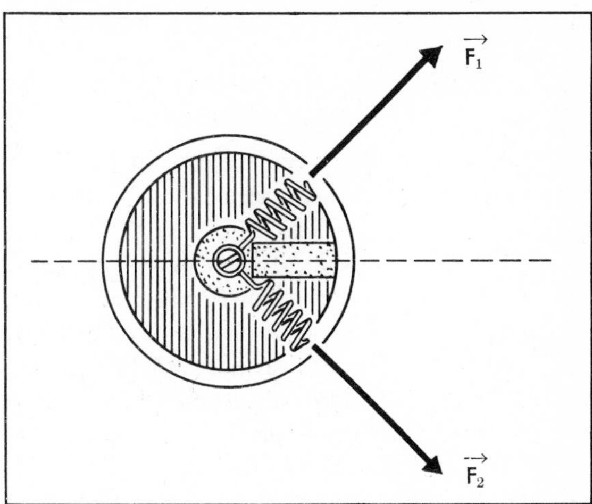

20–13. Two forces of equal magnitude act at an angle to each other. The object accelerates along the dotted line bisecting the angle between the directions of the two forces. We conclude that the net force acted along this line.

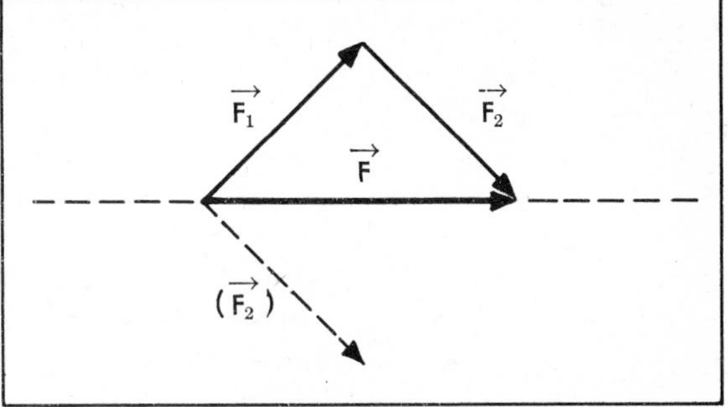

20–14. The vector addition of the two forces that are shown in Fig. 20–13. The sum is the net force which determines both direction and magnitude of the acceleration of a given mass.

opposite to it. As a result of these net forces we change the speed of the object but not the direction of its motion. Forces, however, can be applied in other directions. We can shove a moving ball out of its course by pushing across its direction of motion. In general, then, we see that forces change the velocity vector describing the motion of an object either in magnitude or direction, or both. The force is itself a vector and Newton's law connects it with the rate of change of the vector velocity. We should write the law as

$$\vec{F}\Delta t = m\Delta\vec{v}$$

or

$$\vec{F} = m\frac{\Delta\vec{v}}{\Delta t} = m\vec{a},$$

where $\vec{a}$ is the vector acceleration. In the next chapter we shall see some of the evidence for the vector nature of Newton's law and discuss some of its implications.

20–11. Forces in Nature

When we pull an object, we cannot usually be sure that the force we exert is the only force acting on the object (Fig. 20–15).

Sometimes the origin of forces on an object is not immediately apparent, or forces may arise as a result of the motion of the object. For example, the wind pushing on the surface of a balloon can exert a force, and we must pull on the balloon in the opposite direction to prevent it from blowing away. Even if the air is still, when we move the balloon through it, the air gives rise to a force opposing the motion. When the balloon is in motion its acceleration is not given by the force we apply. It is given by the net force. If the net force is zero the acceleration is zero and the balloon moves at constant speed.

We can measure the force exerted by a steady wind going past the balloon by measuring the extension of a spring in a string holding the balloon still. This force increases with the speed of the wind. As we all know, when the wind blows faster, it blows harder. When we then pull the balloon through still air, we must subtract this force from the force we exert to get the net force that is responsible for the acceleration.

Frictional forces become evident when we try to move an object along a surface. Unlike the retarding force which arises when we pull a balloon through the air, frictional forces are often nearly independent of the speed of the object. It was undoubtedly the common occurrence of friction that led the Greeks to conclude that force was needed to maintain a constant motion. The force needed is equal and opposite to the forces of friction and air resistance. The net force is zero.

20–15. The force we exert may not be the only force that is acting.

The idea of force as a cause of motion is valuable because it enables us to predict what motion will occur in a given situation. The same forces occur over and over again whenever the same situation arises. Some forces are independent of motion; for example, the force of gravitational attraction, the weight of a body. As we shall see in the next chapter, this force is the same, whether the body moves or stands still. If we know our geographical position, we know what gravitational force to expect, and we can make predictions about the motions of a falling object. Other forces depend on the relative motion of one body with respect to another. One of the essential jobs we face is to learn about the forces in nature. Then we can use the observed forces to make predictions about motion and to design mechanical apparatus.

FOR HOME, DESK, AND LAB

1. A ball is released from rest on the left-hand incline of Fig. 20–4 at a height of 10 cm above the lowest point.

(a) If there is no friction, how high vertically will it rise on the right-hand incline?

(b) If the right-hand incline rises 1 cm for every 10 cm of horizontal distance, how far will the ball travel horizontally on it?

(c) If the incline rises only $\frac{1}{2}$ cm for every 10 cm of horizontal distance, how far will the ball go?

2. Why is it dangerous to step from a moving vehicle onto the ground? In what direction would you tend to fall?

3. Why is it particularly dangerous to drive on an icy highway?

4. A certain force exerted for 1.2 sec raises the speed of an object from 1.8 m/sec to 4.2 m/sec. Later, this same force is applied for 2.0 sec. How much

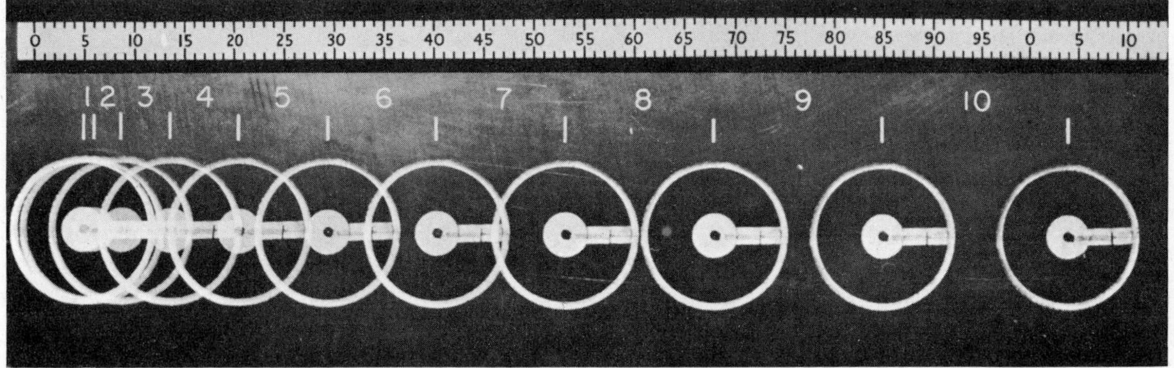

20–16. For Problem 15. The interval between flashes is $\frac{1}{5}$ second; the scale is in cm.

does the speed change in the 2-sec period? (In both cases, the force is applied in the direction of motion.)

5. A body is pulled across a smooth horizontal surface by a spring that is kept stretched by a constant amount. It is found that the body is accelerated at 15 cm/sec². What will be the acceleration of the body if it is pulled by two springs, each just like the first spring, side by side and stretched by the same amount? [See Fig. 20–8(a).]

6. An object sliding on a low-friction bearing is pulled with a constant force. In a time interval of 0.3 sec the speed changes from 0.2 m/sec to 0.4 m/sec. In a second trial, the object is pulled with another force. In the same length of time the speed now changes from 0.5 m/sec to 0.8 m/sec.

(a) What is the ratio of the second force to the first?

(b) If the body is pulled with the second force for 0.9 sec, what change in speed results? (Note that the forces are in the direction of motion.)

7. In Section 20–4 we discussed a way in which a stretched spring could be calibrated so that it exerts twice as much force as a standard spring stretched a given amount. Be ready to discuss in class how you would determine when a stretched spring exerts one-half as much force as the standard.

8. Suppose you accelerate an object with a steady force and find that the change in speed during a time interval Δt of 1 sec amounts to 2.4 m/sec. You now repeat the measurement using the same force with a second object. It gains 3.3 m/sec in 0.5 sec.

(a) Which body has the greater inertial mass?

(b) What is the ratio of the inertial mass of the second object to that of the first?

9. (a) Two blocks, made of different metals, identical in shape and size, are acted upon by equal forces which cause them to slide across a frictionless horizontal surface. The acceleration of the second block is found to be 4.18 times that of the first. What is the ratio of the mass of the second block to that of the first?

(b) The first block is known to be made of lead. Using the densities given in Table 2, Section 7–4, decide of what material the second block might be made.

10. Why is the flask in Fig. 20–10 closed? Be prepared to explain in class.

11. A body with a mass of 0.5 kg is accelerated at 4 m/sec². How large a force is acting?

12. A force of 3 newtons is applied to a mass of 0.6 kg. How fast does it accelerate?

13. A force of 5 newtons gives a mass m_1 an acceleration of 8 m/sec², and a mass m_2 an acceleration of 24 m/sec². What acceleration would it give the two when they are fastened together?

14. You have two objects, A and B, which balance each other when placed on opposite sides of an equal-arm balance. When you place both these objects on one side, they balance a third object C on the other side. Object A accelerates at 3.8 m/sec² when you apply a certain force. Suppose you now apply this same force to C. What is its acceleration?

15. In Fig. 20–16 measure Δx, the distance traveled in each interval, for intervals 5 through 10.

(a) What is the speed $\Delta x/\Delta t$ in each interval?

(b) What are the changes in speed Δv in each interval?

(c) What is the acceleration $\Delta v/\Delta t$ in each interval?

(d) Has a constant force been acting?

(e) Assuming the disc has a mass of 2 kg, what is the average applied force?

16. A force of 3.0 newtons is exerted on an object and it speeds up at 1.5 m/sec².

(a) Assuming that this is the only force on the object, what is the mass?

(b) How would you make an independent measurement of the mass?

(c) Suppose this measurement indicates that the mass determined by the first method is greater. What might you suspect?

17. Two bodies, one of mass 8.0 kg and the other of mass 2.0 kg, stand at rest on a smooth table top side by side. The 8-kg mass is accelerated from rest by a force of .70 newton and the 2-kg mass is accelerated from rest in the same direction by a force of 1.4 newtons. Both bodies start accelerating at the same instant of time.

(a) How long does it take before the separation of the bodies is 5.0 m?

(b) What is the velocity of each at this instant of time?

18. A block of mass 3.0 kg is moving along a smooth horizontal surface with a speed v_0 at an instant of time $t = 0$. A force of 18 newtons is applied to this body opposite to the direction of its motion. This force reduces v_0 to one-half its value while the body moves 9.0 m.

(a) How long does it take for this to occur?

(b) What is v_0?

19. If the distance covered by a moving object varies directly as the time, what conclusions could you draw about the motion and the forces?

20. You observe an object covering distance in direct proportion to t^3, where t is the time elapsed.

(a) What conclusion might you draw about the acceleration? Is it constant? Increasing? Decreasing? Zero?

(b) What might you conclude about the forces? Be prepared to discuss in class.

21. You pull a sliding disc with a constant force, starting from rest. The speed increases 0.10 m/sec in each Δt of 0.30 sec.

(a) How fast is the body moving after 1.2 sec?

(b) Now you begin pulling with the same force in the opposite direction. You continue pulling in the reverse direction for 0.90 sec. How fast is the body moving?

(c) In what direction is it moving?

22. A block of mass 2.0 kg is pulled on a frictionless table by a constant force of 6.0 newtons. The block starts from rest.

(a) What is the acceleration of the block expressed in meters/sec²?

(b) What is the speed of the block 3.0 sec after the force starts acting?

(c) How far does the block travel in 2.0 sec?

(d) If at the end of 3.0 sec, the block splits in two equal pieces — one piece still being pulled by the force of 6.0 newtons, and the other free — how far apart will the two pieces be 2.0 sec after the break occurs?

23. A block of mass 8.0 kg, starting from rest, is pulled along a horizontal table top by a constant force of 2.0 newtons. It is found that this body moves a distance of 3.0 m in 6.0 sec.

(a) What is the acceleration of the body?

(b) What is the ratio of the applied force to the mass?

(c) Since your answer to part (b) is not equal to that of part (a), (at least, it shouldn't be), what conclusions can you draw about this motion? Give numerical results, if possible.

24. A 6.0 kg object is acted upon by two forces of 3.0 newtons each.

(a) If these forces act at an angle of 90° with each other, what is the magnitude and the direction of the acceleration?

(b) What is the acceleration if the forces act in the same direction? In opposite directions?

25. A 3.0-newton force and a 4.0-newton force act on a 9.0-kg mass. The two forces act at an angle of 60° with each other.

(a) If the object starts from rest, how fast will it be moving after 3.0 sec?

(b) In what direction will it be moving?

26. Two men wish to pull down a tree by means of a rope fastened near the top. If they use one rope, the tree will come down on top of them. To prevent this, they tie two ropes 10.0 meters long to the same point and stand on the ground 10.0 meters apart when they pull. If each pulls with a force of 300 newtons, what is the force exerted by the ropes on the tree?

27. Find the applied force required to accelerate a 450-kg rocket from a standing start to a velocity of 60 m/sec along a 100-meter horizontal track. The retarding force of friction is 93 newtons.

28. The retarding force of air resistance on a balloon is proportional to the square of the velocity. For a certain balloon, inflated a certain amount, this force is given in newtons by $F_R = .2v^2$ where v is the velocity in m/sec. The balloon and the air inside have a combined mass of 10 gm.

(a) Draw graphs of the balloon's acceleration as a function of velocity when you pull it with a 1.8-newton force and with a 7.2-newton force.

(b) What is the maximum velocity that the balloon will reach in each case?

(c) If the mass were 5.0 gm, how would this affect the maximum velocity?

(d) What do you think would be the effect on the maximum velocity if you inflated the balloon to a larger volume?

29. Aristotle taught that a constant force was required to produce a constant velocity and from this he concluded that, in the absence of force, bodies would come to rest.

(a) Name several situations where a constant force seems to produce a constant velocity.

(b) How do you explain each of the situations in (a) in the light of Newton's law of motion?

30. How would you define a unit of mass if people had placed a standard spring at Sèvres instead of a standard mass?

FURTHER READING

COHEN, I. B., "Isaac Newton." *Scientific American*, December, 1955. A brief account of his life.

COHEN, I. B., *The Birth of a New Physics*. Doubleday, 1960: A Science Study Series paperback.

GALILEO, *Moments of Discovery*. Edited by G. Schwartz and P. Bishop, Basic Books, 1958 (p. 332). Galileo's own description of the laws of acceleration of falling bodies.

HOLTON, GERALD, *Introduction to Concepts and Theories in Physical Science*. Addison-Wesley, 1952. Chapter 4 gives a summary of Newton's law and Galileo's principle of inertia.

KNEDLER, J. W., Jr., *Masterworks of Science*. Doubleday, 1947. Chapters on Galileo and Newton describe their lives and work.

NEWTON, SIR ISAAC, *Mathematical Principles of Natural Philosophy* and his *System of the World*. Edited by Florian Cajori, University of California Press, 1947.

SCIAMA, D., "Inertia." *Scientific American*, February, 1957. A thought-provoking "second look" at the idea of inertia described in this chapter.

MOTION AT THE EARTH'S SURFACE

CHAPTER 21

IN THIS chapter we shall start our study of the forces occurring in nature. We shall determine them from the motions of the bodies on which they act, or, when possible, by balancing the unknown forces against known forces that we can apply. Here on the surface of the earth the force of gravity which pulls objects toward the center of the earth is familiar to us all. We shall first study this gravitational attraction.

21–1. Weight and the Gravitational Field of the Earth

We have already learned in Chapter 7 that objects on the surface of the earth are pulled toward its center. Different objects are pulled down by gravitational forces of different magnitude. The magnitude of this force on an object is called the weight of the object. It may be measured by hanging the object on a spring calibrated in newtons.

If we take a standard kilogram mass and measure its weight anywhere on the surface of the earth, we find it to be very nearly 9.8 newtons. Actually the weight of an object differs slightly from place to place on the earth's surface. However, the fractional variation in weight is the same for all objects. For example, at the North Pole a 1-kg mass weighs 9.83 newtons and at the equator it weighs 9.78 newtons. At the pole a mass of 2 kg weighs 19.66 newtons, and at the equator it weighs 19.56 newtons. Both masses change weight by $\frac{1}{2}$ per cent, when moved from pole to equator. The weight of the 2-kg mass is always exactly twice that of a 1-kg mass at the same place. Therefore, the gravitational force F acting on an object of gravitational mass m_g can be written

$$\vec{F} = m_g\vec{g},$$

where $\vec{g}$ is the proportionality factor between the gravitational force and the gravitational mass. The mass is independent of position on the earth's

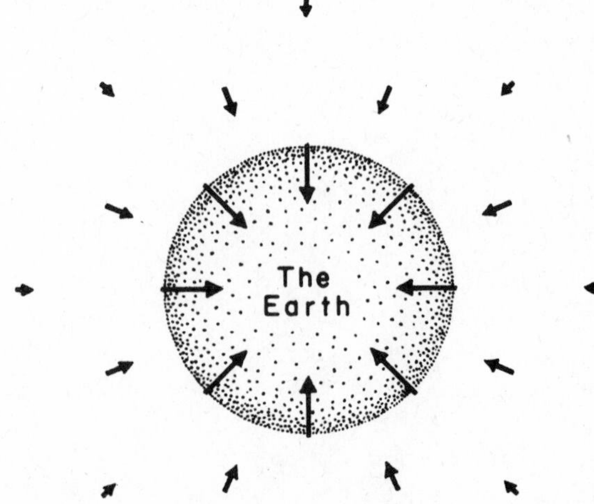

21–1. The gravitational field of the earth. The inner vectors represent the magnitude and direction of the field at the earth's surface. The middle set gives values for a height of 3×10^6 meters. The outer vectors are for a height of 6×10^6 meters. (The radius of the earth is 6×10^6 meters.)

surface — if two masses balance (on an equal-arm balance) at one place on the earth, they balance at all other places. Therefore, we learn that the proportionality factor $\vec{g}$ varies slightly from place to place near the surface of the earth, and it is the same for all masses at any one place.

The factor $\vec{g}$ is the gravitational force per unit mass. It is a vector with the dimensions of newtons per kilogram. We can measure and tabulate it for a large number of locations on the surface of the earth. Such a collection of physical quantities depending on position is called a field; and in particular the gravitational force per unit gravitational mass at different locations relative to the earth is called the gravitational field of the earth. Fig. 21–1 represents part of the gravitational field around the earth, and Table 1 gives its magnitude at a number of different places.

Table 1

Gravitational Field of the Earth

Place	Latitude	Altitude, Meters	Magnitude of the Field, newtons/kg
North Pole	90°	0	9.832
Greenland	70°	20	9.825
Stockholm	59°	45	9.818
Brussels	51°	102	9.811
Banff	51°	1376	9.808
New York	41°	38	9.803
Chicago	42°	182	9.803
Denver	40°	1638	9.796
San Francisco	38°	114	9.800
Canal Zone	9°	6	9.782
Java	6° South	7	9.782
New Zealand	37° South	3	9.800

21–2. Free Fall

How does an object move in the gravitational field $\vec{g}$ of the earth? Suppose we let it fall. Its motion depends on the net force acting on it and on its *inertial* mass. The net force $\vec{F}$ acting on the falling body is given by the vector sum of the gravitational attraction $\vec{F}_g = m_g\vec{g}$ (the weight of the body) and the air resistance $\vec{F}_a$. It is

$$\vec{F} = \vec{F}_a + m_g\vec{g}.$$

According to Newton's law of motion, the acceleration of the object is proportional to this net force and inversely proportional to the inertial mass m_i; that is,

$$\vec{a} = \frac{\vec{F}}{m_i} = \frac{\vec{F}_a + m_g\vec{g}}{m_i}.$$

Now for objects which are relatively dense, air resistance is very small at low speeds and can be neglected compared to the weight. In such circumstances, the gravitational attraction alone is important, and we expect the acceleration of the object to be

$$\vec{a} = \frac{m_g}{m_i}\vec{g}.$$

Here something remarkable appears. As we found out in Chapter 20, the ratio $\frac{m_g}{m_i}$ is the same for all objects. Consequently the acceleration does not depend on the mass of the object. In fact, by measuring m_i and m_g in terms of the same standard kilogram, we have made m_i equal to m_g, that is, $\frac{m_g}{m_i} = 1$. It then follows that for a freely falling body

$$\vec{a} = \vec{g}.$$

In other words, we predict that all objects moving under the influence of gravitation alone are accelerated in just the same way when located at the same place in the gravitational field. In addition, we should be able to measure the gravitational field strength g at any given location by observing the acceleration of any object as it moves through this position.

What do we find in fact? All bodies of sufficiently high density (large mass per unit volume) do fall with the same acceleration at the same place. The magnitude of the acceleration with which they fall is very nearly 9.8 m/sec^2 anywhere near the surface of the earth. It makes no difference whether we measure it in a laboratory on the first floor of a building or on the top floor, whether the body starts from rest or has been projected with any reasonable vertical velocity.

Careful measurements of the multiple exposure photograph of a falling object (Fig. 21–2) lead to the results shown in Table 2. The exposures are at $\frac{1}{30}$-sec intervals. These results illustrate our statement that the gravitational field near the earth's surface results in an acceleration of falling objects of about 9.8 m/sec^2 directed down.

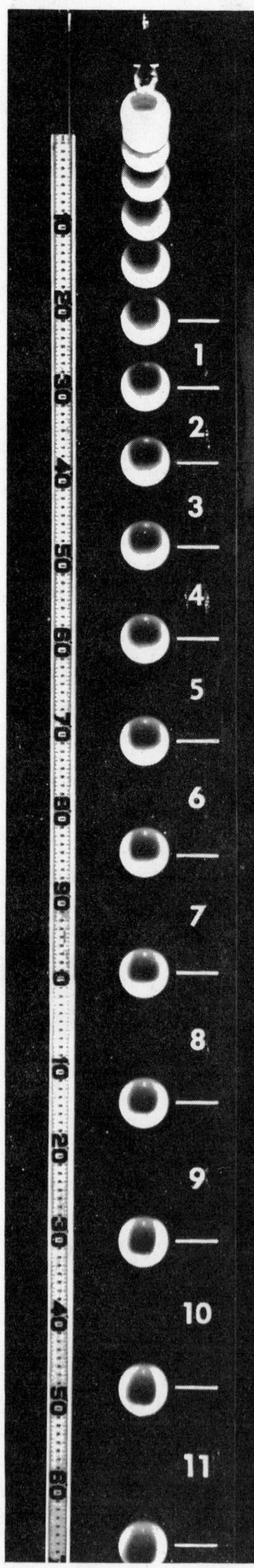

21–2. A flash photograph of a falling billiard ball. The distance scale is in centimeters, and the time interval between successive positions of the ball is $\frac{1}{30}$ second. This motion is analyzed in Table 2.

Table 2

Interval Number	Interval Length Δx(cm)	Average Velocity $\Delta x/\Delta t = v$(cm/sec)	Change in Velocity Δv(cm/sec)	Acceleration $\Delta v/\Delta t$(m/sec^2)
1	7.70	231	32	9.6
2	8.75	263	31	9.3
3	9.80	294	32	9.6
4	10.85	326	34	10.2
5	11.99	360	33	9.9
6	13.09	393	32	9.6
7	14.18	425	32	9.6
8	15.22	457	32	9.6
9	16.31	489	35	10.5
10	17.45	524	32	9.6
11	18.52	556		
			Average acceleration	9.8

The analysis of the motion shown in Fig. 21–2. The calculated values of the acceleration are constant within the limits of accuracy of our measurements. Even though an accurate ruler was brought right up to the picture of the ball, the last significant figure in the Δx column is quite uncertain; just a reasonable estimate of a fraction of a millimeter. It has been retained, however, to reduce successive errors that would accumulate if we rounded off early. Notice that we have kept only three significant figures in the velocity column.

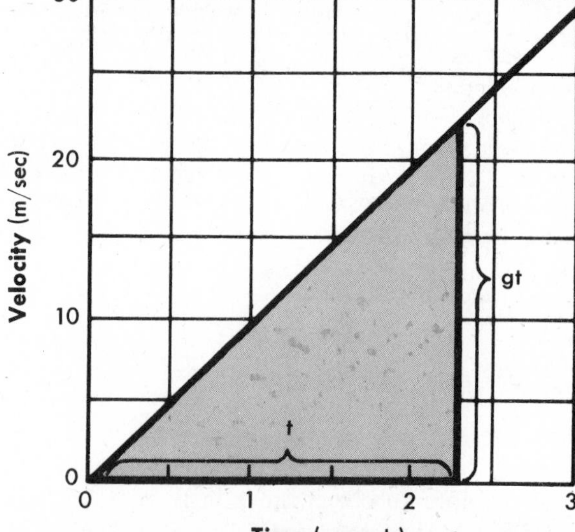

21–3. A velocity-time graph of a freely falling body. The distance fallen is given by the area under the curve — the area of the triangle with base t and height gt. This area is $\frac{1}{2}gt^2$.

We have limited our attention to compact, dense objects carefully selected to minimize the frictional resistance of the air. But if you drop a ping-pong ball it falls only a short distance before the force of air resistance balances the force of gravity, and the ball moves at constant speed. In general, air resistance becomes greater with higher speed. Therefore, if an object falls far enough, it will gain so much speed that the air resistance

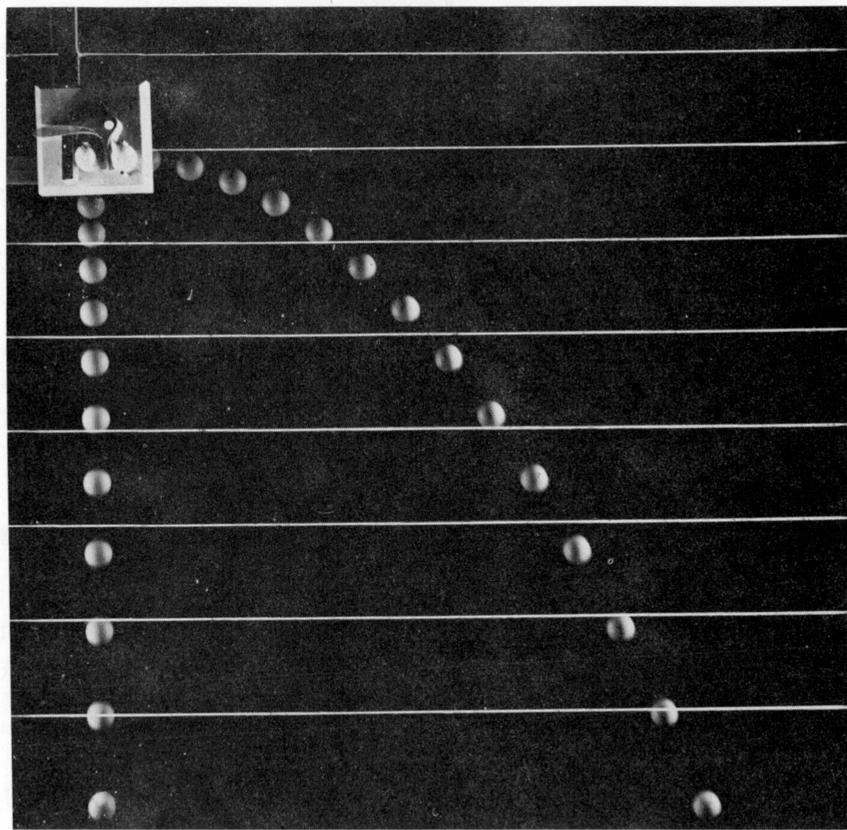

21–4. A flash photograph of two golf balls, one projected horizontally at the same time that the other was dropped. The strings are 6 inches apart, and the interval between flashes was 1/30 second. This photograph is the same as Fig. 6–19.

becomes equal to the weight. Then the body continues to fall with constant speed. This final constant speed is called the terminal velocity of the falling body. (Problem: What happens if you throw a light bulb down faster than its terminal velocity?)

We can check that these deviations from free fall are indeed the result of air resistance by performing experiments in a vacuum. When we remove the air, we find that all objects, regardless of shape or density, fall with the same acceleration at a particular position near the earth's surface. Furthermore, because $\vec{g}$ does not change direction or magnitude appreciably unless we move through distances comparable with the size of the earth, the acceleration is closely the same for objects falling anywhere within a room, within a building, a city, or even a state. In the region within which the gravitational field $\vec{g}$ is effectively constant and where gravitation alone is important, all objects fall with constant acceleration equal to $\vec{g}$. Starting from rest, in time t they pick up *downward* speed

$$v = gt$$

and move down through the distance

$$d = \tfrac{1}{2}gt^2$$

given by the area under the curve of speed versus time (Fig. 21–3). By using the flash photo of Fig. 21–2 again, you can show that the distance d moved from rest increases as $\frac{1}{2}gt^2$.

21–3. Projectile Motion: The Vector Nature of Newton's Law of Motion

Objects that drop straight down under the influence of gravitational attraction alone all accelerate at the same rate. Do all objects also accelerate at that same rate when they move in other directions in the gravitational field? Fig. 21–4 shows a series of flash photographs of two balls. The first ball started falling from rest at the moment that we projected the second one horizontally. We see that the vertical motions of the two balls are identical despite the fact that the horizontal motions differ. Also we see that the horizontal motion is at constant horizontal velocity, like motion when there is no force. The presence of the downward force does not change the horizontal motion; and the existence of horizontal

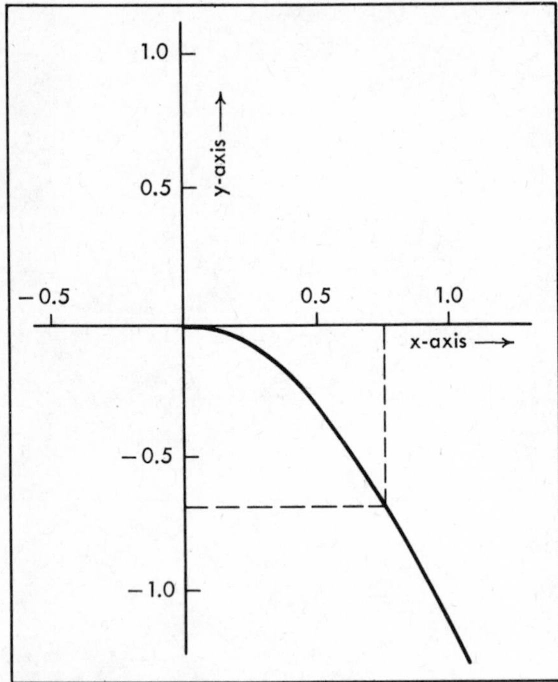

21–5. The path of the second ball in Fig. 21–4 is plotted on a pair of coordinate axes. The scales on the figure measure the distance along the coordinate axes in meters. The x coordinate of the ball at any time t is $v_o t$ (v_o = 2 m/sec), and its y coordinate is $-\frac{1}{2}gt^2$. For example, when t = 0.38 sec, x = 0.75 m and y = −0.7 m.

motion does not change the effect of the downward force on the vertical motion. Our observation shows that the horizontal and vertical motions are independent. Each one follows from the appropriate component vector of the force: $\vec{F}_v = m\vec{g}$, and the vertical motion is the same as free fall; $\vec{F}_h = 0$, and the horizontal motion is without acceleration.

At the end of the last chapter we found that the net force $\vec{F}$ acting on a body is a vector. As we know from Chapter 6, the acceleration $\vec{a}$ is also a vector. This suggested that Newton's law of motion is a vector law. In addition, when the force $\vec{F}$ acts in the direction of motion, the acceleration $\vec{a}$ is related to the force by $\vec{F} = m\vec{a}$. In the last chapter, however, we did not investigate any motion in which the net force $\vec{F}$ acted at an angle to the velocity $\vec{v}$. We might, therefore, ask the questions: Is Newton's law of motion valid when $\vec{F}$ and $\vec{v}$ are in different directions? Is the acceleration still in the direction of the force? Is the magnitude of $\vec{a}$ the same for the same size force?

Projectile motion is the first case we have examined in which $\vec{F}$ and $\vec{v}$ are in different directions. The observed fact is that the vertical gravitational force $\vec{F}$ produces the same vertical acceleration no matter whether there is horizontal motion or not. Although this observation is not enough to prove that $\vec{F} = m\vec{a}$, it provides supporting evidence for the idea that Newton's law in this simple form holds regardless of the direction of motion. After discussing the path of a projectile, we shall examine experiments with other forces acting across the direction of motion. We shall see that the vector law $\vec{F} = m\vec{a}$ also holds for those experiments.

21–4. Projectile Motion: Determination of the Path

In studying the motion of a projectile we encounter a new problem. Previously in our study of dynamics, we considered objects moving in a straight line under the action of a net force along the line of motion. The second ball in Fig. 21–4, however, traveled in a curved path. One of the important problems in dynamics is the determination of the path in such a situation.

If we know the position and velocity of an object at one moment, the path it follows as a function of time can be found from the force on the object and Newton's law of motion. For the projectile, however, we do not need to go all the way back to Newton's law and the gravitational force. We can find the path by combining the known vertical and horizontal motions. (As we saw in the last section, they go on independently in agreement with Newton's law and the known gravitational force.) For this purpose we choose a horizontal axis of reference (the x axis) and a vertical reference axis (the y axis) so placed that the origin ($x = 0$, $y = 0$) is at the point where the body is projected. (Fig. 21–5.) When the ball is projected with horizontal velocity v_o, we know that it continues to move along the x direction at this velocity. After a time t, the x coordinate of the position of the ball is therefore $x = v_o t$. We also know that the vertical motion is the same as free fall. The y coordinate at the same time t is therefore $y = -\frac{1}{2}gt^2$. (The minus sign just tells us that the ball goes down rather than up). These equations contain all the information about bodies projected horizontally with an initial velocity equal to v_o. The common value of the time t in the equations relates them to the motion of one single body rather than to the motion of two different bodies.

The path which the body follows is a curve, and we can express this curve by an equation relating the vertical position y to the horizontal position x at the same instant of time. To find this equation we eliminate the time t from the two equations $y = -\frac{1}{2}gt^2$ and $x = v_o t$. From the second equation we see that $t = x/v_o$; and putting this expression for t into the first equation, we get

$$y = -\tfrac{1}{2}gt^2 = -\tfrac{1}{2}g\left(\frac{x}{v_o}\right)^2 = -\frac{g}{2v_o^2}x^2.$$

The equation

$$y = -\frac{gx^2}{2v_o^2}$$

is the equation of the path of the object. As shown in Fig. 21–5, the path is a parabola with its vertex at the place where the object is moving horizontally.

In Fig. 21–6 we have plotted several possible paths which correspond to different values of the initial horizontal velocity v_o. As we see, when the horizontal velocity is large, the parabola is rather flat. The projectile moves a long way sidewise before falling any great distance. On the other hand, small values of v_o give sharply curved parabolas. The projectile moves a shorter distance horizontally in the time it takes to fall a given amount.

Here we have analyzed the problem of a projectile which is fired horizontally. The more general case of a projectile fired with an initial velocity $\vec{v}_o$ at any angle with the horizontal can be handled in the same way. We again use the fact that the vertical and horizontal motions are independent. From the initial velocity vector $\vec{v}_o$, we find the initial horizontal and vertical components. The horizontal component of velocity never changes, and the vertical component undergoes a uniform change at the rate

$$\frac{\Delta v_y}{\Delta t} = -g.$$

On working through the details the result is

21–6. Several possible paths for a body projected horizontally. Note that the shape of the parabola depends on the magnitude of the horizontal velocity v_o.

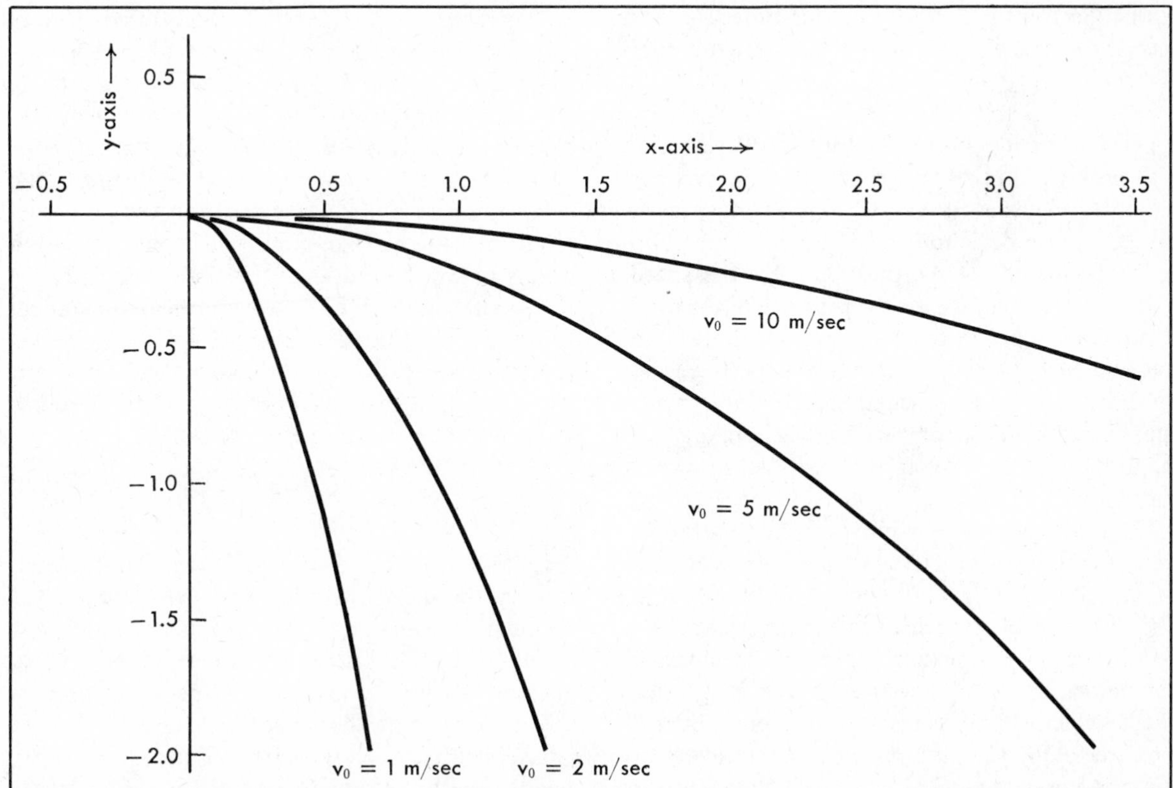

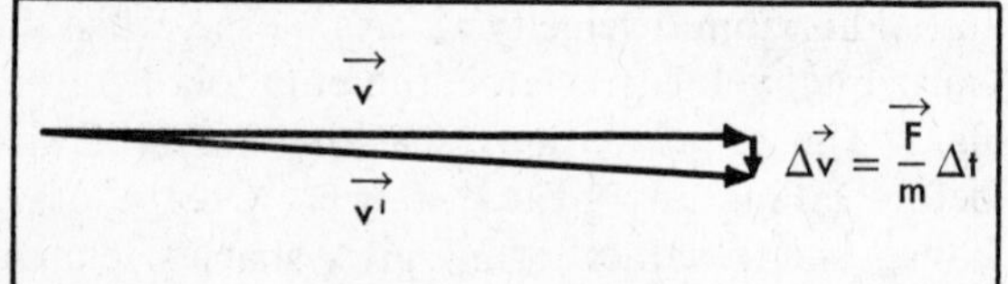

21–7. The change in the velocity of a body when a force acts perpendicular to its path. Such a force changes the direction of the motion, but not the speed. The magnitude of $\vec{v}'$, the velocity after the force $\vec{F}$ has acted for time Δt, is the same as that of $\vec{v}$.

again a parabolic path with a flat region whose extent is determined by the horizontal speed. The only difference is that the top of the parabola is not at the starting point of the motion.

What we learned in this section on projectile motion resembles what we learned earlier in Chapter 6. (Fig. 21–4 is exactly the same as Fig. 6–19.) Yet there is an important difference. In Part I we dealt only with the description of motion (kinematics) whereas here we considered the force which caused the motion (dynamics). The gravitational force $m\vec{g}$ and Newton's law in vector form allow us to predict as well as describe what happens. In our study of the dynamics of other motions we shall lean heavily on kinematic descriptions given in Part I. If you review Sections 6–5 to 6–7 at this time, the next sections of this chapter should be easier to understand.

21–5. Deflecting Forces and Circular Motion

A projectile moves on a curved path because the force that pushes it has a component perpendicular to the direction of motion. The component of force along the path changes the speed, but it does not change the direction. On the other hand, a force perpendicular to the motion shoves the projectile sidewise so that the path curves. It leads to a perpendicular acceleration which changes the direction without changing the magnitude of the velocity vector as shown in Fig. 21–7.

While the projectile is moving on its parabolic path, the force of gravity acting on it has components both along the path and perpendicular to it. The direction of the velocity changes because the perpendicular component of force produces a perpendicular acceleration, and the magnitude of the velocity changes because the component of the force along the path produces an acceleration along the path.

In this section we shall concentrate on change in direction alone. Therefore we shall look for examples of motion in which the speed is constant. Only direction changes.

The direction of a motion is the direction of its velocity vector. The simplest example of motion with changing direction occurs when the velocity vector rotates uniformly. Uniform rotation is familiar to all of us. The sweep second hand of a watch or clock, the turntable on your record player, the earth itself, all rotate uniformly. In Part I, Fig. 6–29, we have already met a sequence of vectors corresponding to uniform rotation.

How is such uniform rotation produced? Suppose we push steadily on a body, always pushing at right angles to its motion. Because there is never a component of force in the direction of motion, there is no acceleration along the path; the speed of the body stays constant while the direction of motion changes. Now if we keep the magnitude of the force constant, the direction of the path will change the same amount in every equal time interval, and the path must be a circle. Each time the body moves at constant speed around the circle, the velocity vector rotates uniformly through 360 degrees.

Thus we have reached the important conclusion that a deflecting force of constant size perpendicular to the motion makes a body move in a circle with constant speed. The force and the acceleration of the body are directed toward the center of the circle, and the velocity vector is tangent to the circle at every point. The position vector drawn from the center of the circle is of constant length and equal to the radius of the circle. (Fig. 21–8.)

We shall now obtain two useful mathematical formulas for the acceleration in this circular motion. Since the motion occurs with constant speed v, and the body goes around the circumference $2\pi R$ of the circle in the time T

$$v = \frac{2\pi R}{T}.$$

T is called the period of the motion. In the same time T the direction of motion has also turned completely around and now points the way it did originally. The direction of motion rotates around steadily, always staying perpendicular to the radius, but the speed does not change. Consequently the velocity vector just turns steadily, with the same period T. (See Fig. 21–8.)

In Fig. 21–8 (b) we see (as we already noted in Chapter 6) that the velocity is carried around by an acceleration perpendicular to it — just as the radius vector is carried around by a velocity perpendicular to it. The end of the velocity vector therefore goes around a circle of radius v and circumference $2\pi v$ in the time T; and the magnitude of the acceleration which produces this change is

$$a = \frac{2\pi v}{T}.$$

By combining the last two equations, we can eliminate either T or v, expressing the acceleration alternatively as

$$a = \frac{v^2}{R}$$

or as

$$a = \frac{4\pi^2 R}{T^2}.$$

These expressions will be valuable in studying satellite motion, the planetary system, and atomic physics.

The acceleration vector is perpendicular to the velocity vector; and the velocity vector is perpendicular to the position vector $\vec{R}$. The two right angles add up to 180°. Therefore, the direction of the acceleration vector is opposite to that of $\vec{R}$. (See Fig. 21–8.) Using this information about the direction of $\vec{a}$ and the last formula for its magnitude, we can write the vector relation

$$\vec{a} = -\frac{4\pi^2 \vec{R}}{T^2}.$$

If we imagine $\vec{a}$ with its tail on the body, we will see that it points from the body toward the center of the curve around which the body moves. For this reason the acceleration is called *centripetal* (center-seeking) *acceleration.*

Now let's go back to the force that produces this acceleration. Newton's law $\vec{F} = m\vec{a}$ tells us how the force and acceleration are related. Therefore, with our mathematical expression for the acceleration in terms of the radius R of the motion and its period T, we can relate the force to the circular motion it produces. The result is

$$\vec{F} = m\vec{a} = -\frac{m4\pi^2\vec{R}}{T^2}.$$

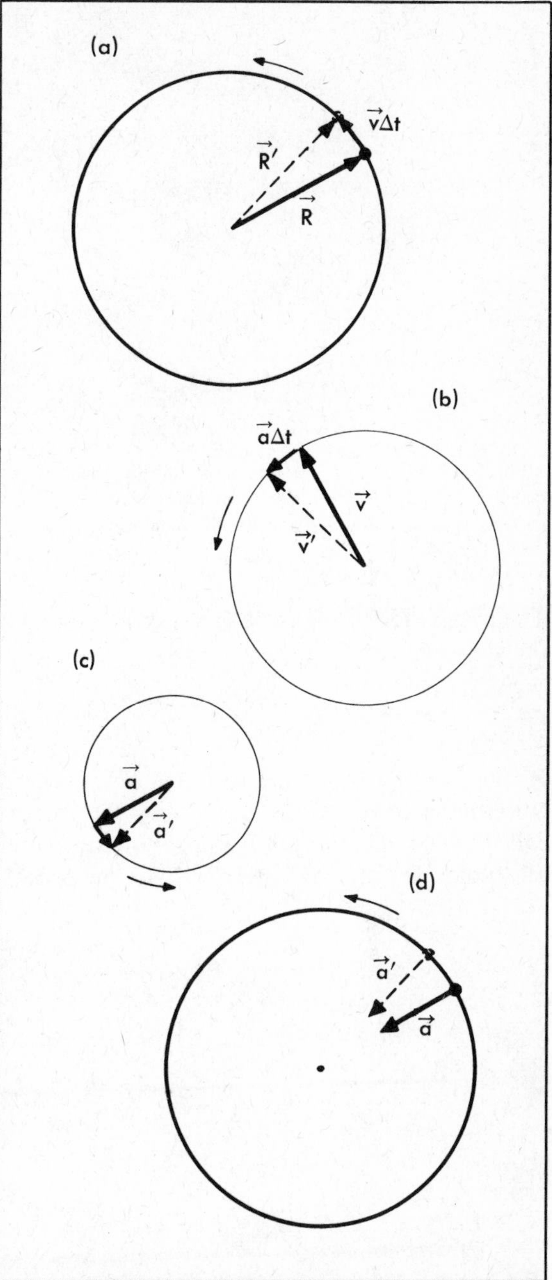

21–8. (a) The path of a body moving in a circle at constant speed. Its position vector $\vec{R}$ rotates uniformly. During a complete period T, the body moves around the circle a distance $vT = 2\pi R$. (b) The changing velocity vector of the body. $\vec{v}$ rotates at the same speed as $\vec{R}$, but at an angle of 90° to it. In a short time interval Δt, the velocity changes an amount $a\,\Delta t$. In one revolution, the tip of $\vec{v}$ moves through the distance $aT = 2\pi v$. Part (c) shows the changing acceleration vector, which is always perpendicular to the velocity. Part (d) again shows the circular path of the body. Here we have drawn the acceleration vectors in the same direction as in (c), but with their tails on the body. The acceleration vector always points from the body toward the center of the circle in which it moves.

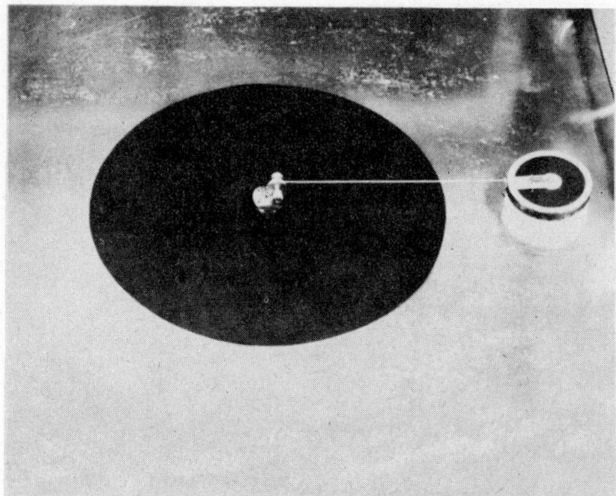

21–9. An arrangement for measuring the centripetal force acting on a body moving in a circular path. The disc is at rest; no force is acting; the spring on the disc is not extended.

The magnitude of the force can also be related to the speed v and radius R as

$$F = \frac{mv^2}{R}.$$

Remember that the direction of F is inward, toward the center of the circle, and the force is called *centripetal* force. The last equation actually holds for any path where F is the perpendicular deflecting force and R the radius of curvature (the radius of a circle which just fits the actual path near the point in question).

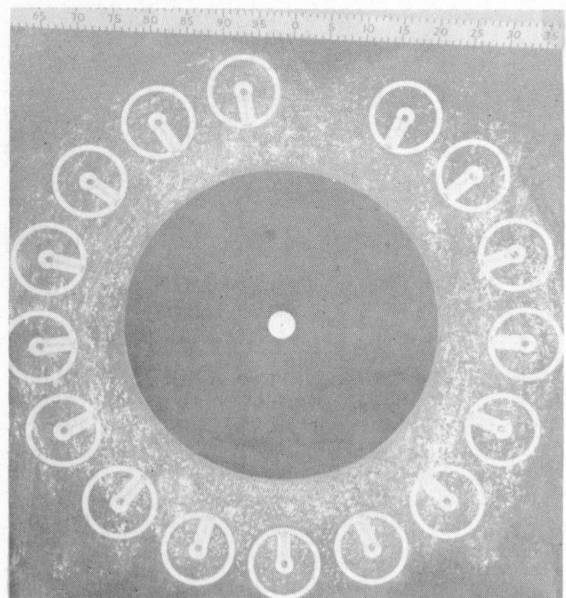

21–10. A disc moving in a circle at uniform speed. Note that the spring is extended the same amount at each position, indicating that a constant force is acting.

We can check our equations experimentally. Fig. 21–9 shows an apparatus designed to do this with a Dry Ice disc. The disc rests on a smooth horizontal table. One end of a string is attached to the center of the table; the other end is connected to a spring on the disc. The extension of the spring measures the centripetal force.

In the experiment the disc was given just the right push to make it move around a circle. Fig. 21–10 is a stroboscopic flash photograph of the motion. The light flashed five times a second and was stopped before one complete revolution was registered. The spacing between successive pictures of the disc shows that the speed was essentially constant. The spring on the disc is stretched as you see by comparing with Fig. 21–9. The stretch stays the same throughout the motion, and from it we can find the force which makes the disc run around in a circle.

The measured extension of the spring tells us that the force was 1.18 newtons. The time taken to move through the fifteen intervals from the first position to the last was $0.2 \times 15 = 3.0$ sec. In this time the disc moved around through a measured angle of 320° or $\frac{8}{9}$ of a complete revolution. Therefore the time T for one revolution is $(\frac{9}{8})(3.0 \text{ sec}) = 3.4$ sec. The radius was 0.33 meter and the mass of the disc and spring was 1.03 kg. Using these values in our expression for the magnitude of the centripetal force F which should make the disc go around the circle, we get

$$F = \frac{m4\pi^2R}{T^2} = \frac{(1.03 \text{ kg})\, 4\pi^2(.33 \text{ m})}{(3.4 \text{ sec})^2} = 1.2 \text{ newtons}.$$

We see that this experiment confirms our expression for the centripetal force to within the accuracy of our measurements.

Suppose the string breaks. The disc no longer moves in a circle, since the centripetal force has been removed. Since no external force now acts on the disc, *it moves in a straight line at constant speed.* This motion is shown in Fig. 21–11, where the string was burned through by a gas torch. Notice that after the string breaks, the disc moves along a tangent to the original circle; it does not move out along a radius.

21–6. Earth Satellites

Only for distances small compared to the earth's radius is the weight of a body constant in direction and magnitude. When we throw a projectile as fast as is now possible with rockets, it may travel so far that we can no longer neglect the change in direction of the force of gravity. Because the earth is almost spherical, we conclude that the force of gravity always points toward its center. But if we look from outer space we see that the center of the earth lies in opposite directions from any two points which are on opposite sides (Fig. 21–1).

If a projectile is launched horizontally with the right initial velocity it will move at constant speed in a circular orbit around the earth. However, since it is very difficult to project an object in exactly the right direction, and with just the right speed, artificial satellites actually follow elliptical orbits (see next chapter). We shall analyze only the special case of circular motion of a satellite since it is relatively simple mathematically.

The earth satellites which have been successfully launched are multistage rockets. The last stage is fired almost horizontally at high altitude where air resistance is small. There is no essential difference in the dynamical behavior of a man-made satellite and one found in nature, such as the moon. But the radii of their orbits are different and, as a result, their periods of revolution (that is, the times for one trip around the earth) are different.

Let us compute the period of revolution of a satellite moving around the earth. For motion in a circle the magnitude of the acceleration is $a = v^2/R$, and since the centripetal force is the gravitational attraction of the earth, the magnitude of this acceleration must be equal to g, the gravitational field. Hence the speed of the satellite is given by

$$\frac{v^2}{R} = g \quad \text{or} \quad v^2 = gR,$$

where R is the radius of the circle and g is the value of the acceleration of gravity where the satellite is. Suppose the satellite is 400 km above the earth. Then R = radius of earth + 400 km $= 6.8 \times 10^6$ meters; and g is about 8.6 m/sec^2 out there. Therefore

$$v^2 = gR = 8.6 \times 6.8 \times 10^6 \text{ m}^2/\text{sec}^2,$$

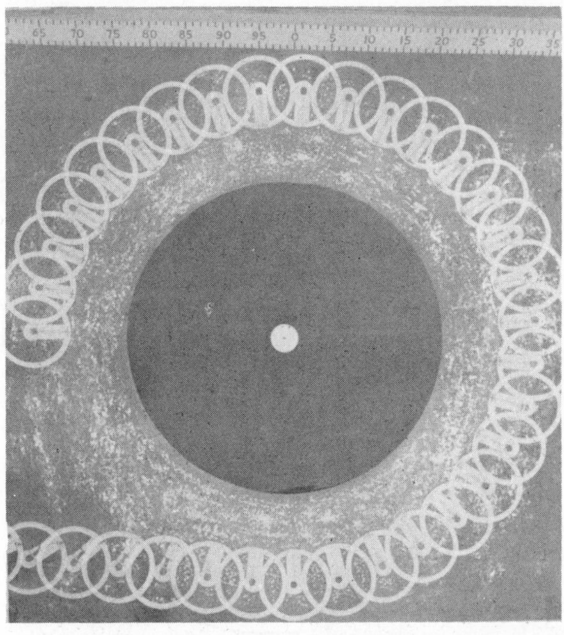

21–11. A disc in circular motion photographed at a flash rate of 10 per second. When the disc reached the bottom of the photograph, the string attached to it was burned with a torch. The disc continued to move in a straight line with the velocity it had when the string broke.

and $$v = 7.6 \times 10^3 \text{ m/sec}.$$

This is a speed of about 5 mi/sec or 18,000 miles per hour.

To get the period T, we note that the circumference of the circle ($2\pi R$) is the distance covered in one revolution at constant speed v. Therefore

$$2\pi R = vT \quad \text{or} \quad T = \frac{2\pi R}{v}.$$

We can estimate the period of the satellite by substituting $R = 6.8 \times 10^6$ m and the value $v = 7.6 \times 10^3$ m/sec that we have just computed. The result is

$$T = 2\pi \frac{6.8 \times 10^6}{7.6 \times 10^3} = 5.6 \times 10^3 \text{ sec} = 93 \text{ min}.$$

The calculations we have made for the period and velocity of an artificial satellite were needed to put the first artificial satellite in orbit. Newton suggested the possibility of launching a satellite by firing a projectile from a high mountain with a velocity of about 5 miles per second, and drew the diagram of Fig. 21–12 to explain his proposal.

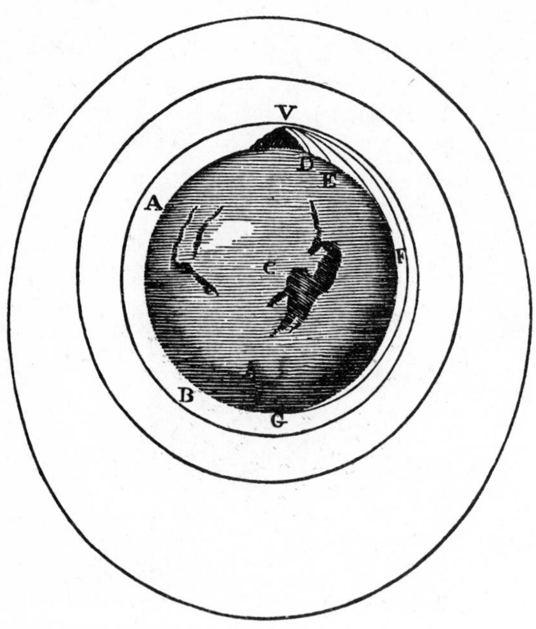

21–12. A drawing from Newton's "System of the World" (attached to later editions of the "Principia"), showing the paths that a body would follow if projected with various speeds from a high mountain. As you can see, Newton was aware that a body would go into an orbit around the earth if its speed was great enough. The orbits from V ending at D, E, F, and G are for projectiles thrown with higher and higher horizontal velocities. Newton recognized that air resistance would prevent the motion of satellites close to the earth from following his ideal paths or from continuing for a long time. He pointed out that satellites could move permanently in the outer orbits.

It is one of the triumphs of the development of the dynamics of Galileo, Newton, and others that it was possible to discuss such projects with confidence in their ultimate possibility.

Why, then, was the first artificial satellite not placed in orbit in the seventeenth century? You can guess the answer. There were no guns or rockets powerful enough. Man's understanding of broad scientific laws often runs ahead of technology. The detailed application of scientific knowledge requires much time and labor.

Sometimes it is the other way round — technology runs ahead of science. Now that our technology has enabled us to establish artificial satellites, we will gain new observations of the universe. Some of these observations have previously been denied us by the curtain of the earth's atmosphere. The new data will give us new knowledge of cosmic rays and of the density of matter in interplanetary space, and will help shape our ideas of the universe. In the long run basic knowledge and technological applications go hand in hand — one helps the other.

21–7. The Moon's Motion

The moon is an earth satellite. We can compute its centripetal acceleration from the following observations. The period of the moon's motion is 27.3 days, or 2.3×10^6 sec; and the distance from the earth to the moon is about 3.8×10^8 meters (about 240,000 miles). The magnitude of the moon's acceleration toward the earth is

$$a = \frac{4\pi^2 R}{T^2} = \frac{4 \times \pi^2 \times 3.8 \times 10^8 \text{ m}}{(2.3 \times 10^6 \text{ sec})^2}$$
$$= 2.7 \times 10^{-3} \text{ m/sec}^2.$$

This acceleration is much smaller than the acceleration of a satellite near the earth's surface. Comparing it with $g = 9.8$ m/sec^2, we see that the gravitational attraction has fallen off by a factor of about 2.7×10^{-4}. This evidence of the weakening of gravitational attraction as the separation increases was one of the things that led Newton to his law of gravitation, as we shall see in the next chapter.

21–8. Simple Harmonic Motion

When we stretch a spring, it pulls back with a force proportional to the stretch (Fig. 21–13). If we attach a mass to a stretched spring and let it go, it will oscillate to and fro. We often find such forces which are proportional to the distortion, at least for small distances. We can describe them by $\vec{F} = -k\vec{x}$, where $\vec{x}$ is essentially the distortion or stretch distance, and the minus sign indicates that the force is a restoring force which pulls the system back toward its equilibrium position.

Linear restoring forces like these always lead to similar to-and-fro motions, called simple harmonic motion, and we want to know what this motion looks like. If we were to use Newton's law directly to predict the motion, we would be confronted with a mathematically complicated problem; but the motion can be derived from circular motion, as we shall now show. Circular motion in a plane looks just like the simple harmonic to-and-fro motion if we examine it from the edge of the plane. To get an idea of

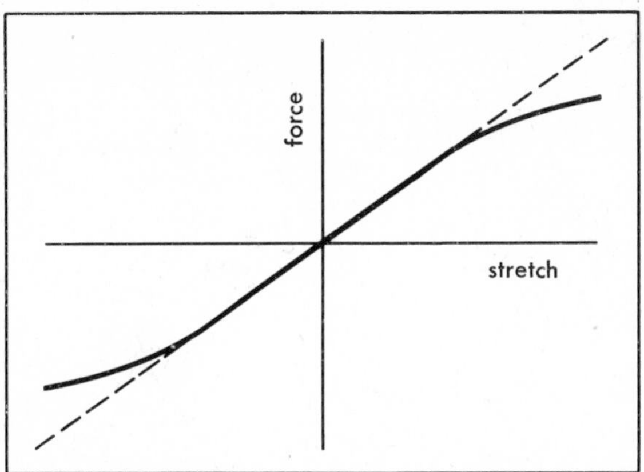

21–13. The force exerted by a spring as a function of its stretch, or of its compression. When the distortion of the spring is not too great, the force is directly proportional to the distortion. The curve in this region can be approximated by a straight line, the ends of which are shown dashed.

the motion, move your thumb steadily around a horizontal circle level with your eye. The straight-line motion you see is simple harmonic motion, as we can tell by matching such a motion with the motion of a mass on a spring (Fig. 21–14).

To study this motion we once again return to the fundamental property of vectors which allows us to represent any motion in a plane as the combination of two independent motions in fixed directions at right angles to each other. We shall apply this independence to the components of circular motion with constant speed. We shall find the motion of one component and we shall also find the force which gives the motion in that direction.

Fig. 21–15 shows a circle around which a body of mass m is moving with constant speed; we shall examine the horizontal component of this motion. In Fig. 21–16 we have drawn a right triangle with the position vector $\vec{R}$ and its vector component $\vec{x}$ in the horizontal direction. We have also drawn

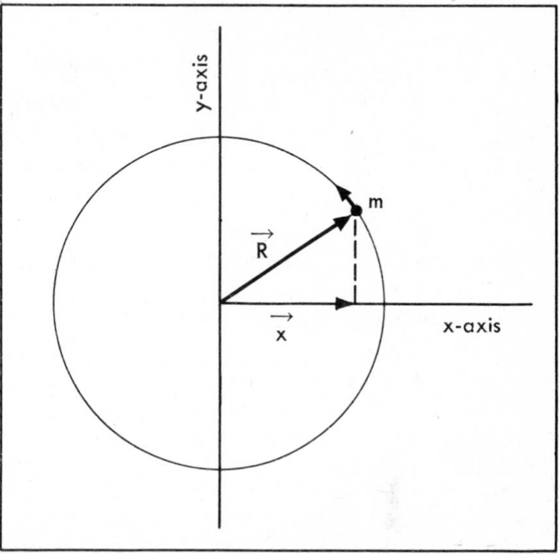

21–15. A mass m is moving around a circle at constant speed. This motion can be thought of as consisting of two components at right angles — a horizontal and a vertical component. We shall look closely at the horizontal x component.

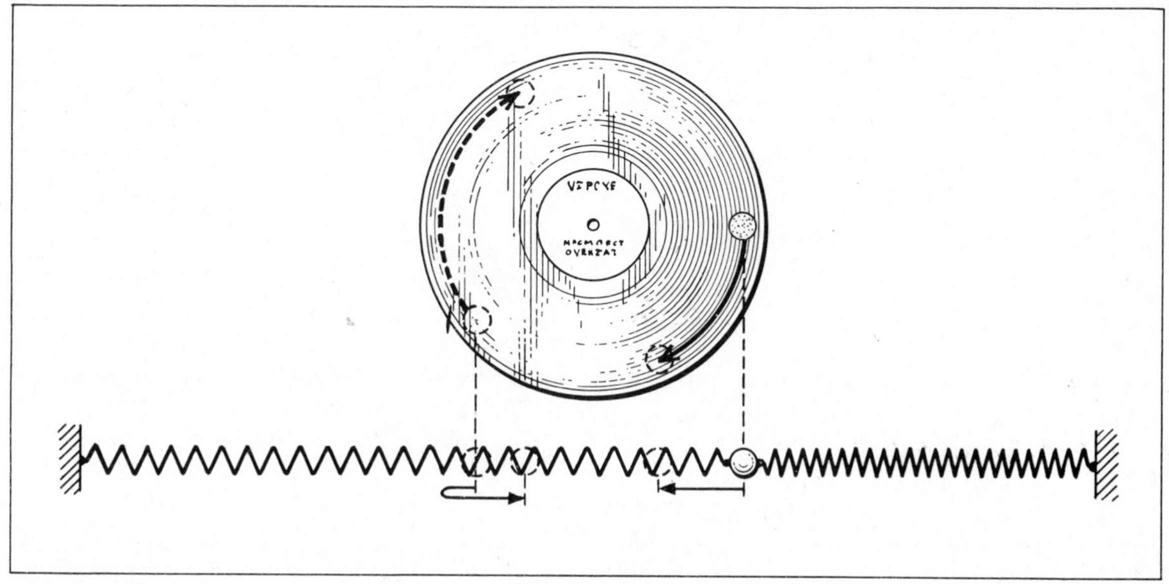

21–14. The to-and-fro motion of a mass on a spring can be matched by one component of the motion of a mass on a circular turntable. We must choose an appropriate radius for the turntable and turn it at the right speed.

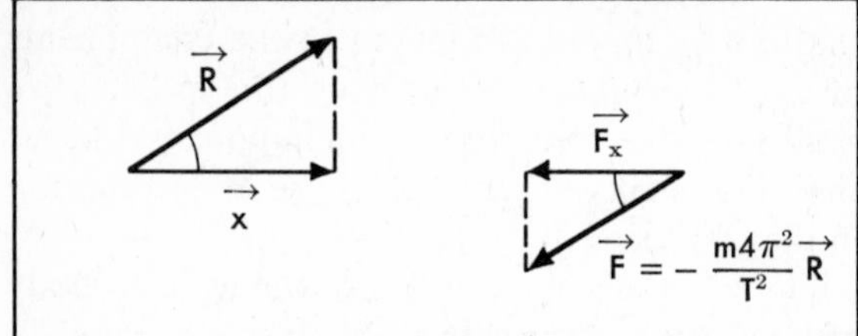

21–16. A right triangle is formed by the position vector $\vec{R}$ and its horizontal vector component $\vec{x}$. The centripetal force $\vec{F}$ and its horizontal component $\vec{F}_x$ form another right triangle. The triangles are similar because the angle between $\vec{R}$ and $\vec{x}$ is equal to the angle between $\vec{F}$ and $\vec{F}_x$ ($\vec{R}$ is parallel to $\vec{F}$, and $\vec{x}$ is parallel to $\vec{F}_x$).

the similar right triangle with the centripetal force $\vec{F}$ and its vector component $\vec{F}_x$. From these similar triangles we see that the magnitudes of $\vec{F}_x$ and $\vec{x}$ are in the same ratio as those of $\vec{F}$ and $\vec{R}$ and they point in opposite directions.

Since $\vec{F} = -\frac{m4\pi^2}{T^2}\vec{R}$ (see Section 21–5), the relation between $\vec{x}$ and $\vec{F}_x$ is therefore

$$\vec{F}_x = -\frac{m4\pi^2}{T^2}\vec{x}.$$

(This equation is simply the x component of the equation $\vec{F} = -\frac{m4\pi^2}{T^2}\vec{R}$.)

Since the mass m and the period T are constant for any particular motion, $m4\pi^2/T^2$ is a constant, and the equation can be more simply written

$$\vec{F}_x = -k\vec{x},$$

where the factor $k = m4\pi^2/T^2$ is the constant of proportionality between $\vec{F}$ and $\vec{x}$. This shows that the force $\vec{F}_x = -k\vec{x}$ is the force that produces the to-and-fro motion of $\vec{x}$. Because the motion along the x axis depends only on the force along the x direction, any such force produces a motion exactly like the motion of point N at the end of $\vec{x}$ in Fig. 21–17 when the point P in the figure goes steadily around the circle.

We have now linked up the x component of circular motion with the motion of any mass m when acted on by a restoring force $\vec{F} = -k\vec{x}$ no matter what provides the force, and this link enables us to calculate the period. If we have a mass m moving under a force $\vec{F} = -k\vec{x}$, we can always imagine a suitable circular motion that will match the motion of m. The period of the actual motion of m is the same as that of this matching circular motion.

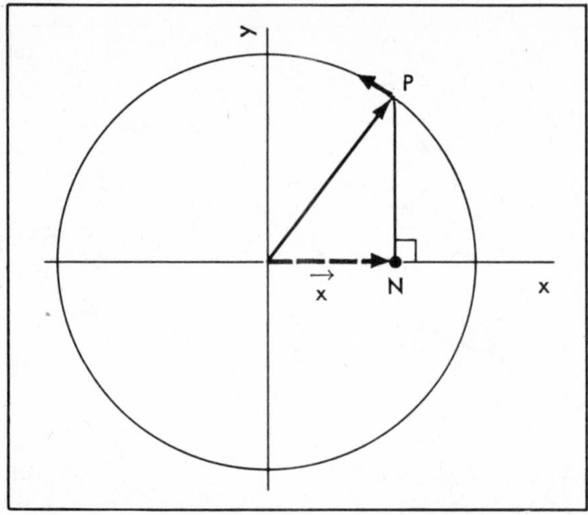

21–17. If a mass at N is acted on by a force such that $\vec{F} = -k\vec{x}$, it will move along the x axis. Its motion will be the same as the x component of the motion of a point P moving uniformly in a circle.

We can use our earlier discussion to find the relation between the force constant k in $\vec{F} = -k\vec{x}$ and the period in which the mass moves to and fro. The period depends only on the mass m and on the force constant k. By rearranging $k = \frac{m4\pi^2}{T^2}$, we find

$$T = 2\pi\sqrt{\frac{m}{k}}.$$

This expression is reasonable. If the restoring force increases rapidly with distance (that is, if k is large), the mass is pushed back and forth rapidly: T becomes small. On the other hand, if the mass is large it responds more sluggishly to the force; and so the period is greater the larger the mass. One result of our reasoning may seem astonishing: the period does *not* depend on the amplitude R of the motion. This is a result you can easily check experimentally. Try it.

A simple pendulum is just a mass m on the end of a string of length l. Its motion is very close to simple harmonic motion. To show this, we start by finding the force along the path s (Fig. 21–18); this force shoves the mass m back toward its equilibrium position. As we see in Fig. 21–19, the magnitude of the force F_s along the path is given by

$$\frac{F_s}{mg} = \frac{d}{l} \quad \text{or} \quad F_s = \frac{mg}{l}d,$$

where d is the horizontal displacement of m from equilibrium. There is almost no difference be-

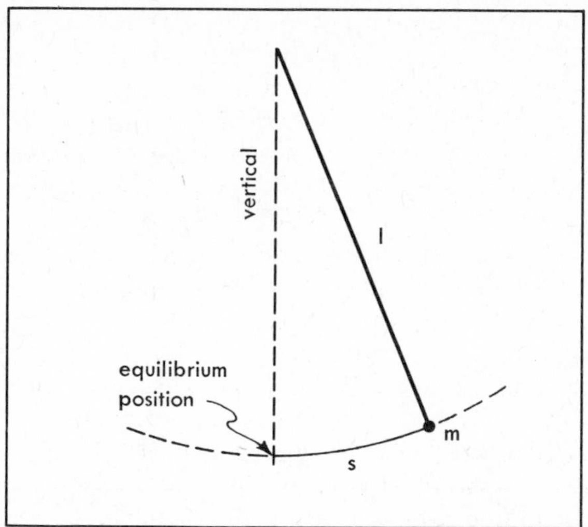

21–18. A simple pendulum: a mass m on a string of length l moves along the path s.

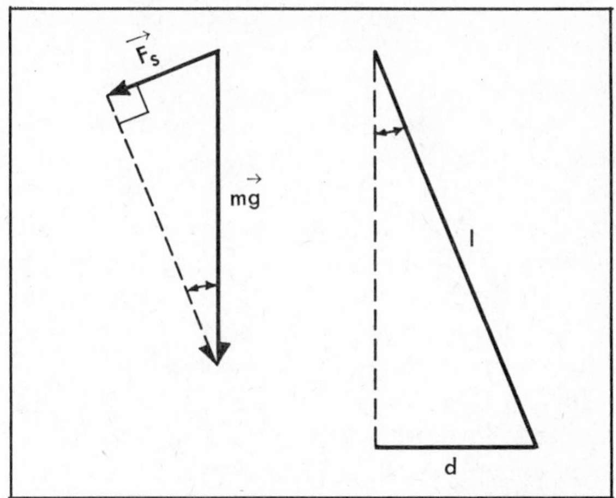

21–19. Two similar triangles. In the left-hand triangle we show $\vec{F}_s$ acting along the path, the weight $\vec{mg}$ acting vertically downward, and the pull on the string (dashed line). The other triangle shows the string of length l, d, the horizontal distance of m from the center line, and the center line. These triangles are similar because $\vec{mg}$ and the center line are both vertical, and the pull on the string, which is perpendicular to $\vec{F}_s$, must therefore be in the same direction as l.

tween the lengths or directions of d and s (Fig. 21–20); we therefore see that F_s is also closely proportional to s with the proportionality factor mg/l. Also, F_s always points back toward the central position, and so we have a linear restoring force:

$$F_s = -\frac{mg}{l}s.$$

This force has the form $F_s = -ks$; and for any particular pendulum the constant k is given by the mass m and length l of the pendulum. From

$$k = \frac{mg}{l}$$

we can find the period of the pendulum. We substitute this expression for k in

$$T = 2\pi\sqrt{\frac{m}{k}}.$$

The result is

$$T = 2\pi\sqrt{\frac{l}{g}}.$$

The period depends only on the length of the pendulum and the gravitational field strength. As always when the force is basically gravitational, the mass does not matter. The amplitude or size of the swing also does not matter as long as it is so small that d and s are closely the same. A pendulum of accurately known length and a good independent clock like the rotating earth can thus be used to measure g accurately.

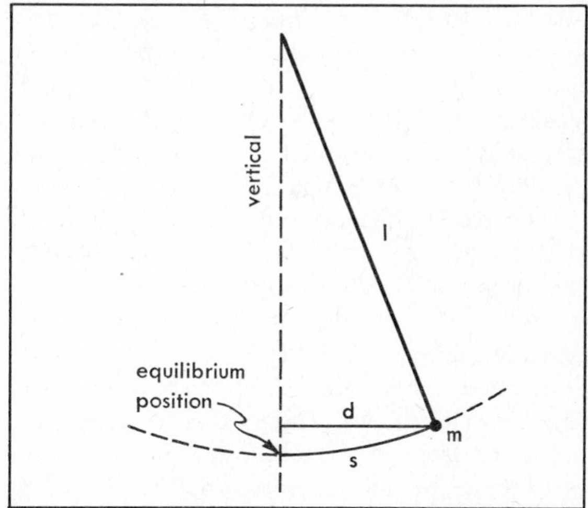

21–20. When the mass is displaced only a short distance from its equilibrium position, there is very little difference between the length of the path s and the horizontal displacement d. Imagine that the displacement is much smaller than it is shown here, compared to the length of the pendulum.

21–9. Experimental Frames of Reference

Turn around. Apparently the room rotates the other way. The corner of the room goes around a circle; so does a marble on the table. But no force mv^2/r on the marble is required to accelerate the marble while it moves in its apparently circular path. Under the action of no net force the marble is simply at rest when we describe it with respect to the room, but it appears to be accelerating when you describe its motion with respect to yourself.

Suppose you are in a car that is accelerating in a straight line. You look out and see a ball flying through the air. It appears to curve violently in the horizontal plane, although you realize that it moves on a straight path over the ground. If you describe the motion of the ball with respect to the car, the ball undergoes an acceleration which does not correspond to any sensible forces.

In Part I frames of reference were discussed in connection with the description of motion — that is, in connection with kinematics. The essential point made there is that any frame of reference can be used to describe a motion truly. So the sensible thing to do is to use the frame of reference that provides the *simplest* description. In other words, we have complete freedom of choice and use this freedom to make life as easy as possible.

But how about dynamics? Have we the same freedom? It is sad but true that here we no longer can use every reference frame and keep Newton's law of motion. Newton's law of motion is *not* correct in all frames of reference. To give a dynamical description in some frames requires more complicated laws. How then do we select reference frames in which Newton's law of motion is correct? The answer is: from experimental observations. Remember how we were led to Galileo's principle of inertia and to the statement of Newton's law of motion; and remember that any conclusion which is drawn from experimental observation is true only within the accuracy of the measurements. Since we arrived at Newton's law of motion from laboratory experiments on the earth, we know that a frame of reference rigidly attached to the earth is a good one — at least within the accuracy of our measurements. On the other hand, an accelerating car is not a frame of reference in which Newton's laws hold.

21–10. Fictitious Forces in Accelerated Frames

We are all aware of the strange forces which appear when motion is observed in some frames of reference. If we ride in a closed car at constant speed on a straight, smooth road, no forces act on us except those which act when we sit in a chair at rest. But when you drive around a curve, especially at high speed, you are conscious of a force: the door of the car pushes on your body. If you think of this experience in the frame of reference of the car, it appears to be a cause for concern. A force acts on you, but you do not move. You are likely to say that another force pushes you against the door and holds you there. This new centrifugal force acting away from the center of the curve just balances the force exerted by the door. In this way you may explain why you don't move with respect to the car. But here is a real dilemma: how can a change in the motion of a reference system (the car) actually create new forces? Is this centrifugal force real?

To answer these questions we start by looking at a simple experiment. We take a Dry Ice puck, for example, hold it at rest on a flat, frictionless surface, and let it go. What happens? Exactly nothing. The puck stays at rest, and we conclude from this observation that no net force acts on it. In particular, no horizontal force acts on the ice puck.

Now we perform the same experiment on a frictionless table located on a large, rotating merry-go-round. Our whole laboratory rotates uniformly with respect to the earth. Now what do we observe when we let the puck go? The puck does *not* stay at rest but moves *relative to us* — that is, relative to the merry-go-round — in a curve of the sort seen in Fig. 21–21. It is called an involute.

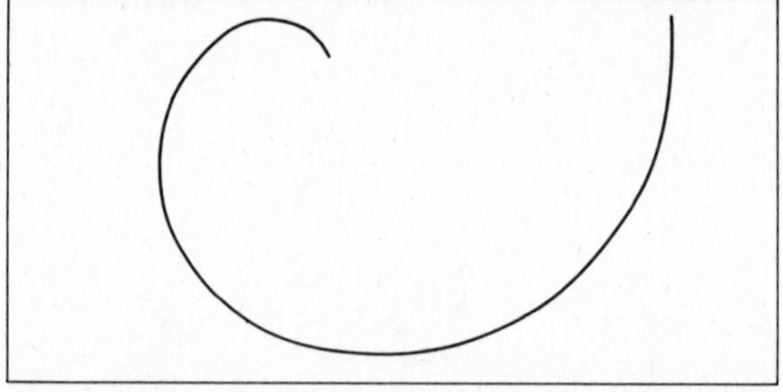

21–21. If we release a puck on a frictionless table when we are in a room on a large merry-go-round, it seems to move on a curved path. Such a path is called an involute.

Now we are really in trouble! Here our observations show that, in the absence of forces, a body moves in an involute, not in a straight line with constant speed. What a contradiction of Galileo's principle of inertia! How can we properly reconcile our observations with Galileo's law? We might say: we are mistaken to think that no force acts on the puck; such a motion shows that there *is* a complicated force. But what exerts this force?

Nothing of which we are aware. So we are right back in the quandary from which we started.

Now look at the whole situation from the standpoint of an observer on the ground. He sees us moving in a circle with constant speed. We are holding an ice puck which moves in the circle with us. When we let go of the puck, it moves in a straight line, tangent to the circle, at constant speed, as Galileo's principle says it must. The man on the ground understands our dilemma and points out to us that our troubles have come, not from a breakdown of the laws of dynamics, but from the fact that we made our observations in a rotating system of reference. This rotating system is an accelerated system, and we can solve all our problems by allowing for the motion of our rotating reference system. Now we know the cause of our trouble. The apparent violation of Galileo's principle and Newton's law of motion is due to the *acceleration* of the rotating frame of reference relative to the ground.

Thus if the observer on the merry-go-round holds the puck at rest relative to him, he finds that he must pull on it with a force which is constant in magnitude and directed inward toward a fixed point. He reasons that, since the puck is at rest (relative to him) there must be an equal and opposite force acting outward *on the puck*. This somewhat mysterious force he calls *centrifugal* force. On the other hand, the observer on the ground sees that the puck is accelerated toward the center of the merry-go-round and that the rotating observer is applying the needed centripetal force. The observer on the ground has no need for the centrifugal force.

Now what about the force that we actually feel when we sit in a car going around a corner? This is the force from the door on us. This force is real enough; but it may be mysterious when we forget that we are moving around a curve. In the reference system of the earth everything is clear. The door of the car must exert a real *centripetal* force on us to cause us to go around the corner instead of straight ahead. In this example the motion in the frame of reference where Newton's law holds is accelerated, and the forces producing the acceleration are real. The car, including the door and us, will not turn the corner unless it is pushed sidewise by the road. The *centrifugal* force, on the other hand, is *not* real. If it were, the net force would be zero, and we would not go around the curve. The centrifugal force is a fiction, something we invent to make it appear that Newton's law of motion applies in the frame of reference of the car.

We see that centrifugal force is really not a force in the sense of a push or a pull exerted by one object on another; rather it is a fictitious or "phony" force that we introduce to correct for the acceleration of our rotating frame of reference. Such fictitious forces which are needed to take into account the acceleration of a frame of reference are called inertial reactions. They are not real pushes and pulls that we ourselves can exert.

Centrifugal force is a term which is widely used and poorly understood. If we use it at all, we must remember that it is a device used to make corrections for the dynamical description of motions in a rotating frame of reference. In a frame in which Newton's description is valid, it simply does *not* exist.

21–11. Newton's Law and the Rotation of the Earth

Now we have raised another problem. We know that the earth spins about its axis once a day relative to the sun or to the fixed stars. Are we in a rotating frame of reference, or are the sun and the fixed stars themselves rotating about the earth? In other words, is Newton's law "really" valid when we use the earth as the reference frame, or is it more accurate in some other frame of reference with respect to which the earth turns? If Newton's law really applies to some frame of reference other than the earth, we should be able to find out by noticing that to explain the observed motions of bodies with respect to the earth we must introduce fictitious forces like centrifugal force. These fictitious forces must be small or they would long since have been apparent in our experiments. Also, we expect them to be small if they correspond to the daily rotation of the earth. To force a mass m to go around daily at the equator requires a centripetal force (Section 21–5)

$$4\pi^2 mR/T^2 = 3 \times 10^{-2} m \text{ newton}$$

or about $\frac{1}{300}$ of the force of gravity. An experiment to make sure that $\frac{1}{3}$ per cent of g is used to produce this motion must be more precise than the experiments we performed in establishing Newton's law of motion.

The French physicist Foucault performed a famous experiment to demonstrate the fact that the earth rotates on its axis in a frame of reference where Newton's law holds. To perform this experiment we construct a pendulum by hanging a bob on a string, the top end of which is fastened to the ceiling. When set in motion, this pendulum will swing back and forth; and, if the amplitude of the motion is not too large, the bob will perform the simple harmonic motion which we have met in Section 21–8.

To start such a bob in motion we might, for example, pull the bob aside from its equilibrium position and release it from rest. It will then oscillate in very nearly straight-line motion. If we are in a proper frame of reference for Newton's law, the motion of the pendulum should continue indefinitely in the plane containing the line of oscillation and the point of suspension of the pendulum (see Fig. 21–18). There is no component of force perpendicular to this plane, nor has the pendulum bob an initial velocity component perpendicular to the plane. Therefore Newton's law of motion predicts that, if such a pendulum starts swinging in this plane, it will continue to swing in the same plane indefinitely. This is what will happen in an inertial frame of reference, one in which Newton's law is valid.

When we perform this experiment in the laboratory we find that a pendulum does pretty well; it seems to stay in the plane in which it started and obeys Newton's law of motion in fine shape. But if we wait long enough — hours instead of minutes — we find that slowly but inexorably the plane of the motion rotates relative to its initial orientation. In fact, if we performed this Foucault pendulum experiment at the North Pole we would find that in just 24 hours the plane in which the pendulum swings has rotated completely around through 360 degrees, as seen by us (Fig. 21–22). This provides the experimental evidence, obtained from an experiment done on the earth, that the earth is indeed in rotation and that frames of reference rigidly attached to it are rotating frames of reference. It also shows again how little we are likely to notice the effects of the earth's rotation in laboratory experiments. A pendulum with a period of one second oscillates about 10^5 times in a day. If the frictional forces on such a pendulum were so small that it could really swing completely free in the inertial frame, the plane of oscillation would appear to us to rotate through an angle of about 10^{-3} degree in each swing at the North Pole.

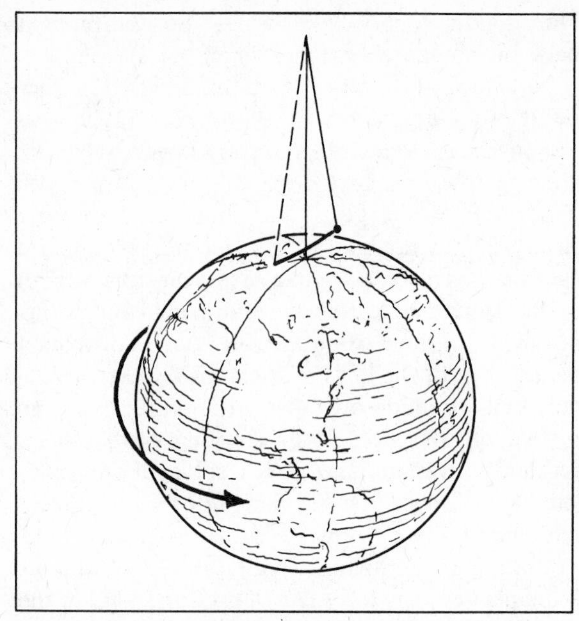

21–22. A Foucault pendulum at the North Pole. The pendulum swings in nearly straight-line motion while the earth rotates beneath it. To a man standing on the earth, the plane of the pendulum's motion would seem to rotate.

These experiments show that the earth is indeed a rotating frame of reference in which Newton's law is not exactly valid. But for all except the most precise experiments we may ignore effects of the earth's rotation. If we want to be as accurate as possible, however, we must use Newton's law in the frame of reference of the fixed stars rather than in that provided by the earth.

FOR HOME, DESK, AND LAB

1. (a) Approximately what is the gravitational force on a mass of 100 gm at the earth's surface?
(b) What is the approximate mass of a weight of 49.0 newtons?

2. The gravitational field at the surface of the moon is one-sixth of that at the surface of the earth.
(a) How much would a 70-kg man weigh on the moon? On the earth?
(b) What would be his mass on the earth? On the moon?

3. The earth's gravitational field at a certain point out in space accelerates a 1-kg mass at 5 m/sec². How much will it accelerate a 3-kg mass?

4. If different objects had different ratios of their inertial and gravitational masses, would they all accelerate at the same rate in the gravitational field of the earth? Explain.

5. * Throw a baseball as hard as you can (outdoors) and note how fast it goes. Then throw a crumpled-up piece of paper equally hard.
(a) Does the paper seem to slow down appreciably?
(b) What is the terminal velocity in a horizontal direction for any object thrown through the air?
(c) What do you expect to happen to any object thrown downward at a speed greater than its terminal velocity?

6. What would you expect to happen if a stone were dropped into a hole that extends through the center of the earth from the North Pole to the South Pole? Would you expect the stone to undergo constant acceleration all the way to the center? Can you reason out crudely how the g field changes inside the hole as you approach the center of the earth? Be prepared to discuss this in class.

7. A stone drops from the edge of a roof.
(a) How long does it take to fall 4.9 meters?
(b) How fast is it going at the end of that fall?
(c) How much longer does it take to fall an *additional* 3 meters?
(d) How fast is it going at the end of this 7.9-meter fall?
(e) Through what distance does it move during the third second?

8. A ball is thrown straight up with a velocity of 15 m/sec.
(a) How fast will it be going after 1.2 sec?
(b) How far above the ground will it be at that time?
(c) How fast will it be going after 2.3 sec?
(d) How far above the ground will it be at that time?
(e) What is the ball's acceleration at the top of its rise?

9. A stone is dropped off a cliff h meters high. At the same instant a ball is thrown straight up from the base of the cliff with initial velocity of v m/sec.
(a) Assuming the ball is thrown hard enough, at what time t will stone and ball meet?
(b) When they meet, is the ball still rising?

10. Two 0.5-kg Dry Ice discs on a flat table are tied together by a string.
(a) What is the total gravitational force on these discs?
(b) At what rate will they speed up if pulled across the table by a horizontal force equal to the gravitational force found in (a)?
(c) If one disc remains on the table and the other hangs over the edge, what will be the acceleration of the discs? Neglect friction.

11. An object of mass m is moving on a frictionless inclined plane that makes an angle of 30 degrees with the horizontal.
(a) What is the net force on the object?
(b) What is its acceleration down the plane?

12. * As an easy project, try rolling one marble slowly off the edge of a table at the same instant that you snap another marble off the table horizontally with your finger. Do they hit the floor at the same instant? Explain.

13. A baseball thrown horizontally starts at a height of 2.0 meters with a velocity of 30 m/sec.
(a) Plot the trajectory of the ball, using 1/10-sec intervals.
(b) How long before the ball strikes the ground?
(c) Determine both the magnitude and direction of the velocity of the ball at the instant it strikes the ground.

14. A bullet is dropped from the same height and at exactly the same moment that another bullet is fired horizontally. Discuss the motion of each of the bullets.

15. A baseball is thrown from center field to home plate. If the ball is in the air 3.00 seconds and we neglect air resistance, to what vertical height must it have risen?

16. Plot the trajectory of an object that is thrown into the air with an initial velocity of 10 m/sec at an angle of 45 degrees with the horizontal.

(a) How high does it rise?
(b) How far does it go?
(c) At what velocity does it strike the ground?

17. A stone drops from the edge of a roof and is observed to pass by a window which is 2.0 meters high in 0.10 second. How far is the roof above the top of the window?

18. A boy on a cliff 49 meters high drops a stone and one second later throws a second stone after the first. They both hit the ground at the same time. How fast did the boy throw the second stone? Neglect air resistance.

19. Show that the expression $\frac{v^2}{R}$ for centripetal acceleration has the units of acceleration.

20. The minute hand of a large tower clock is 2.0 m long.
(a) At a quarter past the hour, what are the direction and magnitude of the velocity of the end of the minute hand?
(b) What is its acceleration?

21. (a) What is the centripetal acceleration of a hammer thrower's hammer if his axis of rotation is 2.0 m from the hammer and he turns around once every $\frac{2}{3}$ seconds?
(b) If the hammer weighs 70 newtons, what force must the hammer thrower exert to maintain this centripetal acceleration?

22. How fast must a plane fly in a loop-the-loop of radius 1.00 km if the pilot experiences no force from either the seat or the safety belt when he is at the top of the loop? In such circumstances the pilot is often said to be "weightless."

23. Some people speak of a pilot coming out of a power dive in a jet airplane as weighing several times his own weight. We sometimes say that the same pilot, falling free before opening his parachute is weightless.
(a) Do these statements make sense in the light of our definition of weight as the force of gravity on an object?
(b) What is meant by "several times his own weight" and "weightless" above? Be prepared to discuss these questions in class.

24. A pendulum bob with a mass of 0.40 kg swings through the bottom part of its arc with a velocity of 0.70 m/sec. The distance from the point of suspension to the bob is 1.0 m. What is the tension on the string at this lowest point?

25. A string 5.0 m long of diameter 2.0 mm just supports a hanging ball without breaking.
(a) If the ball is set to swinging, the string will break. Why?
(b) What diameter string of the same material should be used if the ball travels 7.0 m/sec at the bottom of its swing?

26. An electron (mass = 0.90×10^{-30} kg) under the action of a magnetic force moves in a circle of 2.0 cm radius at a speed of 3.0×10^6 m/sec. At what speed will a proton (mass = 1.6×10^{-27} kg) move in a circle of the same radius if it is acted upon by the same force?

27. A body moving with a speed v is acted upon by a force that always acts perpendicular to the motion of the body but increases steadily in magnitude.
(a) Draw a sketch of the trajectory.
(b) Does the speed of the object increase, decrease, or remain unchanged?

28. * As a home project, carry out the experiment indicated in Fig. 21–14. You may want to use a pendulum in place of the mass on the end of a spring. Make your own pendulum. If the period of your pendulum does not match the period of rotation of the phonograph turntable, what do you do?

29. A spring of force constant $k = 196$ newtons/m hangs vertically from a peg with its lower end at $y = 0$. Then a 2.00-kg mass is hung on the spring.
(a) Plot the net force on the mass as a function of the y coordinate of its position from $y = -.250$ meter to $y = +.250$ meter.
(b) At what position on the y axis should the mass be released from rest if you want it to stand still?
(c) Suppose the mass is released from rest at $y = 0$. Describe its subsequent motion. How far will it move before it again is momentarily at rest? How long a time does it take?

30. A block of mass m rests on a horizontal platform. The platform is driven vertically in simple harmonic motion with an amplitude of 0.098 meter. When at the top of its path, the block just leaves the surface of the platform. (This means that at this point its acceleration is 9.8 m/sec^2 downward.)
(a) What is the period of the simple harmonic motion?
(b) When at the bottom point of its path, what is the acceleration of the block?
(c) What is the force exerted by the platform on the block at this bottom point?

31. (a) What is the period of a pendulum consisting of a mass of 2.0 kg suspended on a light cord 2.4 meters long if $g = 9.8$ newtons/kg?
(b) Notice that we can use a pendulum to measure g. If the period of this pendulum is 3.0 sec, what is g?

32. While a bus is in motion along a level, straight road, we roll a marble from one side to the other across the floor of the bus. Its path is a straight line relative to the bus. Later we roll it again, and this time the path is a parabola which bends toward the front of the bus (concave toward the front of the bus). Describe the motion of the bus in each case. Be prepared to discuss in class.

FURTHER READING

EINSTEIN, A., and INFELD, L., *The Evolution of Physics.* Simon & Schuster, 1938 (pp. 12 ff.).

HEISKANAN, W. A., "The Earth's Gravity." *Scientific American*, September, 1955. Why the earth's gravity varies slightly from place to place, and the effect on athletic records.

HOLTON, GERALD, *Introduction to Concepts and Theories in Physical Science.* Addison-Wesley, 1952. Projectile motion, circular and simple harmonic motion are described at length in Chapters 2, 3, and 5.

NEWTON, SIR ISAAC, *Mathematical Principles of Natural Philosophy* and his *System of the World.* Edited by Florian Cajori, University of California Press, 1947.

NEWTON, SIR ISAAC, *Moments of Discovery.* Edited by G. Schwartz and P. Bishop, Basic Books, 1958 (p. 278). Newton's own description of his universal laws of motion.

UNIVERSAL GRAVITATION AND THE SOLAR SYSTEM

CHAPTER 22

THERE are few people who do not recognize the Big Dipper in the night sky. The most striking fact about the heavens is that the constellations, groups of stars such as the Big Dipper, maintain unaltered shapes. They move just as though they were tacked on the inside of a large rotating sphere, and we were at the center of this sphere watching (Fig. 22–1). Against this background of "fixed stars" the sun and moon move smoothly, as if they were attached to other spheres rotating at different rates about the earth. According to this view, the earth, large and immobile, is located at the center of a universe made of celestial matter which revolves about it. Such a universe is called geocentric (earth-centered).

22–1. A one-hour time exposure taken with the camera pointed at the North Star. The circular arcs show the apparent motion of the stars. It was this circular motion that led the Greeks to visualize the stars as attached to a sphere which turned about the earth. (Yerkes Observatory Photograph.)

Seven heavenly bodies which appeared to move among the fixed stars were known to ancient man. The sun and moon, Mercury, Venus, Mars, Jupiter, and Saturn were called planets from the Greek word meaning "wanderer." With the exception of the motion of the sun and moon, the motions of these bodies appear irregular when viewed over long periods of time (Fig. 22–2). Their erratic motion focused the attention of ancient men on the planets. They were brighter than the stars; and because their brightness changed, their distances from the earth seemed to change. They became associated with various

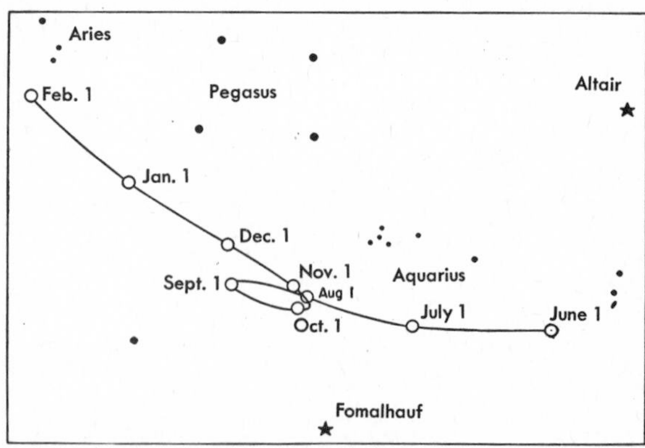

22–2. The peculiar apparent motion of the planet Mars with respect to the fixed stars. Mars, at various intervals, appears to reverse its direction of motion. From: R. H. Baker, "Astronomy," D. Van Nostrand Co., Inc.

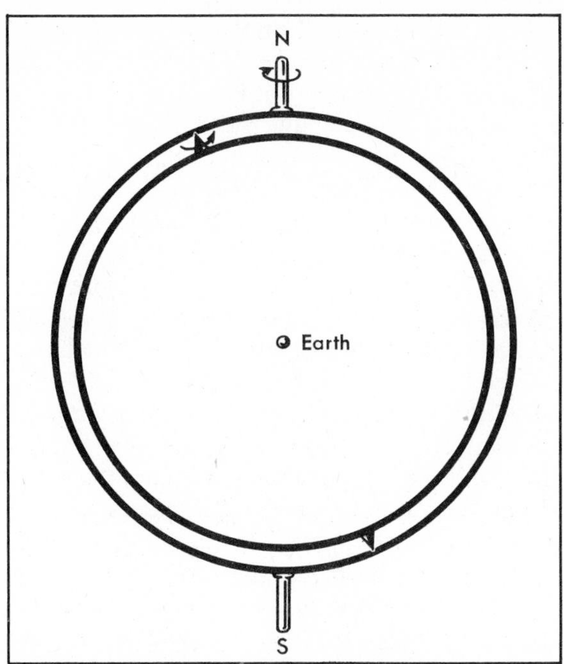

22–3 (a). Eudoxus's planetary system. The motions of the sun, moon, and planets can be approximated by an arrangement of spheres turning within spheres. Here the outer sphere is the sphere of the fixed stars. This sphere rotates once every 24 hours from east to west on an axis through the earth's north and south poles. The inner sphere has the sun fixed to a point on its surface. This sphere rotates about once a year.

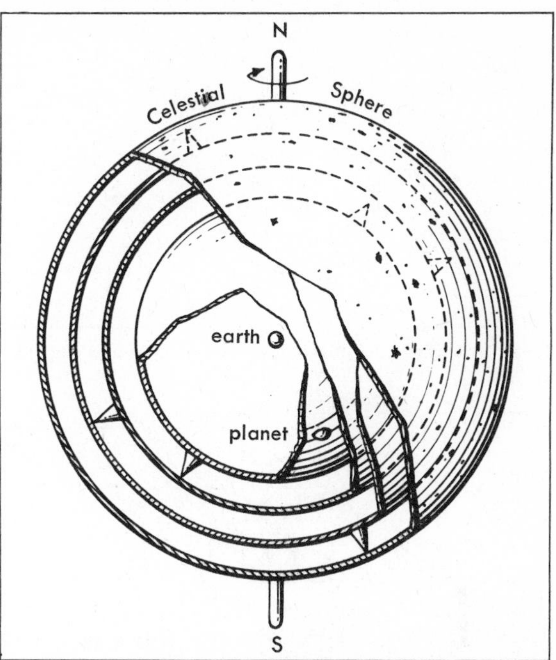

22–3 (b). Here a planet is mounted on the surface of the innermost sphere. The axis of each sphere is connected to a pair of points on the inner surface of the next one. By placing the axes at the proper angles, and choosing suitable speeds and directions of rotation, the motion of a planet against the background of the fixed stars as observed from the earth can be reproduced to a good approximation.

human endeavors and emotions (Venus with love, Mars with war, etc.), as though they formed an intermediary between the immutable perfection of the stars and the restless imperfection of the earth. Later, the astrologers saw in the planetary positions indications of the future course of the lives of human beings.

Finding a reasonable explanation for the peculiar observed motion of the planets was a major concern of the ancient astronomers. It is related that Plato, the Greek philosopher (427–347 B.C.), set the following problems for his students: The stars, as we can see, move in perfect circular paths around the earth, but the planets seem to trace irregular figures. What are the combinations of perfect circular paths along which the planets really move? The form of this question reveals the fact that the circle was believed to be the most perfect of all curves and hence alone worthy of describing celestial motions. The efforts of all astronomers for many centuries were devoted at least partly to answering this question.

22–1. Early Planetary Systems

Plato's pupil Eudoxus tried to represent planetary motions by a collection of moving spheres, each with its center at the earth. Each planet was attached to the surface of a sphere which rotated uniformly about an axis attached to two opposite points on the surface of a larger sphere (Fig. 22–3). While the inner sphere spun uniformly on its axis, the axis itself was carried around by a uniform motion of the outer sphere. In fact, the axis of the outer sphere might itself be attached to the surface of a still larger sphere; in this way the number of spheres could be extended to represent more complex motions. Finally, the whole system spun around inside the celestial sphere which carried the fixed stars. With a sufficient number of spheres moving around inside of other spheres, Eudoxus obtained a good approximation to the motion of a planet. His successors improved the accuracy of his model by using still more spheres. In the course of history many planetary systems depending on the motions of the spheres were developed, and large numbers of spheres were

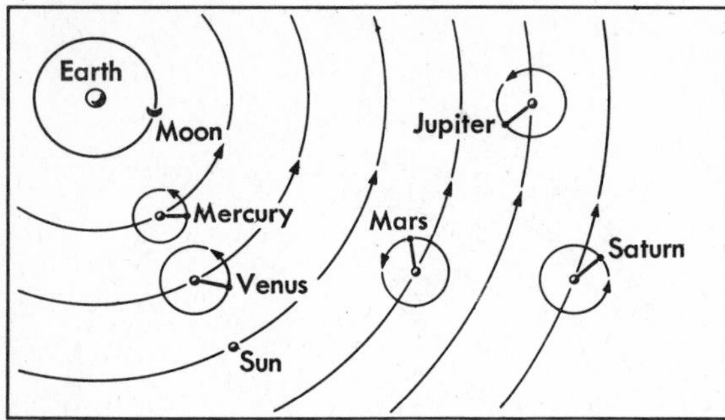

22–4. A simplified diagram of the Ptolemaic system of planetary motions.

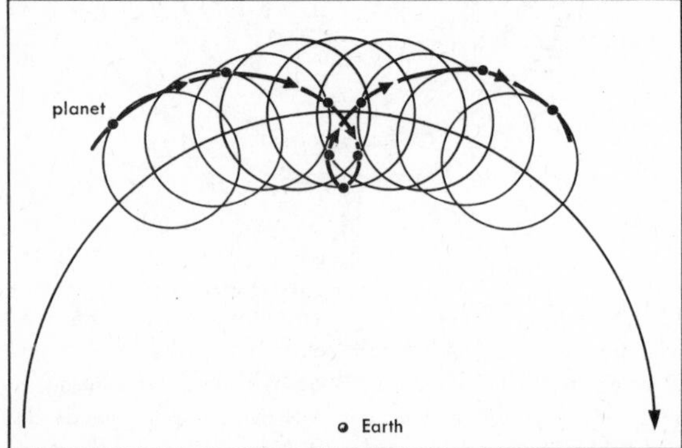

22–5. The motion of a single planet in the Ptolemaic system. The planet was considered to revolve in a small circle whose center moved in a circular orbit about the earth.

eventually employed. In one system, there were thirteen spheres for Mercury alone.

Other Greek astronomers tried to solve Plato's problem in a different way. For example, Apollonius and Hipparchus (third and second centuries B.C.) developed a system in which a planet moves on a circle the center of which moves on another circle. The work of these early Greek astronomers led to the system of Claudius Ptolemy of Alexandria in the second century A.D. His system of circles moving on other circles reproduced the observed motions of the planets reasonably accurately (Fig. 22–4). But his curves describing the planetary orbits were so complicated that there were many complaints from those who studied them. Alphonso X, King of Castile in 1200, was prompted to say that, had he been consulted at the creation, he would have made the world on a simpler and better plan. A simplified Ptolemaic orbit of a planet is shown by the heavy line in Fig. 22–5; the circular motions from which this orbit as supposed to have originated are also shown.

22–2. Copernicus' Planetary System

The Polish astronomer Nicolaus Copernicus (born in 1473) felt that the Ptolemaic system was too complex. The simplicity of uniform circular motion desired by Plato had been buried in complicated constructions. The truth, Copernicus thought, must be simpler. He therefore set out to give a simpler answer to Plato's problem by choosing a different center for the system of circles.

Like others before him, Copernicus realized that the motion of the fixed stars might be explained by assuming that the earth rotates.* Our situation with respect to the heavens is then much like that of a passenger in an airplane. As the airplane turns in flight above a big city, the streets and avenues seem to go around. So as the earth rotates, the stars appear to move.

Once he imagined that the earth rotates daily, Copernicus found that the orbits of the planets could be greatly simplified by choosing the sun rather than the earth as the center of the planetary system. Then the earth would be neither at the center of the universe nor at rest. Perhaps it was a planet, and revolved along with the other planets about the sun. In Fig. 22–6 we show the simple orbits followed by the earth and the planets as they move around the sun according to Copernicus.

Copernicus justified his proposal that the earth moved by saying, "And although it seemed to me an absurd opinion, yet, because I knew that others before me had been granted the liberty of supposing whatever circles they chose in order to demonstrate the observations concerning the celestial bodies, I considered that I too might well be allowed to try whether sounder demonstrations of the revolutions of the heavenly bodies might be discovered by supposing some motion of the earth . . . I found after much and long observation, that if the motions of the other planets were added to the motions of the earth, . . . not only did the apparent behavior of the others follow from this, but the system so connects the orders and sizes of the planets and their orbits, and of the whole heaven, that no single feature can be altered without confusion among the other parts and in

*Although the main current of Greek and medieval thought embodied a geocentric theory, Heracleides (about 370 B.C.) believed that the earth rotated on its axis, and Aristarchus (third century B.C.) thought that the earth moved around the sun.

all the universe. For this reason, therefore, . . . have I followed this system."

Copernicus' system also included a large, immobile sphere on which the fixed stars were located. About it he said: "The first and highest of all the spheres is the sphere of the fixed stars. It encloses all the other spheres and is itself self-contained; it is immobile; it is certainly the portion of the universe with reference to which the movement and positions of all the other heavenly bodies must be considered. If some people are yet of the opinion that this sphere moves, we are of a contrary mind; . . ." Then describing the planetary spheres and their periods of rotation in which the earth appears as one of six planets while the moon is clearly designated as a satellite of the earth, he concluded: "In the midst of all, the sun reposes unmoving. Who, indeed, in this most beautiful temple would place the light-giver in any other part than that whence it can illumine all the other parts? . . ."

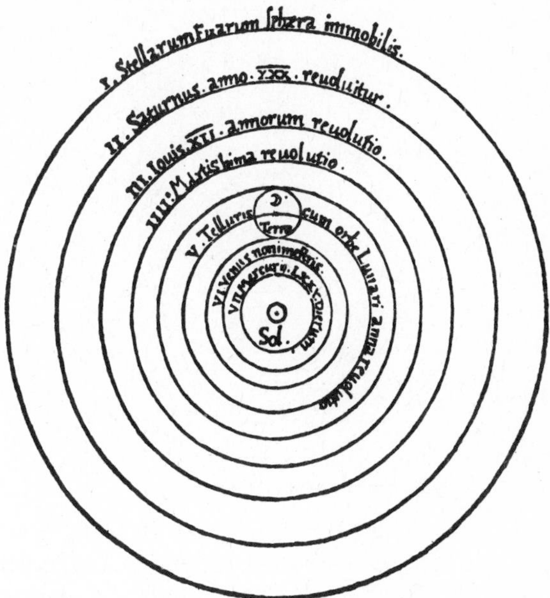

22–6. The orbits of the planets according to the planetary system of Copernicus.

22–3. Objections to Copernicus' Theory

It must be understood that in order to achieve his simplified orbits Copernicus was obliged to discard the entire picture of the universe that had been developed from the time of Aristotle. The question as to whether or not the earth moved was a very serious one. All of medieval cosmology and physics was based on the idea that the earth was at rest at the center of the universe. In part this belief was based on man's inner conviction that his earth must be at the center of things. But in addition there seemed to be good evidence of the earth's special position. For one thing, if the earth moves, what is pushing it and why is this motion not felt? Or, to take another example, why do stones fall toward the earth if it is not the center of the universe?

Copernicus expected a great deal of criticism, and he delayed publication of his book so long that he first saw a printed copy of it on the day he died. Anticipating many of the objections, he attempted to answer them beforehand. To the argument that his earth rotating so rapidly about its own axis would surely burst like a wheel driven too fast, he countered: "Why does the developer of the geocentric theory not fear the same fate for his rotating celestial sphere — so much faster because so much larger?" To the argument that birds in flight would be left behind by the rapidly moving earth, Copernicus answered that the atmosphere is dragged along with the earth.

In fact, there were many arguments and counter-arguments. The Copernican theory was denounced as "false and altogether opposed to the Holy Scriptures." Martin Luther branded Copernicus a fool and a heretic. The argument over this bold new concept of the universe raged for more than 100 years before the notion that the earth could move was generally accepted.

22–4. Tycho Brahe

Tycho Brahe, the Danish astronomer, born in 1546, could not accept the Copernican system, despite its simplicity. He contributed instead an improved geocentric system in which the sun goes around the earth and the other planets go around the sun [Fig. 22–7 (a)]. Also, to test astronomical models, he set out to make a really accurate map of the positions of the fixed stars and to determine the apparent positions of the planets as seen from the earth over a long period of time. He began his observations with an instrument consisting of a pair of joined sticks, one leg to be pointed at a fixed star, the other at a planet. In this way he could measure their angular separation. Later he constructed great sextants and compasses with which he made wonderfully care-

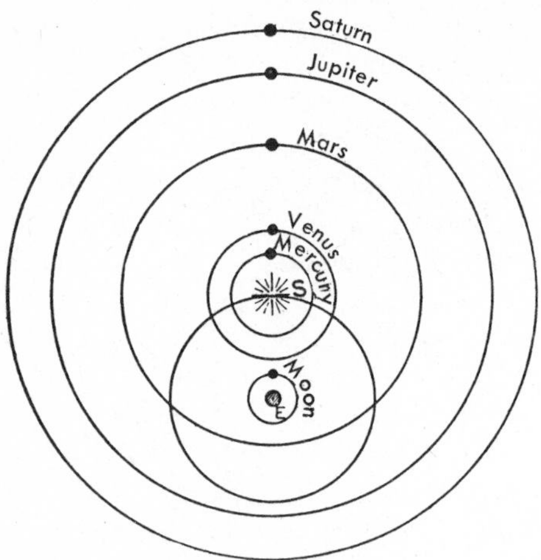

22–7 (a). Tycho Brahe's geocentric system.

ful observations [Fig. 22–7 (b)]. He catalogued the positions of a thousand stars so accurately that his observations are still used, and his measurements of the planetary angular positions over a period of twenty years contain no error larger than 1/60 of a degree. This angle is about the same as the angle subtended by the head of a pin five meters from your eye.

Tycho's observations of planetary positions were far more accurate than those available to Copernicus. They soon showed that the Copernican orbits were only roughly correct. A search then began for a more accurate description of the orbits. This objective was reached, after Tycho's death, by one of his students, the German scholar Kepler.

22–7 (b). Tycho Brahe's mural quadrant. A brass arc of over 6-foot radius was mounted on a wall and equipped with movable sights. An observer (upper right) sighted on a star through the window in the wall at the left. Other assistants noted the time and recorded the angle of the observation. The sector of wall enclosed by the arc is covered with a mural painting of Tycho and other aspects of his work.

22–5. Kepler

Johannes Kepler, born in 1571, was a striking contrast to Tycho Brahe. Tycho possessed tremendous mechanical ability and skill but relatively little interest in mathematics. Kepler was clumsy as an experimenter but was fascinated by the power of mathematics. He was akin to the ancient Greeks in his reverence for the power of numbers and was intrigued by puzzles concerning number and size.

After Kepler had learned the elements of astronomy, he became obsessed with the problem of finding a numerical scheme underlying the planetary system. He wrote, "I brooded with the whole energy of my mind on this subject." He devoted his life to the analysis of the tables of planetary positions which Tycho had left him. In tackling the problem of translating the observations of Tycho Brahe into mathematical descriptions of planetary motions, Kepler acted like any scientist today who attempts to explain experimental findings in terms of simple mathematical laws rather than mere tables of numbers. With mathematical laws we can not only reproduce observed data, but we can predict the results of observations not yet made. Furthermore, mathematical laws are easier to remember and to communicate than mere tables of numbers.

In his first book Kepler described his attempts to understand why there were precisely six planets in the solar system. He established a connection between the six orbits and the five regular geometrical solids* (Fig. 22–8). From this construction he obtained ratios of radii agreeing fairly well with the values then known for the planetary orbits.

*By a regular solid body we mean a symmetrical body with equal flat faces. Only five kinds of regular solid bodies can be constructed.

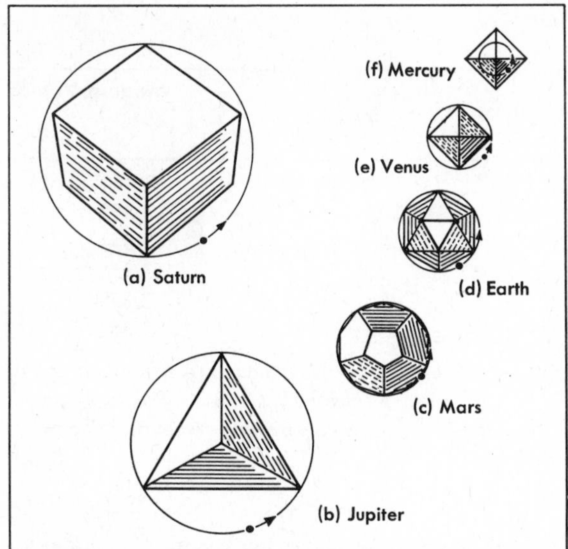

22–8. Kepler's law of planetary orbits was based on the five regular solids. According to the law, a sphere, with a radius equal to that of the orbit of Saturn, is circumscribed about a cube (a). A sphere inscribed within this cube has a radius equal to the radius of the orbit of Jupiter.

In (b) the sphere of the orbit of Jupiter is shown with a tetrahedron inscribed. A sphere inscribed within the tetrahedron gives the radius of the orbit of Mars.

In (c) the sphere for Mars has a dodecahedron inscribed. A sphere inscribed within that gives the orbit of the earth (d).

We may continue this process of alternate inscribing of spheres and regular solids, using the icosahedron (20-sided) and the octahedron. These will give us the orbits of Venus (e) and of Mercury (f), which is on a sphere inscribed inside the octahedron. Kepler considered the five solids as bridging the intervals between planetary orbits. Since there are only five regular solids, Kepler believed there could be only six planets.

Kepler was ecstatic. He wrote, "The intense pleasure I have received from this discovery can never be told in words. I regard no longer the time wasted; I tired of no labor; I shunned no toil of reckoning, days and nights spent in calculation, until I could see whether my hypothesis would agree with the orbits of Copernicus, or whether my joy was to vanish into air."

The relation between the radii of planetary orbits is typical of the kind of result Kepler set out to achieve with Tycho's data. It often happens, however, that even the prettiest correlation of the data turns out to have no deep meaning in explaining the nature of things. Today this discovery of Kepler's is all but forgotten. His system is destroyed by the fact that there are more than six planets. But a seventh planet was not discovered until many years after his death.

Kepler discovered other mathematical relations, relations which have survived the test of later observations. He began his great analysis of Tycho's data with an exhaustive study of the motion of Mars. On what sort of curve had Mars moved during the twenty years of Tycho's observations? Observations of planetary positions had of necessity been made from the earth. Would Mars move in a simple curve if one imagined the earth to be at rest, or if one imagined the earth to be in motion as Copernicus believed? Kepler adopted the Copernican idea that the earth spun about its axis while moving in an orbit about the sun. Following tradition, he first tried a system of circles moving on circles to obtain possible orbits. He made innumerable attempts, each involving long and laborious calculations. He had to translate each of Tycho's measurements of the angle between Mars and the fixed stars into a position of the planet in space with respect to a fixed sun about which the earth itself was moving.

After about seventy trials using the "eccentric circle" type of orbit, Kepler found one scheme which agreed fairly well with the facts. Then, to his dismay, he found that this curve, when continued beyond the range of the data he had used, disagreed with other observations that Tycho had made of Mars' position.

The disagreement between Brahe's data and Kepler's calculations was about $\frac{8}{60}$ of a degree. (This is the angle through which the second hand on a watch moves in about 0.02 second.) Might not Tycho have been wrong by this small amount? Could not the cold of a winter's night have numbed his fingers or blurred his observations? Kepler knew Tycho's methods and the painstaking care he took. Tycho could never have been wrong even by such a small amount. Thus, on the basis of Tycho's data, Kepler rejected the curves he had constructed. What a tribute this was to the memory of his teacher!

Saying that "Upon this eight minutes [he] would yet build a theory of the universe," Kepler began again. Discarding the ancient and cherished belief in uniform motion, he considered possible changes of the speed of a planet as it moved in its orbit about the sun. He now made his first great discovery. He found that a line from the sun to a planet sweeps out equal areas in equal times. This has come to be known as Kepler's second law (Fig. 22–9).

Kepler's Third Law

Planet	Radius R of orbit of planet in A.U.	Period T in days	R^3/T^2 (A.U.)^3/(day)^2	Modern Values R^3/T^2 m^3/sec^2
Mercury	0.389	87.77	7.64×10^{-6}	3.354×10^{18}
Venus	0.724	224.70	7.52	3.352
Earth	1.000	365.25	7.50	3.354
Mars	1.524	686.98	7.50	3.354
Jupiter	5.200	4,332.62	7.490	3.355
Saturn	9.510	10,759.20	7.430	3.353

The values of the orbits and periods in this table are those used by Kepler. In Kepler's day, the radii were known only in terms of the radius of the earth's orbit. The radius of the earth's orbit is called an astronomical unit (A.U.) of length. The nearly constant values of R^3/T^2 illustrate Kepler's third law. The last column is based on accurate modern measurements of the orbits and periods.

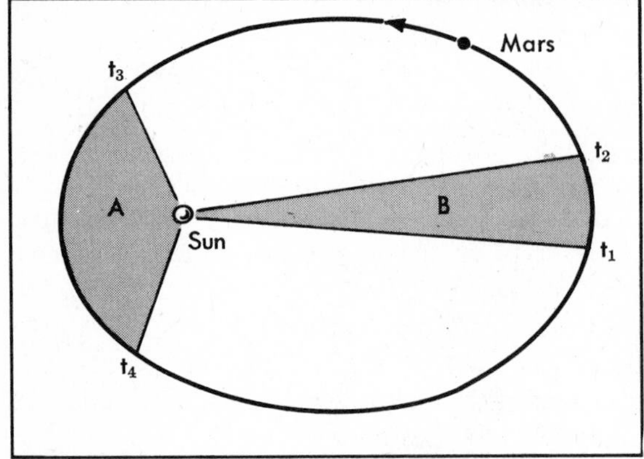

22–9. Kepler's law of equal areas. Mars travels along its orbit with varying speed, moving fastest when it is closest to the sun. Kepler found that for equal time intervals, $t_2 - t_1 = t_4 - t_3$, the areas swept out by a line between the sun and the planet were equal (area B = area A). In the drawing, the elongation of the ellipse has been exaggerated to illustrate the equal-area law more clearly.

After the discovery of his second law, Kepler finally abandoned his attempts to construct planetary motions out of combinations of uniform circular motions and began to try various ovals as possible orbits. After many more laborious calculations, he finally achieved one of his most important results — his so-called first law. Each planet, he found, moves in an elliptical orbit with the sun at one focus. Imagine Kepler's delight. After years of effort, he had finally found a simple curve which described the motions of planets.

Kepler then set to work to find a connection between the size of a planet's orbit and its period, the time of one revolution of the planet about the sun. After many trials he found the precise relation for which he was searching: for all the planets the ratio of the cube of the radius of the orbit to

The Solar System

Object	Mass (kilograms)	Radius (meters)	Period of Rotation (seconds)	Mean Radius of Orbit (meters)	Period of Revolution (seconds)
Sun	1.98×10^{30}	6.95×10^{8}	2.14×10^{6}	—	—
Mercury	3.28×10^{23}	2.57×10^{6}	7.60×10^{6}	5.79×10^{10}	7.60×10^{6}
Venus	4.83×10^{24}	6.31×10^{6}	2.6×10^{6}(?)	1.08×10^{11}	1.94×10^{7}
Earth	5.98×10^{24}	6.38×10^{6}	8.61×10^{4}	1.49×10^{11}	3.16×10^{7}
Mars	6.37×10^{23}	3.43×10^{6}	8.85×10^{4}	2.28×10^{11}	5.94×10^{7}
Jupiter	1.90×10^{27}	7.18×10^{7}	3.54×10^{4}	7.78×10^{11}	3.74×10^{8}
Saturn	5.67×10^{26}	6.03×10^{7}	3.60×10^{4}	1.43×10^{12}	9.30×10^{8}
Uranus	8.80×10^{25}	2.67×10^{7}	3.88×10^{4}	2.87×10^{12}	2.66×10^{9}
Neptune	1.03×10^{26}	2.48×10^{7}	5.69×10^{4}	4.50×10^{12}	5.20×10^{9}
Pluto	?	?	?	5.9×10^{12}	7.82×10^{9}
Moon	7.34×10^{22}	1.74×10^{6}	2.36×10^{6}	3.8×10^{8}	2.36×10^{6}

the square of the period is the same.* Once he happened upon this ratio, the regularity was striking. (See top of page 350.) The constancy of the ratio R^3/T^2 is called Kepler's third law.

With this triumph Kepler wrote, "... what sixteen years ago I urged as a thing to be sought... that for which I joined Tycho Brahe... at last I have brought to light and recognize its truth beyond my fondest expectations... The die is cast, the book is written to be read now or by posterity. I care not which — it may well wait a century for a reader as God has waited six thousand years for an observer."

Kepler had carried astronomy through a momentous advance. He had translated the magnificent tables of data of Tycho Brahe into a simple and comprehensive system of curves and rules. Kepler's system earned him the title "Legislator of the Heavens."

*The radius R of an orbit is defined by taking one-half the sum of the shortest and longest distances between the sun and the planet. Because the planetary orbits are not very different from circles, the distance from the sun to any point on a planetary orbit will do for most purposes.

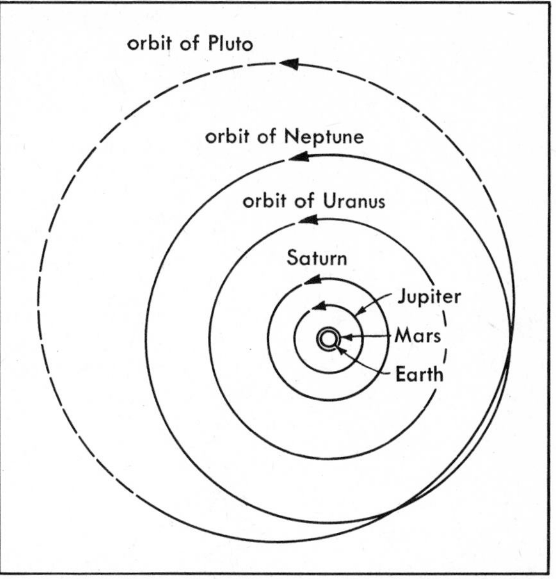

22–10. Approximate orbits of the principal planets. (The orbits of Mercury and Venus are too small to show on this drawing.) They are very nearly circles, except for Pluto, and are in almost the same plane. Only careful measurements show them to be ellipses. The orbits of Pluto and Mercury are the most elliptical, and the plane of Pluto's orbit makes an angle of about 17° with the planes of the other orbits. In the figure, the portion of Pluto's orbit below the plane of the paper is shown by a dashed line.

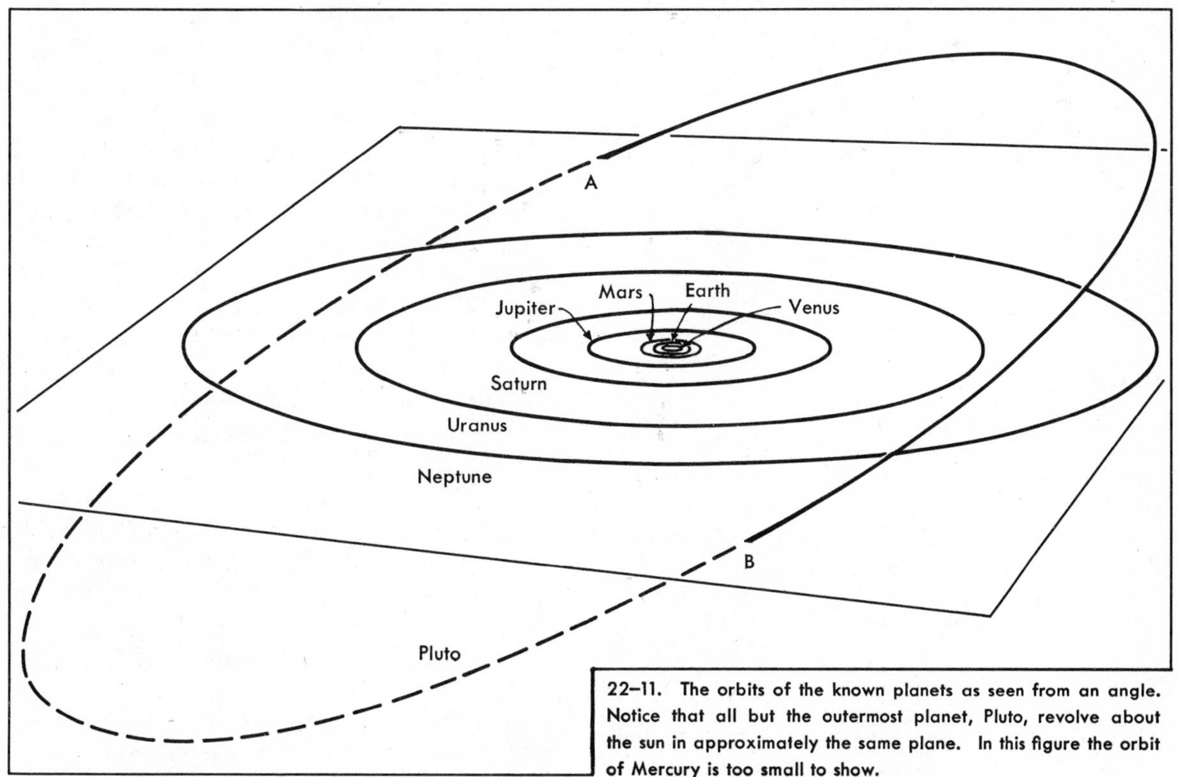

22–11. The orbits of the known planets as seen from an angle. Notice that all but the outermost planet, Pluto, revolve about the sun in approximately the same plane. In this figure the orbit of Mercury is too small to show.

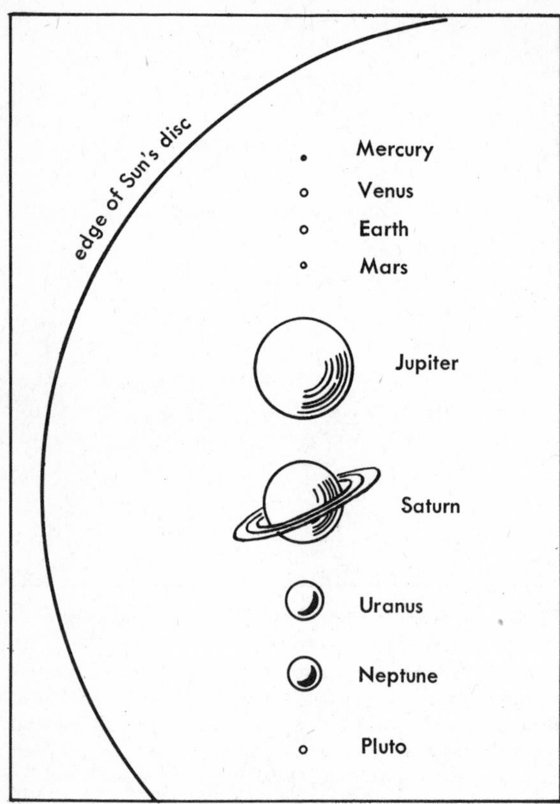

22–12. The approximate sizes of the planets compared to the sun. The total mass of all the planets equals only 1.34×10^{-3} of the sun's mass.

A Scale Model of the Solar System

It is impossible to show in a small drawing both the relative sizes and the distances of the planets on the same scale. The following table gives some idea of the relative sizes and distances in terms of common objects. To get the true dimensions of the solar system, every dimension should be multiplied by 4.4×10^9.

Object in the Solar System	Object in the Model	Distance from "Sun"
Sun	basketball	
Mercury	half a pinhead	13 m
Venus	appleseed	25 m
Earth	appleseed	34 m
Mars	small appleseed	52 m
Jupiter	golf ball	180 m
Saturn	ping-pong ball	320 m
Uranus	a marble	0.65 km
Neptune	a marble	1.0 km
Pluto	?	1.3 km
Nearest star	basketball	8×10^3 km

Here are statements of Kepler's three laws:

I. Each planet moves in an elliptical path with the sun at one focus.

II. The line joining the sun and the planet sweeps out equal areas in equal times.

III. The ratio $\frac{R^3}{T^2}$ is the same for all planets.

If this constant ratio is called K, the third law may be written

$$\frac{R^3}{T^2} = K.$$

Kepler's three laws give a more accurate representation of the planetary orbits than had been obtained from either the Ptolemaic or the Copernican system with all their complexity of circles moving on circles.

22–6. Kinematic Description and the Dynamical Problem

Kepler's laws are the kinematics of the planetary system. They give a simple, accurate description of the motions of the planets, but they do not provide an explanation of the motions in terms of forces. Ptolemy's description of the planetary motion is also kinematics. What is the essential difference in the two kinematic descriptions?

Both descriptions are reasonably accurate. Each allows us to predict where we shall see a particular planet at a given time. The difference lies in the point of view. Kepler's description appears simpler to us. He followed Copernicus in choosing the fixed stars as a framework with respect to which the planetary motions are specified, and like Copernicus he used the sun as the origin from which to measure the planetary positions. It is simpler to describe planetary motions using the sun as the origin than it is to describe the motions as seen from the earth, and we can conclude from this simple description what the planetary motions must look like when viewed from earth.

On the other hand there is nothing wrong in describing the motion directly, using the earth as the origin. It is merely difficult and confusing because the motions we see look complicated and irregular. Convenience — not principle — determines the frame of reference and origin we use in kinematics.

The situation is like that of the man on the ground watching the motion of a point on the edge of the wheel of a car (Chapter 6). He sees the point move on a cycloidal path with a speed that varies periodically from zero to a maximum value. On the other hand, a man who describes the motion with respect to the axle of the wheel finds that the point moves at constant speed around a circle. Both men are right; and if we take account of the motion of the axle with respect to the ground, the two descriptions are equivalent. In just the same way geocentric and heliocentric descriptions of the planetary systems can be equivalent, as are the systems of Tycho Brahe and of Copernicus (Figs. 22–6 and 22–7); and which we adopt is a matter of convenience. For navigation, for example, the earth-centered view is preferable — we don't care how simple the motions would appear from the sun. We want to know where we are when we see the planets in certain directions at a certain time. Consequently, the geocentric language is used in celestial navigation of ships and airplanes today.

When we wish to explain planetary motions, however, the situation is different. In the first place we should certainly suspect that the dynamical explanation will be easier to arrive at and to understand the simpler the description of the motion. In the second place we already know that Newton's law of motion applies only in certain frames of reference. Even the uniform motion that goes on in the absence of a net force on an object will not look uniform to an observer who spins around like a top. In this case we know that complicated fictitious forces will appear, and then we can not find a simple dynamical explanation. Consequently in making the transition from kinematics to dynamics, it is important to find a preferred frame of reference where fictitious forces do not confuse us.

To explain planetary motion dynamically we need to choose an appropriate frame of reference. Can we choose that frame so that the earth is at rest in it? To this question the answer seems to be "no." In any such frame, the motions of the planets imply irregular forces and no dynamical explanation has been found. We can only retire to the Aristotelian view that planets are different from other matter and behave according to their own special laws of motions.

The Ptolemaic system was appropriate to this Aristotelian view. It also fitted with a geocentric dynamics for earthly objects. It led to the idea that the orbits of the planets should appear simplest when viewed with the earth as center (and not around some other point). The greater simplicity of the planetary orbits in Kepler's heliocentric description thus undermines the whole Aristotelian picture.

In the heliocentric system, on the other hand, the earth becomes a planet like other planets. Then there is no reason left to have a special geocentric dynamics. Instead we can look again for a single dynamics that includes the motions of objects on the earth and of all the planets including our own. Indeed the heliocentric view provided the clue from which we have constructed a dynamical explanation of planetary motion.

In the rest of this chapter we shall see how the heliocentric system fits in with the new dynamics of Galileo and Newton. There we shall follow in the footsteps of Newton. With the heliocentric description and a frame of reference tied to the fixed stars we shall find that a simple law of force between chunks of matter leads to the observed planetary motions. It explains them on the basis of the same dynamics that applies here on earth. Since the time when this law of gravitational force was postulated by Newton, it has also been experimentally tested for small pieces of matter here on earth. It is valid here as well as through astronomical distances. Thus the search for a dynamics in which motions here and in the heavens are of just the same kind have been successful. On a geocentric picture no such unified explanation is available.

22–7. Newton

Isaac Newton was born in 1642, the year Galileo died. He brought together the discoveries of Copernicus, Kepler, Galileo, and others in astronomy and in dynamics. To these he added his own findings and fused them into a structure that still stands today, one of the greatest achievements of science. So profound and clear was his understanding, that he was able to apply the laws of motion successfully to an astonishing number of phenomena, from the movement of the planets to the rise and fall of the tides.

Between the time of Kepler and that of Newton a great change had taken place in scientific thought. After Galileo's work the feeling grew that there were universal laws governing the motion of bodies and that these laws might apply to

22–13. Sir Isaac Newton.

motion in the heavens as well as on earth. The scientific discussions in the Royal Society of London often centered about the question, "What sort of force does the sun exert on the planets which causes the planets to move according to the laws which Kepler has discovered?" With Kepler's laws as a guide Newton answered this question. He created a planetary dynamics which was so successful that for many years scientists complained that nothing was left to be done.

Newton's first effort to understand the motion of celestial bodies was directed toward a study of the motion of the moon. Newton knew that if no force acted on the moon it would move in a straight line with constant speed. However, as viewed from the earth, the moon follows a nearly circular path. Consequently, there must be an acceleration toward the earth and a force which produces it. He stated:

"Nor could the moon without some such force be retained in its orbit. If this force was too small, it would not sufficiently turn the moon out of a rectilinear course; if it was too great it would turn it too much and draw the moon from its orbit toward the earth."

What is the force that causes the moon to move about the earth? Newton said that the answer came to him while he was sitting in a garden. He was thinking about this problem when an apple fell to the ground; the force which the earth exerted on the apple might, he thought, also be exerted on the moon. The moon might be a falling body.

In Chapter 21 we calculated the acceleration of the moon toward the earth and found it to be about 2.7×10^{-3} m/sec^2, nowhere near the value of 9.8 m/sec^2 which is the acceleration of a falling body at the earth's surface. Newton carried out essentially the same calculation. At first he did not have available a very accurate value for the radius of the moon's orbit. He did know, however, that it was about sixty times the radius of the earth; and, using a rough value for the earth's radius, he could obtain the radius of the moon's orbit and calculate the moon's acceleration. When he found out how small the acceleration of the moon is, Newton must have asked himself questions like these: Why is the acceleration of a falling body so much greater than that of the moon? Does the force with which the earth attracts a body decrease as the body gets farther and farther away? If so, what is the exact relation between the force and the distance of separation?

Newton had assumed that the earth pulled on the moon in the same general way that it pulled on the falling apple. If this assumption was to be retained, any postulated law of force would have to explain the acceleration g of a body at the earth's surface and the much smaller value of the acceleration of the moon. Newton explained many years later that he was led to the correct force law by working backwards from Kepler's third law. He temporarily left the forces that were exerted by the earth and considered instead the forces exerted by the sun on the planets, the centripetal forces which kept the planets moving in their orbits. Newton wanted to know how the force on a planet varied with the radius of the planet's orbit. We shall now see how this force may be calculated.

One of Kepler's triumphs was his description of planetary orbits as ellipses. But the planetary orbits are nearly circular, and for simplicity we shall approximate them as circles with the sun at their common center. Let us consider a planet moving around the sun with a period T in a circular orbit of radius R. As we learned in Section 21–5, the centripetal acceleration of a planet or any object moving uniformly around a circle is $a = \frac{4\pi^2 R}{T^2}$. Therefore the centripetal force on the planet must be

$$F = ma = \frac{m4\pi^2 R}{T^2},$$

where m is the mass of the planet. This is the force that acts on the planet.

In order to eliminate the period T and express the force as a function of R and m alone, Newton used Kepler's third law $\frac{R^3}{T^2} = K$, or $T^2 = \frac{R^3}{K}$. On substituting $\frac{R^3}{K}$ for T^2 in the equation $F = \frac{m4\pi^2 R}{T^2}$, we find the force on the planet is

$$F = 4\pi^2 K \frac{m}{R^2}.$$

The force is proportional to the mass of the planet and inversely proportional to the square of the distance from the sun (Fig. 22–14).

Eventually Newton was able to show that any body moving under the action of this force must move in an elliptical orbit with the sun at one focus and that the line connecting the sun with the body will sweep out equal areas in equal times. Furthermore, we know from the method by which we found the force that Kepler's third law will follow from it. The whole system of planetary motion described by Kepler's law therefore follows from this law of force and Newton's law of motion.*

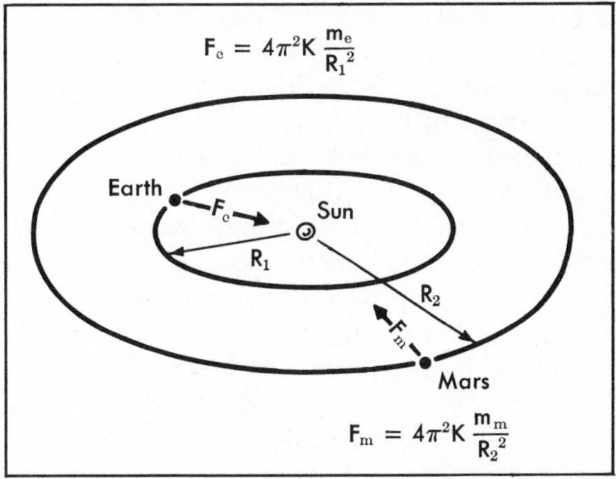

22–14. The gravitational force exerted by the sun on a planet is proportional to the mass of the planet and inversely proportional to the square of its distance from the sun.

22–8. Universal Gravitation

Notice that the factor $(4\pi^2 K)$ in the law of force between the sun and a planet enters the equation from the law of periods. It applies to any planet of any mass on any orbit around the sun. Therefore, $(4\pi^2 K)$ depends only on the properties of the sun; it measures the strength of the sun as the source of the force of attraction.

The gravitational force between the sun and a mass m is

$$F = \frac{(4\pi^2 K_s)m}{R^2},$$

where $4\pi^2 K_s$ refers to the sun and R is the distance between the sun and the mass m. Perhaps the force between the earth and a mass m is

$$F = \frac{(4\pi^2 K_e)m}{R^2},$$

where $(4\pi^2 K_e)$ is the strength of the earth as a source of gravitational attraction and R is now the distance between the earth and the mass m. With such ideas Newton returned to the problem of the moon's motion about the earth. Measuring R from the center of the earth, the value of the gravitational field g (the acceleration of a mass falling at the earth's surface) is then

$$g = \frac{F}{m} = \frac{(4\pi^2 K_e)}{R_e^2},$$

where R_e is the radius of the earth, the distance between the center of the earth and a mass m at its surface. Also, the value of the gravitational field at the distance of the moon, which is the acceleration of the moon toward the earth, is

$$a_m = \frac{(4\pi^2 K_e)}{R_m^2},$$

where R_m is the distance from the center of the earth to the center of the moon. On dividing this equation by the last one we get

$$\frac{a_m}{g} = \frac{R_e^2}{R_m^2} \quad \text{or} \quad a_m = g\,\frac{R_e^2}{R_m^2}.$$

Since Newton knew that $\frac{R_e}{R_m}$ is about 1/60 and g is 9.8 m/sec², he found that $a_m \approx 2.7 \times 10^{-3}$ m/sec². This is about the same value of a_m that he obtained from the radius and period of the moon (Section 22–7).

Now Newton had obtained the acceleration of the moon in two different ways: from R_m and the period of the moon's motion without any reference to the inverse-square law of force, and from g at the earth's surface by using the inverse-square

*Huygens and Hooke also used Kepler's third law and Newton's law of motion to infer that F is proportional to $1/R^2$, but they did not show that Kepler's other laws then followed. Newton provided the law of motion, found the law of force, and also showed that it resulted in Kepler's description of planetary motions.

law in the ratio $(R_e/R_m)^2$. The approximate agreement of the values he obtained gave him support for the idea that the force between earth and moon was of the same kind as that between the sun and the planets. They were both gravitational forces like the force on the falling apple.

Newton probably did not show that all of Kepler's laws follow from the law of gravitational force until several years after his original discoveries. But he discovered the law of force and applied it to the problem of the moon when he was twenty-four years old. Of this period Newton later wrote: "And the same year I began to think of gravity extending to ye orb of the Moon, and . . . from Kepler's Rule (Third Law) . . . I deduced that the forces which keep the Planets in their Orbs must (vary) reciprocally as the square of their distances from the centers about which they revolve: and thereby compared the force requisite to keep the Moon in her Orb with the force of gravity at the surface of the earth, and found them to answer pretty nearly. All this was in the two plague years of 1665 and 1666, for in those days I was in the prime of my age for invention, and minded Mathematicks and Philosophy more than at any time since."

Newton certainly suspected that the inverse-square law of attraction applied not only to the sun and planets, not only to the earth and moon, but also to any two chunks of matter. This suspicion leads immediately to the question: What property of a body determines its gravitational attraction for other masses? What property of the earth determines how large $4\pi^2K_e$ is for the earth? What determines $4\pi^2K_s$ for the sun? Perhaps $4\pi^2K$ depends on a new property of a body; but if gravitational attraction is a property of all bodies, it is reasonable to suppose that $4\pi^2K$ depends on the quantity of matter in the body. The simplest assumption is that $4\pi^2K$ is proportional to the mass of the body. Then $4\pi^2K_e = Gm_e$ for the earth; and $4\pi^2K_s = Gm_s$ for the sun. G is the proportionality factor between $4\pi^2K$ and m for any body.

Newton made this assumption. With it, the gravitational force of attraction that a body of mass m_1 exerts on a body of mass m_2 at a distance R becomes

$$F = (4\pi^2K_1)\frac{m_2}{R^2} = Gm_1\frac{m_2}{R^2}.$$

Furthermore, because every mass attracts every

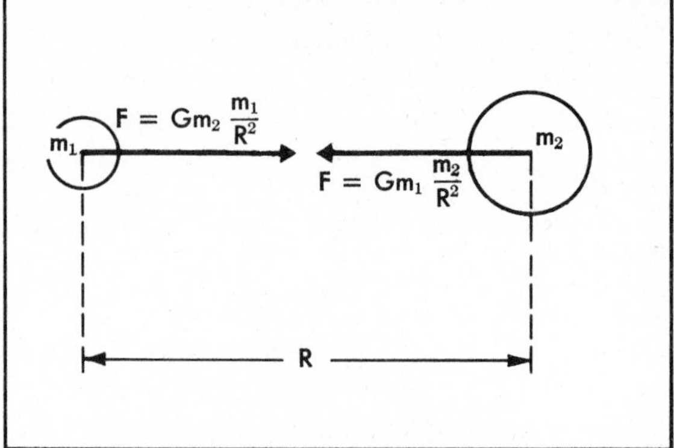

22–15. The force of gravitation exerted by m_1 on m_2 is equal and opposite to the force exerted by m_2 on m_1.

other piece of matter gravitationally, the mass m_2 also exerts a gravitational force on m_1. Since $4\pi^2K_2 = Gm_2$, this force of attraction exerted by m_2 on m_1 is

$$F = (4\pi^2K_2)\frac{m_1}{R^2} = Gm_2\frac{m_1}{R^2}.$$

Although these two forces are opposite in direction they are equal in magnitude (Fig. 22–15). The expression $F = G\frac{m_1m_2}{R^2}$ for the magnitude of the attraction summarizes Newton's law of universal gravitation: any two bodies attract each other with a force proportional to the mass of each and inversely proportional to the square of the distance between them. The universal gravitational constant, G, does not depend on what objects are considered, where they are, or what their state of motion may be.

We do not know in detail how Newton arrived at the law of universal gravitation. In addition to the reason that we have given to make the law plausible, a number of other considerations may have suggested the same result. For example, as we shall see in the next chapter, Newton eventually assumed that the forces of interaction between two bodies are always equal and opposite, and he may already have had this idea in mind when he formulated the law of universal gravitation. Whatever the steps by which Newton was led to the law of universal gravitation, the law eventually stands or falls by the consistency between the predictions we can make from it and the actual behavior of the universe. On the basis of this law Newton was able to take great strides in building up a theoretical system of the universe.

Satellitum tempora periodica.

1d. 18h. 28′ $\frac{3}{5}$. 3d. 13h. 17′ $\frac{9}{10}$. 7d. 3h. 59′ $\frac{3}{5}$. 16d. 18h. 5′ $\frac{1}{5}$.

Diſtantiæ Satellitum à centro Jovis.

Ex Obſervationibus	1.	2	3	4	
Caſſini	5.	8.	13.	23.	
Borelli	5 $\frac{2}{3}$.	8 $\frac{2}{3}$.	14.	24 $\frac{2}{3}$.	
Tounlei *per Micromet-*	5,51.	8,78.	13,47.	24,72.	Semidiam.
Flamſtedii *per Microm.*	5,31.	8,85.	13,98.	24,23.	Jovis.
Flamſt. *per Eclipſ. Satel.*	5,578.	8,876.	14,159.	24,903.	
Ex temporibus periodicis.	5,578.	8,878.	14,168.	24,968.	

Hypoth. VI. *Planetas quinque primarios Mercurium, Venerem, Martem, Jovem & Saturnum Orbibus ſuis Solem cingere.*

Mercurium & Venerem circa Solem revolvi ex eorum phaſibus lunaribus demonſtratur. Plenâ facie lucentes ultra Solem ſiti ſunt, dimidiatâ è regione Solis, falcatâ cis Solem; per diſcum ejus ad modum macularum nonnunquam tranſeuntes. Ex Martis quoque plena facie prope Solis conjunctionem, & gibboſa in quadraturis, certum eſt quod is Solem ambit. De Jove etiam & Saturno idem ex eorum phaſibus ſemper plenis demonſtratur.

Hypoth. VII. *Planetarum quinque primariorum, & (vel Solis circa Terram vel) Terræ circa Solem tempora periodica eſſe in ratione ſeſquialtera mediocrium diſtantiarum à Sole.*

Hæc à *Keplero* inventa ratio in confeſſo eſt apud omnes. Eadem utique ſunt tempora periodica, eædemq; orbium dimenſiones, ſive Planetæ circa Terram, ſive iidem circa Solem revolvantur. Ac de menſura quidem temporum periodicorum convenit inter Aſtronomos univerſos. Magnitudines autem Orbium *Keplerus* & *Bullialdus* omnium diligentiſſimè ex Obſervationibus determinaverunt: & diſtantiæ mediocres, quæ temporibus periodicis reſpondent, non

Aaa 2 diffe-

22–16. A page from Newton's "Philosophiae Naturalis Principia Mathematica" (London, 1687). The periods of revolution of the four largest moons of Jupiter are given at the top of the page. The table gives the radii of the orbits of the moons as measured by different observers. The bottom line of the table gives the radii as calculated from the periods using Kepler's third law.

22–9. Some of Newton's Later Accomplishments

Newton applied the law of universal gravitation to a wide variety of problems. As we already mentioned, he derived all three of Kepler's empirical laws from the law of universal gravitation. He then examined the tides and explained them on the basis of the gravitational force exerted by the moon, both on the earth and on the oceans. He began to analyze the small irregularities (perturbations) of planetary orbits. These small deviations of the planets from their predicted elliptical paths can be explained by the small gravitational interactions among the planets themselves. Not only is the earth attracted by the sun but also in varying degree it is attracted by each of the other planets. These attractions are relatively small because of the small masses of the planets in comparison with the mass of the sun; but their effects can be observed and they are predicted correctly by Newton's theory.

Later this perturbation theory led to the discovery of a new planet. In the nineteenth century seven planets were known. Of these the original six behaved well; but the seventh, Uranus, which had been discovered by Herschel in 1781, did not act quite as expected. When the perturbations of its orbit by the other planets had been computed, the result did not agree with the details of the observed motion. The astronomers Adams and Leverrier arrived independently at the conclusion that there must be another yet undiscovered planet (still farther away from the sun but close enough to influence the motion of Uranus); and on September 23, 1846, the astronomer Galle found the new planet where Leverrier had told him to look. This new planet was named Neptune.

Among the many other problems to which Newton applied the law of universal gravitation, one is of particular interest to us. It concerns the calculation of the acceleration of the moon from the inverse-square law of force and the value of g at the surface of the earth (Section 22–8). When he originally performed this calculation, Newton used the distances R_e and R_m from the center of the earth. Although the center of the earth is a natural place from which to measure R, Newton was not sure that it was the right place. Because he suspected that the inverse-square law of attraction applied to any two pieces of matter, Newton thought that the gravitational attraction of the earth for an object should be the resultant of the forces attracting it toward each piece of matter in the earth.

The different pieces of matter in the earth are located at various distances from an object at the earth's surface. Do they, all acting together, produce the same force on this object that they would produce if all were concentrated at the center of the earth? Does the force fall off as $1/R^2$ even close to the surface of the earth? Before he would be satisfied, Newton had to solve the mathematical problem of adding up all the forces arising from all the pieces of matter of which the earth is made. He had to prove that this vector sum gave the inverse-square law of force outside the surface of the earth.

Now we can solve this problem by applying an elegant mathematical theorem; but in Newton's time this theorem and its basis were unknown. Newton himself invented the mathematics (now called the calculus) necessary to solve this and similar problems. When he obtained the answer it turned out that his original assumption was correct. When the forces from each piece of matter fall off as the square of the distance, spherical bodies do attract each other as though their entire mass were concentrated at their centers. Newton was delighted.

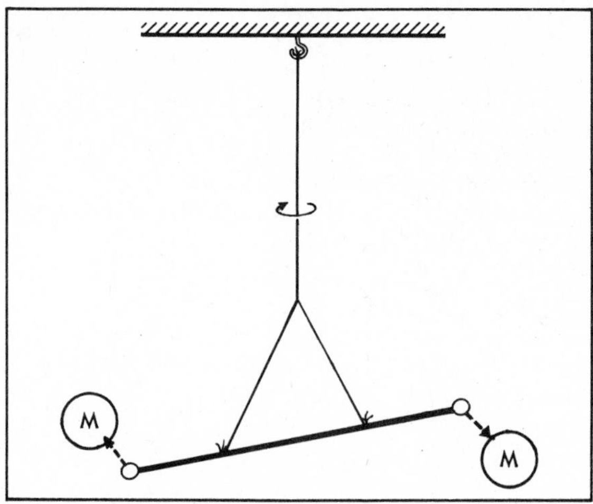

22–17. A simplified diagram of the apparatus used by Cavendish to verify the law of universal gravitation for small objects and to measure the gravitational constant G.

22–10. Laboratory Tests of the Law of Universal Gravitation

The direct way to see if Newton's law of universal gravitation is consistent with the behavior of all matter is to measure the gravitational forces between chunks of matter in the laboratory. We should find the gravitational attraction between two masses and measure the force on each; we should use objects of various materials to see that the mass alone determines the attraction. If we found that the law is consistent with our measurements, we would then naturally evaluate the universal constant of proportionality G.

Such experiments are difficult. Even when two stones are placed close together, they do not attract each other noticeably. With a crude estimate of G we can see why. According to the law of universal gravitation, the gravitational force on a mass m at the surface of the earth is

$$F = G\frac{m_e m}{R_e^2}.$$

The gravitational field g is therefore

$$g = \frac{F}{m} = G\frac{m_e}{R_e^2}.$$

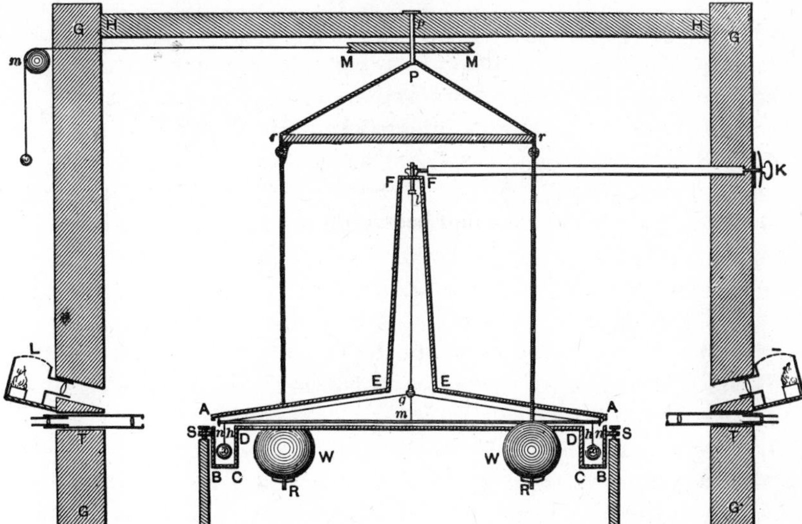

22–18. The sketch of the Cavendish apparatus which appeared in Cavendish's original paper. The two large masses are labeled *W* and the small masses *x*. Notice that the whole device is mounted in a large case *G* with outside controls to move the weights and adjust the horizontal rod. Scales at *A* near the ends of the rod were illuminated by the lamps *L* and observed through the telescopes *T*.

In this equation we know g; it is 9.8 m/sec^2. We know the radius of the earth $R_e = 6.38 \times 10^6$ meters; and Newton knew an approximate value for it. To determine G, therefore, we need only to estimate the mass of the earth.

Newton made such an estimate. He guessed a reasonable value for the average density of the earth, about five times the density of water, and multiplied it by the volume of the earth. The mass of the earth is then estimated as about 6×10^{24} kg; and the order of magnitude of G is $10^{-10}\,\frac{m^3}{\text{kg-sec}^2}$. We now know G accurately. It is $G = 0.667 \times 10^{-10}\,\frac{\text{m}^3}{\text{kg-sec}^2}$. Applying this result to two stones 10 cm apart and each of 1 kg mass, we find that their gravitational attraction should be about 10^{-8} newtons, about one billionth of the force pulling them toward the earth. Newton also concluded that "the gravitation [between such stones] must be far less than to fall under the observation of our senses." He therefore directed his attention to the calculations about the gravitational interactions of the planets and their satellites which we mentioned in the last section.

One hundred years later, in 1798, Lord Cavendish succeeded in measuring the gravitational interaction of laboratory-sized objects. The apparatus he used is diagramed in Fig. 22–17. Two small spheres were mounted on opposite ends of a light rod 2 meters long. This rod hung horizontally with its center below a fine vertical wire from which it was suspended. At the ends of the rod and on the side of the case which contained the apparatus, Cavendish mounted ivory rulers with which to measure the position of the rod. When Cavendish placed two large masses near the small spheres at the ends of the rod, the small spheres were attracted toward the big masses and the wire suspension twisted.

Cavendish recorded the position of the rod with the suspension twisted when the big masses were located as shown in Fig. 22–17. Then he moved each of the large masses to the symmetrical position on the other side of the little spheres. The gravitational attraction twisted the suspension in the opposite direction, and he measured the new position. By measuring the changes in position when known forces were applied to the small balls, Cavendish could find the strength of the gravitational forces between the small balls and the large masses.*

*The force at various twists of the suspension can be found dynamically by taking away the large masses and letting the rod carrying the small balls swing horizontally, twisting and untwisting the wire suspension. The motion of the rod then depends on the known masses of the small balls and on the forces exerted on them by the twisted suspension. The size of these forces can therefore be determined from the motion. Now consider the whole system at rest with the large masses in position. The net force on each ball must be zero; but the suspension is twisted because of the gravitational forces between the large masses and the balls on the rod. The net force, zero, is the resultant of the gravitational force and the force exerted by the twisted suspension. The gravitational force is therefore equal in magnitude and opposite in direction to the force exerted by the suspension. Since we now know the force exerted by the suspension, we also know the gravitational force.

Actually Cavendish performed numerous experiments. He had to evaluate possible extraneous effects such as convection currents in the air due to slight temperature differences. He wanted to make sure that he was not measuring magnetic forces by mistake. He needed many determinations to make sure that his results were reproducible and to determine their accuracy. With these experiments Cavendish determined G. He expressed his answer in terms of the mean density of the earth which he found to be close to $5\frac{1}{2}$ times that of water, very close to Newton's estimate.

By using different substances for the various objects, we can modify the Cavendish experiment to show that the masses alone determine the gravitational attraction. By changing the relative positions of the small and large masses, we can check up on the inverse-square law at laboratory rather than planetary distances. Many modifications of the Cavendish experiments have been carried out, and so far Newton's law of universal gravitation is consistent with all of them.

22–11. A Small Discrepancy

It has been almost 300 years since Newton's work on gravitation. During that time the law of gravitation has been tested through the most detailed calculations of the motion of the planets and their moons. In almost every case, the calculations have predicted orbits which are in agreement with actual observation. There is, however, one exception: an extremely small irregularity in the orbit of the planet Mercury which is not predicted by Newton's law of gravitation. Even though the discrepancy is minute, an improved theory is needed to explain it.

Such a theory was provided by Albert Einstein in his general theory of relativity. At the heart of his theory lies the remarkable equivalence of gravitational and inertial mass. Einstein welded them into one entity. His theory is built upon the theory of Newton just as Newton's theory was built on the work of Galileo and Kepler. Out of it come all the results of Newton's theory (but the calculations are more difficult). Actually, when we say it gives the same results, we mean that the differences between the predictions of Einstein's gravitational theory and Newton's mechanics are usually so small that they cannot be observed. Only under exceptional circumstances are the predicted differences observable. Mercury's orbit is one of these rare exceptions. Here Einstein's predictions of the orbit bring theory into accord with observation.

FOR HOME, DESK, AND LAB

1. * As a project, observe the position of one of the planets with respect to the fixed stars once or twice a week for a month or two. Begin by plotting a map of the stars surrounding the planet. Then mark the new position of the planet on this map at each observation.

2. * Another project: The four largest moons of Jupiter can be seen through reasonably good binoculars. One of the moons moves so fast that its motion relative to Jupiter can be detected by observations just a few hours apart. With your binoculars, observe the positions of the moons every clear night for about three weeks.

   (a) Plot their positions relative to Jupiter for each observation.

   (b) Can you determine the period of revolution for each moon?

   (c) Which of these moons is nearest to Jupiter?

3. The fixed stars go around in about one day as seen by an observer on the earth. About how long do the following revolutions appear to take?

   (a) The sphere of the fixed stars as seen by someone on the moon.

   (b) The earth about the moon as seen from the moon.

(c) The sun as seen from the moon. Does the sun appear to rotate as if it were one of the fixed stars? Does it appear to rotate faster or slower? Remember that the earth and moon go around the sun once every year.

4. The earth's orbit around the sun is nearly circular, and the moon moves in a nearly circular orbit around the earth. The radius of the earth's orbit is 1.5×10^{11} meters, and that of the moon's orbit is 4×10^8 meters.

(a) How often is the moon between the earth and the sun?

(b) How far has the moon moved around the sun in the interval between two successive times when the moon is between the earth and the sun?

(c) Sketch the orbit of the earth going around the sun and on the same figure sketch the orbit of the moon going around the sun.

(d) Does the moon show retrograde motion as seen by an observer at the sun? (Retrograde motion is motion like that shown in Fig. 22–2.)

5. In addition to planets, the solar system contains other "wanderers" called comets. Many comets reappear at regular intervals, apparently becoming brighter and larger in a few weeks as they approach the earth and then becoming dimmer and smaller until they are invisible for a period of years. What kind of orbit do you think they have?

6. How fast, in m^2/sec, is area swept out by

(a) the radius from sun to earth?

(b) the radius from earth to moon?

7. Astronomers have observed that Halley's comet has a period of 75 years and that its smallest distance from the sun is 8.9×10^{10} meters, but its greatest distance from the sun cannot be measured because it cannot be seen. Use this information together with the second footnote in Section 22–5 to compute its greatest distance from the sun. (It was Newton who told Halley how to compute the orbit of a comet. Halley found and calculated the orbit and period of the comet that bears his name in the course of a general analysis he made of comets' orbits.)

8. Three fireflies X, Y, and Z are on a moving bicycle at night. X is at the very center of one of the axles, which turns with the wheel. Y is on the rim of the wheel. Z is on the frame of the bike outside the circumference of the rim. Draw sketches and use a few words to describe the motions

(a) of X and Y as viewed by Z.

(b) of Y and Z as viewed by X.

(c) of X and Z as viewed by Y.

(d) of all three as seen by an observer standing near the bicycle.

9. Two skaters of equal mass on a circular rink go around the rink in the same time. One skater is twice as far from the center of the rink as the other. Compare

(a) the velocities of the skaters.

(b) the centripetal forces acting on them.

(c) What exerts the centripetal force on them?

10. At what height above the earth's surface will a rocket have half the force of gravity on it that it would have at sea level?

11. (a) At what height will a satellite moving in the plane of the equator stay over one place on the equator of the earth? One way to get the answer is to compare this satellite with the moon, which is at 59.5 earth radii from the center of the earth and takes 27 days to go around the earth.

(b) How fast is the satellite accelerating toward the earth?

(c) Using the inverse-square law and g at the surface of the earth, find the gravitational field at the height of the satellite. Compare with your answer to (b).

12. A satellite circles the earth once every 98 minutes at a mean altitude of 500 km. Calculate the mass of the earth. The masses of planets are actually calculated from satellite motions, and one reason for establishing artificial earth satellites is to get a better value for the mass of the earth.

As stated in Section 22–10,

$$G = 0.667 \times 10^{-10} \frac{m^3}{kg\text{-}sec^2}$$

13. (a) If T is the period of a satellite circling around just above the surface of a planet whose average density is ρ, show that ρT^2 is a universal constant.

(b) What is the value of the constant?

14. Compute the periods of a satellite in an orbit close to the surface of

(a) the earth.

(b) the sun.

15. Find the weight of a 100-kg man on planets with the following masses and radii.

	m	R
Mars	6.4×10^{23} kg	3.4×10^6 m
Earth	6.0×10^{24} kg	6.4×10^6 m
Jupiter	1.9×10^{27} kg	7.2×10^7 m

16. A 70-kg boy stands 1 meter away from a 60-kg girl. Calculate the force of attraction (gravitational) between them.

17. Find the gravitational attraction of the two atoms in a hydrogen molecule.

18. (a) If a planet of twice the diameter of the earth has a mass six times as great, how does the gravitational field at its surface compare with the gravitational field at the surface of the earth?

(b) How would the densities of the two planets compare?

19. The earth is acted upon by the gravitational attraction of the sun. Why doesn't the earth fall into the sun? Be prepared to discuss your answer.

20. (a) What is the speed of the moon around the sun compared to that of the earth around the sun?

(b) If the earth could be removed suddenly without disturbing the motion of the moon, what would be the subsequent path of the moon?

(c) Calculate the ratio of the force of attraction exerted by the sun on the moon to the force exerted by the earth on the moon.

(d) Why does the sun not capture the moon, taking it away from the earth?

21. Assume the earth is perfectly round and has a radius of 6400 km.

(a) How much less does a man with a mass of 100 kg apparently weigh at the equator than at the poles because of the rotation of the earth?

(b) How fast would the earth have to spin in order that he would exert no force on a scale at the equator?

(c) How many times larger is the speed of rotation in (b) than the actual speed?

22. The two stars of a double star, far away from any other large masses, revolve in circular orbits, always remaining the same distance apart. Sketch their orbits if

(a) they have equal masses,

(b) one has twice the mass of the other.

(c) What is the ratio of the radii of the two orbits in each case?

23. Assume that the gravitational attraction exerted by m_1 on m_3 in Fig. 22–19 is not influenced by the presence of m_2, and the attraction of m_2 on m_3 is not changed by the presence of m_1.

(a) Using the universal law of gravitation, show that the force of attraction exerted on m_3 by the single "body" made of m_1 and m_2 together is proportional to its mass.

(b) If m_1 and m_2 were far apart compared to their distance from m_3, would they act like a single body?

22–19. For Problem 23.

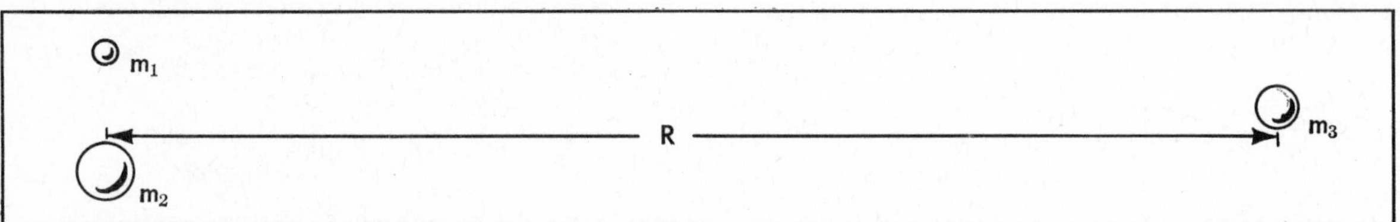

FURTHER READING

ABETTI, G., *History of Astronomy*. Abelard-Schuman, 1952.

ANDRADE, E. N. DA C., *Sir Isaac Newton*. Doubleday Anchor Books, 1958.

BAKER, R. H., *Astronomy*. Van Nostrand. A standard textbook.

COPERNICUS, N., *Readings in the Literature of Science*. Edited by Dampier and Dampier, Harper, 1959 (pp. 11–13). Also Galileo, pp. 14–30.

HOLTON, G., and ROLLER, D. H. D., *Foundations of Modern Physical Science*. Addison-Wesley, 1957; Part III, *The Study of Planetary Systems*.

Moments of Discovery. Copernicus, p. 217; Tycho Brahe, p. 232; Galileo, p. 240; Kepler, p. 265. Their own reports of their contributions to planetary systems.

NEWTON, SIR ISAAC, *Mathematical Principles of Natural Philosophy* and his *System of the World*. Edited by Florian Cajori, University of California Press, 1947.

WHIPPLE, F. L., and HYNEK, V. A., "Observations of Satellite I," *Scientific American*, December, 1957. An account of the observations made in computing the orbit of an artificial satellite.

MOMENTUM AND THE CONSERVATION OF MOMENTUM

CHAPTER 23

23–1. Impulse

Try to make a baseball and a 16-lb shot go at the same speed. As you know, it is a lot harder to get the shot going. If you apply a constant force $\vec{F}$ for a time Δt, the change in velocity is given by $m\Delta\vec{v} = \vec{F}\Delta t$. So, in order to get the same $\Delta\vec{v}$, the product $\vec{F}\Delta t$ must be greater the greater the mass m you are trying to accelerate.

To start a 16-lb shot from rest and give it the same final velocity as a baseball (also started from rest), we must push either harder or longer. What counts is the product $\vec{F}\Delta t$. This product $\vec{F}\Delta t$ is the natural measure of how hard and how long we push to change a motion. It is called the *impulse* of the force.

We can exert a given impulse in many different ways: a big force for a short time, a smaller force for a longer time, or even a force that changes while it acts. In Fig. 23–1 we have plotted a constant force F against the time it acts. The plot is just a horizontal straight line of height F above the time axis and of length $\Delta t = t_2 - t_1$, equal to the time during which the force acts. The area of the rectangle under this line is $F\Delta t$, the size of the impulse in the time interval. (The direction of the impulse is the same as that of the force.) For any constant force acting for any time interval, we can always get the magnitude of the impulse as the area under the force-time curve for this time interval, and the direction is the direction of the force.

Now suppose the force changes, as in Fig. 23–2 for instance. For a time Δt_1 the force is constant and the impulse is $\vec{F}_1\Delta t_1$. This impulse makes the change $m(\Delta\vec{v})_1$ in the motion. In the next time interval, Δt_2, the force is again constant, this time $\vec{F}_2$, and there is an impulse $\vec{F}_2\Delta t_2$ which results in the change $m(\Delta\vec{v})_2$ in the motion. That is,

$$\vec{F}_1\Delta t_1 = m(\Delta\vec{v})_1$$

and

$$\vec{F}_2\Delta t_2 = m(\Delta\vec{v})_2.$$

If we add these two statements vectorially we get

$$\vec{F}_1\Delta t_1 + \vec{F}_2\Delta t_2 = m(\Delta\vec{v})_1 + m(\Delta\vec{v})_2 = m[(\Delta\vec{v})_1 + (\Delta\vec{v})_2].$$

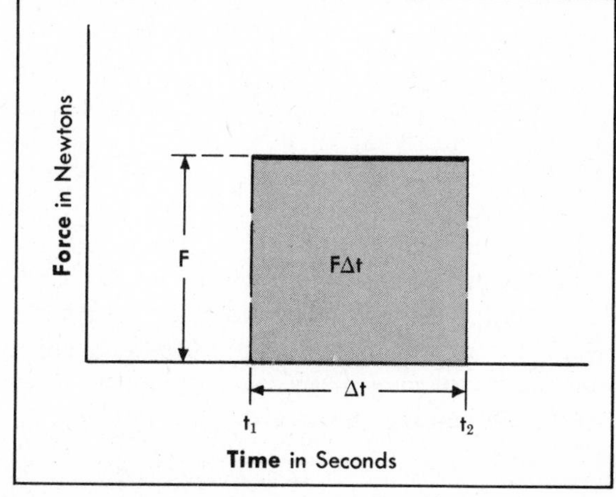

23–1. A constant force F is plotted against time for the interval $t_2 - t_1 = \Delta t$. The area $F\Delta t$ under the curve gives the impulse of this force in time Δt.

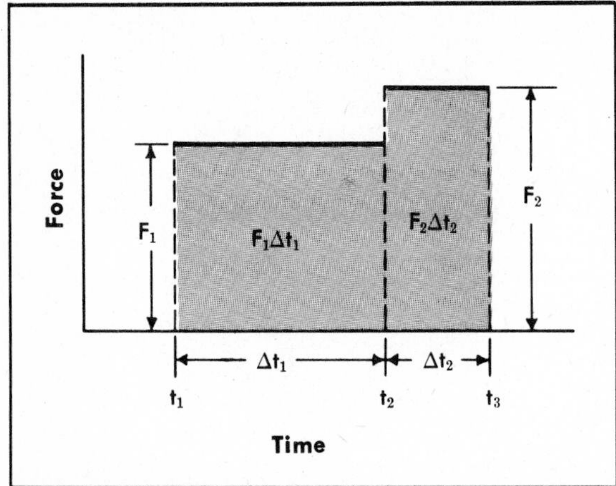

23–2. The force is F_1 in the time interval Δt_1, and changes to F_2 in time interval Δt_2. If the direction does not change, the total impulse in time $\Delta t_1 + \Delta t_2$ is $F_1 \Delta t_1 + F_2 \Delta t_2$, the shaded area under the curve.

Can we lump the two impulses on the left together into a single "total impulse"? Earlier we saw that the impulse is that combination of force and of the time it acts which produces the change in velocity $\Delta\vec{v}$ of the mass affected. Now we see that $\vec{F}_1 \Delta t_1 + \vec{F}_2 \Delta t_2$ does produce the change in velocity $\Delta\vec{v} = \Delta\vec{v}_1 + \Delta\vec{v}_2$ which occurs in the motion of m between the onset of the force $\vec{F}_1$ and the removal of the later force $\vec{F}_2$. Consequently the sum $\vec{F}_1 \Delta t_1 + \vec{F}_2 \Delta t_2$ is equal to the total impulse acting in that time. Finally since $\vec{F}_1 \Delta t_1$ and $\vec{F}_2 \Delta t_2$ are the two individual impulses which act on m in that period, we can conclude that the vector sum of successive impulses gives the overall impulse.

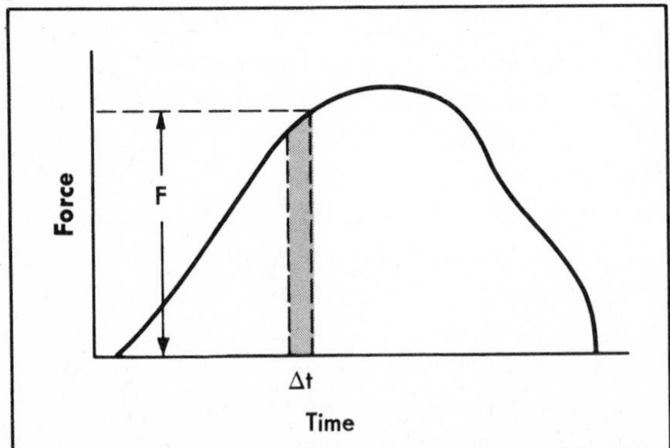

23–3. When the force is continually changing, we can break up the area under the F-t curve into a large number of small areas that are nearly rectangles. (See shaded areas.) Each such area $F\Delta t$ is a little impulse. The total impulse is the sum of all these small impulses. Therefore, as long as the force points in the same direction, the area under the curve is the total impulse.

When we deal with a continuously varying force we can still obtain the total impulse by adding up all the impulses in short time intervals. We can take each time interval so short that $\vec{F}$ is essentially constant during it. Then the total impulse, which is the sum of all the $\vec{F}\Delta t$'s, gives the total change $m\Delta\vec{v}$ in the motion.

When the force changes magnitude but always points in the same direction, we can add the impulses up by finding the area under the $\vec{F}$–t curve. A simple case is shown in Fig. 23–2, and an example in which the force changes continuously in Fig. 23–3. If the force changes direction, however, this graphical method is not enough. We must add the little impulses $\vec{F}\Delta t$ in their correct directions. Because each little impulse causes a change $m\Delta\vec{v} = \vec{F}\Delta t$ in the direction of the force then acting, the total impulse between any initial time t and any final time t' must be added up *vectorially*. This vector sum then gives the net change $m\vec{v}' - m\vec{v}$ in the motion. (We shall often use the symbol ′, which is read "prime," to distinguish velocity at a later time from that earlier.) Briefly, the total impulse is the *vector* sum of all the little $\vec{F}\Delta t$'s. It equals the vector sum of all the little $m\Delta\vec{v}$'s. This is the same as m times the vector sum of all the little $\Delta\vec{v}$'s and equals $m(\vec{v}' - \vec{v})$.

Often a large force acts only for a very short time interval. Think what happens when you hit a tennis ball with a racket, or when two steel balls collide. Without the most elaborate equipment it is very hard to tell the size of the forces which act during the collision. But the total impulse of the force is easily found by observing the net change in mv. Forces which act for a short time and for which only the product $\vec{F}\Delta t$ is known are called impulsive forces.

23–2. Momentum

When a mass m is moving with velocity v, we feel that there is a certain quantity of motion. Furthermore, if two masses, each m, are moving with the same velocity, we should have a measure of quantity of motion which is twice as large as for one mass. We can establish various measures of motion which are proportional to the mass and increase with the speeds — for instance, mv, mv^2, mv^3), etc. Two such measures are of great importance in physics. At this time we can develop one of them.

23–4. This high-speed photograph shows a familiar example of an impulsive force. Notice the large distortion of the racket and the ball. (Courtesy: Harold E. Edgerton.)

One measure of the quantity of motion of a body is the impulse necessary to set it moving at its velocity $\vec{v}$ starting from rest. As we know from the last section, the impulse required is determined by $m\Delta\vec{v}$, the mass times the change in velocity; and for a mass that starts from rest the change in velocity is equal to the final velocity $\vec{v}$. The impulse that would give the body its present motion is therefore equal to $m\vec{v}$, the mass times its present velocity. Because this product $m\vec{v}$ is proportional to the mass and to the velocity, it is a measure of motion of the type we described in the first paragraph. We call it the *momentum* of the body, and measure it in kilogram-meters per second. Because we shall use *momenta* often, we introduce the symbol $\vec{p}$ to represent the momentum of a body: $\vec{p} = m\vec{v}$.

Velocity and momentum, although related, tell us different things. The knowledge of the velocity only tells how fast (and in which direction) an object moves. It tells us nothing about the effort required to get it moving, or, for that matter, to stop it. The momentum, on the other hand, does not tell the speed of the object (although it tells us the direction in which it moves), but it determines the impulse necessary to get it going and the impulse necessary to stop it. Briefly the velocity is a kinematical quantity — one which enters the geometrical description of where and when — whereas the momentum is a dynamical one, connected with the impulses and therefore with the causes of changes in the motion of masses.

Notice that the momentum does not depend

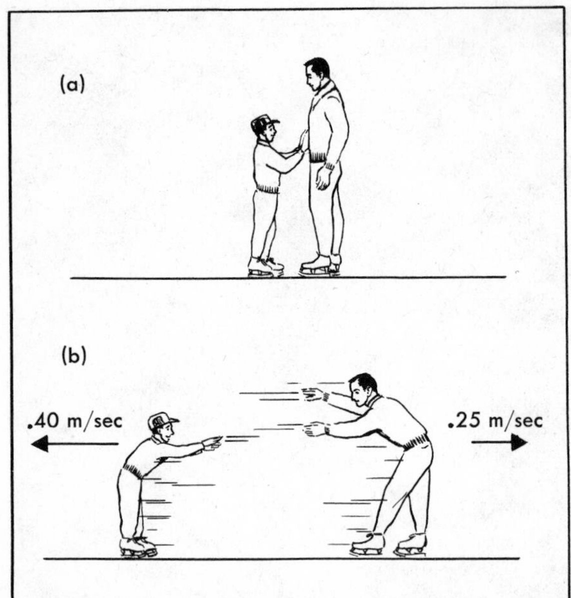

23–5. On a frozen pond a 50-kg boy pushes an 80-kg man hard enough to give him a speed of .25 m/sec. The boy moves off at .40 m/sec.

on the way in which the body acquired its present motion. $\vec{p} = m\vec{v}$ contains nothing but the mass and its motion now. The impulse which set it going may have been delivered in any of an infinite number of ways (as we know from the last section), or the mass may always have been moving with momentum $\vec{p}$, for all we care. Similarly, the impulse required to bring the mass to rest may be applied in infinitely many ways or not at all; we still know from the present momentum how big it would be. It would cost a reverse impulse equal to $-m\vec{v}$ to stop the body whether we use a big force and short time or a little force and long time.

Because of its connection with the impulse which occurs naturally in Newton's law $\vec{F}\Delta t = m\Delta\vec{v}$, we expect momentum to fit naturally into Newtonian dynamics. In fact, Newton expressed his law of motion in terms of the momentum $m\vec{v}$, which he called the quantity of motion. We can easily express Newton's law in terms of the change in momentum instead of change in velocity: $\vec{F}\Delta t = m\Delta\vec{v} = m(\vec{v}' - \vec{v})$ where $\vec{v}$ and $\vec{v}'$ are the velocities before and after the impulse $\vec{F}\Delta t$. But the right-hand side of the last equation can be written as: $m(\vec{v}' - \vec{v}) = m\vec{v}' - m\vec{v} = \vec{p}' - \vec{p} = \Delta\vec{p}$, the change in the momentum. Therefore $\vec{F}\Delta t = \Delta\vec{p}$; or, in words, the impulse equals the change in the momentum. Finally, dividing by Δt, we find $\vec{F} = \Delta\vec{p}/\Delta t$; the force equals the rate of change of the momentum. It was in this form rather than in terms of $\vec{F} = m\vec{a}$ that Newton originally formulated his law.

For the discussion of the motion of a single object, both forms of Newton's law are equally convenient. The great importance of momentum will become apparent in the next sections where we deal with the motions of two objects which exert forces on each other.

23–3. Changes in Momentum when Two Bodies Interact

A boy and a man are standing next to each other on a smooth sheet of ice. The boy shoves the man; and they both start to move, sliding away in opposite directions with the boy moving away somewhat faster than the man. If we perform such experiments, we find that whenever two people are at rest and one pushes the other, they go off in opposite directions. We also find that their speeds are inversely proportional to their masses. For example, if a 50-kg boy shoves an 80-kg man hard enough so that the man goes off at .25 m/sec, we find that the boy goes off in the opposite direction at .40 m/sec (Fig. 23–5).

These experimental facts are most easily expressed in terms of the momentum of the man and the momentum of the boy. The momentum of the man is $mv = 80 \text{ kg} \times 0.25 \text{ m/sec} = 20 \text{ kg-m/sec}$, and the momentum of the boy in the opposite direction is $mv = 50 \text{ kg} \times 0.40 \text{ m/sec} = 20 \text{ kg-m/sec}$. After the shove their momenta are equal in magnitude and opposite in direction.

With discs mounted on Dry Ice bearings we can perform an accurate experiment of the kind that we have been describing. We screw one end of a spring to the edge of one disc; we bend the spring and tie the ends together with a thread (Fig. 23–6). Then we put a second disc close to the first as shown in the figure. When the thread is broken the spring will snap out and shove the second disc away. When the two discs are at rest on a level metal plate, we burn the thread and see what happens when the spring "explodes." The subsequent motion of the discs is shown in Fig. 23–7.

23–6. The apparatus used to show a simple kind of explosion. A compressed spring is held between two Dry Ice discs. The spring is screwed to the larger disc and secured by a thread.

In this experiment the mass of the large disc, including the spring mounted on it, was 2.28 kg, and the mass of the small disc was 1.10 kg. A glance at the picture shows that the two discs went off in opposite directions. In each interval between flashes of the light the small disc moves farther than the large one. The small disc must have been given a higher velocity than the large one. By making measurements on the photograph you can tell that the small disc was moving at 0.206 m/sec after the shove, and the large disc was moving at 0.100 m/sec. The rightward momentum of the small disc was $mv = 1.10$ kg $\times$ .206 m/sec = .227 kg-m/sec, while the leftward momentum of the large disc was 2.28 kg $\times$ .100 m/sec = .228 kg-m/sec. Within experimental accuracy these momenta are equal and opposite.

By observing the motions of two bodies starting from rest and interacting with each other, we find time after time that the resulting changes in momentum are equal and opposite. It does not matter what produces the forces of interaction. They may arise from our muscles, from a distorted spring, or from a chemical explosion.

Take a chemical explosion as another example. When a man fires a rifle, the gases from the explosives exert violent forces inside the barrel. The bullet is pushed out in one direction and the rifle is pushed back in the other. We can show that the rifle's momentum and the bullet's momentum are equal and opposite: we suspend the rifle on long strings, take suitable flash photographs of the bullet, and time the very much slower motion of the recoiling rifle. In ordinary use the recoil velocity of the gun is rapidly decreased by an impulse from the man's

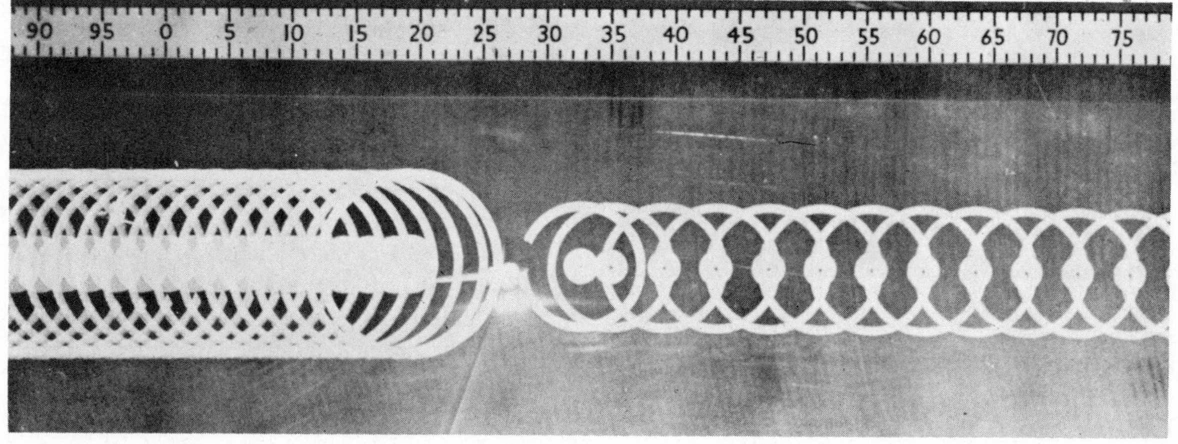

23–7. A multiple-flash picture of the motion of the two discs after being pushed apart by the spring. The flash rate was 5 per second, and the scale is in centimeters.

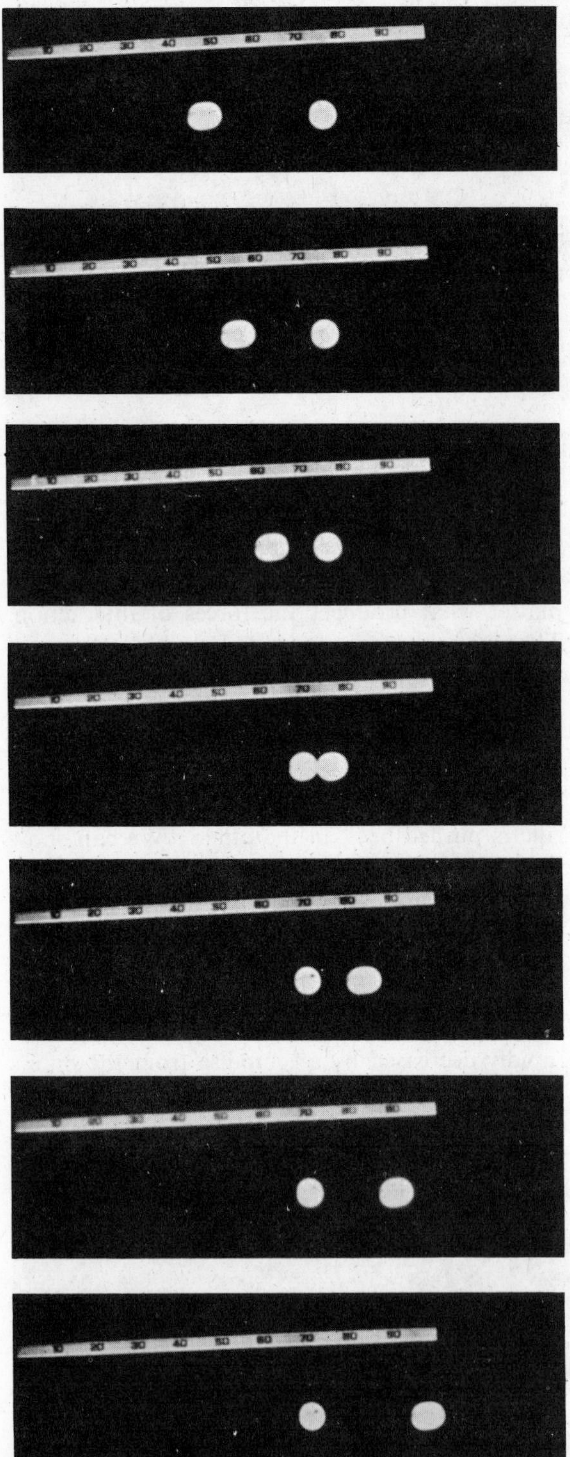

23–8. Enlarged movie frames showing a head-on collision between two billiard balls of equal mass. The time interval between pictures is $\frac{1}{48}$ second; the scale is in centimeters. Notice that all of the momentum of the incident ball is transferred to the ball initially at rest.

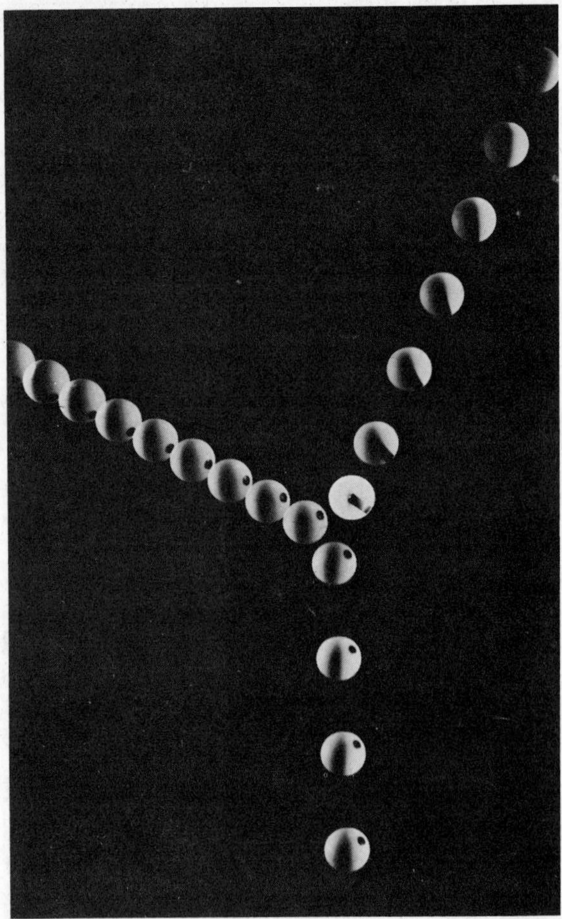

23–9. A multiple-flash photograph (flash rate 30 per second) of an off-center collision between two balls, each of mass 173 grams. The dotted ball entered at the bottom of the picture and struck the striped ball at rest. (The camera was pointed straight down and the balls were moving horizontally.) To get the velocities and momenta diagramed in Fig. 23–10, we used the fact that the photograph is about $\frac{1}{7}$ actual size. Could this approximation affect the conclusion that $\Delta\vec{p_1} = -\Delta\vec{p_2}$?

shoulder, and a later measurement of its momentum does not show the equality and opposition so directly.

So far we have only examined examples in which both of the interacting bodies were originally at rest. What can we say about the changes in the momenta of two interacting bodies when one or both are originally in motion?

In Fig. 23–8 a moving billiard ball collides with a billiard ball at rest. The incident ball stops and the ball it hits goes off with the same velocity with which the incident ball came in. The two billiard balls have the same mass. Therefore, the momentum of the second ball after the colli-

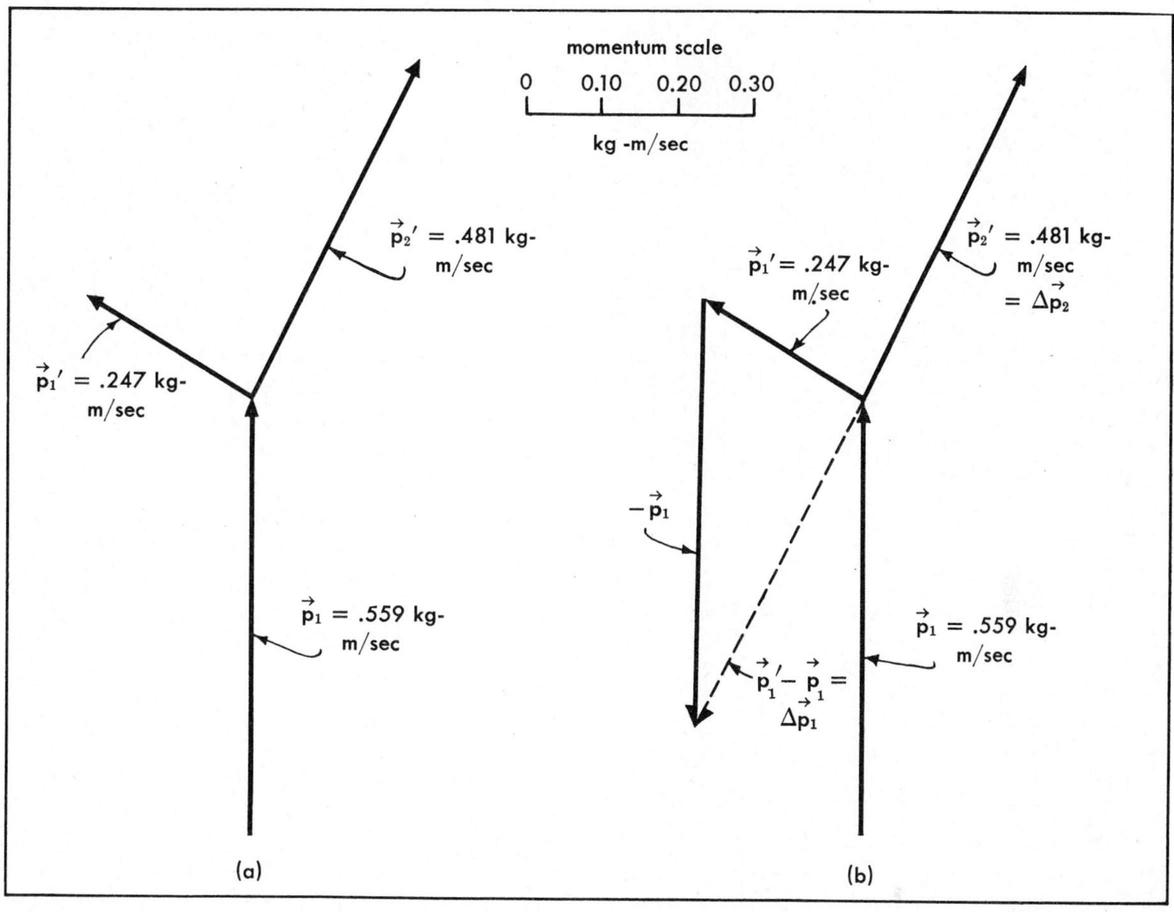

23–10. (a) The vectors representing the momenta of the balls in Fig. 23–9. $\vec{p}_1$ is the original momentum of the dotted ball; $\vec{p}_1'$, its momentum after the collision; and $\vec{p}_2'$ the momentum acquired by the ball originally at rest. In (b) we obtain $\Delta\vec{p}_1 = \vec{p}_1' - \vec{p}_1$ graphically. We subtract $\vec{p}_1$ from $\vec{p}_1'$ by drawing $-\vec{p}_1$ from the head of $\vec{p}_1'$, then drawing the resultant (shown dashed in the figure). Note that $\Delta\vec{p}_1$ is closely equal and opposite to $\Delta\vec{p}_2 = \vec{p}_2'$.

sion is the same as that of the incident ball before collision. The incident ball has lost all its momentum, and the ball it struck has gained exactly the momentum which the incident ball lost. The changes in momentum are again equal and opposite.

The collision illustrated in Fig. 23–8 is a very special one: the incident billiard ball hit the ball at rest head on. Usually one billiard ball hits another somewhere on the side, and the two balls go off in different directions. Such a collision is illustrated in Fig. 23–9. In the picture the ball originally in motion came in at the bottom. After the collision, as we would expect, one ball goes off to the right; the other goes off to the left.

The flash photograph shows the speeds and directions of the balls both before and after collision. The speeds are measured by the distances the balls travel between flashes. Using these measured speeds and the observed directions of motion, we find the velocity vectors, $\vec{v}_1$, $\vec{v}_1'$, and $\vec{v}_2'$, representing the velocity of the first ball before and after the collision and that of the second ball after the collision. (We shall generally use primes — that is, 's — to distinguish velocities after collision from those before.) Then we obtain the momenta of the balls by multiplying the vector velocities by the masses: $\vec{p} = m\vec{v}$ for each ball. Because the masses of the balls here are equal, using $\vec{p}$ instead of $\vec{v}$ just changes the scale in this case. In Fig. 23–10 (a) we have plotted the momentum vectors $\vec{p}_1$, $\vec{p}_1'$ and $\vec{p}_2'$, representing the momentum of the incident ball before the collision, and the momentum of each ball after the

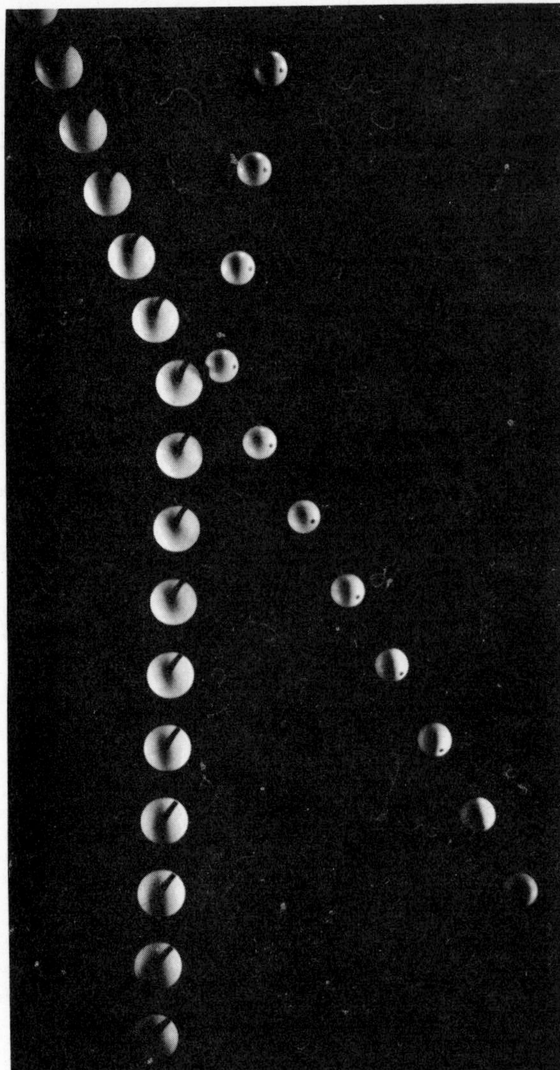

23–11. A multiple-flash photograph of a collision between two balls — one of mass 201.1 gm and the other 85.4 gm. Again the flash rate was 30 per second and the setup was the same as that described in Fig. 23–9. Both balls were initially in motion and entered from the top of the picture.

collision. (When the second ball was at rest before the collision, it had no momentum.)

Now we shall find out whether the momenta of the two balls change by equal amounts in opposite directions in this experiment.

In Fig. 23–10 (b) $\Delta\vec{p}_1$ is obtained graphically. We draw $-\vec{p}_1$, from the head of $\vec{p}_1{}'$. The vector $\Delta\vec{p}_1$ is the resultant of $\vec{p}_1{}'$ and $-\vec{p}_1$. It extends from the tail of $\vec{p}_1{}'$ to the head of $-\vec{p}_1$, and we see that it is equal and opposite to $\Delta\vec{p}_2 = \vec{p}_2{}'$, the change in the momentum of the struck ball. The change in momentum of the incident ball is compensated by an equal and opposite change in the momentum of the other ball, or

$$\Delta\vec{p}_1 = -\Delta\vec{p}_2.$$

23–4. The Law of Conservation of Momentum

In the last section we have seen examples in which two bodies interact. The motion of each body changes, and the change in momentum of one body is equal and opposite to the change in momentum of the other. As we go further we shall come across more and more examples. No single example can yield a general proof that the momenta of two interacting bodies always change equally and oppositely. But our experience with the interactions of two bodies, in all circumstances, strongly suggests that equal and opposite changes of the momenta are the invariable rule in nature.

This rule of nature can be stated in a different form. We introduce the total momentum $\vec{P} = \vec{p}_1 + \vec{p}_2$ of the two bodies. Because any changes in the momenta $\vec{p}_1$ and $\vec{p}_2$ are just opposite, the total momentum $\vec{P}$ never changes. That is, $\Delta\vec{P} = 0$, or $\vec{P}$ is constant. We call the statement that the total momentum is constant the law of conservation of momentum.

Let us look at the conservation of momentum when two balls of different masses, both initially in motion, collide. Such a collision is illustrated in Fig. 23–11. By measuring the distances that the balls have moved between flashes, we determine their velocities. The velocity vectors are indicated in Fig. 23–12 (a). Multiplying by the masses, which were measured as 85.4 grams for the first ball and 201.1 grams for the second, we obtain the momentum vectors for the individual balls before and after the collision [Fig. 23–12 (b)]. Then, on the left in Fig. 23–12 (c), we have added together the momentum vectors of both balls before the collision to obtain the total momentum; and on the right we have added together the momentum vectors of the two balls after the collision. We see that the two measured values of the total momentum are almost precisely the same. This experiment is consistent with the law of conservation of momentum.

Let us try one more kind of collision: one where the two colliding masses stick together and continue as a unit after the collision. Fig. 23–13 shows a collision between a golf ball and a putty

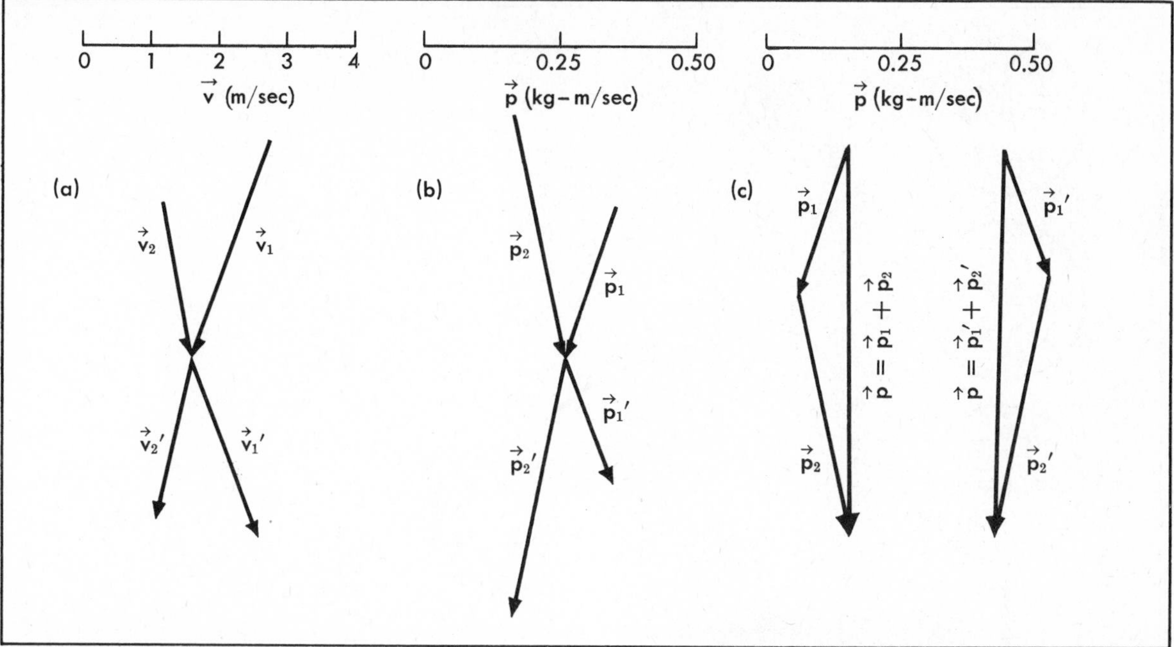

23–12. (a) The velocity vectors of the balls shown in Fig. 23–11. The subscript "1" refers to the smaller ball, and "2" to the larger. The primes indicate velocities and momenta after the collision. (b) The momentum vectors before and after the collision. (c) On the left we have added the momenta before the collision. On the right we have done the same for the momenta after. As you can see, $\vec{p}_1 + \vec{p}_2 = \vec{p}_1{}' + \vec{p}_2{}'$. In fact, when we made the original drawing, they were equal within about 1 part in 200.

ball. The golf ball had a mass of 45.7 gm, and the putty ball, originally at rest, had a mass of 69.7 gm. The combined mass of the two balls stuck together after the collision was therefore 115.4 gm. This total mass was 2.53 times the mass of the incident ball. By measuring the ratio of the incident and final velocities in the flash photograph, you will find that the incident speed was about 2.53 times the final speed. Therefore the final momentum was just equal to the initial momentum.

From now on we shall assume the conservation of momentum for two interacting bodies. We consider it to be a general law based on experience. Indeed the kind of experience which we have summarized in our discussion here is the kind that originally led to the conservation law. Because the laws of collisions were of such obvious importance for the development of mechanics, in

23–13. A flash photograph of a collision between a golf ball and a putty ball. The golf ball moved in from the left and struck the putty ball. The two balls moved off to the right, stuck together. Measure the ratio of the incident and final speeds yourself, and check them against the calculation in the text.

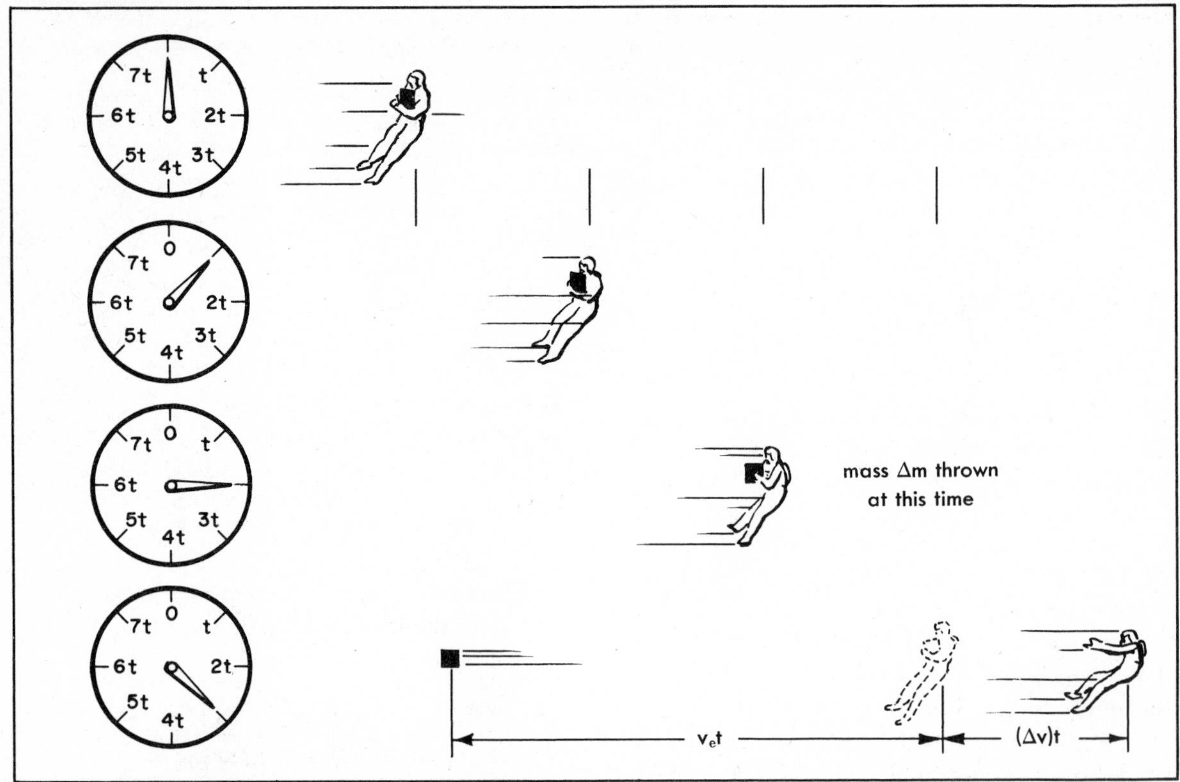

23–14. The successive positions of a man moving through outer space. He is shown at equal time intervals t. In the first two pictures he is moving with uniform velocity. In the third he throws away a small mass Δm, with a velocity v_e with respect to his original motion. In the next interval his ghost moves at the original speed, while he goes $\Delta v = \frac{\Delta m}{m} v_e$ faster. He therefore ends up $(\Delta v)t$ farther than the ghost. The small mass ends up $v_e t$ behind the ghost.

1668 the Royal Society of London (then only eight years old) initiated an investigation into the problem. Three able men produced almost similar solutions: John Wallis, an English mathematician; Sir Christopher Wren, the English scientist and architect who designed St. Paul's; and Christian Huygens, a Dutch physicist. Wallis was first, and so he gets the credit for the general principle of conservation of momentum.

In a paper published in 1669, and later in his book "Mechanica" (1670) Wallis developed fairly clear ideas of impulse and momentum and the connection between them. He believed that an impulse which started one body toward another would give the same momentum to the single body or to the two bodies combined after collision. He thus arrived at the conservation of momentum for one kind of collision. He also argued that conservation applied to other collisions. All his arguments really involve assumptions about the forces or impulses between the colliding bodies. The French physicist Mariotte demonstrated these conclusions by a series of experiments on pendulums that could strike one another. Huygens made similar experiments, and other experiments in which hard spheres in close contact were struck by a similar sphere moving in a straight-line groove. In the "Principia" Newton described these experiments and his own careful experiments. The law of conservation of momentum was established as one of the foundations of modern physics.

23–5. Rockets

Imagine a man in a space suit moving in interplanetary space. His mass is m, and in his hand he holds a small object of mass Δm, which evidently moves through space at the same speed that he does (Fig. 23–14). Now the man throws away the small mass Δm with a velocity $\vec{v}_e$ with respect to his original motion. Its momentum changes by an amount $(\Delta m)\vec{v}_e$. According to the principle of conservation of momentum, the velocity $\vec{v}$ of the man undergoes a change in magnitude Δv in the opposite direction, and his momentum will change by an amount $m\Delta v$, just equal in magnitude to the momentum change $(\Delta m)v_e$ of the small object. Therefore

$$m\Delta v = (\Delta m)v_e$$

and the man's speed changes by

$$\Delta v = \frac{\Delta m}{m} v_e.$$

This man is much like a rocket ship: he changes his momentum by throwing out mass. If he wants to increase his speed toward the east, he throws out mass to the west.

In a rocket ship the mass thrown out is in the form of a stream of gas. The gas is shot out from the ship at a high exhaust velocity; and the momentum of the ship changes in the opposite direction. We must be careful to remember that m is the mass of the ship *after* the small mass Δm has been thrown out. It includes the fuel, the passengers, the casing — everything left on board.

Let us find out what happens to a rocket that ejects mass at a constant exhaust velocity v_e with respect to the rocket. How will the mass of the rocket decrease as it picks up speed? To get an idea of the relation between decreasing rocket mass and increasing rocket speed, we shall pretend that the gas is ejected in bursts. For instance, we might make each burst just equal to $\frac{1}{10}$ of the total mass m_t of the rocket at the time the burst is ejected. Then at each burst $\frac{1}{10}m_t$ is shot out and $\frac{9}{10}m_t$ continues forward faster. We see then that $\Delta m = \frac{1}{10}m_t$ and $m = \frac{9}{10}m_t$. When we divide the first equation by the second we find

$$\frac{\Delta m}{m} = \frac{1}{9}$$

in every burst. Also, as we found in the case of the man who threw away a small mass,

$$\Delta v = \frac{\Delta m}{m} v_e.$$

On combining these two equations we have

$$\Delta v = \tfrac{1}{9}v_e.$$

This equation shows that we have chosen the bursts so that the change Δv in the speed is the same for each. In starting from zero, then, the speed v of the rocket increases to $\frac{1}{9}v_e$, then $\frac{2}{9}v_e$, $\frac{3}{9}v_e$, and so on with successive bursts.

Now let's look at what happens to the mass of the rocket as the speed goes up. In each burst its mass changes from m_t to $\frac{9}{10}m_t$. Therefore, after the first burst it is $\frac{9}{10}m_o$, where m_o is the original total mass before the rocket was fired. After the second burst the mass is $\frac{9}{10} \times \frac{9}{10}m_o$ or $(\frac{9}{10})^2\, m_o$; after the third it is $(\frac{9}{10})^3\, m_o$, and so on. In Fig. 23–15 we have plotted the fraction of the original mass left against the speed attained, measuring this speed as a multiple of v_e.

The molecules of gas ejected by a rocket are such tiny masses compared to the mass m that we may think of a continuous ejection of mass. Bursts of $\frac{1}{10}$ of the mass give a crude approximation to continuous ejection. But we can make better and better approximations by using bursts of $\frac{1}{100}$ of the mass, $\frac{1}{1000}$ of the mass, and so on. The graphs we then obtain (Fig. 23–15) are slightly different, but as the bursts get smaller the curves get more nearly the same, and for sufficiently small bursts — still far larger than individual molecules — we approach the single mathematical curve for continuous ejection. This curve, called the exponential curve, will tell us the relation between the speed we can hope to attain and mass left over.* Because we can attain high exhaust velocity only when we eject individual molecules, this relation tells us the highest speed we can attain with a given fraction of the mass left over. The exponential decay (Fig. 23–16) is the same curve which tells the fraction of radioactive atoms left in a sample as time goes on (Chapter 7).

We now can estimate how much of the mass of a rocket we must throw away to get an earth satellite into orbit. We already know that we need a satellite speed of about 8 km/sec for circular motion around the earth. To get this with the smallest loss of rocket mass, we should make the exhaust velocity v_e just as high as

*The graphs show $\frac{m}{m_o}$ vs $\frac{v}{v_e}$, the relation between the mass remaining and the velocity. They do not show anything about the time taken. The final speed depends only on v_e and the fraction of the original mass remaining. You can see that the time taken to burn the fuel does not affect the final speed, by imagining that the engine is turned off for a while. During that time the rocket coasts without changing speed.

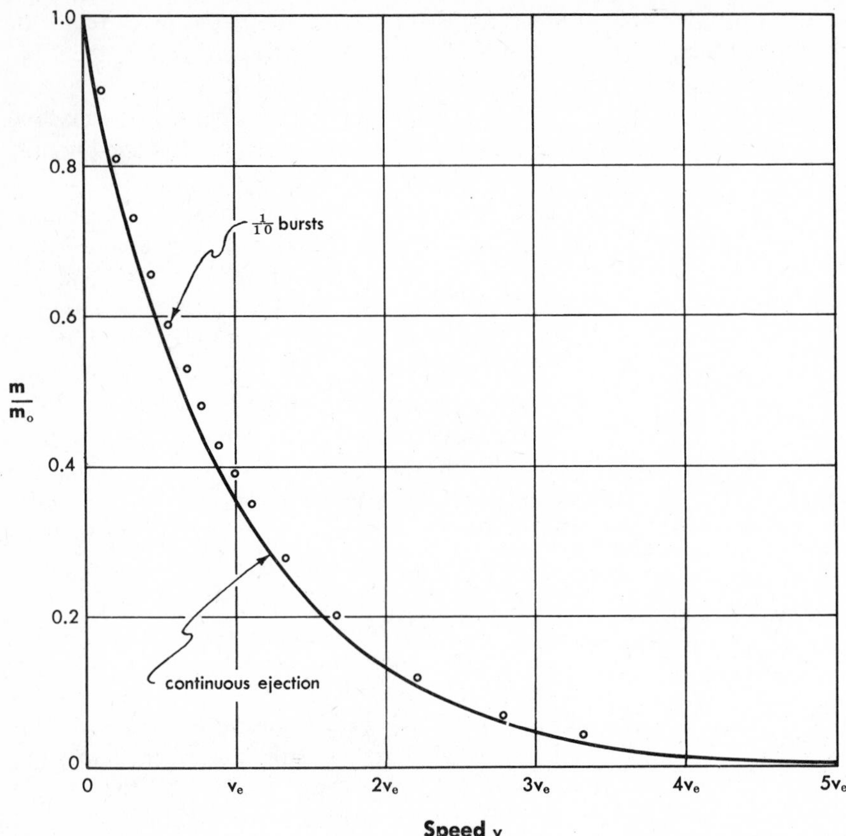

23–15 (a). Left. A rocket throws out mass to gain speed. The fraction of the original mass remaining is plotted as a function of the speed v attained. This speed v is given as a multiple of the exhaust velocity v_e. The unconnected dots show the relation of the mass and speed when we throw out bursts of $\frac{1}{10}$ the mass then present. The smooth curve slightly below shows this relation when mass is thrown out continuously — this is the exponential.

23–15 (b). Right. A semi-log graph of the same relation. Equal distances along the vertical scale represent the multiplication of the mass by equal number. For example, when $\frac{m}{m_o}$ changes from 1.0 to 0.1 or from 0.1 to .01 (multiplication by $\frac{1}{10}$), the distances on the vertical scale are equal.

23–16. The exponential curve of the radioactive decay of polonium (Section 7–13). This shows us the fraction of the original atoms remaining after various time intervals.

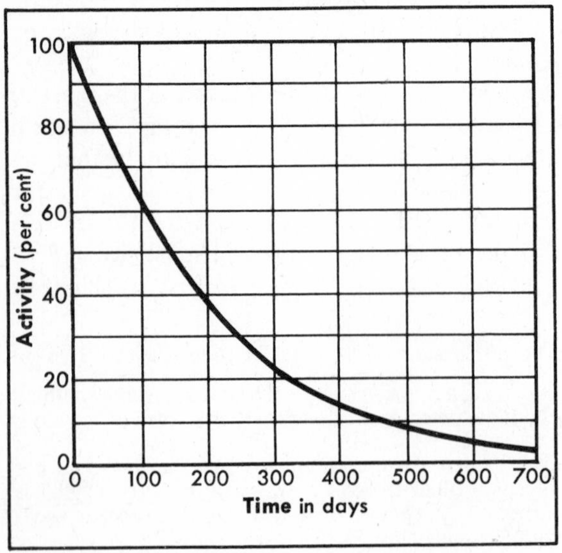

possible. How large can we possibly make v_e? This depends on the fuel, and for chemical fuels we can at best get something like 3 km/sec. These chemical fuels are just not powerful enough to get us higher exhaust velocities. Furthermore, the maximum possible v_e is probably not yet obtained in practice. Therefore, we shall use $v_e = 2$ km/sec. This corresponds to gas temperatures of better than 3000°C, and only skillful nozzle design prevents much of the gas from bombarding the rocket casing and vaporizing it.

When $v_e = 2$ km/sec, v/v_e for a rocket that would circle the earth is $\frac{8}{2}$, or 4. Referring again to Fig. 23–15 (b) we see that at this velocity ratio the mass ratio, m/m_o, is 0.02, or $\frac{1}{50}$. Ninety-eight per cent of the original mass has to be ejected so that the remaining 2 per cent attains a velocity of 8 km/sec. In addition we have to get the rocket up to its orbit, forcing it up against air resistance and the gravitational pull of the earth. This means that we must eject still more mass; and only about $\frac{1}{200}$ of the original mass goes into orbit. You can see why it takes tons of rocket to get kilograms of satellite into orbit.

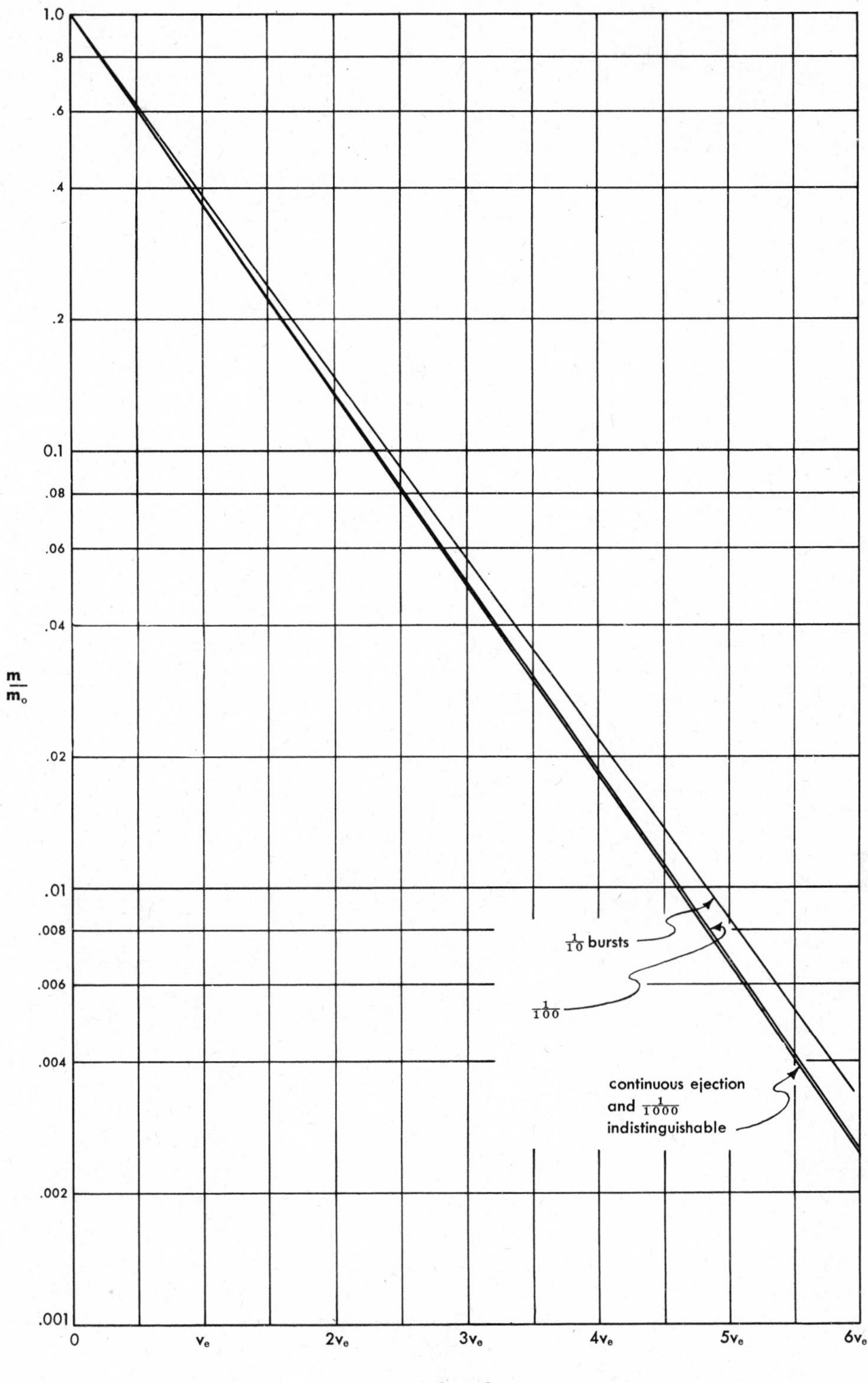
1.0
.8
.6
.4
.2
0.1
.08
.06
.04
.02
.01
.008
.006
.004
.002
.001
$\frac{m}{m_o}$
0
v_e
$2v_e$
$3v_e$
$4v_e$
$5v_e$
$6v_e$
Speed v
$\frac{1}{10}$ bursts
$\frac{1}{100}$
continuous ejection
and $\frac{1}{1000}$
indistinguishable

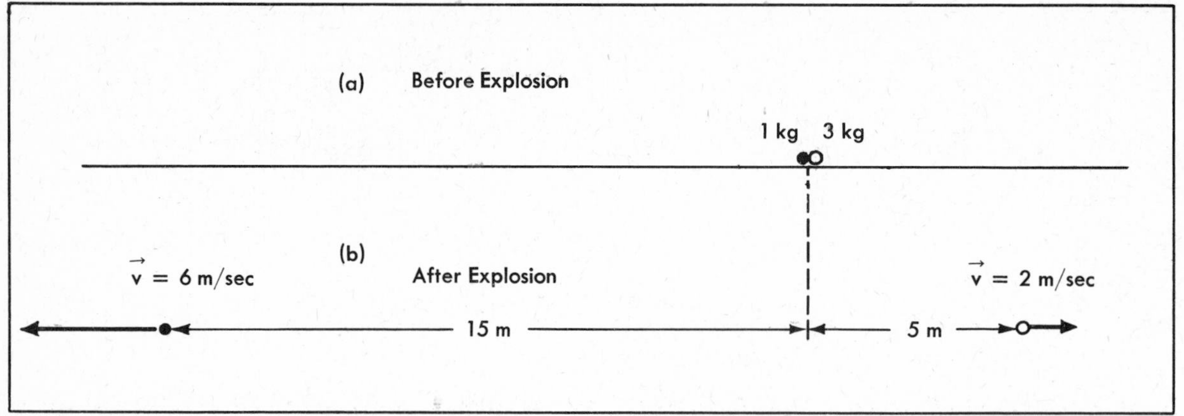

23–17. Two masses, one of 3 kg and the other of 1 kg, are on a horizontal frictionless table. In (a) they are held together by a thread, with a small spring compressed between them. Their center of mass is at the position of the masses. In (b) the thread has been burned and the masses have moved apart — the large mass 5 meters and the small mass 15 meters. Where is the center of mass now?

23–6. The Center of Mass

Think of a Fourth of July rocket which explodes while it is moving along through the air. After the explosion, if you saw all the fragments on one side of the path you would be sure that something was wrong. This kind of experience tells us that somehow the fragments into which the rocket explodes have an average motion along the original trajectory. There is a special point, known as the center of mass of the fragments, that moves along in the same way whether the rocket explodes or not. By using the law of conservation of momentum we can find out how to describe that point; but the reasoning would appear rather complicated if we dealt with the many fragments into which Fourth of July rockets explode. In this section, therefore, we shall discuss the center of mass only for the simpler case of two fragments.

Let us go back to the "rocket man" of the last section. (Fig. 23–14.) We shall use him and the small mass he carries as the two interacting masses. Suppose that like the ghost in that figure, you are moving along beside the rocket man, at the same velocity, before he throws away the mass Δm. Now, when he throws the mass Δm, he will move away from you with the velocity $\Delta \vec{v}$, and Δm will move away from you with velocity $\vec{v}_e$ which is in the opposite direction — you keep your original motion. Furthermore, the speeds of the mass and the man as they recede from you are inversely proportional to their masses.

You are at an important position. Even if you became invisible we could tell where you were by finding the point that correctly divides the distance between the little mass Δm and the man m. This point is entirely specified by the masses Δm and m and their positions, and it moves along just as if the total mass $\Delta m + m$ were still located there. It is known as the center of mass. Briefly, the center of mass of two masses is the point that divides the distance between them in inverse proportion to the masses.

Look at a simple example (Fig. 23–17). A mass of 3 kg and a mass of 1 kg have an elastic spring between them. Suppose we push them close together and tie them with a string. We now burn the thread. The masses move apart as in an explosion. If the large mass is sliding away at 2 meters a second when the spring has finished pushing, the small mass will be sliding away at 6 meters a second — because momentum is conserved. Whatever the actual speeds, the small mass moves three times as fast as the large one; and in a given time it travels three times as far. Before the thread was burned the center of mass was at the position of the combined masses. Suppose that after a certain time the small mass has traveled away 15 meters; then the large mass has traveled 5 meters. Where is their center of mass now? The masses are 20 meters apart, and the center of mass divides the line between them in the ratio 3 to 1. The point is three-quarters of the way from the small mass to the large one, and one-quarter of the way from the large mass to the small one: it is 15 meters from the small mass (Fig. 23–17). That point is the

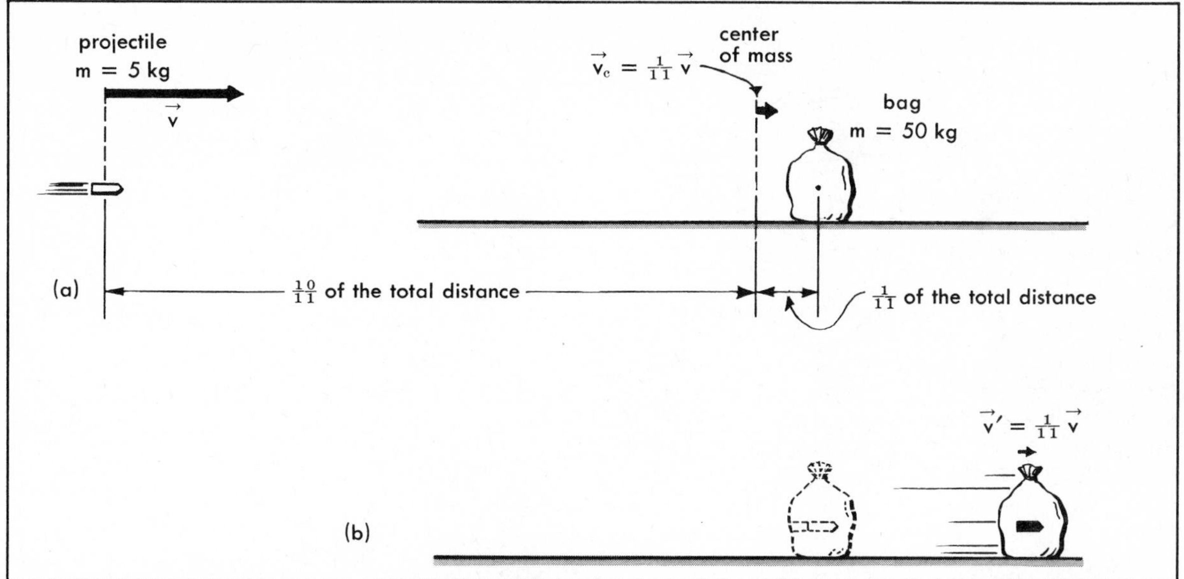

23–18. (a) A 50-kg bag is at rest on a frictionless floor. A 5-kg projectile is approaching it. The center of mass is $\frac{1}{11}$ of the way from the bag to the projectile. The projectile moves toward the bag with velocity $\vec{v}$, but the center of mass moves in with velocity $\vec{v}_c = \frac{1}{11}\vec{v}$. (b) The projectile and the bag together continue with velocity $\vec{v}' = \frac{1}{11}\vec{v}$.

same as the starting point. In other words, the center of mass sits still.

Now suppose the combined masses are already moving when the thread is burned. That motion continues. Both the masses and their center of mass keep that motion unchanged. In addition, the masses gain extra motions from the spring, motions which do not affect the center of mass. It simply keeps going as if there had been no "explosion."

Let us look at the center of mass of two masses that interact in a different way. Suppose we shoot a projectile of mass $m = 5$ kg horizontally into a sand bag of mass $M = 50$ kg. The bag is originally at rest on a frictionless level floor. As the projectile approaches the bag, where is the center of mass and how does it move? To find it we must divide the distance between the projectile and the bag in the ratio of 10 to 1 (Fig. 23–18); and therefore the center of mass is $\frac{1}{11}$ of the distance from the bag to the projectile. As the projectile approaches the bag at velocity $\vec{v}$, the center of mass only approaches it at the velocity $\vec{v}_c = \frac{1}{11}\vec{v}$. When the projectile buries itself in the bag, the bag with the projectile in it moves off with velocity $\vec{v}'$. According to the law of conservation of momentum, the total mass now has the same total momentum $\vec{P}$ as the projectile had before:

$$\vec{P} = (m + M)\vec{v}' = m\vec{v}$$

or

$$(5 + 50)\vec{v}' = (5)\vec{v}.$$

So the velocity $\vec{v}'$ of the bag and projectile is

$$\vec{v}' = \tfrac{5}{55}\vec{v} = \tfrac{1}{11}\vec{v}.$$

This is the same velocity as that of the center of mass before the collision. The center of mass has now buried itself inside the bag, and it continues to travel with the same velocity as before. This velocity ($\vec{v}_c$ or $\vec{v}'$) times the total mass, always gives the total momentum. Some ballistics experts measure the velocity $\vec{v}'$ of the bag and projectile to learn the original velocity $\vec{v}$ of a projectile.

We can show that the center of mass of two interacting bodies must always act this way. It always moves as if all the mass were concentrated there. To see that this is so we shall again imagine that we move with the center of mass. We shall move with it wherever it goes and observe the motion of the two interacting masses m_1 and m_2 from the center of mass. The two masses are always in opposite directions from the center of mass. Their distances from the center of mass are always in inverse ratio to their masses: if the distance to m_1 is x_1 then the distance to m_2 is

$$x_2 = \frac{m_1 x_1}{m_2}.$$

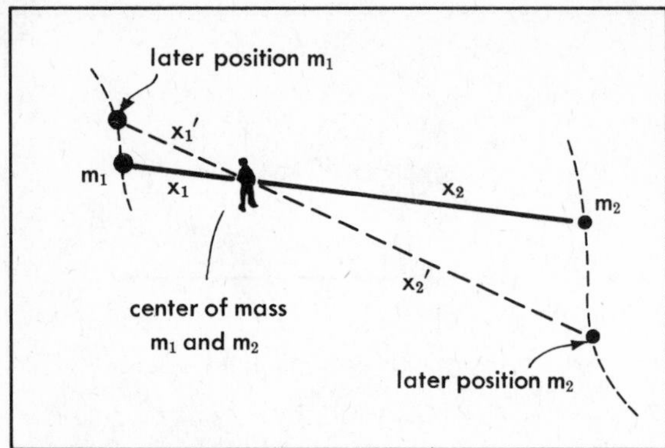

23–19. The motion of two masses as we see it when we are moving along with their center of mass. They will always be in opposite directions from the center of mass, at distances inversely proportional to their masses.

If at one moment the masses are at the positions shown in Fig. 23–19 with respect to the center of mass, a little later as the result of their motions they will be at positions such as those indicated at the ends of the dashed lines. The distances x_2' and x_1' are still in the ratio $\frac{x_2}{x_1} = \frac{m_1}{m_2}$ because we are measuring the distances from the center of mass.

Fig. 23–20 shows the motion of the two masses in a short time interval Δt. With respect to the center of mass they are moving with velocities $\vec{V}_1$ and $\vec{V}_2$; $\vec{V}_1\Delta t$ and $\vec{V}_2\Delta t$ give the distances moved. Since the two triangles in the figure are similar, the magnitudes $V_1\Delta t$ and $V_2\Delta t$ are related

by $$\frac{V_1\Delta t}{V_2\Delta t} = \frac{m_2}{m_1} \quad \text{or} \quad m_1V_1\Delta t = m_2V_2\Delta t,$$

just as $$\frac{x_1'}{x_2'} = \frac{m_2}{m_1}.$$

Also, we see that $\vec{V}_2$ is exactly opposite in direction to $\vec{V}_1$. Therefore,

$$m_1\vec{V}_1 = -m_2\vec{V}_2,$$

where the minus sign says that the directions are opposite. In other words, from our point of view as we ride with the center of mass, the momenta of m_1 and of m_2 are always equal and opposite: the total momentum $m_1\vec{V}_1 + m_2\vec{V}_2$ that we see is always zero.

Now let us get back to earth. What does an observer on earth see? The velocity $\vec{v}_1$ of m_1 that he sees is made of the velocity $\vec{v}_c$ of the center of mass plus the velocity $\vec{V}_1$ of m_1 with respect to the center of mass: that is

$$\vec{v}_1 = \vec{v}_c + \vec{V}_1.$$

Similarly, $\vec{v}_2$ is

$$\vec{v}_2 = \vec{v}_c + \vec{V}_2.$$

Therefore the total momentum of m_1 and m_2 with respect to the earth is

$$\vec{P} = m_1\vec{v}_1 + m_2\vec{v}_2 = m_1(\vec{v}_c + \vec{V}_1) + m_2(\vec{v}_c + \vec{V}_2)$$

or $$\vec{P} = (m_1 + m_2)\vec{v}_c + m_1\vec{V}_1 + m_2\vec{V}_2.$$

But by riding with the center of mass, we learned that $m_1\vec{V}_1 + m_2\vec{V}_2$ is always zero. So finally we have

$$\vec{P} = (m_1 + m_2)\vec{v}_c.$$

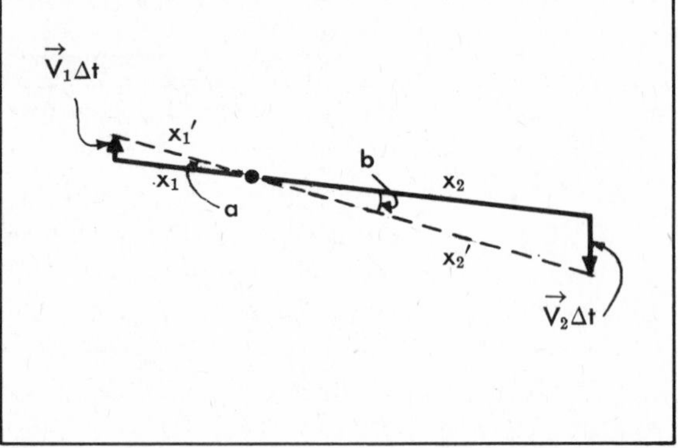

23–20. The masses of Fig. 23–19 move during a short time Δt. $\vec{V}_1\Delta t$ and $\vec{V}_2\Delta t$ give the distances moved. The two triangles are similar, since angle a = angle b and $\frac{x_1'}{x_2'} = \frac{x_1}{x_2} = \frac{m_2}{m_1}$.

The total momentum is the same as if the total mass moved with the center of mass.

The parts of a body may move with respect to each other. They may move around the center of mass or they may move in and out, toward and away from the center of mass. No matter what these internal motions, the center of mass of the body moves as though all the mass were there (Fig. 23–21).

When the two masses interact only with each other, we know that $\vec{P}$, the total momentum, is constant. So we also conclude that the velocity of the center of mass never changes. The center of mass acts like a single body with no net force on it. It moves in accord with Galileo's principle of inertia. Since there is no force acting from the outside — only the interaction of m_1 with m_2 — it is pleasing to find that the two interacting masses do act like a single body in this respect.

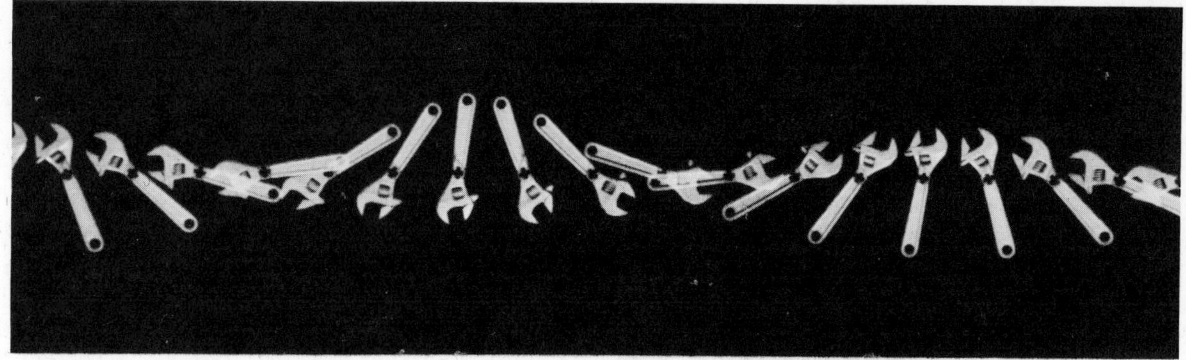

23–21. A multiple-flash photograph ($\frac{1}{30}$ second between flashes) of a moving wrench. The black cross marks its center of mass.

23–7. The Conservation of Momentum in General

In this chapter we have seen many examples of the conservation of momentum of two bodies. The conservation of momentum applies equally well to any number of interacting bodies. In this section we shall follow one line of reasoning that shows the relation between conservation of momentum in general and the conservation of momentum for two bodies. In the next section we shall sketch another line of reasoning showing the same connection for the simple case of "Newtonian" forces. Our belief in the conservation of momentum of many bodies does not depend on reasoning alone. It is also backed by a huge accumulation of experimental evidence.

In Fig. 23–22 we see a diagram of two bodies. One is a single ball and the other is made of two balls which are tied together by a very light spring. Suppose that the second body is at rest, and the first one hits it, moving with momentum $\vec{p}_1$. After the collision, ball number 1 travels away with a momentum $\vec{p}_1{}'$ while the compound body moves off with momentum $\vec{p}_2{}'$.

We know from the experiments we have been discussing that the momentum of two interacting bodies is conserved. Here, before the collision, the total momentum $\vec{P}$ is just the momentum $\vec{p}_1$ of the first body. After the collision the total momentum $\vec{P}$ is $\vec{p}_1{}' + \vec{p}_2{}'$. Consequently

$$\vec{p}_1 = \vec{p}_1{}' + \vec{p}_2{}'.$$

All we have said so far comes from considering the two bodies 1 and 2. Now let us take a closer look at body 2. It is made of the balls a and b. We know from the last section that its center of mass momentum $\vec{p}_2{}'$ is the sum of the momenta of the two balls of which it is made:

$$\vec{p}_2{}' = \vec{p}_{2a}{}' + \vec{p}_{2b}{}'.$$

If we put this expression for $\vec{p}_2{}'$ into the preceding equation we get

$$\vec{p}_1 = \vec{p}_1{}' + \vec{p}_{2a}{}' + \vec{p}_{2b}{}'.$$

23–22. The single ball, body No. 1, collides with body No. 2, which is made of two parts a and b, connected by a light spring.

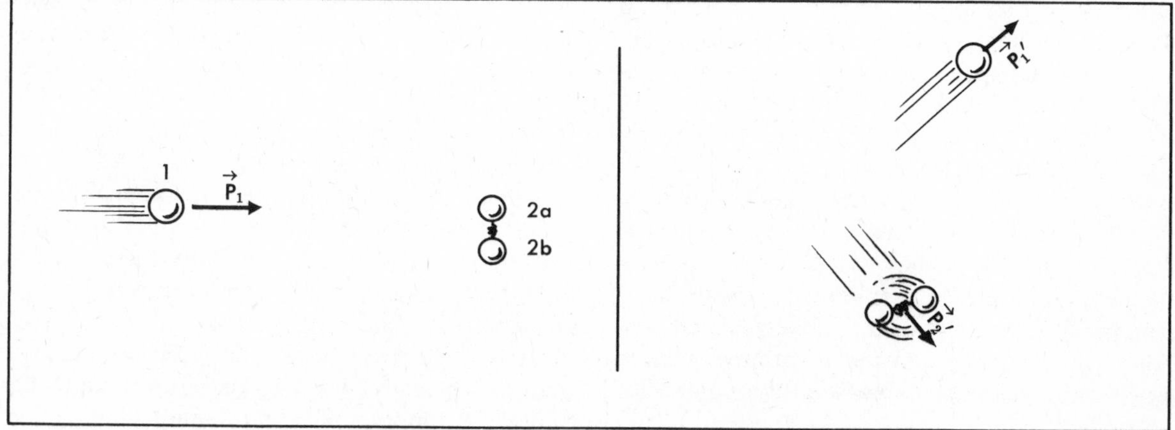

This reasoning shows that the total momentum is conserved for three bodies (1, a, and b) just as well as two — at least when two of the three bodies are tied together. But the fact that balls a and b were connected by a spring really does not matter; the spring never entered the reasoning at all. The center-of-mass momentum $\vec{p}_2{}'$ of body 2 is constant and equal to $\vec{p}_{2a}{}' + \vec{p}_{2b}{}'$ no matter if there is a spring holding the balls together or not.

The experiment we just analyzed is no different from some of the other experiments we have considered. Fig. 23–9 is a picture of a moving body colliding with one at rest. If you take a close look at that picture you can see that after the collision the ball that was hit rotates as well as moving along as a whole. The momentum that we measured for the struck ball in Fig. 23–9 was really the momentum of the center of mass. Just as we can think of the collision that we discussed in the last paragraph as a collision between three bodies rather than two, we could have called the collision in Section 23–3 a collision of three bodies by mentally dividing the struck ball into two halves, for instance the half with the black mark on it and the one without. Because of the forces holding the two halves together, these two halves are two bodies interacting with each other. After all, what we call a body is our choice. We decide whether to call that collection of arms and legs a chair or to split it into eight bodies called arms, back, seat, and legs.

By looking at the balls 1, a, and b above as a system of three bodies we showed that when three bodies interact the total momentum stays the same. The conservation of momentum applies just as well to three bodies as it did to two. We can now see that the conservation of momentum does not depend on the number of bodies at all. If we have any system of pieces that interact only among themselves, any isolated system, we can divide it into any number of bodies we choose. The same kind of reasoning that we just went through will show us that the total momentum does not change and does not depend on what we decide to call a body. The conservation of momentum therefore applies to any isolated system. It appears to be a perfectly general law. All experience, with interactions of any sort and any number of bodies, bears out this powerful conclusion.

23–8. Forces of Interaction

We can connect the conservation of momentum for two interacting bodies with the general law of conservation of momentum in another way. This line of reasoning involves the forces. We show that the forces in an interaction of two bodies are equal and opposite. Then we consider a number of bodies interacting and assume that the forces between every pair of bodies are still equal and opposite. With this assumption we find the total momentum of all the bodies is conserved.

In every interaction between two objects that we have studied, momentum is conserved; what one mass loses the other gains: $\Delta\vec{p}_1 = -\Delta\vec{p}_2$. Furthermore if we indicate the force that m_1 exerts on m_2 by $\vec{F}_{1-2}$ and the force that m_2 exerts on m_1 by $\vec{F}_{2-1}$, then $\Delta\vec{p}_1 = \vec{F}_{2-1}\Delta t$ and $\Delta\vec{p}_2 = \vec{F}_{1-2}\Delta t$. The Δt must be the same for both masses suffering the collision. If I push you, you automatically push me back and I cannot push you for a longer time than you push me. Thus,

$$\Delta\vec{p}_1 = -\Delta\vec{p}_2$$

becomes

$$\vec{F}_{2-1}\Delta t = -\vec{F}_{1-2}\Delta t,$$

and that now leads to

$$\vec{F}_{2-1} = -\vec{F}_{1-2}.$$

The idea that forces of interaction must be equal and opposite was stated by Newton (after his experiments on momentum conservation): "To every action there is always opposed an equal reaction, or the mutual reactions of two bodies upon each other are always equal and directed to contrary directions." This statement is often called his third law of motion, although you can see that it is a law about the forces in interactions and that the motions are inferred from it by applying Newton's law of motion to each body.

Even before we studied momentum, we studied one force of interaction with some care. In the last chapter we saw that the gravitational attraction between two bodies applies equal forces to each of the bodies, and the forces are directed oppositely along the line between the centers. The pull of the sun on the earth is equal and opposite to the pull of the earth on the sun. The pull of the earth on the moon is opposite to the force of the moon on the earth, and so on. Later in this volume we shall often study what goes on when the forces are of this particularly simple kind. We shall call them Newtonian forces.

Now let us trust Newton's third law to relate the forces between two bodies even when many bodies interact. Then we can use it to give an alternative demonstration of "universal" momentum conservation. We have a number of masses moving about in any way in an isolated system, exerting various forces one on another. Since all the forces occur in pairs with $\vec{F}_{2-1} = -\vec{F}_{1-2}$, their effects on the momenta of the bodies also occur in equal and opposite pairs. Therefore, while one body gains some momentum, another loses an equal and opposite amount. And in the whole isolated system there can be no net change of momentum.

If Newton's third law is true, momentum conservation follows. But it is possible that momentum may be conserved for many bodies even if some of the forces are not Newtonian. In fact, as we shall see in Part IV, some forces are not Newtonian.

Here is one example in which the forces are not obviously Newtonian. Every once in a while a tremendous bright light flares up somewhere out in space — a supernova. The light gets dimmer exponentially, falling off by the factor $\frac{1}{2}$ every 55 nights (with the same half-life as the new radioactive element Californium). Compared to the millions of years light takes to reach us from a supernova, the light takes only a short period to die down. The supernova has burned out long before the light gets here.

When the light arrives here from a supernova, it gives us a slight shove. But nobody would think that we give the dead supernova a counter shove at the same moment. If we think of forces of interaction between us and the supernova at the same moment, there is no reason to expect them to be equal and opposite.

The conservation of momentum is all right, however. What we must do is to include the light as one of the bodies in our description of the universe. When the light was emitted, the star gave it a shove and was given a shove backwards. Some of the light took off toward us carrying momentum; and when it arrived here millions of years later, the light shoved on us and we shoved on it, so that as the light was absorbed here its momentum was transferred to us.

This description may not seem so far-fetched if we return to the people sliding around on the ice. This time we imagine them playing ball. The man throws the ball to the boy. When he throws it, he gives it momentum in one direction and he receives momentum in the opposite direction. Later on, when the boy catches the ball, the momentum is transferred from the ball to him. (Of course the mass of the ball is included with him after he catches it.) The changes in the momenta of the man and of the boy with the ball are equal and opposite. And the interaction between the man and the boy occurs with a time delay. The time delay is considerably shorter than that which occurs between the emission of light by a supernova and its absorption at the surface of the earth; nevertheless, it is an appreciable and measurable time delay. If we forget about the ball, the interaction between the man and the boy does not appear Newtonian; and momentum seems to be lost for a while, when the ball is in the air. But everything makes sense when we include the ball in the system; and in just the same way everything makes sense in the case of the earth and the supernova when we include the light.

Looking at light as a ball thrown across from man to boy helps to make the time delay in the interaction less mysterious; and it gives a sense of assurance that momentum is still conserved in the over-all interaction. The ball-throwing scheme is a "model" for the transfer of light — a model in which we can use Newtonian interactions. In fact, light is not a ball — balls do not appear when thrown and disappear when stopped, but light does. So we should not take the model too literally. When we study interactions with light, magnetic fields, etc. in Part IV, we could continue to devise models to keep our description Newtonian in appearance; but the models are apt to be too complicated and to look artificial. We usually drop them and just hold on to the over-all conservation of momentum.

By examining the emission and absorption of light (as we shall do to some extent in Part IV), we shall find that the idea that momentum is carried by light makes a consistent picture. We can, and indeed we must, extend the law of conservation of momentum beyond those interactions in which the momentum is solely carried by material objects. We must include the momentum traveling around in radiation. The inequality in the forces between earth and supernova occurs while momentum is moving in radiation. There are many other similar examples. The same sort of thing happens when radiation is emitted by one atom and absorbed by another. When the momentum in radiation is included, the conservation of momentum spans our universe.

FOR HOME, DESK, AND LAB

1. How great is the impulse exerted by a 3.00-newton force for 6.00 sec?

2. How great is the impulse that gives an 8.00-kg mass a change in velocity of 4.00 m/sec?

3. What happens to the velocity of an object when an impulse of 2.00 newton-sec is applied to it? Suppose this impulse is applied

(a) to a 6.00-kg object

(b) to a 3.00-kg object.

4. A constant force applied to a 2.0-kg object at rest moves it 4.0 m in 2.0 sec. What impulse was applied to the object?

5. A skier with a mass of 75 kg is moving on level ground at a constant speed of 10 m/sec. Through some miscalculation, he finds himself brought to a stop in a snowbank during a Δt of 1.5 sec.

(a) What impulse did the snow apply to the skier?

(b) What was the average force exerted by the snowbank to produce this change of speed?

6. An object with a mass of 10 kg moves at a constant speed of 10 m/sec. A constant force then acts on the object for 4.0 sec, giving it a speed of 2.0 m/sec in the opposite direction.

(a) Calculate the impulse acting on the object.

(b) What is the magnitude and direction of the force?

(c) What is the momentum of the object before and after the force acts?

7. A 0.50-kg ball is thrown straight up at 3.0 m/sec.

(a) What is the initial momentum of the ball?

(b) What is the momentum at the top of the rise?

(c) What impulse stopped the ball? For how long did the impulse act?

(d) If the ball had a mass of 1.0 kg, what would be different in (a), (b), and (c)?

8. A body is made of two masses m_1 and m_2, 2.00 kg and 0.500 kg respectively, tied together by a light thread. [Fig. 23–23 (a).] It moves on a friction-

23–23. For Problem 8.

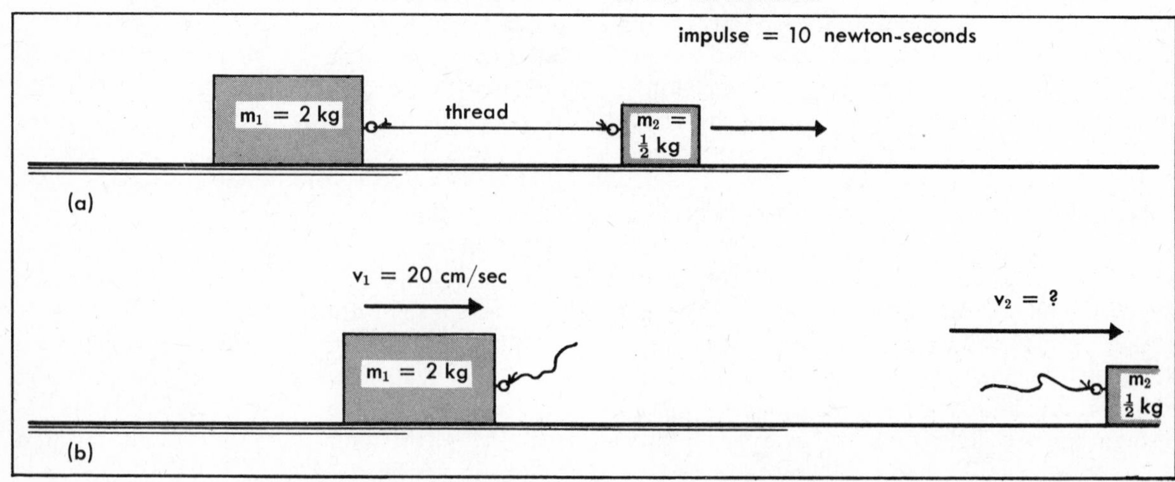

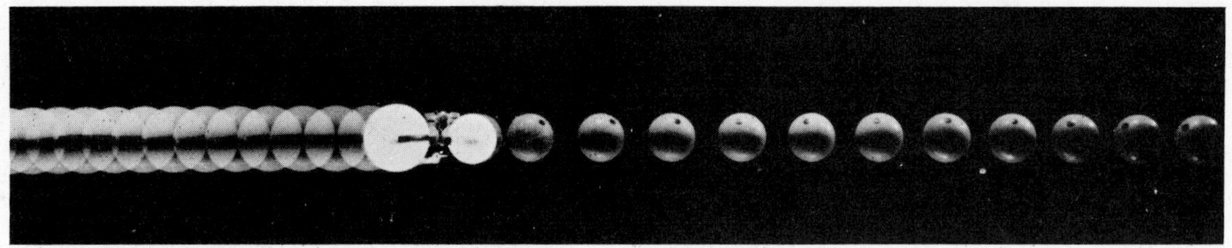

less table starting from rest. We set it in motion by applying an impulse of 10 newton-sec to the body, but unfortunately the thread connecting m_1 and m_2 breaks during the course of the impulse. [Fig. 23–23 (b).] As a result, m_2 goes off with great speed while m_1 at the end is only moving at a speed of 0.20 meters per second.

(a) How big an impulse did m_1 receive?

(b) How big an impulse did m_2 receive?

(c) How fast is m_2 moving at the end of the impulse?

9. Fig. 23–24 shows a multiple-flash photograph of an "explosion" of two billiard balls. The mass of the larger ball is 201 gm and that of the smaller ball 85 gm. The light flashes were $\frac{1}{30}$ sec apart. Your measurements on the photograph should give you a simple check on the conservation of momentum. If you find that the momenta of the two balls are not equal in magnitude, how would you explain this?

10. A man is at rest in the middle of a pond on perfectly frictionless ice. How can he get himself to shore?

11. A 20-kg cart is moving with a speed of 2.0 m/sec. A boy whose mass is 60 kg jumps off the cart. When he hits the ground, he is

(a) moving at the same velocity as the cart

(b) not moving relative to the ground

(c) moving with twice the initial velocity of the cart.

In each case, what is the change in velocity of the cart?

23–24. For Problem 9.

12. The same boy gets on the same cart as in Problem 11 and moves along at the same initial speed. Then he jumps off the cart again, applying a steady force to the cart for 0.20 sec and giving the cart a forward impulse of 20 newton-sec.

(a) What force did he apply?

(b) What was the final velocity of the cart?

(c) With what horizontal velocity did he hit the ground?

13. Two heavy frictionless carts are at rest. They are held together by a loop of string. A light spring is compressed between them (Fig. 23–25). When the string is burned, the spring expands from 2.0 cm to 3.0 cm, and the carts move apart. Both hit the bumpers fixed to the table at the same instant, but cart A moved 0.45 meters while cart B moved 0.87 meters. What is the ratio of:

(a) the speed of A to that of B after the interaction?

(b) their masses?

(c) the impulses applied to the carts?

(d) the accelerations of the carts while the spring pushes them apart?

14. A freight car of mass 10^4 kg is coasting along a track at 2 m/sec. A second freight car of twice the mass comes toward it in the opposite direction. If both cars come to rest upon collision, how fast was the second car moving?

23–25. For Problem 13.

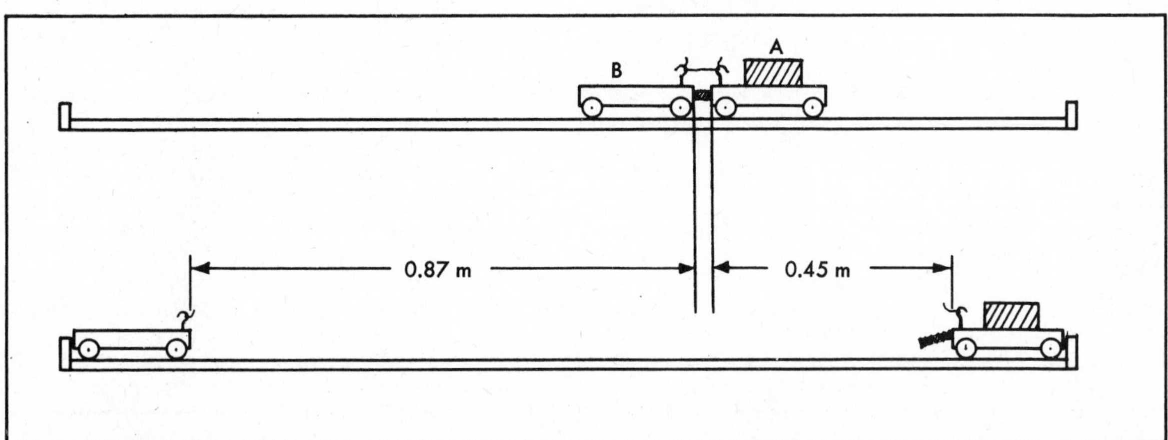

15. A proton (mass 1.67×10^{-27} kg) with a speed of 1×10^7 m/sec collides with a motionless helium nucleus and the proton bounces back with a speed of 6×10^6 m/sec. The helium nucleus moves forward with a speed of 4×10^6 m/sec after the bombardment.

(a) Can you compute the mass of the helium nucleus? If so, what is it?

(b) Can you compute the force that acted during the collision? If so, what is it?

(c) If you answered "no" to either (a) or (b), be prepared to discuss in class why you gave this answer.

16. In Fig. 23–26 the large ball came in at the top of the picture and the little ball at the bottom. As you see, a collision took place in the middle.

(a) Draw the vectors which represent the change in the velocity of the large ball and the change in velocity of the small ball. Plot these vectors to the same scale and make sure that each one is in the right direction.

(b) Are these changes of velocity opposite in direction?

(c) Are they equal in magnitude?

(d) If their magnitudes differ, what should be their ratio?

(e) The mass of the large ball is 201 gm. What is the mass of the small ball?

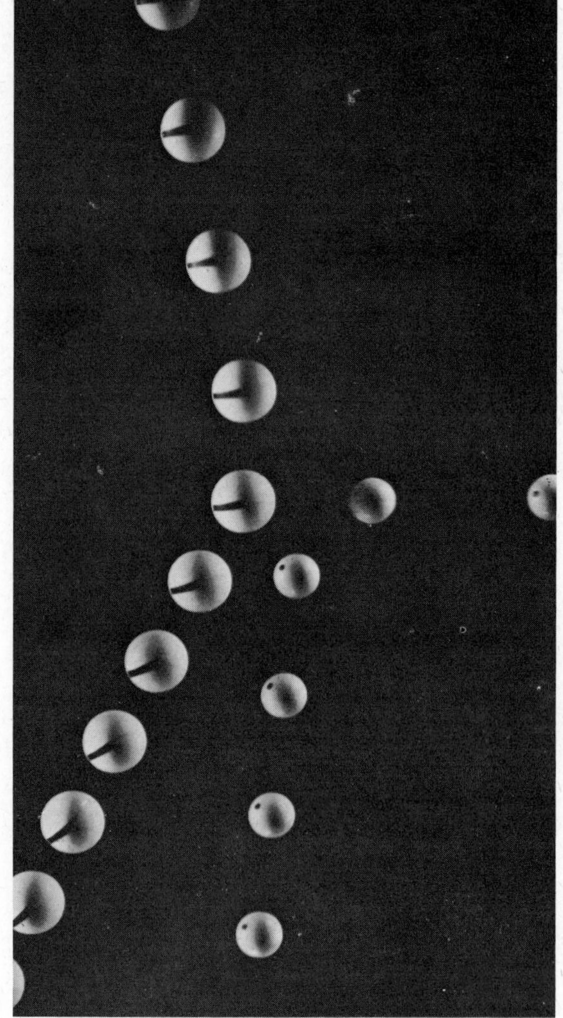

23–26. For Problem 16.

17. A double star consists of two large masses that attract each other gravitationally. By observing the motion of both masses, we can see that they rotate around each other.

(a) What do you think happens to the momentum of each of the masses in a double star as time goes on? Explain your answer.

(b) When observed carefully, the bright star Sirius seems to wobble about, instead of having a uniform motion of the center of mass. From this and other evidence astronomers believe that Sirius has a dark companion. It is really a double star. How does this explain the peculiar observed motion?

18. A stationary refrigerator car with mass 2.0×10^4 kg is rammed by a loaded gondola car with mass 3.0×10^4 kg. Before impact, the gondola car was going 1.0 m/sec. If they lock together, what is the new velocity?

19. When a proton (mass 1.67×10^{-27} kg) collides with a neutron (mass 1.67×10^{-27} kg) the two can stick together forming a deuteron (whose mass is 3.34×10^{-27} kg). (Actually the neutron is slightly more massive than a proton and the deuteron is slightly less massive than the sum of the two. However, these differences are less than 1 part in 400.) With what velocity will the deuteron move if it is formed from a proton moving with a velocity of 7.0×10^6 m/sec to the right and a neutron moving with a velocity of 3.0×10^6 m/sec to the left?

Note: Actually, in this collision an X ray is given off. The momentum carried in the X ray is about 20 per cent of the final momentum of the deuteron. An answer that neglects this is therefore somewhat in error.

20. A fire hose with a nozzle that we can turn on and off squirts bursts of water into a truck from behind. The truck can roll along a level surface with very little friction. The body of the truck is not leaky, and the water stays in it.

(a) Suppose the truck has a mass of 4.5 tons (4.5×10^3 kg) and that it is at rest when the first burst of water goes into it. The water comes squirting in at 20 meters per second horizontal speed, and the first burst is half a ton. What is the momentum of the truck after receiving the first burst? With what speed is it moving?

(b) We now squirt a second burst into the truck. The water moves at the same speed, 20 meters per second, with respect to the ground. How large does the second burst have to be so that the truck gains the same amount of speed the second time?

(c) If you increase the speed with which the water is shot out so that each burst moves with the same relative velocity with respect to the truck, what would this do to your answer to part (b)?

21. A rocket is out in free space shooting out a stream of exhaust gases and picking up speed in the opposite direction. What happens to the center of mass of all the matter, that which is ejected and that which is left in the rocket?

22. In an unsuccessful attempt to put a satellite in orbit, the carrier rocket moving vertically upward at 3000 meters/sec explodes and breaks into two pieces. One of the pieces continues upward at an angle of 45° with the vertical, and with a speed of 3500 meters/sec immediately after the explosion.

(a) What is the velocity of the second piece if its mass is 0.60 that of the first piece?

(b) What is the velocity of the center of mass of the rocket immediately after the explosion?

(c) What is the change in center-of-mass velocity in the next second?

23. A 2.0-kg brick with no horizontal motion is dropped on a 2.0-kg cart moving across a frictionless table at 0.40 meter/sec.

(a) What is the change in velocity of the cart?

(b) What is the velocity of the center of mass of the system composed of cart and brick before the brick is dropped?

24. A machine gun fires ten 100-gram bullets per second at a speed of 600 meters/sec.

(a) What impulse does the gun apply to the bullets in ten seconds?

(b) What impulse do the bullets apply to the gun in ten seconds?

(c) What is the average force applied to the gun?

(d) Sketch rough graphs of:

(i) *Average* force on gun *vs.* time

(ii) *Actual* force on gun *vs.* time

(e) How are the graphs (i) and (ii) related?

25. An explosion blows a rock into three parts. Two pieces go off at right angles to each other, a 1.0-kg piece at 12 m/sec and a 2.0-kg piece at 8.0 m/sec. The third piece flies off at 40 m/sec.

(a) Draw a diagram to show the direction in which it goes.

(b) What is its mass?

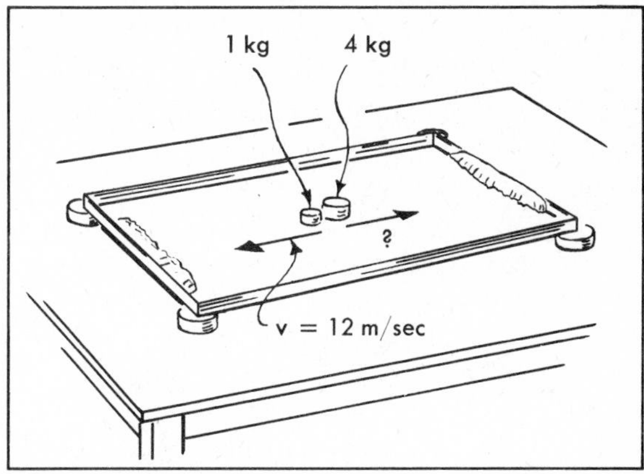

23–27. For Problem 26.

26. The system shown in Fig. 23–27 consists of a 5.0-kg frame with a 1.0-kg and a 4.0-kg mass in the middle. At either end of the frame are stops made of putty. The two masses and the frame are mounted on Dry Ice discs. (The mass of the Dry Ice is included in the values given above.) The center of mass of the whole system is at the center of the frame. An explosion pushes the two masses apart. The 1.0-kg mass goes off with a speed of 12 m/sec. Eventually each mass is trapped by the putty.

(a) What is the speed of the 4.0-kg mass immediately after the explosion?

(b) What is the center of mass of the whole system after 1 sec? After 2 sec?

(c) What is the velocity of the frame and the attached masses after 100 sec?

(d) Describe the motion qualitatively from the time of explosion to 100 sec.

(e) How far does the frame move?

FURTHER READING

EHRICKE, K. A., and GAMOW, GEORGE, "A Rocket to the Moon." Scientific American, June, 1957. An elementary description of the speed, orbit, and fuel requirements of any object that is to return to earth after a trip to the moon.

HOLTON, GERALD, *Introduction to Concepts and Theories in Physical Science.* Addison-Wesley, 1952. The conservation of momentum is the subject of Chapter 16.

WORK AND KINETIC ENERGY

CHAPTER 24

ALTHOUGH energy may be hard to define precisely, it is familiar to us all. Food is the fuel that supplies us with energy to live and work. We need other fuels, too; wood, coal, and gasoline release great quantities of heat energy, for cooking, warming homes, or moving our cars. Prometheus, or whoever it was that lighted the first fire, taught man how to use the energy of sunshine stored by growing trees. For thousands of years man used the energy released by burning fuels for such purposes as keeping warm and on a small scale in arts and crafts. Until only recently, heavy work was done by muscles. Since the Industrial Revolution, however, man has been using more and more fuel to replace muscular effort. Burning fuels now supply most of the energy that operates our farm machinery, runs our factories, and drives our trains, autos, ships, and airplanes. All this fuel energy contributes significantly to our material comfort. One good measure of the material well-being of a country is the energy taken from fuel for each citizen during a year.

In everyday language, we often speak of energy in the following way. We get up in the morning eager and ready to do a job or take on a challenge, and we say we feel full of energy. Perhaps we are energetic enough to mow a lawn, shovel snow, or play football, baseball, or tennis. But when we have been active for some time we get tired and say we have lost our energy. A good night's rest and nourishing food will re-establish our capacity to do a job. This common use of the word "energy" is closely related to the scientific concept of energy.

Of course we might mow the lawn with a power mower instead of using our own muscles. Electric motors, steam engines, and gasoline engines can all do useful jobs, and they all require fuel. And for the human body, looked on as a machine, food is the fuel. These facts suggest a close connection between energy and fuels which enable machines and muscles to do useful jobs.

Some jobs need no fuel: supporting a roof, coasting across a frictionless icy lake, remembering a table of logarithms. (Given a start, each of these jobs can be carried on by something that uses no fuel: a concrete pillar, continuing momentum, a printed table of logarithms.) In our study of energy, we are not concerned with that kind of job. We shall deal only with "fuel-using jobs" such as raising a cable car, driving a lawn mower, heating a house, speeding up a train. For the moment, we shall say that energy is the essential thing involved in jobs — not the creation of energy but its transfer from one form to another.

24–1. Energy Transfer

Jobs are done by the transfer of energy from one form to another or from one place to another — for example, from energy in fuel to energy in a speeding train; from heat in a boiler to heat in a room. Fuels, then, hold energy in stored form, ready for use. A given amount of fuel contains a given amount of energy. You will see later that energy is never created or destroyed but only transferred (from one form to another or from one place to another). It is somewhat like cash, which changes hands only when someone buys something.

Consider what we could do with the energy stored in some gasoline. We might burn the gasoline in an automobile engine and use the energy to run the car up an incline. Or we might burn the gasoline under a steam boiler. There the energy is transferred to heat in the steam. The steam can expand and move a piston which can raise a load, thus making a further transfer of energy. The load may then be hitched to the axle of a car by a rope passing over a pulley; and if the load falls it can pull the car up the incline. The energy has again been transferred and at least some of the energy in the fuel has ended up in raising the car by a more roundabout method. In the final stage, energy stored in the raised-load system is changed to energy stored in the raised-car system. A detailed accounting, reckoning energy changes by jobs or by fuel (or by work, which we shall discuss next) shows that energy is not created or lost; energy is conserved.

24-2. Work: A Measure of Energy Transfer

When energy is transferred in some fuel-using job, we can measure the transfer, the cost of the job, either by (a) the number of unit jobs (e.g. number of lawns to be mowed, or the number of houses to be heated), or by (b) the amount of fuel used (e.g. the number of gallons of gasoline).

In the jobs just described, forces are exerted and things move. We say that work has been done in those transfers of energy, and we shall now develop the idea of work as a precise and reliable measure of energy transfer. For the moment, we shall use *work* to mean the measure of the job done or of the fuel used. Notice that these two measures of energy transfer agree with each other. Think of any job: you will see that the number of unit jobs in it and the amount of fuel used are proportional. To do two equal jobs we need twice as much fuel as for one. For instance, we can cut twice as much lawn with two pints of gasoline in the mower as we can with one pint.

We now want to find a combination of force and motion to serve as a measure of energy transfer. We therefore look for such a combination which is proportional to the fuel used and to the number of unit jobs done. We shall call this combination the "work."

Suppose a gasoline engine pulls cable cars up to the top of a mountain. How does the fuel consumption for the job depend on the *force* exerted by the cable? It takes a certain amount of fuel to lift one car up the mountain, pulling the cable with a definite force for a definite distance. It takes the same amount of fuel again to lift a second, identical car. The fuel used to lift two cars is twice that used to lift one of them, because there are two equal jobs. Furthermore, we could pull two cars up the mountain at the same time with separate cables, each run by an identical engine. In this way we could lift them simultaneously, exerting twice the force and burning twice the fuel needed to lift one. We could tie the two cables together, side by side, and that would make no difference to the fuel burned or to the job done. We could even replace this double cable by a single cable supporting both cars, and use one engine to do the job — but that engine would have to burn fuel faster. The fuel used to lift the two cars would still be twice that needed to lift one. The fuel needed is doubled when the force exerted is doubled. So we say work, which we are going to use as the measure of energy transfer, is proportional to the force exerted (Fig. 24–1).

Now consider how the fuel used depends on the distance a car moves up the mountain (Fig. 24–2). Lift the car up halfway, then up to the top. To lift the car up the second half of the mountain, the engine exerts the same force and moves the same length of cable as it does to lift the car up the first half. The same job is done twice; so it takes twice as much fuel to move a car all the way as it does to move it halfway. The fuel used is doubled

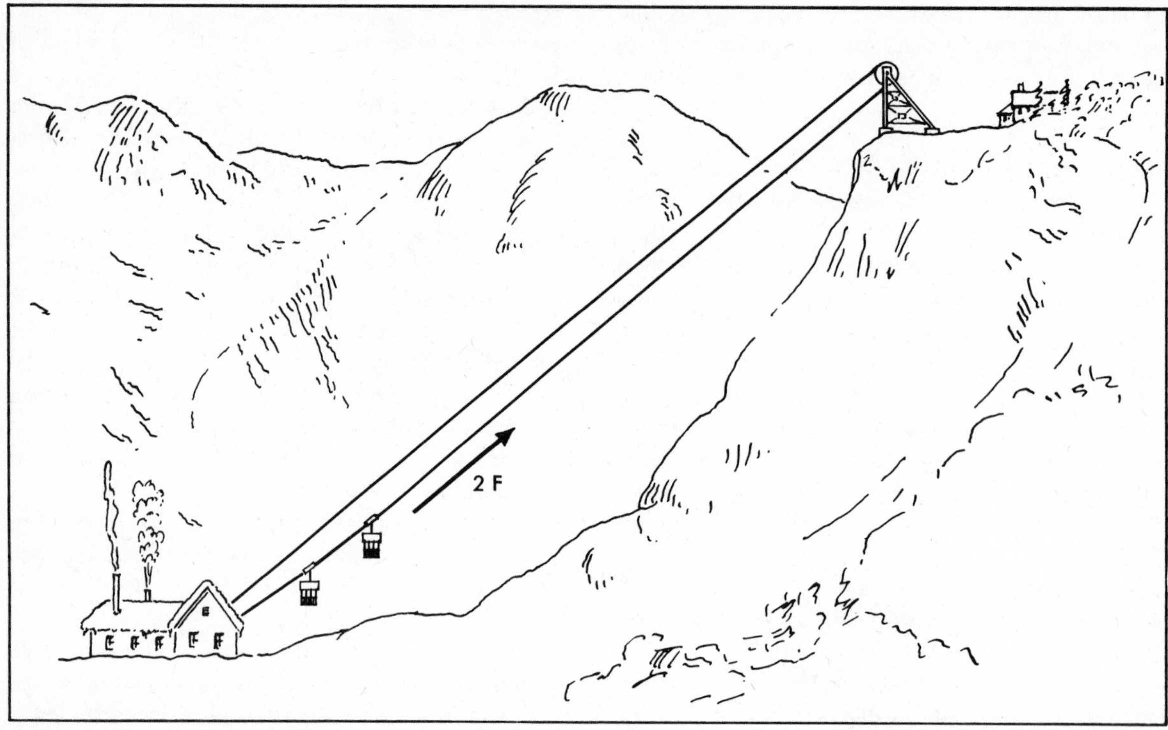

24–1. Above. Pulling two cable cars up the mountain requires twice the fuel needed to haul up one; the force is doubled also. Thus we see that the work must be proportional to the force.

24–2. Below. It takes twice as much fuel to pull the cable car to the top of the mountain as it does to pull it up half way. Work is therefore proportional to the distance moved.

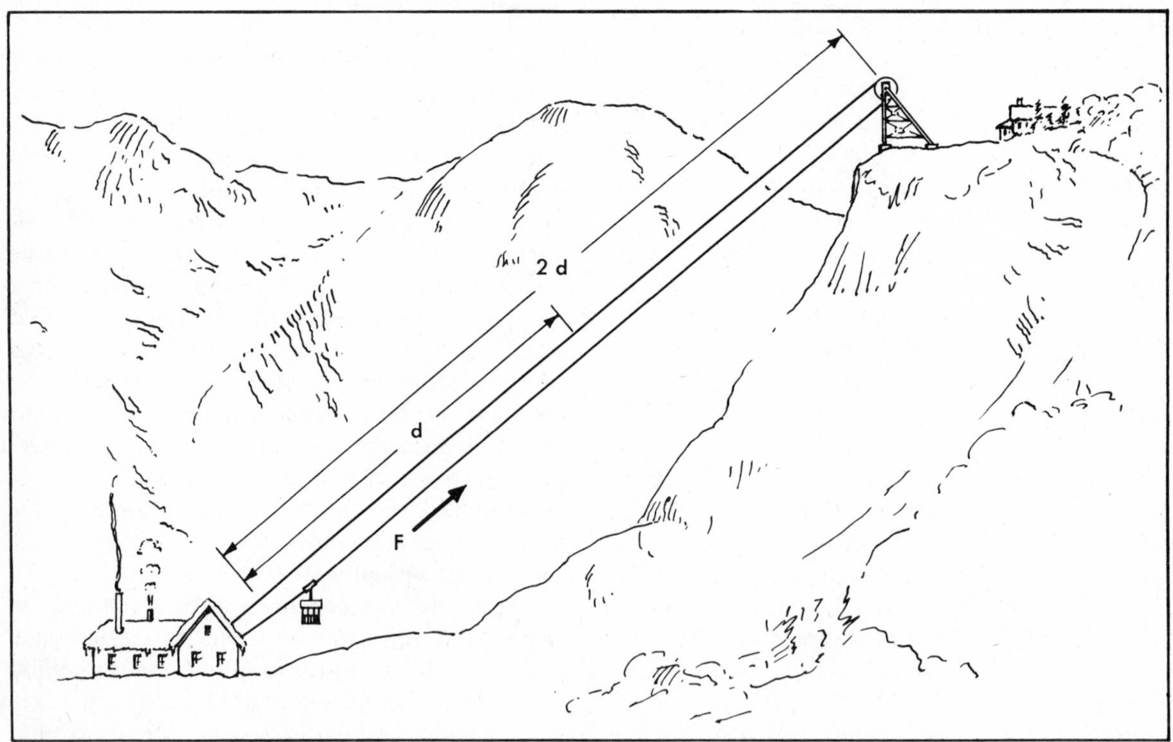

when the distance is doubled; so we say work is also proportional to distance moved. Combining these results we define work as

force $\times$ *distance moved.*

From a study of many other examples we have concluded that "work" thus defined is a good way of measuring energy transfer.

The unit of work must be *unit force* times *unit distance: one newton* times *one meter*, or *one newton-meter.* We call this unit one joule after the English physicist James P. Joule (1818–1889), who did some of the first careful experiments in measuring energy transfers to establish the conservation of energy. If we move a body 10 meters while pushing with a force of 2 newtons in the direction of motion we do 20 joules of work.

When we lift a car up the mountain rapidly, we use practically the same amount of fuel as when we lift it slowly. Time has nothing to do with the amount of work in the job. As an extreme case, we can do half the job today and half tomorrow, and still use the same amount of fuel.

If we put the brakes on and turn off the engine, the car stops and thereafter no energy is transferred to it from the fuel. Although a force is still exerted to hold the car there, no work is done because there is no distance moved.

But energy can be taken from fuel without doing a useful job. We can disengage the cable from the engine and let the engine run, burning fuel even though it is not pulling the car up the mountain. The fuel gives energy to the motion of the pistons, moving them through distances with forces opposite to those of friction. In this way, energy goes into heating the engine. Energy is still being transferred from fuel to other forms and places though none is used to do the job of lifting the car. Even when the engine is pulling the cable car up the mountain, some of the fuel's energy does these other things. The amount of fuel actually burned may differ from trip to trip — for example, if the pistons are poorly lubricated on one trip, more fuel will be used. Correcting for these effects, however, we find that the fuel used for the job of lifting the cable car — or for any other particular job — is always the same.

24–3. More About the Definition of Work

We developed the definition of work as force times distance from the example of a cable pulling a car which moved along the direction of the pull. When the force is in the direction of motion, there is a transfer of energy; work is done. On the other hand, there is no energy transfer when we exert a force on a body perpendicular to the direction of its motion. For example, in our study of motion we used bodies sliding along horizontal, smooth surfaces on practically frictionless bearings. The supporting surface exerts on the body a vertical force equal in magnitude and opposite in direction to its weight [Fig. 24–3 (a)]. After receiving an initial push, the body will continue to move along the horizontal surface with practically constant velocity. No fuel is used in maintaining this motion, and we thus conclude that the force exerted by the supporting surface does not perform any work.

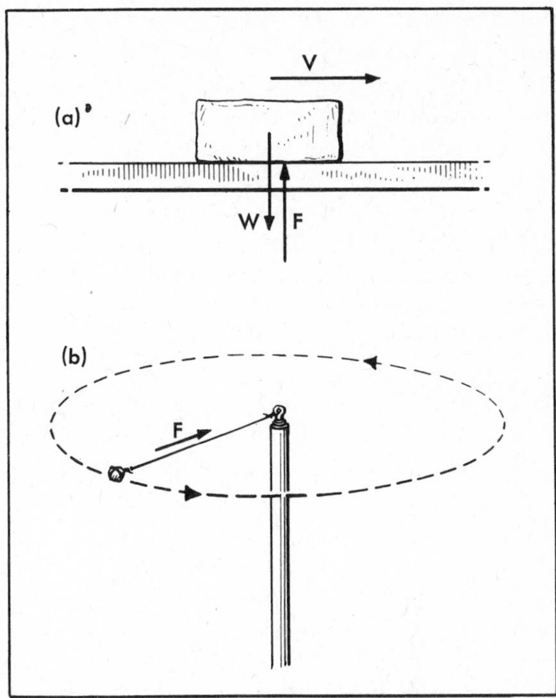

24–3. (a) When a body slides along a table, the vertical supporting force does no work. (b) A stone at the end of a string is whirling around a post. The string is attached to a frictionless bearing on the post. No work is done transferring energy to the stone because there is no component of force in the direction of the stone's motion.

Take another example in which the motion occurs in a direction perpendicular to the force. Consider a stone whirling around on the end of a string which is tied to a rigid post [Fig. 24–3 (b)]. The stone moves around and around without changing speed. Time and time again it comes to the same place moving at the same speed; and therefore its energy is unchanged. At the other end of the string, the post remains motionless. It burns no fuel, and transfers no energy to the string. Therefore, the string neither gives nor receives energy; so its pull does no work.

What happens if we pull with a force at some other angle to the motion? Then the force has a component in the direction of motion, and this component speeds up the stone. After that, because it is moving faster, the stone can do more work pulling something as it comes to rest. It therefore has more energy. The component of force in the direction of motion has done work on the stone, transferring energy of motion to it.

Briefly, the component of any force perpendicular to the motion does no work. *The work done on an object is equal to the component of the force along the direction of motion times the distance moved.*

24–4. Kinetic Energy

Our definition of work as the force times distance has been designed to agree with the idea that equal amounts of fuel will supply equal amounts of energy. Does this definition of work also enable us to say how much energy a moving body has? The value of our definition of work depends on the answers to questions like this.

Suppose we apply a force to a body on a frictionless table. The body accelerates, gaining speed. While the force acts, we do work transferring energy to the body. We calculate the work done on the body as it moves a measured distance under the action of the force. This work is the energy transferred, and it gives us an expression for the energy of motion of the body. This energy is called kinetic energy. We want to find an expression for it *in terms of the motion,* using the object's speed v. We shall find that we also need to use its mass m, but nothing else.

We start the object from rest and pull with force F for a distance x. (Fig. 24–4.) The energy transferred is Fx, and since the object started from rest this energy transferred to it *is* its energy of motion or kinetic energy. How can we express Fx in terms of m and v? We have

$$F = ma,$$

so

$$Fx = max.$$

Since F is constant, a is constant; and we already know (from Section 5–7, Equation 3) that

$$v^2 = 2ax$$

or

$$ax = v^2/2.$$

Therefore,

$$Fx = max = mv^2/2.$$

The work $W = Fx$ done accelerating the mass m from rest is equal to the quantity $mv^2/2$, or in other words, $mv^2/2$ is equal to the energy transferred to the body in setting it in motion. We call it E_K, the *kinetic energy* of the body: that is

$$E_K = \frac{mv^2}{2}.$$

Notice that the kinetic energy $mv^2/2$ is defined purely in terms of the mass and its motion. It shows no sign of the force used to give the body this energy, and no sign of the distance moved. It does not depend on the way in which the energy was transferred to the mass. If we know the mass, we can evaluate the kinetic energy by observing how fast the body moves. In other words, our definition of E_K is in terms of the state of motion of the mass without reference to its history. Whenever the mass is in the same state of motion, $mv^2/2$ is the same. The body has the same kinetic energy.

We can easily see that the work to give a body that starts from rest a certain $mv^2/2$, a certain kinetic energy, is always the same. Try using

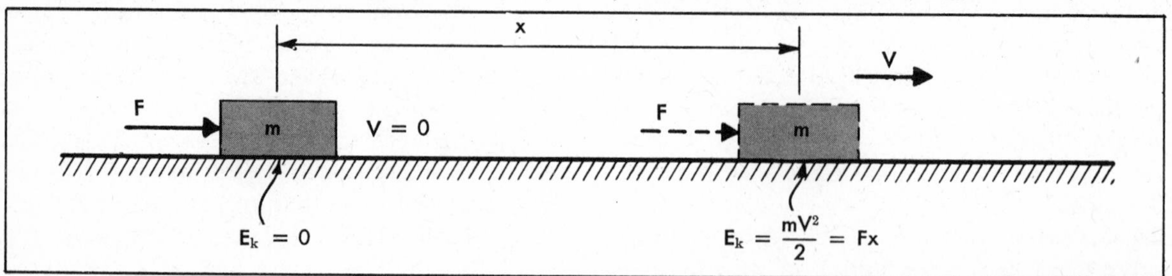

24–4. A force F is exerted on a mass m, which moves a distance x starting from rest. The energy transferred to m is Fx, equal to $mv^2/2$, which we call the kinetic energy of the body.

double the force for half the distance, you will get the same $mv^2/2$ for the same work. Suppose that the force changes to a new value when the body is already moving with speed v_1, and the work $W_1 = mv_1^2/2$ has been done. The body now is accelerated with a different constant acceleration a', and from Section 5–7, we know that after an additional distance Δx its speed v is given by

$$v^2 = v_1^2 + 2a'\Delta x.$$

On multiplying by $\frac{m}{2}$ we see that $\frac{mv^2}{2}$ at the end is

$$\frac{mv^2}{2} = \frac{mv_1^2}{2} + ma'\Delta x.$$

Since ma' is the new force F',

$$ma'\Delta x = F'\Delta x.$$

This is the additional work ΔW; and the equation above shows that it increases the kinetic energy from $mv_1^2/2$ to $mv^2/2$. The total work is therefore the sum of the work W_1 (which gives transfer of energy from zero to $mv_1^2/2$) and the additional work ΔW (which gives the change from $mv_1^2/2$ to $mv^2/2$). The total work from rest to speed v, this time given by $W_1 + \Delta W$, again gives $mv^2/2$.

If the force continually changes during the motion (as in Fig. 24–5, for instance), we can always take small intervals during which its value is nearly constant. In each interval, as we have just seen, the work will give the *change* in $mv^2/2$. So the total work will always give the total change in $mv^2/2$. Indeed, even if a force points in some direction other than that of the motion, we still get the same result. Only the component of force along the motion enters the work, and only the component along the motion changes the speed. Consequently, our definition of kinetic energy as $mv^2/2$ is such that the same amount of work always gives the same change of kinetic energy.

If a mass m is moving with speed v, its kinetic energy is $mv^2/2$. This amount of energy had to be transferred to it to accelerate it from rest to the speed v. When a force acts on the mass to slow it down, the kinetic energy decreases. Energy is transferred from kinetic energy of the mass to energy in the system that exerts the retarding force. The work $F_x\Delta x$, when the force F_x retards the motion, measures the energy coming out of the moving mass as it slows down. By using the same reasoning as above, we see that if the body has

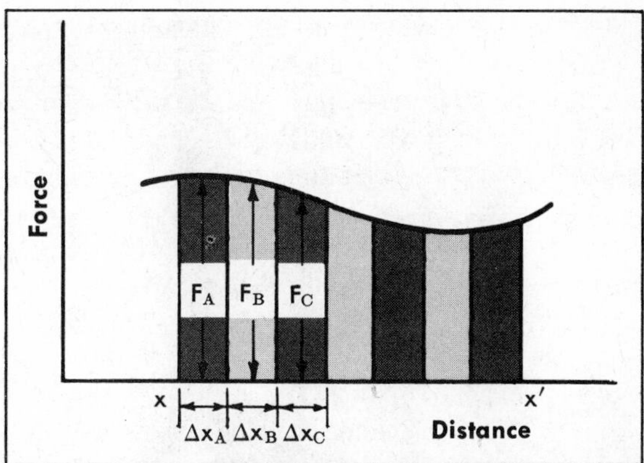

24–5. The total work done by a changing force can be calculated by taking the sum of the areas of the many small rectangles with base Δx and height F. This total work gives the total change in $mv^2/2$. In moving from x to x', it is represented by the area shaded.

$mv^2/2$ kinetic energy, it can do just that amount of work before coming to rest no matter how it is slowed down.

In summary, when work is done by a force acting on a mass in the direction of its motion, the kinetic energy of the mass is increased. The work measures the transfer of energy from the outside into kinetic energy of the mass. When a force opposes the motion, the transfer of energy is in the opposite direction and the work measures the transfer of kinetic energy of the mass into energy of something else. We can express the kinetic energy of a mass m moving with a speed v directly in terms of its motion as $mv^2/2$.

24–5. The Transfer of Kinetic Energy from One Mass to Another

So far we have examined what happens when one object gains or loses kinetic energy. This gain or loss is measured by the work done in transferring the energy to or from the object. We believe that energy transferred to the object comes from someplace, and energy transferred from it goes somewhere. For example, when one ball hits another at rest, the first ball transfers energy to the second one. Fig. 24–6 shows a flash photo of a billiard-ball collision. By measuring the distances the balls move between flashes, we can find the kinetic energy of the ball with the dot as it came in from the left; we can find its kinetic energy after collision as it went off more slowly to the lower right, and also find the kinetic energy of the

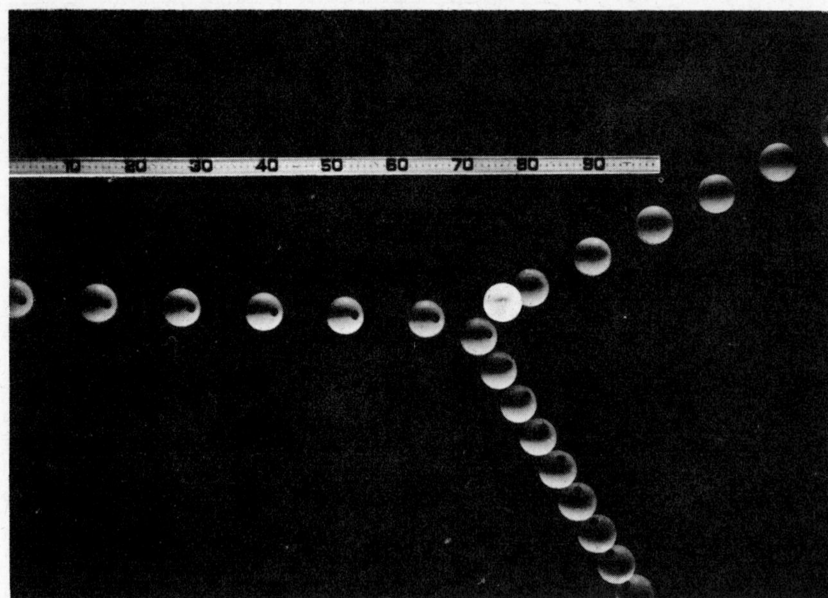

24–6. A multiple-flash photograph of a collision between two billiard balls, each of mass 173 gm. The interval between flashes was $\frac{1}{30}$ sec. The dotted ball came in from the left and struck the unmarked ball at rest. The unmarked ball appears whiter where it was at rest and was photographed during several flashes.

dotless ball after the collision set it in motion toward the upper right. We find that the kinetic energy lost by the dotted ball is almost exactly equal to that gained by the other ball.

How does the energy transfer actually occur in a billiard-ball collision? The balls approach, exerting no force on each other until they are very close, and we say they are "in contact." Then repulsion sets in: each ball pushes the other. These forces change in magnitude, growing and decreasing again as the balls distort each other and finally push each other away. Because the forces are changing, a billiard-ball collision is difficult to analyze in detail. We shall be able to understand the transfer better if we start with an easier example in which the force has a simpler behavior. After we see the details in this simple case we can return to billiard balls.

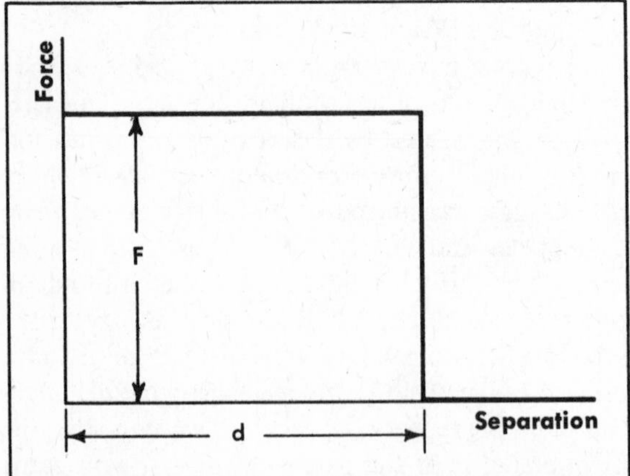

24–7. The graph of a force acting between two bodies. This force is zero when the separation *s* is more than *d*, and a constant value *F* when the masses are closer together than *d*.

To make a simple preliminary study of collisions and energy we shall study an artificial case in which two colliding bodies exert no force on each other until they get within a distance d and then exert a constant repulsion F on each other as long as the separation is less than d (Fig. 24–7).

Suppose the collision takes place along a line. (Fig. 24–8.) Moving along this line with velocity v_1, the mass m_1 approaches the mass m_2 which is at rest. Nothing happens until m_1 gets to the distance d away from m_2. From then on, however, m_2 is pushed forward with force F, and m_1 is pushed backward just as hard. Consequently m_2 speeds up while m_1 slows down. Because m_1 is moving and m_2 standing still when the repulsion sets in, the masses continue to get closer together for a while. But soon they reach a stage when they are as close as they will get and are moving along with the same velocity. (If m_1 were still going faster it would still be gaining on m_2; and if m_2 were going faster, the masses would be separating.) Still pushed apart by F, m_2 continues to speed up and m_1 to slow down. The masses therefore separate until eventually they are d apart again. Then, because they are getting farther apart, the force falls to zero, and they continue their further motion without changes in velocity. The collision is over, with m_1 and m_2 now moving with definite energies that no longer change.

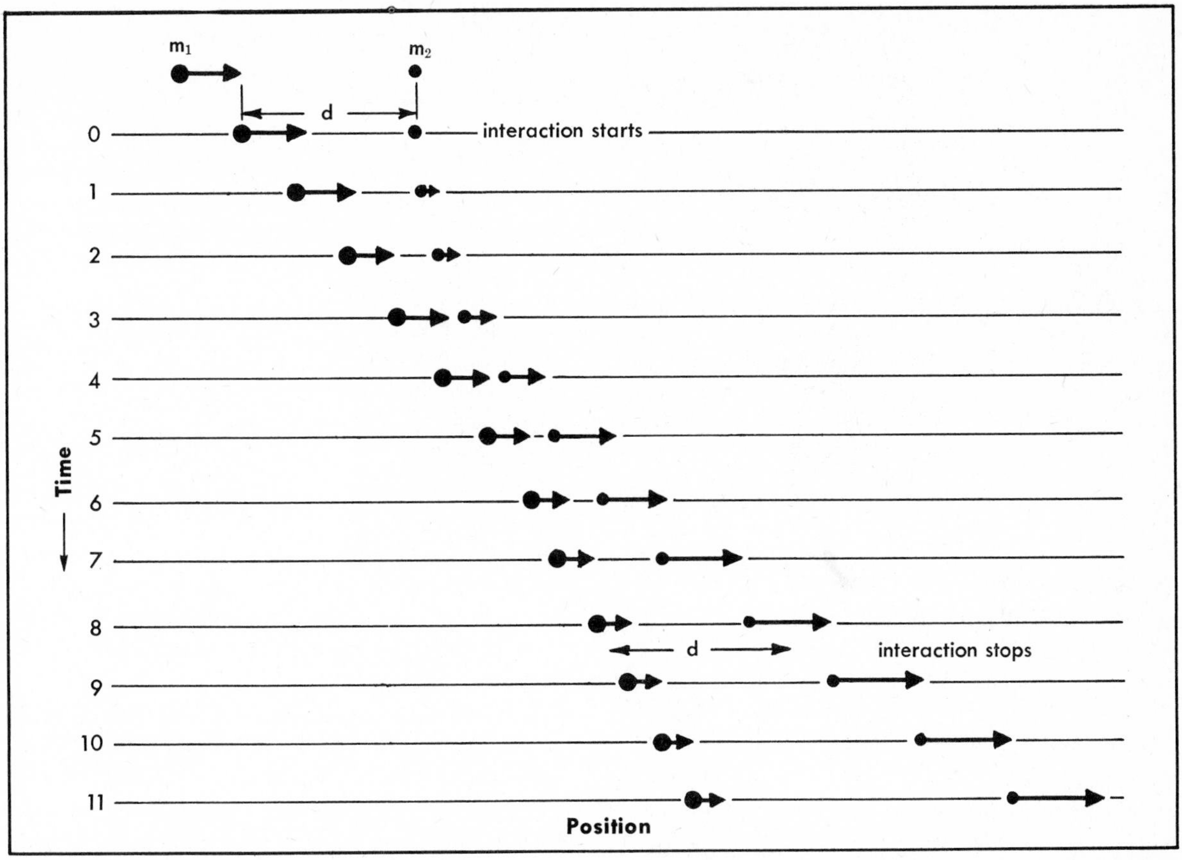

m1 m2
d
0 interaction starts
1
2
3
4
5
6
7
8
d interaction stops
9
10
11
Time
Position

24–8. The positions and velocities of two masses m_1 and m_2 as they interact along a line, with the force shown in Fig. 24–7. The masses are shown at equal time intervals. Mass m_1 comes in from the left. When the distance between masses is less than d, m_1 slows down and m_2 speeds up from rest. After $8\frac{1}{3}$ time intervals, in this particular case, the separation is again greater than d; the force drops to zero; and the two masses move apart with constant speeds. The gain in kinetic energy of m_2 over the whole interaction is equal to the loss of kinetic energy of m_1.

For this collision with a steplike force, we can calculate the details of the motion of each mass. This we have done, using Newton's law, for masses such that $m_1 = 3m_2$; and we constructed Fig. 24–8 in this way. But we do not need to go through the details of calculating the motion to find out whether the transfer of kinetic energy from m_1 is the same as the transfer of kinetic energy to m_2. Because the force has the constant value F during the interaction, the energy transferred into kinetic energy of m_2 is F times the distance that m_2 moves during the collision. Also, the kinetic energy transferred from m_1 is F times the distance m_1 moves during the collision. (m_1 loses kinetic energy because the force on it opposes the motion.) We can show that the kinetic energy lost by m_1 is just the amount gained by m_2 if we show that m_1 and m_2 move the same distance during the collision. To see that, look at Fig. 24–9. There we show the positions of the masses when the interaction starts and when it stops. Notice that d plus the distance m_2 moves during the interaction (top line) is equal to d plus the

24–9. The positions of m_1 and m_2 at the beginning (top line) and the end (bottom line) of an interaction. Comparing the two lines, d plus the distance m_2 moves is equal to d plus the distance m_1 moves. Thus m_1 and m_2 move the same distance during the interaction.

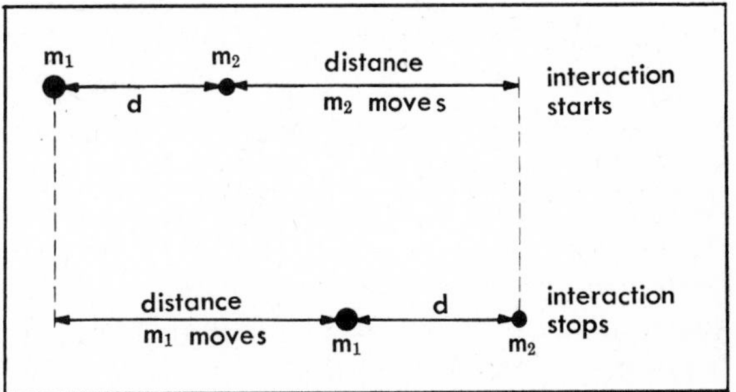

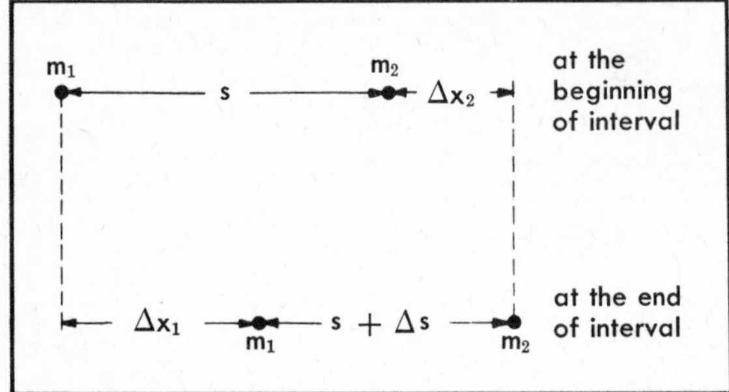

24–10. During a short time interval, while m_1 and m_2 interact, Δx_1 is the distance m_1 moves and Δx_2 is the distance m_2 moves. s is the original separation between m_1 and m_2, and $s + \Delta s$ is the separation at the end of the interval. Δs therefore is the change in the separation. Comparing the top line of the figure with the bottom line, we see that $s + \Delta x_2 = \Delta x_1 + (s + \Delta s)$. Then, subtracting $(\Delta x_1 + s)$ from both sides, we get the result $\Delta x_2 - \Delta x_1 = \Delta s$.

distance m_1 moves (bottom line). Consequently the distances moved by m_1 and by m_2 are the same during the complete interaction. The force times distance moved during the collision is therefore equal and opposite for the two masses; and as we anticipated, the kinetic energy from m_1 just goes into kinetic energy of m_2.

24–6. Another Look at the Simple Collision

There is a slightly different way of looking at this special example that will make it easier to see what happens in a real collision when the pattern of force is more complicated. In order to study real collisions we wish to find what kind of forces must be acting if all the kinetic energy lost by one mass is gained by the other. To find the nature of these forces we shall examine the sum of the two kinetic energies directly rather than each one individually. If the sum at the end is the same as at the beginning, what is lost by one mass must be gained by the other.

When we look at the changes in kinetic energy during the course of a collision, we shall see that at *intermediate stages* the loss of kinetic energy of m_1 is not equal to the gain of kinetic energy of m_2.

To find out how the total kinetic energy changes during a collision we shall concentrate on a small time interval during a collision between two masses m_1 and m_2 (Fig. 24–10). At the beginning of this time interval, we shall call the separation between the masses s. At the end of the time interval the separation is $s + \Delta s$. The change in separation Δs is given by the difference between the distance Δx_2, which m_2 moves, and the distance Δx_1, which m_1 moves in the same direction:

$$\Delta s = \Delta x_2 - \Delta x_1.$$

If m_2 moves the distance Δx_2 in the direction away from m_1, the separation is increased by this distance; but if m_1 moves by Δx_1 in the same direction, that is, toward m_2, the separation is decreased by that distance.

Now when the force of interaction F in this interval is repulsive, the kinetic energy transferred to m_2 is $F\Delta x_2$. This is the work done in accelerating m_2. On the other hand, the kinetic energy taken from the motion of m_1 is $F\Delta x_1$. This energy is transferred from the motion of m_1 because the force on m_1 is in the opposite direction from the motion Δx_1. Consequently, the change in the total kinetic energy in the interval when these motions take place is given by

$$\Delta E_K(\text{tot}) = F\Delta x_2 - F\Delta x_1 = F(\Delta x_2 - \Delta x_1).$$

Since, $\Delta x_2 - \Delta x_1 = \Delta s$, we can write the change in the total kinetic energy as

$$\Delta E_K(\text{tot}) = F\Delta s.$$

For example, in Fig. 24–11 as the separation changes from s to $s + \Delta s$, the total kinetic energy changes by the amount given by the shaded area, F high and Δs wide.

$\Delta E_K(\text{tot}) = F\Delta s$ is exactly the result we need. It shows that the change in the total kinetic energy in any interval depends only on the force of interaction and the change of separation that takes place. These were the only quantities that entered our calculations. We never have to say where the masses are with respect to any other objects. Equally it does not matter what the interaction force may be at some other separation. Consequently, the force that acts at other separations need not have the same value that it has in the interval we just considered. It is for this reason that we shall be able to apply our results to collisions in which the force of interaction depends in any way on the separation alone. We shall see how to use $\Delta E_K(\text{tot}) = F\Delta s$ for such forces in the next section. We shall end this section by using this equation to show the conservation of kinetic energy in the simple collision we studied in the last section.

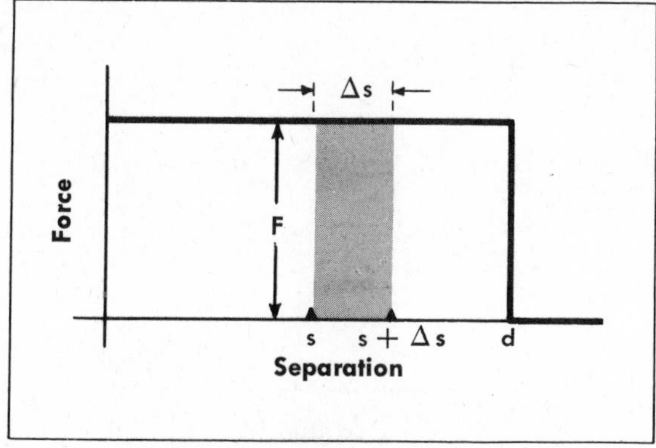

24–11. When the separation changes from s to $s + \Delta s$, the change in the total kinetic energy is given by the shaded area.

For a collision with the force shown in Fig. 24–11 (that is, F at all separations less than d, and zero at larger separations), the total kinetic energy decreases at the beginning of the collision. When m_1 first arrives at the distance d from m_2, it is moving toward m_2 while m_2 is standing still. As we see by looking back at Figure 24–8, in the next interval of time m_1 moves considerably farther than m_2. Since the forces on m_1 and m_2 are equal and opposite, the kinetic energy taken from m_1 is greater than the kinetic energy given to m_2. There is a net loss in kinetic energy. This result follows from $\Delta E_K(\text{tot}) = F\Delta s$ because the separation between m_1 and m_2 has decreased, and so $F\Delta s$ is negative.

As long as m_1 is coming closer to m_2, kinetic energy continues to disappear. Eventually, however, the total kinetic energy is regenerated. While m_1 continues to slow down, m_2 picks up speed so that finally the separation increases again. When the separation becomes d once more, the value of Δs, measured from the beginning of the collision, is zero. Consequently $\Delta E_K = F\Delta s = 0$. The kinetic energy which was lost as the two bodies approached each other, has been regained. After that the masses go apart still farther but there is no force acting on the masses. Consequently E_K stays the same. The collision is over and the kinetic energy remains at its final value, the same value that it had before the collision began.

24–7. Conservation of Kinetic Energy in Elastic Interactions

In the collision we studied in the last sections, the transfer of kinetic energy from one mass to the other ends up without loss. This result does not depend on the interaction range d, within which the force F acts, nor on the magnitude F of the force between the two interacting masses. In any interaction with any interaction range, d, and any constant force, F, we find the same total kinetic energy at the beginning and the end of any collision. The result is more general than we might have anticipated. How general is it?

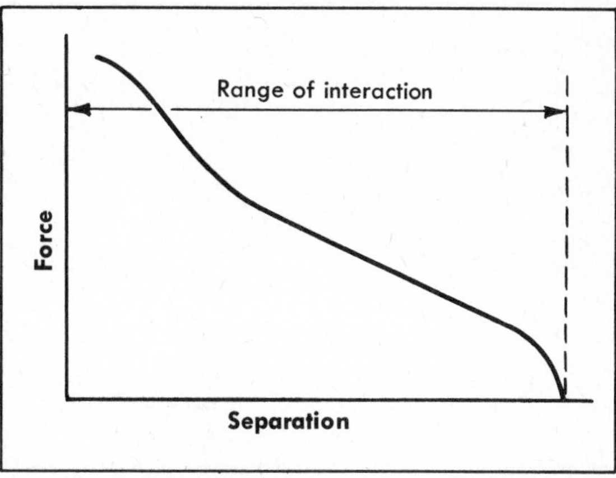

24–12 (a). The graph of a force which is a function of the separation of two bodies. The force is zero beyond the range of interaction.

We shall now show that the total kinetic energy at the end of a collision is the same as at the beginning, whenever the force of interaction depends only on the distance of separation of the two masses.* The equal and opposite forces F on the two masses may be any function of the separation of the two masses as long as F is zero beyond some definite range, so that we can define a complete interaction. Such an interaction starts with the masses farther apart than this distance and ends when they are again separated by more than this range [Fig. 24–12 (a)].

We can now apply the result $\Delta E_K(\text{total}) = F\Delta s$ to any force of interaction which depends on the separation alone — for example, the force illustrated in Fig. 24–12 (a). Consider for a moment what happens to the total kinetic energy when the separation of the two bodies decreases by the Δs shown in Fig. 24–12 (b). The force is almost constant; and $F\Delta s$, represented by the shaded

*This merely means that the force is the same on the way out as on the way in to the collision. This excludes forces like friction which reverse on the way out — so that they are always "against the motion."

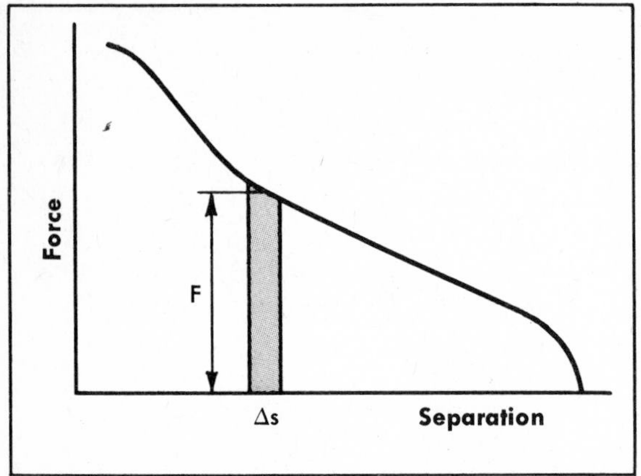

24–12 (b). During an interaction, when the separation changes by Δs, the kinetic energy E_K changes by $F\Delta s$ — the shaded area under the curve.

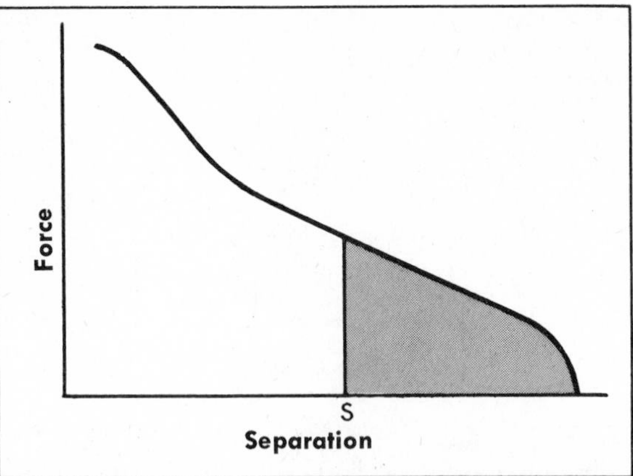

24–13. If two bodies approach each other from a long distance to a separation s, they lose a total amount of kinetic energy equal to the shaded area under the curve. When they move apart again, they regain the same amount of kinetic energy provided only that the force as a function of separation is the same on the way out as on the way in.

area, gives the decrease of the total kinetic energy. On the other hand, if the bodies are moving apart at this separation, their kinetic energy increases by the same amount as their separation increases by the same Δs. We see then (Fig. 24–13) that as two interacting masses move closer together from large separation to separation s they lose all the kinetic energy represented by the area under the F versus s curve. Then, in going apart again, they gain back all the kinetic energy represented by the same area. At the end of the interaction they have the same kinetic energy as at the beginning, provided only that the force as a function of separation is the same when the masses go apart as it was when they came together. We have now extended our theorem of the conservation of kinetic energy over a completed collision to apply to any interaction in which the force depends only on the separation. An interaction of this kind is called an elastic interaction or an *elastic collision.*

The interactions we see about us, such as collisions between billiard balls, or between a baseball and a bat, are never perfectly elastic, but many are very nearly so. As we saw in Section 24–5, when a moving billiard ball strikes one at rest, practically no kinetic energy is lost. When we come to the physics of atoms and of elementary particles such as the electron, we shall find collisions which are even more nearly elastic. When one electron hits another one, no loss of kinetic energy is normally detectable, although in collisions with very rapidly moving electrons a noticeable amount of energy may be radiated away.

24–8. Kinetic Energy and Momentum

When two bodies interact elastically, their kinetic energies E_{K1} and E_{K2} change by equal and opposite amounts over the whole interaction; that is:

$$-\Delta E_{K1} = \Delta E_{K2}.$$

This must be true because there is no change in the total kinetic energy $E_{K1} + E_{K2}$. Also, as we learned in Chapter 23, the changes in momenta of the two bodies are equal and opposite:

$$-\Delta\vec{p}_1 = \Delta\vec{p}_2.$$

This vector relation is always true for two bodies forming an isolated system; in particular, therefore, it is true for elastic collisions.

The similarity between the equation relating the changes in momentum and the equation relating the changes in kinetic energy goes further. A change in momentum is given by the impulse $F\Delta t$, which is the measure of the transfer of momentum from one body to another, just as the transfer of energy is given by the work $F\Delta x$.

From the fact that in these two transfers no momentum and no kinetic energy is lost, we can learn a great deal about the final motion of the two masses which interact. The two equations contain a large part of the information needed to determine the final speeds v_1' and v_2'. In particular, if the motion takes place along a straight line, we find that

$$v_1' = \frac{m_1 - m_2}{m_1 + m_2} v_1$$

and that

$$v_2' = \frac{2m_1}{m_1 + m_2} v_1.$$

If the collision is not head-on, we need some more information to tell us how far off the center it is and therefore in what direction the masses will go after the collision. For details of finding v_1' and v_2' for such head-on collisions see the box.

In making Fig. 24–8, we used a constant F within the range of interaction d; and we chose $m_1 = 3m_2$. Then from Newton's law we found that $v_1' = \frac{1}{2}v_1$ while $v_2' = \frac{3}{2}v_1$, as you can read off the figure. If you calculate v_1' and v_2' from the equations in the last paragraph based on the conservation of momentum and of kinetic energy, you will get the same results.

On the Derivation of the Formulas for v_1' and v_2'

We can determine the final speeds v_1' and v_2' that result from the collision discussed in Section 24–5 by using the equality and opposition of the changes of kinetic energy and of momentum. Here the form

$$-\left(\frac{m_1 v_1'^2}{2} - \frac{m_1 v_1^2}{2}\right) = \frac{m_2 v_2'^2}{2}$$

for the changes of E_K will be useful. Notice that we can write this equation as

$$-(m_1 v_1' - m_1 v_1)\left(\frac{v_1' + v_1}{2}\right) = (m_2 v_2' - 0)\left(\frac{v_2' + 0}{2}\right).$$

We see that each side of this energy equation is the product of the momentum change of one mass times the average of the initial and final speed of the mass. Because we know that the momentum changes are equal and opposite, we can cancel $-\Delta p_1 = -(m_1 v_1' - m_1 v_1)$ on the left with $\Delta p_2 = (m_2 v_2' - 0)$ on the right. We therefore obtain the additional information that

$$v_1' + v_1 = v_2'.$$

On substituting v_2' from this equation into the equation of the conservation of momentum

$$-(m_1 v_1' - m_1 v_1) = m_2 v_2'$$

we find

$$v_1' = \frac{(m_1 - m_2)}{m_1 + m_2} v_1.$$

The energy and momentum relations thus lead to a specific prediction for the final speed of m_1 when its initial speed is given. Furthermore, by putting this value of v_1' into $v_2' = v_1' + v_1$, we get

$$v_2' = \frac{2m_1}{m_1 + m_2} v_1$$

which tells us the final speed of the second mass.

Actually in getting this answer for the final speeds, we have put in quite a bit of information. Most of this information was introduced when we assumed that the collision was head-on so that the masses move only along the x axis. If we had allowed one mass to approach the other off center (Fig. 24–6), the problem would be more complicated to handle, and we would have to put in the information representing the distance off center in order to get the answer. We also specified that m_2 is initially at rest. These equations do not apply if m_2 is in motion at the start of the interaction. The more general equations that apply then are, however, easy to derive by the same method.

Furthermore, we should note that we made one tacit assumption in finding v_1' and v_2'. We assumed that there *was* a change in momentum in the interaction. It is possible even in our head-on collision to get another answer: if $v_1' = v_1$ and $v_2' = 0$, the momentum is unchanged and no energy transfers from one body to the other over the complete interaction. We shall not worry about this possible answer too much, however, because m_1 must pass right through m_2 in this case.

The results of using either Newton's law or the conservation laws must always agree. But it is not always so easy to apply Newton's law directly. If F is a complicated function of separation, finding the motion from Newton's law is a slow numerical procedure. Often, in fact, we do not know the details of F as a function of separation even though experience may indicate that the total kinetic energy is the same before and after every collision. In such a situation, we cannot describe the motion completely, but the conservaion laws still provide a large part of the answer.

For example, billiard-ball collisions are of this kind. The detailed forces between colliding balls are unknown to us; but observation shows that the kinetic energy of the balls is almost the same after they interact as it was before. Therefore, the forces must be functions only of the separation of the centers of the balls, and the force is zero when the centers are apart by more than the diameter. In particular, then, we can use the last two equations with $m_1 = m_2$ to describe a head-on collision between a billiard ball in motion and one at rest. From the equations we then get $v_1' = 0$ and $v_2' = v_1$ or, in other words, if one billiard ball smacks another head-on, the moving ball should stop and the ball at rest take off with the speed the other used to have. That m_1 stops and m_2 goes on with the speed v_1 is just what we observe, as Fig. 23–8 shows.

The same kind of analysis is often of importance in modern high-energy physics. Here the colliding masses may be protons, neutrons, mesons, or the recently discovered hyperons ("elementary" particles with masses greater than the neutron). For some of their interactions we do not know the details of the forces. But sometimes we can pick out the elastic collisions by observing the kinetic energies before and after interaction.

Sometimes visible masses (particles whose tracks we can see) collide with particles which are invisible to us. Then we can still try to apply the conservation of kinetic energy and of momentum, assuming that every invisible particle has the same mass.

In much this way James Chadwick discovered the neutron in 1932. In his experiments protons at rest were hit by unknown invisible particles which came from a region where beryllium was bombarded by the alpha particles from polonium. After the collisions the tracks of protons could be "seen" and their kinetic energy measured. After examining a large number of collisions, Chadwick concluded that one kind of invisible particle of a mass almost equal to the proton would explain all the observations. Furthermore, when the invisible particles hit atoms, the energy transferred was just what was expected. The "invisible" particle that Chadwick thus discovered is called the neutron. It is one of the building blocks out of which atoms are made; but its existence was only suspected before Chadwick's work. One of Chadwick's experiments is described in more detail in the box opposite.

24–9. Work and Kinetic Energy When More Than One Force Acts

In much of this chapter we have studied the gains and losses of the kinetic energy of a body when it is acted on by a single external force. Even when we dealt with the interaction of two bodies, each body was acted on by a single force. If we now consider more than two bodies, each body will be acted on by the forces of interaction with every other body. How then do we find the changes in kinetic energy of the various bodies?

Let us consider one of the bodies. How does the work which transfers kinetic energy in or out of the body depend on all the forces acting on it and on the distance through which it moves?

We can arrive at the answer to our question in either of two ways. First, if we add all the forces acting on the body, we obtain the net or resultant force on it. This resultant force acting alone produces the same acceleration of the body as a whole — the same acceleration of the center of mass — as all the forces acting together. All our statements about work and kinetic energy are true if the force we use is the *net* force. The kinetic energy we get this way is the energy of motion of the body as a whole, excluding the energy of internal motions like vibration or rotation of the parts about the center of mass.

Second, we can compute the work done by any one of the forces acting during a specified part of the motion, and add together the amount of work done by each. The sum will be just equal to the work done by the net, or resultant, force. To see how this result comes about, suppose that the motion of the body is along the x axis. Then the

Discovery of the Neutron

Here is a schematic diagram of the apparatus Chadwick used in one of his experiments leading to the discovery of the neutron. The beryllium gave off unknown, invisible particles when struck by alpha particles from the polonium.

These invisible particles then struck either hydrogen or nitrogen atoms at rest. As a result of the collisions, protons or nitrogen nuclei were knocked out, and Chadwick measured their velocities.

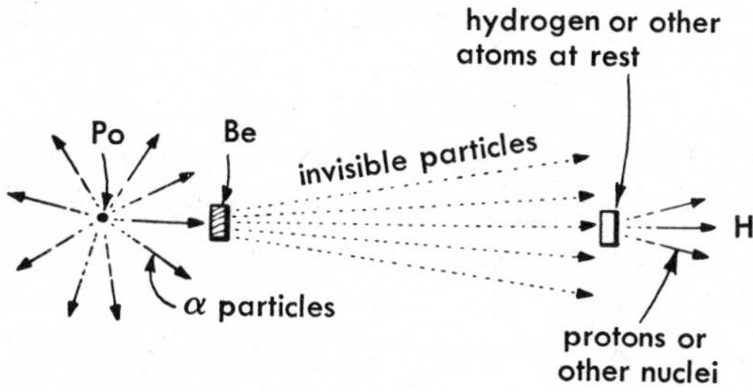

24–14. Diagram of Chadwick's apparatus.

Suppose we select head-on collisions by looking in the region H (see Fig. 24–14), and we assume that they are elastic. Then, calling m the mass of the invisible particle, and v its velocity, and calling m_p the mass of the protons and v_p' their velocity, we have:

$$v_p' = \frac{2m}{m + m_p} v.$$

In the same way, calling the mass of nitrogen and its speed m_N and v_N,

$$v_N' = \frac{2m}{m + m_N} v.$$

In this equation we can replace m_N by $14m_p$ because, as we know, the mass of nitrogen is 14 atomic mass units and that of hydrogen is about 1 amu. (See Chapter 8.) After replacing m_N by $14m_p$, we divide the first equation by the second one. This eliminates the unknown speed v of the invisible particle with the result:

$$\frac{v_p'}{v_N'} = \frac{m + 14m_p}{m + m_p}.$$

In his experiments, Chadwick measured the speeds v_p' and v_N'. He found that the ratio $\frac{v_p'}{v_N'}$ was about 7.5. Therefore

$$\frac{m + 14m_p}{m + m_p} \approx 7.5$$

or

$$m \approx 1.00m_p.$$

Chadwick repeated the experiment with other substances in place of hydrogen or nitrogen and found again that an invisible particle with about the mass of a proton fitted in with his measurements. He did a number of other experiments. All were consistent, and one of them determined the mass to within less than 1 per cent. He had proved that the neutron exists.

work done by each of the forces F_a, F_b . . . etc., acting on the body is:

$$W_a = F_{ax}x, \qquad W_b = F_{bx}x, \ldots$$

In each case it is the component of the force in the direction of the motion times the distance x which the body moves. The total work is then the sum

$$W = W_a + W_b + \ldots = (F_{ax} + F_{bx} + \ldots)\, x = F_x x,$$

where F_x is the component of the net force along the direction of motion.

In physical language each force represents the push or pull of some outside agency on the moving body. If the force is in the direction of motion, the work done by this force represents the transfer of energy from the outside agency to the moving body. If the force is opposite to the direction of motion, the transfer is from the moving body to the outside agency. The net result of the whole process will depend on whether the resultant force is in the direction of motion or opposite to it. In the first case more energy is transferred to the moving body than is taken from it. In the second case more energy is taken out of the moving body than is supplied to it. In this way we can generalize the results of this chapter to apply to as many bodies or as many external forces as are present in a complex situation.

24–10. Loss of Kinetic Energy in a Frictional Interaction

If a frictional force acts on a body — a force that does not depend just on the separation between two bodies — energy may be turned into a different form. It may become heat rather than the kinetic energy of the over-all motions of the bodies.

Consider the motion of a mass sliding on a table top. The frictional force exerted by the table top on the mass slows the mass down. The work done is the product of the force and the distance the mass moves. It transfers energy out of the mass because the force is opposite to the motion, and hence the kinetic energy of the mass decreases by the amount of this transfer.

To what is the energy transferred? There is an equal and opposite force exerted by the mass, acting on the table, but the table hardly moves under the influence of this force. Consequently this force on the table does practically no work, and the kinetic energy of the table does not increase appreciably. The kinetic energy of the mass is taken out, but it is not put into the kinetic energy of the table (Fig. 24–15).

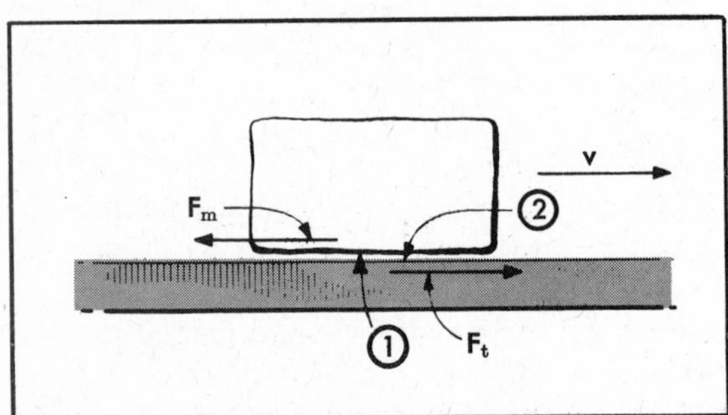

24–15. A mass is sliding along an ordinary table with speed v. A horizontal frictional force F_m acts in region 1 on the lower surface of the mass, taking kinetic energy out of it. The loss of E_K is measured by the work done as the mass moves, slowing down as a result of this frictional force. A frictional force F_t on the table is exerted in region 2 on the surface of the table; it does no work, since the table does not move. The table gains no E_K. Where has this energy gone? Apparently it accumulates in the region of contact around 1 and 2, where we observe an increase in temperature.

It is, however, common observation that the surfaces of the mass and of the table which have been in contact become hot. The energy taken out of the moving mass is associated with this heating. We can already get some idea of the connection between heat and the missing kinetic energy when we recall that the temperature of a gas is proportional to the average mv^2 of its molecules (Section 9–6). This means that heating a body, raising its temperature, increases the kinetic energy of its molecular motions. The energy which does not appear as kinetic energy of the motion of the table as a whole may thus be found in the increased energy of motions of the molecules in the heated regions of the table and the mass.

Let us consider another example of a frictional interaction. When we drop a ball of putty, the interaction between the putty and the floor begins as soon as the ball and the floor come into contact. Forces then begin to act on the putty, slowing it down. Also, the shape of the ball is changed; and, on the rebound, the interaction stops when the ball is closer to the floor than when the interaction began (Fig. 24–16). The force between ball and floor at this position is now zero, whereas when the ball was moving down at this position, the force was not zero. As a result, the total kinetic energy is less after collision than before

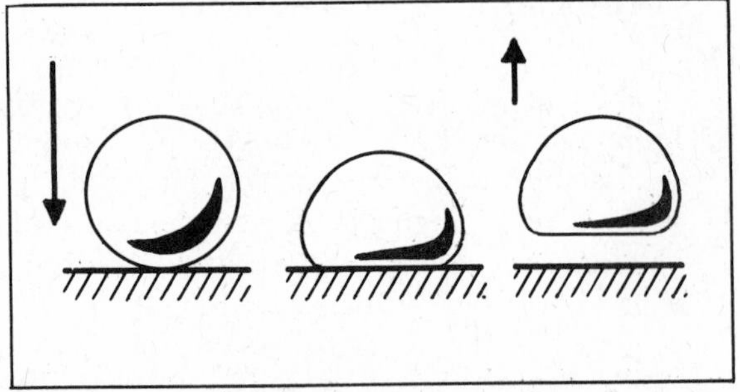

24–16. An inelastic collision. The interaction begins when the ball of putty comes in contact with the floor. The ball is permanently deformed by the interaction and, on the rebound, the interaction ceases before the ball reaches the separation at which the interaction started. As a result, the speed on the rebound is less than the speed at which the ball came in.

and the ball of putty bounces back, moving very slowly. The putty ball seems to lose kinetic energy permanently, but we find the putty hotter after collision with the floor than it was before. This interaction is much like that between the sliding mass and the table. In this example, however, the friction may all occur inside the putty ball when one part of the ball moves with respect to another.

A collision in which the forces are smaller when the bodies separate than when the bodies come together is called an *inelastic* collision. After inelastic collisions extra heat usually is observed. In Chapter 26 we shall discuss heat as a form of energy. For the present we shall keep our attention on situations in which friction and heating effects can be neglected.

24–11. Conclusion

What are the main things that we have found out in this chapter? In the first place, when a force is applied to a moving body, the transfer of energy to the body is given by the work: that is, by the distance the body moves times the component of the force in the direction of the motion. If the force is opposite to the motion, energy is taken from the body. If the force is in the direction of motion, energy is fed into the body. When more than one force acts on a body the net force changes the motion of the body; and correspondingly the total work measures the change in its kinetic energy.

When two bodies interact and the force of interaction depends only on the distance between the bodies, the total kinetic energy after a completed interaction is the same as the total kinetic energy before the interaction. The collision of the two bodies is elastic.

We can make the same kind of statement when many bodies interact. If they all start so far apart that the forces of interaction are zero and all end up far apart again, the kinetic energy at the beginning and at the end is the same. Some bodies may have gained kinetic energy; others may have lost it; but the total comes back to what it was. This statement about the equality of the total kinetic energy at the beginning and at the end of a completed interaction will be proved in general in the next chapter. Here we should emphasize that the statement is correct only if the interaction forces are functions of the separation of the bodies alone. In other words, the forces must be the same whether the bodies are approaching each other or moving apart.

Forces of interaction are not always functions of separations alone. Recall the examples of the mass rubbing on the table and the putty ball bouncing on the floor. They show that when the forces depend on other things the kinetic energy of bulk motion seems to change permanently. But when this kinetic energy disappears heat is usually observed. Later we shall find that this heat is another form of energy.

Even in the course of an elastic collision, the total kinetic energy of the bodies may appear to be lost temporarily. We have found that this lost kinetic energy can eventually be regained. As long as the forces of interaction depend only on the relative positions of the bodies, the "lost" kinetic energy is actually stored in the system. This stored energy we call *potential energy*. It is the subject of the next chapter.

FOR HOME, DESK, AND LAB

1. Coal is burned in a city electric power plant to make steam to run a steam turbine that drives an electric generator. The city water department uses this electric supply to run an electric motor to pump water from a well into a standpipe on a hilltop. List, in order, all the energy changes that take place.

2. A cable pulls a car up a mountain with a force of 4×10^3 newtons at a velocity of 5 m/sec. It takes the car 5 minutes to reach the top.

(a) How much work is done in getting the car to the top of the mountain?

(b) How much work would be done to get the car up the mountain if it traveled 2.5 m/sec?

3. A rotary snow plow uses four gallons of gasoline to plow 10 miles of road in 20 minutes.

(a) About how many gallons would be used in plowing 15 miles at the same speed?

(b) Do you think it would take half as much fuel to plow 15 miles in twice the time? Why? Be prepared to discuss your reason in class.

4. How much energy is transferred to a 15-kg suitcase while

(a) you hold it 5.0 minutes, waiting for a bus?

(b) you run with it a horizontal distance of 10 meters in two seconds at constant velocity in catching the bus?

(c) you lift it 0.80 meter getting into the bus?

(d) you carry it 20 meters down a ramp that makes an angle of 30 degrees with the horizontal?

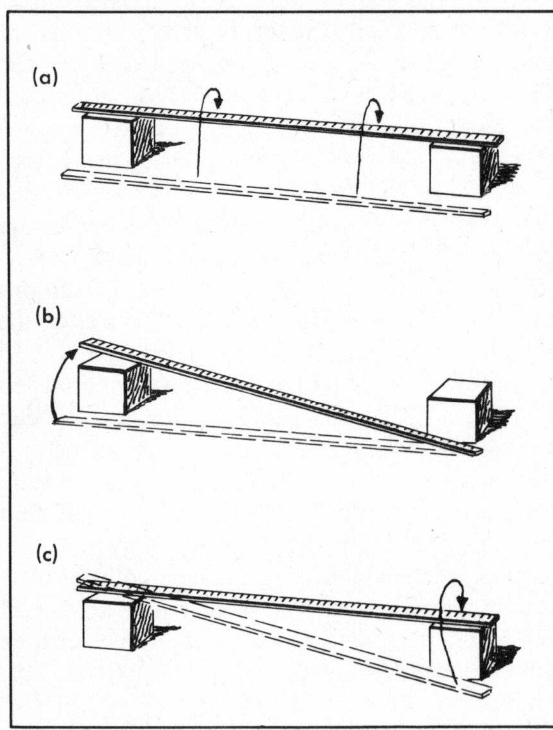

24–17. For Problem 5.

5. A meter stick, mass 0.20 kg, is lying on a table near two blocks 10 cm high (Fig. 24–17).

(a) If you lift the stick, holding it horizontal, and put it on the blocks, how much work have you done?

(b) If you lift one end and set it on one block, and then lift the other end, setting it on the other block, how much work have you done in moving the stick?

6. A force of 10.0 newtons acts on a 2.00-kg roller skate initially at rest on a frictionless table. The skate travels 3.00 meters while the force acts.

(a) How much work is done?

(b) How much energy is transferred to the skate?

(c) What is the final speed of the skate?

7. Compare the work done in lifting a 6.0-kg mass 20 meters and the kinetic energy of the same mass when it has fallen a distance of 20 meters from rest.

8. Compare the kinetic energies of two objects, A and B, identical in every respect except one. Assume that the single difference is:

(a) A has twice the velocity of B.

(b) A moves north, B south.

(c) A moves in a circle, B in a straight line.

(d) A is a projectile falling vertically downward; B is a projectile moving vertically upward at the same speed.

(e) A consists of two separate pieces attached by a light string, each equal in mass to the mass of B.

9. A force of 30 newtons accelerates a 2.0-kg object from rest for a distance of 3.0 meters along a level, frictionless surface; the force then changes to 15 newtons and acts for an additional 2.0 meters.

(a) What is the final kinetic energy of the object?

(b) How fast is it moving?

10. A force of 4.0 newtons applied at an angle of 45 degrees with the horizontal accelerates a 2.0-kg Dry Ice disc, initially at rest, for a distance of 0.50 meter on a horizontal table.

(a) Find the work done on the disc.

(b) What is the velocity of the disc?

11. A 3.0 kg mass moving 5.0 m/sec is acted upon by a force of 4.0 newtons opposite to the direction of motion. If the object is slowed to a speed of 2.0 m/sec, what is

(a) the change in kinetic energy?

(b) the distance moved while the force acts?

(c) the energy gained by the system supplying the force?

12. An automobile of mass 1000 kg is moving at 100 km/hour. We read this speed on the speedometer.

(a) What is its kinetic energy?

(b) How much work was done to provide this kinetic energy?

(c) Can you determine what force acted on the car to provide this kinetic energy? Can you determine through what distance this force acted?

Be prepared to defend your answer in class.

13. A 2.0-kg stone whirls around on the end of a 0.50-m string with a velocity of 2.0 revolutions per second.

(a) What is its kinetic energy?

(b) What is the centripetal force on it?

(c) How much work is done by the centripetal force in one revolution?

14. A body moves along a curve with a constant kinetic energy of 10 joules. Part of the curve is the arc of a circle of radius 0.50 meter.

(a) What is the net force acting on the body while in this part of the curve?

(b) What is the direction of this force?

15. A man pulls with a string on a 20.0-kg mass initially at rest on the floor. He exerts a force of

20.0 newtons horizontally, and the mass moves through 8.0 m. The mass then has a velocity of 3.00 m/sec.

(a) What is its final kinetic energy?

(b) How much energy has been transferred from the man?

(c) How do you explain the difference in your answers to (a) and (b)?

16. Fig. 24–8 illustrates the interaction of two bodies, m_1 and m_2, where $m_1 = 3m_2$. The repulsive force F is constant as long as the separation is less than the distance d, and the force is zero when the separation is greater than d.

Suppose F is 6.0 newtons; d is 20 cm; m_1 is 3.0 kg; and m_2 is 1.0 kg. Also, the initial speed v_1 of m_1 is 16 cm/sec.

(a) Find expressions for Δx_1 and Δx_2 (the distances moved by m_1 and m_2 during the interaction) as a function of time t. Use Newton's law and the relation $\Delta x = v_i t + \frac{1}{2}at^2$. The initial speed, v_i, is the speed v_1 for m_1 and zero for m_2.

(b) At the end of the interaction the masses are again d apart and $\Delta x_1 = \Delta x_2$. How long a time does the interaction last?

(c) Find expressions for v_1' and v_2', the speeds at the end of the interaction, in terms of v_1. Remember that for constant acceleration $v = v_i + at$.

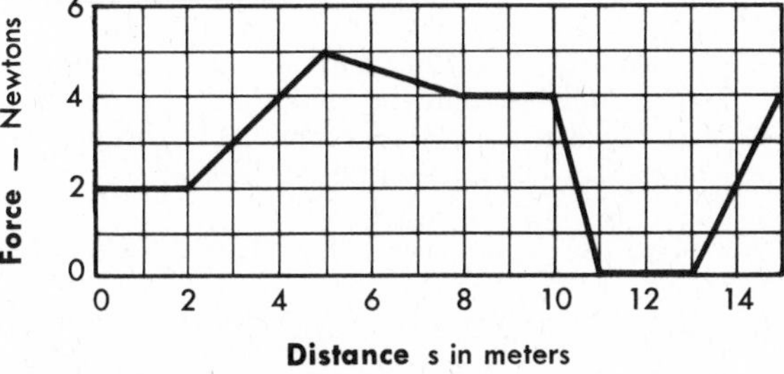

24–18. For Problem 17.

17. A 3.0-kg mass accelerates from rest according to the force function shown in Fig. 24–18. What is the kinetic energy of the object at

(a) $s = 2$ m?

(b) $s = 5$ m?

(c) $s = 13$ m?

(d) $s = 15$ m?

18. A 10.0-kg mass moves 2.00 meters against a retarding force that increases linearly by 4.00 newtons for every 3.00 meters the mass moves (see Fig. 24–19). If the force is zero at the beginning, how much kinetic energy is lost?

19. Two 3.0-kg bodies interact. At a given moment the first body is moving to the right at 0.50 m/sec and the second body is moving to the right at 0.30 m/sec, and so at that instant the speed of approach of one body as measured from the other is 0.20 m/sec.

If the force of interaction is repulsive and equal to 0.10 newton, at what rate is the total kinetic energy decreasing at that time?

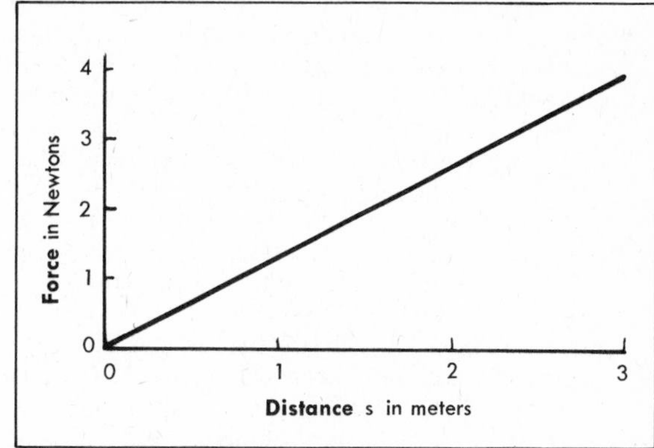

24–19. For Problem 18.

20. A 1.5-kg body is at rest. It is "hit" head-on by a body of mass 0.50 kg moving with a speed of 0.20 m/sec. The interaction force depends only on the separation of the two bodies.

(a) What is the final velocity of each body?

(b) In what direction does each move after the interaction?

21. A moving electron "hits" a stationary proton head-on. The forces between the two depend on the separation only. (The mass of a proton is 1840 times the mass of an electron.) What fraction of the electron's kinetic energy is transferred to the proton?

22. An object of mass $m_1 = 2.0$ kg moving with a kinetic energy of 1.0 joule collides head-on with an object of mass m_2 at rest.

Assuming the force of interaction depends only on the separation, calculate the kinetic energy transferred if

(a) $m_2 = .01$ kg.

(b) $m_2 = 2.0$ kg.

(c) $m_2 = 400$ kg.

What is the ratio of m_1 and m_2 when the transfer of kinetic energy is

(d) a maximum?

(e) very small?

Note: To see this relationship more clearly, you may wish to find the energy transferred for additional values of m_2, and make a graph.

23. A 5.0-kg body is at rest. A 10-kg body approaches it with a velocity of 0.20 m/sec. The interaction force is zero when the separation is greater than 0.10 meter and is 4.0 newtons when the separation is less than this distance. (Note that some of the answers in this problem are easier to get if you use the conservation of momentum.)

(a) What is the kinetic energy of the masses before the interaction?

(b) What will be the kinetic energy of each mass after the interaction is complete?

(c) What will be the kinetic energy of each mass when the separation is at a minimum? Recall that the speeds at minimum separation are equal.

(d) What is the minimum separation? (Your answer to part (c) tells you the net loss of kinetic energy of the two masses at minimum separation.)

24. An antiaircraft shell has a kinetic energy E_K and a momentum $\vec{p}$. Just then it explodes. What can you say about:

(a) the momentum of the pieces?

(b) the kinetic energy of the pieces?

25. (a) In Fig. 24–6 make the necessary measurements and calculate the ratio of the kinetic energy before and after impact of the billiard ball marked with the dot.

(b) What fraction of the initial energy of the dotted ball is gained by the undotted ball?

(c) What is the ratio of the total kinetic energy before the collision to the total kinetic energy after collision?

26. A 3-kg ball with a speed of 6 m/sec strikes another 3-kg ball moving 6 m/sec in the opposite direction. After collision each ball has a velocity equal in magnitude but opposite in direction to its initial velocity. Is this an elastic collision?

27. In one of the experiments that led to the determination of the mass of the neutron, Chadwick measured the velocity of protons that had been hit head-on by neutrons. The speed of the protons was 3.3×10^7 m/sec.

(a) What was the speed of the neutrons before and after collision with the protons?

(b) Chadwick also measured the speed of nitrogen atoms hit head-on by the neutrons. What was it?

(c) What was the velocity of the neutrons after each kind of collision?

28. An empty freight car A of mass 2.5×10^4 kg (25 tons) coasts along a horizontal track at 2.0 m/sec until it couples to a stationary car B of mass 5.0×10^4 kg. There is little friction, and the brakes are off.

(a) What is the initial momentum of car A?

(b) What is the speed of the two cars as they move along the track after the interaction?

(c) What is the total kinetic energy before and after the impact? Is this an example of an elastic collision?

29. Rub the palms of your hands together briskly. Do you do any work? What happens to the energy?

30. I push a finger steadily across a glass table top so that it moves at a constant speed of 3 cm/sec under a 1-newton horizontal force.

(a) What work is done in 1 sec by the force my arm exerts on the finger? What energy does it transfer into the finger each second?

(b) How large and in what direction is the force of friction on my finger? What work is done by the force of friction on my finger each second? In what direction does it transfer energy — in or out of my finger?

(c) What is the net force on the finger? What work does the net force do per second on my moving finger? What happens to the kinetic energy of the finger?

(d) What is the force exerted horizontally on the table by my finger? How far does the table move? What work on the table does this force do each second? In which direction does it transfer energy — in or out of the table?

(e) What happens in the region where finger and table are in contact?

31. A 100-gm light bulb dropped from a high tower reaches a velocity of 20 m/sec after falling 100 m. About how much energy has been transferred to the air?

32. A force of 3.0 newtons and a force of 4.0 newtons are applied simultaneously to a 4.0-kg mass initially at rest. The two forces act at an angle of 90 degrees with each other for 2.0 sec.

(a) What is the net force?

(b) Use the net force to calculate the total work done.

(c) What is the work done by each force separately? How does the sum of these works compare with the answer to (b)?

24–20. For Problem 33.

33. A horseshoe magnet of mass m stands on end on a frictionless table. A steel ball bearing of mass m is rolled toward the magnet from far away with velocity v and goes through the magnet and far beyond. Assume the force of attraction F changes with distance and is the same in front and behind the magnet. (See Fig. 24–20.)

(a) What is the final velocity of the ball?

(b) What is the final velocity of the magnet?

34. A two-stage rocket is moving with velocity v in a region where gravity is negligible. It consists of a final stage, or head, of mass m, and a tail of mass $2m$ which includes an explosive charge to separate the head. The charge is carefully designed so that after separation the tail has the least possible energy. (Assume that the gases from the explosion stay with the tail.)

(a) What is the least possible energy the tail can have?

(b) In this case, how much energy has the head got after the explosion? Give the answer in terms of m and v.

(c) How much kinetic energy did the *head* have before the explosion?

(d) How much energy has the head gained?

(e) How much energy is supplied by the fuel in the explosion?

(f) Why is the answer to (e) different from the answer to (d)?

FURTHER READING

AYRES, EUGENE, "The Fuel Situation." *Scientific American*, October, 1956. A careful look at the world's dwindling supplies of fuel.

POTENTIAL ENERGY

CHAPTER 25

IN THE last chapter we focused our attention on the transfer of kinetic energy from one moving body to another. We found that for complete collisions the loss of kinetic energy of one body must equal the gain of kinetic energy of the other *as long as the force of interaction depends solely on their separation.* Then with the help of the law of conservation of momentum we were able to calculate the final speeds of two bodies colliding head-on in terms of their masses and their speeds prior to the interaction.

In this application, the law of conservation of momentum, $-\Delta\vec{p}_1 = \Delta\vec{p}_2$, and the law of conservation of kinetic energy, $-\Delta E_{K1} = \Delta E_{K2}$, seem strikingly similar; but there is an important difference. The changes in momentum are equal and opposite in any time interval, and the momentum is therefore conserved instant by instant throughout the interaction. On the other hand, even in elastic collisions the total kinetic energy is not the same at all stages of the interaction. Only at the end of the interaction does it return to its initial value. During the collision, the total kinetic energy first decreases and then increases. At intermediate stages some of the kinetic energy has disappeared.

What happens to this lost kinetic energy? Because it all comes back, it must be stored somehow in the interacting system. We call this stored energy the *potential energy* of the system.

25–1. The Spring Bumper

Here is a simple example of energy being stored (Fig. 25–1). Consider a mass m sliding with constant velocity on a horizontal frictionless table. The mass collides with a spring bumper attached to a large body so massive that it hardly moves. When the moving mass hits the spring, the spring is compressed. It exerts a force back on the moving mass, slowing it down. The kinetic energy of the moving body decreases until the speed is zero. At this point the kinetic energy of the moving body has disappeared, and the spring is compressed a maximum amount. All the energy is stored as potential energy. After that the mass picks up speed in the opposite direction. Finally it leaves the spring with its original speed and kinetic energy. All the kinetic energy lost during the compression has been regained. At intermediate compressions, the energy was partly kinetic and partly potential.

In the last chapter we saw that kinetic energy will be completely regenerated if the force depends only on separation. Here compression plays the same role as separation. When the kinetic energy is stored and can be recovered completely, we suspect that the pattern of the force exerted by the spring is the same on the way in, while the spring is being compressed, and on the way out, when it is expanding.

Measurements of the force as a function of com-

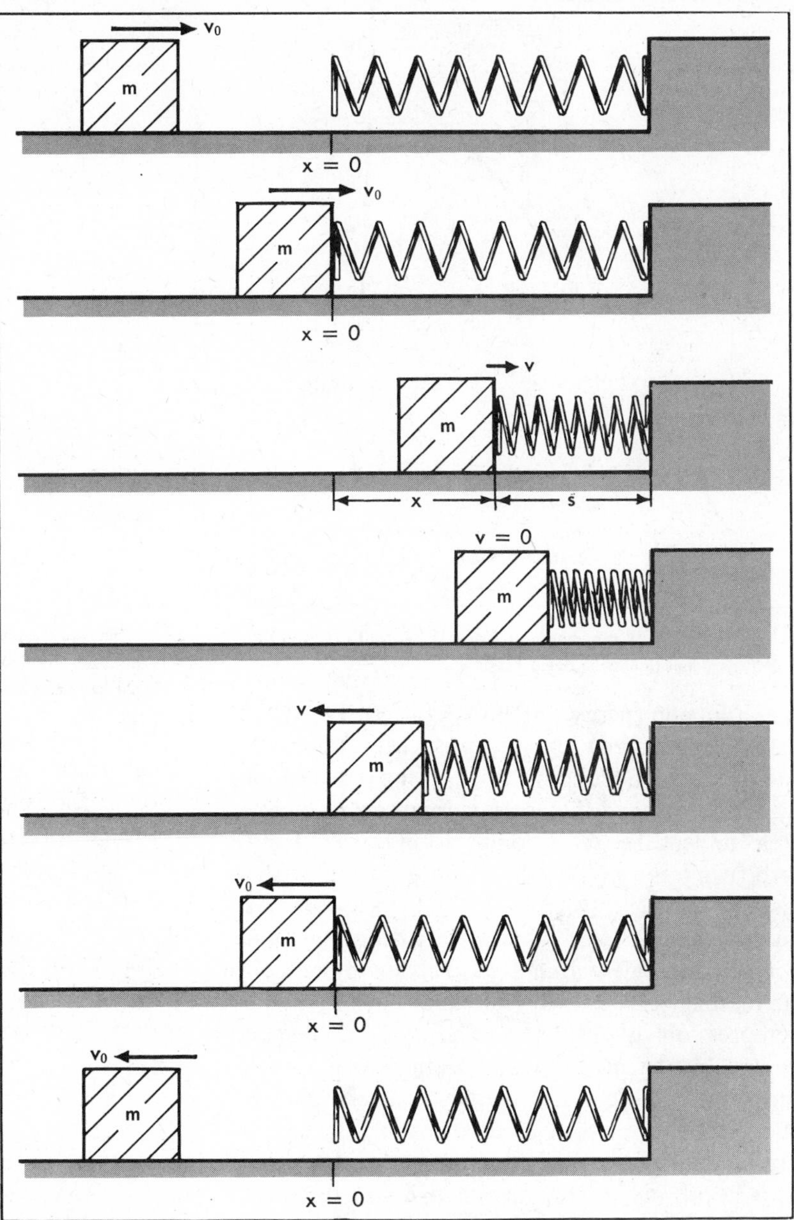

25–1. A collision between a mass m and a spring attached to a mass so large that it does not move appreciably.

pression confirm our suspicion. As we saw in Chapter 21, a typical curve for the restoring force exerted by a good spring looks like Fig. 25–2. The force exerted does not depend on the past history. It has the same value at a certain compression if we have just pushed the spring in that far or if we have pushed it in farther and then let it expand. Furthermore, the force does not depend on the speed of the mass. Since the force is always the same at the same compression, we can represent the pattern of force by a single curve as we have done in Fig. 25–2.

On the other hand, for a poor spring — a copper coil, for instance — the history matters. The forces on the way in and on the way out differ. When such a coil is hit by a moving mass, the mass bounces away, moving slower than when it came in. A copper coil is inelastic like putty and generates heat when it is moved in and out. We do not get a single curve of force versus compression.

When a mass hits a spring, compressing it and

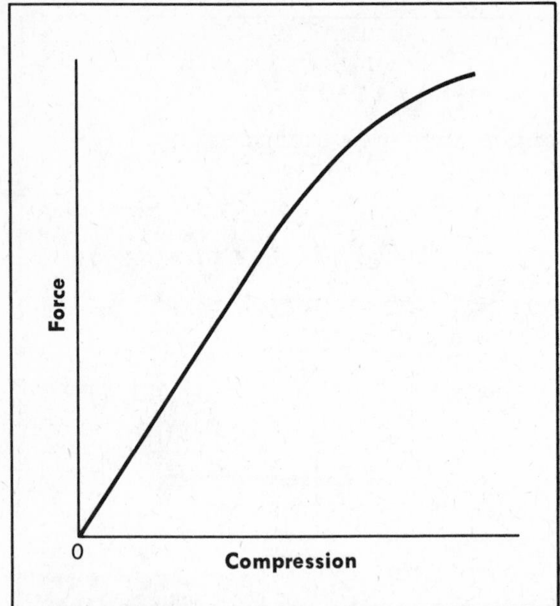

25–2. A graph of the restoring force F exerted by a good spring, as a function of its compression x.

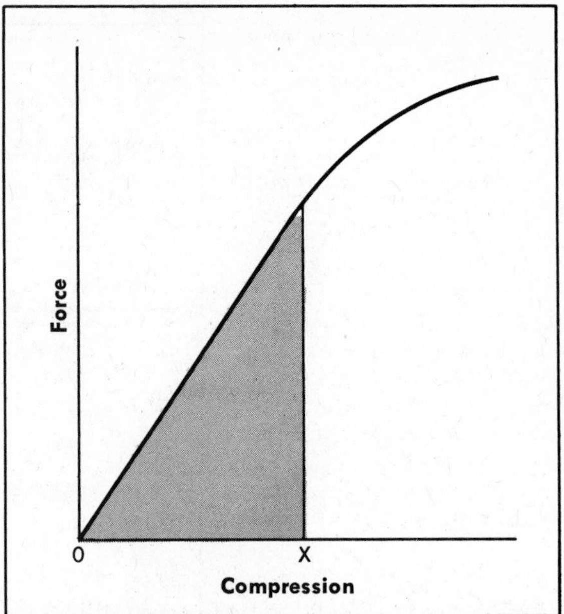

25–3. The work done in compressing a spring is measured by the area under the F versus x curve from zero to any compression x. This represents the potential energy stored in the spring at the compression x.

losing kinetic energy, the transfer of energy from the kinetic energy of the mass into potential energy stored in the compressed spring is measured by the work; and this work is represented by the area under the force-compression curve from zero (when the spring is uncompressed) to x (the distance through which the end of the spring has moved) (Fig. 25–3). When we are dealing with a good spring, one with a single force-compression curve, this work is always the same when the same compression is reached. The *loss* of kinetic energy by the moving mass is therefore always the same. It does not matter what the kinetic energy of the mass is. If m comes in with higher kinetic energy, it will have higher kinetic energy as it is passing x; but the change ΔE_K between zero and x is the same. This *loss* of kinetic energy, this work done in compressing the spring, is the potential energy stored in the spring.

It does not matter whether a moving mass compresses the spring or whether we compress it. If we compress the spring a distance x by hand, place the mass at its end, and let go, the spring will flip the mass off with kinetic energy equal to the work we did by hand. The potential energy of the spring is again given by the area under the force-compression curve, and it is a property of the compression of the spring without any reference to the moving mass.

For a spring with a given force-compression curve we can evaluate the potential energy as a function of the compression x by finding the areas under the curve between zero and various values of x. If we plot these areas against x, we obtain a graph of the potential energy U. Fig. 25–4 is such a graph of U versus x for the spring with the force-compression curve of Fig. 25–2.

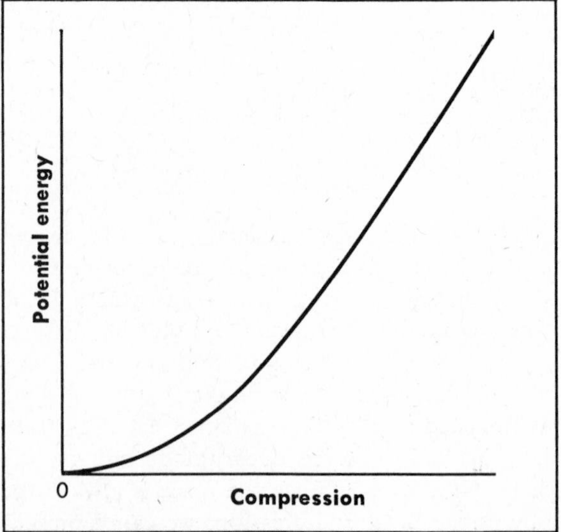

25–4. The graph of potential energy versus compression for the spring with the force-compression curve of Fig. 25–2.

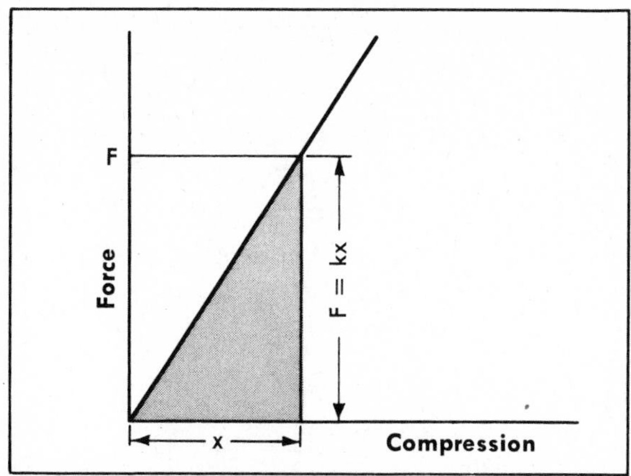

25–5. The graph of F versus x for a spring, when $F = kx$. The area under the curve is the triangle with base x and height kx. The area, and thus the potential energy, is given by $\frac{1}{2}kx^2$.

If the force-compression curve is simple enough, we can find a formula for the potential energy U as a function of x. In Fig. 25–5 we see that when the force is proportional to the compression, $F = kx$, the area under the curve is a triangle with base x and altitude kx. The potential energy is therefore

$$U = \tfrac{1}{2}(\text{altitude})(\text{base})$$
$$= \tfrac{1}{2}(kx)x = \tfrac{1}{2}kx^2.$$

This formula gives the potential energy for a spring with a linear restoring force.

The graph of U versus x can be checked experimentally (whether it was obtained from a formula or from the areas under the force-compression curve). Compress the spring different distances x and let it go, each time accelerating a known mass. Measure the kinetic energy with which the mass ends up. Its value should be the same as U at compression x.

The kinetic energy when the mass leaves the spring is equal to the potential energy when the mass is at rest, because all the potential energy is turned into kinetic energy on the way out. At intermediate points the gain in kinetic energy and the loss of potential energy are equal, and the sum is constant: that is,

$$\tfrac{1}{2}mv^2 + U = E.$$

The constant E is the potential energy at maximum compression when $v = 0$. It is also equal to $\frac{1}{2}mv_0^2$, the kinetic energy when $U = 0$ and the mass is just leaving the spring. E is called the total energy of the spring and the mass.

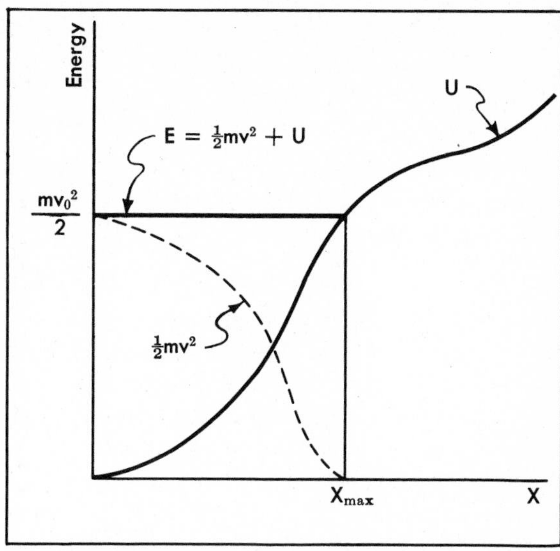

25–6. A graph of the energies of a mass moving on the end of some kind of spring. One curve shows its kinetic energy, the other its potential energy. The sum $U + mv^2/2$ is represented by the horizontal straight line — indicating that the sum of the energies is constant.

When we fasten a mass m to the end of any spring and set the system in motion, it oscillates back and forth. The expression

$$\tfrac{1}{2}mv^2 + U = E$$

enables us to calculate the speed v from the potential energy U at any stage of the motion (Fig. 25–6). For example, if the spring exerts a *linear* restoring force, we know that the mass oscillates in simple harmonic motion. (Section 21–8.) Also we know that $U = \frac{1}{2}kx^2$ for such a force. For simple harmonic motion, then, we see that

$$\tfrac{1}{2}mv^2 + \tfrac{1}{2}kx^2 = E.$$

For example, suppose we have a spring of force constant $k = 2$ newtons/meter. We attach a mass $m = 8$ kg to it and pull it out 1 meter from its rest position. Then we let the mass go. What will be its speed as it passes through the rest position? With what period will the mass oscillate back and forth? To answer the first question, we first notice that the mass is not in motion when we let it go. The kinetic energy $\frac{1}{2}mv^2$ is therefore zero, and the constant total energy E is equal to the potential energy $\frac{1}{2}kx^2$. Therefore, when we let the mass go

$$E = \tfrac{1}{2}kx^2 = \tfrac{1}{2}\left(2\ \frac{\text{newtons}}{\text{meter}}\right)(1\ \text{meter})^2 = 1\ \text{joule}.$$

On the other hand, when the mass passes the rest position $x = 0$, the total energy is all kinetic, that is,

$$E = \tfrac{1}{2}mv^2 = \tfrac{1}{2}(8 \text{ kg})v^2 = 1 \text{ joule}.$$

Consequently, $v^2 = \frac{1}{4}\left(\frac{\text{meter}}{\text{sec}}\right)^2$ and the speed is $\frac{1}{2}$ m/sec.

We can answer the second question — what is the period? — in two simple ways. First we know from Section 21–8 that simple harmonic motion is the motion of a component of steady circular motion. If the maximum displacement in the simple harmonic motion is 1 meter, the matching circular motion goes around in a circle of 1 meter radius and 2π meters circumference. Also, if the maximum speed in simple harmonic motion is $\frac{1}{2}$ m/sec the steady speed of the matching circular motion is that big. Consequently, the period is

$$\frac{2\pi \text{ meters}}{\frac{1}{2} \text{ m/sec.}} = 4\pi \text{ sec.}$$

We can check this result by the second method.

In Section 21–8 we learned that the period is $T = 2\pi\sqrt{\frac{m}{k}}$.

Here this is $T = 2\pi \sqrt{\dfrac{8 \text{ kg}}{2 \dfrac{\text{newtons}}{\text{meter}}}} = 4\pi$ sec.

This agrees with the period as computed by the first method.

25–2. Potential Energy of Two Interacting Bodies

Now consider one mass colliding head-on with another as in Chapter 24. Suppose mass A is projected at mass B, which is at rest (Fig. 25–7). When A reaches the range of interaction d, it begins to slow down and lose kinetic energy while B starts moving faster and faster; but B does not gain as much kinetic energy as A loses. Kinetic energy is disappearing. When A and B are closest together they are both moving with the same speed, and the total kinetic energy is at a minimum. Suppose that at just that instant a light cage (of negligible mass) is dropped over A and B to prevent them from separating. Then the whole system — A and B and their cage — continues with unchanging speed and constant kinetic energy. It will continue to move with this minimum kinetic energy until we remove the cage. If we look at kinetic energy alone, the

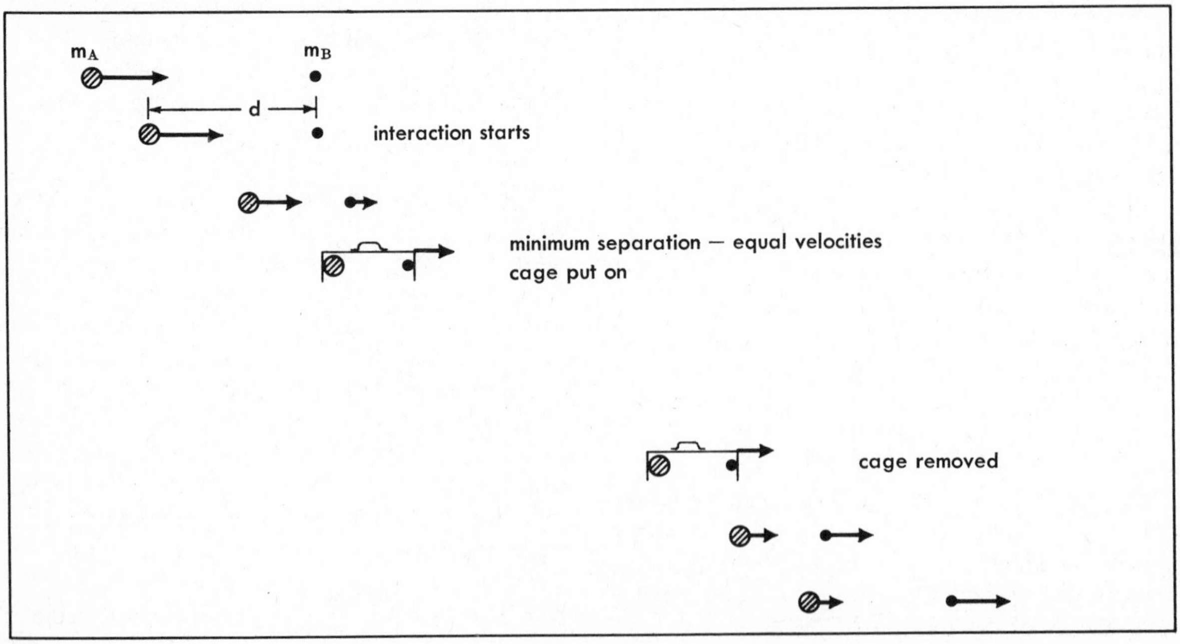

25–7. An interaction between two masses, which begins when their separation is d. At their closest approach, when their velocities are the same, we enclose them in a very light cage. They will continue to move along together at the same speed, with minimum kinetic energy. We can remove the cage at any time; the masses will move apart again and regain the original kinetic energy.

m_A m_B

d

interaction starts

minimum separation — equal velocities
cage put on

cage removed

system seems to have less energy than it had originally. However, if we remove the cage so that *A* and *B* can push apart, we get back to the original kinetic energy, provided the interaction forces depend on the separation alone. Here we are considering only those interactions which provide the same forces at the same separation, whether *A* and *B* are approaching or moving apart. Such forces make the collision elastic.

While the cage is on, we have less kinetic energy than we had originally; and we say that the missing kinetic energy is stored as potential energy. We can keep it stored as long as we like. And whenever we allow the two interacting masses to move apart again, the kinetic energy will increase by just the amount that we stored when we trapped them in the cage.

Whenever the two masses are held at a given separation, there is a definite potential energy. This does not depend on how fast the system is moving or on how the masses were pushed together. And all this energy will come out as kinetic energy when we let them go. The whole arrangement is very much like the spring bumper — where we could have stored the potential energy by applying a latch to hold the spring compressed. However, this time we have no visible spring. All we have is the forces, and we say that this potential energy is stored in the force-field of the interaction. The force-field behaves like an imaginary spring.

Actually we should say things the other way round. In a spring the potential energy is really stored in the force-fields of interactions between its atoms. The visible shape of the spring merely tells us where its atoms are.

To understand more fully what happens to the atoms, consider what happens when two large masses hit with a bang. As they come into "contact" atoms of one body approach the nearest atoms of the other so closely that large interaction forces arise and energy is stored in the inter-atomic force-fields of both masses. We might picture the collision of two freight cars as compressing inter-atomic springs [Fig. 25–8 (b)]. A better picture would show the atoms with no real springs, but only their force-fields to store energy [Fig. 25–8 (c)].

Obviously only some "contact" collisions (for example, those of rubber or steel balls) can store

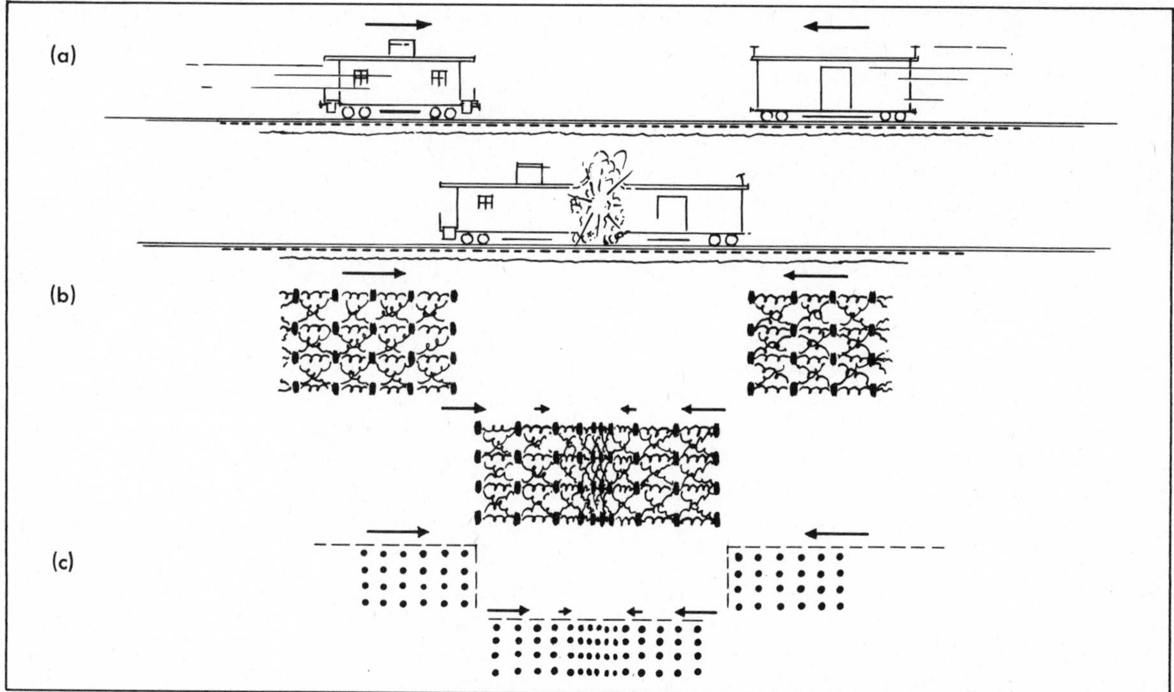

25–8. In (a) two freight cars are colliding. How is the energy stored to make them rebound? We might imagine that the crash compresses a very large number of small springs between the atoms (b). A better picture (c) would show no interatomic springs, but energy is stored in the force fields between the atoms.

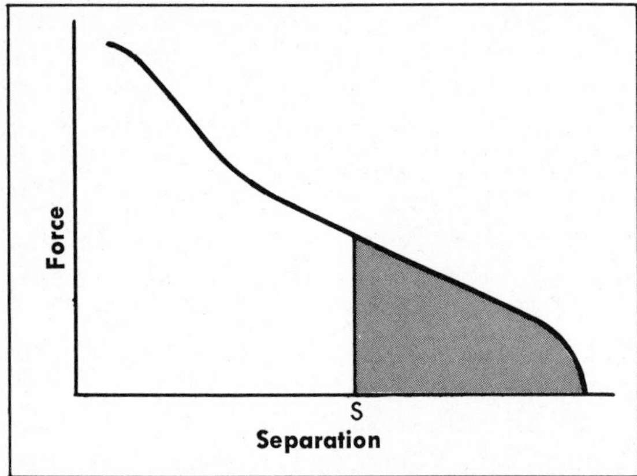

25–9. A graph of force versus separation for two interacting masses. The shaded area represents the work required to bring the masses to separation *s*. It gives their potential energy when they are *s* apart.

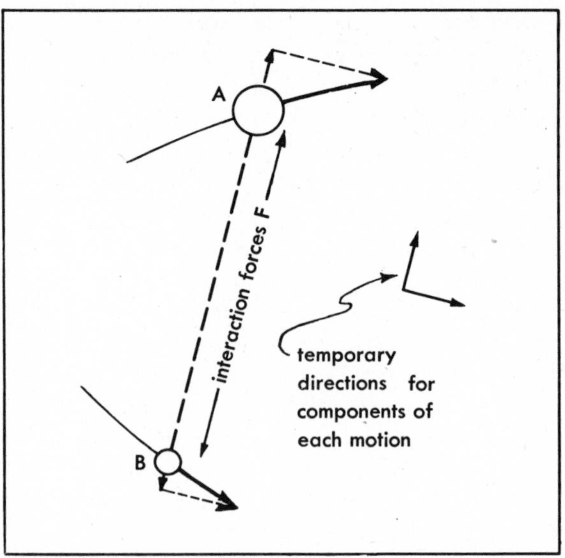

25–10. An interaction between two masses moving in any different directions. The work is given by the force *F* times the component of the motion along the direction of the force.

the energy in returnable form. Others leave the atomic systems in a jangle of motion; the large masses are left hotter and move apart with less visible kinetic energy. The collision is inelastic. When we look at one large mass colliding inelastically with another, we see that the forces are not the same on the outward trip after collision as on the inward trip. Some of the visible kinetic energy of the motion of the large masses disappears permanently. (We calculate it by using $\frac{1}{2}mv^2$ for each large mass and do not go into atomic details.) Because this lost kinetic energy is not directly returnable, we do not regard it as potential energy.

For elastic collisions, the potential energy depends only on the separation s between the masses A and B. It is given by the work necessary to bring them to this separation from a separation larger than the range of interaction. It is the area under the force-separation curve shown shaded in Fig. 25–9. Because the potential energy is only a function of separation, it does not depend on the method of bringing the masses to separation s. We have already seen that we can let the masses collide head-on with any kinetic energy or push them together by hand. The resulting potential energy is the same.

The potential energy is useful because it is a function of the state of the system at the moment and not of its history. Because it is independent of history, we do not need to restrict ourselves to collisions that occur along a fixed straight line. So long as the forces of interaction between the two masses depend only on their separation there is a definite potential energy at a given separation. The masses may be moving in any direction.

Let's look at such a collision in somewhat more detail. The motion of each mass can be split into two components, one along the line joining them and one perpendicularly across it (Fig. 25–10). One of these components is in the direction of the interaction force F and the other is perpendicular to it. From Chapter 24 we know that when force and motion are perpendicular to each other, no work is done. So the components of the motions perpendicular to F are not involved in any transfer of energy. On the other hand, when force and motion are in the same direction, work is done, energy is transferred. Consequently (since the force is in the direction of the separation), the force of interaction times the change in separation measures the transfer from potential to kinetic energy just as it does for a head-on collision.

We can apply the same treatment to any isolated system of masses, however complex, so long as all the forces are Newtonian forces — that is, so long as the forces of interaction between each pair of masses are equal and opposite and depend only on the separation. Under these conditions, the potential energy can be defined and the total mechanical energy (kinetic plus potential) of an isolated system remains constant.

We can now see that potential energy may be related to the energy stored in fuels: in gasoline or in the nuclei of atoms, for example. In using fuels we do not release the energy by removing a cage; but under appropriate conditions, we can turn the energy stored in fuel into the kinetic energy of the motions of large masses — or into the kinetic energy of the random motions of molecules. By using the concepts of kinetic and potential energy, we can understand many of the complex transformations of energy that go on in nature.

A rough analogy may help us to understand kinetic and potential energy. When one man pays another a certain number of dollar bills, the first man is poorer by that number of dollar bills and the second man is richer by the same number. The transfer of dollar bills from one man to the other is analogous to the work which measures the transfer of kinetic energy from one body to another.

Now suppose that the two men have a shoe box labeled "money" into which they can put dollar bills and out of which they can take them. The first man puts some of the bills into the money box, and the bills stay there for some time before the second man takes them out. During the time the bills are in the box, the total number of bills in the pockets of the two men is less. But the other bills are in the box, and the men can take them out later. The store of bills in the box may be compared to potential energy, which acts as a store of energy that can later be taken out as kinetic energy.

The first man might put bills into the box faster than the second man takes them out. The number of bills in the money box then increases. Similarly, one mass interacting with another may lose kinetic energy faster than the second mass takes it up. The potential energy then increases. In neither case is anything lost; the bills are in the box and can be taken out; the potential energy is still available. There is the same total as before.

25–3. Gravitational Potential Energy Near the Surface of the Earth

Let us examine the potential energy associated with the gravitational attraction between the earth and other objects. Consider the system formed by the earth and by a mass m which we assume to be very small compared with the mass M of the earth. If we release the body m above the earth's surface, it will fall. Simultaneously the earth will rise (slightly) toward the body. Each mass gains kinetic energy while the potential energy of the system decreases.

At any one instant of time the momenta of the body and the earth are equal and opposite. Therefore the speed v of the body and the speed V of the earth satisfy the equation

$$mv = MV \quad \text{or} \quad V = \frac{m}{M} v.$$

From this relation we can compute the ratio between the kinetic energies of the earth and the body. For the kinetic energy of the earth E_{Ke} we get

$$E_{\text{Ke}} = \tfrac{1}{2}MV^2 = \tfrac{1}{2}M\left(\frac{m}{M} v\right)^2 = \frac{m}{M}(\tfrac{1}{2}mv^2).$$

Because $(\frac{1}{2}mv^2)$ is the kinetic energy E_{Km} of the mass m, we see that the ratio between the kinetic energy of the earth and the kinetic energy of the small falling mass is always

$$\frac{E_{\text{Ke}}}{E_{\text{Km}}} = \frac{m}{M}.$$

Therefore, if m is very small compared with M, the kinetic energy of the earth can be neglected compared with that of the body. As m falls toward the earth, practically all the potential energy of the system composed of the earth and the mass m is transferred into the kinetic energy of the motion of m.

Now assume that m moves through a distance small compared with the radius of the earth. This is certainly true in any laboratory experiment. Then the force of attraction mg between the earth and the body has a constant magnitude. It has also a constant direction (vertically down).

Under the influence of this force a body starting from rest gains speed with a constant downward acceleration g. As we know from our previous work (Section 5–7), when it has fallen a distance d, its speed is given by

$$v^2 = 2gd$$

and its kinetic energy, E_{Km}, is

$$E_{\text{Km}} = \frac{mv^2}{2} = mgd.$$

The left side of this equation is the kinetic energy while the right side is the work (force times distance) which measures the transfer of potential energy into kinetic energy when the separation between the small mass and the center of the earth *decreases* by the distance d.

In falling from height h above the surface of the earth to height h' a body moves down the distance $d = h - h'$, and the potential energy changes by

$$U' - U = -mgd = -mg(h - h') = mg(h' - h).$$

(The minus sign in $-mgd$ shows that potential energy is lost and kinetic energy gained.) From this result we may conjecture that the potential energy is

$$U = mgh.$$

Indeed this is the right result; and we can show that it is correct by working backward. If

$$U = mgh,$$

then $$U' = mgh'$$

and $$U' - U = mg(h' - h),$$

which we know is the right change in the potential energy. No other expression for U will give this change, but we can add any constant U_o to the expression for U: That is

$$U = U_o + mgh.$$

Because $$U' - U = (U_o + mgh') - (U_o + mgh) = mg(h' - h),$$

the value of U_o makes no difference to our calculation of the change in potential energy.

In physical problems we deal only with changes in potential energy, and the value of U_o can be chosen at our convenience. When we are working near the surface of the earth we often choose $U_o = 0$ (Fig. 25–11). This gives the potential energy the value zero at the earth's surface. On the other hand, when we work with satellites that can go far from the earth we usually choose the potential energy zero infinitely far from the earth. Basically the choice does not matter.

In $$U' - U = mg(h' - h) = -mgd,$$

mgd is the downward force mg on the mass m times the distance d it falls. This expression, therefore, gives the change in the kinetic energy in falling from h to h'; that is,

$$mgd = E_K' - E_K$$

25–11. We may choose any height we want for the location of zero potential energy. The choice is arbitrary and makes no difference, since we deal only with changes in potential energy.

Consequently

$$U' - U = -mgd = -(E_K' - E_K).$$

This equation states that the changes in potential and in kinetic energy are exactly opposite. In falling, the potential energy decreases and the kinetic increases by the same amount. The work mgd measures the transfer. On the way up, the kinetic energy decreases and the potential energy increases by the same amount. Again the transfer is measured by mgd.

Since any change in potential energy is matched by an equal and opposite change in kinetic energy, the sum of potential and kinetic energy remains constant. We can see that this is so by rewriting our last equation as

$$U + E_K = U' + E_K'.$$

The left side of this equation gives the total energy

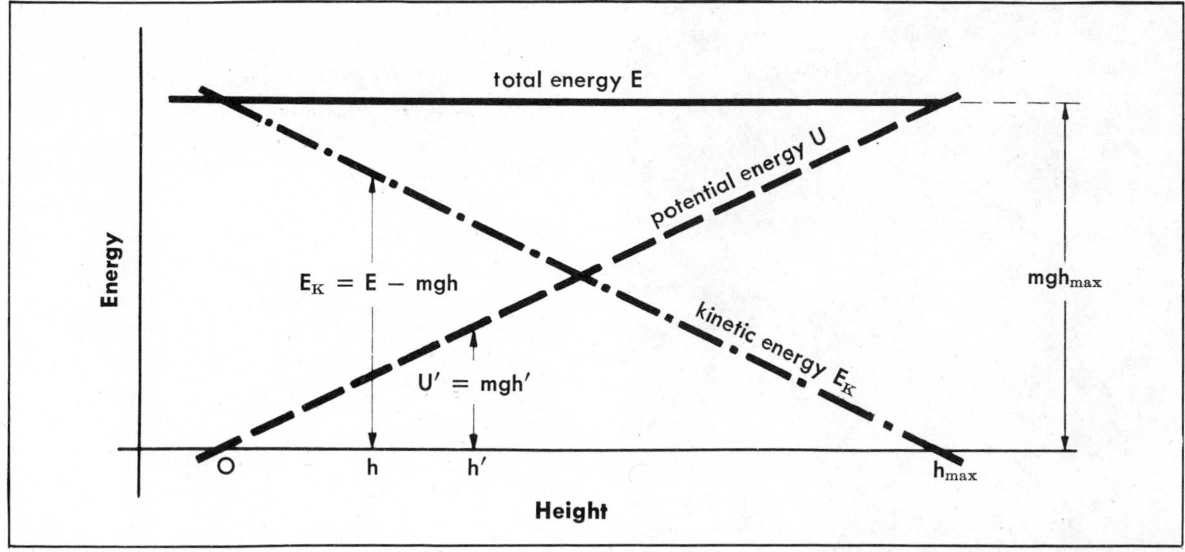

25–12. A graph of the energy of a body moving near the earth's surface. If gravity is the only force acting, the total energy *E* remains the same although the kinetic energy and the potential energy change.

E at one time, and the right side gives the total energy at any other time. The equation shows that this total energy

$$E = U + E_K$$

is the same at any two different times. It is constant, although the values of U and E_K may change. This conservation law applies to the system when it is isolated from external influences which might do work on it and thus change the total energy. It should be clearly understood that no other forces are acting. The relationship between total energy, potential energy, and kinetic energy is shown in Fig. 25–12.

Written out, the equation $U + E_K = E$ is

$$mgh + \tfrac{1}{2}mv^2 = E.$$

This equation is often valuable because it gives us information about the speed of m at different places without reference to the detail of the motion from one place to the other. For example, when a projectile moving upward passes the height h, it has the same speed v that it will later have at the same height on its way down. This must be true because mgh is the same on the way up and on the way down; E is always the same; and therefore, $\tfrac{1}{2}mv^2$ must have the same value even though the direction of motion has changed.

As a specific application of

$$E = mgh + \tfrac{1}{2}mv^2,$$

let us suppose that a mass of 1 kg is moving in any direction with speed 1 m/sec at a height of 3 meters above the earth. What will be its speed when it is 2 meters above the earth?

We can readily calculate its speed if we know its kinetic energy. And since the total energy E does not change, the kinetic energy of the mass at 2 meters above the earth will be the difference between the total energy and the potential energy at 2 meters. The total energy is the sum of the initial potential energy (at 3 meters height)

$$U = mgh = (1)(9.8)(3) = 29.4 \text{ joules},$$

and the initial kinetic energy

$$E_K = \tfrac{1}{2}mv^2 = \tfrac{1}{2}(1)(1)^2 = 0.5 \text{ joules}.$$

That gives

$$E = U + E_K = 29.4 + 0.5 = 29.9 \text{ joules}.$$

At 2 meters height the potential energy is

$$U' = mgh' = (1)(9.8)(2) = 19.6 \text{ joules},$$

and therefore at 2 meters height the kinetic energy is

$$E_K' = E - U' = 29.9 - 19.6 = 10.3 \text{ joules}$$
$$= \tfrac{1}{2}mv^2 = 10.3 \text{ joules}.$$

When we substitute $m = 1$ kg and solve for v we find

$$v = 4.54 \text{ m/sec}.$$

25–13. As the diver moves from the diving board to the water, there are continual changes from kinetic to potential energy and back again.

In each of the above motions, the total energy E remains constant so long as the force of gravity is the only force. But we can change the total energy E by pushing the mass, thus doing some work on it. If we then release it, the mass will move with a new constant value of E.

In this section, just as in the example of the mass colliding with a spring bumper, we have been able to find a potential energy which depends only on the position of the mass. This potential energy decreases by exactly the amount the kinetic energy increases. Just as in the case of the spring bumper, the sum of the potential and kinetic energies remains constant.

Two examples may serve to illustrate the great importance gravitational potential energy has for us. In a pile driver, for example, we increase the gravitational potential energy by raising a large mass. Then by releasing the mass and allowing it to fall freely, we let the gravitational potential energy turn into kinetic energy. This energy drives piles into the earth.

By building dams we can hold water at a greater distance from the center of the earth than that at which it would usually stay. By allowing the water to drop from the top of the dam to a lower level, we convert the potential energy into other forms — for running mills or producing electrical energy to drive motors or light lamps. Each kilogram of water we allow to fall through 10 meters can do work equal to $1(9.8)10 = 98$ joules. By dropping a kilogram through 10 meters every second, we can keep an ordinary light bulb going.

A standard work horse* can do 750 joules work per second. If three of them take shifts, they can light a few light bulbs all year for only a few hundred dollars. The power company will do it for about one-tenth that cost by using the potential energy from stored water or coal.

25–4. Gravitational Potential Energy in General

In the last section we determined the gravitational potential energy when a mass m is near the earth. We assumed that the strength of the gravitational field was constant. On the other hand, we know that when two masses move over larger distances, the gravitational force between them changes. What is the correct expression for the gravitational potential energy in this more general case? What, for example, is the gravitational potential energy of a satellite?

As we know from Chapter 22, the force of attraction between the earth M and a satellite m is GMm/r^2, where r is the distance to the satellite from the center of the earth. The force-separation curve in Fig. 25–14 is a graph of this function.

The area under this curve between two different separations measures the work done as the separation changes. For instance, the green-shaded area represents the work needed to increase the separation from r to r'. Using mathematical methods somewhat more complicated than we wish to discuss here, we can find the area under the force-separation curve from any separation r to infinity. This is the gray-shaded area extending infinitely to the right from r. It is

$$\frac{GMm}{r}.$$

This, then, is the work to pull the bodies apart from separation r to infinite separation. This

*The output of work horses was determined by James Watt in order to make a comparison with the output of his steam engines. More accurately, his standard is 746 joules/sec and is called a horsepower in honor of the horse. A joule/sec is called a watt in honor of Watt.

A Proof That $U_r = -\dfrac{GMm}{r}$ Is the Correct Expression for the Gravitational Potential Energy

The work, which changes the kinetic energy of the satellite as it moves from a point P to a point P', depends only on the two separations r and r', and it is the difference of the potential energy at the two separations:

$$\Delta E_K = -\Delta U = -(U_{r'} - U_r).$$

It is represented by the area under the force-separation curve between r and r'; and because the force is attractive, the kinetic energy decreases when the separation increases. Now if

$$U_r = -\frac{GMm}{r}$$

we find that this work is

$$-(U_{r'} - U_r) = GMm\left(\frac{1}{r'} - \frac{1}{r}\right).$$

Also, if we are correct, it is equal to the gravitational force F times the change in separation: $F(r' - r)$; that is,

$$F(r' - r) = GMm\left(\frac{1}{r'} - \frac{1}{r}\right).$$

Since

$$\left(\frac{1}{r'} - \frac{1}{r}\right) = \frac{r - r'}{rr'} = -\frac{(r' - r)}{rr'},$$

this yields

$$F(r' - r) = -\frac{GMm}{rr'}(r' - r),$$

and on canceling $(r' - r)$ from both sides we get

$$F = -\frac{GMm}{rr'}.$$

Here F is the average force between r and r'. To find it at the point r we must choose r' very close to r. We then obtain $F = -\dfrac{GMm}{r^2}$, which is the correct gravitational force. (The minus sign merely says that the force is attractive, so that the kinetic energy decreases if r' is greater than r.) Obtaining the right force shows that we must have started with the right expression for the potential energy. A different expression for U_r would lead to a different force, and when we found that force we would know that the presumed expression for U_r was wrong.

$U_r = -\dfrac{GMm}{r}$ is therefore the correct gravitational potential energy.

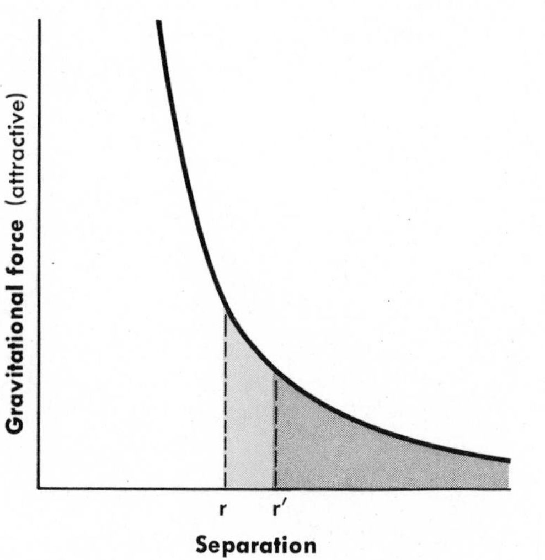

25–14. A graph of the force of gravitational attraction versus the distance to the center of the earth. As the separation increases, the force rapidly decreases.

work measures the energy transferred into potential energy of separation to force the bodies apart. The work is therefore equal to the difference $U_\infty - U_r$ between the potential energy at infinite separation and the potential energy at separation r. That is,

$$U_\infty - U_r = \frac{GMm}{r}.$$

On solving this equation for U_r, we see that the potential energy at the separation r is

$$U_r = U_\infty - \frac{GMm}{r},$$

and if we set the potential energy equal to zero at infinite separation, we get

$$U_r = -\frac{GMm}{r}.$$

Once we have this expression for the potential energy, we can prove that it is correct. This proof is shown in the box.

Now that we have the potential energy, we can get the total energy E by adding the kinetic energy E_K to it. The result is

$$E = E_K + U_r = E_K - \frac{GMm}{r}.$$

Just as we found for masses moved by springs and for objects moving near the earth's surface, the total energy is conserved. For any motion under the influence of the gravitational attraction alone, what is gained in potential energy as the bodies separate is paid for by a reduction in kinetic energy. For instance, as a satellite goes around the earth it goes slowest when it is farthest away and fastest when it is nearest the earth. As the earth goes around the sun the same relations are true.

25–5. Escape Energy, Escape Velocity, and Binding Energy of Satellites

With what energy must we launch a satellite so that it will escape from the earth? In the last section, we found that the work needed to pull two bodies apart from a separation r to infinite separation is

$$\frac{GMm}{r}.$$

Consequently, if a satellite is to escape, we must launch it with at least this much kinetic energy. If the satellite has just this kinetic energy, it will be at rest when the separation is infinitely great. We call this minimum kinetic energy the escape kinetic energy. For a satellite of mass m leaving the surface of the earth it is

$$\text{Escape kinetic energy} = \frac{mv_e^2}{2} = \frac{GMm}{r_e},$$

where v_e is the speed just after launching, r_e is the radius of the earth, and M the earth's mass.

The escape kinetic energy $\dfrac{mv_e^2}{2} = \dfrac{GMm}{r_e}$ rises in direct proportion to the mass m of the satellite. By putting in the numerical values of G, of the mass of the earth M, and of the radius of the earth r_e, we find that this energy is 6.24×10^7 joules per kilogram of escaping satellite. For example, this gives 6.24×10^{10} joules for a 1-ton satellite.

Although the escape kinetic energy that we must supply depends on the mass, the escape speed v_e to which we must bring the satellite is independent of mass. Since the escape kinetic energy is $mv_e^2/2$, the escape kinetic energy per kilogram is $v_e^2/2$. Consequently we can compute the escape velocity (this is the common expression for the speed v_e) from

$$\frac{v_e^2}{2} = \frac{GM}{r_e} = 6.24 \times 10^7 \text{ joules/kg}.$$

[The units may seem strange here, but work them out and you will find that 1 joule/kg = 1 (m/sec)^2.] Then multiplying by 2 and taking the square root, we get

$$v_e = 1.12 \times 10^4 \text{ m/sec} = 11.2 \text{ km/sec}.$$

This is the escape velocity which must be given to any object so that it will go away from the earth and never return.

It is interesting to compare the amount of energy that must be given to a satellite to make it go around the earth in a circular orbit with the energy we must give it in order to make it escape. When the satellite circles just above the surface of the earth, the needed centripetal force mv^2/r_e is supplied by gravitational attraction GMm/r_e^2. Therefore,

$$\frac{mv^2}{r_e} = \frac{GMm}{r_e^2} \quad \text{or} \quad mv^2 = \frac{GMm}{r_e}.$$

This says that the kinetic energy $\frac{1}{2}mv^2$ for orbiting the earth is $\frac{1}{2}$ the escape energy GMm/r_e. In other words, it takes just twice the energy to throw a satellite permanently away from the earth that it does to put a satellite in orbit just above the earth's atmosphere.

The equation for the total energy of the satellite at any separation r is

$$E = \frac{mv^2}{2} - \frac{GMm}{r},$$

and this total energy is constant during the motion. By putting in the values of the escape velocity v_e and the radius r_e at the surface of the earth, we find that the total energy must be equal to zero when the satellite can just escape. Zero total energy thus corresponds to zero velocity and zero potential energy at infinite separation.

If the satellite is to keep moving at infinite separation, the kinetic energy of launching must be greater, and consequently total energy must be greater than zero (that is, positive). On the other hand, for total energies less than zero (that is, negative), the satellite will have its speed cut to zero at a separation r where its potential energy is equal to the total energy.

$$\frac{-GMm}{r} = E$$

At this separation E_K has become zero: there is no kinetic energy, the satellite is at rest; and under the influence of the gravitational attraction of the earth it will start back toward the earth. It cannot get farther away, and in most orbits (where it never comes to rest), it cannot get even this far.

When a satellite has less than enough energy to escape from the earth, we say that it is bound to the earth. Now recall that we chose the zero of energy so that the satellite can just escape when the total energy is zero. If the total energy is greater, the satellite escapes with an excess of kinetic energy; and when there is less, the satellite cannot escape at all. In order to make it escape, we must supply the deficiency. If the total energy is -10^{10} joules, that is, 10^{10} joules less energy than are needed for escape, we must supply $+10^{10}$ joules. The energy that we must supply to overcome the binding is called the binding energy. This energy is just the total energy with the opposite sign. When the binding arises from the gravitational attraction, therefore, the binding energy is

$$\text{Binding Energy} = -E = \frac{GMm}{r} - \frac{mv^2}{2}.$$

The binding energy of a 1-ton satellite circling the earth is 3.14×10^{10} joules. Your binding energy to the earth is about 4 or 5×10^9 joules. That of the earth to the sun is a bit more than 2×10^{33} joules. There are binding energies of importance also in atomic physics, that of the electron to the proton in hydrogen for example, but the scale of this binding energy is quite different, and it arises from electrical rather than gravitational forces. We shall look at atomic binding energies in Part IV.

25–6. Conservation of Mechanical Energy

In this chapter we have investigated the potential energy of systems which interact with Newtonian forces. The masses interact as if they were localized at points which push or pull on each other with equal and opposite forces along the line between them. Even the gravitational attraction of the earth on a mass near by appears to come from the point at the earth's center. But it is not clear that all mechanical systems involve only such simple forces of interaction, nor that their parts can be treated as points. What happens to energy in mechanical systems where we cannot be sure that all interactions are Newtonian?

To answer this question, suppose we have a toy merry-go-round (see Fig. 25–15) which is driven by a weight-and-pulley system. Several turns of string are wrapped round the shaft, and then the string goes through a pulley and down to the mass M. If we let the merry-go-round go, it will start to rotate, gradually speeding up as the mass M falls. No one would try to analyze this system by finding a set of Newtonian interaction forces between all the atoms. But

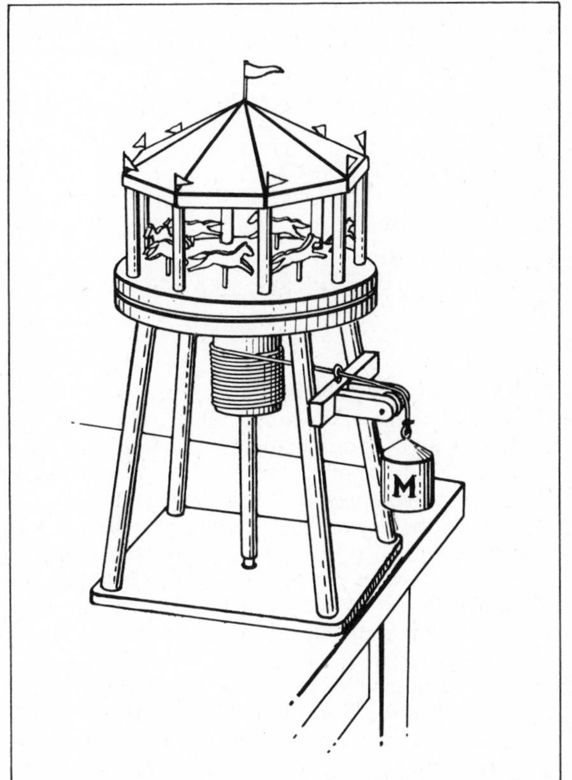

25–15. A toy merry-go-round driven by a falling weight. As the weight falls, the merry-go-round begins to rotate, turning faster and faster. The whirling platform gains kinetic energy which is equal to the loss in potential energy of the weight.

by viewing the merry-go-round as a collection of small masses and finding their speeds, we can calculate the kinetic energy of each piece. Then, adding up, we can find the total kinetic energy of the whirling merry-go-round. We can also measure the distance that the mass M has fallen. When we do such an experiment with a merry-go-round on nearly frictionless bearings, we find that the kinetic energy gained by the merry-go-round is just equal to the decrease in the gravitational potential energy as the mass M falls toward the earth. Eventually the string is unwound, but the whirling merry-go-round continues to turn. The string then wraps around the center post in the other direction. The weight rises, and the merry-go-round slows down. When the merry-go-round stops turning, the mass M is almost back up to its original position. It fails to return to the original height only on account of the energy transferred into other forms through frictional interactions.

We can consider more and more complex mechanical systems; and, without analyzing the forces of interaction in detail, we can often evaluate the kinetic energy and the potential energy. The energy may change back and forth between the two forms, but (when allowance is made for the amount transferred into heat via frictional interactions) the sum remains constant. This common experience suggests that the conservation of energy in mechanical systems may not depend on the detailed form of the interactions. We believe that it applies generally to all mechanical systems.

Sometimes we seem to get into trouble. We find a toy merry-go-round that continues to turn, one which can do work or transfer energy into heat, almost indefinitely. Then if we look far enough, we always find that the energy is being transferred from somewhere else. There is a little motor that burns fuel or one that uses electrical energy. The energy may be transmitted to the toy from the sun in the form of radiation. But as far as we know, energy is never created or destroyed.

In this chapter we have seen that if energy is kept in mechanical form it is conserved. The next chapter will show what happens when transfers to other forms are important. We shall then see why we believe that energy is always conserved.

FOR HOME, DESK, AND LAB

1. A mass of 4.0 kg sliding with a speed of 3.0 m/sec on a frictionless horizontal table collides with a queer kind of spring bumper. The bumper exerts a constant force of 120 newtons on the mass as it moves in (compressing the spring) and the same force on the way out until the spring is back where it was.

(a) Is this an elastic collision? How do you know?

(b) What is the kinetic energy at the beginning of the interaction?

(c) How much is the spring compressed?

(d) What is the ratio of kinetic energy to potential energy when the spring has been compressed 10 cm?

2. A 3.0-kg mass moving with a speed of 2.0 m/sec collides with a spring bumper which exerts a force $F = 100x$, where F is the force in newtons and x is the compression in meters.

(a) Draw a graph of F versus x from $x = 0$ to $x = 0.40$ m.

(b) What is the potential energy stored in the spring when $x = 0.10$ m? What is the kinetic energy of the mass at this point?

(c) What will happen if the spring is compressed 0.10 m by hand and then the 3-kg mass is placed in contact with the spring and the hand is removed?

3. The force-compression curve of a spring is shown in Fig. 25–16.

(a) How much work is done in compressing the spring 0.3 m?

(b) What is the potential energy of the spring when compressed this amount?

(c) Place a 2-kg mass at rest against the spring when it is compressed 0.3 m. Let go. What is the kinetic energy of the mass as it passes the point where the spring is compressed 0.2 m?

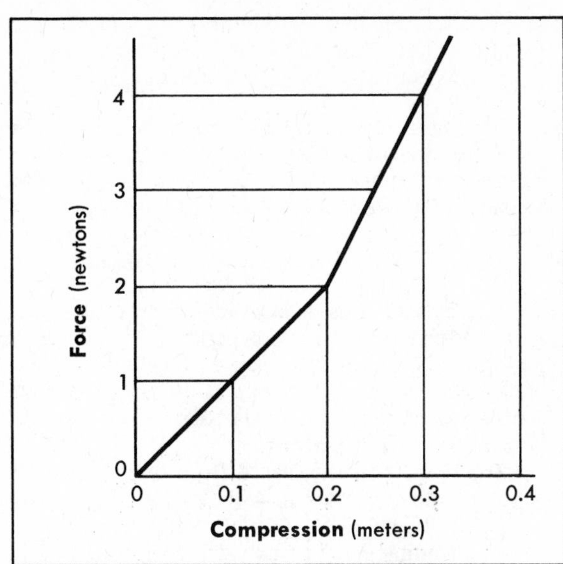

25–16. For Problem 3.

4. Pretend you are given two springs of different sizes. How would you set them up so that the force-compression curve of the system looks like Fig. 25–16?

5. A 1.0-kg mass moving with a speed of 10 m/sec strikes a spring, compressing it a distance of 0.20 m. The mass rebounds with a speed of 8.0 m/sec.
(a) What is the loss in kinetic energy of the mass?
(b) What happens to this lost energy?
(c) Which of the force-compression curves in Fig. 25–17 do you think is most likely correct for this spring?

6. A linear elastic spring is compressed 0.2 m by a force of 20 newtons.
(a) What is the force constant k (or force-compression ratio) of the spring?
(b) What is the equation for the potential energy stored by the spring as a function of its compression?

7. The following table gives the kinetic energy E_K of a 2.0-kg mass when it leaves a spring compressed different distances x.

x Meters	E_K Joules
0.1	0.25
0.2	1.00
0.3	2.25
0.4	4.00
0.5	6.00

(a) Plot the potential energy of the spring against the compression x.
(b) Does the spring exert a linear restoring force?

8. Assume an archer's bow acts like a linear spring.
(a) Compare the initial velocity of an arrow shot when the bow string is pulled back 10 cm with the initial velocity of the arrow when the string is pulled back 20 cm?
(b) How many times higher can the archer shoot in the second case?

25–17. For Problem 5.

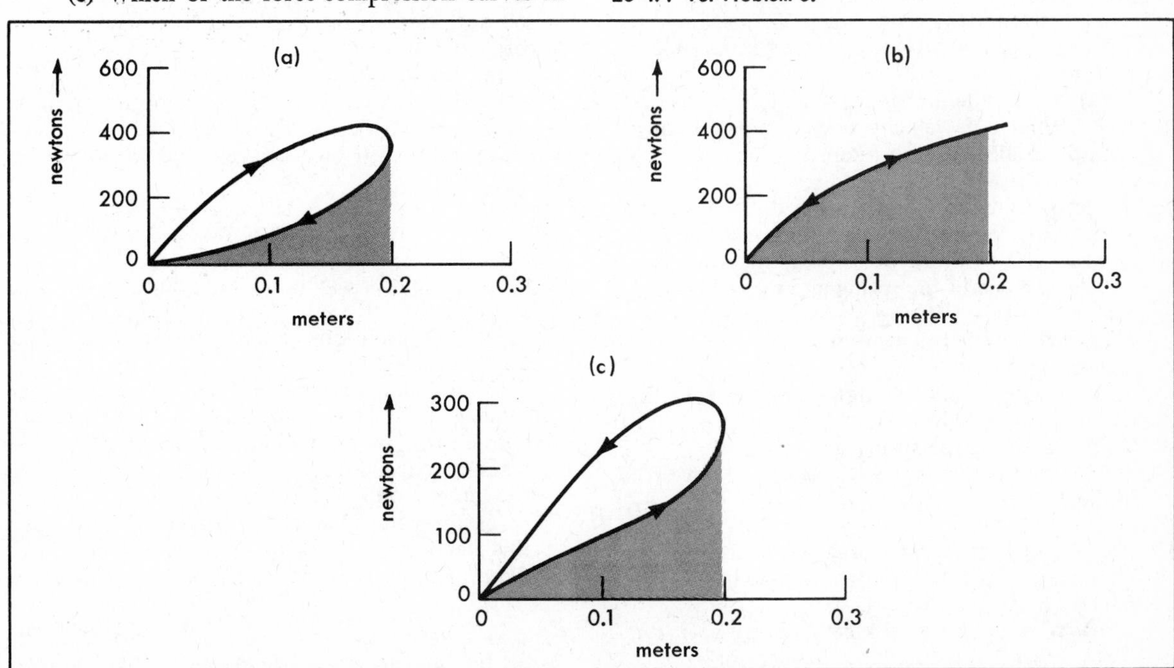

25–18. For Problem 9.

9. Fig. 25–18 shows a roller skate with a mass M mounted on it by four hack-saw blades attached to a base. The mass M is equal to the mass of the roller skate plus the mass of the base. If you hold the roller skate and pull the mass M out to the left, and then let the whole system go, the mass moves to the right and the skate to the left. Be prepared to describe the further motion, indicating the form of the energy at various stages.

10. What will happen if the 3.0-kg mass in Problem 2 hooks itself onto the spring and remains fastened to the spring?

11. A 0.50-kg mass free to slide on a table is attached to a linear spring with a force-extension ratio k of 50 newton/m. The mass is pulled back and released so that it vibrates with an amplitude of 0.10 m.

(a) What is its maximum velocity?

(b) What is its velocity when it is 0.06 m away from its equilibrium position?

12. A spring bumper with restoring force $F = 200x$ where F is in newtons and x in meters is compressed 0.100 meter. A 0.500-kg mass is placed next to the end of the spring and the whole thing let go.

(a) With what momentum will the mass leave the spring?

(b) We do the same thing with masses 0.125 kg, 2.00 kg, and 8.00 kg. What is the momentum of each as it leaves the spring?

(c) What is the energy of each as it leaves the spring?

13. Fig. 25–19 is the graph of the displacements as a function of time of two interacting masses $m_1 = 3$ kg and $m_2 = 1$ kg.

(a) What is the initial kinetic energy of m_1?

(b) What is the final kinetic energy of m_1?

(c) What is the final kinetic energy of m_2?

(d) What is the minimum total kinetic energy?

(e) What is the maximum potential energy?

14. Two masses $m_1 = 1.0$ kg and $m_2 = 2.0$ kg are pushed together despite an elastic interaction force until their potential energy is 27 joules greater than it is when they are beyond the distance at which they interact. If they are let go, what will be the final kinetic energy of each?

15. (a) A ball of mass 0.25 kg is thrown to the right at a speed of 2.0 meters per second. It starts along the frictionless surface at the left of Fig. 25–20. How high up the slope at the right will it go before coming momentarily to rest? What kind of motion will it perform?

(b) If the ball is released from rest at point P, what kind of motion will it perform? How high up the slope on the right will it rise? What is the binding energy (the extra energy needed to make the ball escape from the well in the center of the figure)?

(c) What is the binding energy in part (a)?

16. A linear spring whose force-extension ratio k is 40 newton/m hangs vertically, supporting a 0.80-kg mass at rest. The mass is then pulled down a distance of 0.15 m.

(a) How high will it rise?

(b) What will be its maximum velocity?

(c) How would the answers to (a) and (b) differ if the experiment were done on the moon?

17. A 0.200-kg stone is thrown upward from a point 20 meters above the earth's surface at an angle of 60 degrees with the horizontal and with a speed of 20.0 m/sec.

(a) What is its total energy?

(b) What will be its total energy when it is 15.0 m above the earth's surface?

(c) What will be its speed 15.0 m above the earth?

18. A mass m_1 moving with speed v_1 hits a mass m_2 head on. The mass m_2 is originally at rest, and the collision is elastic. If m_2 equals 10^{24} m_1, estimate the ratio of:

(a) the initial kinetic energy of m_1 to the final kinetic energy of m_1.

(b) the final kinetic energy of m_2 to the initial kinetic energy of m_1. A mass colliding elastically with a spring bumper solidly fastened to the earth loses practically no kinetic energy as a result of the interaction.

(c) Do your answers to (a) and (b) agree with this statement? Be prepared to discuss this.

Note: For parts (a) and (b), use the equations

$$v_1' = \frac{m_1 - m_2}{m_1 + m_2} v_1 \quad \text{and} \quad v_2' = \frac{2m_1}{m_1 + m_2} v_1$$

for the final speeds of m_1 and m_2.

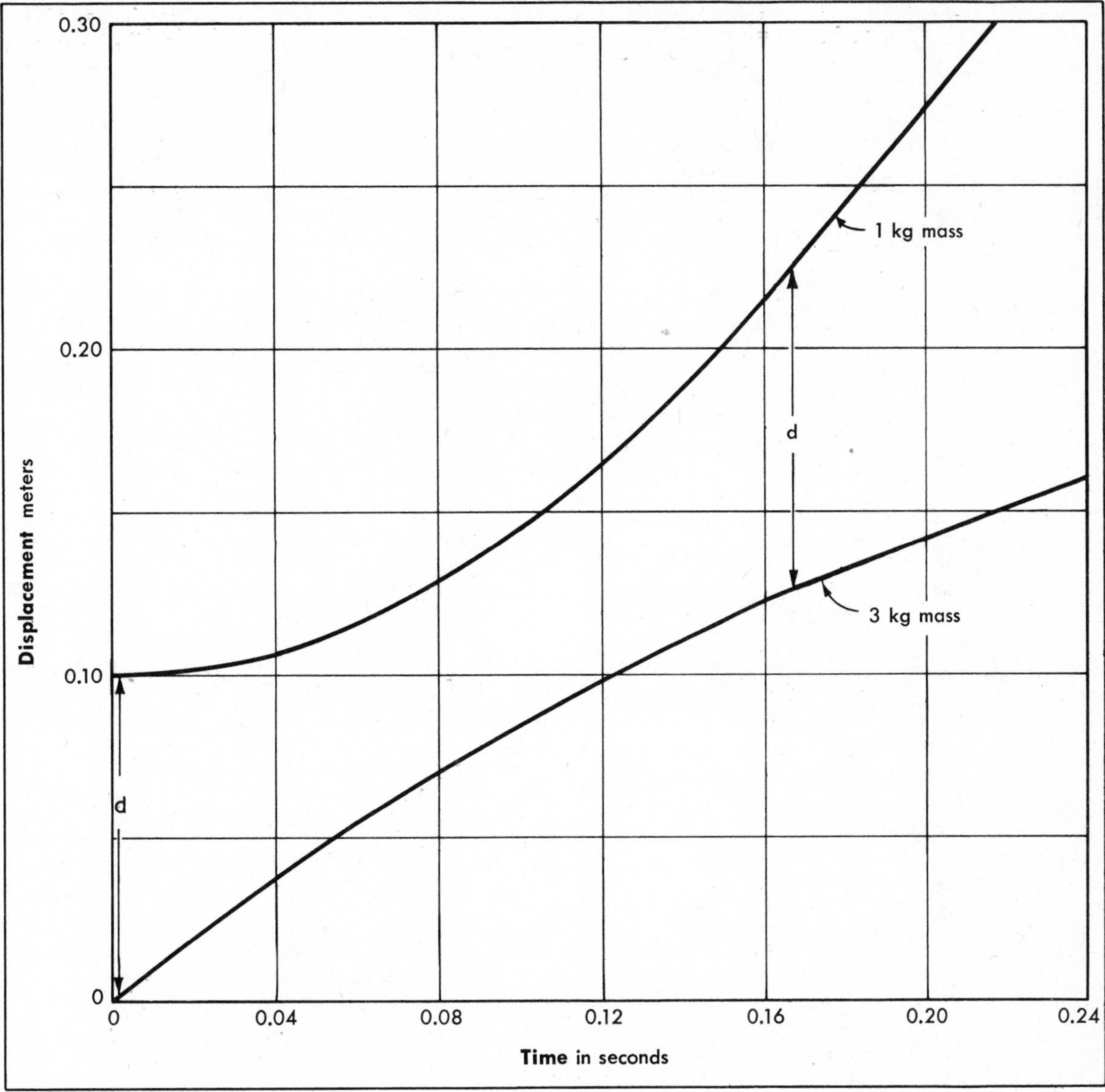

25–19. (Above) For Problem 13.

25–20. (Below) For Problem 15.

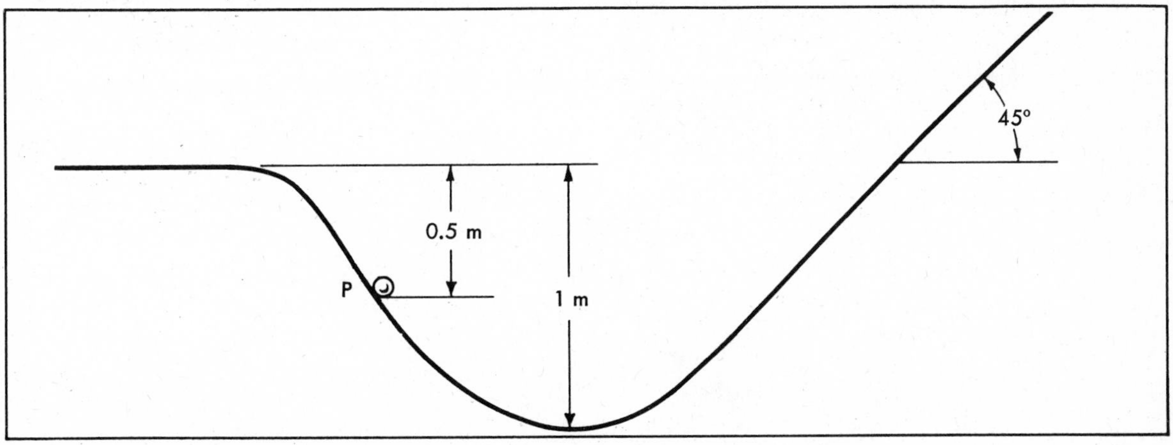

45°

0.5 m

P

1 m

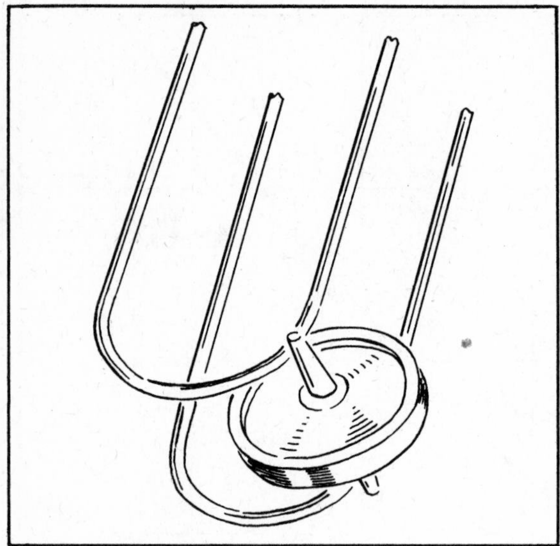

25–21. For Problem 19.

19. Fig. 25–21 illustrates a very common toy consisting of a wheel and shaft held to a support magnetically. When the toy is held upright, the rotor will move down one side starting from rest, round the curve at the bottom, and climb up the other side.

(a) If you have such a toy, find how much energy is lost from mechanical energy (the sum of gravitational potential energy plus kinetic energy) in one period of the motion.

(b) The energy lost is what fraction of the maximum kinetic energy during the motion?

(c) Into what form of energy does the lost energy probably go?

Note: A "period" of the motion is the time it takes the rotor to go completely around the support and return to its initial position.

20. Can you design a simple come-back toy? The outside is a cylindrical container. When the container is rolled away from you on a table, it will come to rest in a short distance, reverse its direction of motion, and come back to you.

21. When an object of mass m moves from r to r' in the earth's gravitational field the potential energy changes by $\Delta U = -GmM\left(\frac{1}{r'} - \frac{1}{r}\right)$, where M is the mass of the earth.

Show that, if the object moves away from the earth a distance $\Delta r = (r' - r)$ which is very small compared to its distance from the earth's center, the above expression reduces to

$$\Delta U = mg\Delta r.$$

22. Find the binding energy, to two significant figures, of:

(a) a 70-kg man to the earth.

(b) the moon to the earth.

23. The force field between a pair of protons is repulsive. Does the potential energy increase or decrease as a pair of protons are brought together?

24. The force of repulsion in newtons between two electrons is given by $F = \dfrac{2.30 \times 10^{-28}}{x^2}$ where x is the separation between them in meters. If each of the electrons has a mass of 9.00×10^{-31} kg and they are held 1.00×10^{-10} m apart and then released, what will be:

(a) the kinetic energy of each when they are 2.00×10^{-10} m apart?

(b) the velocity of each?

25. What is the binding energy of the proton and electron in a hydrogen atom if the proton and electron are 0.50×10^{-10} m apart and the force of attraction between them is given by

$$F = \frac{2.3 \times 10^{-28}}{r^2}$$

newtons, when r is in meters?

Remember, the electron will not stand still long with a force on it. Assume it is moving in a circle around the proton.

26. A drain pipe pointing slightly downhill sticks out from a retaining wall at the side of the road. A ball thrown up the pipe comes back with a greater speed than that with which it was thrown. If this happened to you, would you be surprised? What would you suspect?

27. With about what fraction of the original mass can a rocket using chemical fuel "escape" from the earth?

HEAT, MOLECULAR MOTION, AND CONSERVATION OF ENERGY

CHAPTER 26

WHEN a book sliding on a table comes to rest, energy seems to have disappeared, but the book and the table are slightly warmer. We cannot maintain the idea that energy is conserved unless we can include heat as a form of energy. In this chapter we shall extend our knowledge of energy to include heat. We already know something about heat and temperature from ordinary experience and from our study of gases in Chapter 9. As we mentioned there, experimental evidence indicates that temperature measures the average mv^2 of the gas molecules. As we would say now, the temperature appears to be proportional to the average kinetic energy of the molecular motion. We shall now re-examine the model of a gas developed in Chapter 9 and use our knowledge of dynamics to get more insight into the connections between temperature, heat, and energy. Later in this chapter, we shall see how to establish measures of thermal energy for all sorts of bodies, for liquids and solids as well as gases.

26–1. Gas Pressure

When we developed the molecular model of a gas, we found that the model of moving molecules bombarding the walls of a container related the pressure of a gas to the number, speeds, and masses of the molecules. We now want to find the detailed form of this relation.

Let us start by considering a single molecule approaching a wall, moving straight at it with speed v. If the molecule has mass m, its momentum is mv. When it strikes the wall and comes to rest, this momentum is transferred to the wall. The wall is given an impulse of size mv.

Now consider a small time interval t during which n such molecules hit the wall. The total impulse perpendicular to the wall is mvn. If the number n of colliding molecules is great enough, the wall responds as if to a steady force. This force times the time t is just another way of expressing the total impulse. Consequently,

$$Ft = mvn.$$

From this equation we see that the average force is

$$F = \frac{mvn}{t}.$$

We want to relate the force from this stream of molecules bombarding the wall to the force exerted on an area of wall by the molecular bombardment of a gas. For this purpose we wish to know how many molecules there must be in the little region of space near the wall to provide the bombardment we just considered (Fig. 26–1). We can find out by finding the volume near the wall from which the n molecules came.

Suppose that the molecules land on an area A of the wall. Then all of them must have come from a little volume with the base A and altitude vt. No molecule which started out at the beginning of time t any farther away can have reached the wall, because vt is the distance the molecules travel in time t, and if they start farther away they will fail to arrive in the time t. All the molecules that started out at any distance less than vt must have reached the wall because they will go the shorter distances from their initial positions to the wall in less than time t. We can conclude, therefore, that at the beginning of the time interval t, the n molecules must have occupied the volume vtA. The number of molecules per unit volume that provide this bombardment is, therefore,

$$\frac{\text{number}}{\text{volume}} = \frac{n}{vtA}.$$

In a gas at uniform temperature, every identical volume of reasonable size contains almost the same number of molecules. If the gas is in a container, the number of molecules per unit volume is given by the total number of molecules N divided by the volume V of the container. In our model of a gas, therefore,

$$\frac{n}{vtA} = \frac{N}{V},$$

and

$$n = vtA\,\frac{N}{V}.$$

This equation relates the number of molecules n bombarding the wall area A in time t with the number of molecules per unit volume in a gas. It provides the connection for which we were looking. When we put this expression for n into the equation $F = mvn/t$ for the force on the area A of the wall, we obtain

$$F = \frac{mv}{t}\left(vtA\,\frac{N}{V}\right) = mv^2A\,\frac{N}{V}.$$

The average force per unit area is called the pressure P. According to our simplified gas model, then, the pressure is given by

$$P = \frac{F}{A} = mv^2\,\frac{N}{V}.$$

This is the kind of result we want. The last equation expresses gas pressure in terms of the

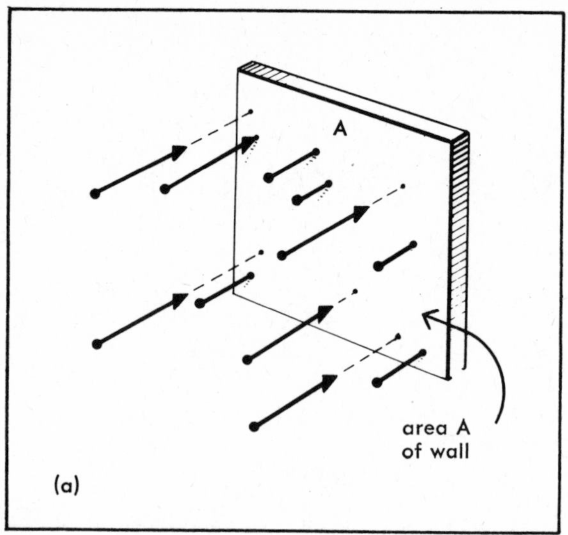

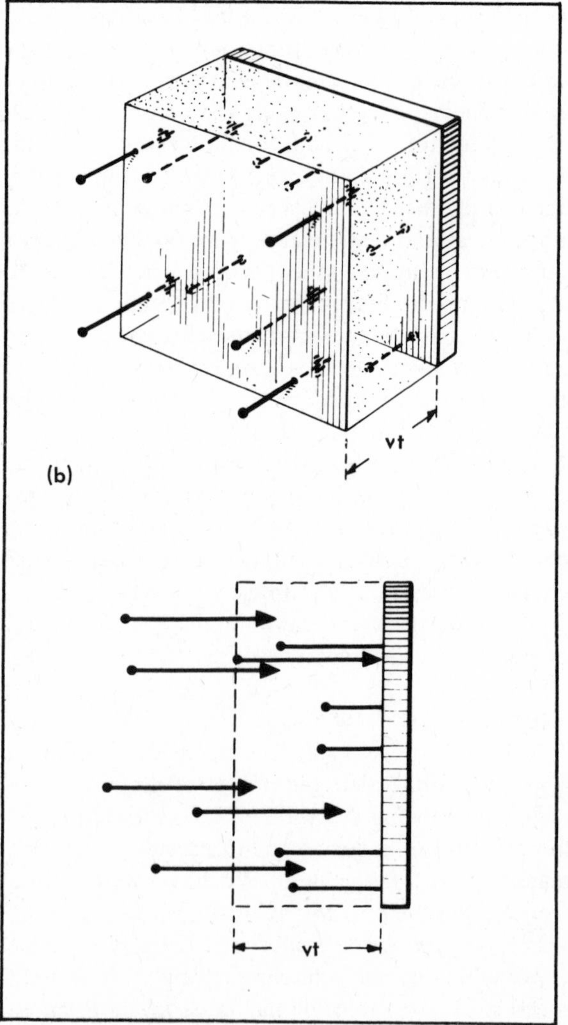

26–1. (a) The molecules move toward the wall with speed v. From what volume do the molecules come that reach the wall area A in time t? (b) The dots show the original positions of the molecules. The arrow heads show how far they get in time t — unless they hit the wall. Notice that all the molecules starting within the distance vt of the wall hit it. All those starting farther away do not get to the wall in time t. Therefore those molecules reaching the wall come from a volume of base A and height vt.

number of molecules per unit volume and the kinetic energy per molecule.

In order to simplify our computations, we have assumed that molecules stop when they hit the wall. In making a model of the behavior of gases this assumption is unrealistic. A molecule may stick to the wall for a while, but certainly a number of molecules must move away from the wall just equal to the number that move toward it. Otherwise the container will soon be emptied of gas. Indeed not only must an equal number of molecules move away from the wall but they must move away from the wall with equal but opposite momentum. If, for example, they went back into the gas moving more slowly, the energy of molecular motion of the gas would decrease. This would happen only when energy is flowing out of the gas, not when the behavior of the gas remains the same.

We can now improve our model of a gas by considering the molecules leaving the wall as well as those that come toward it. For every molecule that brings momentum mv to the wall, another molecule leaves with a momentum that is exactly equal in magnitude but opposite in direction. Consequently the impulse on the wall is twice what we have assumed; and therefore, compared to our first calculation, the pressure is also twice as great. At the same time, however, the number of molecules per unit volume in the gas must also be twice what we computed. In a little volume of the gas next to the wall, in addition to the molecules we have considered which are coming toward the wall, there is an equal number of molecules now leaving the wall. In all there are twice as many molecules per unit volume.

Now look back at our equation for the pressure. When we double the pressure *and* double the number of molecules per unit volume we need make no change in the equation. Consequently,

$$P = mv^2 \frac{N}{V}$$

gives the pressure of a gas of molecules bouncing back and forth between the two walls in a container. It expresses the pressure according to a rather good model of a gas.

In a moment we shall make the model even better, but we already find in this model all the features we discussed in Chapter 9. Briefly the pressure is proportional to the number of molecules per unit volume N/V and to the kinetic energy $\frac{1}{2}mv^2$ of each molecule. This result agrees with Boyle's law and with the idea that the Kelvin temperature is proportional to the kinetic energy. At a given temperature, then, mv^2 has the same value for all kinds of molecules. Consequently, the model predicts that the pressure is proportional to the number of molecules and inversely proportional to the volume they occupy, regardless of the nature of the gas. This is just what we found for real gases as long as the molecules are far apart.

In establishing the relation

$$P = mv^2 \frac{N}{V},$$

we have introduced all the essential factors in a molecular model of gas pressure. However, there are two final improvements we shall make in the model: we shall make the molecules move about in all directions instead of confining them to motion perpendicular to the walls and we shall allow them to have different speeds instead of all moving at the same speed.

In a gas it is the random thermal motions of the molecules that bring them to the walls. The molecules go into the wall at all angles, not just perpendicularly. The net effect (as we show in the box on page 428) is to replace mv^2 by $\frac{1}{3}mv^2$. In a manner of speaking, only $\frac{1}{3}$ of the molecular motions are perpendicular to the wall — the other $\frac{2}{3}$ are parallel to the wall at right angles to each other. Consequently, the gas pressure is

$$P = \tfrac{1}{3}(mv^2) \frac{N}{V}.$$

Now since $\frac{mv^2}{2}$ is the kinetic energy E_K,

$$\tfrac{1}{3}mv^2 = \tfrac{2}{3}\left(\frac{mv^2}{2}\right) = \tfrac{2}{3}E_K.$$

We can, therefore, write our expression for the pressure as

$$P = \tfrac{2}{3}E_K \frac{N}{V}.$$

This equation says that the pressure is $\frac{2}{3}$ of the kinetic energy of a molecule times the number of molecules per unit volume. This form of the equation emphasizes the role of the molecular kinetic energy in determining the pressure.

Finally in a gas the molecular speeds are not all the same and the molecules may have differ-

Taking Account of the Random Directions of Molecular Motion

In Section 26–1 we show that a stream of molecules hitting a wall head-on exerts a pressure on the wall

$$P = mv^2 \frac{N}{V}.$$

When the wall is bombarded by molecules coming at it in all directions, the pressure is

$$P = \tfrac{1}{3}mv^2 \frac{N}{V}.$$

We can account for the extra factor $\frac{1}{3}$ in the case of bombardment in all directions as follows: First, the components of molecular momentum parallel to the wall lead to no force on the wall. This is true because along every line parallel to the wall equal numbers of molecules move in opposite directions. And therefore equal numbers of molecules hit the wall with parallel components in one direction and with parallel components in the opposite direction. Now that we are rid of the parallel components, we look at the perpendicular components. In place of the momentum mv, we must now use the component $mv_\perp$; and in place of v for the speed which brings molecules to the wall, we must use $v_\perp$. Therefore in place of mv^2 we must now have $mv_\perp^2$. In other words, the square of one component of the velocity replaces the square of the velocity.

In the gas the velocities of the molecules must point equally often in all directions. We must therefore find the relation of the average of the square of the particular component $v_\perp$ to the square of the vector v when the vector points equally often in every direction. This can be done by expressing v^2 in terms of the squares of its components along three rectangular directions, say x, y, and z, where we have chosen z as the direction perpendicular to the wall. As Fig. 26–2 shows, $v^2 = v_x^2 + v_y^2 + v_z^2$. Now when v points equally often in all directions, the average values of v_x^2, v_y^2, and v_z^2 must all be the same: that is, $\overline{v_x^2} = \overline{v_y^2} = \overline{v_z^2}$, where the bar means "average." Thus

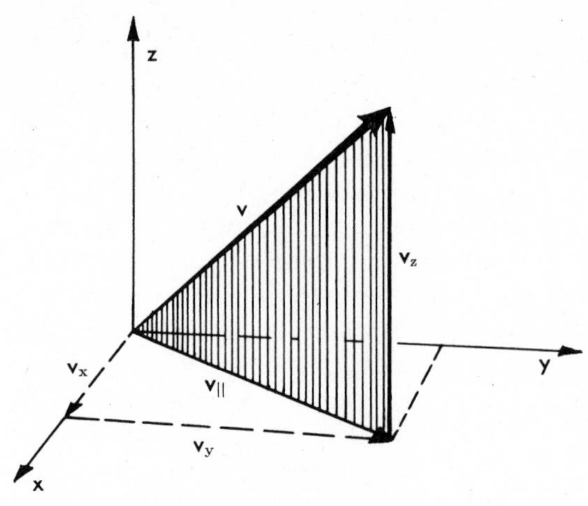

26–2. By the Pythagorean theorem, in the shaded right triangle $v^2 = v_{||}^2 + v_z^2$. And $v_{||}^2 = v_x^2 + v_y^2$ by using the same theorem on the right triangle with sides v_x, v_y, and $v_{||}$. Therefore, $v^2 = v_x^2 + v_y^2 + v_z^2$.

$$\overline{v^2} = \overline{v_x^2} + \overline{v_y^2} + \overline{v_z^2} = \overline{3v_z^2}.$$

And since $v_\perp = v_z$,

$$\overline{v^2} = \overline{3v_\perp^2} \quad \text{or} \quad \overline{v_\perp^2} = \tfrac{1}{3}\overline{v^2}$$

This factor $\frac{1}{3}$ between $\overline{v_\perp^2}$ and v^2 accounts for the difference between the pressure of a stream of molecules hitting a wall head-on and the pressure of molecules hitting a wall from all directions. Since the molecules in a gas move in all directions, the gas pressure is $P = \frac{1}{3}mv^2 \frac{N}{V}$.

ent masses. Here, however, the last equation tells us what to do. It says that on a long enough average each molecule contributes to the pressure in proportion to its kinetic energy. The same equation will therefore tell us the pressure if we interpret E_K as the kinetic energy per molecule *averaged* over all the molecules. The average times the number is the same as adding together the contributions of the individual molecules.

We should be careful to say that the kinetic energy involved is the kinetic energy associated with motions of the centers of mass of the molecules. It is not the kinetic energy of the motion of the parts of the molecule vibrating or rotating about the center of mass. We can see that only the kinetic energy of center of mass motion is in question by remembering that the mv^2 arises from the momentum mv of each molecule times the speed v bringing the molecules to the wall. It is the velocity of the molecules toward the wall that determines how many get to the wall per second and how big an impulse each gives the wall. This is the center of mass motion, and the gas pressure therefore depends on the average kinetic energy in this motion.

26–2. Temperature and Molecular Kinetic Energy; Thermal Energy

In Chapter 9 we learned that all gases at low enough density behave just alike. The predictions of the molecular model of gases fit this common behavior. Boyle's law

$$P = \theta \frac{N}{V}$$

relates the pressure P to the number N of molecules per unit volume N/V of any gas at a particular temperature. Experimentally the proportionality factor θ depends only on temperature, not on the nature of the gas.

The molecular model, as we found in the last section, predicts that

$$P = (\tfrac{2}{3}E_{\mathrm{K}}) \frac{N}{V},$$

where $E_{\mathrm{K}} = mv^2/2$ is the average kinetic energy of the center of mass motion of a molecule in the gas. This is exactly the same as Boyle's law, but it goes further. It tells us that the proportionality factor θ is $\frac{2}{3}$ of the average kinetic energy of a gas molecule:

$$\theta = \tfrac{2}{3}E_{\mathrm{K}}.$$

Because θ is the same for all gases at the same temperature, we learn that the average kinetic energy is the same no matter what the mass of the molecule.

As we change the temperature from melting ice to boiling water or to any other value, all low-density gases still behave alike. At constant pressure they expand in the same proportion (or at constant volume the pressure rises in the same proportion for all of them). In Section 9–4, this identical behavior of PV/N for all gases as the temperature rises led us to select gases to define the basic temperature scale. We used

$$\frac{PV}{N} = \theta = kT$$

to define the absolute temperature scale. We adjusted the proportionality factor k, so that the value of the temperature of melting ice is 273° Kelvin. (Then there are 100 degrees between the temperature of melting ice and the temperature of boiling water as in all common scientific thermometers.)

Now we can make our most important conclusion. We know that the proportionality factor θ in Boyle's law measures the temperature; and we know that θ is $\frac{2}{3}$ of the average kinetic energy of a molecule. Consequently (as we anticipated in Chapter 9 and in Section 26–1), the temperature is a measure of the thermal kinetic energy — a measure of energy of the random molecular motions.

Just how much energy is there on the average in the center of mass motion of one molecule at a particular temperature? From

$$\frac{PV}{N} = \theta = kT$$

we can calculate k. (For example, you can use atmospheric pressure 1.01×10^5 newtons/m²; a mole of any gas, that is 6.025×10^{23} molecules; and 22.4 liters $= 2.24 \times 10^{-2}$m³, which is the volume that a mole occupies at 273°K and this pressure.) The result is

$$k = \frac{\left(1.01 \times 10^5 \,\frac{\text{newtons}}{\text{m}^2}\right)(2.24 \times 10^{-2}\text{m}^3)}{(6.025 \times 10^{23}\text{ molecules})(273°\text{K})} = 1.37 \times 10^{-23} \,\frac{\text{joule}}{\text{molecule} - °\text{K}}.$$

This gives us the numerical relation between the temperature and the average molecular kinetic energy. Since

$$\tfrac{2}{3}E_{\mathrm{K}} = \theta = kT,$$

we find that the average kinetic energy of a molecule is $\frac{3}{2}kT$. Putting in the value of k we get

$$E_K = \frac{3}{2}(1.37 \times 10^{-23})\, T = 2.05 \times 10^{-23} T,$$

where E_K is measured in joules per molecule and T is measured in °K. At room temperature, for example, a molecule has about 6×10^{-21} joules of kinetic energy on the average in its center-of-mass motion.

The temperature is a measure of the average kinetic energy of an individual molecule, the kinetic energy of its center-of-mass motion. In any gas the molecules have this energy, and perhaps other forms of energy in addition. So one mole of any gas should have

$$6.025 \times 10^{23} \times 2.05 \times 10^{-23} = 12.4$$

joules of energy in this form for each Kelvin degree of temperature.

We can put energy into a gas in many ways — beating it with an egg beater, rubbing the container, letting heat flow into it are a few of the possibilities. (Here we do not mean throwing a bottle full of gas across the room — that gives energy to moving the whole bulk, while we are now interested in feeding the energy into the inside of the gas without moving the whole works.) When we feed energy into some gases, it all appears to go into the energy of the motions of the centers of mass of the molecules. If we feed 12.4 joules into a mole of helium or any other noble gas the temperature rises by 1°K. We can put in the energy in many ways; all give the same result. The energy we put in is completely accounted for by the increased motion of the centers of mass of the molecules.

The molecules of the noble gases are especially simple. They are single atoms (He, A, Ne, etc). More complicated molecules — like O_2, N_2, CH_4 which are made of two or more atoms — do not behave the same way. To raise their temperature one degree Kelvin may require more than 12.4 joules per mole. Raising their temperature takes more energy because the atoms in a complicated molecule vibrate and rotate around the center of mass (Fig. 26–3). And when we feed in energy, only part of it ends up increasing the energy of center-of-mass motion; the rest goes to increase the energy of rotation and vibration. Since the temperature measures only the part of the energy in the center-of-mass motion, more energy must be fed into the gas to produce a given rise in the temperature.

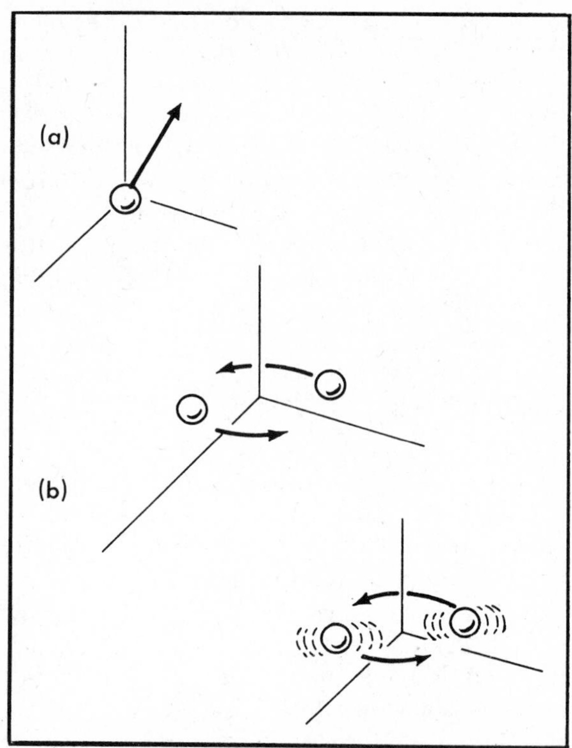

26–3. All the energy fed into a gas of monatomic molecules goes into center-of-mass motion of the molecules, as indicated in (a). Complex molecules, like those in (b), can also rotate and vibrate. Therefore, part of the incoming energy goes into rotation and vibration, and not all of it raises the temperature.

The energy of the motions of the centers of mass of the molecules and the energy of rotation and vibration of the atoms in a molecule are often called thermal energy. Actually not all thermal energy is necessarily kinetic energy; it may include the mutual potential energy of the atoms as they change their separations inside the molecules. Briefly, thermal energy is any energy that is fed into a sample when we raise its temperature and comes out when the temperature falls.

When thermal energy is fed into a gas, some of it may go into internal potential energy — inside the molecules. When the molecules are closer together, as in a liquid or solid, they continually exert appreciable forces on each other. Then, in addition to their kinetic energy, there is an average mutual potential energy of the interactions between the molecules; and when we feed energy in from the outside some of it goes into changing the average potential energy of the interacting molecules. The thermal energy then includes potential energy of molecular interaction.

The distinction between temperature and thermal energy (or heat) should now be clear. The temperature measures only the average energy of the center-of-mass motion. It gives the center-of-mass energy per molecule. The thermal energy also includes the energy in all the other internal motions and even the potential energy which changes when the molecules move farther apart or closer together with changing temperature. The thermal energy per molecule can therefore be different in two samples even though the temperature is the same. For example, while water is boiling, its temperature stays constant, but we must supply a large amount of energy to pull the molecules apart. When water vapor condenses, the molecules cluster together without appreciable change in kinetic energy, but a large amount of "latent heat" is released and must be taken away while the average separation of the molecules and the average intermolecular potential energy decrease. The latent heat is usually classed as thermal energy; it is not the energy of center-of-mass motion of the molecules, as we see, because the temperature stays the same.

26–3. Mechanical Energy of Bulk Motion and Internal Energy

When bodies isolated from the rest of the world interact with each other, their total momentum does not change. Momentum, as we saw in Chapter 23, is conserved. Mechanical energy, however, is conserved only if there are no dissipative forces such as friction. When there are frictional forces that depend on something besides the separations of the visible masses, the visible mechanical energy decreases, as in the example of a book sliding on a table. Is the law of conservation of energy really limited, unlike the law of conservation of momentum, or has the energy only changed form or location, so that its presence is no longer obvious?

Consider for a moment a closed box with two balls of equal mass m moving back and forth inside. Suppose that one ball goes north at speed v when the other goes south at the same speed, and they pass each other at the midpoint. The system has no total momentum at any time, and from outside we see no motion. No kinetic energy is apparent unless we can look inside.

Now think of this whole system of box and balls moving north past us at speed V while the balls move back and forth inside with speed v relative to the box. The apparent kinetic energy $\frac{1}{2}MV^2$ is only a part of the total kinetic energy. The total kinetic energy E_K is made up of the kinetic energy of the box M_b moving at speed V, plus the kinetic energy of the balls. If the box were transparent, you would see one ball m moving at speed $V + v$ and the other going at speed $V - v$. The total kinetic energy E_K is therefore

$$E_K = \tfrac{1}{2}M_bV^2 + \tfrac{1}{2}m(V+v)^2 + \tfrac{1}{2}m(V-v)^2 \\ = \tfrac{1}{2}MV^2 + 2(\tfrac{1}{2}mv^2),$$

where the total mass is $M = M_b + 2m$. As the last term on the right shows, in addition to the kinetic energy $\frac{1}{2}MV^2$ of bulk motion, the total energy may contain any amount of energy of internal motion. That energy cannot normally be seen from outside.

On the other hand, the apparent momentum of the bulk motion *is* the total momentum. By adding the momentum of each mass, we get

$$M_bV + m(V+v) + m(V-v) \\ = (M_b + 2m)\,V = MV,$$

which is exactly the momentum of the total mass in its visible motion.

This simple example illustrates a very common situation. Energy is often locked up in forms that do not appear as the kinetic energy of the motion of visible bulk masses, while momentum is less frequently hidden from our view. Consider, for example, the experiment of Section 23–6, in which a projectile is fired into a bag of sand. When the bullet buries itself in the bag, the bag moves off with the total momentum. If the bullet of mass m moved with speed v, the bag of mass M now moves with speed V such that $(M+m)V = mv$, and

$$V = \frac{mv}{M+m}.$$

Before the bullet strikes the bag, the kinetic energy is $E_K = \frac{1}{2}mv^2$, while afterwards the kinetic energy of the visible bulk motion is only

$$E_K' = \tfrac{1}{2}(M+m)V^2.$$

This is far less than the original kinetic energy, as we find by substituting $V = \dfrac{mv}{M+m}$ in the expression for E_K'. The result is

$$E_K' = \left(\frac{m}{M+m}\right) E_K.$$

The final kinetic energy E_K' is down by the factor $\frac{m}{M+m}$ from the original kinetic energy E_K. The fraction $\frac{M}{M+m}$ of the original energy has disappeared from view. For example, if a 5-kg projectile is fired into a 50-kg sandbag (and stays in the bag!), 50/55 or 91 per cent of its original kinetic energy becomes invisible.

What has happened to this energy? We think that when the bullet knocks into the sand, it sets the molecules in the sand and in itself into more rapid motion, with accompanying changes of potential energies. It has thus transferred a great deal of its kinetic energy into the energy of the random motions of the atoms and molecules in its surface and along its path through the sand. Because these internal motions of the atoms inside the bag are little motions that go in all directions, we do not see them; and we lose track of this part of the energy while seeing only the small amount of energy that goes into the bulk motion of the bag.

We would like to believe that no energy has really been lost; but if we can see only a very small part of the total energy, how can we know that all the energy is still around? We must find a way to measure the energy that has gone into internal motions or changes of atomic separations. In principle perhaps we could look at the position and motion of every microscopic or submicroscopic particle of matter; but in practical life we need some way of evaluating the energy stored in large chunks of matter without resorting to microscopic examination.

Here we are at the threshold of a great extension of the idea of conservation of energy. What we need is a measure of internal energy changes that depends on a few common measurements like temperature and volume. This will allow us to extend the conservation of energy to a whole new domain. With such a measure we can evaluate energy changes without seeing the actual position and motion of every microscopic particle of the object with which we deal.

We already have clues to the evaluation of the energy stored in internal motions and positions. When the bullet stops in the sand, they both heat up. When a car is stopped suddenly, its apparent kinetic energy is lost; but the brakes heat up. When a meteor is slowed down in the earth's atmosphere, it gets so hot that it usually vaporizes completely. Where energy disappears from the visible motions and from the potential energy of the separation of visible bodies, we frequently notice a rise in temperature.

The temperature of a gas is a measure of the average mv^2 of its molecules. At least in the case of simple gases, the number of molecules affected times the change in temperature measures the energy which is fed into or out of the random thermal motions. For other substances (for which we do not have such a simple model), the energy fed in may also go into changing internal potential energy, increasing the separations of atoms, for instance, as well as into the random mv^2's of the thermal dance. Nevertheless, as long as we keep the bulk volume of any substance the same, we might expect that the increase of internal energy would be reflected in a temperature change. Heat, we may guess, is a form of energy; and a hotter body contains more internal motion than a colder one.

Now we can look back on the history of the idea that heat is energy. It had early been recognized that heat phenomena might be explained in mechanical terms. Bacon, Galileo, Boyle, Hooke, Newton, and others conceived that the temperature of a body might be related to the "degree of motion" of the particles of which it was made. Boyle gave an illustration in the motion of a nail driven into a board. When the head prevents further motion of the nail, repeated blows of the hammer then serve to heat the nail: the motion of the hammer can no longer be imparted to the nail as a whole, Boyle said, and so is transferred to the "corpuscles" in the nail, making them move more quickly, and so producing a hot nail.

There are many claimants to the full proof that heat is energy. Count Rumford heated cannon by boring them, using mechanical energy supplied by horses. The energy became heat. Soon afterwards, the use of steam engines made it clear that heat could also be turned into mechanical energy. The idea that heat *is* energy was clearly formulated by the German physicist Julius Robert Mayer (1814–1878) and the British physicist James Prescott Joule (1818–1898).* By the time of Mayer

*Mayer was a physician whose interest in animal heat led him to the study of heat in general. Joule, the owner of a successful brewery, was a pupil of Dalton. Joule made many distinguished contributions to science, especially in the fields of electricity and heat.

and Joule, there were available many processes of *energy conversion:* heat to mechanical energy, electricity to heat, electricity to mechanical energy, etc. Joule made measurements of *many* such conversions. In each experiment, he expressed his results in terms of *heat*, measured by warming up some water, and *mechanical energy*, measured by raising a load against gravity. He used the constancy of the conversion factor between those two measures to show that heat is a form of energy. This is our next job.

26–4. The Equivalence of Mechanical and Thermal Energy

We have just asserted that when gross mechanical energy is lost it often turns up as thermal energy — the energy of random molecular motion. But such an assertion must be backed by more than the qualitative observation that heat is found when mechanical energy is lost.

The British physicist Joule showed that the same amount of heating occurs — the same thermal energy appears — whenever a given amount of mechanical energy is lost. Suppose that water is placed in an insulated container, for example in a large vacuum bottle. In the water there is a paddle wheel which can be turned by a falling mass m as shown in Fig. 26–4. When the bearings of the paddle wheel are well lubricated, the work done by the gravitational forces on the mass m measures the energy transferred from gravitational potential energy of m and used to churn up the water. When the mass is stopped, the paddle wheels stop, and the water quiets down. Finally it is at rest; but we find that the temperature of the water has increased. From beginning to end only two things have changed. The mass has fallen slowly through the distance h, so that mgh gravitational energy has disappeared, and the water has become hotter.

If mechanical energy and "heat" are equivalent, we shall always obtain the *same* temperature rise

26–4. The apparatus for a Joule experiment, to observe the conversion of mechanical energy into heat. As the masses go down, the paddle wheels turn, churning up the water. When the masses have fallen the distance h, gravitational potential energy mgh has disappeared and the water has been heated. (m = the total mass that goes down.) Note that the masses go down without attaining much speed, and their kinetic energy is small.

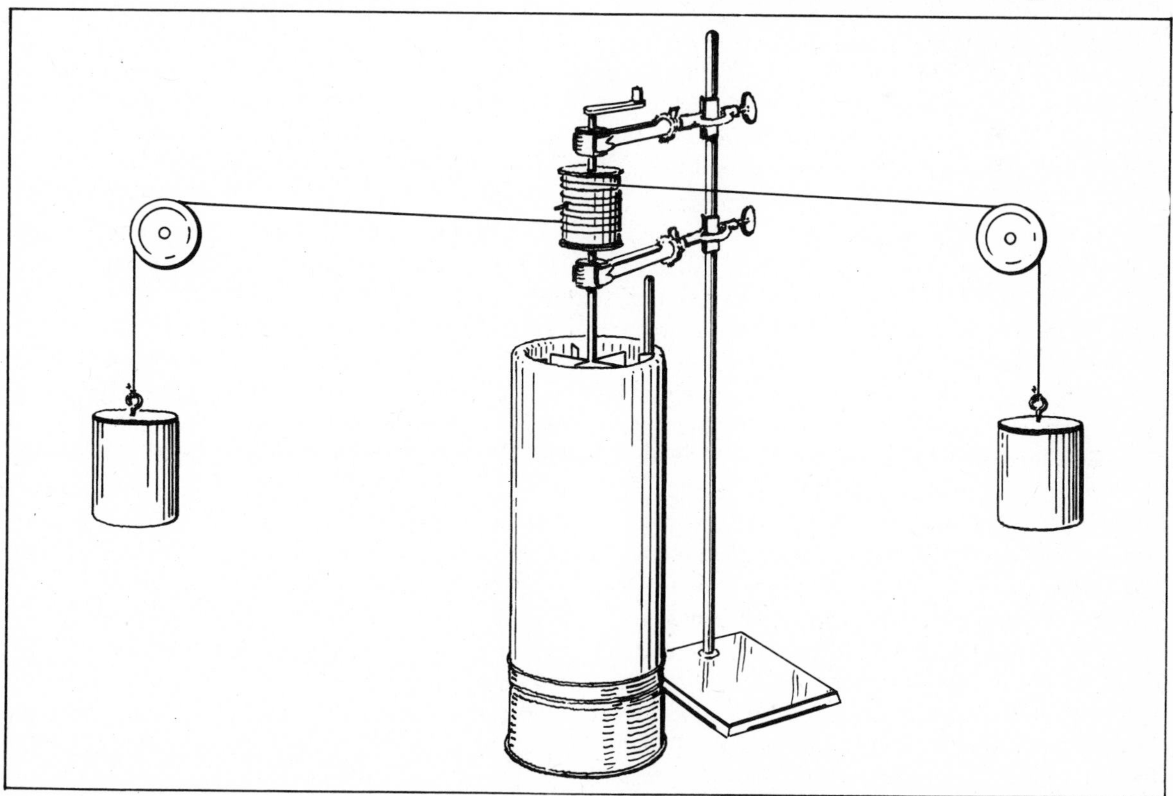

when a *given* amount of work is done in heating a given amount of water. In fact, a lot of different experiments have been done. They show that the temperature rise depends only on the energy transferred and not on the force or distance or the design of the paddle wheels. For example, if we double the mass of the falling body and allow it to fall only half the original vertical distance, the work done by the gravitational forces is the same as before. And we find that the temperature rise of the water is exactly the same, even though the process has been carried out considerably faster.

26–5. Heat Flow

The dissipation of mechanical energy through frictional forces is not the only method of increasing the temperature of an object. You can warm your hands either by rubbing them together or by dipping them into hot water. When they are in hot water, there is a transfer of energy from the more lively random molecular motions of the hot water to the more sluggish random molecular motions of your cold skin. When such a transfer of thermal energy from a hotter to a colder body occurs, we say that heat *flows* from the first to the second body.

We can trace a given amount of energy from gross mechanical energy into internal thermal energy of a given sample through either of two routes. The energy may be converted from mechanical to thermal energy in the sample or it may be converted to thermal energy elsewhere and reach the sample by heat flow. By experiment we can show that the method of transfer does not matter. The same amount of thermal energy winds up in the sample either way.

Suppose that we have two containers, one containing a certain amount of water, as in the Joule experiment, and the other a different amount of another liquid, such as oil. We perform the Joule experiment described in the last section separately on each liquid; and we find that it takes x joules of work to raise the temperature of the water one degree and that it takes y joules of work to raise the temperature of the oil one degree. Now we start again with the water and oil at their original common temperature. We churn the water alone until we have dissipated $(x + y)$ joules of mechanical work. The temperature of the water rises more than one degree. Then we place the container of oil in contact with the container holding the water. We keep the whole system insulated. The temperature of the oil rises and that of the water drops. Finally equilibrium is reached: the temperature of both liquids becomes the same and remains constant. We measure the final temperature of the water and oil, and we find that each is one degree higher than it was at the start.

We conclude the following: of the $(x + y)$ joules of work done on the water, y joules have been transferred to the oil by *heat flow*. We make this conclusion because we know that exactly y joules of work are necessary to produce a temperature rise of one degree in the oil. The remaining x joules have produced the one-degree temperature rise of the water. Thus we have shown that the work necessary to produce a definite temperature rise in a given liquid is the same whether the energy is transferred to the liquid by heat flow or whether the mechanical energy is dissipated directly in the liquid.

26–6. Quantitative Relation of Energy Dissipation and Temperature Rise

Let us be specific about the energy that must be dissipated to raise the temperature of a gram of water by 1°C. If we dissipate mechanical energy, we find that we must transfer 4.2 joules. Alternatively, we can put the energy in by heat flow from hot oil. We can calibrate the hot oil by a Joule experiment. Then we find that the oil must lose 4.2 joules by heat flow to warm the water. Whichever way they are received, 4.2 joules of energy will raise the temperature of the water just the same amount.

We can combine the two ways of heating up a mass of material. Suppose we have a gram of water surrounded by a bath of hot oil, all insulated from the rest of the world, and with a little insulating shaft leading to paddles in the water. Now we dissipate 1 joule of mechanical energy in the gram of water by whirling the paddles; we also allow 3.2 joules to flow into the water from the oil as indicated by the fall in temperature of the surrounding oil bath. We then find that the total transfer into increased internal energy of the gram of water is 4.2 joules. This is indicated by a 1°C rise in temperature, the same rise in temperature that occurs if we let 4.2 joules flow into a gram of water purely by heat flow or dissipate it by mechanical means alone. In general, the transfer into internal energy is given by

$$\Delta W + \Delta Q,$$

the sum of the transfer ΔW by mechanical energy dissipation and the transfer ΔQ by heat flow. This total transfer has the same effect no matter what fraction of it is ΔW and what fraction is ΔQ.

We can dissipate energy in water in innumerable ways — even dropping stones into it will do. The result is always the same. Whenever 4.2 joules are dissipated in a gram of water, its temperature rises 1°C. To raise the temperature of 2 grams takes just twice the energy. Similarly, whenever 12.4 joules are dissipated in a mole of helium (4 grams), its temperature rises 1°C. The rise in temperature is different for different substances as the examples show, but in any one substance, we always get the same results over the same temperature range.

Precise measurements show that 4.185 joules are necessary to raise the temperature of 1 gram of water 1° from 14.5°C to 15.5°C. This amount of energy is called a calorie.* The calorie is just another unit of energy. We could measure the kinetic energy of the bulk motion of an object in calories just as well as in joules; for instance, a 3-kg mass moving 2 m/sec has $\frac{1}{2}(3)(2)^2 = 6$ joules or $\frac{6}{4.185} \approx 1.45$ calories of kinetic energy; however, the joule connects directly with our units of force and distance so that the joule is usually more convenient. We shall stick to joules. One unit is enough.

26–7. Conservation of Energy

When gross mechanical energy is changed into heat, the same number of joules of mechanical energy gives the same heating. If we put the heat into a standard amount of water, for instance, we always get the same temperature rise. But Joule experiments and heat-flow experiments fail to answer all the questions we can ask about heat and mechanical energy. Can we turn heat into mechanical energy at the same rate of exchange at which the mechanical energy turns into heat? Can we get 4.2 joules of gross mechanical energy from the heat that comes out of a gram of water when its temperature falls 1°C? Our earlier experiments suggest that we should get 4.2 joules, but we need direct evidence. Lots of things — even door latches — act one way when going in one direction and differently when reversed.

The simple way to check up on the change *from* heat *to* mechanical energy would be to pour a known amount of heat ΔQ into a heat engine and measure the work ΔW the engine does. We must be sure, however, to leave the heat engine at the end with the same energy it had at the beginning; otherwise we must know how much extra energy the engine has retained or how much it has given us from its original stock.

The usual way to make sure that the engine is not contributing energy is to get the engine back at the end into exactly the same condition it was in at the beginning. We then find, however, that the engine does not simply take in the heat ΔQ and produce work. It takes in the heat ΔQ, produces some work, *and* pours out some heat. (It is to get rid of that rejected heat which must be poured out that cars and all other heat engines have radiators.) If we wish to see whether thermal energy can be turned into gross mechanical energy joule for joule, we must use the net flow of heat — that going in minus that coming out — to compare with the work. Consequently, we must measure all the heat taken in and all the heat coming out by observing the temperature changes of the surroundings. Then we can compare the *net* flow of heat into the engine with the *net* work measured by forces times distances. Such experiments have been carried out. The Frenchman Hirn even chased all the heat and all the work in and out of the steam engine of a textile mill. The result is that the heat does turn into mechanical work at par. When we can change 4.2 joules of heat into mechanical energy, we get 4.2 joules of mechanical energy.

Although the energy equivalence of heat and mechanical energy is complete — the same when the transfer is in either direction — there is an

*Units like the calorie came into use for measuring heat even before heat was agreed to be a form of energy. They are used because it is so easy to estimate a quantity of heat by giving it to a known mass of water and measuring the temperature rise. Note that there is a larger unit, the "kilocalorie" or Calorie with a capital C, which is 1000 times as big as the small-c calorie. The Calorie is the unit commonly used today in specifying energy yields from food.

essential difference between transfers in the two directions. We can easily change *all* of a supply of gross mechanical energy into heat; but we can normally change only a fraction of the heat available into gross mechanical energy. We pour the heat into an engine at a high temperature; some of it must be poured out again at a lower temperature; and the remainder turns into mechanical energy at full value. The fact that whatever energy is changed in form is converted at full value is a version of the first law of thermodynamics. The question of how large a fraction can be converted is the subject of the second law of thermodynamics.

We now believe that heat and mechanical energy are just two different forms of energy, and no energy is lost or gained in turning one into the other. Energy, like momentum, is conserved; but to see that it does not change amount we have had to find measures of heat and keep track of the amount that is locked up in internal energies as well as the energy of bulk motions and raised weights. No single experiment leads all by itself to our conviction that energy is conserved. But we assume conservation in thinking about all kinds of physical and chemical processes. Innumerable such processes go on daily: chemicals react, heat is released, engines run. And energy bookkeeping balances out time after time. If any substantial amount of energy were disappearing, we should have felt the loss long since. If there were mysterious sources from which energy entered, the gain should have become apparent. It is on this overall check of conservation as well as on innumerable detailed checks of all sorts of transformations that our belief in energy conservation really rests.

By adding heat flow to mechanical work, we have extended the conservation of energy beyond simple mechanical systems. The extension was made by including a new transfer mechanism. Heat flow was the first new mechanism to be added to work, but we have since discovered that other mechanisms have to be included. For example, the energy reaching us from the sun does not arrive here either through mechanical work or through the kind of heat flow that occurs between a hot and a cold body in contact. Radiation — visible and invisible light — carries the energy. If we want the conservation of energy to span our universe, we must take account of this energy of radiation in the same way that we had to include the momentum of radiation to explain the behavior of bodies which emit or absorb light.

Experiment and theory combine to assure us that energy is indeed conserved when radiation is included. But, whereas the transfer of thermal energy by ordinary heat flow can be viewed as a microscopic version of the transfer of energy through work, the transfer through radiation is different. We cannot be satisfied that we understand that mechanism until we have studied radiation. Here we shall not try to go through the details. Even without studying the mechanism, however, we can extend the conservation of energy to include radiation by performing experiments like those with which we extended the conservation of energy to include heat flow. We can use a measured amount of energy to run a light for a while and absorb the emitted radiation on a black surface. The surface gets hot and we can measure the energy which goes into heating the black surface and the energy left as heat in the source of light. We find the sum is equal to the energy we fed in. Part of the energy has gone from the light source to the absorber. And it has gone without loss or gain.

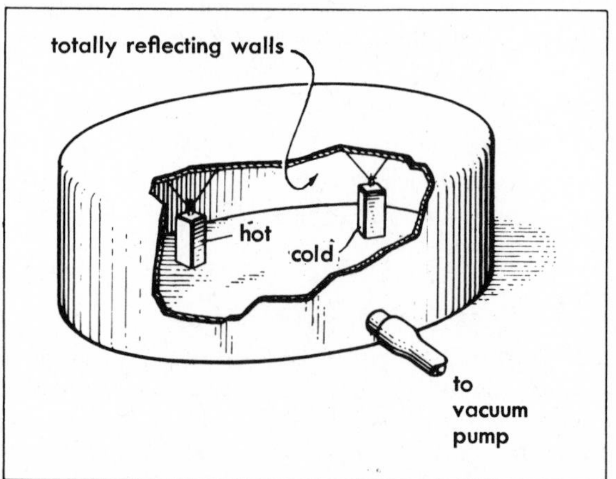

26–5. A hot object and a cold object are placed in a container with reflecting walls. There is a good vacuum in the container, so that energy is not transferred by the air molecules. Even so, the warm body cools off and the cold body warms up as energy is transferred by radiation.

The radiation need not be visible. For example, we can put a hot body and a cold body inside of a very good reflector of radiation (Fig. 26–5). We make such a good vacuum inside the reflector that ordinary heat flow cannot take place. Nevertheless, the hot body loses energy and the cold one gains energy. The energy flows from one to the other as radiation. We find the total energy is conserved.

Like the transfer of momentum the transfer of energy by radiation takes time. The light from the sun transfers its energy and momentum to us here 8.3 minutes after it leaves the sun. As far as we know, nothing ever moves faster. Energy transfer by other mechanisms is slower, but usually the distances are so short that we may fail to detect the time lag.

For many ordinary mechanical systems — such as billiard balls colliding or the earth going around the sun or even the operation of a steam engine — the part played by radiation in energy transfer is so small that we can usually ignore it. But radiation must be considered not only when we look into the energy transfer from stars but also whenever we consider atoms emitting or absorbing light.

All physical happenings, from the evolution of a star to the life of a firefly, are in essence transformations of energy from one form to the other. Even on a cosmic scale, we can trace its flow. Physicists have now learned about the nuclear energy that supplies the radiant energy of the stars. Our physical knowledge is consistent with a universal conservation of energy. To the best of our knowledge, the total energy in a region changes only when an exchange of energy occurs between the region and its surroundings. Then, if our region is the whole universe, we can expect no change of the total energy — because, by definition, there is nothing outside the universe. This assumption, that the total energy of the universe is constant, is the basis of most cosmological theories. But that is a daring generalization from our limited experience. We live in a small corner of the universe, and we have tested the validity of our physical laws over a very limited period of time. It is conceivable that these laws, including the law of conservation of energy, are not rigorously correct. In our limited view, energy *is* conserved with great precision; but a tiny rate of destruction or creation may have escaped our notice — if, for example, the total energy of the universe had doubled in the course of several billion years, we probably should not be aware of this change. Indeed, some cosmological theories assume a continuous creation of energy.

Here is one of the live scientific questions of today. Cosmologists are working hard to find out whether energy *is* completely conserved over the whole universe. And just now, for the first time, there is a possibility of actual experiments to decide between the rival theories.

FOR HOME, DESK, AND LAB

1. A machine gun fires a stream of 10-gram bullets at the rate of 400 rounds per minute. The bullets, moving at velocity 300 m/sec, hit a wall of solid rock and stop dead. Calculate:

(a) the force on the wall.

(b) the kinetic energy of the bullets arriving at the wall in one minute.

(c) the kinetic energy of the bullets in 1 meter length of the stream as they approach the wall. Compare twice this answer with your answer to (a).

2. Suppose there is a tiny sticky area on the wall of a container of gas. Molecules hitting this area stick there permanently.

(a) Is the pressure there greater or less than on the ordinary areas of the wall?

(b) If the sticky region is cut out, leaving a hole, what is the pressure on the hole?

Be prepared to discuss your answers in class.

3. In a certain gas $\frac{2}{5}$ of the energy of the molecules is tied up in motion of the atoms around each other and $\frac{3}{5}$ in motion of the centers of mass.

(a) On the average, what is the kinetic energy of the center of mass motion of one such molecule when the temperature is 300°K?

(b) If the temperature is raised 1°C, what energy must be supplied to a mole (0.6025×10^{24} molecules) of the gas?

4. A gas in a cylinder pushes a piston out, increasing its volume by ΔV. The gas exerts a pressure P

on the face of the piston, which has an area A. The force exerted by the gas moves the piston a distance Δx, transferring energy $F\Delta x$ to some outside machinery. Show that the work $F\Delta x$ is equal to $P\Delta V$.

Note: This is a very useful expression for work whenever we deal with a gas or a liquid pushing a piston: work equals the pressure times the change in volume.

5. One mole of an ideal monatomic gas (in practice, helium or argon) is placed in a cylinder at temperature 273°K. The gas is at atmospheric pressure, 1.02×10^5 newtons/m². At this pressure and temperature the gas occupies 2.24×10^{-2} m³.

A piston in the cylinder is then pushed in to decrease the volume by 2.45×10^{-4} m³.

(a) How much mechanical work must be done to push the piston in? (Neglect the change in pressure.)

(b) What is the final temperature of the gas if the container is completely insulated? (Remember 12.4 joules of energy raise its temperature one degree.)

6. In Problem 5, by what fraction of its original value does the pressure change?

7. Suppose we take 18 grams of water (one mole) at boiling point and turn it into vapor in a cylinder. The cylinder is closed by a frictionless piston, which is so light that the gas remains at atmospheric pressure at all times.

(a) What volume will the water vapor occupy if it behaves as an ideal gas? (Water vapor is not an ideal gas, but the error due to the assumption will be less than 10 percent.)

(b) What work must be done in pushing the piston out against atmospheric pressure as the whole of the water vaporizes?

(c) Given that each gram of water takes 540 calories to tear its molecules apart into vapor, how much heat is needed to convert the water to vapor *and* push the piston out?

(d) What fraction of the total heat needed is converted to work in pushing the piston out?

8. (a) Estimate the speed of oxygen molecules at room temperature from the following data: 32 grams of oxygen at room temperature (20°C) at one atmosphere pressure, 1.02×10^5 newtons/m², occupy 2.4×10^{-2}m³.

(b) The same volume of hydrogen at the same temperature and pressure weighs only 2 grams. Estimate the average velocity of hydrogen molecules at room temperature.

(c) From your answer to (a), estimate the average velocity of nitrogen molecules at room temperature, *within 10 percent.*

(d) What is the average velocity of air molecules at room temperature correct within 10 percent?

(e) What is the velocity of oxygen molecules at room temperature and two atmospheres pressure?

9. A large bag of sand is hung from a tree by a long rope. A boy shoots a bullet into the sand bag and the bullet stays in the bag.

(a) Describe the energy changes.

(b) Suppose a 10-gram bullet is moving at 300 m/sec when it hits the bag, and the bag is a 1990-gram bag of sand. Calculate the amount of kinetic energy:

(i) the bullet had originally.

(ii) the bullet and bag have after collision.

(iii) that disappears.

(c) What fraction of the original kinetic energy of the bullet goes into heat?

10. A machine gun fires lead bullets at a wall and they stop dead. Describe the changes of energy from the stage when it is in the explosive to the stage when the bullets have been lying on the ground at the bottom of the wall for several hours.

11. In one of his most famous experiments, Joule churned water with a paddle wheel driven by two loads, each of mass 14 kg, each falling vertically about 2 meters. He had about 7 kg of water to be heated. After each churning he hauled his loads up and let them fall again. What temperature rise would you expect him to find after twenty falls?

Note: this is a reversal of the logic of Joule's great experiment. *You* know that 4.2 joules will always raise the temperature of a gram of water 1°C; Joule was trying to find this out.

12. * A project: (a) Make or obtain a small spring of steel wire. Stretch it and let it go many times. Hold it to your cheek to feel whether it grows warmer.

(b) Make a similar spring of soft copper wire and repeat the trial.

Note: If you overstretch the spring, just push it back into close coiling.

13. * A project: Swing a hammer fast and give several violent blows to a small block of lead on a firm anvil of stone or iron. Feel the lead before and after. Make rough estimates of the kinetic energy lost by the hammer and of the thermal energy gained by the lead. (Assume that 1 kg of lead needs about 130 joules to raise its temperature 1°C.)

14. * A project: (a) Obtain an electric egg beater and run it at full rate for 5 minutes in a measured mass of water. (If you put the water in an aluminum pan, you may allow for the heating of the pan also. 1000 grams of aluminum take as much heat as 200 grams of water. An ingenious way to avoid having a container that takes heat is to hold the water in a thin plastic bag like the ones used in a deep-freeze — but this makes a good deal of mess if the egg beater touches the bag.)

(b) Repeat the experiment for twice the time; and again with half or twice the mass of water.

In each case, estimate the heat delivered by the egg beater per minute.

15. * A project: Estimate the energy delivered in 5 minutes by a small electric light of known wattage.

(a) Do this experimentally by running the lamp in ink (why ink?). (You can use an automobile headlight bulb connected to a 6-volt battery. Do not use a bulb of higher voltage, because of danger of shock!)

(b) Do this by calculation from other knowledge: note that one kilowatt hour, which is likely to cost you 3 or 4 cents, is worth 3.6×10^6 joules.

16. A high-speed swimmer uses 120,000 joules of energy in a half-minute race. Three quarters of the energy is released as waste heat; the rest is dissipated by his hands and legs, by mechanical work.

(a) In 30 seconds he swims 50 meters. Estimate the average force opposing his motion.

(b) Describe the changes of form of energy in the swimming.

(c) Where and in what form is the energy that has been released when he has finished the race?

17. (a) With what velocity must a 2-kg block of ice at 0°C be thrown against a stone wall so that the entire mass of ice melts upon contact? (1 kg of ice takes 3.36×10^5 joules to melt.)

(b) What effect does changing the mass have on the velocity?

(c) What makes this problem unrealistic?

18. One mole of helium at 24°C is placed in contact with water at 26°C insulated from the rest of the world. The final temperature of both is measured to be 25°C. How much water was there?

19. A mountain climber can climb about 1500 feet or 500 meters vertical rise per hour.

(a) How much energy does such a climber gain as gravitational potential energy in a five-hour climb up a mountain?

(b) The human body is an inefficient chemical-mechanical machine. At best its muscles deliver only 25 percent of the chemical energy used as useful mechanical energy. The other 75 percent or more is dissipated as waste heat. Assuming this efficiency, how much chemical energy does the climber use in 5 hours?

(c) Assume that, aside from mountain climbing, he needs 2.2×10^6 small calories per 24 hours. How much total energy should he take in in his daily diet if he makes that climb every morning?

(d) If the climber walks down the mountain every afternoon, he loses the potential energy he gained. Why does that not help him to reduce his diet?

20. Suppose you have two large boxes of negligible mass. Box A contains one mole of hot helium at 60°C, the other box, B, contains one mole of cool argon (also a noble gas) at 10°C.

(a) The two boxes are placed side by side in contact with all their outer surfaces insulated. After some time, both gases are at the same temperature. What is the temperature and why?

(b) Instead of being placed side by side, the two boxes are joined together to make one large box, without change of volume, so that the gases mix. What will be the final temperature of the mixture?

(c) Now suppose that box B contains one mole of cold nitrogen at 10°C instead of the argon. The hot helium and cold nitrogen are allowed to mix as in (b) above. Will the final temperature be the same as in (b) or higher or lower?

(d) Give a clear reason for your answer to (c).

21. A new small airplane is to be tested. To maintain secrecy, the test is conducted in a large, closed hangar whose walls are completely insulated from the outside world. The airplane is filled up with 10 kg of gasoline, flies around and around the hangar for half an hour, and then lands with its gas tanks empty again.

(a) In what form was the energy that the airplane uses in flying supplied to it originally?

(b) Discuss the changes of energy during the flight.

(c) Where is the energy and in what form, half an hour after the flight?

22. A rocket is equipped with insulated containers full of very hot gas instead of combustible fuel. The hot gas rushing out of a nozzle drives the rocket forward.

(a) Where does the momentum that the rocket acquires come from?

(b) Where does the rocket's kinetic energy come from?

(c) If the gas is ejected into a box standing on the ground as the rocket starts out, and the temperature of the gas collected in the box is measured after the rocket has left, do you expect that temperature to be higher, lower, or the same as the original temperature of the store of gas in the rocket?

23. Imagine you have a light bulb in a perfectly reflecting box which is otherwise empty — a perfect vacuum.

(a) By running the light bulb do you produce

(i) kinetic energy of bulk motion?

(ii) potential energy of the bulk matter of the box?

(iii) thermal energy of internal atomic motion?
(iv) thermal energy in the form of intermolecular potential energy?
(v) internal energy in some form?
(vi) no additional energy in the box?
(b) By running a light bulb, do you produce
(i) momentum of bulk motion?
(iii) momentum of thermal motion of atoms?
(vi) no momentum in the box?
Be prepared to discuss your answer in class.

24. (a) A cylinder containing helium gas is closed with a movable piston which has negligible friction. A man pushes on the piston and drives it in quickly, compressing the helium. The helium heats up. Why does the helium heat up? Discuss the mechanism of the heating up in terms of molecular behavior.

(b) A cylinder with a movable piston contains compressed helium. The piston is released and the helium pushes it out and cools. Explain in terms of molecular behavior how the helium cools.

(c) A large box with a good vacuum in it contains a small bottle of compressed helium. A trigger is arranged to remove the stopper of the helium bottle. When the helium is let out of the bottle no change of temperature is observed after the release is all over. Explain, from the point of view of molecular behavior, why the helium does not change temperature when it expands into the big box.

(d) Although compressed helium shows no final change of temperature, some other gases show a noticeable cooling after they have expanded into vacuum from high compression. What does that tell you about these other compressed gases?

25. A rocket of mass 2×10^3 kg has been fired in an attempt to "escape" from the earth. However, when it is several thousand kilometers from the earth, its speed is only 30 m/sec, so it is evident that the rocket will fall back into the atmosphere. The control center on the surface therefore sends a radio impulse which fires off a small explosive charge (several kilograms) in the rocket. It explodes into two parts — one of them, with mass 0.5×10^3 kg, continues forward at 330 m/sec.

(a) Calculate the velocity of the other fragment.

(b) Calculate the kinetic energy of the original rocket, and of each piece after the separation.

(c) Why is there more kinetic energy afterwards than before?

26. * A project: Experiment with the radiation from a glowing electric heating element. Place a sheet of asbestos tile (or a piece of damp cardboard will serve temporarily) between the heater and you. Make a small hole about 1 in. in diameter to let radiation through to you. Hold the back of your hand near the hole and feel the effect of radiation on your skin. Then try the following changes:

(a) Place a sheet of cardboard between the hole and your hand, and remove it quickly.

(b) Place a sheet of window glass between the hole and your hand and remove it quickly.

(c) Cover your hand with aluminum leaf (most easily done by clenching your fist, licking the back of your hand to make it wet with saliva, and placing a sheet of very thin aluminum leaf gently on it). Try the metal-coated skin near the hole.

(d) Keep the aluminum leaf on your hand but paint a little black paint or India ink on top of it. Again try that near the hole.

27. * A project: Use the skin of the back of your hand or, better, your cheek to detect the radiation from a hot surface. For the source, use either a bright metal can of boiling water or, better, a bright sheet of copper which has just been made very hot with a gas flame. In each case, paint one side of the source black (a mixture of soot and alcohol serves well). Then make your estimate near each surface, bright and black, in turn.

FURTHER READING

DYSON, F. J., "What Is Heat?" *Scientific American*, September, 1954. A description of our modern ideas and a brief history of their development.

GAMOW, GEORGE, "The Evolutionary Universe." Also in *The Universe*, cited above.

HART, IVOR B., *James Watt and the History of Steam Power*. Henry Schuman Co., 1949.

HOLTON, GERALD, *Introduction to Concepts and Theories in Physical Science*. Addison-Wesley, 1952. Heat, molecular motion, and the conservation of energy are dealt with in Chapters 17, 18, and 20.

HOYLE, FRED, "The Steady-State Universe." *The Universe*, A Scientific American Book, Simon & Schuster, 1957.

PART IV

ELECTRICITY AND ATOMIC STRUCTURE

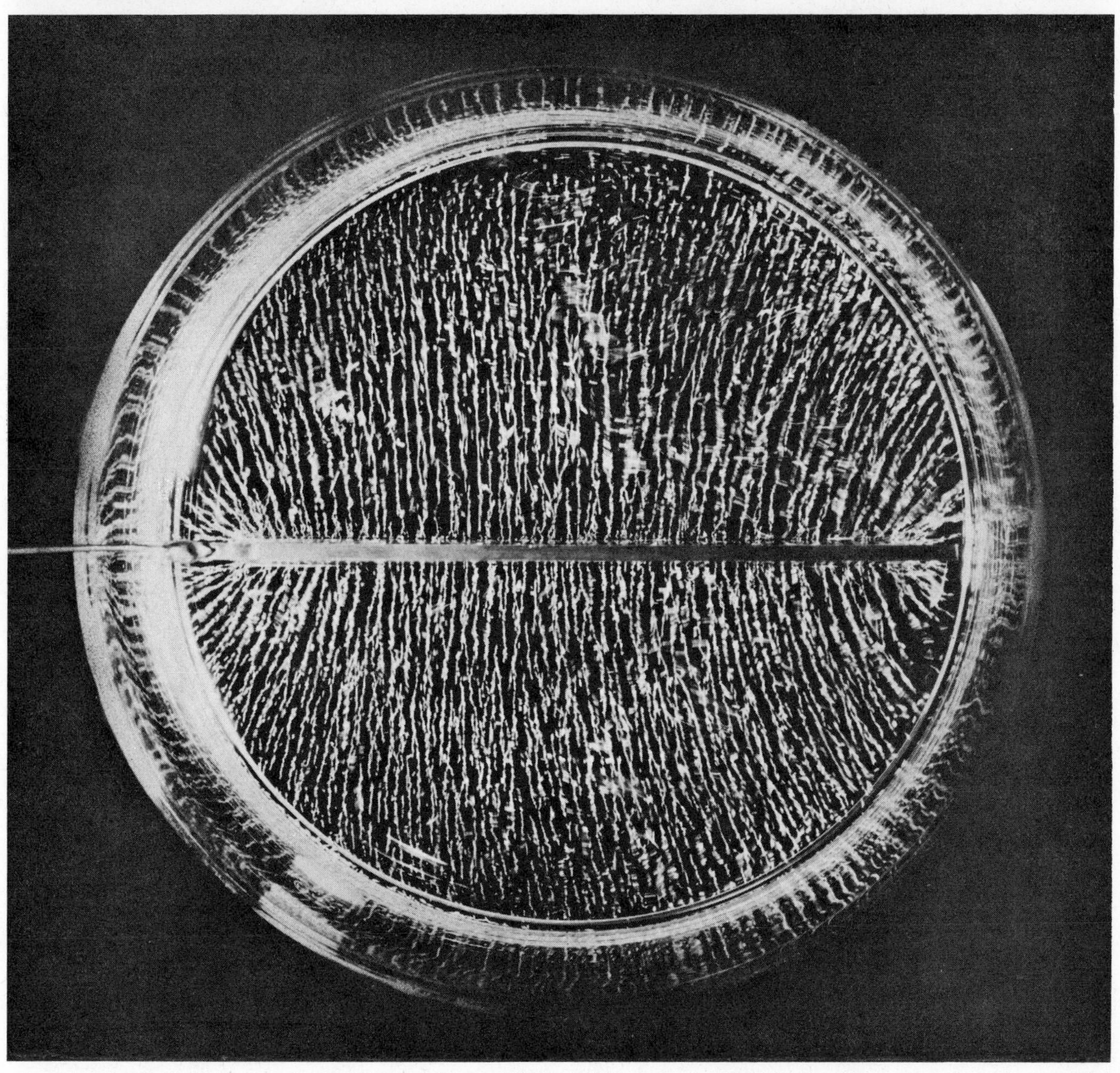

The electric field around a charged conducting plate outlined by grass seeds in an insulating liquid. The study of electric force fields will help us understand the nature of light and the forces that hold atoms together.

SOME QUALITATIVE FACTS ABOUT ELECTRICITY

CHAPTER 27

In Part III we learned that every material body attracts every other material body with a force known as the *gravitational force.* This gravitational attraction has practical consequences only when at least one of the interacting bodies has enormous mass, something like a whole planet. However, gravitational forces are not the only forces acting at a distance between material bodies. Sometimes other forces are enormously greater. A small magnet will lift a steel nail off the table against the gravitational attraction of the entire earth. A comb rubbed on your sleeve will lift bits of paper. These are examples of *magnetic* and *electric* forces, respectively.

The existence of such forces has been known since antiquity. The ancient Greeks were familiar with the peculiar properties of the lodestone, an iron ore (magnetite) which is a natural magnet. The word *magnet* comes from the name of the city of Magnesia in Asia Minor, near which this ore was found. Also, the Greek philosopher Thales is said to have observed the action of electric forces about twenty-five centuries ago. He found that when amber is rubbed, it attracts light objects. The word *electricity* comes from "elektron," the Greek word for amber.

It was only during the Renaissance, however, that a systematic study of electricity and magnetism developed, and physicists did not gain a clear understanding of these subjects until the end of the past century. Hardly ever has a scientific achievement had such profound and far-reaching consequences. There have been innumerable practical applications. The harnessing of electric power and the development of electrical communications have changed our whole way of life. On the scientific side, we have learned that electric forces control the structure of atoms and molecules. Electricity is associated with many biological processes — for instance, with the action of our nerves and brain.

27–1. Attraction and Repulsion Between Electrified Objects

We shall now examine some of the basic facts of electric and magnetic behavior and discuss their interpretation. Let us begin with a simple electrical experiment. Rub a glass rod with a piece of silk and then place it horizontally in a stirrup hung on a silk thread (Fig. 27–1). Then rub a second glass rod, and bring it near the first. The two rods *repel* each other.

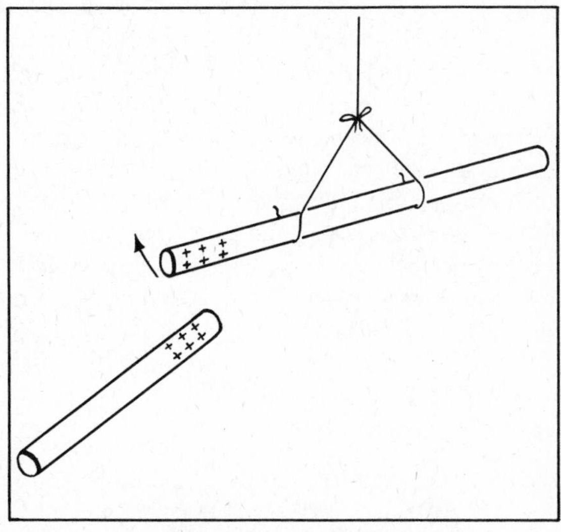

27–1. Two electrified glass rods repel each other.

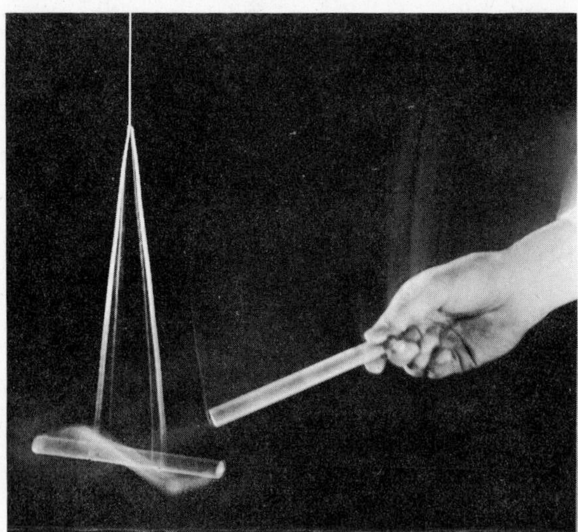

27–2. Two electrified plastic rods also repel each other when they are brought close together. This photograph is a time exposure, made while one rod was brought near the other. The repulsive force pushed away the near end of the suspended rod.

Repeat this experiment with two rods of plastic rubbed with a piece of fur. These two rods repel as the two glass rods did. (Fig. 27–2.)

Finally rub a glass rod with silk and a plastic rod with fur. Place one rod in the stirrup and bring the other near it. We now find that these rods *attract* each other.

We can perform similar experiments with a number of other materials. Objects of the same material which have been "electrified" by the same procedure always repel. Different electrified objects may either attract or repel.

We find that electrified objects fall into two groups. Only two "electric states" exist, one similar to that of the glass rod and one similar to that of the plastic rod of the previous example. Following the common usage, which dates back to Benjamin Franklin, we shall say that the glass rod and all other electrified objects which behave like it are *positively charged.* Similarly we shall say that the plastic rod and all other electrified objects which behave like it are *negatively charged** Any two positively charged objects repel each other, just as two electrified glass rods do. Similarly any two negatively charged objects repel each other. Any positively charged object attracts any negatively charged one.

*The words "positive" and "negative" are used because the forces exerted by neighboring positively and negatively charged objects on any third body tend to cancel.

27–2. Electric Forces Between the Building Blocks of Matter

We have learned that matter is made of atoms and that the atoms themselves may be made of smaller units. But so far in this book we have not faced the question of whether there are any ultimate building blocks from which all atoms are made. The study of electricity will give us some important information about this question.

To begin with, it is natural to think that the force between two bodies is the vector sum of the forces acting between their building blocks. Since two electrified objects attract or repel each other, we suppose that there are similar forces of attraction or repulsion between some of the parts of which the two objects are made. Because there are electrically positive and electrically negative objects, we assume that among the building blocks of matter there are two types of particles: *electrically positive* and *electrically negative.* Two particles of the same sign repel and two particles of opposite sign attract. Some of the building blocks of matter belong in a third group: for example, neutrons (Section 24–8) do not act like either positive or negative electric particles.

Although the electrical forces between particles are enormously greater than the gravitational forces, when ordinary "uncharged" pieces of matter are placed near each other, they exert no appreciable electric forces on each other. This does not mean we have to give up the idea that there are positive and negative electric particles in matter. Since a positive and a negative particle exert forces in opposite directions on any third electric particle, we merely note that the forces exerted by the two kinds of particle can cancel. When the effects of the positive and negative particles cancel exactly, we say the object is uncharged or electrically neutral. We can even picture a neutral atom in this way.*

If we add some positive particles to an electrically neutral object, there is no longer a balance. The effect of the positive particles is greater than the effect of the negative particles; and we say the object is positively charged. We can also

*If every small volume of a body is neutral, the resultant force exerted by all the electric particles upon any electrical particle outside is zero. However, a body can be neutral on the average and nevertheless contain local concentrations of charge. Then an electric particle near one of the local concentrations is subject to a force.

charge an object positively by *removing* some *negative* particles, leaving an excess of positive ones. (Similarly, we can make a neutral object electrically negative either by adding some negative particles to it, or by taking some positive particles away from it.)

We have seen that rubbing a glass rod with silk makes the rod electrically positive. How can this happen? We may think of two possibilities. Perhaps there is a transfer of positive particles from the silk to the rod; perhaps there is a transfer of negative particles from the rod to the silk. In either case the silk must become electrically negative as the glass becomes electrically positive. We can check this conclusion by bringing the silk near the suspended glass rod. We find that the rod is attracted by the silk. Also the silk will repel a negatively charged plastic rod.

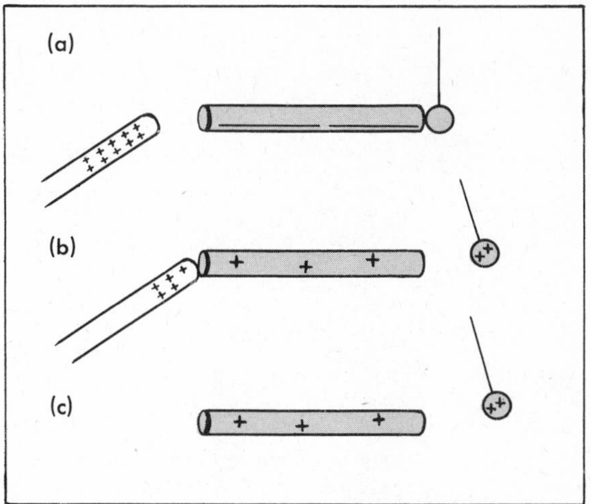

27–3. In (a) the metal ball and rod are uncharged. The charged rod is some distance away. (b) The initially charged rod is touching the metal rod and has pulled off some negative particles. The ball and the metal rod are now positively charged and repel each other. (c) With the initially charged rod removed, the ball and metal rod are still charged; they still repel.

27–3. Insulators and Conductors

We often classify different materials by saying that one is an electrical conductor and another an insulator. This classification is based on experiments like those we shall now discuss. Suppose we hang a light metal-coated ball on a silk thread. Then we support a metal rod horizontally on a glass or plastic stand so that one end touches the ball (Fig. 27–3). Now we electrify a piece of glass, and rub the glass against the other end of the metal rod. As we rub the glass against the metal, the ball swings away. We repeat the experiment, using a rod of plastic in place of the metal rod. Now the ball does not move. (Fig. 27–4.) We therefore see that the metal and the plastic rods act differently.

To account for this difference we need only assume that in a metal some electric particles are free to move from point to point, while in the plastic no electric particles can move freely. Suppose, for example, that the free particles in the metal are negative. When the positively charged glass touches the neutral metal rod, the glass pulls some of the free negative particles off the metal rod and the ball. Both the ball and the rod therefore become positively charged, and they repel each other. Even after the glass is removed, there will be a shortage of negative particles on both the rod and the ball, and they will continue to repel.

We can equally well assume that the free particles are electrically positive. Then, when we touch the metal rod with the electrified glass, positive particles will pass from the glass to the metal and spread along it to the ball. Again, the rod and the ball will both become positively charged and will repel each other.

Now let's picture what happens when we replace the metal rod with the plastic one. In the plastic neither positive nor negative particles can move freely. Thus only the part of the rod in direct contact with the charged glass acquires an excess of positive particles. The rest of the rod remains electrically neutral, and so does the ball. Consequently, there is no force pushing the ball away from the rod.

Substances that behave like the metal in this kind of experiment we call *conductors.* Substances that behave like the plastic we call *insulators.* All conductors contain freely moving electric particles and insulators do not.

Toward the end of this chapter we shall learn how to determine the sign of the freely moving particles in different kinds of conductors. We shall find that when liquids and gases conduct electrically, both positive and negative particles move. In metals, however, the conductivity is due solely to the motion of electrically negative particles. To keep the discussion brief, in the next few sections we shall assume that only negative particles move.

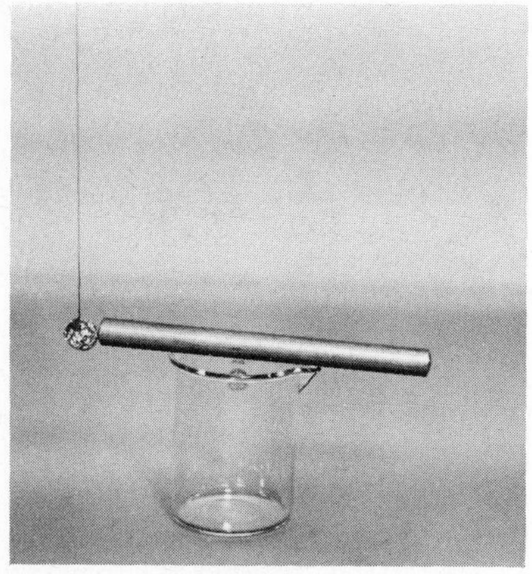

27–4 (a). A metal rod on a beaker is in contact with a light metal-coated ball.

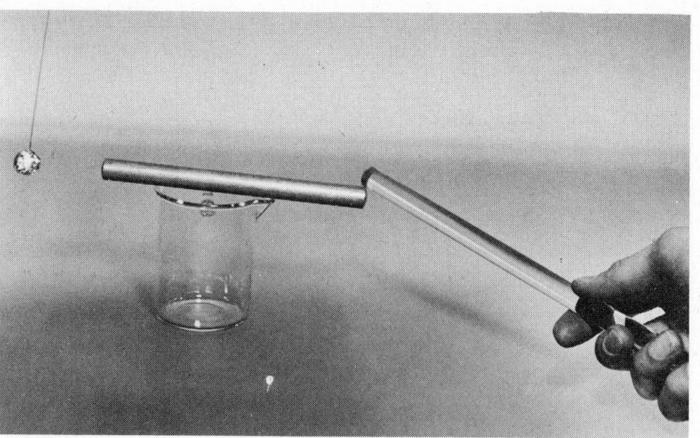

(b) We touch the end of the metal with a charged rod, and the ball at the other end is repelled.

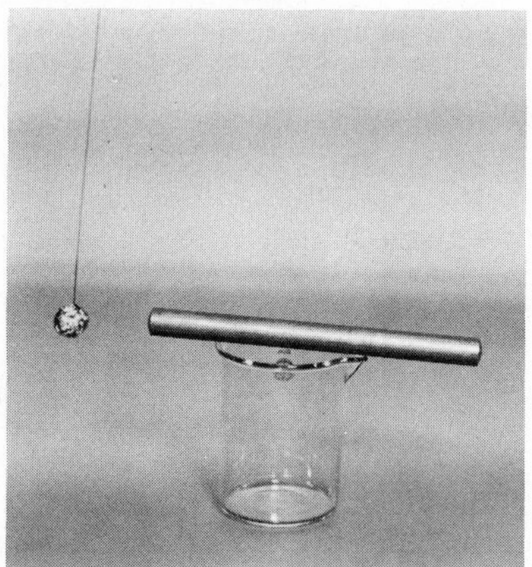

(c) After the charged rod is removed, the metal rod still repels the ball.

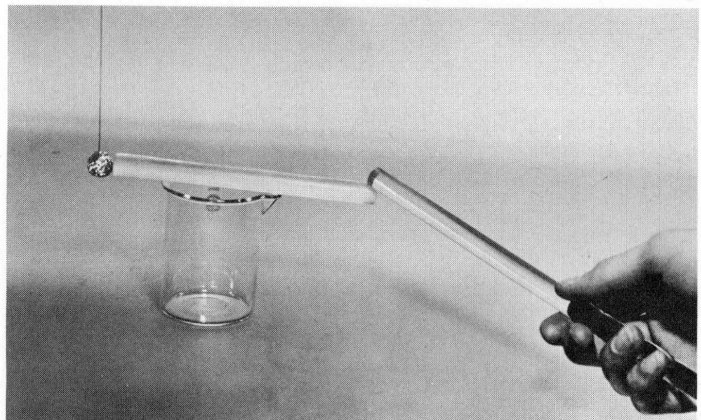

(d) We repeat the experiment with a plastic rod in place of the metal one. The ball stays still.

27–4. Some Experiments with an Electroscope

An electroscope is an instrument for detecting the presence of electric charge. The simplest version of this instrument is an old-fashioned *gold-leaf electroscope.* It consists of two thin gold leaves hanging from a metal rod in a glass jar (Fig. 27–5). We shall now explain how it works.

If we touch the knob at the upper end of the metal rod with a charged piece of plastic, the gold leaves spring apart. What has happened? Electrically negative particles passed from the plastic to the metal rod and spread immediately to the leaves. The leaves repel each other because they are both electrically negative. Since they are very light, a small charge is enough to cause a visible divergence of the leaves. (The leaves would also diverge if we used a glass rod rubbed with silk in place of the plastic rod. In this case, however, the leaves would be electrically positive.)

Give a charge to an electroscope and then touch the knob with an uncharged metal ball on an insulating rod. (Fig. 27–6.) The leaves fall a bit because we have taken some charge away. The charge is shared between the electroscope and the ball. Try again with a bigger ball. The leaves fall much farther, because the bigger ball takes a bigger share of charge. The same thing happens if we join the electroscope knob to a big ball with a wire. Some of the charge runs along the conducting wire to the big ball. With a very big ball, practically all the charge goes to the ball, and the electroscope is left with so little charge that the leaves fall completely. We can use the largest

27–5. A gold-leaf electroscope. The leaves stand out because they are charged.

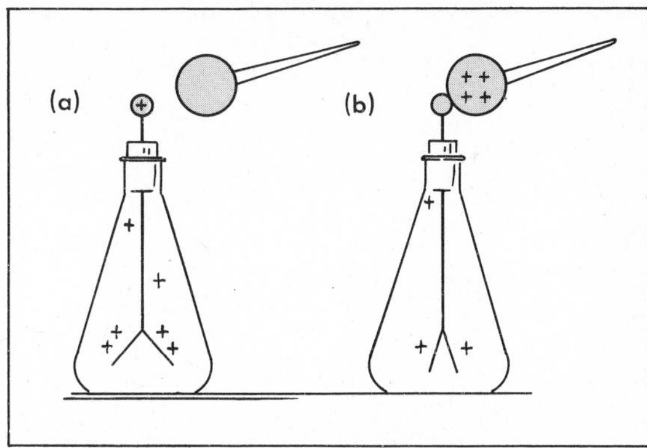

27–6. (a) A charged electroscope, with the leaves repelling each other strongly. (b) We have touched the knob with a metal ball on an insulating handle. The charge is now shared between the ball and the electroscope; and the leaves have now fallen considerably.

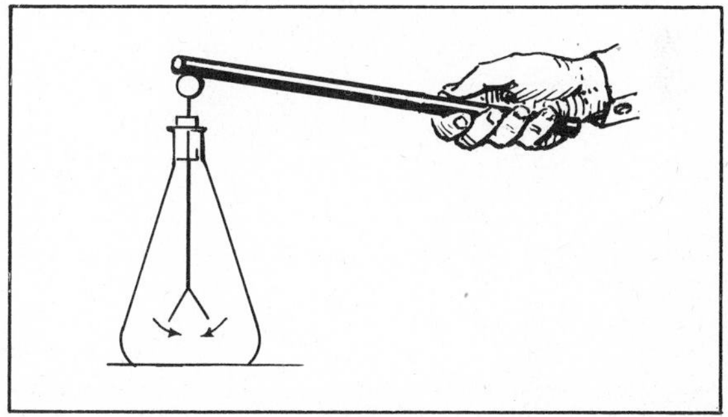

27–7. When you touch the knob of a charged electroscope with a stick of graphite, the leaves fall. Both you and the graphite are conductors.

available ball of all, the earth. When we connect a charged electroscope to the earth, practically all the charge runs away — there is far too little left to notice. (This process of sharing charge with the earth is often called "grounding.")*

Although you are not as large as the earth, you too are a conducting ball. If you charge the electroscope and then touch the knob with a finger, the leaves collapse. If there was initially an excess of negative particles on the metal rod and leaves, some of these particles must have gone onto your body. They may have passed through your body to the ground. But even if your shoes are insulators, the electroscope leaves will fall. In this case, you are sharing the charge with the small electroscope.

If the electroscope is positively charged, you will still discharge it by touching the knob. Some negative particles must have gone from you to the electroscope neutralizing the positive charge on the leaves. In either case, from these experiments we conclude that the human body is an electrical conductor.

We can determine what other substances are conductors. For example, suppose we charge the electroscope again and touch the knob with a stick of graphite, such as the lead from a pencil. (Fig. 27–7.) The leaves fall immediately, showing that graphite is also a conductor. On the other hand, the leaves of a charged electroscope do not move if we touch the knob with uncharged glass, hard rubber, porcelain, or plastics. These substances are electric insulators. If we touch the knob with a wooden match, the leaves fall, but very slowly. Apparently in wood some electric particles can move, but not as freely as in metals; wood offers a much greater "resistance" than metals to the motion of electric particles.

*The earth has some patches of nonconductor — desert sand, some rocks, etc. — but underground there is a good-enough conducting material so that the charge is quickly shared all over the earth. A metal pipe, such as part of the water system, is often used to make sure of the connection to the conducting region underground.

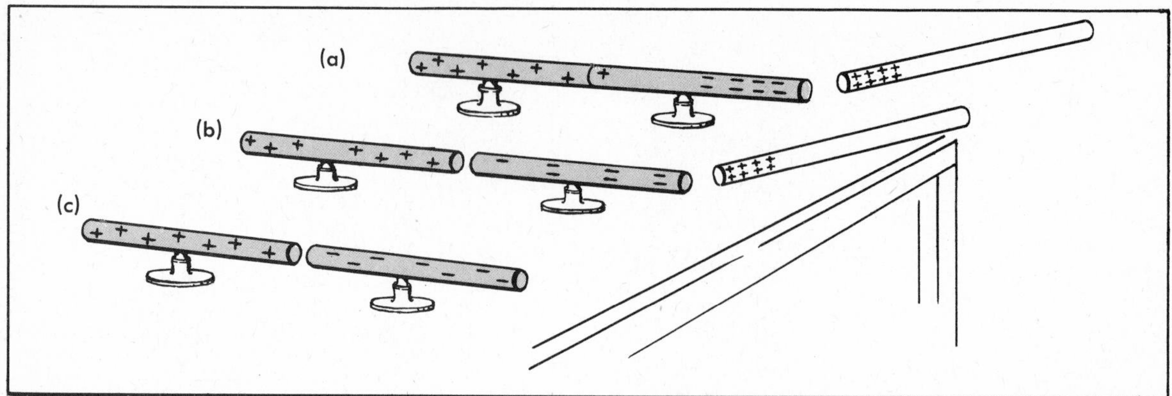

27–8. Electrostatic induction. (a) Two metal rods are in contact; a positively charged object is near by. Negative particles are attracted to the right, leaving a positive charge to the left. (b) The rods are separated with the charged body still near by. The right-hand one has a negative charge and the left-hand one positive. (c) The rods retain their charges even when the charged object is taken away.

27–5. Electrostatic Induction

We do not need to touch a conductor in order to move charges around on it. Suppose we have two metal cylinders on insulating stands. We put them in contact to form one long conductor as in Figs. 27–8 and 27–9. Then we bring a positively charged glass rod near one end of the conductor. The positive charge on the glass rod will attract negative charges on the conductor and repel positive charges. As a result, the near end of the conductor acquires an excess of negative electric particles and the far end is left positive. Now we separate the two metal cylinders by pulling the insulating stands apart while the positively charged glass is near by. The near cylinder should have a net negative charge and the far one a net positive charge. We can verify this conclusion by taking the glass away and bringing up a light, positively charged ball on a thread. Then we see

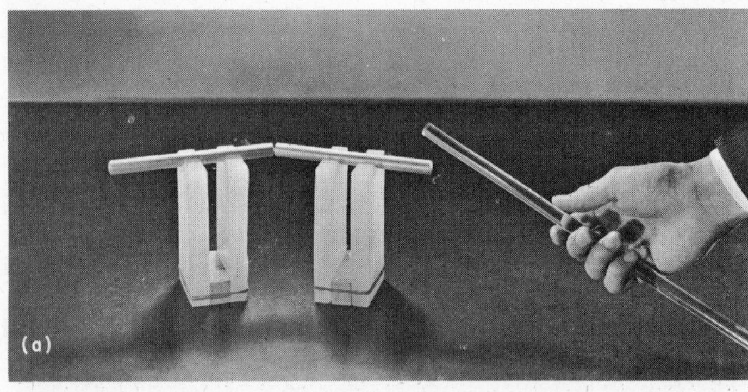

27–9. Electrostatic induction. (a) Metal rods in contact, positive charge near by. (b) The rods are separated. (c) We test the charge on each rod with a positively charged ball. The rod at left repels — it is positively charged. The one at right attracts — it is negatively charged.

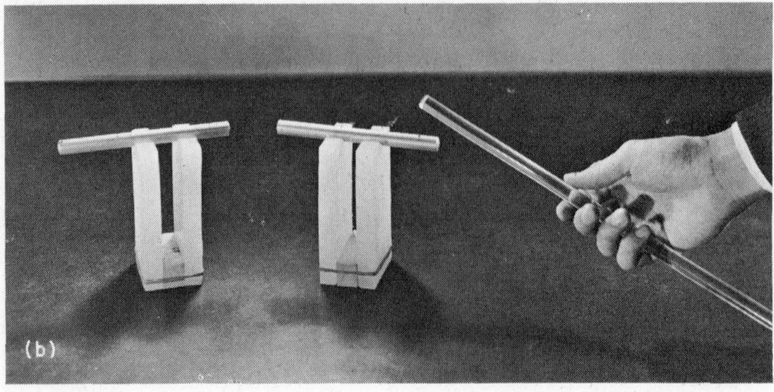

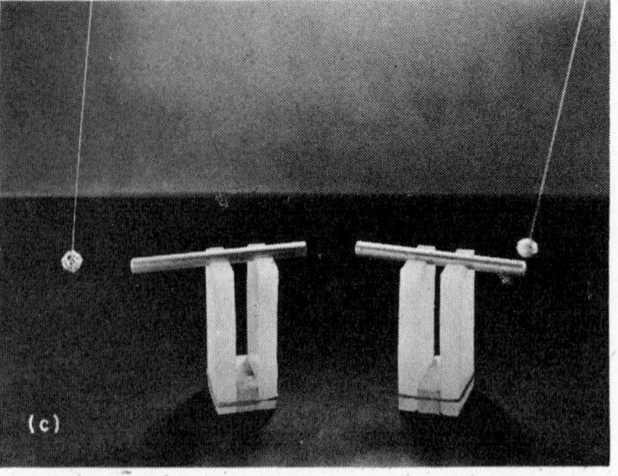

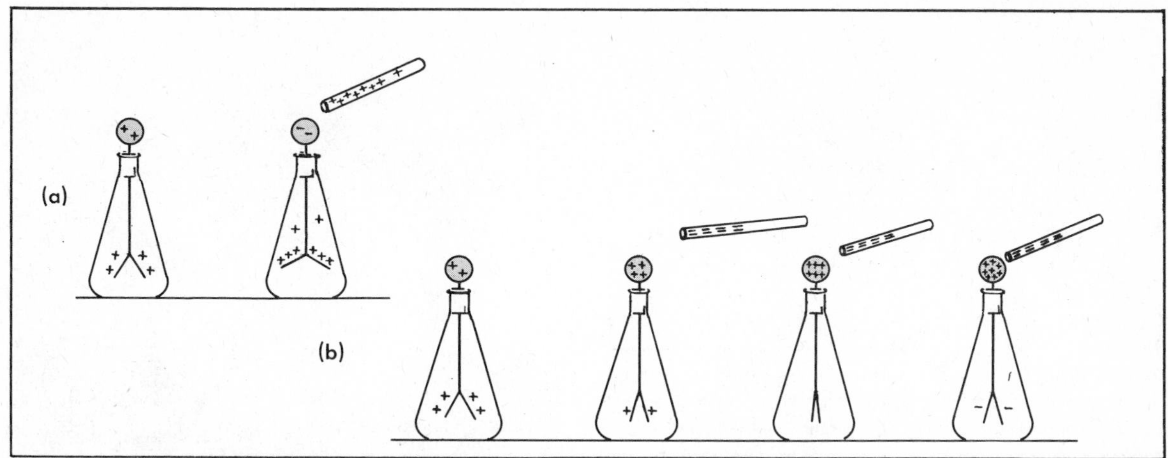

27–10. Using an electroscope to detect a charge and determine its sign. In (a) we bring a positive charge near a positively charged electroscope. The leaves diverge still farther. In the series of pictures (b) we move a negative charge nearer and nearer to the knob of a positively charged electroscope. More and more negative charges are repelled toward the leaves, and they fall. Finally, if a big negative charge gets very close, we may push so many minus charges on the leaves that they are given a net negative charge. They then diverge again.

that the near cylinder attracts the positively charged ball and the far one repels it.

The separation of positive and negative charges on a conductor induced by the presence of a charged object near by is called *electrostatic induction;* and the local excesses of positive and negative charge which accumulate in different regions of the conductor are called *induced charges.*

Electrostatic induction allows us to use an electroscope to detect the presence of a charge without transferring it to the electroscope. In fact, we can even determine the sign of the charge. To do this, we first charge the electroscope, let us say positively. Then we bring the unknown charge near the knob. If the charge is positive, it induces a negative charge on the knob and thus increases the positive charge on the leaves. Consequently, the leaves diverge farther [Fig. 27–10 (a)]. If, on the other hand, the unknown charge is negative, the induction goes just the other way. The net positive charge on the leaves decreases, and the leaves fall [Fig. 27–10 (b)].

Electrostatic induction also enables us to understand the force of attraction exerted by an electrified body on a neutral conductor. Suppose that the electrified body *A* is positively charged (Fig. 27–11). It will induce a negative charge on the nearest part of the conductor and a positive charge on the part farthest away. The negative induced charge is attracted toward the positive charge on *A*, and the positive induced charge is repelled by it. However, the repulsion is weaker than the attraction because the positive induced charge is farther from *A* than the negative one. As a result, there is a net force on the conductor pulling it toward *A*.

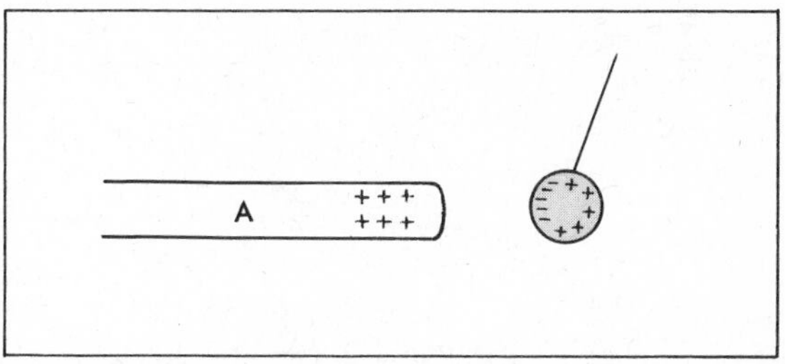

27–11. Attraction of a neutral conductor. When a neutral conductor is near a positively charged body, negative electric particles are attracted to the end near the positive charge. A positive charge is left on the rest of the conductor. Since the induced negative charge is nearer the positive body, there is a net force of attraction.

There is a similar but smaller force of attraction between a neutral insulator and a neighboring charge. In an insulator, neither the positive nor the negative particles can wander freely from their atoms, but they can be pushed or pulled over short distances. For example, we may imagine that an insulator is made of positively charged particles nailed down so that they remain in place in the insulator, and negative particles held near the positive ones by springy forces. The springy forces prevent the negative particles from moving any great distance. But when we

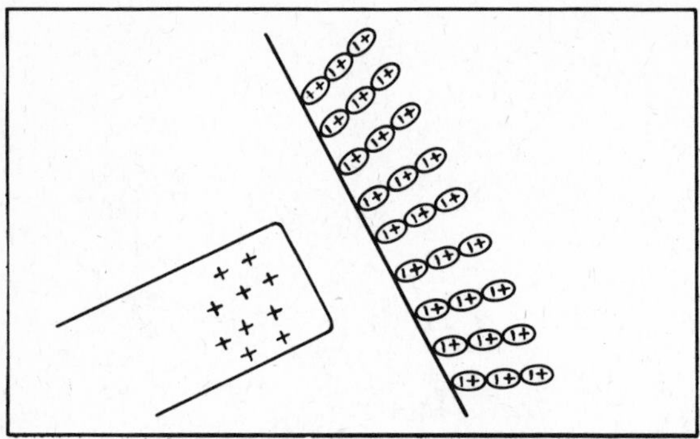

27–12. Attraction of a neutral insulator. A positively charged object is near an uncharged insulator. There are no electric particles free to move through the insulators, but the positive and negative particles in each molecule can be displaced slightly. The negative particles are thus all slightly nearer the plus charge, giving again a net force of attraction. Note that in fact the molecules are extremely small and so are the charges on them. This diagram is far from a realistic picture.

27–14. A simple electroscope shielded by a metal case — a coffee can. Instead of thin metal leaves, the sensitive element is a metal-coated drinking straw hung by a pin that fits through two holes in the frame.

bring a positively charged body near the insulator, the negative particles are attracted toward it. Consequently, they move a short distance away from the positive particles toward the attracting body (Fig. 27–12). Because the negative particles are slightly nearer the positively charged body than are their positive counterparts, the force of attraction on them is slightly greater than the repulsion exerted on the positive particles. As a result, there is a net force of attraction between the insulator and the positively charged body.

27–6. Improved Electroscopes and Electrometers

When the gold leaves of an electroscope hang in a glass bottle (as in Fig. 27–5) the electroscope is sensitive to charges anywhere near by. Such charges exert forces on the leaves, both directly (when the leaves are charged) and by electrostatic induction. For many purposes, however, we would like an electroscope to respond only to charges on the leaves or near the knob.

We can cut out unwanted electric effects by replacing the glass bottle with a metal case and using an insulating sleeve to keep the case and the leaves electrically separated. (Fig. 27–13.) Suppose we bring a positively charged body, *A*, near an electroscope with a metal case. The charge on *A* induces negative charges on the near side of the metal case, and positive charges are left on the opposite side. We find experimentally that if the electroscope is completely surrounded by a metal shield, the leaves are entirely uninfluenced by the presence or absence of charges such as *A* outside the shield. The induced charges exert forces on the leaves, and apparently these forces just balance the force exerted by the positive charge of *A*. A shielded electroscope is therefore a far more dependable instrument than our crude one in a glass bottle. It is insensitive to irrelevant outside influences. You can make a shielded electroscope like the one in Fig. 27–14.

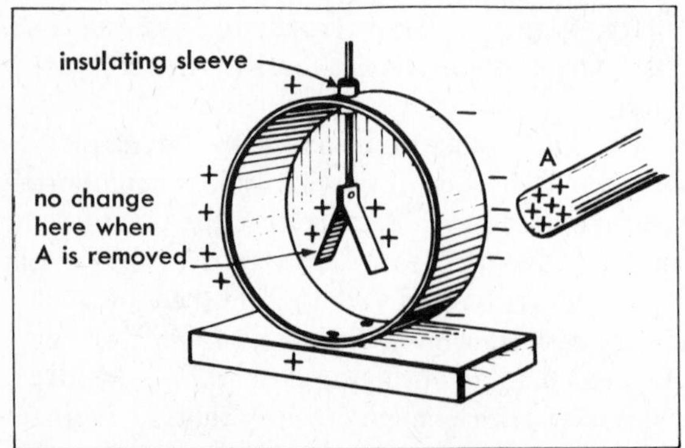

27–13. When a charged body is brought near a shielded electroscope, charges are induced on the case. Inside the case the forces from the induced charges just cancel those from the outside charge. Try it.

Sometimes we wish to detect charges smaller than those which cause an ordinary gold-leaf electroscope to respond noticeably. By changing the design — making the moving part of light

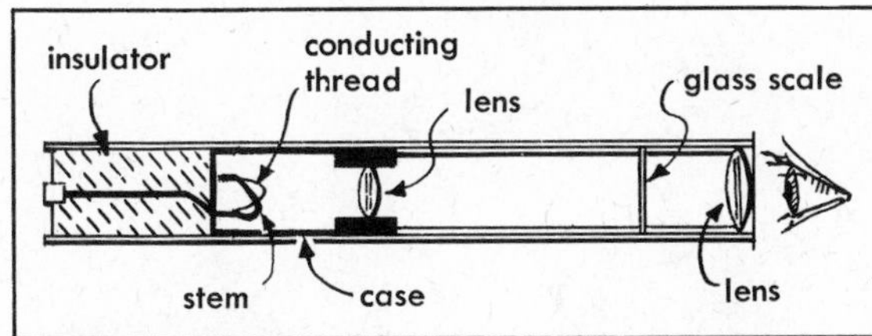

27–15. Sensitive electroscopes. (a) Schematic diagram of a radiation dosimeter, which gets its high sensitivity by using a stem made of a very small and light conducting fiber.

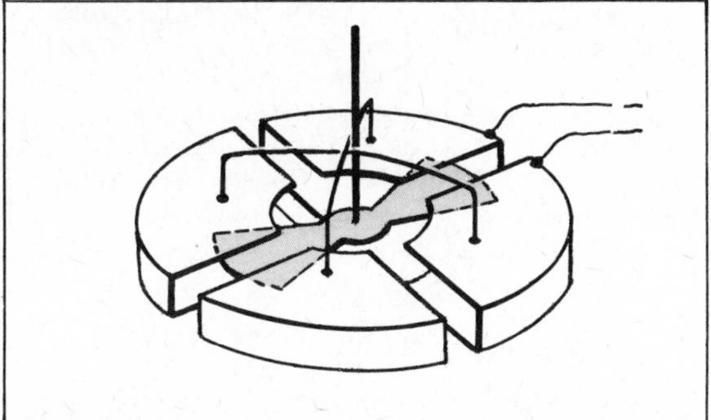

(b) The stem of a quadrant electrometer. A very light "needle" is suspended in the hollow space inside the four quadrants, forming a torsion balance. The needle is given an initial charge by a battery, and the charge to be measured is put on the quadrants. The charges are distributed in such a way that a very small charge gives a large deflection.

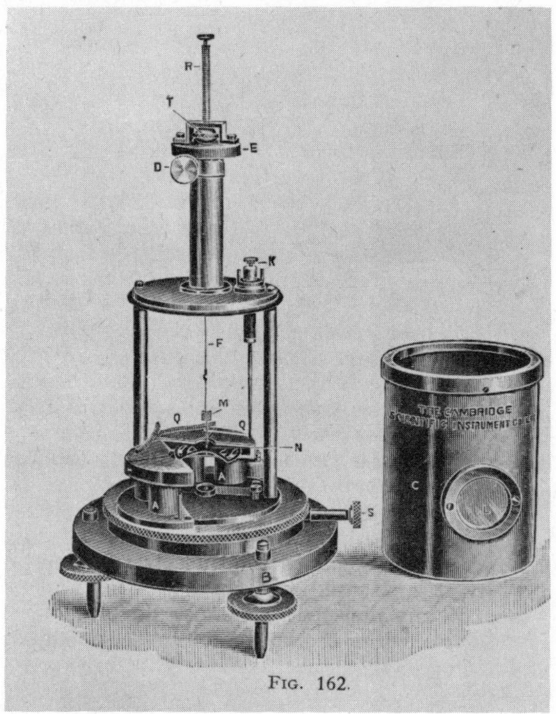

(c) A complete quadrant electrometer. (From S. G. Starling and A. J. Woodall, "Electricity and Magnetism," Longmans, Green & Co., New York.)

conducting thread, changing the structure of the rod, and making the dimensions smaller — we can build electroscopes which are far more sensitive. Each of these sensitive instruments has a metal case for shielding and a sensitive element that plays the role of the rod and the leaves of our simple model. We shall call any such sensitive element the stem of the electroscope. With a well-designed stem in a good metal shield, we can measure a thousandth or less of the charge detectable with the usual gold-leaf model.

Sensitive electroscopes are now fairly common (Fig. 27–15). The radiation dosimeters used to find out when someone has been exposed to radioactive radiation are really sensitive electroscopes. They have a scale added so that we can make quantitative measurements of the position of the thread which replaces the leaves of our simple instrument. (An electroscope with a scale is usually called an *electrometer*.) When the dosimeter is charged, the thread moves across the scale. Further charging moves it farther across the scale, and discharging will move it in the opposite direction.

In designing an electrometer, we took advantage of metal shielding. The observation that a metal shield separates the electrical universe into two parts really does far more than allow us to design a better instrument. The observed cancellation of the electric effects of a charge outside the metal case gives us information about the electrical forces. With careful reasoning we can show that complete cancellation occurs only in the case of forces which vary as the inverse square of the distance.* The Coulomb experiment which we shall discuss in the next chapter shows directly that electrical forces are of this kind.

27–7. Batteries

Rubbing two things together (such as a plastic rod and a woolen cloth) is not the only method of separating electrically positive from electrically

*We shall not go through this reasoning here. An example of it is given in the PSSC film on Coulomb's law, and a related discussion is given in the box in Section 28–3.

27–16. Charging an electroscope with batteries. The three radio "B" batteries required to produce this deflection of the leaf are equivalent to 180 flashlight cells in series. The effect of a single flashlight cell would not be detectable.

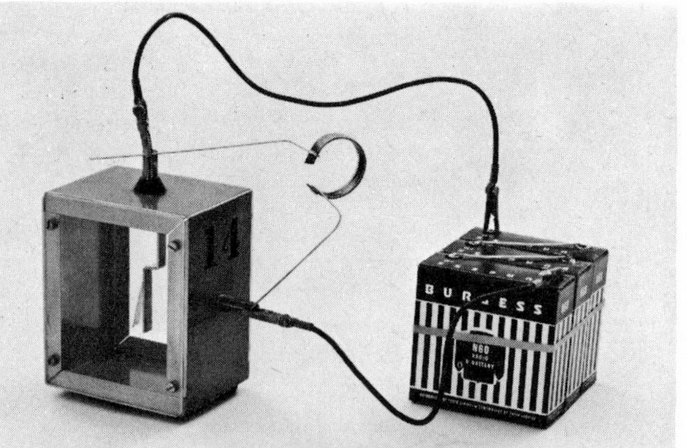

27–17. An electroscope connected to a battery stays charged even though the stem and the case are joined by a high-resistance wire. Since the resistance wire is very fine and has to be very long, it is wound up in a coil around the circular form. If the battery is disconnected, the electroscope discharges.

negative particles. Batteries (and other electric generators) are really machines for separating charges.

A good gold-leaf electroscope will detect the charge separation produced by enough batteries (Fig. 27–16). A couple of "B" batteries (available at radio stores) will charge up a civil-defense dosimeter so that the thread has been shoved entirely across the scale.

The charge that a battery puts on an electrometer is the same kind of electricity that we put on from a rubbed glass rod or from any other charged body. When the plus terminal of a battery is connected to the knob of an electrometer and the minus terminal to the metal case, the knob gets charged with the same kind of charge that we get from rubbed glass — positive charge. When the battery is connected the other way round, the knob becomes negatively charged; and these negative charges can be canceled off by just a small part of the positive charge from rubbed glass.

A battery, then, is a complicated chemical mechanism which shoves plus charges to the positive terminal and minus charges to the negative terminal, despite the forces of electrical attraction which tend to pull these charges together. When the battery is connected to the metal case and to the stem of an electrometer, the case and stem are given opposite charges. The charges quickly accumulate until after a brief time the electric forces shoving the charges back toward the battery compensate the forces exerted by the chemical action driving them out of the battery.

27–8. Electric Currents

As we have just seen, we can charge an electrometer by momentarily connecting the stem and the metal case to the terminals of a battery. When we disconnect the battery the electrometer stays charged. But if we then join the stem to the metal case with a metal wire, the electrometer quickly discharges. Electric particles must have moved through the wire between the stem and the case. We shall assume that these are negative particles.

Now suppose that we leave the battery permanently connected to the electrometer. Then if we connect the stem to the case with a poorly conducting wire (Fig. 27–17), the electrometer remains partially charged.* There is now a continuous flow of electric particles in the wire. As these negative particles reach the positive battery terminal, they cancel some of the positive charge there; as they leave the negative battery terminal, they drain negative charge from it. The battery, on the other hand, keeps providing a supply of charges at the terminals. Chemical changes continuously drive negative particles across inside the battery from the positive to the negative terminal (or positive particles in the other direction). The rate at which the battery moves these charges is controlled by the rate at which the charges outside the battery flow through the wire and cancel.

*A long thin wire of a nickel-chromium alloy will do.

A flow of electric particles in a conductor is called an *electric current.* In particular, the steady flow imposed by a battery is called a *steady current.* Electric currents have many different effects. For example, a metal wire carrying a big-enough current heats up. We can build instruments to detect these effects and thus measure electric currents. In the next few sections and in Chapter 29 there is much more discussion of electric current and its measurement.

27–9. Conductivity of Gases; Ionization

Let us charge an electroscope, for example by momentarily connecting the stem to the positive terminal and the case to the negative terminal of a battery. The electroscope, of course, is full of air. What would happen if some of the air molecules were electrically positive and some electrically negative? The positive molecules would be attracted toward the negatively charged case and the negative molecules toward the positively charged stem. The arrival of the electrically negative molecules would neutralize the excess of positive particles present on the stem, and the electroscope would gradually discharge. (Fig. 27–18.)

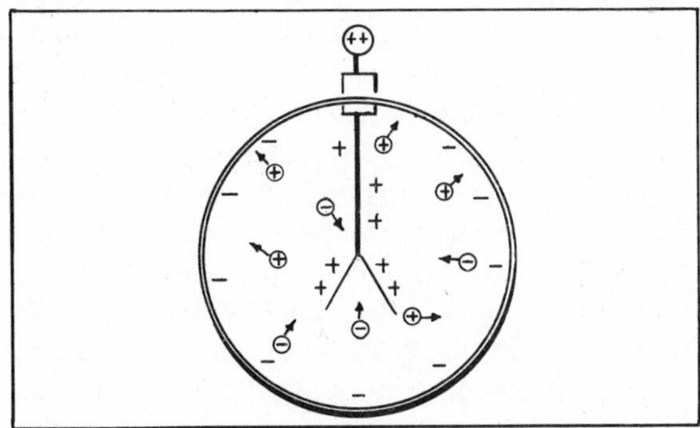

27–18. If air contains electrically positive and negative particles, the charge on an electroscope will be rapidly canceled. Normally this is not true; but the air can be ionized.

Nothing of this kind happens. Under ordinary circumstances, the electroscope remains charged for a long time. The gas in it is an effective insulator. And this means that the molecules of air are *electrically neutral.* Also if we fill the electroscope with other gases, such as carbon dioxide, helium, argon, etc., we always find the same result, even when the gases are monatomic. Thus complete molecules, including those that are single atoms, are electrically neutral.

But now let us bring some radioactive material near the charged electroscope, or let us direct a beam of X rays toward it. The electroscope will gradually discharge. Furthermore, if we remove the radioactive material (or shut off the X-ray beam) before the electroscope has lost all its charge, it will stop discharging.

We can interpret these results by assuming that the X rays, or the radiations from the radioactive material, break up the gas molecules into electrically charged fragments. Some of these fragments may be identical with the ultimate building blocks of matter that we have been talking about. Others may be composed of several such particles. Some may be made of a charged fragment of a molecule that has attached itself to a neutral molecule, thus producing a heavier charged unit. The charged molecular fragments or more complex units are called *ions;* and a gas containing ions is said to be *ionized.*

While an ordinary gas is an insulator, an ionized gas behaves like a conductor. A positively charged object immersed in an ionized gas attracts the negative ions; a negatively charged object attracts the positive ions. In either case the ions, as they come in contact with the object, gradually neutralize the original charge.

There are many experiments we can do to show that the conductivity of gas results from ionization. For example, we can make sure that the discharge of an electroscope placed in a beam of X rays is not due to a direct effect of the X rays on the stem of the electroscope. The experiment illustrated in Fig. 27–19 shows that the X rays are acting on the gas. In this experiment we pump air into the electroscope through a tube, part of which can be irradiated. We charge the electro-

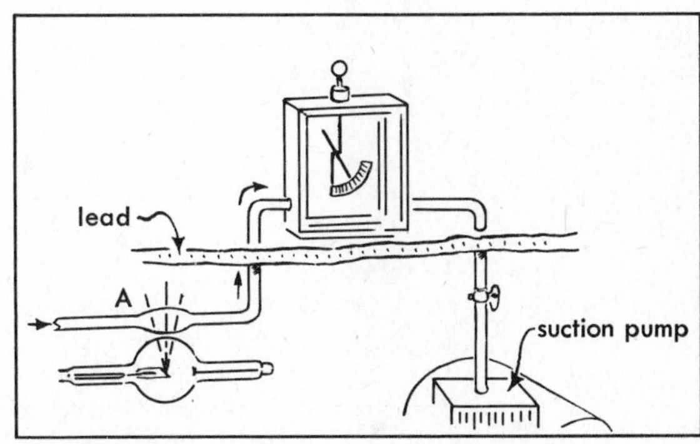

27–19. X rays ionize the air at *A*. When this air with the ions reaches the electroscope, the leaves fall.

scope and start the pump. Then we turn on the X rays. The electroscope begins to discharge because ions formed by the X-ray beam are carried into the electroscope case by the moving air. With the X-ray machine still running, we stop the pump. The flow of air stops, and the ions formed in the tube no longer reach the electroscope. The gradual discharge of the electroscope also stops.

At the beginning of this section we said that gases usually are good insulators. We might have said that in the absence of ionizing radiation they are perfect insulators. As a matter of fact, however, a small amount of radiation is present everywhere. Most materials around us contain minute traces of radioactive substances. And although we can eliminate radiation from materials near by, cosmic rays will make some ions. Even exceedingly thick shields made of materials free from radioactivity are incomplete protection against these penetrating radiations that originate outside of our atmosphere. Thus gases are always slightly ionized and therefore slightly conducting. This conductivity, however, is so small that it can only be detected with very delicate apparatus.

27–10. The Cloud Chamber

Figs. 1–6 and 7–17 show the visible tracks left by fast-moving particles in the near-boiling liquid of a bubble chamber and in photographic emulsions. Actually only fast-moving *charged* particles leave these tracks. Each track is an indirect effect of the electric forces exerted by the passing charged particle upon the atoms of the emulsion or the liquid.

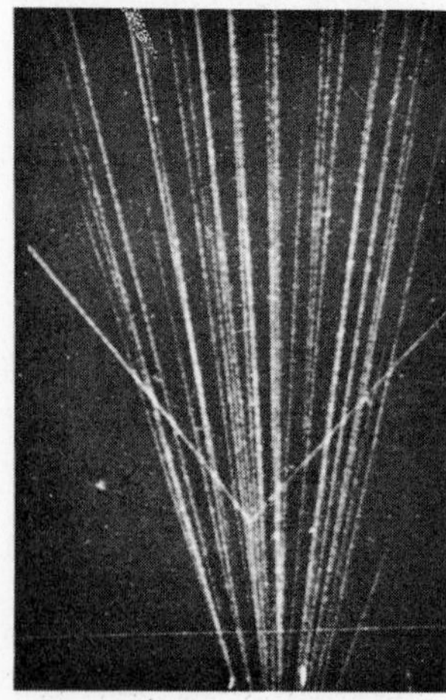

27–20. A cloud-chamber photograph showing the paths of alpha particles in a chamber containing helium. (From P. M. S. Blackett, in Proceedings of the Royal Society, 107A, 349, 1925.)

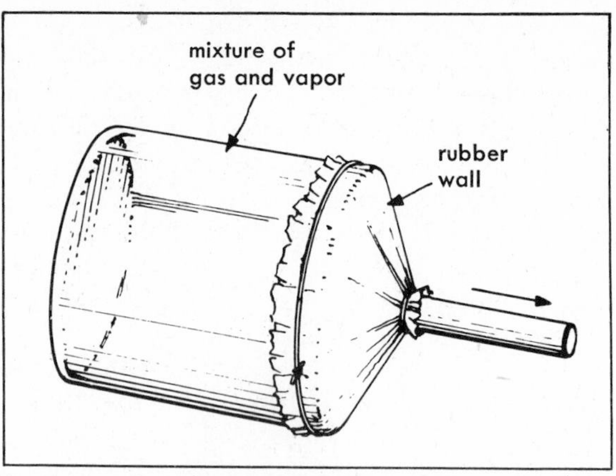

27–21. An expansion cloud chamber. When the rubber wall is moved out rapidly, the vapor in the chamber is cooled and drops condense where ions are formed.

A *cloud chamber* also enables us to "see" the paths of charged particles in gases (Fig. 27–20). The particles leave a trail of positive and negative ions; and the operation of the cloud chamber is based upon the observed fact that vapors condense more easily around such ions than in open space.

One form of cloud chamber (the expansion chamber) consists of a glass box with a movable wall (Fig. 27–21). The chamber contains a mixture of a vapor like alcohol and a gas such as air or argon. The vapor, which is normally liquid at room temperature, condenses easily. If we suddenly pull the movable wall outward, the enclosed gases expand and their temperature drops. If the temperature falls enough, the vapor condenses into droplets everywhere, and a general fog will appear. If the temperature change is somewhat smaller, the vapor condenses only around ions. Consequently, if a charged particle traverses the chamber at about the time of the expansion, the trail of ions along its path will become a trail of visible droplets.

There is another type of cloud chamber called a diffusion chamber. A simple version of it consists of a shallow cylindrical box, the bottom of which is kept cold while the transparent top is kept at a higher temperature (Fig. 27–22). On the wall of the chamber there is a wick of cloth or of blotting paper soaked in alcohol. The alcohol continuously evaporates from the wick and condenses on the cold floor. Just above the floor there is a region where the alcohol vapor does not condense spontaneously but will condense around any ion formed. When a charged particle

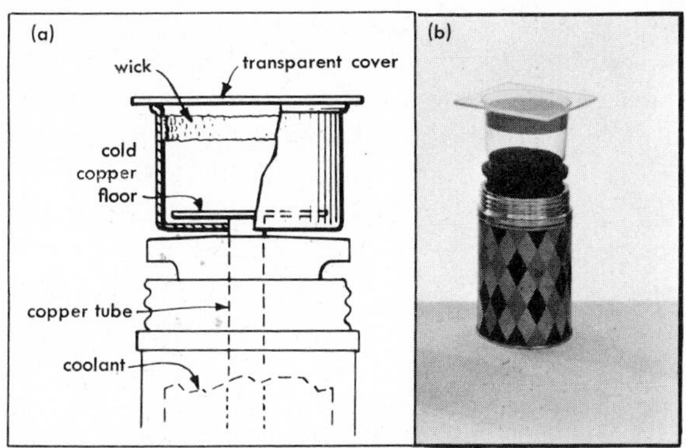

27–22. A simple diffusion cloud chamber. (a) The chamber itself is a plastic box with a transparent cover; around the top is a wick soaked in alcohol. In the bottom of the box is a copper plate painted black, and soldered to it is a copper tube which is immersed in a coolant. (b) In use, the copper tube extends down into a mixture of Dry Ice and alcohol in a vacuum bottle. You will see occasional tracks from cosmic rays at all times. To see more tracks, put a weak radioactive source (such as a numeral from a luminous watch dial) into the chamber.

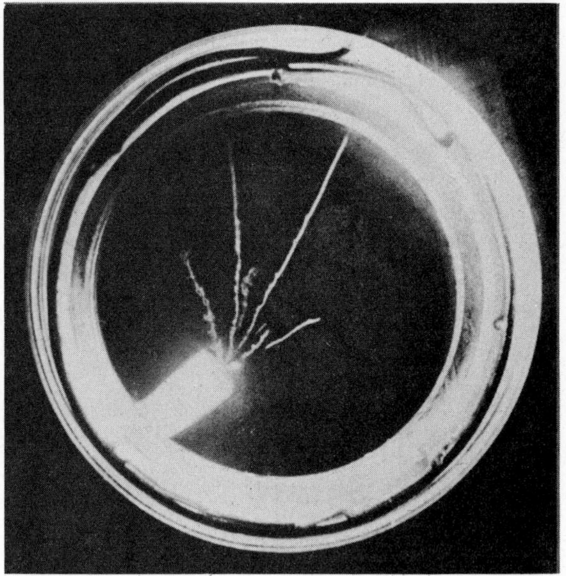

27–23. Tracks of alpha particles in the diffusion cloud chamber.

traverses this region, its track becomes visible. This cloud chamber is cheap to make, and it runs continuously. With it we can see the passage of an occasional charged cosmic ray. Also, by putting a bit of radioactive material in the chamber we can see the tracks of the charged fragments emitted in radioactive decay as in Fig. 27–23.

27–11. Conductivity of Solutions

Some liquids are electrical conductors; others are insulators. The behavior of water and of water solutions is particularly interesting. In order to study this behavior experimentally we shall use the arrangement shown in Fig. 27–24. In series we connect a metal plate, an electric current meter, a battery, and a second metal plate. Then we stick the metal plates (called electrodes) into a glass of water.

If the water is pure, the meter shows no current. Since the molecules in liquids are free to move, the absence of current proves that the water molecules are electrically neutral.

When we dissolve some table salt in the water, the meter shows a current in the circuit. The same thing happens with many other chemical compounds such as hydrochloric acid, sulfuric acid, copper sulfate, potassium chloride, etc. We can explain the conductivity of these solutions by assuming that the table salt (or the other dissolved substance) breaks up into positively and negatively charged fragments, which we shall again call positive and negative ions. This explanation

27–24. Apparatus for studying electrical conduction in a liquid. When salt is dissolved in the water, the meter shows a current. The charge is carried through the solution by positive and negative ions.

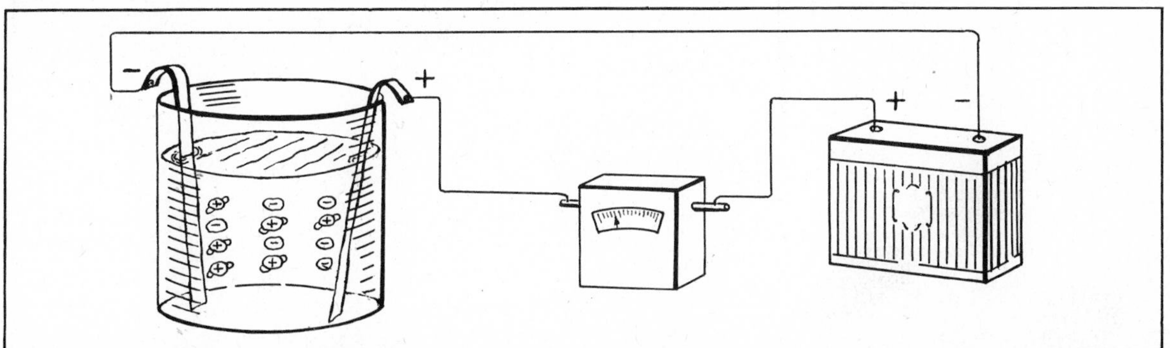

is much like the explanation of electric conduction in gases. In liquids, however, unlike gases, no outside ionizing agent is needed. The ions seem to be formed in a spontaneous breakup of the dissolved substance.

We get convincing support for our explanation of the electrical conductivity of solutions by observing what happens at the electrodes. If we have a copper salt (for instance copper sulfate) dissolved in the water, we find that when there is an electric current the negative electrode gradually becomes coated with a film of copper. If, instead, we fill the cell with a solution of a silver salt (such as silver nitrate), we find that the negative electrode becomes coated with a film of silver. This suggests that when copper sulfate or silver nitrate breaks up in solution, the *metal* atoms are carried by the *positive* ions. The motion of these ions in the electric current involves a detectable transport of matter.

The phenomenon described above is known as *electrolysis.* It is commonly used in electroplating and in many other manufacturing processes, such as refining copper, producing hydrogen gas, and producing aluminum. In Section 29–4 we shall see how to use electrolysis to measure electric current.

27–12. Electrons in Metals

Metals are the commonest kind of conductor. What kind of electric particles are free to move in them, making them conduct? Are these particles positive or negative or both? No single experiment is capable of answering this question in such a clear-cut manner as in the case of conducting gases and liquids. However, one observation gives us a very suggestive clue; and together with other pieces of circumstantial evidence it provides an answer.

It is natural to think that the electric particles in metals are in a state of thermal agitation like the molecules of a gas (see Chapter 9 and Chapter 26). Yet experiments show that a charged piece of metal in a vacuum holds its charge indefinitely. Consequently, we know that the electric particles cannot ordinarily escape from the metal. And we conclude that, when they are near the surface of the metal, the moving particles experience forces that prevent their escape by attracting them back into the metal.

Now suppose we heat the metal. As the temperature increases, the speeds of the particles must increase, just as the speeds of gas molecules do. At high-enough temperatures an appreciable fraction of the particles should have sufficient speed to escape. Like rockets moving fast enough to escape from the gravitational attraction of the earth, these high-speed particles should not fall back into the metal. They should get out beyond the reach of the attractive forces.

With the apparatus shown in Fig. 27–25 we can do experiments to see what actually happens when we heat a metal. The essential part of this equipment is a hollow metal cylinder with a thin metal wire filament stretched along its axis. The cylinder and the filament are sealed in a glass vessel, which is thoroughly evacuated. To heat the filament we connect it to a battery — marked *A* in the figure. We also connect the filament through a current meter to the negative terminal of a "B" battery. The positive terminal of the "B" battery is connected to the cylinder.

27–25. Apparatus for investigating electrical conduction in metals. The electric current from battery *A* heats the filament. We can raise the temperature of the filament by removing resistance wire from the "A"-battery circuit. The current meter connected to the "B" battery shows when charge flows through the space between the filament and the cylinder.

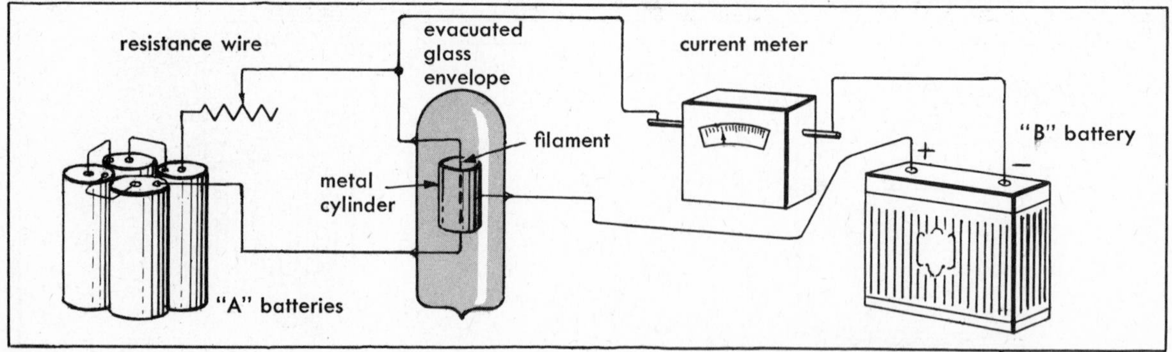

When the filament is at ordinary temperatures, there is no current in the "B"-battery circuit. But if we gradually raise the temperature of the filament, the meter will eventually register a current, indicating that electric particles pass through the empty space between the filament and the cylinder. As we raise the temperature of the filament further, going from orange hot to white hot, this current increases very rapidly.

We repeat the experiment, reversing the connections to the "B" battery. The cylinder is now *negatively* charged and the filament *positively.* In this case the meter shows no current, even when the filament is white hot.

What do these results mean? Suppose first that the hot filament boils out negative particles. When the filament is negative and the cylinder positive, these particles are repelled by the filament and attracted by the cylinder. Therefore they travel from the filament to the cylinder; they then flow through the metal wire to the positive battery terminal and from the negative terminal through the metal wire back again to the hot filament. Thus the emission of negative particles from the filament effectively bridges the gap between the filament and the cylinder so that a steady current is observed in the circuit.

Suppose, on the other hand, that the filament emits positive particles. They would bridge the gap when the filament is positive and the cylinder negative; and we would then observe a current in the "B"-battery circuit. Consequently the fact that there is no current with the filament positive proves that the filament emits no positive particles. And we conclude that all the electric particles boiled out of a hot metal are negatively charged.

We are naturally led to believe that we see here, boiled out into the vacuum, the same particles which move around inside a metal. These particles are called *electrons.* The emission of electrons by metals is known as thermionic emission. Further experiments indicate that electrons are the same in all metals. In the experiment described above, we can make the filament and the cylinder of different metals — for example, tungsten and nickel. We then run a thermionic current for a long time (but at a temperature at which tungsten does not evaporate appreciably). We find no trace of the filament's metal on the cylinder, no matter how long electrons have been flowing across. There is no change in the chemical composition of either the cylinder or the filament. The electrons that have come out of the tungsten must be identical with the electrons already inside the nickel.

This conclusion is supported by similar evidence from metals in contact. We can leave a nickel wire connected across the brass terminals of a battery and let a current run for days in succession without noticing any change in the wire itself or in the battery terminals. A great many electrons have gone from one metal to the other across the contact, but no change takes place in the brass or the nickel. The electrons of nickel and brass are thus indistinguishable.

Finally, we conclude that electrons must be among the ultimate building blocks of all metals and in fact of all atoms. Today the correctness of this conclusion is beyond doubt. We shall meet more of the evidence for it in later chapters.

27–13. Diodes, Electron Guns, Cathode-Ray Oscilloscopes

Thermionic emission has many practical applications; one of the most important is in radio tubes. The device we used to demonstrate thermionic emission is a simple type of radio tube called a diode (Fig. 27–26). (In radio language the hot

27–26. A photograph of a commercial diode. The white metal tube in the center is heated internally and emits electrons. When it is charged negatively and the outer cylinder is positive, the electrons move through the space between.

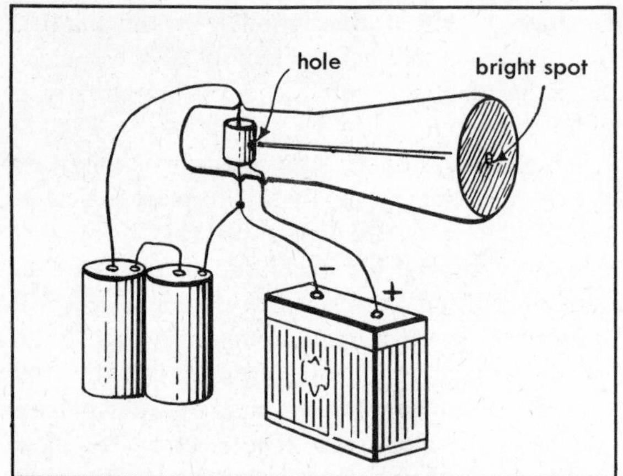

27–27. The simple diode can be converted to an electron gun by drilling a hole in the cylinder and extending the glass envelope. One end of the tube is coated with a fluorescent substance that glows where the beam of electrons strikes it.

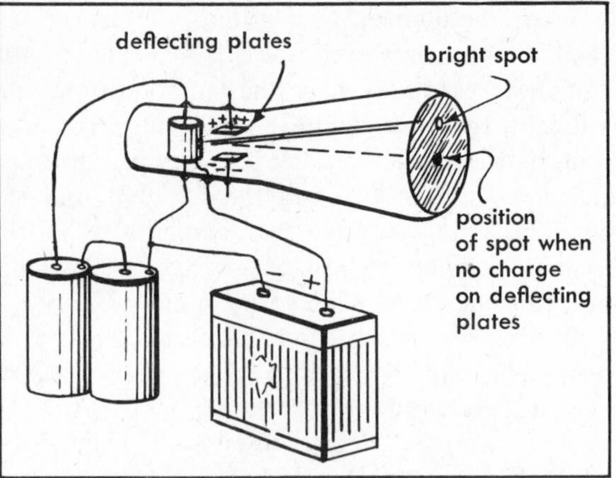

27–28. The electron gun can be made to serve as an electrometer by putting a pair of horizontal metal plates in front of the hole. If, for example, we put a positive charge on the upper plate and a negative charge on the lower, the electron beam will be deflected upward. The movement of the spot away from its center position is a measure of the charge on the plates.

wire from which the electrons are emitted is called the cathode, and the electrode to which the electrons travel is called the plate.) In a diode electrons flow from the cathode to the plate, but not in the opposite direction. It can therefore be used as a valve (or "rectifier" or "detector") to change a current that flows alternately in each direction in a circuit into a current that flows intermittently but in one direction only.

We can also use a diode to make an electron gun by drilling a hole in the plate (see Fig. 27–27). Although most of the electrons driven across from the hot filament hit the plate, those moving straight toward the hole go through and travel on until they meet the wall of the tube. If the wall opposite the electron gun is covered with fluorescent paint, a bright spot appears where the electrons hit.

With one more modification, the tube we have described becomes a cathode-ray oscilloscope. We put two small horizontal metal plates in the tube so that the electron beam passes between them (Fig. 27–28). If one plate is charged positive and the other negative, the electrons are shoved vertically toward the positive plate and hit the fluorescent screen at a new place. Even a single flashlight battery connected across the deflecting plates produces a visible deflection of the spot. Consequently, we can use this oscilloscope as an electrometer. And if we couple it with an amplifier like the one in a radio, it can be a far more sensitive instrument than the electrometers we described previously.

In addition to its sensitivity as an electrometer, the cathode-ray oscilloscope has an even more useful property, the speed of its response. Because of the mass of its moving parts, an ordinary electrometer takes an appreciable time to reach the equilibrium position after it has been charged. The electrons, on the other hand, have astonishingly small mass compared to the lightest mechanical part. Consequently, the deflection of the electron beam occurs practically instantaneously. Thus the cathode-ray oscilloscope is capable of showing very rapid changes of charge, something that ordinary electrometers cannot do.

With the cathode-ray oscilloscope we can even study in detail how a rapidly changing charge varies with time. For this purpose we equip the oscilloscope with a second pair of metal plates arranged to deflect the beam horizontally (Fig. 27–29). A "sweep circuit" gradually charges this pair of plates and then discharges them suddenly, only to start charging them again. During the gradual charging the bright spot where the electrons hit swings horizontally across the screen at a constant speed; then on discharge it returns quickly to the starting point. At the same time the first pair of plates produces a vertical deflection corresponding to their charges. As a result of the two deflections the spot traces a curve which gives a graphical picture of the way the charge on the vertical plates changes with time (Fig. 27–30).

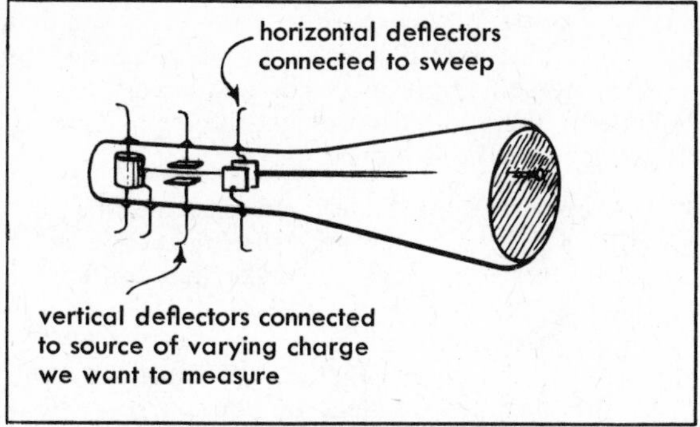

27–29. An oscilloscope tube has a second pair of plates to give a horizontal deflection. Charging these plates swings the spot across the face of the tube.

The cathode-ray oscilloscope has many applications. Television and radar tubes are special types of cathode-ray tubes. The pictures they paint are produced by deflecting the electron beam horizontally and vertically over the face of the tube while the strength of the beam is varied to make each little region of the screen glow bright or stay dark in response to signals from the TV camera.

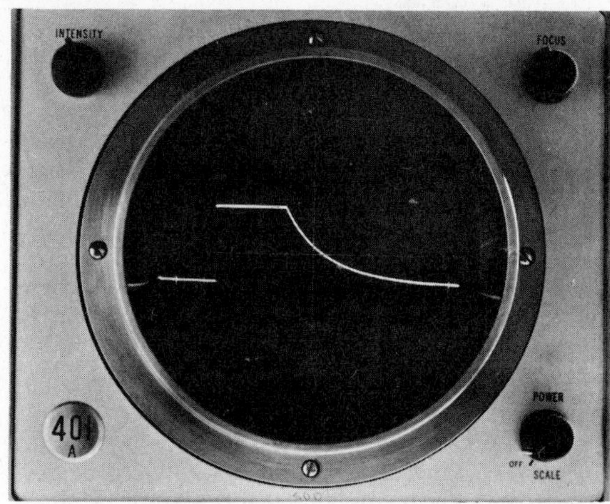

27–30. A photograph of a trace on the face of an oscilloscope tube. While the sweep circuit moved the beam from left to right, a battery rapidly charged two metal plates connected to the vertical deflection plates of the tube. A moment later they were allowed to discharge more slowly through a wire of high resistance.

FOR HOME, DESK, AND LAB

1. Suppose that you have electrified a plastic rod by rubbing it with wool.

(a) Do you expect the wool to become charged?

(b) How could you find out if it does?

2. In filling the gasoline tank of an airplane, the metal nozzle of the hose is always carefully connected to the metal of the airplane by a wire before the nozzle is inserted in the tank. Be prepared to explain why this procedure is followed, and to describe how it accomplishes its purpose.

3. (a) When you touch a metal object like a door handle on a dry winter day, you are likely to see a spark and feel a definite shock. We usually explain this by saying that we have built up a static charge. How could you tell the sign of the charge you are carrying? Why does this not happen on a humid day in the summer?

(b) If you accumulate a static charge and then touch the wooden frame of a door, you often find no spark or shock — although there would be if you touched the metal handle. Why?

(c) Sometimes, if you touch the wooden frame and then touch the metal handle, there is no spark or shock in either case — although there would have been if you had touched the handle first. Suggest an explanation.

4. (a) Why can't you electrify a metal rod by rubbing it while *holding it in your hand?*

(b) What could you do to electrify a metal rod?

5. * A short project: Charge a plastic coat hanger and suspend it by a light string.

(a) Find out whether the charge is positive or negative.

(b) What happens when you bring your finger near the charged hanger?

(c) How do you explain your result in (b)?

6. (a) Describe the steps you would follow to charge an electroscope positively by induction.

(b) Using labeled sketches, describe the movement of negative electric particles during the charging process.

7. Three metal blocks in contact are resting on a plastic table top. You place two objects with strong positive charges, one at each end of the line of blocks, close to but not touching the blocks. You then poke the blocks apart with an insulating (uncharged) rod, while the objects with strong positive charges are near by. Finally you remove the two positively charged objects.

(a) What charge is now on each block?

(b) Explain how the blocks acquired these charges by describing the motion of negative particles.

8. * As a project you can make a device called an electrophorus. You will need an old phonograph record and a metal plate somewhat smaller than the record. Attach an insulating handle at right angles to the plate. A small aluminum pan (an empty frozen-pie container) with a candle stuck to it will do.

Charge the record by rubbing it with wool. Place the pan on the record and ground the pan momentarily with your finger. Then remove the pan and use it to charge an electroscope. What charge does the pan have? What charge does the record have? To charge another pan in the same way, would you have to recharge the electrophorus?

9. Before the invention of the magnetic telegraph, numerous schemes were proposed for long-distance signaling over wires, using electric repulsion or attraction. Suggest a simple arrangement for such communication.

10. * A project: Do an experiment to find out whether Scotch tape will discharge an electroscope. If you find some sign of conduction, try cutting the tape to half width, and repeat the test. Also try using twice the length.

11. * A project: (a) Charge an electroscope and bring a lighted match near the knob. What do you observe? Does it make any difference whether you have a positive or negative charge on the electroscope?

(b) Hold a match far enough from the knob so the electroscope does not discharge. What happens when you fan the heated air very gently toward the knob? How do you explain this result? Is the discharge the direct effect of heating the knob, or does heating make the air conducting?

12. We have seen that electric charge will flow through certain solutions, such as copper sulfate in water. In this case there is a deposit of copper built up on the negative electrode. Recall the explanation given for this in Section 27–11, and think how this process might be used as a current-measuring device. Be prepared to discuss your ideas in class.

13. Section 27–13 is concerned with a simple type of radio tube called a diode. A triode is similar, but it has a second cylinder of open wire mesh between the filament and the plate [Fig. 27–31 (a)]. Suppose first that the wire mesh (or "grid") is connected to the earth so that the grid remains

27–31. For Problem 13.

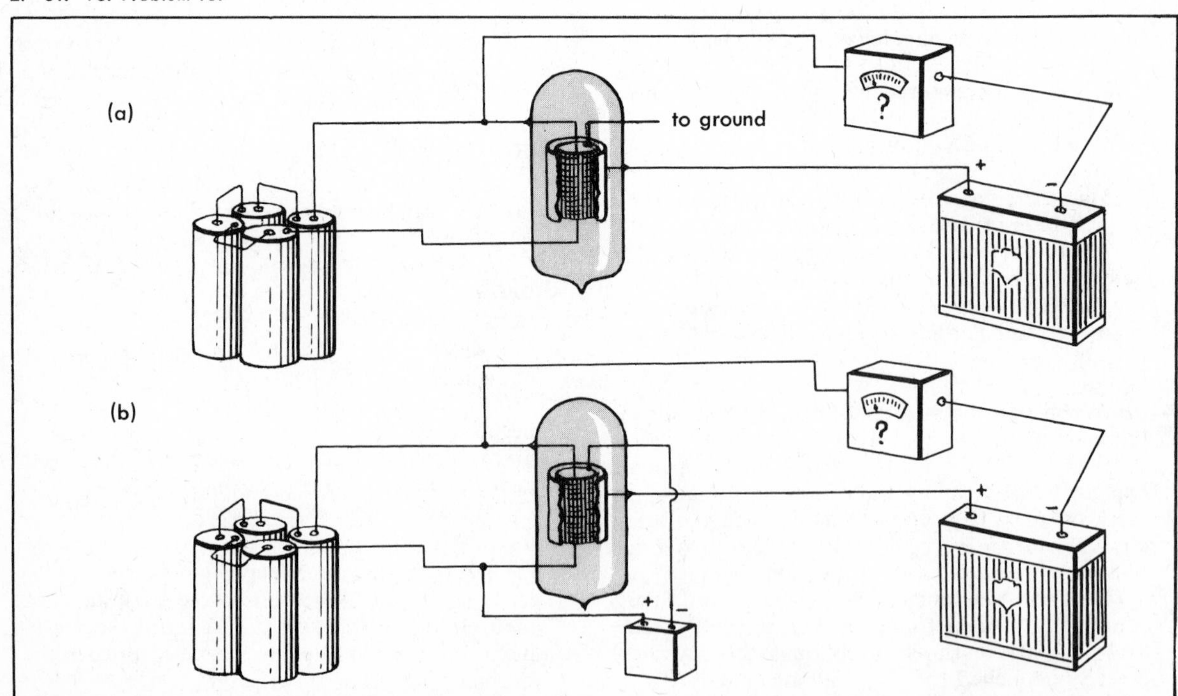

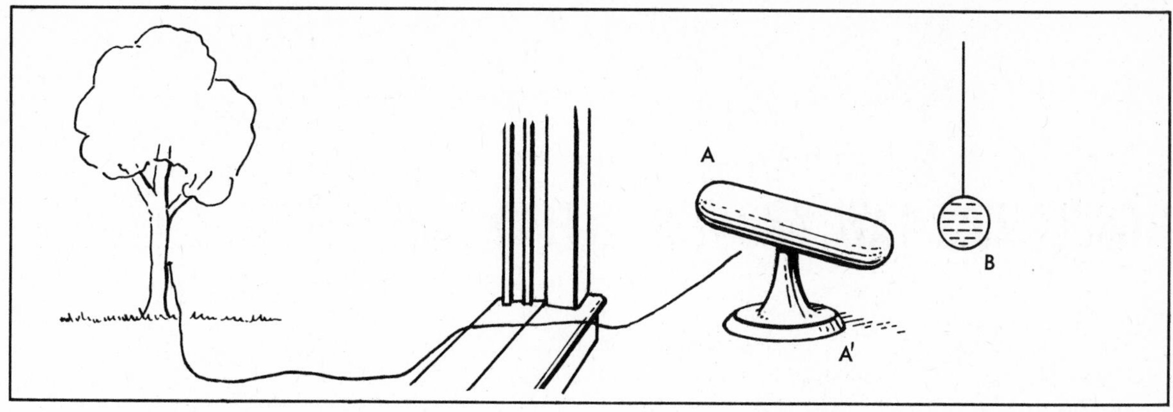

27–32. For Problem 17.

uncharged. Then we connect a battery [Fig. 27–31 (b)] so that there is a negative charge on the grid. Compare the currents in the "B" battery circuit in these two cases.

14. Suppose we have a large number of identical particles. Any two of them at 10 cm separation repel with a force of 3×10^{-10} newtons.

(a) If one of them is at 10 cm from a group of *n* others, how strongly do you expect it to be repelled?

(b) Suppose you measure the repulsion and find it is 6×10^{-6} newtons; how many particles were there in the group?

15. Suppose we have a large number of positive and negative electric particles, all exactly the same (except for sign). This means that any pair of them either attract or repel depending on their signs, but the magnitude of the force between them is the same as long as the separation distance is the same. For example, the force between any two of them at 10 cm is 3×10^{-10} newtons.

A single positive particle is 10 cm from a group containing *P* positive particles and *M* negative particles.

(a) How strongly will it be repelled? (b) You are unable to count the particles, but you measure the force and find it is 6×10^{-6} newtons. What does this tell you about *P* and *M*?

16. We think the earth has a slight electric charge. How would you go about testing for it?

17. In the following experiment changes or motions of electric charge occur. An oblong horizontal conductor *A* (Fig. 27–32) is supported on an insulating stand *A′*. A conducting ball *B* hung on an insulating thread carries a strong negative charge. *A* is uncharged.

(1) *B* is then brought near *A*.

(2) A wire then connects *A* to an enormous conducting object situated outside the laboratory (e.g. a wet oak tree).

(3) The conducting wire is removed.

(4) *B* is taken away.

(5) The conducting wire is again touched to *A*.

(a) Suppose that only negative particles are movable in the conductors (and neither negative nor positive in insulators) and say what charges move where in each of the stages of the experiment described.

(b) Now suppose the conductors are made of some material in which only positive particles can move (there are some, but they are special). Repeat the explanation asked for in (a), in full detail.

(c) Now suppose that the conductors have both positive and negative particles that move freely (which is what you would have if the conductors were blocks of insulator painted with brine). Repeat the explanation asked for in (a), in full detail.

FURTHER READING

Furry, W. H.; Purcell, E. M.; Street, J. C., *Physics for Science and Engineering Students.* Blakiston, 1952 (Chapter 22).

Gilbert, N. E., *Electricity and Magnetism.* Third Edition, Macmillan, 1950.

Skilling, Hugh H., *Exploring Electricity.* Ronald Press, 1948.

Steinbach, H. B., "Animal Electricity." *Scientific American*, February, 1950.

Taylor, Lloyd, *Physics, the Pioneer Science.* Dover, 1959 (Chapter 40).

Wilson, Mitchell, *American Science and Invention.* Simon & Schuster, 1954 (Franklin: pp. 16–23).

COULOMB'S LAW AND THE ELEMENTARY ELECTRIC CHARGE

CHAPTER 28

So FAR, our study of electric forces has been qualitative. It indicated that the electric attraction and repulsion between large bodies is due to attraction and repulsion between the subatomic particles of which they are made. Our next task will be to describe experiments that provide quantitative information about these forces.

28–1. Force vs. Distance

The way in which the attraction or repulsion between charges depends on distance was established experimentally by the French physicist Charles Coulomb in 1785. In his experiment Coulomb used a torsion balance, like the instrument Cavendish used later to study gravitational attraction (see Section 22–10). Fig. 28–1 is a diagram of this kind of apparatus. When the charged sphere A is put in place, the electric force it exerts on the charged sphere B pushes the horizontal arm around. The arm then comes to rest in a new position with the suspension twisted. The more the suspension is twisted, the greater the force must be. From the angle of twist, therefore, Coulomb could measure the electric force. And by changing the distance between the charged spheres, he measured the force as a function of separation. Because the charges are distributed

28–1. Below: schematic diagram of Coulomb's torsion balance. At right: a sketch of Coulomb's apparatus which appeared in his original paper.

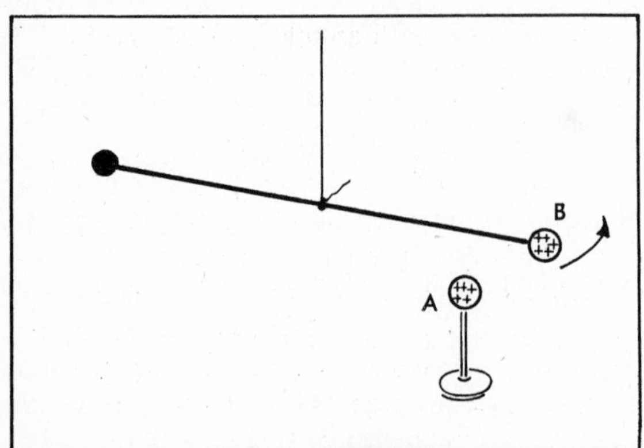

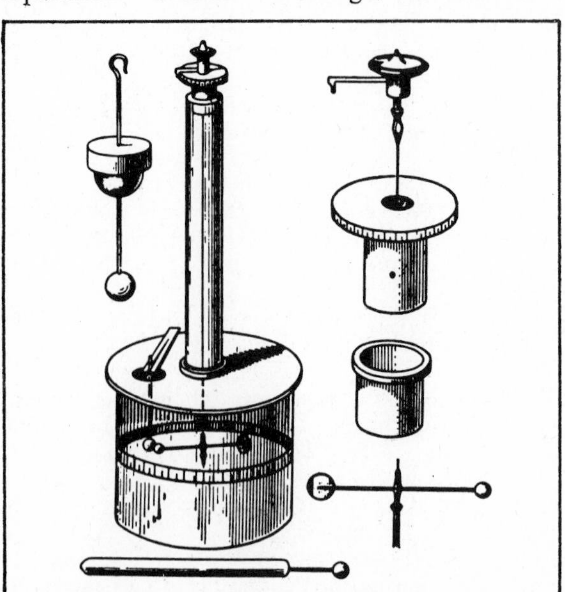

about on the spheres, the spheres must be far enough apart so that the slight differences in distance and direction do not matter.*

Using both positive and negative charged spheres, Coulomb showed that the electric force is always inversely proportional to the square of the distance between the charges. He established this result with an accuracy of about 3 per cent. Later indirect tests — using the shielding effect of conductors — have shown it with much higher precision. Cavendish attained 1 per cent accuracy; and in the latter part of the nineteenth century Maxwell established the exponent 2 (the *square* in the inverse square), to within one part in 40,000. It is now known to one part in 10^9. Note that electric forces and gravitational forces vary with distance in exactly the same manner. We have no explanation of this similarity, but because of it we can often understand gravitational and electrical effects in the same way.

We believe that the force of attraction or repulsion between any two charged objects is the vector sum of all forces that the electric particles of one object exert upon the electric particles of the other. And in all cases, we find experimentally that the force varies in inverse proportion to the square of the separation. So we naturally conclude that *the force between individual electric particles varies as the inverse square of their separation.*

Since 1910 a great many experiments have been done with subatomic particles. We can fire them at one another or at the charged nuclei of atoms. As we shall see in Chapter 32, these experiments also show that the electric force between the particles varies as the inverse square of the separation.

28–2. Electric Charge and Electric Force

In an electrically neutral body the effects of positive and negative electric particles cancel. A positively charged body contains uncanceled positive particles and a negatively charged body contains uncanceled negative particles. Thus the charge of a body depends on the uncanceled excess of positive or of negative particles, measured from neutral.

*When charged bodies are far apart compared with their dimensions, they are often called point charges because the detailed positions of the charges on the bodies are then unimportant.

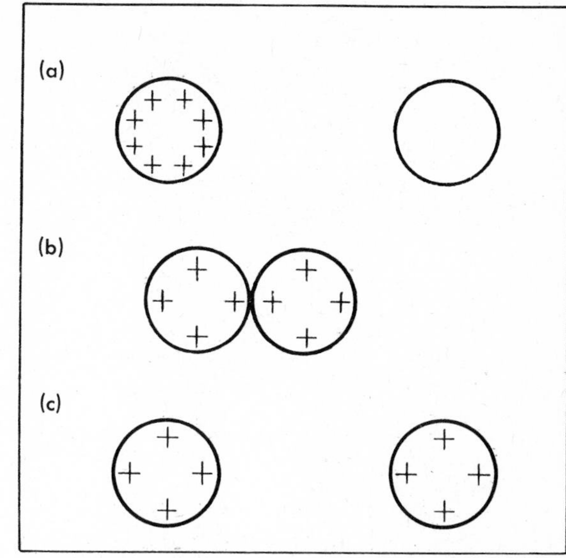

28–2. The sharing of electric charge. When a charged sphere is touched to an identical uncharged one, the excess of electric particles divides equally. The final distribution of charge must be symmetrical, as shown in (c).

The force between two charged bodies depends on their separation and increases with the excess of positive or of negative electric particles on each body. Just how does the force depend upon the excess of electric particles? To answer this question we need a scheme to divide the excess of particles in a known way — in half, into thirds, etc. Suppose we touch a charged metal sphere with an identical uncharged sphere (Fig. 28–2). Then the electric particles will move around until they are shared equally by both spheres. Each sphere will have half the original charge.

What happens to the electric forces when charges are shared? Measure the force of repulsion between two charged spheres A and C at a certain separation. Then halve the charge on A by sharing it with an identical sphere B. The force of repulsion between A and C (still at the same separation) is *also* cut in half. Furthermore, we get the same force when A is replaced by B, the identical sphere with which it shared its charge. Apparently, charge and force are proportional, as we might have guessed.

Such experiments give us a way of comparing charges quantitatively. Two charges are equal if they experience equal forces at a given distance from any third charge. One charge is twice another when it experiences twice the force. Fur-

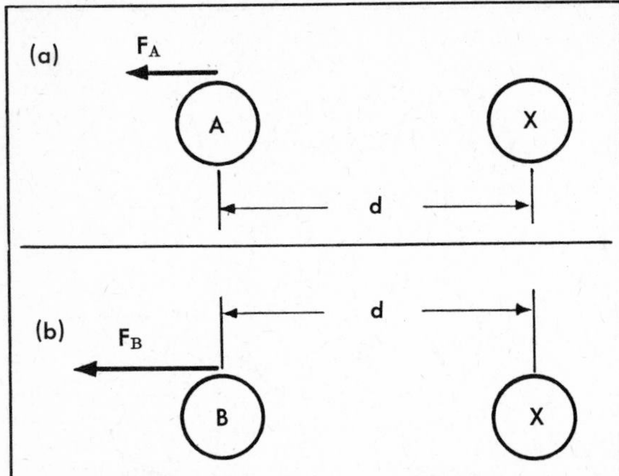

28–3. To compare two charges, *A* and *B*, we place them in turn at the same distance from any other charge *X*, and measure the forces. The ratio of the charges equals the ratio of the forces: $q_A/q_B = F_A/F_B$. What do you think is the ratio of the forces exerted on *X*?

thermore, the force experienced by a charge and the force exerted by it go together. When a charge is halved by charge sharing, the force it exerts on a third charge is also halved. In general, charges are compared by the ratio of the forces they exert on and experience from any other charge at a given distance. This *ratio* does not depend on the magnitude of the "other" charge nor on the distance apart (Fig. 28–3).

Now let us summarize our knowledge in algebraic language. The electric force on a charge q is proportional to the charge: $F \propto q$. When this force is the force of interaction between the charge q and another small body of charge Q, the force is also proportional to the other charge. We can write this proportionality to both the charges as $F \propto qQ$.

We now have a definite meaning for charge, and we know how the electric force depends on the charges. We can combine this knowledge with Coulomb's experiments. They tell us that the force is inversely proportional to the square of the separation r between the charges. So we arrive at the complete expression for the force of interaction between two charges. It is

$$F = \frac{kQq}{r^2}$$

where the proportionality factor k depends only on the units in which we measure forces, separations, and charges. We shall call this expression for the force *Coulomb's law*, and the force itself the Coulomb force.

When we first began speaking of electric charge, we gave this word only a qualitative meaning. An electric charge was simply the result of adding or removing some positive or negative electric particles from a neutral object. Now, however, we have learned to compare charges numerically; and we can speak of the charges of the individual particles themselves. We shall say that two particles have the same charge if they experience the same force when placed at a given distance from another charge. If the forces experienced by the two particles are different, we shall say that their charges are in the ratio of these forces. The "charge" on a "large" object may be thought of as the excess of electric particles of one sign. But the charge of one electric particle can only be defined by the force it exerts.

One thing is still missing. We need a standard unit of charge, something reproducible so that we can compare charges at widely separated places. For this purpose many different arbitrary units have been used. Fortunately, however — as we shall see in Section 28–5 — nature itself provides a fundamental unit.

28–3. Electric Force Fields

Suppose we move a charge to various positions near another small charged body fixed at a particular place. The force varies inversely as the square of the separation and always points along

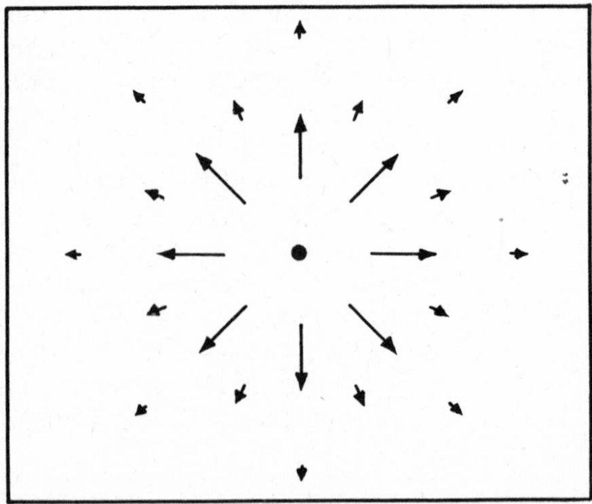

28–4. The electric force field around a fixed charge. It is a set of vectors showing the force on a movable charge of the same sign as the fixed charge.

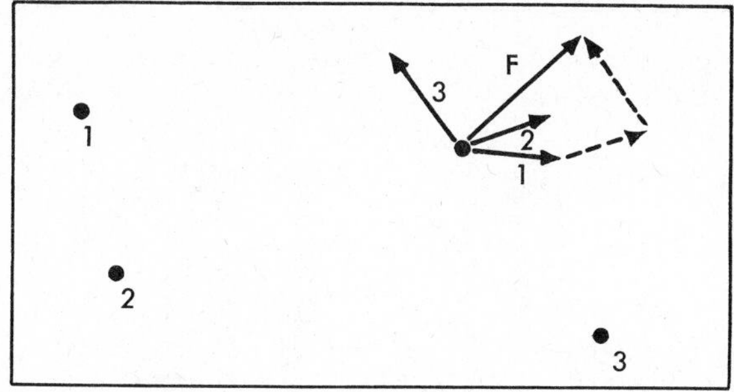

28–5. Three fixed charges 1, 2, and 3 exert forces on a movable charge. The net force $\vec{F}$ on it is the vector sum of the three forces, 1, 2, and 3, exerted by each of the fixed charges.

the line between the charges. We can draw a diagram of the force vectors around the stationary charge, showing the size and the direction of the force on the movable charge at a large number of points. Fig. 28–4 shows such a set of vectors. It is just like the set of vectors indicating the gravitational field around the earth (Fig. 21–1) — except that the vectors here all point away from the stationary charge. They point away because the charge we moved around happened to be of the same sign as the stationary charge. Just as Fig. 21–1 shows the gravitational field of the earth, this diagram shows an electric force field around the stationary charge. Such a force field is simply a collection of values of the force at various points in space as it is felt by a movable charge.

Now suppose we have a collection of many charges nailed down at different positions. They exert a force on a movable charge placed at any position, and this force is the vector sum of the forces that each of the nailed-down charges would exert individually (Fig. 28–5). The net force on the movable charge in this situation does *not* vary as the inverse square of the separation from any one of the nailed-down charges. But we can compute the net force by adding all the individual forces, or we can measure it experimentally. We can represent it by making a plot of the net force vectors at a large number of positions; and we thus get an idea of the field of force from the whole collection of nailed-down charges.

As an example, suppose we have a large number of charges spread evenly on a large plane. We then find that the net force does *not* increase noticeably as we move closer to the plane. Al-

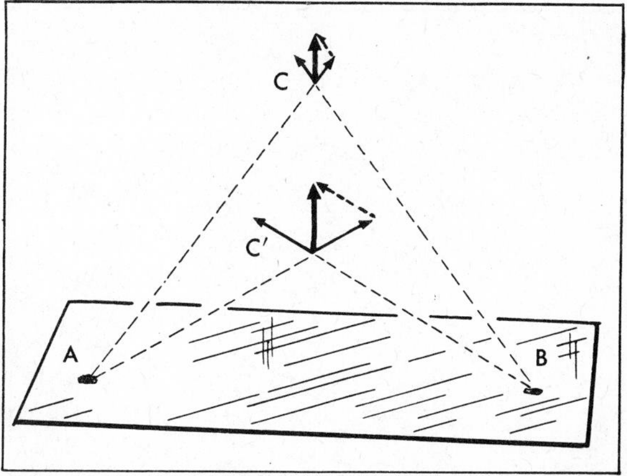

28–6. Two fixed charges *A* and *B* on a plane exert forces on a movable charge C. As C moves nearer to the plane, the forces tend to push against each other. So the net force does not increase as much as we might expect. What is the sum of the forces exerted by *A* and *B* when C is just in between them?

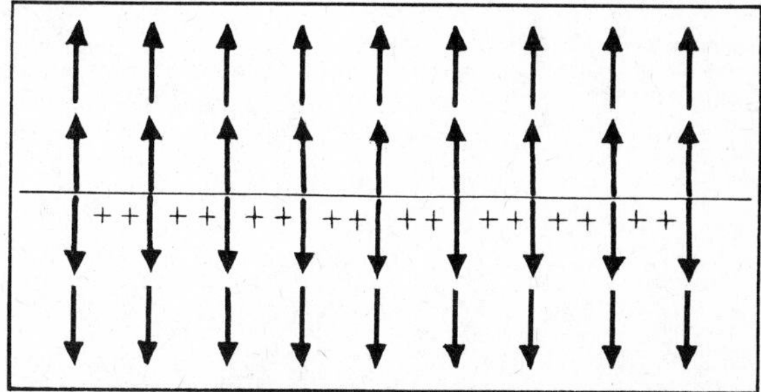

28–7. The electric force field around an evenly charged plane.

though we are getting nearer to the charges, the forces from them push more and more nearly in opposite directions and become progressively less effective (Fig. 28–6). When we actually carry through the vector addition of all the forces, we find that the net force does not change either in magnitude or direction as we approach the plane. The force field is uniform. (A proof is outlined in the box on page 468.) If the charges on the plane and the movable charge are of the same sign, this uniform force field points straight away from the plane. Fig. 28–7 is a diagram of this field. We shall get an experimental demonstration of its uniformity in the next section.

Often instead of drawing a collection of net-force vectors, we represent an electric force field in a slightly different way by drawing a number of electric field lines. A line is constructed by moving a point continuously in the direction of the force exerted on a movable particle. As the force changes direction, so does the line. The

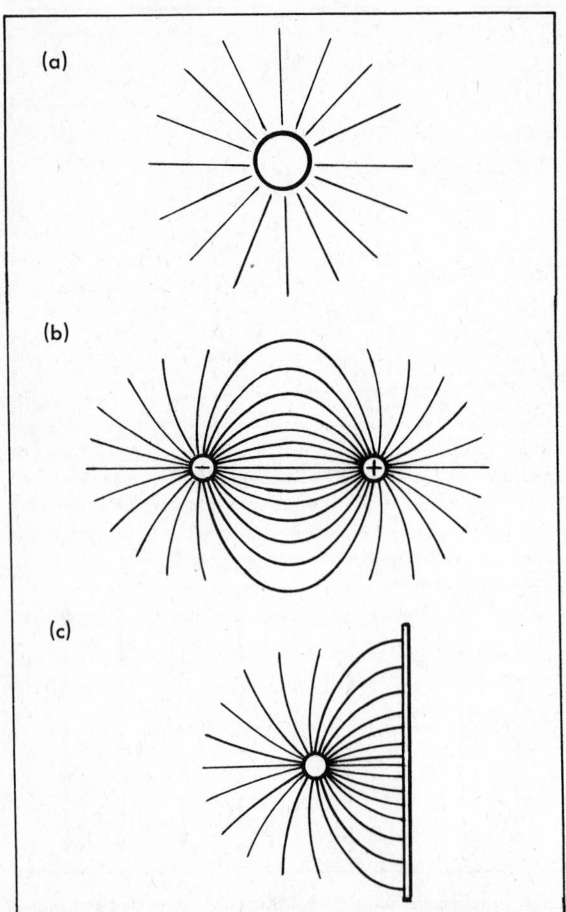

28–8. (a) The electric force field around a single isolated charged sphere. (b) The electric force field of two charged spheres of opposite sign. (c) The electric force field of a small charged sphere near a large plane conductor. Note that close spacing of the field lines indicates a region where the field is strong. Diverging lines indicate that the field is growing weaker.

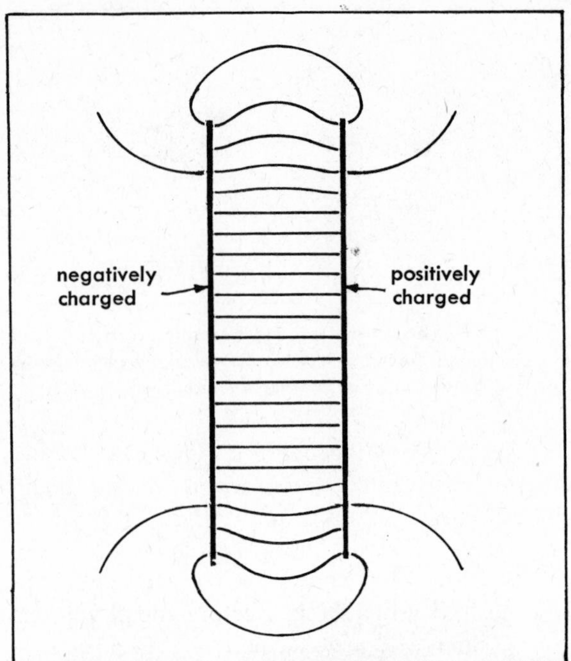

28–9. The field of two oppositely charged metal plates placed close together and parallel to each other. In the center the field lines run straight across. The force on a charge is the same anywhere in this region — the force field is uniform.

patterns of electric field lines around a single small charged object and around several separated charged bodies are illustrated in Fig. 28–8. Sometimes we can show the electric field lines experimentally by taking advantage of the fact that small oblong bodies will line up along them. For example, we can suspend grass seed in an insulating liquid. Then, if we make an electric field by putting charged objects in the liquid, the seeds line up forming a picture of the field. Fig. 28–10 shows photographs of the grass seed patterns of several electric fields. [Compare the center of Fig. 28–10 (f) with Fig. 28–7.]

In Fig. 28–10 the charged objects are metal conductors. Notice that the electric field lines meet their surfaces at right angles. This is easy to understand. In a metal conductor electrons are free to move from point to point within the metal, but cannot easily leave its surface. If the electric forces which act on the electrons in a metal surface have any component parallel to that surface, they drag the electrons along the surface. This flow of electrons is a current. The currents will continue until the electrons have so arranged themselves that electric field lines become perpendicular to every metal surface. This rearrangement takes a very small fraction of a second; what we measure in these experiments is the field after the charges have stopped moving.

In the next section we are going to use the electric force on a small object between two oppositely charged plane parallel metal plates close together (Fig. 28–9). Except at the edges, the charge on each plate spreads out evenly over the inner surface. Consequently, in the region between the plates, the electric field should be uniform and point straight across from one plate to the other. As long as a charge between the plates is not too close to the edges, the force on it should be the same at every point. This force is proportional to the charges on the plates.

28–10. Photographs of electric force field patterns formed by grass seeds in an insulating liquid.

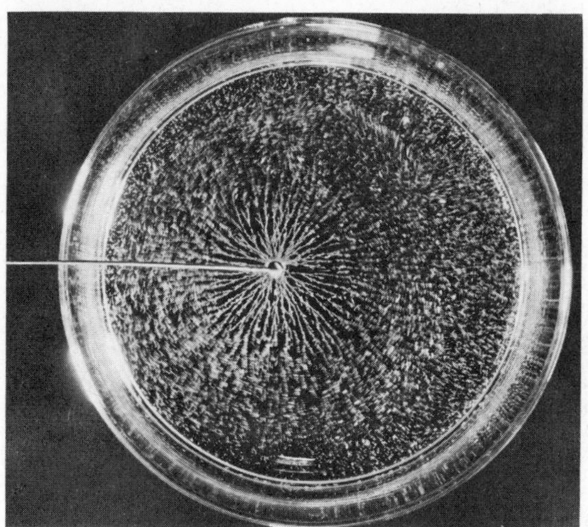

(a) A single charged rod.

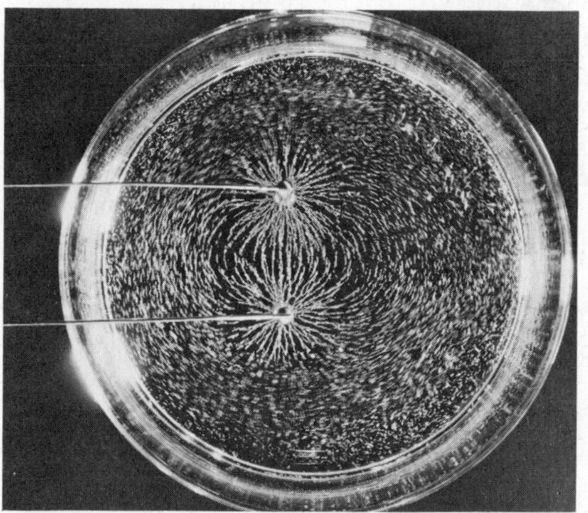

(b) Two rods with equal and opposite charges.

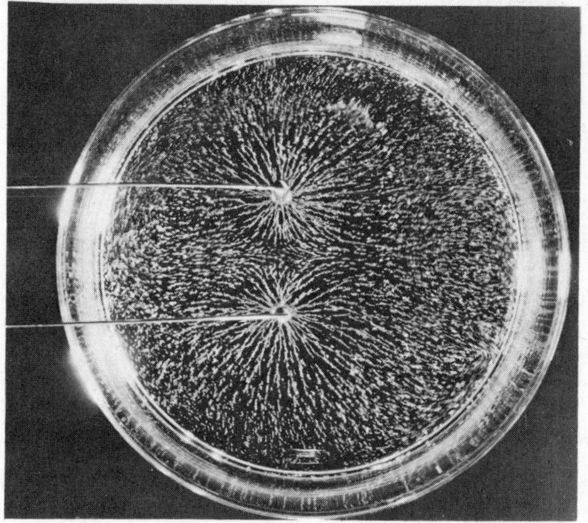

(c) Two rods with the same charge.

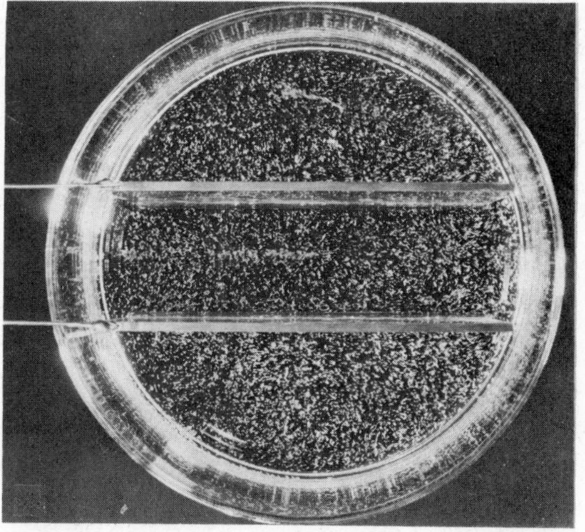

(d) Two parallel plates, no electric field.

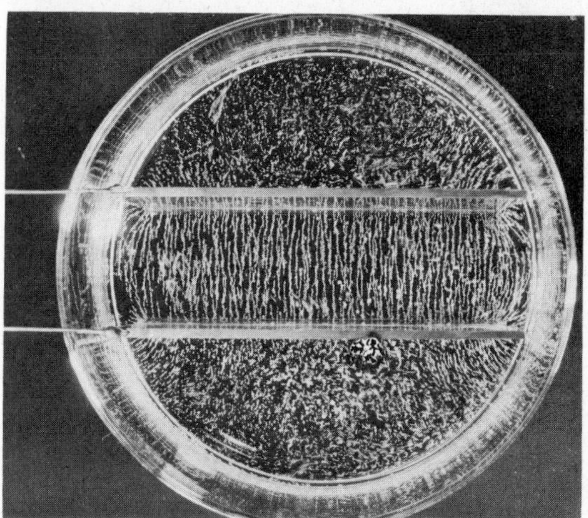

(e) Two parallel plates with opposite charges.

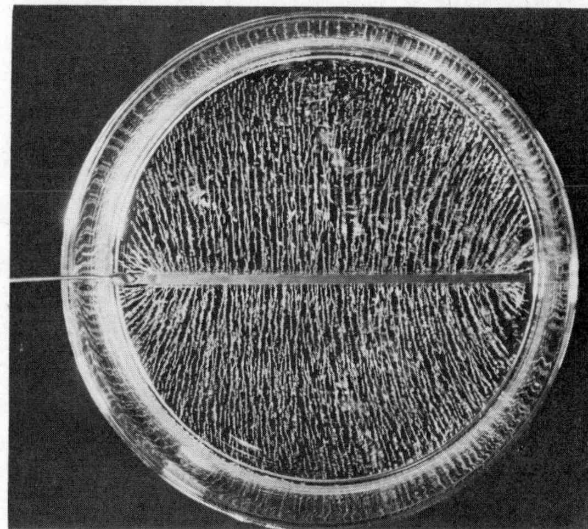

(f) A single charged metal plate.

The Electric Force on a Charge above a Uniformly Charged Plane

Imagine you are on the charge. The plane is directly below you; and you look down on it, looking at some angle to the vertical through a small cone — like a long, thin megaphone (Fig. 28–11). The area of the little patch of plane you see through the cone increases with the square of your height above the plane. For example, if you move twice as far from the plane, you see a patch of twice the original length and twice the original width on the plane. The patch has four times the original area, and therefore the charge of the patch is four times the original charge seen at that angle. Also, this charge is twice the original distance away. So the force from a given amount of charge is one-quarter what it was originally. The ratio of the force at a given angle to the original force at that angle is changed by two factors, the factor 4 from the fourfold charge and the factor $\frac{1}{4}$ from the square of the doubled distance. The net effect — because $4 \times \frac{1}{4} = 1$ — is to give exactly the original force.

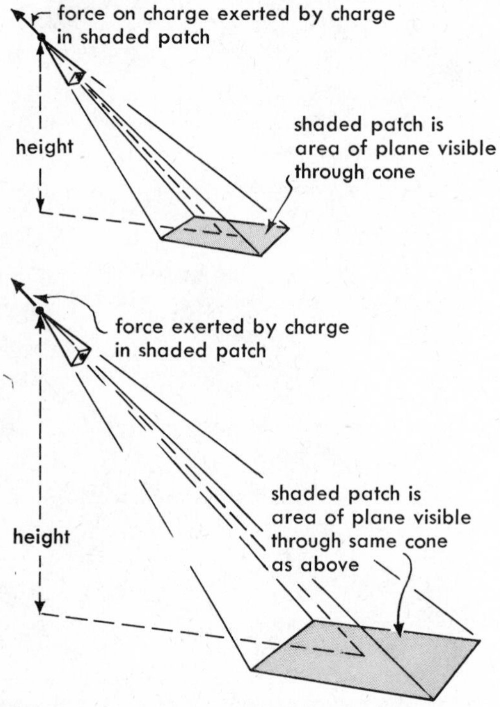

The falling off of the force from a given amount of charge and the increase in the amount of charge seen through the megaphone always compensate — $1/r^2$ and r^2. Therefore the force coming up at any angle is the same at all heights as long as we do not have to look off the edge of the plane.

Finally, since all the forces coming up at all angles stay the same, the net force also stays the same. It does not depend on the height above the plane. Note that with any other force law you would not obtain a uniform force field. The $1/r^2$ force law is the only one that will cancel with the geometrical r^2. Consequently, the observation of a uniform force field in this case verifies Coulomb's law.

Of course, at really great heights, so great that the whole charged plane looks like a point, the force falls off as $1/r^2$. The force starts to decrease appreciably when we get about $\frac{1}{20}$ as far away as the smallest dimension of the charged region.

28–11. Looking down at a plane through a narrow cone, you see an area of the plane that depends upon your height above it.

28–4. Measuring Small Electrical Forces

As we shall see, ions have charges of very few particles, often an excess of only one or two. By studying them we shall find that electric particles all have charges of the same size. Charge comes in separate grains; and every grain, whether positive or negative, is of the same magnitude as any other. The identity of the grains of charge, like the identity of atoms of matter, provides us with natural units. Their discovery is one of the great landmarks distinguishing modern physics from ancient.

This discovery allows us to specify the charge on an object by counting the extra number of electric particles of one sign as compared with those of the other sign. It makes our picture of charge simple. Of course, the fact that elementary charges all have the same magnitude does not guarantee that particles are the same in all other respects. As we shall see later, there are particles of several different masses, all with the same charge. Eventually we classify particles by a number of properties.

At the moment we shall study the small electric forces on ions, and then use them to establish the units of charge.

The electric forces we can exert on ions are small; these forces will not move ordinary-sized objects or stretch springs appreciably. In any case, we cannot tie single ions to a spring or be sure that we have only one ion on any object of visible size. We must therefore find a way of handling really tiny objects with an excess of only a few elementary electric particles on them. In this section, we shall discuss one method of manipulating such objects and of measuring the minute electrical forces we can exert on them. Then we shall be equipped to understand the evidence given in the next section for the natural unit of charge.

We need objects which are much larger than ions or gas molecules and yet small enough to be moved about by the electric forces we can exert on ions. Objects visible to the naked eye are too massive for our purpose. Microscopic plastic spheres about 1.8×10^{-6} meter in diameter turn out to be about right (Fig. 28–12). Although they are large enough to be seen as spots of light through an optical microscope, the mass of each is only 2.9×10^{-15} kg — about 3 micro-micrograms. Since these spheres are manufactured for calibrating the distances seen with electron microscopes, a large number of almost identical spheres are available.

In air these spheres move rather slowly. Driven downward by the gravitational force, they fall 1 millimeter in about 10.6 seconds. Looking at them, we see that they fall steadily (Fig. 28–13) with only a slight amount of Brownian motion, and no apparent acceleration. On the average the net force on them must be zero. This zero net force is the vector sum of the gravitational driving force which pulls a sphere down and the opposing force of air resistance. When a sphere starts falling the air resistance is zero, but the faster the sphere goes the greater the air resistance. So the drag of the air increases quickly until it balances the gravitational driving force; and the speed of the steady motion we observe is a measure of the size of that force.

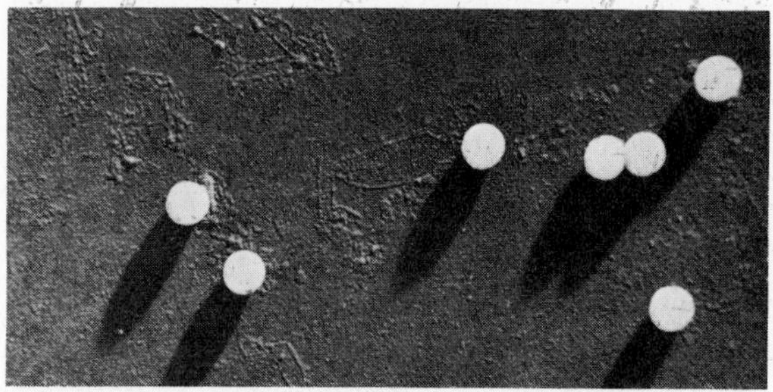

28–12. An electron-microscope photograph of a few plastic spheres magnified about 2500 X.

Now we come to the point of the game. The little plastic spheres usually carry a few ionic charges; and because air molecules are neutral, the charge on a sphere stays the same for quite a long time. If we place ordinary charged bodies near a falling sphere, they will exert electric forces on these ionic charges, forces comparable with the small gravitational force pulling the sphere down. When such an electric force is present, the driving force pushing a sphere along is the vector sum of the gravitational force and the electric force. Therefore, by changing the charges near by, we can change the driving force exerted on the sphere. When the driving force changes, the speed of the sphere changes. If we increase

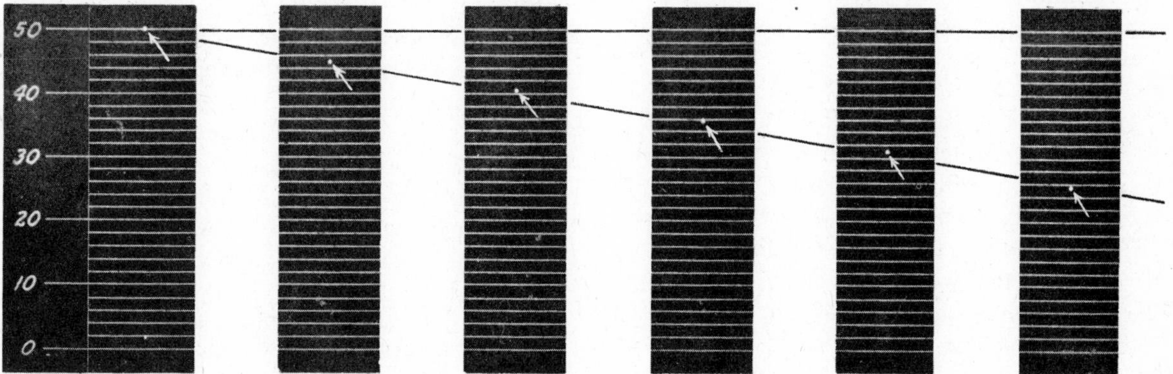

28–13. Photographs of a plastic sphere driven downward by gravity, taken through a microscope at one-second intervals. The sphere falls about the same distance in each interval across a grid slightly over 1 mm long.

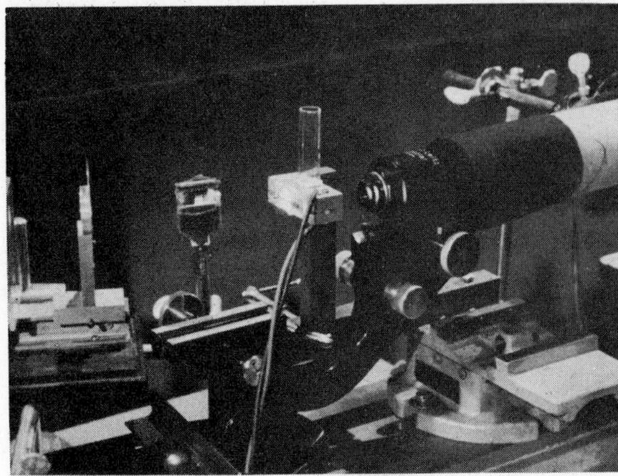

28–14. The micro-microbalance. The plastic spheres are observed in the space between the metal plates in the center of the picture. The microscope is on the right, and to the left is a bright source of light.

28–15. The plates of the micro-microbalance. Note the connecting wires from the battery used to charge the plates. The spheres are put into the plastic tube above the plates, and one or two will drift through a small hole into the region between the plates.

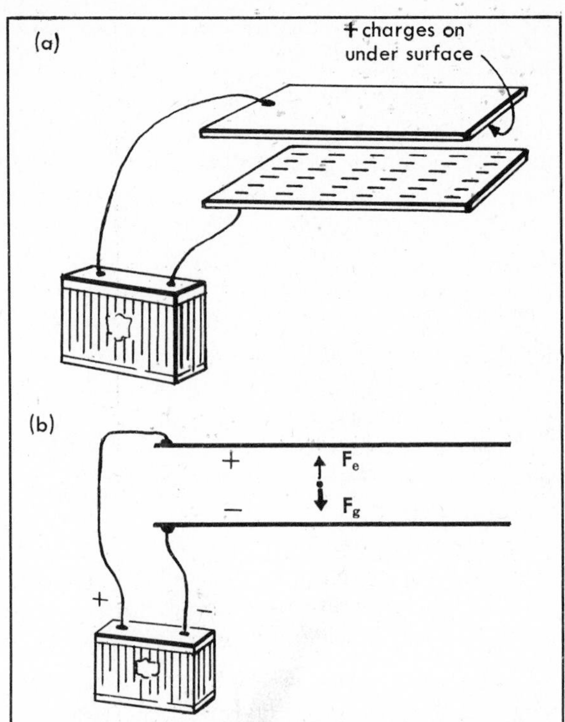

28–16. By choosing the right battery and the right plate separation, we can hold a sphere motionless between the plates. The electric force and the gravitational force must be equal: (a) shows the way the plates and the battery are arranged; (b) is a sketch of the same apparatus with schematic plates.

the driving force, the speed goes up until the increased drag of the air restores the balance, and the net force is again zero. The observed change in the steady speed of the sphere measures the contribution of the electric forces. In this way we get a micro-microbalance with which to measure the electric forces on the tiny ionic charges (Fig. 28–14).

Here is the description of a real experiment. We put one of our small spheres into the space between two parallel metal plates (Fig. 28–15). By connecting the plates to a battery, thus charging them, we hang the sphere motionless in midair. To do this we choose the battery and set the separation of the plates so that the electrical force on the sphere just compensates the gravitational attraction (Fig. 28–16). There is then no driving force pushing the sphere in any direction, and the sphere stands still. (If the sphere was moving beforehand it immediately comes to rest because of the air resistance.) Because we know the gravitational force on the sphere, this balance tells us the electric force. The downward gravitational force on a sphere of 2.9×10^{-15} kg is 2.8×10^{-14} newtons.* The balancing electric force must be 2.8×10^{-14} newtons upward, exactly compensating the downward gravitational pull.

If we remove the electric force, by connecting the two metal plates so that their charges cancel, the sphere starts to fall. It goes down steadily, moving 1 mm each 10.6 seconds. When we put the battery back on, re-establishing the electrical force, the sphere stops. By putting more charge on the metal plates we can haul the sphere back up. (The extra charge can be pushed on by add-

*For really accurate results we should subtract the bouyant force of the air from the gravitational attraction. Because this correction is only about one part in 1000, we shall neglect it here.

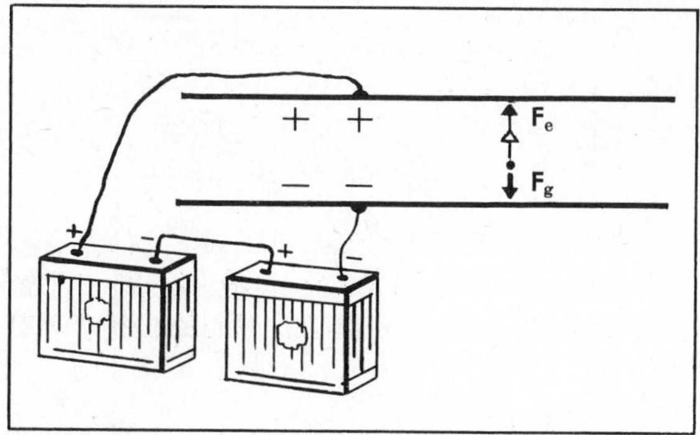

28–17 (a). We can make the sphere move upward by adding another battery in series, pushing more charge onto the plates.

28–17 (b). A sequence showing the sphere being hauled up by the electric force when another battery is used as shown in (a).

ing another battery in series [Fig. 28–17 (a) and (b)].) In this way we can keep the sphere in view for a long time while we play with it.

From observing the sphere fall under gravity alone we already know that a driving force of 2.8×10^{-14} newtons results in a steady velocity of 1 mm every 10.6 seconds. We also know how to get an *electric* force of this size on the sphere. Now we are going to find out what steady speed results from a different driving force. We can get a known force just twice the gravitational attraction by turning the electric force upside down and adding it to the gravitational one. All we have to do is to connect the balancing battery in reverse so that the charges on the plates are interchanged. Then an electric force of 2.8×10^{-14} newtons is pushing down on the charged sphere in addition to the equal gravitational force (Fig. 28–18). The driving force is therefore 5.6×10^{-14} newtons. Watching the sphere through the microscope, we observe that it now falls steadily, going 2 mm instead of 1 mm in each 10.6 seconds.

28–18. With the connections of the balancing battery reversed, the electric force now acts downward. The driving force is twice the gravitational force. The speed is 2 mm in 10.6 sec.

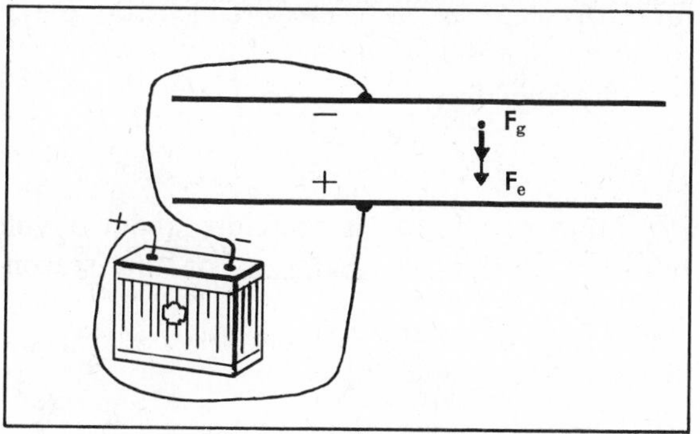

This experiment suggests that the drag of the air is just proportional to the speed; so when the driving force doubles, the speed doubles, bringing the drag back into balance.

If we can exert other known driving forces on the sphere, we can check that the speed with which the sphere moves is directly proportional to the driving force. To establish another known force, we adjust the electric force so that it hauls the sphere up at a speed of 1 mm in 10.6 seconds — just equal to the downward speed imposed by gravity alone. [We get this upward speed, it turns out, with two batteries in series as in Fig. 28–17 (a).] Since the driving force that gives this speed must be equal in magnitude to the gravitational force, the electric force upward must be twice the gravitational force downward. Therefore the electric force with two batteries connected is 5.6×10^{-14} newtons. When we turn this force upside down and add it to the gravitational pull on the sphere (Fig. 28–19), we get a

28–19. When we have two batteries in series, we know [see Fig. 28–17 (a)] that the electric force is twice the gravitational force. Now if they are reversed so that the electric force acts downward, the *driving* force is three times the gravitational force. The sphere moves down at a speed of 3 mm in 10.6 sec.

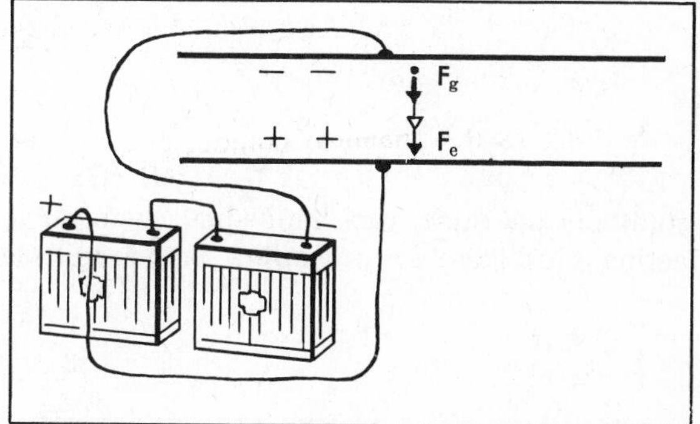

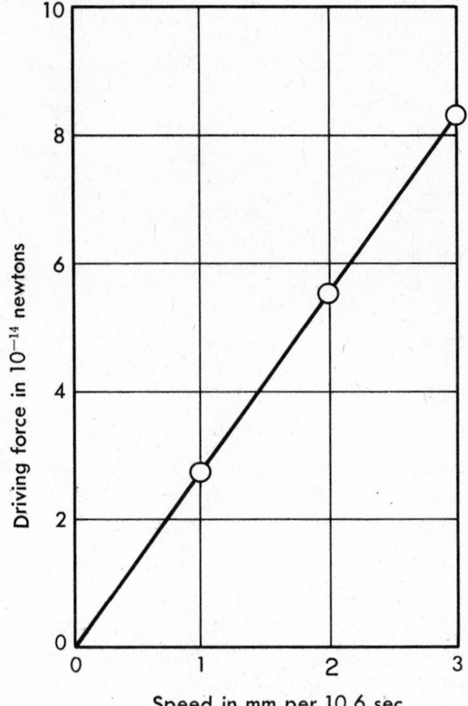

28–20. A graph of driving force versus velocity. Since the graph is a straight line, the force driving a standard sphere is proportional to its velocity.

downward driving force of $(5.6 + 2.8) \times 10^{-14}$ or 8.4×10^{-14} newtons. This is a new known driving force, just three times the gravitational force.

How does the sphere move when driven by this force? In the belief that the speed is proportional to the force, we predict that it will go at about 3 mm in 10.6 seconds, and it does. Now whenever we see the sphere move at a steady velocity we know the force driving it (Fig. 28–20). And by taking account of the 2.8×10^{-14} newtons of gravitational attraction, we can find the electric force. We have a micro-microbalance with which we can measure the electric force on a standard sphere.

With the micro-microbalance we can learn several useful things about batteries. For example, we can show that the electric force is proportional to the number of batteries connected in series to charge the plates. We already connected two

SUMMARY OF SECTION 4

The logic of this section is rather long. Here is a summary that puts it all together. (See Fig. 28–21.)

(a) When the plates of the micro-microbalance are uncharged, the sphere is driven downward by the force of gravity, F_g. Because of the drag of the air, it falls at the constant speed v_0.

(b) With the balancing battery connected, the plates are charged and there is also an electric force on the sphere. The sphere stands still, so we know that the electric force is equal and opposite to the gravitational one.

(c) When the battery is reversed, the electric force *and* the gravitational force both push the sphere down. The driving force is twice the gravitational force. We observe that the sphere falls at the speed $2v_0$.

(d) With two balancing batteries connected in series, the plates have larger charge and a larger electric force is exerted on the sphere. We observe that the sphere rises at speed v_0. This shows that the net driving force is upward and equal to the gravitational force. Therefore the electric upward force is two times the gravitational force.

(e) When the two batteries are reversed the driving force is three times the gravitational force and downward. The sphere falls with speed $3v_0$.

From (a), (c), and (e) we see that the speed is proportional to the driving force; and we can measure the driving force by observing the speed. The driving forces we can measure are of the order of 10^{-14} newtons.

(f) With three batteries in series the charge on the plates and the electric force on the sphere are again bigger. The sphere moves up with speed $2v_0$. Therefore the driving force is twice the gravitational force and in the opposite direction. It is made of the gravitational force downward and an electric force equal to three times the gravitational force pointing upward.

From (b), (d), and (f) we see that the electric force is proportional to the number of batteries. So also, therefore, is the electric charge on the plates.

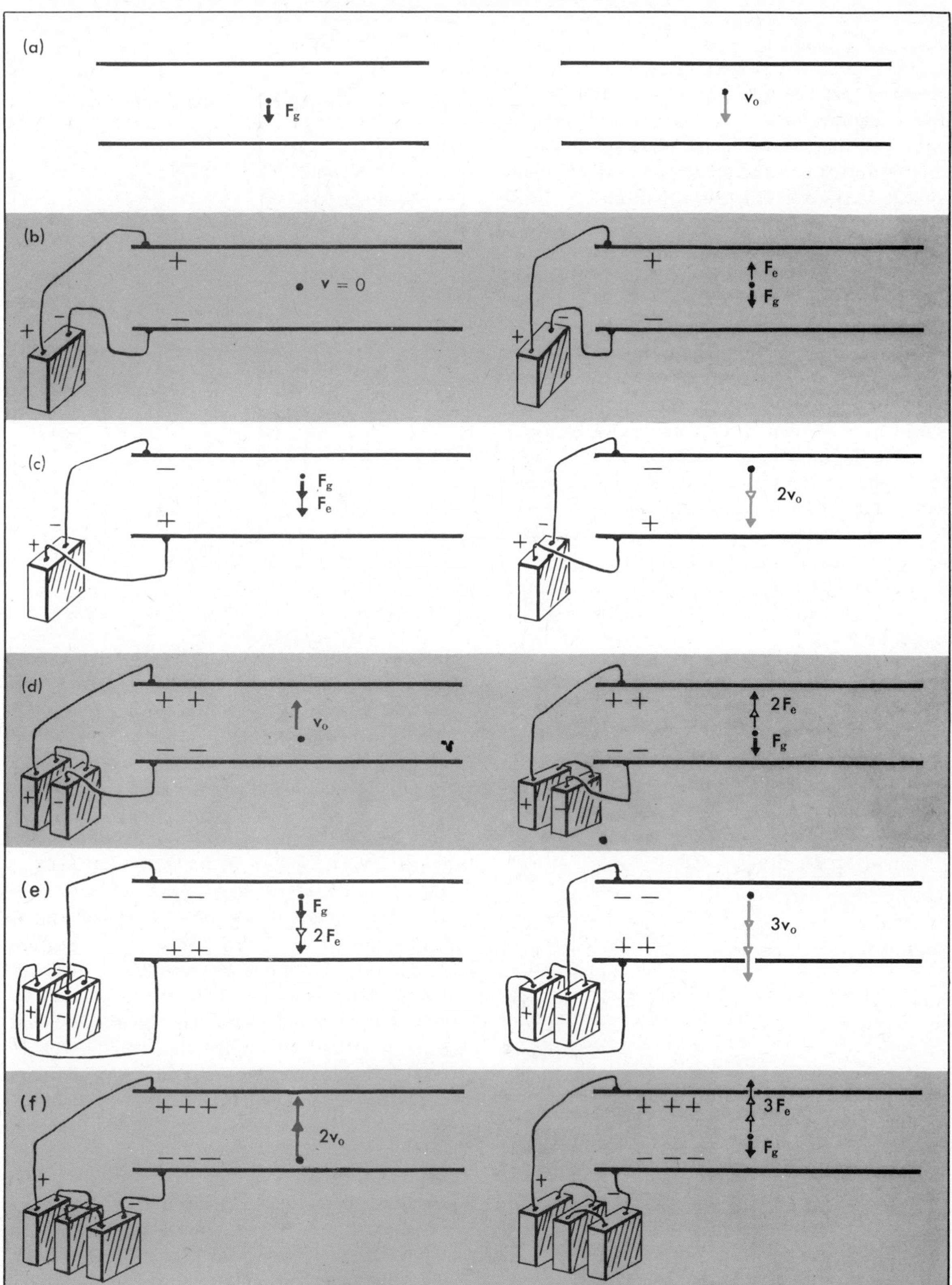

28–21.

batteries in series and looked at the motion of the sphere. We found that the electric force is then twice that put on by either battery — we used one battery to balance the sphere and one more to drive the sphere upward as fast as gravity would drive it down. Now we try three of the same batteries in series. The sphere goes up at 2 mm in 10.6 seconds. The extra battery has contributed another equal electric force between the plates. Since the electric forces are proportional to the charges on the plates, we can also conclude that the amount of charge the batteries put on the plates is directly proportional to the number of identical batteries.

Let us note one more thing we have demonstrated in this section. As we hauled the charged sphere up and down between the metal plates, it moved at the same steady speed, no matter where it was between the plates. The electric force was therefore the same at all points between the plates. This is an experimental proof of the constancy of the electric force field between charged planes. It agrees with the theoretical conclusion stated in the last section where we asserted that the field *should* be constant.

28–5. The Elementary Charge

Suppose somebody gives you a set of stiff paper bags, sealed shut, with various numbers of marbles in them. He challenges you to tell whether the marbles he put in are all alike and how many are in each bag — without breaking the seals. You weigh the bags and find the masses for the marbles given in Table 1. By plotting these masses as in Fig. 28–22, you see that they are all multiples of 0.00560 kg. Then you might very well decide that all the marbles have equal mass. This would make sense, because with marbles of 0.00560 kg there would be

Table 1

Bag	Mass of marbles in the bag	Supposed number of marbles	Mass per marble
A	0.02800 kg		
B	0.00560 kg		
C	0.01680 kg		
D	0.01120 kg		
E	0.02240 kg		

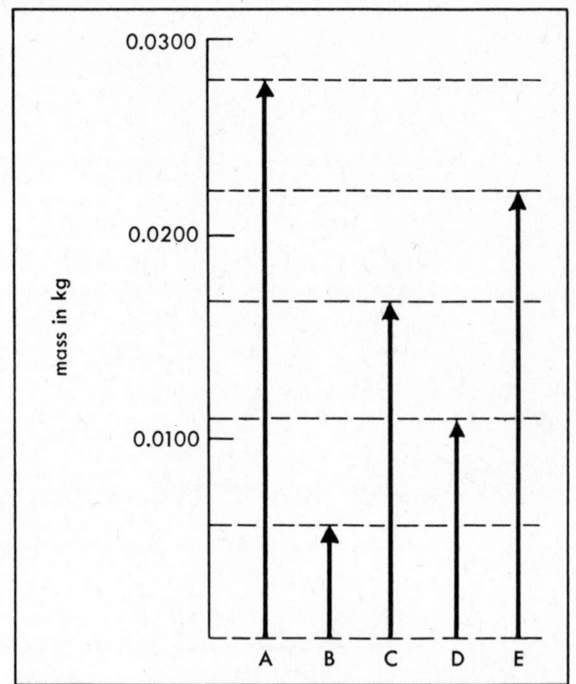

28–22. The masses of the five bags of marbles. The horizontal broken lines are to make comparison easier.

5 in bag *A*, 1 in bag *B*, 3 in C, 2 in D, and 4 in *E*. (You would probably rattle bag *B* to see whether your idea was correct.)

On the other hand, if there are huge numbers of marbles in each bag, you probably will not suspect that every marble has the same mass. For example, suppose that the collections of marbles have masses of 5.76 kg, 6.27 kg, 3.24 kg, 4.82 kg, etc., that is about 1030, 1120, 580, 860 . . . marbles. With such masses, even if you suspect that the marbles are identical, you will find it hard to convince yourself. In order to be sure that all the collections are whole numbers of identical marbles, you would have to measure to a small fraction of 1-marble accuracy. That means weighing to something like 1 part in 10,000, which is a much more difficult and much less convincing job. If the numbers of identical objects involved are still larger, like the numbers of atoms in a mole — 6×10^{23} of them — the job would be hopeless.

Because there are so many atoms even in a very small sample, the masses of atoms were not established by weighing small numbers of them. A less direct method was used (see Chapters 7–9). For the same reason, the elementary unit of charge was not discovered by measuring large charges and seeing that they come in multiples of a single unit. The charges we normally deal with involve huge numbers of elementary electric charges, millions of millions of them, and the presence or absence of one more charge is far too hard to detect. Consequently, the earliest evidence for an elementary charge came indirectly, in the nineteenth century. Because this evidence is indirect and because it is tied to other aspects of atomic theory, we shall deal with it in Section 29–4. Here instead we shall look at some evidence which became available early in this century. At that time micro-microbalances like the one described in the last section were being developed for measuring ionic charge. In 1909 R. A. Millikan perfected a balance much like the one we have described, and he performed a series of experiments which clearly show the existence of the elementary unit of charge. Where we use plastic spheres of known mass, he used tiny oil drops — and he had to measure their masses while examining their charges. Our experiment is therefore easier than his but otherwise it is nearly the same.*

For our experiment we go back to the micro-microbalance of Section 28–4. With the plates charged by one standard battery and the sphere still charged the same amount as in Section 28–4, the sphere is in balance. Now we shall leave the charge on the plates alone while we change the charge on the sphere.

We can make the charge on the sphere change when we want to by ionizing the gas near it (or knocking charge off it) with an X-ray beam. When the electric force on the sphere changes, the driving force is no longer zero. It is now given by the extra electric force exerted on the charge just added on the sphere. The sphere therefore starts to move, gaining a steady speed which measures the electric force on this added charge.

Exactly what happens next depends on chance — on what ions the sphere happens to pick up, or on what charge the X-ray beam knocks off the sphere. In one run the following sequence took place. From balance the sphere suddenly started off with a downward velocity of 0.54 mm per 10.6 sec. Later a dose of X rays made the sphere pick up some more ions. The sphere then rose at the speed of 0.50 mm per 10.6 sec. Next it went up at the speed of 0.96 mm per 10.6 sec. It was necessary to let the sphere fall and to haul it up to convenient positions for measurement several times. But with enough patience, enough charge changes and speed measurements, we took the data in Table 2. There in the left-hand column are the observed speeds, and in the right-hand column the forces to which they correspond. We know from Section 28–4 that each millimeter in 10.6 seconds means a force of 2.8×10^{-14} newtons. Consequently, 0.54 mm per 10.6 sec corresponds to $0.54 \times (2.8 \times 10^{-14}$ newtons), that is to 1.51×10^{-14} newtons. The other forces were calculated in the same way.

*In Millikan's time there were no standardized plastic spheres and no electron microscopes with which to see that they are all the same. He was forced to do something different.

Table 2

Speed in millimeters moved in 10.6 seconds. (+ indicates rise, and — fall)	Electric force exerted on the charge added to the sphere since balance, in units of 10^{-14} newtons
− 0.54	− 1.51
+ 0.50	+ 1.40
+ 0.96	+ 2.7
+ 1.46	+ 4.1
+ 1.98	+ 5.55
+ 0.58	+ 1.6
− 0.52	− 1.45
0.0	0.0
+ 1.00	+ 2.80
+ 2.5	+ 7.0
+ 1.98	+ 5.55
+ 0.50	+ 1.40
− 0.52	− 1.45

Figure 28–23 shows several series of observations of the motion of the sphere. In each sequence of observations, spread out horizontally on the figure, the charge on the sphere is different. You can see the effect of the different electrical forces by comparing the vertical motions during equal time intervals. Notice that in the four sequences the vertical motions are in the ratios of 1 to 2 to 3 to 4.

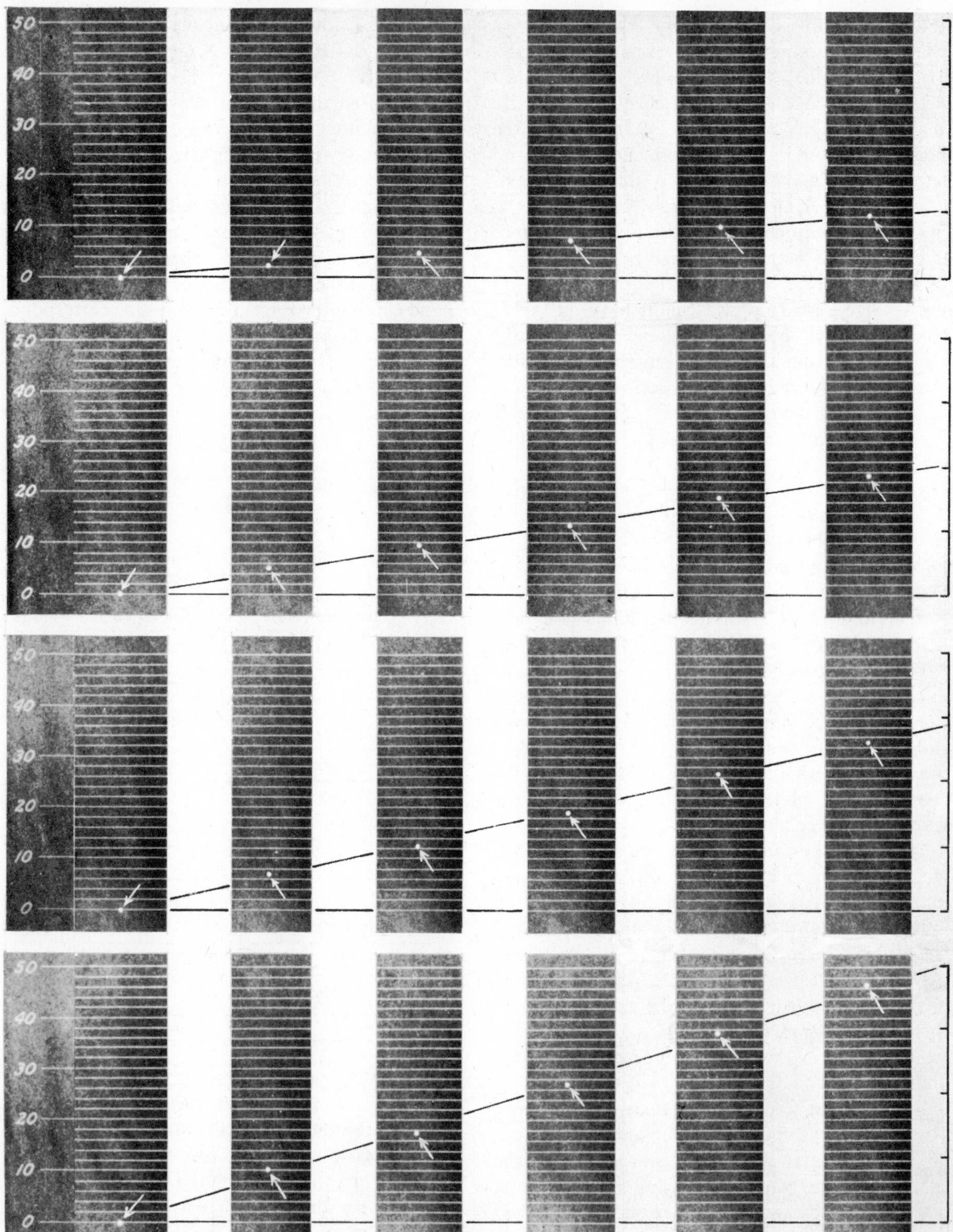

28–23. Four sequences of pictures taken at 1-sec intervals, showing the motion of a standard sphere. (The plates were connected to the same battery at all times, giving them the charge needed to balance the sphere before its charge was changed.) How are the four speeds related? What does this relation tell you about the forces and the charges on the sphere?

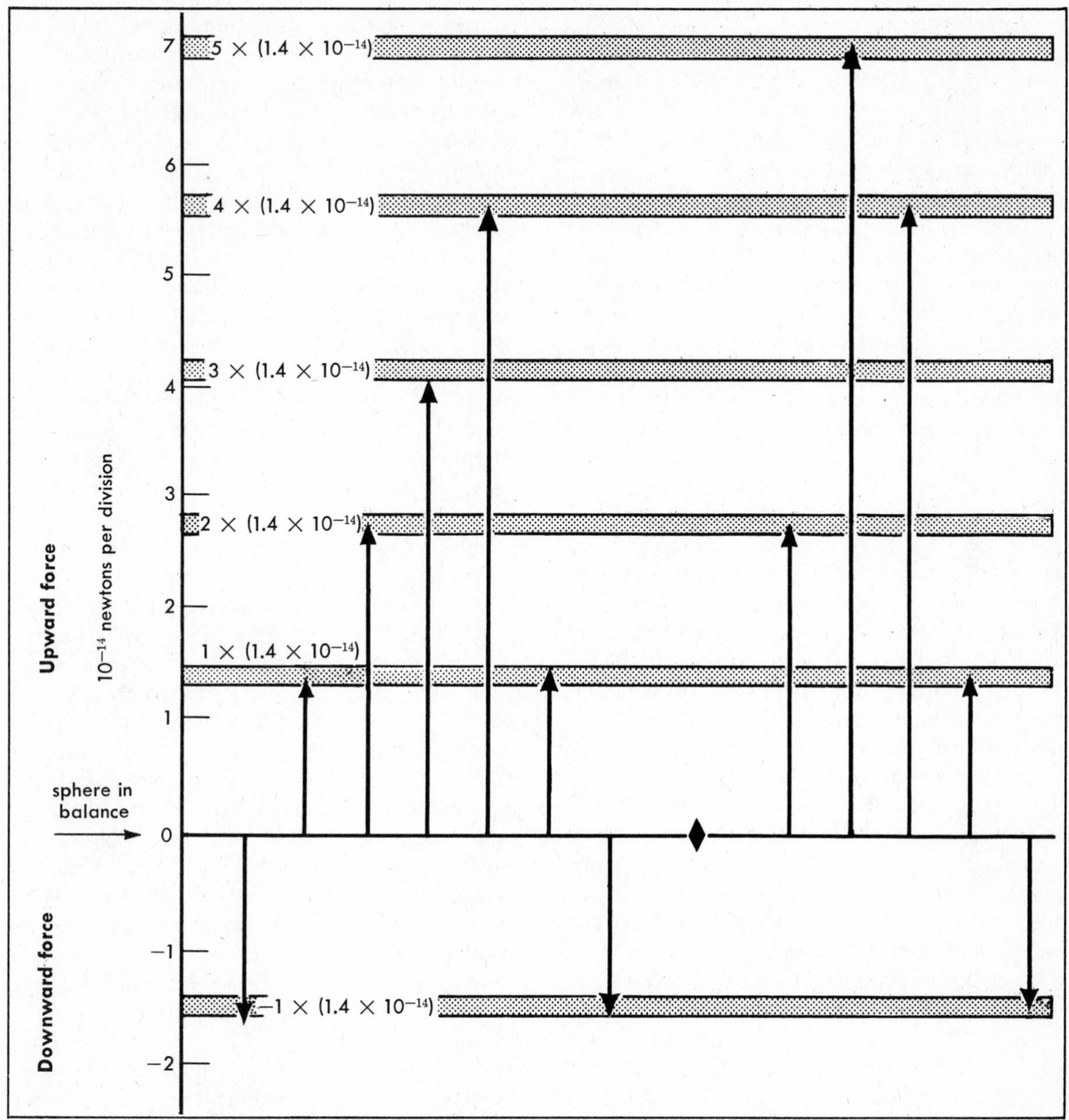

28–24. The arrows indicate the forces measured on a plastic sphere in a Millikan experiment as the charge on the sphere changes. The horizontal bands are drawn where the forces are whole-number multiples of 1.4×10^{-14} newtons. The force measured is the electric force on the charge added to the sphere since balance.

Fig. 28–24 is a graph of the forces from Table 2. The different forces all are very close to 1.4×10^{-14} newtons or to 2, 3, 4 . . . times this number. No intermediate values of the force are found between 1 and 2 times this force or in the region between 2 and 3 times this force, or between any successive small whole numbers. What does this mean? Because we have maintained the same charge on the plates, the force on the sphere at any time is proportional to the extra charge put on the sphere since balance. The charge added (or knocked off) is therefore 1, 2, 3, or some other small whole number of unit charges.

Here is striking evidence of the grainy structure of electricity. No charge of less than a certain amount ever goes on or off the sphere. There is a smallest grain size. But that is not all: the evidence says much more. The atoms of electricity are all of the same size. There are no charges of $1\frac{1}{2}$ units or π or any amount like that — only 1, 2, 3, 4 of these smallest grains. All the charges are made up of the basic units.

This is a sweeping conclusion, and we must check it in other ways. We worked only with the *changes* in the charge on the sphere. What of the original charge? Is it a multiple of the unit for charges? The answer is "yes." In our experiment the electric force to balance the sphere against gravity was 2.8×10^{-14} newtons, and the force on each unit charge was 1.4×10^{-14} newtons. The sphere therefore started with 2 of the same unit charges on it.

What would happen if we had a different initial charge on the sphere? In our experiment the plates were 3.1×10^{-3} meters apart; and our standard balancing battery was made by putting three 90-volt "B" batteries in series. If the same sphere starts with 3 charges, it must be balanced by using a different battery to charge the plates. We then find that two 90-volt batteries make the balance. Also we then find that the force on the apparent unit of charge is 0.9×10^{-14} newtons — that is, two-thirds of the old force. But this is just right, for two-thirds the original balancing battery should give only two-thirds the force on the same charge. So the elementary charge again comes out the same.

We can do other experiments like this with spheres of different size and different material, and many were done by Millikan. For example, with a sphere of twice the mass, the balancing force is twice as big. The ratio of speed to driving force is also different. But when we take all the changes into account, we find that all the experiments give the same natural unit of charge. We can use different gases; we can ionize them in different ways; we can even send in electrons or other charged particles — we always find the same unit. We shall call it the elementary charge.

28–6. A Large Electrical Balance

With a micro-microbalance we can measure the charge of an object as a certain number of elementary charges. We know that this method will work when the number of elementary charges is small and the object is microscopic. Will it also work for large numbers of elementary charges? A really large number of elementary charges will not stay on a microscopic object. Perhaps even more important, not all objects are microscopically small. Consequently, in a literal sense, the answer is, "No, the micro-microbalance will not work."

How, then, are we going to measure a large charge as a number of elementary charges? There are several ways, but the most obvious is to build a bigger balance. We want a balance large enough to accommodate a sphere from a Coulomb experiment (see Sections 28–1 and 28–2) or some similar object. If we can measure the charge on such an object in terms of the number of elementary charges, we should then be able to measure all charges as numbers of elementary charges. Indeed, we shall see in the next section that once we have measured one big charge, the Coulomb experiment will let us measure any other in terms of elementary charges.

The new balance must be large enough to accommodate a reasonably large object, and at the same time we must know the electric force on an elementary charge between the plates. (Unless we know the force on an elementary charge in the balance, we can use it only to measure big charges in terms of an arbitrary unit of charge.) If we could do an accurate Millikan experiment in a large balance, we could compare a big charge directly with an elementary charge. Unfortunately, to do a Millikan experiment with a large balance is impractical. However, there is a way around this difficulty: we can build a large balance in which the force on each elementary charge between the plates is exactly the same as the force on an elementary charge in the micro-microbalance. To design the large balance in this way, we must learn how the dimensions of a balance are related to the force it exerts. Then we can increase the size of the balance without changing the force.

In order to scale up a balance, we shall have to change both the area of the plates and their separation. We can learn the effect of each of these changes by experiment, both with the micro-microbalance and with widely separated charged plates exerting forces on large charges.

When we use plates of larger area at the same distance apart and connected to the same battery (Fig. 28–25), the force on a charge between them

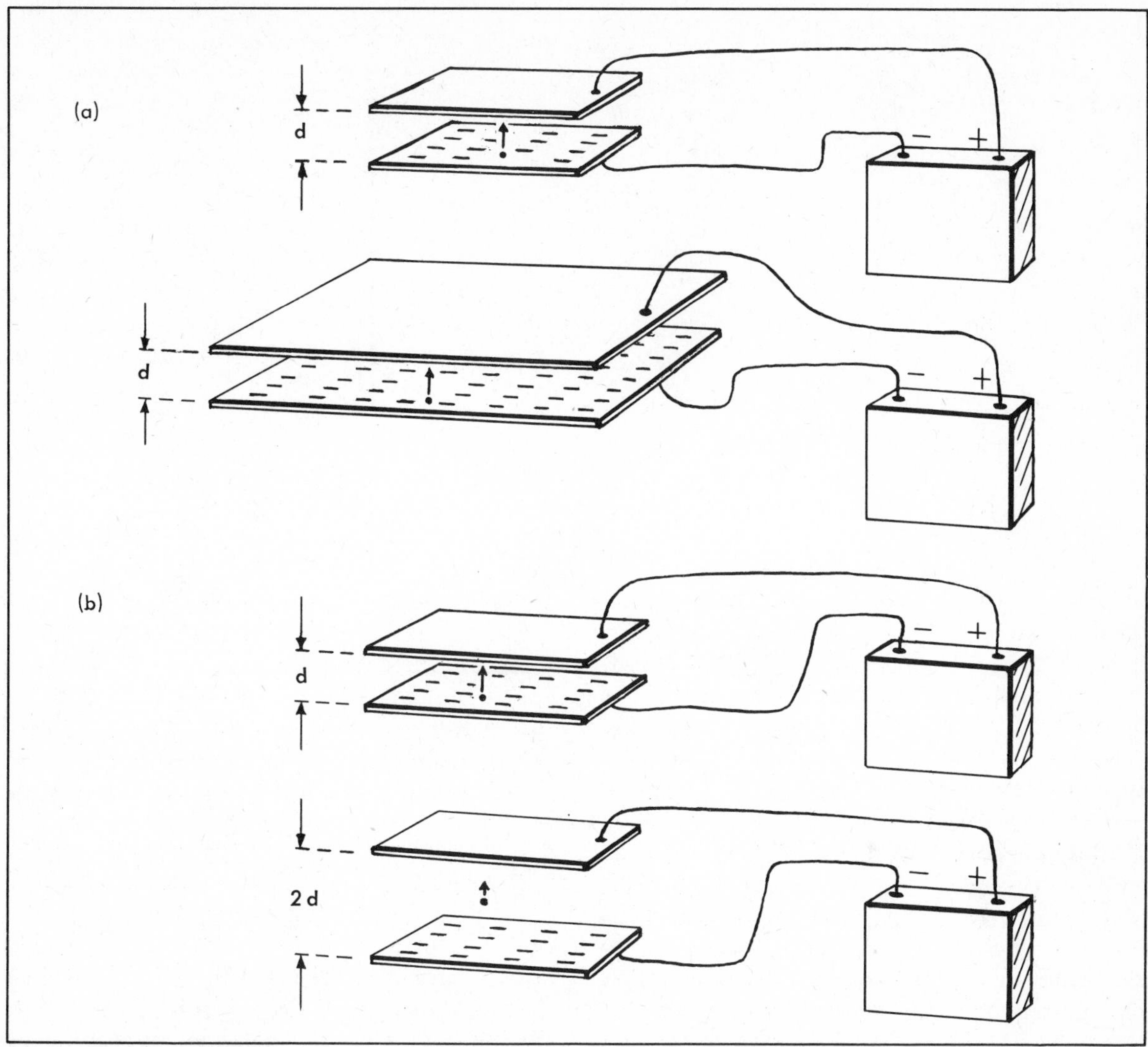

28–25. **(a) If we increase the area of the plates without changing the separation or the battery, the force on an elementary charge anywhere between the plates remains the same. (b) If we double the distance between the plates with the same battery connected, the force is halved. In general, the force is proportional to $1/d$, where d is the distance between plates.**

is the same. When we separate the plates, however, with the same battery connected, the force decreases, going in inverse proportion to the separation. We can compensate the decrease of the electric force by using more batteries to charge the plates. Since the force increases in proportion to the number of batteries (Section 28–4), we must double the number of batteries whenever we double the separation of the plates. Direct tests demonstrate the same thing. As long as the plates are big compared with their distance apart, we keep the same electric force by increasing the separation and increasing the number of batteries in the same proportion. The exact area of the plates does not matter. Therefore, to scale up the electric micro-microbalance to a convenient size, we use big parallel metal plates a convenient distance apart. And we make sure that the electric force on an elementary charge between the plates is the same as in the micro-microbalance by charging the plates with a sufficient number of batteries in series.

In order to measure the number of elementary charges on an object of ordinary size, we shall place the plates 31 cm apart, a hundred times the separation of the plates in our micro-microbalance. We shall charge them by using a hundred

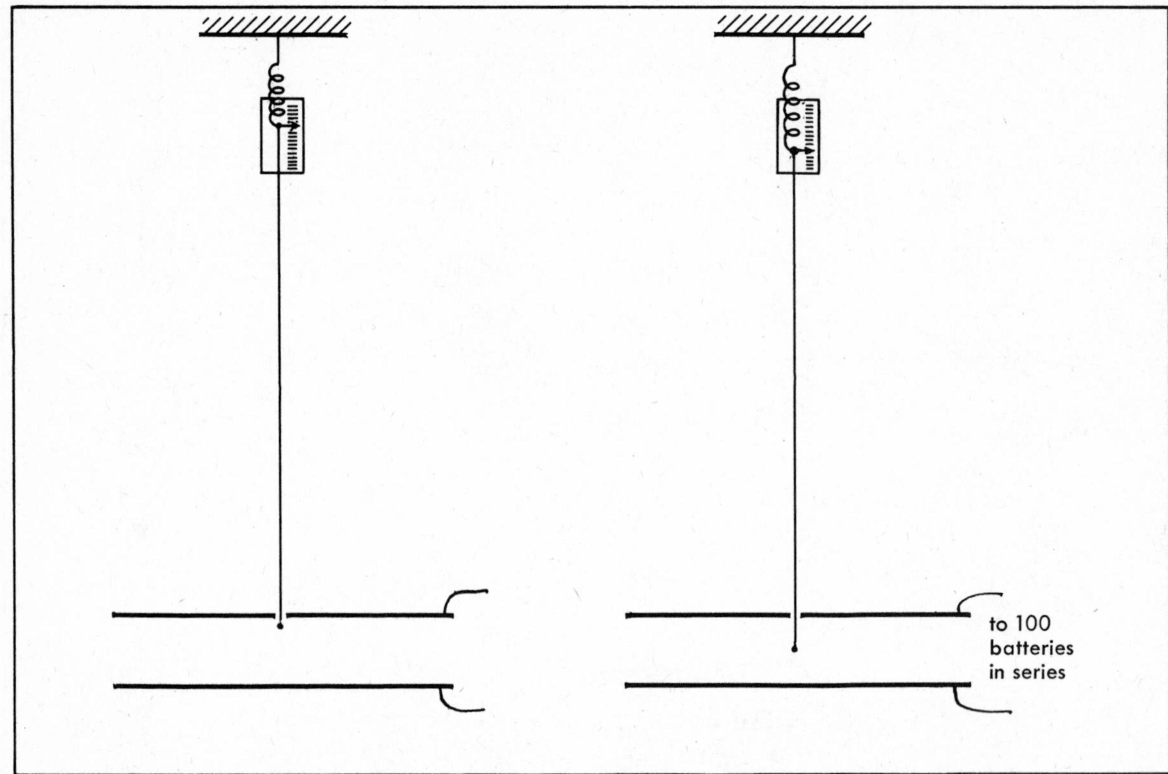

28–26. A large electric balance. The electric force on the charged sphere is measured by the extension of the spring. The extension is calibrated with known weights. Electric forces on the spring may be avoided by having it far above the upper plate.

of the 270-volt balancing batteries placed in series.* (This is a lot of batteries, but we need to do this experiment only once, and there are plenty of batteries made.) We now have a space 31 cm wide with an electric force field in it that will exert 1.4×10^{-14} newtons on an elementary charge, the same number of newtons per elementary charge exerted in the micro-microbalance.

28–7. The Constant in Coulomb's Law; the Force Between Elementary Charges

Consider a typical Coulomb experiment with two equally charged spheres. In one such experiment, when the spheres were 0.10 meters apart, they repelled each other with a force of 8.8×10^{-5} newtons. How many elementary charges were there on each sphere? To find out, we put one sphere between the plates of the large balance described at the end of the last section.

In order to introduce the sphere from the Coulomb experiment between the plates of our large electric balance, we hang it on insulating thread on the end of a spring (Fig. 28–26) or on the end of an insulating balance arm as we show in Fig. 28–27. When the sphere is hanging between the plates, which are discharged and disconnected from the batteries, we note the position of the end of the spring. Then with the plates charged so as to pull the sphere down, we measure the extension of the spring. Finally, with the plates again discharged, we find the weight that will give the same spring extension; it is 8.4×10^{-4} newtons. This must be equal to the electric force on the sphere between the plates. Because the electric force is 1.4×10^{-14} newtons per elementary charge, this tells us that the charge on the sphere is

$$q = \frac{8.4 \times 10^{-4} \text{ newtons}}{1.4 \times 10^{-14} \text{ newtons/elem. ch.}}.$$

That is 6.0×10^{10} elementary charges.

*In the actual experiment we used a trio of 90-volt "B" batteries to make each 270-volt "balancing" battery.

When we discussed Coulomb's law and the electric charge in Sections 28–1 and 28–2, we found that

$$F = k\frac{q_1 q_2}{r^2}$$

where F is the force one charge exerts on the other, q_1 and q_2 are the charges, and r is the separation between them. The proportionality factor k is a constant. Its value depends on the units in which we measure force, separation, and charge. Now we are in a position to evaluate the constant k in Coulomb's law. We know the charges q_1 and q_2: each is 6.0×10^{10} elementary charges. We also know that at a separation of 0.10 meters the repulsive force is 8.8×10^{-5} newtons.

On putting these measured values into Coulomb's law, we can obtain k. From

$$k = \frac{Fr^2}{q_1 q_2}$$

we get

$$k = \frac{(8.8 \times 10^{-5} \text{ newtons})(0.10 \text{ meters})^2}{(6.0 \times 10^{10} \text{ elem. ch.})(6.0 \times 10^{10} \text{ elem. ch.})}$$

$$= 2.4 \times 10^{-28} \frac{\text{newton-m}^2}{(\text{elem. ch.})^2}.$$

We can check on the value of k by doing other Coulomb experiments and using the large balance to measure the charges. As we expect, the value of k always comes out the same. It is one of the universal constants of nature. A great deal of work with all sorts of experiments has gone into measuring k accurately. The results of all these experiments are in close agreement, and the value given by the best experiments is almost exactly $2.306 \times 10^{-28} \frac{\text{newton-m}^2}{(\text{elem. ch.})^2}$. Consequently, we now write Coulomb's law as

$$F = \left(2.306 \times 10^{-28} \frac{\text{newton-m}^2}{(\text{elem. ch.})^2}\right)\frac{q_1 q_2}{r^2}$$

where q_1 and q_2 are the numbers of elementary charges and r is the separation.

As we remarked in the last section, once we can measure an ordinary charge by counting the elementary charges, we should be able to devise a procedure for measuring any charge in terms of elementary charges without going to the extreme of bringing each charge into a large electrical balance. Our knowledge of the value of k is the key to measuring charges. By charge-sharing we can always get two equal charges. After measuring the force between them at a definite distance we know F, r, and k in Coulomb's law, and we can therefore work out q in elementary charges. Using one of the charged bodies as a standard, we can then measure the number of elementary charges on any other body by measuring the force between it and the standard.

28–27. A photograph of an electric balance. The charged ball is suspended between the large plates on a plastic arm, pivoted on a vertical rod visible in the center of the picture. Just to the right of this rod is a light spring. Note the stack of a hundred 270-volt batteries in the background.

In addition to giving us a practical way of counting the numbers of elementary charges by measuring electric forces between ordinary-sized objects, the constant, $2.3 \times 10^{-28} \frac{\text{newton-m}^2}{(\text{elem. ch.})^2}$, is the direct measure of the force between two elementary charges one meter apart. They exert just 2.306×10^{-28} newtons on each other. No doubt that force looks absolutely negligible. But in fact it is huge. The gravitational attraction between two hydrogen atoms at this distance is about 2×10^{-64} newtons. The electric force between two elementary charges is 10^{36} times bigger. (If you say this in terms of millions of millions, you have to say the word "million" six times over.) The force is so big that two moles of elementary charge (two collections of 6×10^{23} charges) placed one on each side of the earth would push on each other with a force of half a million newtons — 50 tons. Two moles of the heaviest atoms placed at opposite ends of a diameter of the earth would have no appreciable gravitational effect on each other.

28–8. Conservation of Charge

Our picture of particles of electric charge leads to the idea of the conservation of charge. When we charge bodies by rubbing them, we transfer charged particles from one to another. What one body gains in charge the other one loses. When we charge the plates of an electric balance with a battery, the battery transfers charge from one plate to the other. The charges of the plates are equal and opposite.

In certain very unusual circumstances we can "create" charged particles, but we shall find that we always create them in pairs, and the charge of one particle is equal and opposite to the charge of the other. Sometimes nature "creates" charged particles automatically: for instance, a neutron turns into a proton and an electron. The proton and electron thus created have equal and opposite charges. The total charge is zero before and after the creation.

All our evidence indicates that the total amount of charge never changes. Like the conservation of energy, the conservation of charge is a law of nature which extends over everything we know.

28–9. The Electric Charge of Electrons and other Particles of Matter

We already know that electrons have a negative electric charge, but we have yet to find out whether their charge equals one or several elementary charges. We can determine the charge of an electron by counting electrons as we add them to a neutral body and then measuring the charge on the body in numbers of elementary charges.

With an electron gun (Section 27–13) we can produce a beam of high-speed electrons which will make a luminous spot on a fluorescent screen. If the number of electrons passing per second in the beam is small enough, the individual electrons will cause individual scintillations like the scintillations with which we counted radioactive disintegrations in Sections 7–13 and 8–3. Although each scintillation gives off very little light, the scintillations can be detected by looking at them with a photoelectric cell. Thus the electrons can be counted individually. The electrons can also be counted directly by using a special kind of amplifier called an electron multiplier. With such counting, we can determine experimentally the number of electrons passing per second in the electron beam.

After we have measured the number of electrons per second in the beam, we can catch the beam in a metal bottle (Fig. 28–28). The electrons which enter the bottle stop in the metal walls, and even if they eject other electrons from the inner surfaces of the wall, hardly any particles will find their way out of the small neck of the bottle. The bottle therefore is charged up only by the charge brought in by the electrons. After a sufficiently long time, the bottle will acquire enough charge to be measured, and we can therefore determine the charge brought into the bottle in each second. By dividing the charge per second by the number of electrons per second in the beam, we then find the charge of an electron. It is exactly one negative elementary charge.

We can also use the same kind of measurement to measure the charge of the particles shot out in the radioactive disintegration of polonium. Indeed, the first experiment of this kind was done by Rutherford and Geiger in 1908 in order to find the charge of these atomic fragments, which we usually call alpha particles. They found that

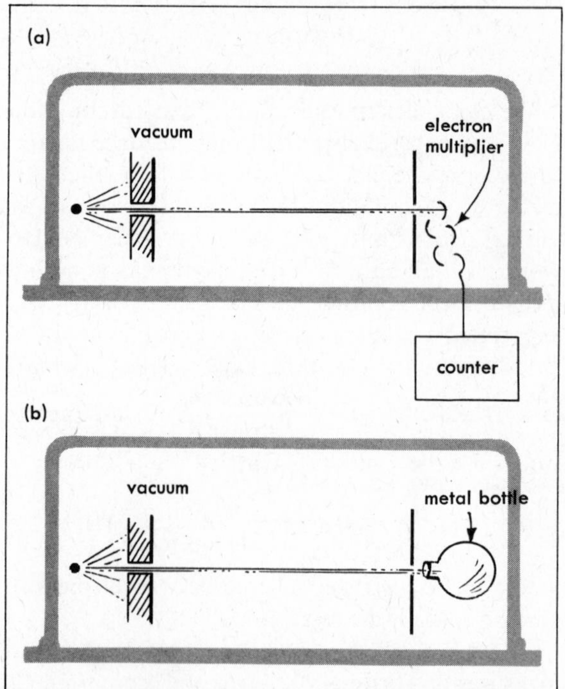

28–28. (a) We can measure the number of electrons per second passing by in an electron beam by directing the beam at a counter. (b) We can determine the rate at which the same beam carries charge by firing the beam at a "bottle" with a narrow opening for a long enough time to accumulate a measurable charge on the bottle.

an alpha particle carries exactly two positive elementary charges. Later experiments showed that an alpha particle can be decomposed into more basic units, into two protons and two neutrons. As we already know, the neutrons are neutral. Each of the protons, on the other hand, has one positive elementary charge. A number of other charged particles are now known which differ in mass from electrons or protons. But when we carry the decomposition of matter far enough, all the electric particles found always have either one positive or one negative elementary charge.

FURTHER READING

FURRY, W. H.; PURCELL, E. M.; STREET, J. C., *Physics for Science and Engineering Students.* Blakiston, 1952 (Chapter 22).

MILLIKAN, R. A., *Electrons, Protons, Photons, Neutrons, Mesotrons, and Cosmic Rays.* Revised Edition, University of Chicago Press, 1947.

WILSON, MITCHELL, *American Science and Invention.* Simon & Schuster, 1954 (Millikan: pp. 328–339).

FOR HOME, DESK, AND LAB

1. Two electrified objects *A* and *B* are separated by 0.03 meters, and repel each other with a force of 4.0×10^{-5} newtons.

(a) If we move body *A* an additional 0.03 meters away, what is the electric force now?

(b) Does it make any difference which body we move? Explain.

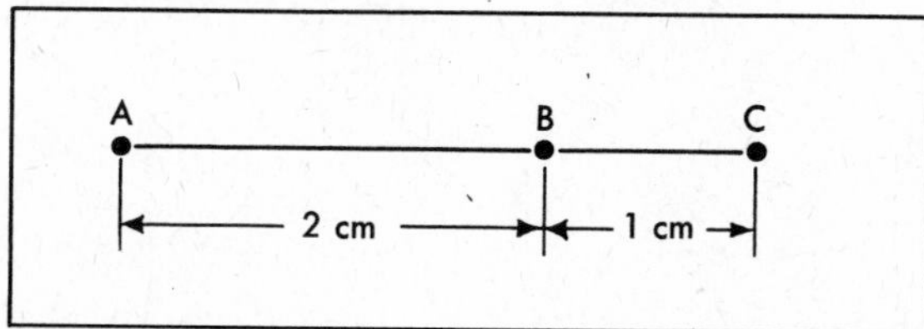

28–29. **For Problem 2.**

2. Three equally charged objects are located as shown in Fig. 28–29. The electric force exerted by *A* on *B* is 3.0×10^{-6} newton.

(a) What electric force does *C* exert upon *B*?

(b) What is the net electric force on *B*?

28–30. **For Problem 3.**

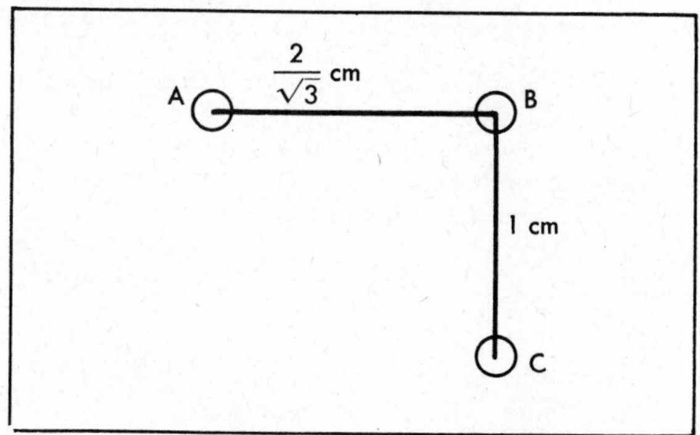

3. Suppose that we place three small charged spheres, with equal charges on them, as shown in Fig. 28–30. *A* and *C* are fixed in position and *B* can move. *C* exerts a force of 4×10^{-6} newtons on *B*.

(a) What force does *A* exert on *B*?

(b) What is the net force on *B*?

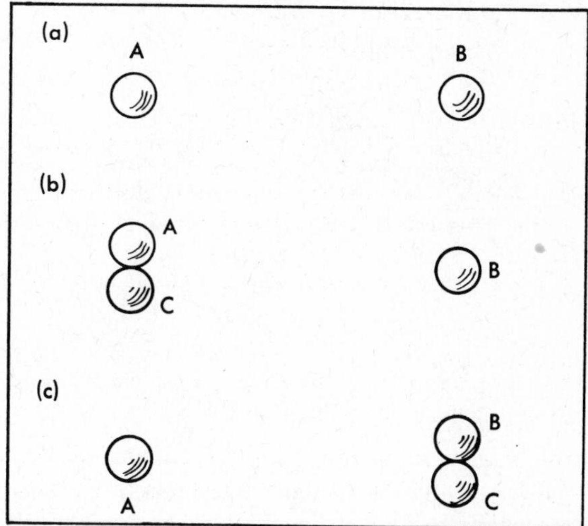

28–31. **For Problem 4.**

4. Two equally charged identical conducting spheres *A* and *B* repel each other with a force of 2.0×10^{-5} newtons. (Fig. 28–31 a.) Another identical uncharged sphere *C* is touched to *A* (Fig. 28–31 b) and then moved over right next to *B* (Fig. 28–31 c).

(a) What is the electric force on *A* now?

(b) What is the net electric force on *C* (after having touched *A*) when it is halfway between *A* and *B*?

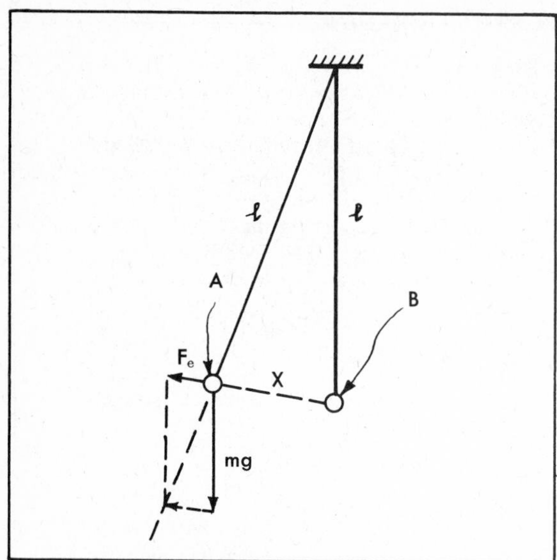

28–32. For Problem 5.

5. Two charged balls A and B each with mass m are placed as shown in Fig. 28–32. The ball A is free to move; B is fixed in position.
   (a) How does the force F_e between them depend upon X?
   (b) Find the relationship between the electric force F_e and the weight mg in terms of X and l.
   (c) If the charge remains the same and the separation X is cut in half, how must the weight have changed?

6. Suppose we have a *very* long charged wire.
   (a) Draw the electric field lines around the wire, looking (i) from the side, and (ii) looking from one end. Note: Because of the symmetry the field can depend only on distance from the wire.
   (b) How does the field vary with distance from the wire? Note: You can use much the same method as was used in the box on page 468.

7. The graph in Fig. 28–33 shows the electric force of repulsion on a tiny charged conducting sphere as a function of its separation from a large conducting sphere. The large sphere has a radius of 1 cm, and has 10 times the charge of the small sphere.

28–33. For Problem 7.

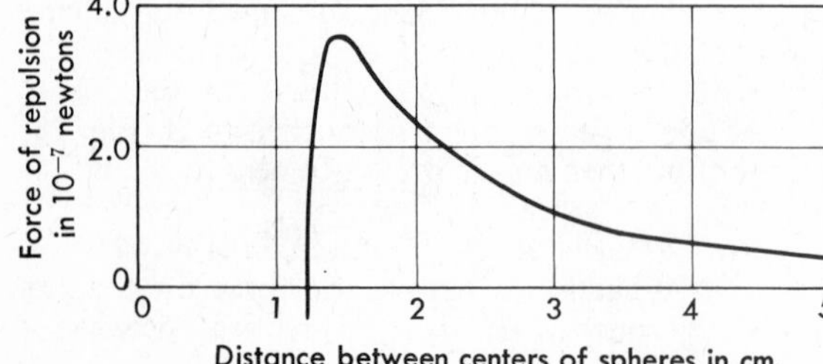

   (a) How is the force changing as the separation changes from 5 cm to 3 cm?
   (b) Explain the behavior of the force between separations 2 cm and 1 cm.

8. Why was it possible to ignore the changes in mass of the spheres used in the Millikan experiment when they picked up ions?
   (a) Compute the maximum mass of an ion made of an O_2 molecule which has lost a charged fragment.
   (b) What fraction of the mass of the sphere is one such ion?

9. Suppose we measure the speed of the standard plastic spheres (weight 2.8×10^{-14} newtons) between the plates of a micro-microbalance and find it is three halves of their speed under gravity alone.
   (a) What is the electrical force on them if they are moving upward?
   (b) If they are moving downward?

10. The following table gives possible data on the motion of the samé plastic spheres used in the Millikan experiment described in Sections 28–4 and 28–5.

Distance moved in 10.6 seconds, in millimeters (+ indicates rise and − fall)	Electric force exerted on the charge added to the sphere since balance, in units of 10^{-14} newtons
+ 0.96	+ 2.68
− 1.98	− 5.54
+ 1.00	+ 2.80
+ 3.00	+ 8.40
− 0.98	− 2.74
− 4.01	− 11.5

   (a) What are the forces in units of the smallest force? Since force is proportional to charge, what are the charges in units of the smallest charge?
   (b) How many balancing batteries in series were used in this experiment, assuming the plates are at the same separation as in Sections 28–4 and 28–5?
   (c) How many elementary charges were on the sphere in balance?

11. Only one of several identical metal spheres is charged. The charged sphere A experiences a force $F = 1.0 \times 10^{-4}$ newtons when placed midway between certain charged parallel plates.
   (a) Sphere A is then touched to one of the uncharged spheres (B). What force does A now experience when placed between the same plates?
   (b) A is touched to another of the uncharged spheres (C). What force does A now experience?
   (c) What force is exerted on sphere B when it is between the plates? On sphere C?

12. In a Millikan experiment we connect three balancing batteries in series to the plates so the electric force adds to the gravitational force. What will be the velocity of the plastic sphere?

13. Two large metal plates are separated by 0.10 m. They are connected to the terminals of a battery. A small charged ball halfway between them experiences an electric force of 3×10^{-4} newtons. The plates are now moved apart until the separation is 0.15 m. The same battery is connected to them.

(a) What force now acts on the ball?

(b) If we add two more identical batteries in series at the new separation, what is the force on the ball?

14. You can use the Millikan apparatus to measure the *strength* of batteries. We have found that we can double the force on a charged plastic sphere between the plates by connecting two identical batteries in series. This evidently puts double the charge on the plates. In general we can get any whole-number multiple of the force (and of the charge on the plates) provided by a single battery by connecting the correct number of identical batteries in series.

Fractions of a single battery can be obtained by using a "potentiometer" (a kind of battery fractionator). We can connect a *uniform* poorly conducting wire across two batteries as shown in Fig. 28–34. The connection to the plates is then made with the movable contact *C*. We find the interesting result that when *C* is at the middle of the wire the plates are charged as though only *one* battery were connected.

(a) When the slide wire is connected across three batteries, where should *C* be placed to give the effect of one?

(b) of two?

(c) Suppose it were connected across one battery. How would you get the effect of half a battery?

(d) Why is it necessary that the slide wire be uniform?

15. A plastic sphere of mass 3.06×10^{-15} kg is in an electric force field which exerts an upward force of 1.00×10^{-14} newtons on each positive electric particle. The electric force exerted on the sphere is sufficient to balance the force of gravity on it.

(a) What is the excess of electric particles on the sphere?

Suppose that each molecule has a mass of 3.00×10^{-26} kg.

(b) How many molecules are there in the sphere?

(c) What fraction of the molecules in the sphere have lost or gained an elementary charge?

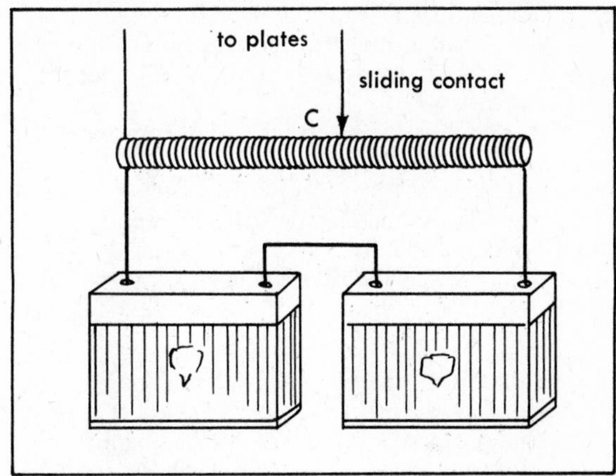

28–34. For Problem 14.

16. A sphere of mass 4.5×10^{-3} kg is hanging on a string 2.0 meters long between two oppositely charged parallel plates as shown in Fig. 28–35. At equilibrium the ball has been pulled 2.0 cm from its original position.

(a) What is the magnitude of the electric force on the sphere?

The electric force field between the plates is 3.0×10^{-14} newtons per elementary charge.

(b) What is the excess of electric particles on the ball?

28–35. For Problem 16.

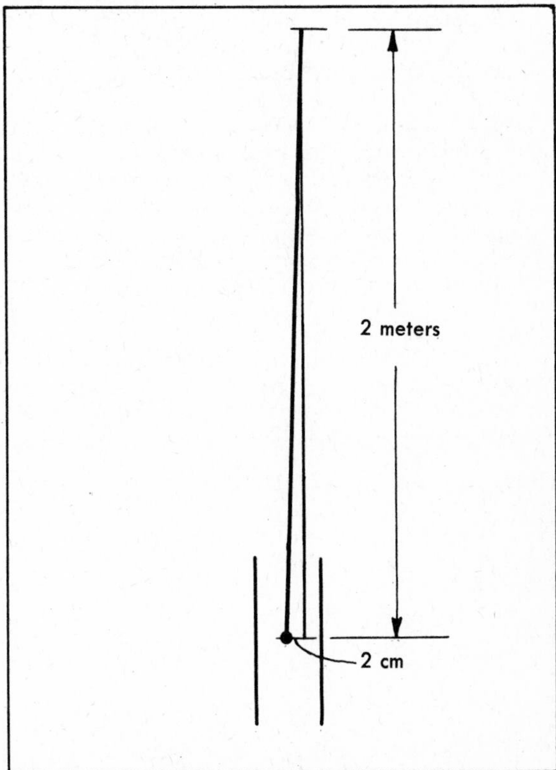

17. The mass of an electron is 9×10^{-31} kg.

(a) What is the gravitational force of attraction between two electrons at a distance of 1 meter?

(b) What is the electric force of repulsion?

(c) What is the ratio of electrical to gravitational forces?

(d) What is the electric force of repulsion and the gravitational force at 0.5 meters?

(e) How has the ratio changed?

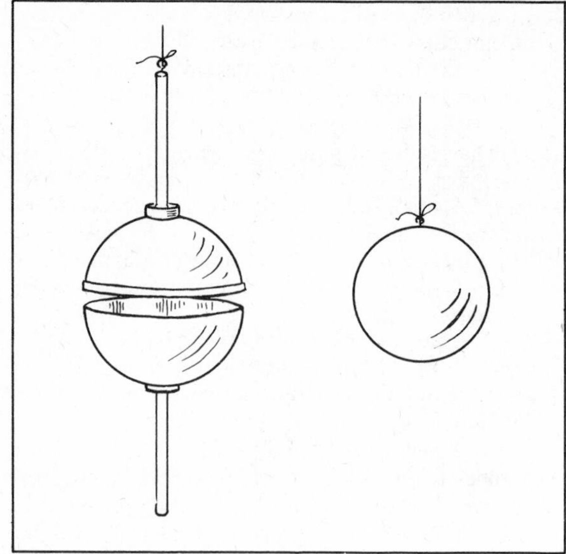

28–36. For Problem 18.

18. We have two hollow metal spheres, one slightly larger than the other. The bigger sphere is made so that it can be taken apart into two hemispheres by means of two small insulating handles (Fig. 28–36). Each sphere is originally charged exactly the same amount, as can be verified by noticing that each exerts the same force on a third charged body. Then the big sphere is taken apart without discharging it, and fitted together around the little sphere.

(a) When the combined sphere is now placed the same distance from the third charged body, what force will it exert?

(b) Is your answer consistent with the experiments on charge sharing?

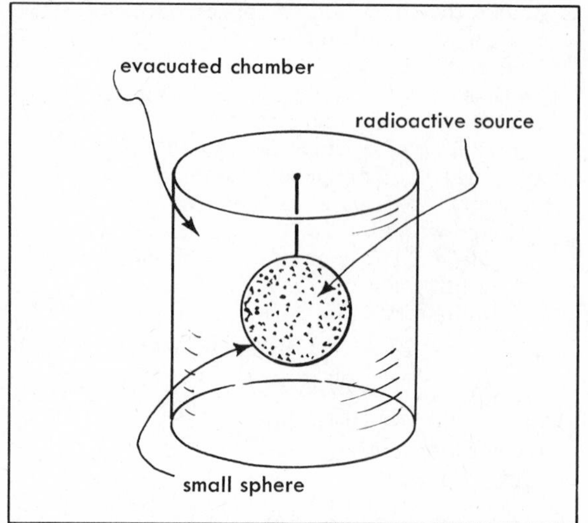

28–37. For Problem 19.

19. A thin layer of radioactive material emitting beta particles is painted on a small conducting sphere. The sphere is then hung on an insulating thread in an evacuated chamber (Fig. 28–37).

After 50 days we measure the charge on the sphere and find it to be 4.32×10^{10} positive elementary charges. (The sphere has been kept in an evacuated chamber, so very few charges have leaked off.) In a separate experiment with a Geiger counter we find beta particles shooting out at the average rate of 1.00×10^{4} per second.

(a) What is the charge of one beta particle?

(b) What do you think beta particles may be?

ENERGY AND MOTION OF CHARGES IN ELECTRIC FIELDS

CHAPTER 29

THIS chapter deals with the motions of charges in electric fields. We shall use these motions to determine the masses of charged particles and to discuss the currents in electric circuits. In particular we shall find the masses of positive hydrogen ions and of electrons, because these charged particles will be central to our later study of atoms. When charged particles accelerate, their kinetic energy changes. Energy is transferred to the particles. The energy transfers (from chemical stored energy, to the energy of moving charges, to thermal energy) will allow us to consider all kinds of electric circuits from a single point of view.

A. MOVING CHARGED PARTICLES

29–1. Motion of Electrons and Protons in a Uniform Electric Force Field

In this section and the next we shall describe experiments in which the electrons and positive hydrogen ions move in the uniform force field between two charged metal plates. In order to study the motion under the influence of the electric force alone, we shall do the experiments in vacuum, so that the drag of the air which we used in the micro-microbalance in the last chapter is eliminated. Furthermore, because the hydrogen ions and the electrons are so light, less than 10^{-11} times the mass of the standard spheres we used in the micro-microbalance, we can neglect the gravitational forces in comparison with the electric forces in these experiments.

To get a known electric force we connect a 90-volt "B" battery to two metal plates which for convenience we place 9.3 mm apart. In this way, we use one-third of the balancing battery we used in the experiments of the last chapter; and the separation of the charged plates is three times that of the plates in the micro-microbalance. We know that the force on each elementary charge between the plates is proportional to the number of batteries and that it falls off in inverse proportion to the separation of the plates. Consequently, we know that we have one-ninth the force we had in the micro-microbalance in the last chapter. The force is therefore

$$\frac{1.4}{9} \times 10^{-14} \text{ newtons} = 1.55 \times 10^{-15} \text{ newtons}$$

on each elementary charge.

If an object moves the distance d in the direction of a force F, the work Fd tells us the change of kinetic energy of the object. (For instance, if the object starts from rest, $Fd = \frac{1}{2}mv^2$ where m is the mass and v the final speed of the object. See Section 24–4.) Consequently, as any body carrying one elementary charge is shoved across from one plate to the other, it gains

$$\begin{aligned} Fd &= (1.55 \times 10^{-15} \text{ newtons}) \times (9.3 \times 10^{-3} \text{ m}) \\ &= 1.44 \times 10^{-17} \text{ joules} \end{aligned}$$

of kinetic energy. And if the body carries q elementary charges, it acquires a kinetic energy q

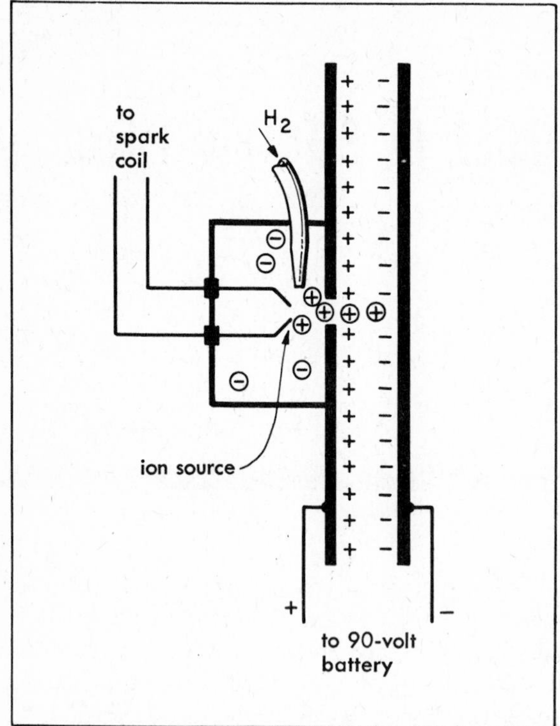

29–1. Apparatus for accelerating hydrogen ions in an electric force field. The ions are formed in the box at the left, and some drift through the hole into the region between the plates. The whole set-up is enclosed in an evacuated chamber.

times greater. For example, if we ionize some hydrogen next to one of the charged plates (Fig. 29–1) and let some of the ions drift through a small hole into the region between the plates, the ions will accelerate across this region and end up at the other plate moving with a kinetic energy $\frac{1}{2}mv^2 = 1.44 \times 10^{-17}$ joules per elementary charge.

In the next section we shall use the known value of $mv^2/2$ as part of an experiment to measure the ionic mass m. Since we know the value of $mv^2/2$ from F times d, we can determine the mass m by measuring the speed v.

29–2. The Mass of the Electron and of the Proton

As we saw in Section 29–1, we can find the mass of an ion by accelerating it through a known distance in a known electric force field and then measuring its final speed. We shall measure this speed directly by timing the flight of an ion as it moves through vacuum with no force exerted on it.

Let us start with hydrogen ions which we accelerate from rest in the apparatus we described in the last section. The ions starting at the left-hand plate accelerate toward the right-hand plate, acquiring the speed v. In the right-hand plate we have also drilled a small hole, and some of the ions will pass through the hole into a chamber 0.50 meters long. This chamber, which you see on the right in Fig. 29–2, is made of a conductor. Consequently, there is no electric force inside it, and the ions move its entire length without changing their speed. It takes the ions only a few microseconds (a few times 10^{-6} seconds) to go the whole distance. Although this time interval is very short, with a special timer we can measure it accurately. Then we can find an accurate value of the speed v of an ion.

In order to measure the time it takes for the ions to pass from one end of the long chamber to the other, we must record the time at which a particular ion passes a given point at the left and the time at which the same ion reaches the far end on the right. (You can understand the idea of such a measurement by considering the experiment discussed in the box, page 490.) To mark the time when a given ion enters the long chamber, we place a couple of small deflecting plates near the entrance. (See Fig. 29–3.) With these deflecting plates we can control the direction of the beam of hydrogen ions. When the deflecting plates are charged, the hydrogen ions are subject to a sidewise electric force which bends them out of their normal path. But when the deflecting plates are discharged, the beam of ions will pass through the whole apparatus. The moment at which the deflecting plates are discharged, therefore, marks the time at which a small group of ions is allowed to start down the long chamber toward the far end. Their arrival 50 cm farther away is then signaled by a detector placed at the end of the chamber (Fig. 29–3).

To measure the time interval, we connect the deflecting plates in the chamber to the vertical deflecting plates of an oscilloscope (Fig. 29–4). When we discharge the plates in the long chamber, the time of the discharge is recorded as a spike in the curve traced on the face of the oscilloscope. We also connect the detector at the far end of the long chamber to the same vertical deflecting plates of the oscilloscope. (We make the electrical connections at both ends of the chamber

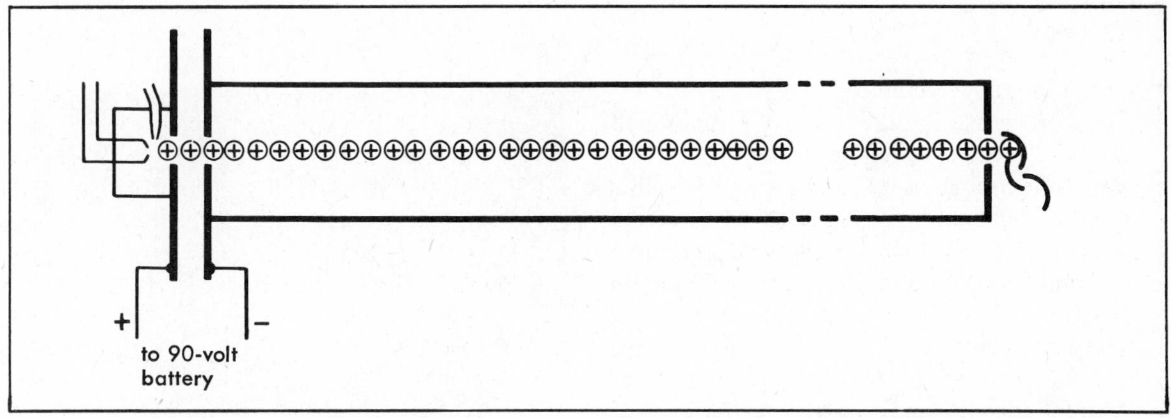

29–2. To measure the mass of hydrogen ions, we drill a hole in the right-hand plate, allowing some ions to enter a long chamber on the right, where they move without forces.

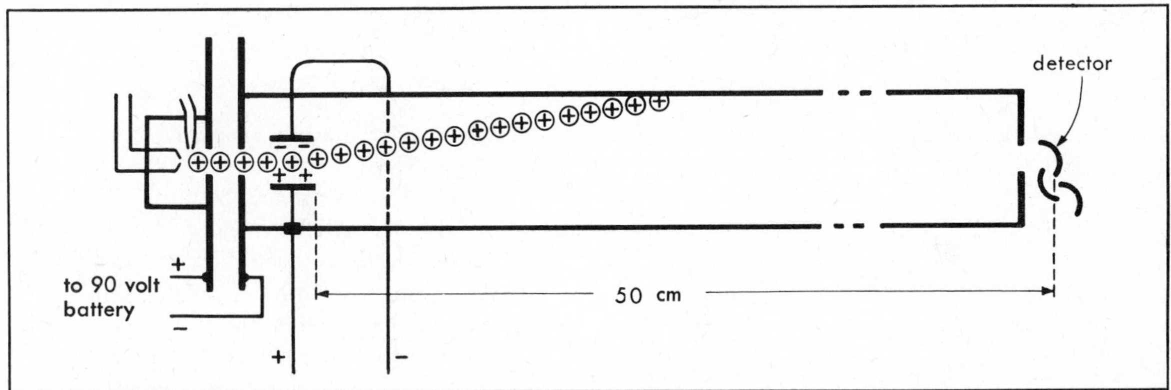

29–3. When the deflecting plates are charged, the electric force swings the beam to the side. When the plates are uncharged, ions go straight ahead and hit the detector.

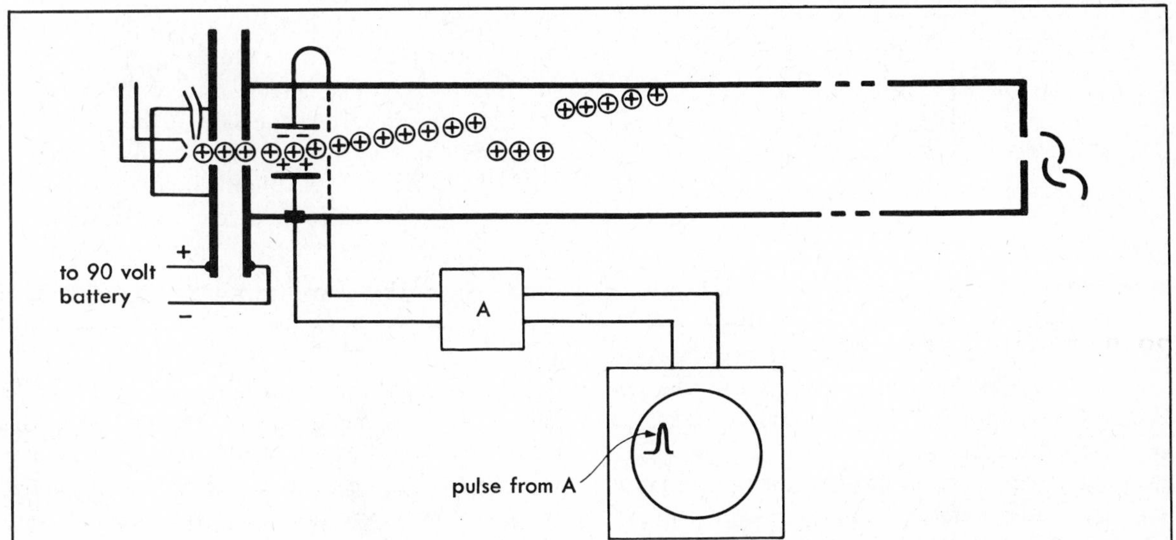

29–4. When we momentarily discharge the plates, we let through a short pulse of ions that goes straight along the chamber to the detector. The discharge is recorded as a spike on the oscilloscope, marking the time that the pulse begins its flight.

A MEASUREMENT OF SPEED BY TIME OF FLIGHT

We can understand the idea of this experiment by measuring the speed of a metal ball moving steadily along a trough. In Fig. 29–5 the trough is shown. At two points on the ball's path there are contacts in the trough; and as the ball passes each contact, it completes a circuit. When the ball passes the first contact a current flows for a moment from a battery in Box *A* through the ball. At the same time, triggered by the flow of current, Box *A* sends a pulse to the oscilloscope so that a spike appears on the oscilloscope face. The horizontal position of this spike tells the time at which the ball passes the contact.

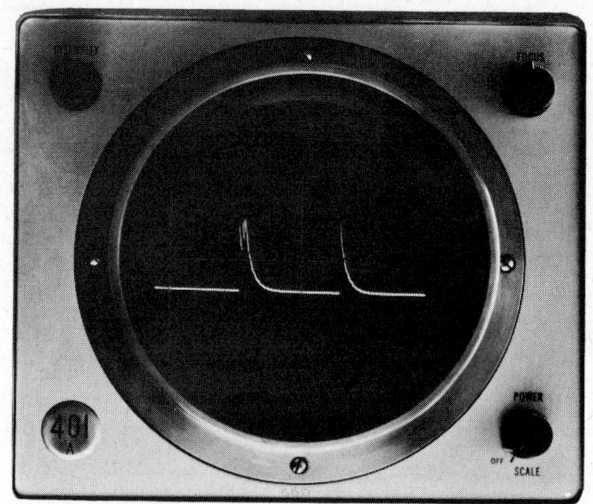

29–6.

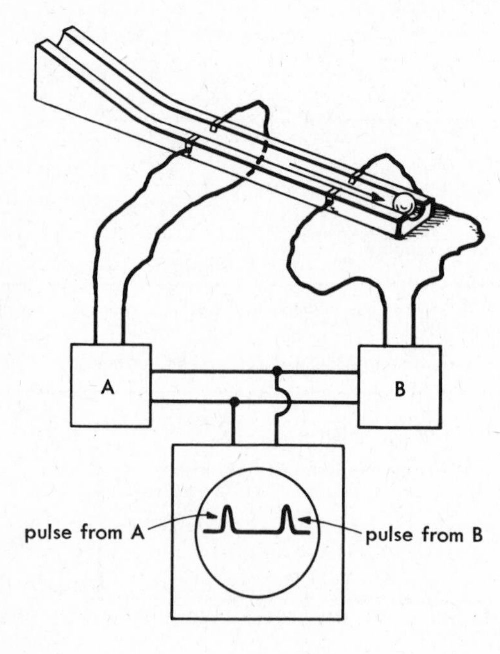

29–5.

While the ball moves from the first contact to the second one, the sweep circuit of the oscilloscope continues to trace the curve on the face from left to right. When the ball passes the second contact, an identical mechanism in Box *B* puts a second spike on the face of the oscilloscope. The position of this second spike corresponds to the time when the ball passes the second contact. The distance between the two spikes measures the time interval, the "time of flight" of the ball, between the first and second contacts in the trough. Fig. 29–6 shows a record plotted out on the face of an oscilloscope in such a measurement. The sweep traced the curve steadily, moving from one side of the grid of lines on the face of the oscilloscope to the other in 1 second. So the distance between spikes corresponds to 0.38 sec. In this time the ball moved 24 cm from contact to contact. So its speed was 0.63 meters per second.

identical.) When the beam of ions hits the detector, a second spike then appears on the face of the oscilloscope (Fig. 29–7). The two spikes occur at different places on the tube face because they are made at different times. During the intervening time interval the sweep circuit in the oscilloscope has moved the electron beam horizontally across the face. The electron beam in the oscilloscope moves the distance between the spikes in the same time that the hydrogen ions move the 50 cm through the chamber. (You may want to look again at the same reasoning applied to the simpler experiment described in the box.)

With a modern oscilloscope, the sweep circuit can move the electron beam horizontally across the face of the tube from one side to the other in

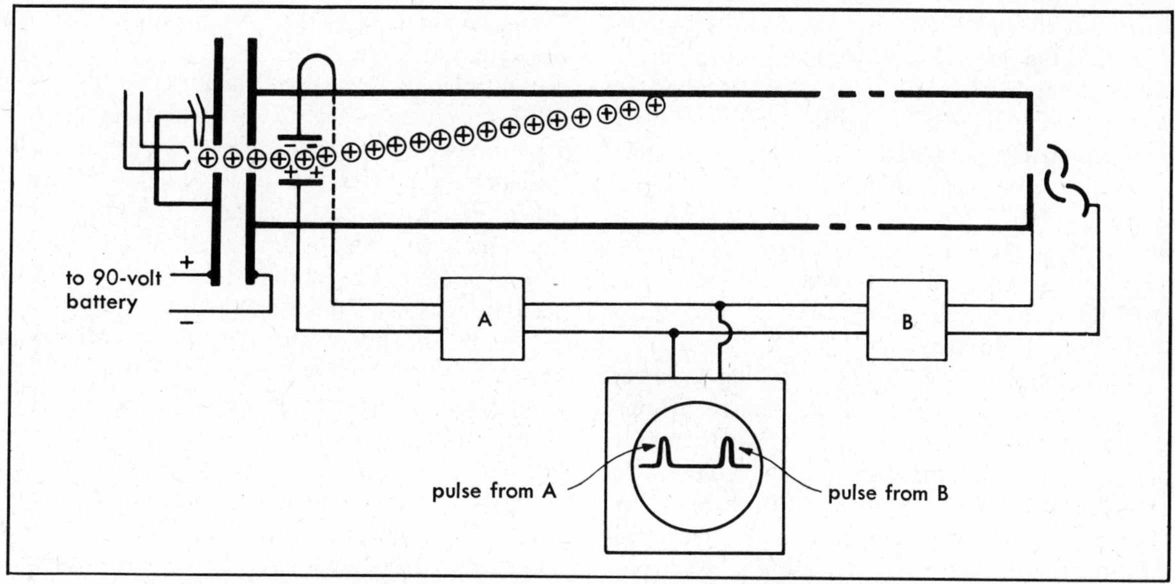

29–7. When the ion pulse strikes the detector, a second spike appears on the oscilloscope. The distance between the two spikes measures the time of flight of the ions.

a few hundredths of a microsecond. To measure the speed of the ions, we adjust the sweep circuit to make the whole curve represent 5 microseconds. The two spikes on the curve are then well separated on the face of the oscilloscope. By measuring the distance between the spikes, we measure the time it takes the beam to cross the long chamber. We obtain the time interval from the moment when the beam is allowed to go straight ahead to the moment when it hits the detector, with an accuracy of about one-hundredth of a microsecond. With hydrogen ions and a 90-volt battery providing the accelerating electric force, the time of flight is 3.82 microseconds. From this, we compute the speed of the ions in the long chamber. It is

$$\frac{0.50 \text{ meters}}{3.82 \times 10^{-6} \text{ sec}} = 1.31 \times 10^5 \text{ meters per second.}$$

Now what do we know? Let us assume that each hydrogen ion carries one elementary charge. Then its kinetic energy is $\frac{1}{2}mv^2 = 1.44 \times 10^{-17}$ joules. (This is the kinetic energy transferred to any particle as it is accelerated across from plate to plate by the electric force on one elementary charge.) We also know that the actual speed with which the hydrogen ions are moving after that acceleration is 1.31×10^5 meters per second. By putting this value of v into $\frac{1}{2}mv^2 = 1.44 \times 10^{-17}$ joules, we can compute the mass of the hydrogen ion. It comes out to be 1.7×10^{-27} kg.

But this mass is familiar to us. To within our accuracy it is the same as the mass of the hydrogen atom. We computed that mass in Chapter 8. There we found that the mass of a mole of hydrogen atoms is very close to 1 gram, and the number of atoms in a mole is 6×10^{23}, so the mass of one hydrogen atom is about 1.7×10^{-24} grams, or 1.7×10^{-27} kg.

We can now state our result. If the hydrogen ion is singly charged, we find it has almost the same mass as the hydrogen atom. In fact, we can go one step further and assert that the hydrogen ion actually does carry a single charge and does have practically the mass of the atom. This must be true because the assumption that the ion carries more charge leads to an absurd result. For example, if an ion carried two elementary charges, the actual value of $mv^2/2$ would be just twice what we used above. Since we measured v, this could only mean that the mass of the ion is twice what we found. Such a hydrogen ion would have twice the mass of the atom of which it is a fragment. And that conclusion is unlikely enough so that we reject it.

We have already had indications that electrons are small building blocks common to all atoms. Presumably a hydrogen ion is a hydrogen atom that has lost an electron. Furthermore, we never see a positive fragment of hydrogen with two positive elementary charges either in these or any other experiments. This is one of many indications that the positive hydrogen ion is an elementary building block. It is the proton. And as we mentioned in Chapter 28, protons are also found in alpha particles and fragments of heavier atoms.

When hydrogen is split into charged fragments, as we just found out, the proton has almost the whole mass of the atom. The electron therefore must be very light. We can use the same apparatus to measure the electron mass and thus verify this conclusion.

If hydrogen ions are made by taking an electron out of a hydrogen atom, the source of ions at the left of our apparatus should also provide electrons. By turning the battery around, we can accelerate the electrons that drift through the hole in the left-hand plate and reject the hydrogen ions. (Alternatively we can use the electrons boiled out of a hot filament — with either source we get the same results.) Since the electrons are pushed across between the plates with the same force through the same distance, they will gain the same value of $mv^2/2$ — that is

$$mv^2/2 = 1.44 \times 10^{-17} \text{ joules.}$$

Because they are much lighter than the positive ions, they will be moving faster when they pass through the hole in the second plate and cross the long chamber. Consequently, when we measure the speed with which the electrons pass through the long chamber, we find that we are closer to the limits imposed by our apparatus. With the sweep circuit adjusted so that the distance across the tube face corresponds to a time interval of about 0.12 microseconds we can see the two spikes recorded on the face of the oscilloscope. They are about nine-hundredths of a microsecond apart. However, to measure the exact time interval between them to better than 10 per cent accuracy requires an unusually fast oscilloscope and very sharp spikes. Taking 0.090 microseconds as a first approximation, we find that the speed is about 5.6×10^6 meters per second. Consequently, the mass of an electron (computed in the same way as the mass of positive ions) is about 0.9×10^{-30} kg. Accurate measurements of the mass of the electron give 0.911×10^{-30} kg, about a two-thousandth of the mass of a hydrogen atom.*

In measuring the masses of the ions, we can change the details of the experiments so that we use different known electric forces and different separations between the plates. We then get different values of $mv^2/2$. But we always get the same masses. We can use other methods to measure the masses — and we shall describe another one in the next chapter. The results are the same. Indeed, the masses of many ions are now extremely well established, and they lead to accurate masses of the atoms.

The experiments we have just described tell us about two of the fundamental building blocks from which atoms are made, protons and electrons. In interpreting these experiments, we naturally used the Newtonian mechanics that we studied in Part III. Because our results are sensible and consistent, we can now conclude that Newtonian mechanics can be applied over an enormous range. It gives an accurate description of the motions of large masses at large distances, of the planets in the solar system; it applies to moderate masses at the moderate dimensions of everyday life; and it also applies to the small masses of electrons moving through relatively small distances at huge speeds. Consequently, it is reasonable to try to apply the same mechanics and the same forces to the electrons within atoms. In particular, we can make a model of a hydrogen atom in which a single electron moves around the relatively massive proton under the influence of the Coulomb force. Because the Coulomb force has the same inverse-square dependence as the gravitational force between the sun and a planet, we shall call this model a planetary model of the atom. In the planetary model of hydrogen, the electron moves around the proton in an elliptical orbit like a planet around the sun. The planetary model, as we shall see in Section 32–5, meets with some difficulties, but it is a good first approximation to actual atomic behavior. Since Rutherford introduced it in 1911, it has played a central role in our understanding of atoms.

*With modern fast oscilloscopes and amplifiers, we can measure time intervals to within 10^{-9} sec. Therefore it is now possible to use this technique to get an accuracy of about 1 per cent. Earlier, precision measurements were made by other methods which we shall come to in Section 30–9.

29–3. Electric Current

The beams of protons and electrons in the experiments described in the last section are electric currents. The natural measure of these currents is the number of elementary charges transported per second.

If we catch a beam of positive particles in a metal cup, the cup becomes more and more positively charged as time goes on. For this reason we say that the direction of this electric current is into the cup. The current is in the same direction as the motion of the positive particles.

A beam of negative particles is also an electric current. But when we catch it in a metal cup, the charge of the cup decreases. If we catch beams of positive and of negative particles at the same time, they neutralize each other. When the same number of positive and of negative particles arrive in the cup per second, the charge of the cup does not change. There is no incoming electric current. Even though the beam of negative particles moves *toward* the cup, it constitutes an electric current *away* from the cup, emptying the cup of positive charge as fast as the positive beam fills it. In other words, a beam of negative particles constitutes an electric current in the direction opposite to the motion of the negative particles.

In general an electric current can be brought about by the motion of both positive and negative particles. The total electric current is made of the number of positive elementary charges passing per second (contributing to the electric current in their direction of motion) *plus* the number of negative elementary charges passing per second (contributing to the electric current in the direction opposite to their motion).

You already know an example of an electric current made of charges of both signs moving in opposite directions. In an electrolytic cell such as that shown in Fig. 29–8, ions move in both directions. The positive ions moving from A to C are part of an electric current toward C. The rest of that electric current is given by negative ions moving in the opposite direction.

The total electric current does not begin or end in the electrolytic cell. It comes in through the wire from the positive battery terminal to A and it goes out through the wire from C to the negative battery terminal. In each of these wires the moving charged particles are electrons, and

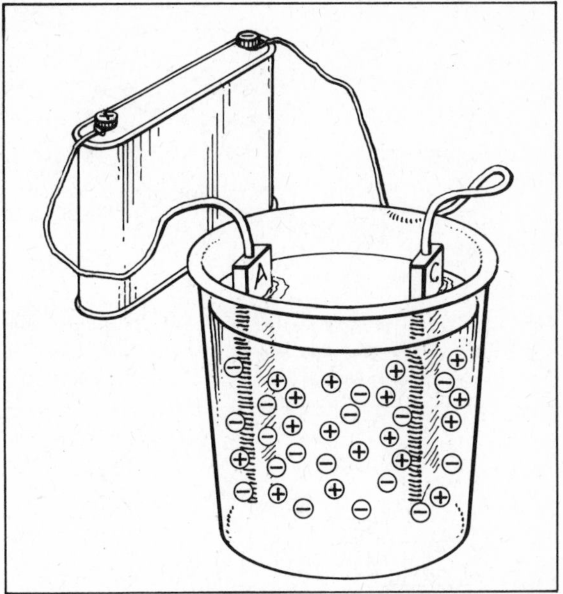

29–8. An electrolytic cell in series with a battery. The current in the cell is made up of the positive ions moving from A to C plus the negative ions moving from C to A.

these negative particles move in the opposite direction from the electric current. For example, they go from A to the positive terminal, causing the effective transport of positive charges from the terminal to A. Looking at the whole circuit we see that the electric current is flowing from the positive to the negative battery terminal around the external circuit. Inside the battery, on the other hand, the current goes from the negative to the positive battery terminal. The battery moves more positive charges to the positively charged terminal and negative charges to the negative terminal despite the electric repulsions. In this process the battery uses chemical energy to force the charges onto the terminals.

The net rate of flow of elementary charges is the same all around the circuit. This must be true because, when the current is running steadily, charge does not accumulate in any region of the circuit. The same number of elementary charges, therefore, goes in one end of any region as comes out the other (Fig. 29–9).

The steady electric current cannot be measured by observing changes in charge; but we may imagine an observer who can count elementary charges passing any particular point in the circuit. If he watched the charges passing through the wire at a particular place, he would find I

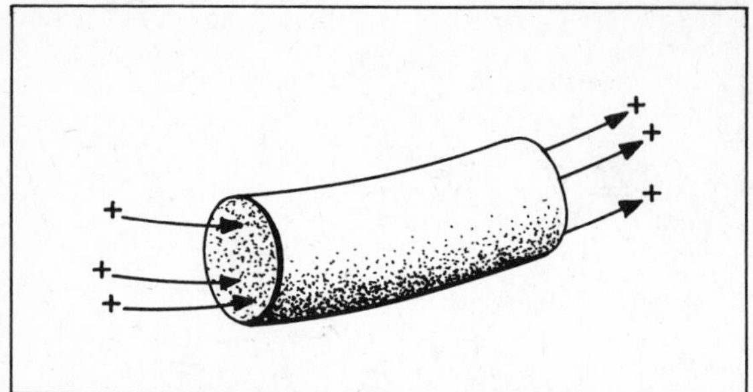

29–9 (a). When the same number of elementary charges goes in one end and out the other end of a section of a circuit, no charge accumulates in that section.

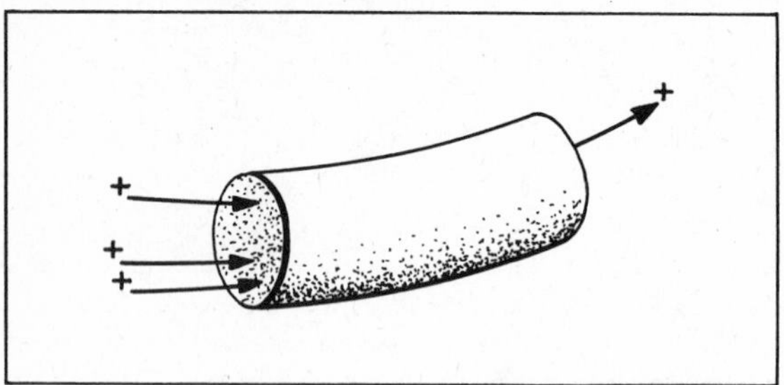

29–9 (b). If more elementary charges go in than go out, charge accumulates in the region. Therefore the observation that charge does not accumulate shows that the current into one end of the region must equal the current out the other end.

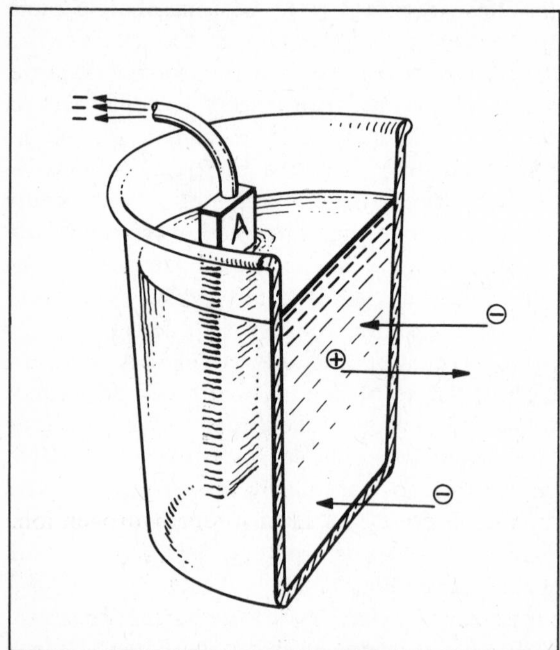

29–9 (c). In the region of the circuit shown, electrons flow through the wire and ions move in the electrolytic cell. Because no charge accumulates, we know that the sum of negative and positive ions passing through the center of the cell must equal the number of electrons passing through the cross section of the wire.

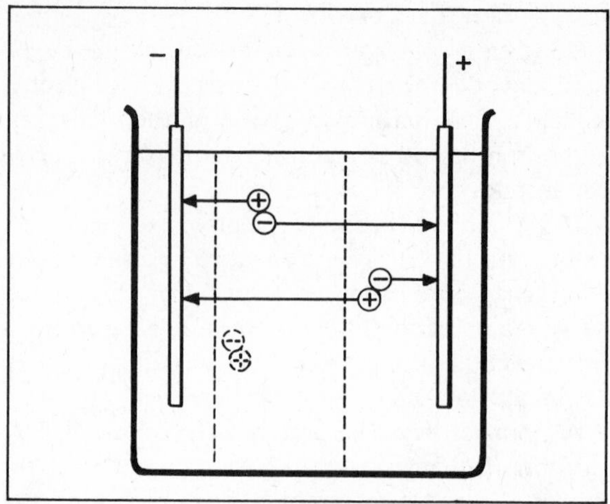

29–10. When any number of ion pairs is produced in the cell, this number of positive ions will be collected at the negative electrode, and this number of negative ions will be collected at the positive electrode. The arrows show how the ions go to the electrodes. Count the arrows passing through the dotted boundaries. The total number of positive and negative ions crossing any boundary between the electrodes is the same. Try adding the pairs produced at any place you want.

negative elementary charges, I electrons, passing per second. If he looked at the charges passing through the electrolytic cell at a particular place, he would also see I elementary charges passing. But here he must count the negative ones moving one way and the positive ones moving the opposite way and add the two numbers in order to get the total electric current which measures the net transport of charge (Figs. 29–9 and 29–10). In the next section we shall see how a real measurement of a steady current can be carried out.

29–4. Electrolytic Measurement of Electric Currents

The observer who can see elementary charges passing is imaginary. But in certain circumstances, we can make equivalent observations. For instance, we have already counted electrons in a weak beam from an electron gun. In this section we shall describe the measurement of the number of elementary charges by observing the amounts of mass transported by ions in solution.

For this purpose we connect a number of electrolytic cells *in series* with a battery as shown in Fig. 29–11. With this arrangement, the same amount of charge flows through each cell. The various cells contain solutions of salts of different metals, for example silver and copper. The elec-

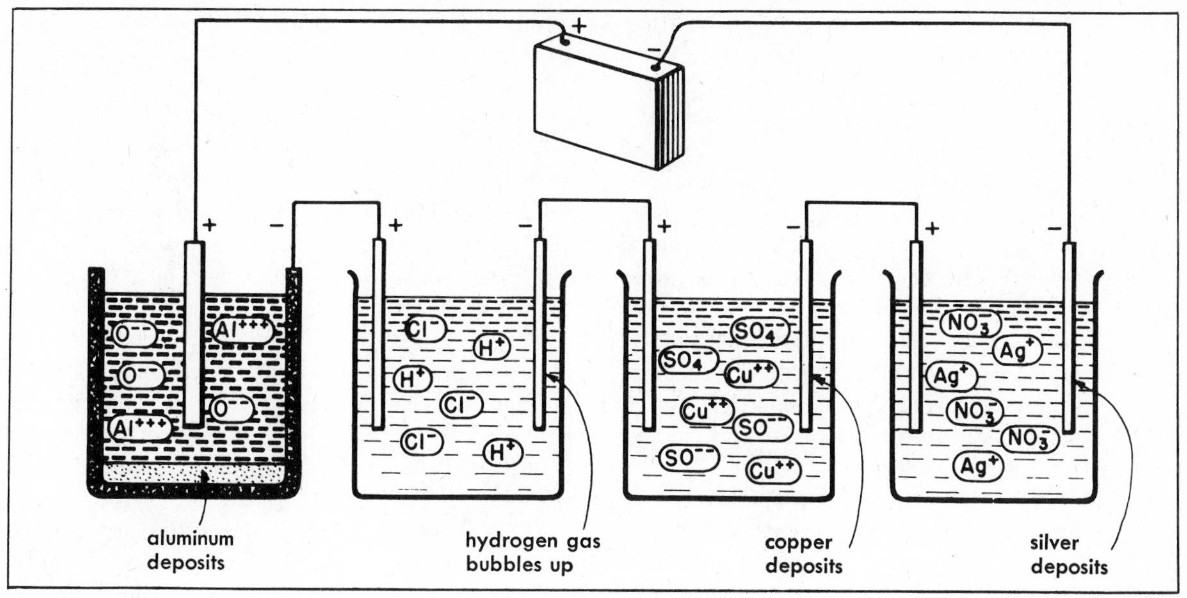

29–11. Electrolytic cells in series with a battery.

trodes are made of platinum (or carbon) which does not react chemically with either of these solutions. We also include a cell filled with dilute acid such as hydrochloric acid (HCl), whose molecules contain hydrogen instead of a metal, and a complicated cell containing aluminum in the compound Al_2O_3. The electrolytic cells for copper, silver, and hydrogen ions are ones that you can handle. The cell for the aluminum ion is different. Aluminum oxide, Al_2O_3, is dissolved in molten cryolite, and the aluminum which goes to the negative electrode is also molten. This kind of cell is actually used in refining aluminum.

As ions move through the solutions, the negative electrodes become coated with the metals present in the dissolved salts. Also, hydrogen gas bubbles out at the negative electrode of the cell full of acid. This shows that when the molecules of the salts are ionized, the positive ions carry the metal atoms with them (or perhaps they *are* positively charged metal atoms). When these ions arrive at the negative electrodes, the metal atoms usually remain attached to the electrodes. It also shows that the hydrogen ions are positive, and when they are neutralized at the negative electrode the hydrogen gas is formed.

By weighing the electrodes before and after an electric current has passed through the cells, we can determine the mass of metal that has been deposited in each cell. From this mass and from the mass of a mole of the metal we can compute the number of moles deposited. Similarly, we can determine the number of moles of hydrogen. When these computations are made a remarkable fact appears. For each mole of silver deposited there is a mole of hydrogen atoms, half a mole of copper, and one-third of a mole of aluminum.

Since a mole of any element contains the same number of atoms, we see that the charge carried by one ion of silver is the same as that carried by one ion of hydrogen; the charge carried by one ion of copper is twice that carried by one ion of silver; and the charge carried by one ion of aluminum is three times as large. In general, we find that the charges of all ions in solution are small whole-number multiples of a unit charge, the charge of the silver ion (or of the hydrogen ion). This great discovery was made by Faraday in 1833. It was the first cogent evidence of the existence of an elementary charge.

The smallest charge carried by an electrolytic ion, the charge of the silver ion or hydrogen ion, must be equal to the elementary charge we found in the Millikan experiment in Section 28–5. There are a number of reasons for being sure that this is so. For example, when an electrolytic hydrogen ion moves to the negative electrode in an electrolytic solution, it is made neutral by an electron from the platinum. Then the neutral hydrogen atoms combine to form hydrogen gas which bubbles out at the negative electrode. Because the platinum supplies ordinary electrons — there are no other — and because the hydrogen gas released is the same as any other hydrogen, the hydrogen ions in solution must be the same as the hydrogen ions whose mass we measured in Section 29–2. Like those hydrogen ions, these ions must carry exactly one positive elementary charge which can be neutralized by the negative elementary charge of the electron.

At the other electrode in the same electrolytic cell, negative ions are neutralized and neutral gas molecules are formed. The negative charge of each ion is taken off at the metal and carried away by an ordinary electron.

In general the ions of any kind which come to the electrodes in any electrolytic cell are turned into neutral atoms or molecules, and this neutrality is brought about by combining with ordinary electrons from a platinum electrode or by supplying ordinary electrons to the electrode. All the ionic charges must therefore be multiples of the elementary charge, and presumably the smallest ionic charge is the same as the elementary charge we detected in the Millikan experiment.

By itself the kind of evidence we have mentioned is reasonably convincing. There is no reason to assume that there are two kinds of unit charges in the universe; and the unit charge found in electrolysis seems to fit together perfectly with the unit charge found in the Millikan experiment. We shall be able to give another check on this conclusion in the next section. Furthermore, by the end of this part of the book we shall have plenty of evidence to show that atoms are made of electrons and of positively charged particles which exactly neutralize them. Since we already know that each electron carries one negative elementary charge, it then follows that anything built of atoms must either be neutral or carry a whole number of elementary charges. Because everything including ions is so built, we again conclude the ionic charges are multiples of the elementary charge.

We now know that hydrogen ions and silver ions each carry one positive elementary charge; each copper ion carries two positive elementary charges, and each aluminum ion carries three positive elementary charges. (Also, the charges of some negative ions are indicated in Fig. 29–11.) We can use this information to measure the total amount of charge transported across an electrolytic cell. For instance, when only hydrogen ions come to the negative electrode, the number of elementary charges transported is the same as the number of hydrogen ions that arrive. Consequently, by measuring the mass of hydrogen released and dividing by the mass of one atom, we find the number of elementary charges.

We can use a similar method to measure a current. For instance, by putting an electrolytic cell containing silver ions in a circuit and measuring the *rate* at which silver is deposited, we can measure the electric current in elementary charges per second. Since one elementary charge is transported for each silver atom deposited, the electrolytic cell becomes an electric current meter. Indeed, electrolytic cells depositing silver are often used as standards to measure currents. Usually, however, it is more convenient to employ a different form of meter. We can use any device which responds differently and reproducibly to different currents, but we must calibrate at least one of these other meters. We calibrate any other meter by putting it in series with the electrolytic cell. Since the same current passes through both meters, we can mark the scale of the other meter with the values of the current in elementary charges per second measured by the rate of deposition of silver in the electrolytic cell.

29–5. Experimental Checks: Energy Transfer; Electric Force; Elementary Charges

In Section 29–1 we used a known electric force F to accelerate ions across a distance d. The ions started from rest and acquired the final speed v. We used the relation

$$Fd = \tfrac{1}{2}mv^2$$

to predict their kinetic energy after the acceleration. Now that we can measure an electric current or a total charge transported in terms of elementary charges, we can do an experiment which shows that Fd correctly predicts the kinetic energy $\frac{1}{2}mv^2$ that the ions gain.

For this experiment we use electrons boiled off a hot wire. We accelerate them in a known electric force field between two parallel metal plates, just as we did in measuring the mass of an electron in Sections 29–1 and 29–2. The electrons which are accelerated from the negatively charged plate crash into the positively charged plate and lose their kinetic energy. This energy is transformed into thermal energy, heating the plate. With reasonable currents the heating of the plate can be great enough so that an appreciable rise in temperature occurs within a few seconds. By measuring this temperature rise we can determine the amount of energy transferred. And by measuring the current we can determine the number of elementary charges. We thus obtain the kinetic energy per elementary charge. The results of these experiments confirm our prediction that the kinetic energy per elementary charge is given by the electric force F acting on an elementary charge times the distance d through which the charge accelerates.

It may seem that this verification that $F \times d$ gives the kinetic energy is unnecessary. Indeed there is no surprise in our result, but we can draw two valuable conclusions from it. In the first place, when we computed the work Fd which measures the transfer of energy into the kinetic energy of motions of the electrons, we used the force F per elementary charge that we had already measured on elementary charges at rest or in slow motion in the micro-microbalance of Section 28–4. Up to now we have assumed without experimental evidence that this same force acts on a fast-moving elementary charge. The experiments we have just described show that the electric force on a moving charge is actually independent of its speed. Because electrons which are accelerated between parallel plates charged by three batteries as in the Millikan experiment attain a speed of about 10^7 m/sec, we see that the electric force on an elementary charge is the same at any speed between zero and this enormous value.

Secondly, these experiments show that the unit charge found in electrolytic experiments is the same as the elementary charge found in the Millikan experiment. We measure the currents with meters which are calibrated against electrolytic cells. The number of charges which transfer their kinetic energy into heat at the positive plate is therefore given as the number of electrolytic unit charges. Consequently, our experiments measure the kinetic energy per electrolytic unit charge. On the other hand, we predict kinetic energy in terms of the force in the Millikan experiment. Consequently, the kinetic energy predicted is the kinetic energy per Millikan elementary charge. The agreement between the predicted and the experimental results now shows that the electrolytic unit charge and the elementary charge found in the Millikan experiment must be the same. There is only one elementary unit of electric charge.

Measurements like those we have discussed in this section were performed in 1897 by J. J. Thomson. When he determined the mass per elementary charge of the electron, he made such thermal measurements of the kinetic energy per elementary charge in a stream of moving electrons. Then to complete the determination of the mass, he performed another experiment. He measured the motion under the influence of a known force. Although the details of that experiment were entirely different, it was equivalent to the experiment we described in Section 29–2, where we measured the speed of the electrons. His experiment actually measured their momentum mv, and he then found the mass m and the speed v from the known values of mv and of the kinetic energy $\frac{1}{2}mv^2$. We shall study the method he used in the next chapter.

29–6. Batteries as Energy Sources; Energy Supplied per Elementary Charge

In the last few sections we have discussed the direction of the electric current and the measurement of its strength. Also we have seen that energy is transferred to the charged particles and may be taken from them as thermal energy. Indeed, there is no electric current without some energy transfer.

Clearly, the details of the flow of energy in a circuit are often complex. The electric field serves as a medium through which kinetic energy is supplied to the charges in the external circuit, and inside the battery charged particles are moved against the electric forces from the charges at the terminals. In the rest of this chapter, we shall look at the electric fields and at the energy in more detail. Although we shall not find it practical to establish the exact electric-field patterns for most circuits, we shall arrive at an understanding of the over-all flow of energy in all sorts of circuits.

So far in this chapter we have employed batteries as the source of the energy dissipated as thermal energy elsewhere in the circuit. How much energy does a battery supply and on what does that amount depend? We shall find that a battery which uses stored chemical energy to supply electrical energy usually supplies the same energy for each elementary charge.

Consider, for example, the energy supplied by the battery to each elementary charge in an ion beam accelerated from one parallel metal plate to another. In Chapter 28, we learned that the electric force field between the plates is uniform and, with the battery connected, the magnitude of the force is inversely proportional to the distance between the plates. Consequently the force on an elementary charge times the distance between the plates always comes out the same. As we have just verified in Section 29–5, this force times distance gives the energy transferred to a charge. No matter how we change the plate separation, the force times distance stays the same and the energy supplied per elementary charge by the battery is the same amount. With a 270-volt battery made up, for example, of the three batteries used in the Millikan experiment, the force times the distance between plates always equals 4.34×10^{-17} joules per elementary charge. It is

$$(1.4 \times 10^{-14} \text{ newtons/elem. ch.}) \times (3.1 \times 10^{-3} \text{ m}) = 4.34 \times 10^{-17} \text{ joules/elem. ch.}$$

or

$$(0.7 \times 10^{-14} \text{ newtons/elem. ch.}) \times (6.2 \times 10^{-3} \text{ m}) = 4.34 \times 10^{-17} \text{ joules/elem. ch.}$$

or any similar product of field and separation.

Not only can we change the separation between the plates, but we can also change the plate area. The electrical force on an elementary charge between the plates does not change; and, as we expect, the energy supplied to each ion that passes between the plates stays the same. The battery moves more charges when it initially charges up the plates, but this does not influence the energy supplied per elementary charge moving across in the ion beam.

The energy supplied per elementary charge does not depend on the magnitude of the current. By using a bigger source of hydrogen ions or by boiling more electrons out of a hot wire filament, we can increase the ion currents that we used in our earlier experiments. The energy per elementary charge supplied by the battery does not change. (Later we shall see more evidence that the energy per elementary charge does not depend on the strength of the current.)

We have used the ion currents because they are easy to understand. They are not essential to our result. If we connect a current meter and a high-resistance wire in series between positive and negative terminals of a battery, we can measure the number of elementary charges transported past any point in the circuit in a specified time. In such a circuit almost all the energy that the moving charges acquire from the electric field is turned immediately into thermal energy in the high-resistance wire. By measuring the heat dissipated in the wire, we can calculate the energy supplied by the battery per elementary charge (Fig. 29–12). We find that the energy supplied per elementary charge is the same in this different circuit as it is for an ion beam between parallel metal plates.

All these experiments indicate that a battery is a device which supplies a definite amount of energy per elementary charge; and in particular, a 270-volt battery supplies 4.34×10^{-17} joules per elementary charge. The energy supplied per elementary charge is known as the EMF of the battery. You should read this name as "ee em eff." The old name from which the initials come is the electromotive force, but this name is misleading for we are not dealing with a force in the usual sense at all. Almost everyone now calls the energy per elementary charge the EMF rather than using the old words. We shall symbolize the EMF by the letter $\mathcal{E}$.

Suppose we take three identical batteries, each of which supplies an EMF of 4.34×10^{-17} joules per elementary charge. If we connect them in series in a circuit, each should supply 4.34×10^{-17} joules for each elementary charge. The total EMF — that is, the total amount of energy supplied by all the batteries per elementary charge — should therefore be

$$3 \times 4.34 \times 10^{-17} \frac{\text{joules}}{\text{elem. ch.}} = 1.30 \times 10^{-16} \frac{\text{joules}}{\text{elem. ch.}}.$$

This is exactly what we find; and indeed it is exactly what you would expect on the basis of the experiments with the batteries in series that we mentioned in Section 28–6. There, when we connected one hundred 270-volt "B" batteries in series to make a large electrical balance, we increased the force between the parallel metal plates in proportion to the number of batteries. Consequently, the batteries also supplied energy per

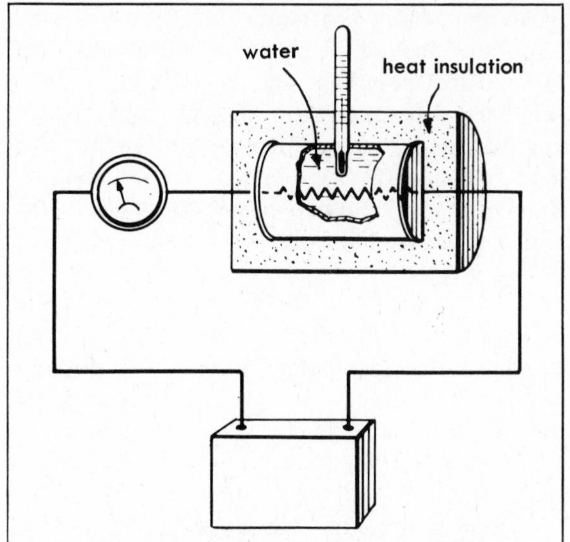

29–12. We can measure the energy dissipated as heat in a resistance wire by the temperature rise of the water surrounding the wire. Since the ammeter indicates the number of elementary charges that pass per second, we can calculate the energy supplied per elementary charge by the battery.

elementary charge in proportion to their number.

Now we are in a position to answer the question of how much energy a battery supplies to an electrical circuit. This energy is just the product of $\mathcal{E}$, the EMF of the battery, times the number q of elementary charges that are transported.

$$q\mathcal{E} = \text{(no. elem. ch.)(joules/elem. ch.)} = \text{joules}$$

If no charges are transported the battery supplies no energy. If there is a current I, the battery supplies energy at the rate

$$I\mathcal{E} = \text{(no. elem. ch./sec.)(joules/elem. ch.)} = \text{joules/sec.}$$

The rate at which energy is supplied to a circuit is known as the power supplied, and the unit of power 1 joule/sec is called a watt after James Watt, the steam-engine maker. In other words, the last equation says when the current is measured in elementary charges per second and the EMF in joules per elementary charge, the power is $I\mathcal{E}$ watts.

29–7. Electric Field and Electric Potential Difference

We have used batteries as the ultimate sources of stored energy. That energy is used to concentrate charges, and the electric force fields originating from these concentrations of charge in turn convey the energy to the ions moving between the metal plates or to the electrons moving in metal wires. The electric force fields are set up whenever we concentrate charges, whether we make these concentrations by the action of a battery, by rubbing, or by any other means. We should, therefore, discuss the energy of an elementary charge in an electric force field without restricting the discussions to a particular source of EMF. For this reason we shall now return to the electric field.

In Section 28–3, we discussed the electric force field produced by a fixed distribution of charges. The electric force field is the pattern of electric force that would be exerted by a given distribution of charges on another charged object. In imagination we place this other charge successively at each point in space, and we either measure or compute the force that would be exerted on it at all the different points.

The magnitude and direction of the electric force at any point depends both on the distribution of the charges exerting the force and on the magnitude of the charge on which the force is exerted. We now define the electric field $\vec{E}$ as the electric force field on one positive elementary charge. Since the force at any particular point in space on one elementary charge is given by the electric field $\vec{E}$ arising from all the other charges, the electric force $\vec{F}$ on a body carrying q elementary charges is q times the electric field, that is, $\vec{F} = q\vec{E}$. Because the electric field times the number q of elementary charges placed in a given position gives the force $\vec{F}$ exerted on those charges, the units of electric field are newtons per elementary charge.

As an illustration, consider the simplest example — the electric field around q_1 elementary charges located at a fixed point. At a distance r away from this point, Coulomb's law tells us that the magnitude of the force on a single positive elementary charge is kq_1/r^2, and the force points directly away from the charge q_1. The electric field $\vec{E}$ is, therefore, represented by vectors of magnitude kq_1/r^2 pointing away from the charge q_1. This expression tells us the electric field at any point in space whether there is a positive elementary charge at that point or not.

Now suppose we place a body carrying q elementary charges at distance r away from the charge q_1. To find the force on it we must multi-

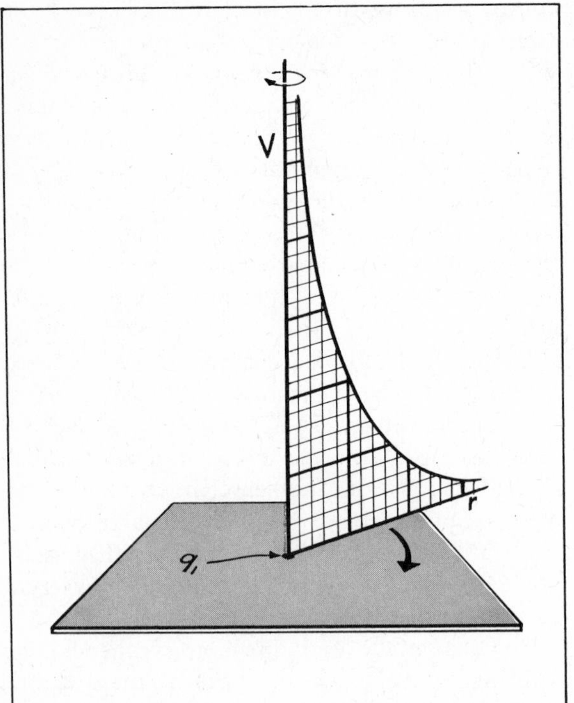

29–13. A graph of electric potential V versus the distance r from a charge.

ply the electric field by q. On multiplying q by the magnitude of the field we find the magnitude of the force. It is $F = kq_1q/r^2$; and since the direction of the field is away from q_1, so is the direction of the force.

As you can see, the electric field here is just an aid that allows us to say what the force will be on any charge q placed at any position. In this simple example, it merely gives us a restatement of Coulomb's law. Also, when the electric field is produced by many different charges, it will give the same result as using Coulomb's law and vector addition to find the force exerted by all the other charges on the charge q.

Although the electric field does not contain any new information, it is a great convenience. At times we can evaluate it without going through the detailed computation of the force based on knowing the magnitude and position of the charges. Later we shall find it even more important. For example, in Chapter 31 we shall discover electric fields that arise in other ways.

We have introduced the electric field here mainly for the purpose of discussing the energy of an elementary charge as it moves from one point in space to another. For the simple case of an elementary charge moving from one point to another around the charge q_1, we already know a great deal about the energy. We know about this energy because the Coulomb field of force has exactly the same form as the gravitational field of force that we studied in Section 25–4. There we found that two masses attract each other with a gravitational force

$$F = -G\frac{m_1m_2}{r^2}$$

and have a corresponding gravitational potential energy

$$U_g = -G\frac{m_1m_2}{r}.$$

The zero of potential energy is chosen to be at infinite separation, and the minus sign indicates that the potential energy is then negative at any separation r. The potential energy is negative because the masses attract each other as indicated by the minus sign in the equation for the force.

Now we know that two charged bodies interact with an electric force

$$F = k\frac{q_1q_2}{r^2}.$$

So in exactly the same way, they have an electric potential energy

$$U_e = k\frac{q_1q_2}{r}.$$

There are no minus signs in these expressions because charges of the same sign repel, instead of attracting each other like gravitating masses. The potential energy of two like charges, which has been taken as zero at infinite distance, will have a positive value for any finite value of r.

In particular, when q_2 is a single positive elementary charge ($q_2 = 1$), the electric potential energy is kq_1/r. We shall call this potential energy per elementary charge the electric potential V at r or the electric potential drop between r and infinity. If the charge q_1 is held in position and a single elementary charge moves from r to infinity, under the influence of the Coulomb force alone, it will gain kinetic energy equal to

$$V = \frac{kq_1}{r}.$$

Since V is the potential energy per elementary

charge, it is measured in joules per elementary charge. It is the EMF of the electric field — the energy stored in its interaction with the additional positive elementary charge and given to that charge as it passes from r to infinity.*

Just as we can work out the electric field $\vec{E}$ throughout space, so we can work out the electric potential V for every point in space, obtaining a field of electric potential drops between r and infinity. To illustrate this field around a charge q_1, we start by plotting a graph of V versus r. (Fig. 29–13.) In this graph the height above a point r shows the value of V. To visualize the field of electric potential at all points on a plane passing through the charge q_1, we swing the graph around a vertical axis passing through $r = 0$. In other words we swing it around the position of the charge q_1. As it sweeps around, the graph generates a potential "hill" whose height above any point on the plane represents the potential at that point. The potential "hill" for a plane passing through a charge located at one point is shown in Fig. 29–14. We shall find this potential "hill" of great value in Chapter 32 when we discuss the motion of one charged particle in the Coulomb field of another.

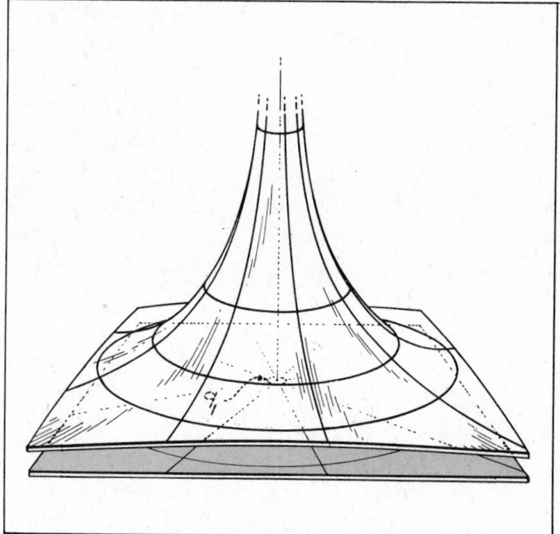

29–14. If we swing the graph of Fig. 29–13 around a vertical axis passing through the charge, we produce a potential "hill." The height of the "hill" above the plane represents the electrical potential at that point on the plane.

The electric potential differences in the electric field of a charge q_1 serve to introduce us to the general idea of electric potential difference. In place of the electric field from q_1 we now consider the electric field produced by any number of charges nailed down at definite positions. Imagine that we move one other positive elementary charge from any point A to another point B in this field (Fig. 29–15). During this motion the electric field transfers the energy V to the charge. Moreover, this energy V is always the same no matter what path we choose from A to B. The path makes no difference because the electric force depends only on the separations between charges. As we saw in Chapters 24 and 25, when the forces depend only on separations, there is a potential energy; and we change that potential energy by the same amount, as long as all the initial and final separations are the same. By changing the position of the positive elementary charge, then, we are changing the electric potential energy between two values that depend only on the positions A and B. The energy V measures the transfer of this electric potential energy. This transfer when we move one elementary charge is what we mean in general by the electric potential difference.

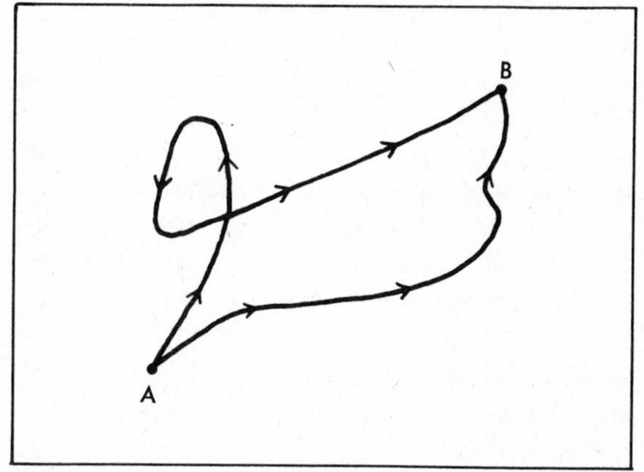

29–15. When we move a positive elementary charge from a point A to a point B in an electric field produced by fixed charges, the energy transferred to the elementary charge does not depend on what path we choose.

For example, in the Millikan experiment in going from the positive metal plate to the nega-

*Any energy transfer per elementary charge may be called an EMF. The EMF may arise as a decrease of electric potential energy as in this example, but it may come from some other source such as the energy stored in a battery or the energy fed in by a generator. We shall use the name electric potential drop when we want to point out that we are dealing with the decrease of electric potential energy that goes with a change in position of an elementary charge.

tive plate connected to the 270-volt battery, we found that the energy given to one positive elementary charge was 4.34×10^{-17} joules. Consequently, the electric potential difference between the plates was 4.34×10^{-17} joule/elem. ch. The electric potential rises 4.34×10^{-17} joule/elem. ch. in going from the negative to the positive plate, and we must supply that energy per elementary charge to force positive charges to move from negative to positive. The electric potential falls by this amount in going the other way, and the field will transfer the 4.34×10^{-17} joules to each positive elementary charge moving from the positive to the negative plate.

29–8. Batteries, Volts, and Amperes

In Section 29–6 we looked at some of the evidence that batteries supply a definite amount of energy per elementary charge, but we did not examine why or how the battery maintains a constant EMF. Although we shall not attempt a detailed explanation here, we shall try to get a crude idea of how this comes about.

Batteries are made by connecting a large number of electrochemical cells in series. In a single electrochemical cell charges are forced onto the terminals against the electric repulsion of the charges already present. Their electric potential energy is thus increased. This increased potential energy of charges at the terminals is supplied by chemical energy released in chemical reactions between the constituents of the cell. In each individual chemical reaction the chemical potential energy is reduced a definite amount. Also because each individual chemical reaction involves a definite number of atoms or ions moving across the cell, this particular amount of energy is used to push a definite number of elementary charges up the electrical hills at the terminals. Therefore the cell gives a fixed energy per elementary charge. Also a battery of cells in series gives an energy per elementary charge in direct proportion to the number of cells.

As long as the chemical composition and the positions of the constituents of a cell stay substantially the same, each individual chemical reaction is just like every other one. So a fixed EMF is maintained. When too much charge has been transferred, however, too many chemical reactions have taken place, and the composition of the cell is changed.

Then the cell no longer provides the same chemical reactions with the same ions moving through the same distances. The EMF falls off and we say that the battery has run down. In some cells, by forcing a current to pass in the opposite direction, we can reverse the chemical reactions, thus "recharging" the battery. Here "recharging" means restoring the chemical energy. We do not change the electrical charge of the battery.

The reactions that go on in electrochemical cells of many different kinds transfer about the same number of joules per individual chemical reaction (the same number of joules per elementary charge), in many cases about 1 or 2×10^{-19} joules per elementary charge. It is therefore convenient to use a practical unit of EMF of about this size. The practical unit that is commonly used is called the *volt*. We define the volt as 1.6×10^{-19} *joules per elementary charge*. A flashlight dry cell, for example, gives 1.5 volts or 2.4×10^{-19} joules per elementary charge; and, as we know, the 270-volt balancing battery gives $270 \times 1.6 \times 10^{-19} = 4.34 \times 10^{-17}$ joules per elementary charge.*

We have defined the volt as a certain number of joules per elementary charge. Thus if we want to measure the number of volts supplied by a given battery, we must perform an experiment using this battery to provide energy to a measured number of charges. However, we need to do this only once, because we can keep our calibrated battery as a standard, just as we can keep a good meter stick on hand to use in distance measurements. (Prescriptions for making standard cells, the Weston cell for instance, will be found in treatises on electricity.)

Using the volt as the unit of EMF will prove convenient not only in practical work dealing with electrochemical cells or batteries, but also in studying the fundamental structure of atoms. The chemical reactions which transfer a few volts — a few times 1.60×10^{-19} joules per elementary charge — are rearrangements of the structure of atoms and molecules. The energy required to pull out an electron or to move one around from one atom to another is therefore about a volt times an elementary charge. For this reason,

*We have defined the volt as 1.6×10^{-19} joules per elementary charge. Often the practical unit of current is defined first; and the volt is defined in terms of it. As we shall see later, the two definitions agree.

physicists often state energies in electron volts. These are parcels of 1.6×10^{-19} joules, and they are of just the right size to measure the energies of individual chemical reactions or the energies required to ionize individual atoms. In the box at the right we have estimated the energy needed to ionize an atom, and you can see that it is a reasonable number of electron volts.

We chose our basic unit of EMF, the joule per elementary charge, so that, when the charge is measured in numbers of elementary charges, $q\mathcal{E}$ gives the energy in joules. We would like to continue to measure the energy in joules even when we shift the unit of EMF to the practical unit, the volt (or 1.6×10^{-19} joules per elementary charge). We therefore introduce a new unit of charge. We design the new unit, the coulomb, so that one coulomb times an EMF of one volt gives one joule,

$$(1 \text{ coul})(1 \text{ volt}) = 1 \text{ joule}.$$

Since 1 volt is 1.6×10^{-19} joules per elementary charge, this is

$$(1 \text{ coul})(1.6 \times 10^{-19} \text{ joules/elem. ch.}) = 1 \text{ joule}.$$

Consequently,

$$1 \text{ coulomb} = \frac{1 \text{ joule}}{1.6 \times 10^{-19} \text{ joule/elem. ch.}}$$
$$= 6.25 \times 10^{18} \text{ elem. ch.}$$

The unit of current that goes along with this unit of charge is called an *ampere*. An ampere is a flow of charge of 1 coulomb per second. Therefore 1 ampere = 6.25×10^{18} elementary charges per second.

When we deal with light bulbs or electric irons the ampere is a more convenient unit of current than the basic current unit of one elementary charge per second. The current that runs an ordinary light bulb is about an ampere. It would be clumsy to say that the lamp current is about 10^{19} elementary charges per second. Most current meters are calibrated in amperes, that is in units of 6.25×10^{18} elementary charges per second. The common name for a current meter is an ammeter.

The volt and the ampere are designed to fit together in the same way that the joule per elementary charge fits with a current measured in elementary charges per second.

In other words, when the current is measured in elementary charges per second and the EMF in joules per elementary charge the power is $I\mathcal{E}$ watts. In just the same way, if we measure the current in amperes (coulombs per second) and the EMF in volts (joules per coulomb), the power $I\mathcal{E}$ again is given in watts. The practical units fit together in the same way as the natural units, be-

Volts and Atoms

We can see that the volt (1.6×10^{-19} *joule per elementary charge*) and the electron volt (1.6×10^{-19} *joule*) are of the right size for atomic affairs by computing the electric potential energy of an electron at the outside of an atom. Since atoms are neutral, such an electron must be acted on by the electric force from one elementary charge at about the distance given by the atomic radius. For hydrogen it is the force exerted by the proton. We know that atomic dimensions are in the range of an angstrom, that is 10^{-10} meters. Then since the charges are of opposite sign and each is one elementary charge in magnitude, the electric potential energy is

$$U_e = k\frac{q_1 q_2}{r}$$
$$= \frac{\left(2.3 \times 10^{-28} \frac{\text{newton-m}^2}{\text{elem. ch.}}\right) \times (1 \text{ elem. ch.}) \times (-1 \text{ elem. ch.})}{10^{-10} \text{ m}}$$
$$= -2.3 \times 10^{-18} \text{ joule}.$$

This energy may not be the only energy. For instance, in a planetary model, as we know from Chapter 25, the kinetic energy of the electron is (positive and) half as great. But in any case this electric potential energy gives us an estimate of the order of magnitude of the energy we must supply in order to take the electron away from the atom. Therefore, the binding or ionization energy of an atom is of the order of 10^{-18} joules. Since electron volts are 1.6×10^{-19} joules at a throw, this estimate is about 6 electron volts. The actual amount of energy necessary to ionize an atom depends on the kind of atom, but it runs from about 2 to about 20 electron volts. This indicates that the electric forces holding the atom together account for the energy necessary to rearrange or pull apart the electric particles of which it is made.

cause we have designed the coulomb so that, in moving through an EMF of 1 volt, a joule of energy is transferred.

Motors, light bulbs, and other electrical appliances are usually designed to use energy at a particular rate. The power, which is the energy they consume per unit time, is usually specified; and so is the voltage at which they will use this power. From the power and the voltage you can determine what current they will draw. For example, a 60-watt, 110-volt light bulb will draw a current of $\frac{60}{110} = 0.545$ amperes when an EMF of 110 volts is placed across its terminals.

Although the volt is a convenient unit of EMF and the ampere is a convenient unit of current, the coulomb turns out to be an appallingly large unit of charge. If two charges, each one a coulomb, are placed a meter apart, the force between them is about ten billion newtons. When dealing with the forces between charges, therefore, it is often more convenient to use the microcoulomb (10^{-6} coulombs) as the unit of charge. A toy balloon charged by being rubbed on a woolly sleeve might have a charge of a few tenths of a microcoulomb.

29–9. Status Report

So far in this chapter we have considered charges that move and energy transferred under the influence of the Coulomb forces exerted by charges at rest. In Section 29–5, we found that as long as the charges exerting the force were at rest, the electric force on a moving charge is the same as the force on a charge standing still at the same position. Because the Coulomb forces depend only on the separations between the charges, there is a well-defined electrical potential energy.

Except for the forces exerted by batteries or generators, in this chapter we have used only the same electric forces that we had studied in the last chapter. Now in considering the forces, two problems remain. In the first place, what can we say about the forces on charges moving through batteries and generators, the forces that apparently move the charges against the Coulomb forces exerted by the concentrations of charge standing still? Secondly, what happens when a charge exerting a force on another charge is itself in motion?

In the next chapter we shall see that Coulomb's law does not adequately describe the force between two charged particles when both of the particles are moving. Then we find that in addition to the Coulomb force, a new force appears — a force that depends upon the motions. This additional force is of great practical importance, for it runs most of our electrical machinery. Furthermore, as we shall see in Chapter 31, this same additional force is responsible for the EMF of electric generators. Finally we are left with the forces and the EMF's supplied by batteries. As we have indicated here, their explanation can be given only in terms of the energy transfers taking place in chemical reactions. In other words, the energy supplied by a battery can be understood only when we look inside the atoms. We shall just be able to start examining the internal energy of atoms in the last chapter of the book.

In the second half of this chapter, we shall look in more detail at energy flow and electric currents. We shall be especially concerned with the application of these ideas to electric circuits.

FOR HOME, DESK, AND LAB

1. Two large parallel metal plates, 6.2 cm apart in a vacuum tube, are connected to the terminals of a 180-volt battery. A doubly charged oxygen ion starts from rest at the surface of one plate and is accelerated across to the other plate.

(a) With what kinetic energy $\frac{1}{2}mv^2$ does the oxygen ion crash into the other plate?

(b) If the ion starts halfway between the plates, with what kinetic energy does it hit the negative plate?

2. (a) In the micro-microbalance experiments of Section 28–4, how much work was done by the electric force on the standard charged sphere when it moved 2 mm upward in 10.6 seconds?

(b) Into what forms did this energy go, and how much into each form?

3. In a time-of-flight experiment like that described in the box on page 490, you have adjusted the sweep circuit of the oscilloscope so that the beam moves across the tube in 0.5 sec. The total length of the trace made in that time is 10 cm. The contact points on the track for the rolling ball are 1.2 m apart. If the spikes on the oscilloscope trace are 8.0 cm apart, what is the speed of the ball?

4. Using the apparatus described in Section 29–2, you perform an experiment to measure the mass of the cesium ion. The hydrogen-ion source is replaced by a source of cesium ions, and the same electric force field is maintained by the same 90-volt battery between the accelerating plates.

(a) What is the kinetic energy $\frac{1}{2}mv^2$ per elementary charge with which the cesium ion goes through the long chamber?

(b) The time of flight of the cesium ions through the long chamber (0.50 m) is about 43.6 microseconds. What is their speed?

(c) What is the mass of the cesium ion if it is singly charged? What is it if it is doubly charged?

5. In the apparatus used to measure the mass of the positive hydrogen ion (proton) of Section 29–2, you use a source of heavy hydrogen and observe a spike which corresponds to ions arriving with a time of flight 1.4 times that of the usual positive hydrogen ions.

(a) What is their mass if they are singly charged?

(b) If doubly charged?

(c) Could they be singly charged helium ions? Doubly charged helium ions?

Remember that the mass of a helium atom is 4 atomic mass units, and the mass of a hydrogen atom 1 atomic mass unit.

6. You ionize some gas between parallel metal plates, making equal numbers of negative and positive ions in every small volume between the plates. There is a battery and a current meter connected in series with the plates, and a steady current is flowing through the circuit. The positive plate is on the left, and the negative on the right.

(a) In what direction do you expect the electric current to go between the plates?

(b) If the current meter measures 10^{16} elementary charges per second, how many positive elementary charges are brought per second by the ions coming to the negative plate?

(c) How many negative elementary charges are coming per second to the negative plate?

(d) In one second, how many positive ions cross to the right through a plane halfway between the plates?

7. A steady electric current passes through an electrolytic cell of dilute hydrochloric acid for a very long time. For ten minutes we collect the hydrogen gas that bubbles up at the negative electrode. At room temperature and atmospheric pressure, the gas collected occupies a volume of 148 cm^3.

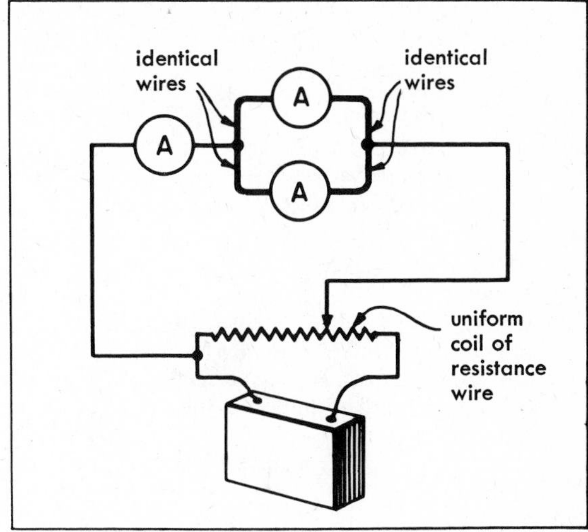

29–16. For Problem 9.

Remember that each hydrogen molecule has two hydrogen atoms. Also 1 mole occupies 2.36×10^4 cm^3 at room temperature.

(a) How many hydrogen molecules were collected?

(b) How many hydrogen atoms were collected?

(c) How many hydrogen ions must have come to the negative electrode in this time?

(d) How many elementary charges were transported across the cell?

(e) What was the current in elementary charges per second?

(f) If there is a cell of copper sulfate solution connected in series with this one, with large electrodes, how much copper is deposited on the negative electrode?

Note: A mole of copper weighs 63.6 grams.

8. You are given some metal wire, batteries, and a calibrated ammeter. How can you calibrate a second ammeter?

9. You are given a half dozen identical ammeters, one of which has a single calibration point — that is, a mark correctly indicating when a 1-ampere current (that is, a current of 6.25×10^{18} elementary charges per second) is passing through it. You also have a few batteries and a large number of identical metal wires. Answer the following questions to complete the calibration of the ammeter.

(a) Assume you have marked a number of ammeters to read one ampere. Then you connect three as in Fig. 29–16. Explain how you can get a 2-ampere calibration point on one of them.

(b) Make sketches showing how to connect the ammeters in order to mark one scale at 3 and 4 amperes.

(c) How would you connect the ammeters so

as to calibrate one of them to read $\frac{1}{2}$ and $\frac{1}{3}$ amperes? (Use sketches.)

10. With the same apparatus as in Problem 1, how many doubly charged oxygen ions would have to go from the positive plate to the negative plate before that plate is heated up by one joule by the dissipation of kinetic energy of the ions?

11. Suppose the doubly charged ions in the last problem were made by ripping electrons off oxygen atoms located halfway between the plates. Then the oxygen atoms are accelerated in one direction and the electrons are accelerated in the opposite direction from the midpoint between the plates. How much energy will the electrons have dissipated heating the positive plate in the time that one joule is dissipated at the negative plate?

12. Think over the evidence available to you that all elementary charges are the same. Be prepared to discuss it in class.

13. (a) You connect a large battery in series with a diode vacuum tube and an ammeter. The ammeter indicates a current of

1.9×10^{16} elem. ch./sec.

The anode of the tube contains a temperature-measuring device that allows you to measure how much energy is dissipated as heat in the anode. You let the current flow for 10 sec and find that 9.6 joules of energy are dissipated in the anode. What is the EMF of the battery?

(b) In a similar circuit you connect another battery to a different diode. In this case, the current is 3.1×10^{16} elem. ch./sec and, after 10 seconds operation, 8.9 joules are dissipated in the anode. What is the EMF of this battery?

(c) You now connect your two batteries in series through an ammeter to a coil of high-resistance wire. The ammeter indicates a current of 2.5×10^{16} elem. ch./sec. Predict the rate at which energy is dissipated as heat in the high-resistance wire.

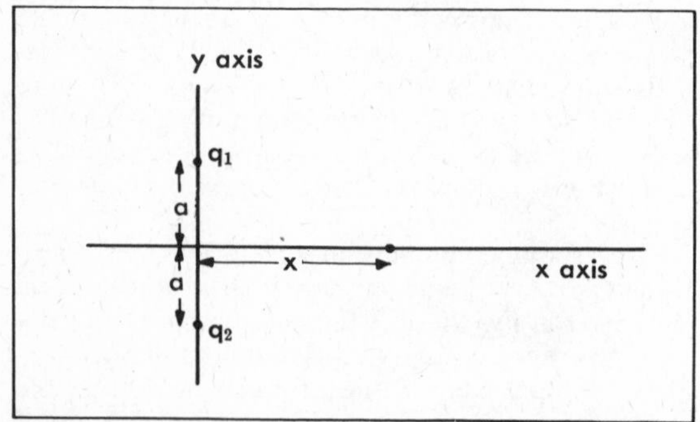

29–17. For Problem 17.

14. (a) What is the electrical potential energy of a small object carrying three elementary electric charges and a small metal sphere carrying ten billion elementary electric charges placed 2 meters away? Take the zero of potential energy at infinite separation.

(b) Suppose the sphere and object have charges of opposite sign. How much energy would have to be used to drag the object out to 20 meters? Does the choice of the zero of potential energy make any difference?

(c) Suppose they have the same sign and you just let the object move out to 20 meters. Describe the energy changes that occur.

15. (a) Find the electric and the gravitational forces on an electron and on a proton between two large parallel metal plates, 20 cm apart. The potential difference between the plates is maintained by 20,000 volts' worth of battery. The plates are horizontal; consider the upper plate positive.

(b) Move the particles up 1 cm. What are the forces now?

(c) What are the changes in gravitational potential energy and in electric potential energy in this motion?

16. (a) Two protons are released from rest 10^{-10} m apart. What will their kinetic energy be at large separation?

(b) Suppose one of the protons is nailed down. What will the kinetic energy be at large separation?

17. Two equal charges, q_1 and q_2, are nailed in place on the Y axis, equal distances a above and below the origin of co-ordinates (Fig. 29–17).

(a) What is the electric potential energy of an elementary charge at point x on the X axis?

Note: Measure the potential energy with the zero chosen when the elementary charge is at infinity. Express your answers in terms of the constant k in Coulomb's law, the value of charges q_1 and q_2, and the distances a and x.

(b) In particular, what is the potential energy of the elementary charge because of its interaction with q_1? with q_2? with both together?

(c) What is its total potential energy if the charges are equal and opposite?

18. (a) In Problem 13, what are the EMF's in volts and the currents in amperes?

(b) Does using volts and amperes change your prediction of the energy dissipation in part (c) of Problem 13?

B. MORE ABOUT ENERGY AND CURRENTS IN ELECTRIC CIRCUITS

29–10. Conductors, Batteries, and Potential Difference

In this section we shall make several applications of the idea of electric field and especially of electric potential difference. In particular we shall consider the fields and potentials of electrical conductors both when they are isolated and when they are connected to batteries.

In charging a conductor, electric charges move; but as we learned in Section 28–3, after charges have rearranged themselves (in response to electric forces exerted by the charged bodies in the neighborhood), all the electric field lines meet the surface of the conductor at right angles. Otherwise charge would move along the surface until the component of electric field in that direction is eliminated. Also there is no electric field inside the conductor, for if there were, charges would be moved by it until the field inside was canceled. What, therefore, is the potential difference between two points either on the surface or inside of a charged conductor? Since there is no electric field either along the surface or through the inside of the body, the force on an elementary charge is zero all along any path passing from one point to the other through the conductor. An elementary charge can therefore be moved without any expenditure of energy. The conductor is all at the same electric potential; there is no potential difference between any of its points. A body which is at a single potential (or a surface all at the same potential) is called an equipotential. In the vocabulary of potential difference we can, therefore, say that any conductor in which charges do not move is an equipotential body.

We have considered what happens when a battery drives charges around an electrical circuit. Now let us consider what happens when the circuit is open. For example, suppose we connect conductors to each battery terminal as shown in Fig. 29–18. Then the battery will move charges, concentrating negative charge on the conductor connected to the negative terminal and positive charge on the conductor connected to the positive terminal. The charges will move as long as the energy to carry one positive elementary charge from the negative to the positive conductor is less than the EMF of the battery. As the charge concentrations are increased, however, any positive

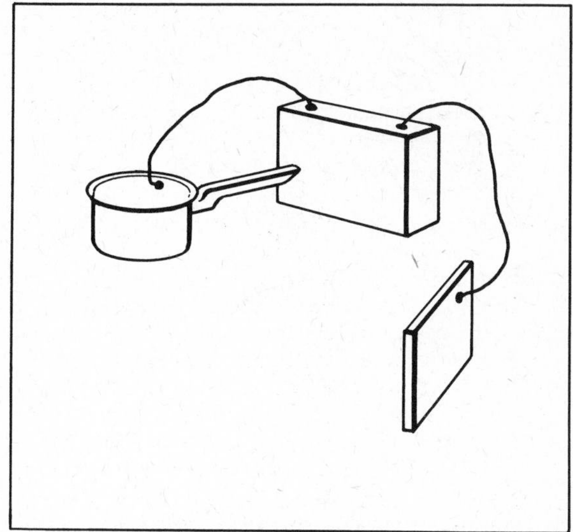

29–18. A battery connected to two conductors.

charge moved between them is attracted to the negative conductor and repelled from the positive conductor with increasingly greater force. Consequently, as the battery charges the conductors, the energy required to move an elementary positive charge rises. And if the charging process went on indefinitely, the energy to move a single elementary charge between the conductors would eventually exceed the EMF. Because the EMF is the energy the battery supplies per elementary charge, the charges stop moving, and the charge distribution stops changing when just enough charge has been transferred so that the energy *required* to move an elementary charge is equal to the EMF.

The energy to move a positive elementary charge from the negative conductor to the positive conductor is exactly what we mean by the electric potential difference (or potential drop) from the positive to the negative conductor. When the conductors are charged up, the potential difference between them is the same no matter what points we select on the conductors, for we already know that each conductor is then an equipotential body. Also, when the conductors are connected to the battery, they are always charged to the same potential difference, equal to the EMF of the battery, no matter how large the conductors are or where they are located. We can hang as many conductors from the terminals of the battery as we wish without influencing this re-

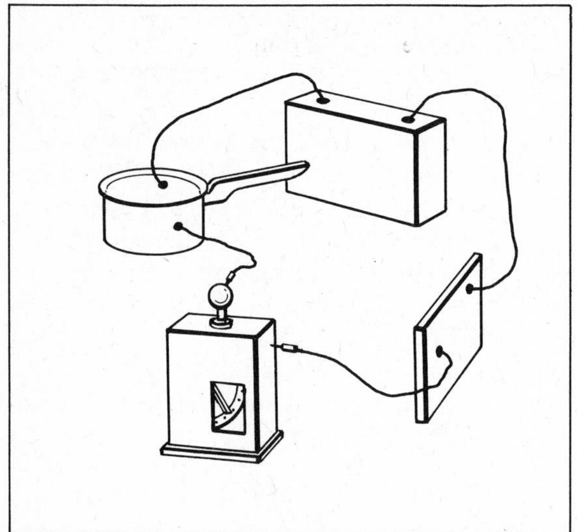

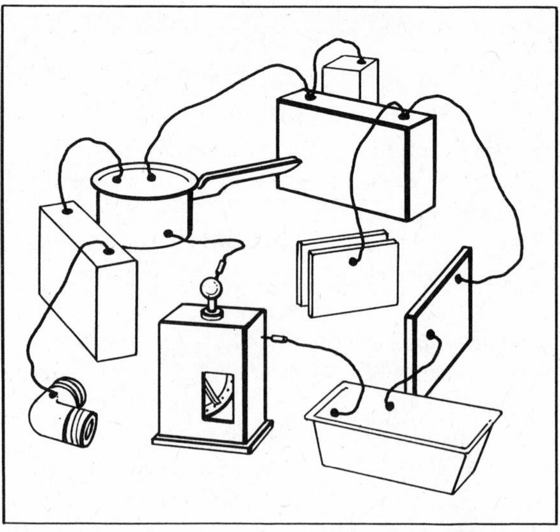

29–19. *Left*, the conductors are extended by connecting them to the stem and case of an electrometer. *Right*, still more conductors are connected. Note that the electrometer reading does not change, giving us an experimental confirmation of our belief that a battery maintains the same potential difference (see Section 29–11). It does not matter where you connect the leads to the conductors.

sult. Even connecting another battery as in Fig. 29–19 does not change the potential difference maintained by the first one. In summary, then, we can view a battery in an open circuit as a machine for maintaining a definite difference in potential, the potential difference given by its EMF.

A conductor in which charge has stopped flowing is an equipotential body. But what of a conductor such as a wire connected to the terminals of a battery? Charge flows steadily through it, driven by an electric field. To find the complete pattern of the field is a more complicated job than we wish to do here, but we can tell a good bit about the field nevertheless. First, the field inside the conductor cannot run into its surface. If it did, charge would flow onto the surface until a canceling field was built up. Indeed, charge concentrations on the surface are built up as soon as the circuit is connected. From then on the field runs along inside the wire from the positive battery terminal to the negative terminal. No matter how many bends there are in the conductor, inside it the field will follow around each curve (Fig. 29–20). This field inside is, therefore, relatively simple compared with the field outside the conductor. The field outside can run in any direction from the charges on the surface. Unlike the field inside, it depends on the location of the battery, the shape of the conductor, and the position of the other charged bodies.

The magnitude of the electric field in the conductor depends on the length of path. In a uniform wire the field is the same all along. (It must be the same to drive the same current, as we shall see in Section 29–13 C.) The field, therefore, adjusts in magnitude so that E times the length l of the wire is equal to $\mathcal{E}$, the EMF supplied. When $\mathcal{E} = El$, the energy supplied per elementary charge is just transferred to an elementary charge as it moves the distance l around the circuit. This adjustment of the field E is made by charges on the wire and at the battery terminals. As we saw for open circuits the battery will force charges to rearrange until $El = \mathcal{E}$.

If the wire is not uniform, the magnitude of $\vec{E}$ varies from point to point. Then if we plot E against the distance along the wire from the positive battery terminal, the area under the curve is equal to the applied EMF. For instance, (Fig. 29–21), if the wire is a good conductor for the length l_1 and a poor conductor for the length l_2 charge will accumulate at the junction between the two conductors until the field E_2 in l_2 is sufficiently stronger and the field E_1 in l_1 is sufficiently weaker so that the same current flows in each. The sum, $E_1l_1 + E_2l_2$, is then the potential difference between the positive and negative battery terminals. This is the energy per elementary charge (the sum of the forces $\times$ distances) that the field will transfer to each elementary charge

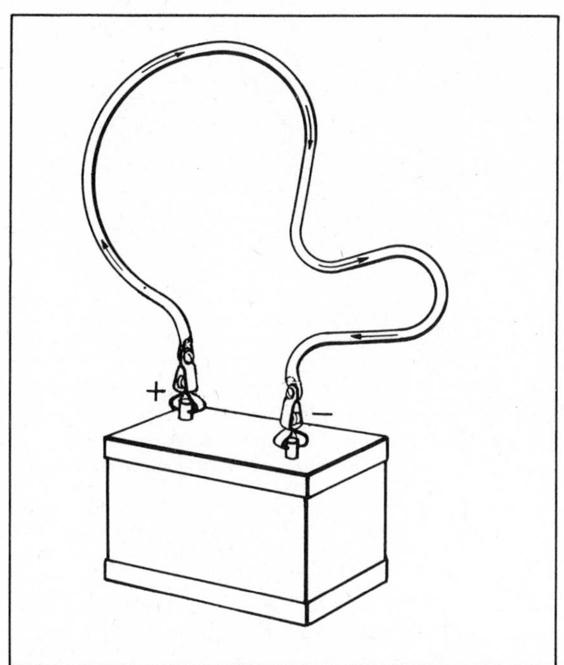

29–20. When a conductor is connected to a battery, there is an electric field inside the wire that runs from the positive to the negative battery terminal.

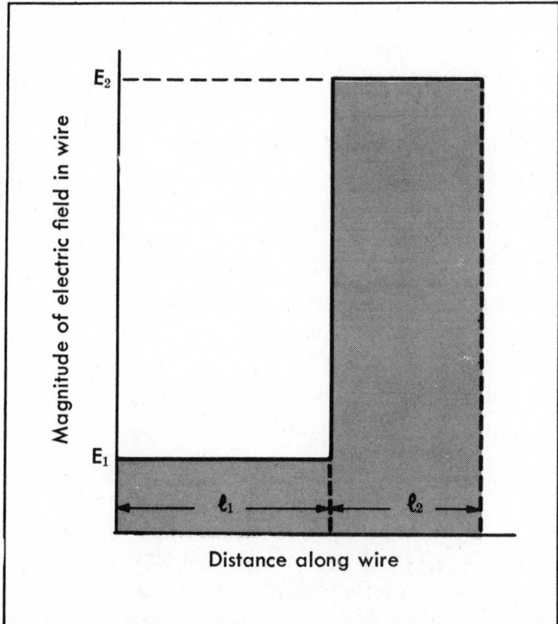

29–21. A graph of the magnitude E of the electric field in a wire vs. the distance l along the wire. Here the wire is a good conductor for one part of its length and a poor conductor for the other. The area $E \times l$ under each part of the curve gives the energy transferred to an elementary charge in this length. This area gives the potential difference between any two points in the circuit.

passing between the terminals and it is determined by $\mathcal{E}$, the EMF of the battery. If it were less than $\mathcal{E}$, the battery would quickly increase it by forcing more positive charge onto the positive terminal and more negative charge onto the negative terminal; if it were more than $\mathcal{E}$, the battery would be prevented from separating charge until the terminals discharged and the energy per elementary charge required to force charges onto them again becomes $\mathcal{E}$.

We have just seen that the EMF of the battery supplies the total potential difference, $E_1l_1 + E_2l_2$, between the positive and negative battery terminal, that is,

$$\mathcal{E} = E_1l_1 + E_2l_2.$$

This potential difference appears on the right-hand side of the equation in two parts; E_1l_1 is the potential difference across the good conductor of length l_1, and E_2l_2 is the potential difference across the poor conductor of length l_2. In fact as we go along the conductor from the positive battery terminal to the negative terminal, the potential difference measured from the positive terminal to any point on the wires changes continuously. From one end to the other of any little length of wire Δl the potential changes by the amount $\Delta V = E\Delta l$ where E is the magnitude of the electric field in this piece of wire. For every elementary charge passing through the piece of wire of length Δl the energy ΔV is transferred first from electrical potential energy to energy of the moving charge. Then as the charge makes collisions with the atoms of the wire, the energy goes into thermal energy heating that section of wire. We shall be able to check up on these statements experimentally as soon as we have discussed measurement of potential difference. (See Section 29–11.) We then find that our conclusions describe the experimental facts.

We have defined the electric potential difference V between a point A and a point B as the energy transferred to an elementary charge moving between A and B. It may seem that if q elementary charges move from A to B, q times this energy would be transferred and therefore the electric potential energy would change by the amount $\Delta U_e = qV$. Often this conclusion is correct. But it depends on the assumption that the neighboring charges which produce the electric field stay in the same positions and thus exert the same

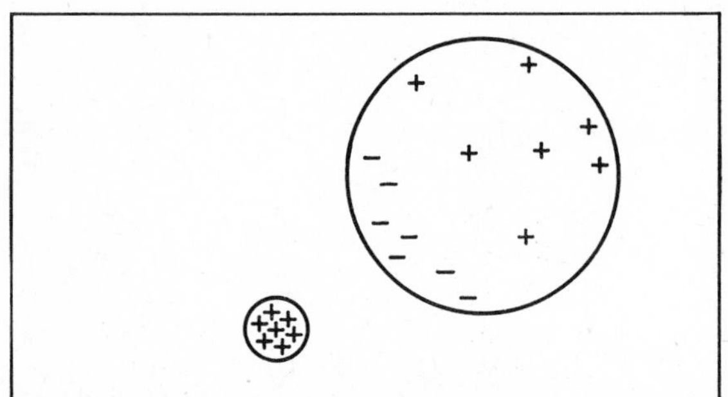

29–22 (a). If we bring a charged body near an uncharged conductor, it induces a distribution of charge. These induced charges exert a force on the charged body, showing that there is an electric field from the induced charges.

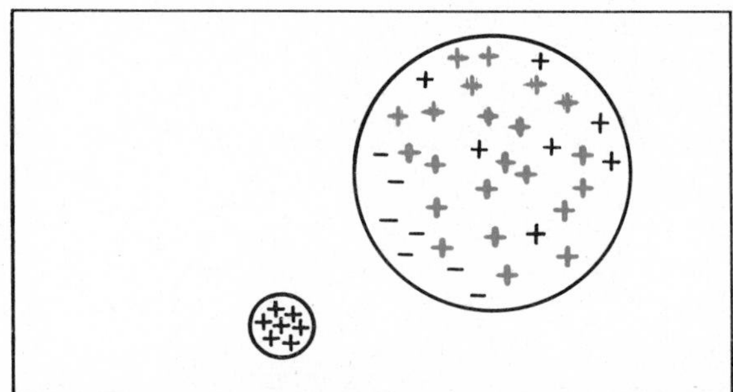

29–22 (b). A charged body is brought near a charged conductor. If the distance apart is great enough, the induced charges on the conductor will be unimportant compared to its initial charge. The field from the conductor is not changed significantly.

forces that they do when we move only a single elementary charge. We know that this assumption is not strictly valid in the neighborhood of conductors. Even a single elementary charge will induce a redistribution of charges when it moves from one place to another in the neighborhood of a conducting body (Fig. 29–22). On the other hand, if the conductor has a large charge to begin with, most of the electric field will arise from that charge. In other words as long as induced charges are negligible, the electric force field is nearly unchanging, and we can compute the change in potential energy by using qV.

In addition to the case in which induced charges are negligible, we have been dealing with another kind of example in which qV yields correct results. When a particular difference of potential V is maintained between conductors by a battery or by some other source of EMF, the motion of a charge q from one place to another is accompanied by just such a redistribution of other charges that the potential difference is maintained. In this case the source of EMF supplies any needed energy or absorbs any excess energy. The energy transfer is correctly given by qV because the potential is not allowed to vary.

Let us end this section by applying the ideas we have discussed to the motion of an ion which moves through space from a positive to a negative conductor. As the ion moves away from the positive conductor, the positive charge is gradually replaced behind it. As it approaches the negative conductor, negative canceling charge gradually concentrates directly in front of it. If the two conductors are connected through a battery, positive charge is gradually transported through the battery in the opposite direction. Thus at the end of the process the canceling negative charge has been supplied to the negative conductor, and a replacement positive charge has been given to the positive conductor. Also, as the charge is transported through the battery, the battery supplies an amount of energy equal to that which goes into the kinetic energy of the positive charge moving between the conductors. For a singly charged ion, this is equal to the EMF of the battery and to the potential difference V between the conductors. When this whole process is finished, the situation on the conductors is the same as it was at the beginning. Only the chemical energy of the battery and the thermal energy of the conductors change. The next charge that goes across between the conductors will get exactly the same energy as the first one, and if q charges go across, they will receive the energy qV.

On the other hand, if there is no battery, the positively charged conductor permanently loses the charge of the ion, and the negative conductor has one of its negative charges permanently canceled. The potential difference between the positive and the negative conductor drops because of the reduction in charge. The next charge to cross between the conductors will, therefore, be given somewhat less energy, and each successive charge crossing will get a progressively smaller amount. Consequently, q charges crossing receive less than the energy qV where V is the original potential difference.

As an extreme example, we consider two oppositely charged metal plates. As elementary charges pass between them, the plates discharge; the potential V also goes to zero, staying proportional to the charges on the plates. Consequently, although the first charge receives the energy V equal to the potential difference between the fully charged plates, successive charges receive smaller and smaller amounts of energy until the last charge receives no energy at all. The average amount of energy received by an elementary charge is just half the original potential difference. Thus the total energy received by all q charges as they pass from one plate to the other is $\frac{1}{2}qV$. You can see that this must be true by looking at Fig. 29–23 where we have plotted the energy transferred per elementary charge vs. the number of elementary charges then on the plates. When all the elementary charges q have been transferred, the total energy transfer is given by the area shaded under the curve. Because it is a triangle that area is $\frac{1}{2}qV$. It represents the energy stored originally when the charges were concentrated on the plates. In other words $\frac{1}{2}qV$ is the electric potential energy of all the charges in their positions on the two plates. Clearly this total electric potential energy is to be distinguished from the electric potential difference V and from the energy qV that would be given to q charges passing between the plates if the potential were maintained by a battery.

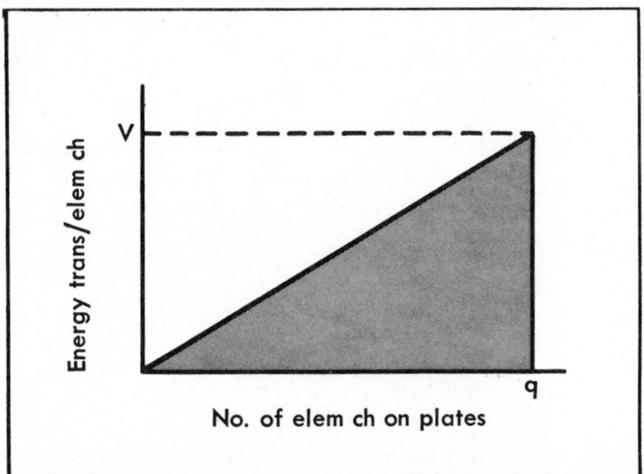

29–23. As charge is transferred from one conductor to another, the potential difference between the conductors rises in proportion to the amount of charge. This graph shows the potential difference as a function of the charge. To move an elementary charge from the negative to the positive conductor requires an energy given by the height of the curve times one unit along the horizontal axis. To charge the conductors to a charge q and potential difference V, the energy required is therefore given by the shaded area under the curve. This is the electric potential energy stored when the conductors are charged.

29–11. Measurement of Potential Difference

We can use a shielded electrometer to measure potential differences (Fig. 29–19). An electrometer gives a particular reading when the forces on the stem have a particular value; and these forces are determined by the charge on the stem and the induced charge on the inside of the shield. For a particular charge on the stem there is a definite electric field in between the stem and the inside of the shield, and the electric potential difference has a particular value. The reading of the electrometer corresponds to this value of electrical potential difference. Conversely, whenever the electrical potential difference between stem and shield has the same value, the fields and charges inside the electrometer must be the same, and the electrometer will give the same reading.

We can measure potential difference with an electrometer. Often, however, it is more convenient to measure potential difference by using a current meter and a high resistance wire in series (Fig. 29–24). When we apply various differences of potential V across the ends of this circuit, the electric fields driving charges through the circuit are proportional to the differences in potential. For example, if the difference of potential is maintained by concentrations of charge on conductors at the two ends of the circuit, the

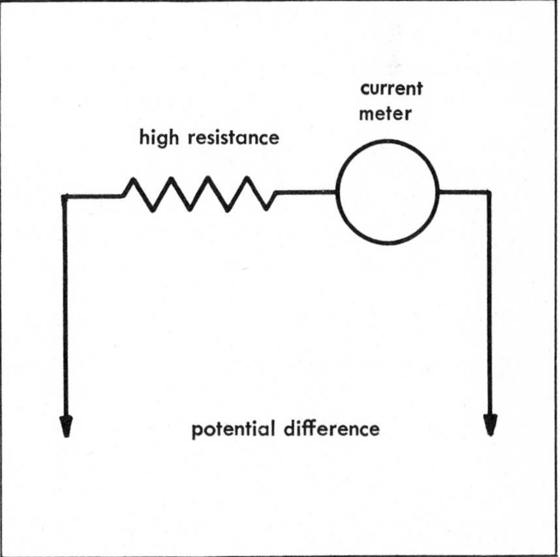

29–24. A voltmeter to measure potential differences is made by connecting a high resistance and a current meter in series. Often the high resistance is included inside the case containing the meter.

fields and the potential difference are proportional to those charge concentrations. Consequently we see that a higher potential means larger forces on the charges which are free to move through the high resistance wire and the current meter. These larger forces lead to bigger currents through the circuit; and the current that we read is a measure of the potential difference. With ordinary resistance wires, as we shall see in Section 29–13, the current is actually proportional to the potential difference, but in any case we can calibrate the current meter with its high resistance wire against known potential differences maintained by batteries. Once we have calibrated the current meter with its high resistance, it becomes a potential-difference meter. Such meters are usually known as voltmeters.

Voltmeters are convenient to use as long as the resistance in them is so high that the current through the voltmeter is small compared to any other currents we would like to maintain in the circuit, or as long as we can make a potential-difference measurement in a time so short that the current does not appreciably change any charge concentrations that we wish to maintain. When these conditions are not met, you must use more complicated circuits, for instance the circuits known as potentiometers which you can explore in the laboratory.

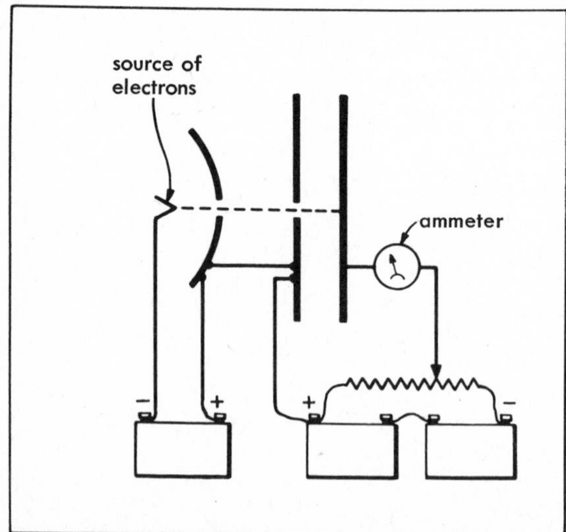

29–25. An experiment to show that the energy gained by charged particles depends only on the potential difference through which they move. The current through the ammeter stops whenever the potential difference measured across the plates becomes greater than the potential difference across the gun.

29–12. A Further Check on Potential Difference and Energy

A battery maintains a constant potential difference and in the absence of currents any good conductor is all at the same electrical potential. Consequently by maintaining a fixed potential difference with a battery, we can accelerate charged bodies to predetermined kinetic energies in the electric field between any two conductors. The conductors need not be large parallel plates.

We can allow some current in the conductors without losing our knowledge of the potential difference between them. Because charges move freely in the conductor practically no energy is required to move a charge from one point to another, and the conductor may be approximately at a single potential even though the charges are forced to move. (We shall make these considerations more quantitative in Section 29–14.)

We can apply these ideas to get a check on our knowledge of potential difference and energy. For example, we can compute the energy of the electrons emitted by the electron gun described in Chapter 27. This gun consists of a hot filament which boils out electrons with negligible speeds, and a plate which is maintained at a constant difference of potential with respect to the filament. The electrons are accelerated between the filament and the plate. Then they pass through a hole in the plate with a kinetic energy which is given by the potential difference. A thousand-volt potential difference between filament and plate will give each electron a kinetic energy of $1000 \times 1.6 \times 10^{-19}$ joules, because the charge of each electron is one elementary charge. The electric field in the region between the filament and the plate is something we need not know in detail. Actually, it is very large near the filament and small near the plate. But the energy given per elementary charge as the particles pass from one to the other depends only on the difference of potential.

We can check up experimentally on this fact by running the electrons from the electron gun into a uniform retarding electric field between parallel plates where we know the retarding force (Fig. 29–25). The electrons will go across the space between the parallel plates as long as the retarding potential difference between the parallel plates is smaller than the accelerating potential difference between the filament and plate of the electron gun. They stop reaching the far end of the system

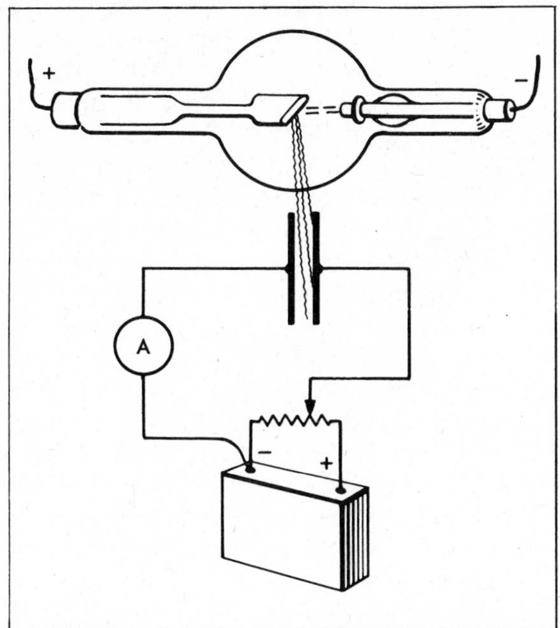

29–26. Apparatus to investigate electric currents in ionized gases.

and the current through the meter stops as soon as the retarding potential difference exceeds the accelerating potential difference. This experiment shows that it is the potential difference imposed by the batteries which determines the energy; the shape of the conductors is irrelevant.

29–13. Current versus Potential Difference

How do the currents in ionized gases, the currents of electrons boiled out of metals, and the currents in metals depend on potential differences maintained across these circuit elements? This is the question we shall now examine.

A. Ionized Gases. We shall begin with the case of ionized gases. The experimental arrangement is shown in Fig. 29–26. Two parallel metal plates are connected to a variable voltage supply, and a sensitive current meter is inserted in one of the connecting wires. The plates are at a distance of several centimeters, and the space between is filled with the gas under investigation. When ionizing radiation (X rays or rays from a radioactive source) passes through the gas, the meter shows a current.

Fig. 29–27 shows how the current depends on the potential difference between the metal plates in one typical experiment. The gas is argon at atmospheric pressure and the radiation comes from a sample of radium. As the potential difference between the plates is increased, the current increases rapidly at first, then more slowly, and eventually reaches a certain limiting value called the saturation current.

The saturation current is reached when all the ions formed are swept out of the gas by the electric field and collect on the appropriate plates. For singly charged ions, such as those produced in argon, the ionization current (in elementary charges per second) equals the number of positive ions per second reaching the negative electrode (and this is the same as the number of negative ions — in this case electrons — reaching the positive electrode). Therefore the saturation current measures the total number of pairs of ions produced every second in the gas between the plates.

Why is the current less when there is a small difference of potential between the plates? The field moving the ions toward the plates is then weaker, and the ions move toward the plates more slowly. As they gradually get pushed toward the plates, they move in all directions because of their random thermal motions, and sometimes a positive and a negative ion will collide. Occasionally they will even recombine to form a neutral atom. When the systematic motion of the ions toward the plates is very slow, many positive and negative ions recombine instead of reaching the plates.

If we increase the potential difference between the plates far beyond the value necessary to establish saturation, we find that the current eventually begins to increase again. Then with a little

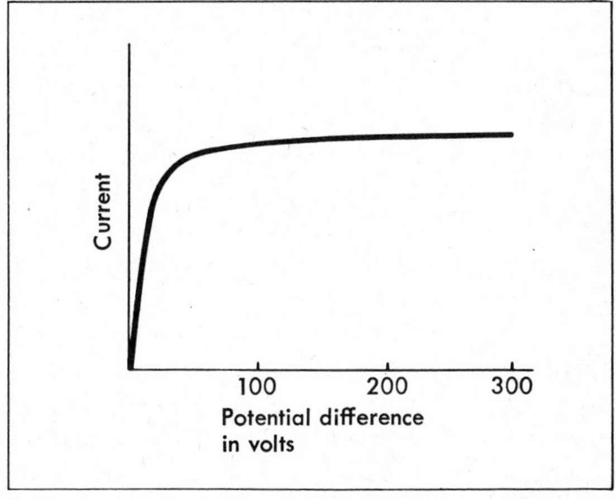

29–27 (a). Current *vs.* potential difference for argon gas at low voltages.

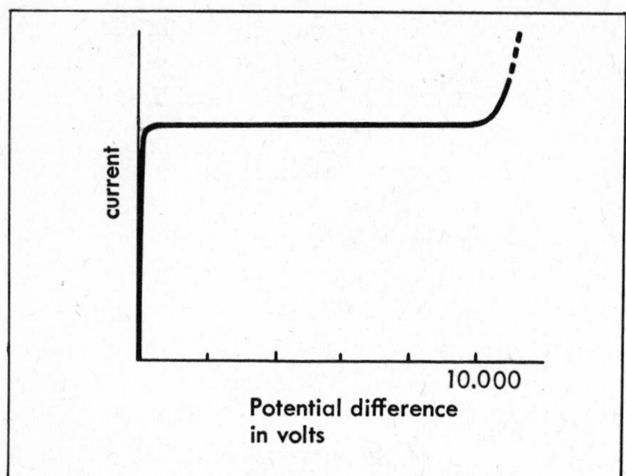

29–27 (b). Current-potential difference curve for argon up to a high voltage.

more voltage it rises to very large values [Fig. 29–27 (b)]. At these potential differences, the gas between the plates glows and there are often crackling noises. Just what we observe at this stage varies greatly with the pressure, the nature of the gas, and the distance between the electrodes. At low pressures the current and the glow are more or less constant. At atmospheric pressure, on the other hand, we have a series of sparks.

These *gas discharges* are quite complex; but we can understand their fundamental cause. The electric field accelerates the positive and negative ions of an ionized gas in opposite directions. Each ion picks up energy until it collides with a gas molecule. On the average, in these collisions, the ions then lose the extra kinetic energy they have acquired since the previous collision; and this energy is transferred to thermal energy of the gas. So the gas warms up.

The situation, however, becomes different when the electric field is very strong. Then in the short time between collisions, some of the ions acquire sufficient kinetic energy to break up the gas molecules against which they collide. The new fragments are themselves ions which are accelerated by the electric field. They too become capable of disrupting the gas molecules which they encounter along their path. So an avalanche of more and more ions is produced. The gas suddenly acquires an enormous electrical conductivity, and a sudden discharge occurs. Geiger counters detect charged particles by using such an avalanche to turn the slight ionization along the track of a particle into an appreciable electric pulse.

B. Thermionic Emission. A somewhat similar relation between current and potential difference occurs for the electrons boiled out by a heated piece of metal (Fig. 29–28). When the potential difference between the heated filament and the surrounding collecting plate is big, we find a saturation current. Raising the potential difference does not change the number of electrons that cross from filament to plate, because all the electrons boiled out of the filament per second at a given temperature are already being pulled over to the plate. When the potential difference is low enough, however, the current drops beneath the saturation value. Apparently the electrons emitted from the filament do not move away sufficiently fast; and while they are in the neighborhood of the filament they push back electrons which would otherwise boil out. Detailed calculations actually show that this "space charge" limitation accounts for the current-voltage curves observed. In Fig. 29–28 typical curves of current vs. potential difference for thermionic emission have been plotted.

If the potential difference between filament and plate is reduced to zero, we observe something else of interest. A small current still passes. Even when the plate is made slightly negative with respect to the filament, a few electrons continue to get across. Apparently some electrons are boiled out of the filament with sufficient kinetic energy to go across despite a slight retarding potential difference. Careful measurements show that the potential difference necessary to stop the current is about two-tenths of a volt.* This corresponds to the thermal energy of a particle at the temperature of the filament.

C. Electrons in Metals. As a last example of the relation between current and voltage, we shall take a metal conductor. Then the relation between potential difference and current is a particularly simple one: the two quantities are proportional to each other. That is,

$$V = RI.$$

The law expressed by this equation is called Ohm's

*To make these measurements it is necessary for all the hot metal to be at the same potential. Otherwise the potential differences from one place to another in the metal may be as large as the potential difference we wish to measure. We therefore use a separate heater instead of having a large electric current flowing in the hot metal.

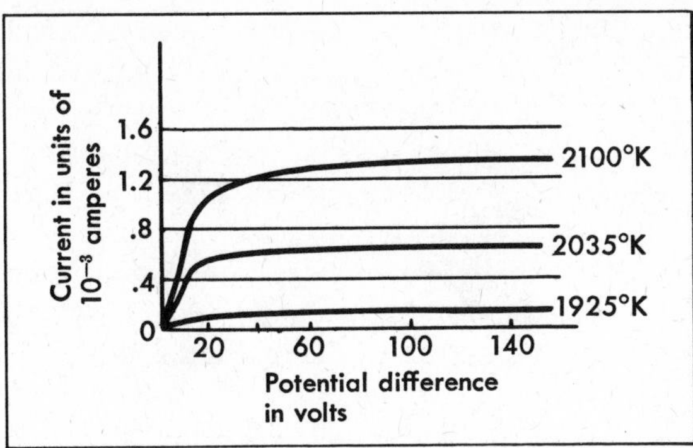

29–28. Current *vs.* potential difference curves for a diode at different filament temperatures.

law, and the proportionality constant R is called the *electric resistance* of the conductor. If V is measured in volts and I in amperes, R is measured in a unit called an ohm.

Ohm's law says that the current in a metal wire is proportional to the potential difference between one end and the other. Because the electric field in a given piece of metal is proportional to the potential difference imposed on its ends, we can just as well say that the current is proportional to the electric field. We can understand this law by returning for a moment to the model of the conductivity of metals, in which we picture electrons running freely around inside the metal like the molecules of a gas (Section 27–12). Because the electrons are so light, at normal temperatures they have tremendous speeds — about 10^5 meters per second. They rush around inside the metal, colliding with the positive metal ions with great frequency. The average time between collisions of a single electron with one or another of the metal ions is extremely short, only about 3×10^{-15} seconds. It is determined by the distance between metal ions and the *thermal speed* of the electrons. Furthermore, at each collision the electron bounces off in a new direction. So a single electron runs in all directions in its random thermal dance.

Now, we add the electric field to our picture. In the short time between collisions, it accelerates the electrons along the wire. The small extra velocity which the electrons acquire along the wire is just proportional to the strength of the field and to the time between collisions. Because of the random changes in direction at each collision, or at worst after every few collisions, the extra velocity along the wire is wiped out and has to be re-established by the action of the field. Our complete picture then looks like this: the electrons rush around in all directions at huge speeds, but superposed on top of these random motions is a small systematic velocity along the wire. This systematic velocity is proportional to the strength of the field and to the time between collisions. With a potential difference of a few volts across a meter of wire, the systematic velocity is about a centimeter a second. It is this systematic velocity that results in a current. The bigger the systematic velocity the bigger the current; so the current is proportional to the electric field. Our model therefore predicts the experimental result embodied in Ohm's law.

The model also makes another prediction about the electrical resistance. It should increase with increasing temperature. As the temperature goes up, so does the speed of the electrons. Therefore the time between collisions diminishes; and the same field yields less current. This conclusion agrees with the experimental observation that the resistance usually does become greater. This agreement is not perfect, however; detailed experiments show that the resistance usually increases in direct proportion to the temperature, while the model predicts that the resistance should only be proportional to its square root. The discrepancy is explained by two facts. In the first place, because of its high density, we should not expect the electron gas to behave like an ideal gas. The electrons are so close together that the forces between them always influence their motion. Secondly, when a gas of identical particles is dense, quantum effects, which we shall study later in this book, become important. When these effects are included, the improved model is in accurate correspondence with the experimental facts. Our model remains useful as one of the essential steps to a more complete description.

29–14. An Over-all View of a Circuit

When a battery lights a flashlight bulb, runs an electric motor, or maintains the current in an electrolytic cell, the battery delivers energy to the external circuit (the bulb, the motor, or the electrolytic cell). There this energy is transformed into heat, or into mechanical energy. If the circuit contains a radio tube with a heated filament, the electrons gain a large amount of kinetic energy as they cross the vacuum from the filament and crash

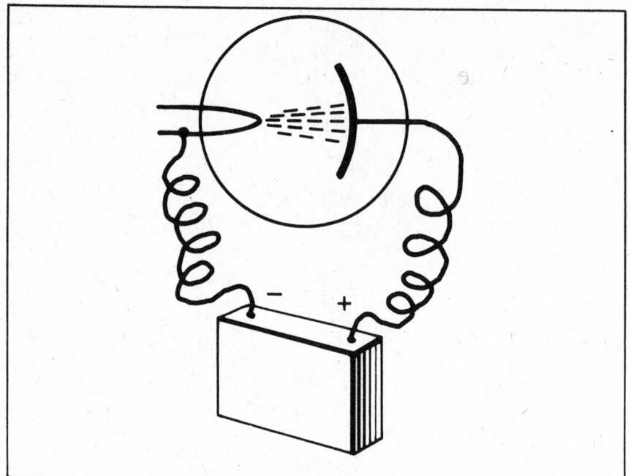

29–29. A large potential difference moves electrons from filament to plate in the diode. Smaller potential differences move the electrons in the wires.

into the plate. In a tube designed so that the electrons hit a small region of the plate, they may make it white hot. In a metal wire the energy supplied by the battery also goes initially into kinetic energy of motion of the electrons. Then as the electrons collide with the atoms of the wire this kinetic energy is transformed into the energy of random motion of the atoms. Because the collisions take place frequently, the electrons never acquire much kinetic energy. The energy fed in becomes heat almost at once. If the circuit contains a motor, most of the energy may be used to raise weights, though some of the energy always comes out as heat.

Let us think of the circuit sketched in Fig. 29–29. Each electron passing from filament to plate is accelerated to a kinetic energy equal to the potential difference maintained between them by the battery. Each electron that goes across takes one negative charge from the filament and cancels one positive charge at the plate. If you disconnected the battery by opening the switch, the current would soon stop. With the battery connected, when one electron moves across, another one is forced along the wire from the negative battery terminal, taking the place of the one that has left. A current equal to the current from filament to plate is thus flowing through the wire. A small electric field in the wire forces the electrons to move. So when the current flows, the different parts of the conducting wire are not exactly at the same potential. If the wire is long and thin enough, and if the current is sufficiently great, the potential difference from one end to the other will be big enough for us to measure.

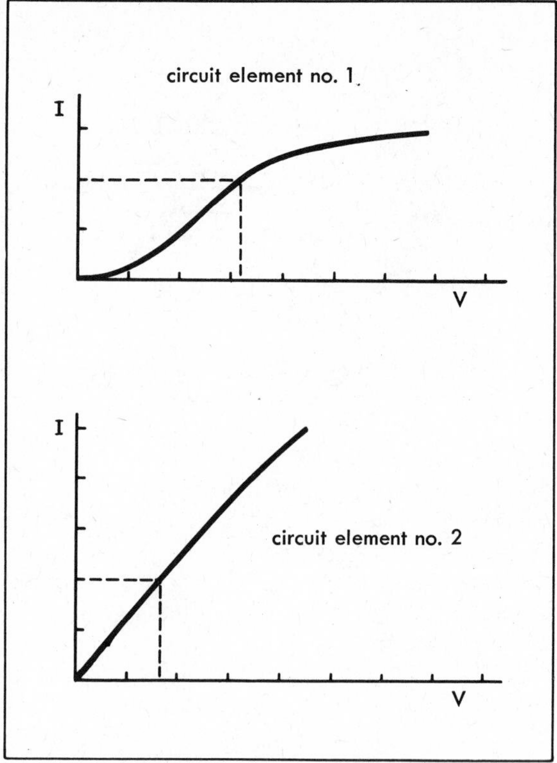

29–30. *I–V* curves for two circuit elements.

The potential difference between the battery terminals — the energy per unit charge supplied by the battery — is split up into potential differences across the various elements of the circuit. A small potential difference drives the electrons from the negative battery terminal to the filament. It accounts for the energy given to each electron and then dissipated in heat as the electron moves through the wire. A large potential difference accelerates the electrons from the filament to the plate and accounts for the kinetic energy with which they crash into the plate. Finally, another small potential difference drives the electrons through the wire back to the positive battery terminal. The sum of these potential differences is the energy given to each elementary charge moved through the battery. All this energy is dissipated, heating the wires or heating the plate. All this energy is supplied by the battery.

How the potential difference imposed by the battery is divided between the various elements of a circuit and how large the current is for a given potential difference depends on the physical nature of the circuit elements. In Section 29–13 we have examined the relation between the currents that occur and the potential differences for a few circuit elements. We can now apply what we learned there to more complicated circuits containing more than one circuit element.

Suppose that we have two circuit elements for which the curves of current vs. potential difference are known, for example, the circuit elements represented by the graphs of Fig. 29–30. If these two elements are connected in parallel as in Fig. 29–31, the potential difference V across their ends from A to B is automatically the same for both elements. The current that comes in at A and goes out at B splits up, and part of it passes through each circuit element. The total current is the sum of the currents through the two elements. It can be found by adding the current I_1 that flows through element 1 at the particular value for the potential difference and the current I_2 that flows through element 2 at the same value of the potential difference. By adding up the two currents determined from Fig. 29–30 at each value of potential difference, we can make a graph of the total current $I = I_1 + I_2$ passing from A to B versus the potential difference V (Fig. 29–32). In this way we combine the two elements in parallel into a new single element represented by the new I versus V graph. This procedure can be extended to handle more circuit elements in parallel by adding the individual currents at each potential difference. Thus, we can always replace a group of circuit elements connected in parallel by an equivalent circuit element that acts in the same way as the whole parallel combination.

For any potential difference V across the parallel combination the energy per elementary charge is still given by the potential difference. Consequently, the power used in the parallel combination is IV, where I is the total current — the current that flows through the combination viewed as a single element. This power used is made up of the power used in each of the individual elements. For example, if there are two elements,

$$IV = I_1V + I_2V,$$

where I_1 and I_2 are the currents through the individual elements that we have connected in parallel. In this equation, each of the terms on the right is the power used in a particular individual circuit element, and their sum on the left is the total power consumed by the whole group combined in parallel.

If we connect individual circuit elements in series, the analysis is somewhat different. The same current must flow through each of the individual elements. Let us start by assuming that this current has a particular value. By using the graphs of current vs. potential difference for each individual circuit element, we can read off the corresponding potential differences. Then to find the potential difference from one end of the series circuit to the other, we must add all of these individual potential drops. On Fig. 29–30, we have marked the same current on each of the current vs. potential difference curves and indicated by the dashed lines how to find the corresponding potential drops. When these two elements are in series, the potential drop across the series

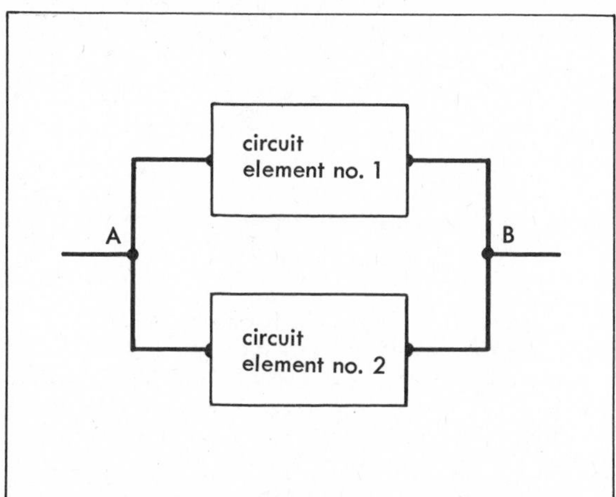

29–31. Two circuit elements connected in parallel.

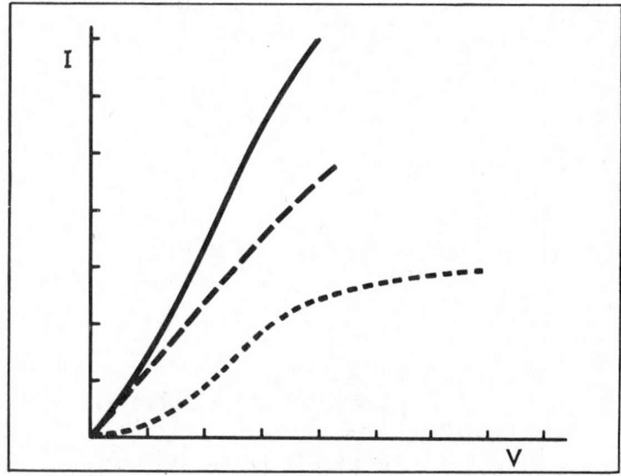

29–32. *I–V* curve for the equivalent circuit element made by placing the circuit elements of Fig. 29–30 in parallel. It is obtained by adding the currents of the two individual circuit elements when the potential difference has the same value for both.

circuit is given by the sum of the two potential drops we read on the horizontal axes of the individual I versus V graphs. By following this scheme for each possible current, we can establish the relation between the current and the potential difference across the whole series circuit. We can again graph it as a curve of current vs. potential difference (Fig. 29–33). In this way we can turn the series circuit into an equivalent single circuit element represented by this new curve of current vs. potential difference.

Now that we have found the behavior of this equivalent single circuit element, we can find the current that will flow through the series circuit when any specified potential difference is applied across its ends. As always, this potential difference represents the energy used per elementary charge passing through the circuit. Again the power consumed is IV, where V is the potential difference from one end to the other of the whole series circuit. In this case, however, V is the sum of the individual potential drops across the individual elements forming the series circuit. If the circuit is made of two elements, that sum is $V = V_1 + V_2$. Consequently,

$$IV = IV_1 + IV_2.$$

In this equation the power consumption of each element is represented by a term on the right-hand side; and the total power consumption IV is just the sum of the power used in each individual element.

We have seen how the potential differences and the currents actually come into adjustment in a real circuit. The results fit into our over-all view

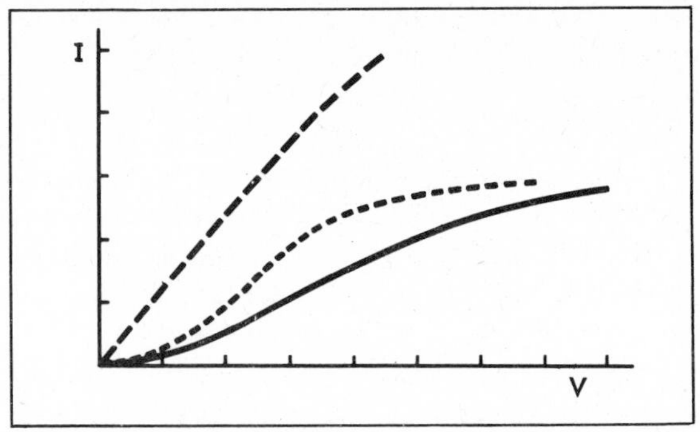

29–33. I–V curve for the equivalent circuit element when the circuit elements of Fig. 29–30 are connected in series. It is obtained by adding the potential differences across the two circuit elements when the current has the same value through both. You can visualize this addition by looking at the picture from the left. There if you pick a given current, the potential difference needed to produce it in circuit element 1 is given by the distance along the V axis to the dotted curve. The potential difference needed to produce this current in circuit element 2 is given by the distance along the V axis to the dashed curve. The sum of these two potentials is the potential difference needed across the circuit elements in series to call forth the same current.

of a circuit. In every case the sum of the potential difference taken in series around the circuit matches up with the EMF's of the batteries or generators supplying the energy per elementary charge. The energy passed out per elementary charge is equal in each circuit element to the difference in potential from one end of the element to the other. The energy thus transferred into other forms such as chemical stored energy, mechanical energy or heat, is supplied by the applied EMF; and the conservation of energy shows us that the sum of the potential differences is always equal to that applied EMF.

For Home, Desk, and Lab

1. (a) How would you connect a 90-volt "B" battery and a 1.5-volt flashlight cell to obtain the maximum potential difference?

(b) How big is that potential difference?

(c) Suppose you disconnect the 90-volt battery; turn it end for end; and then reconnect it. What potential difference do you get?

2. Suppose you were given two electrometers which measure potential differences in the 10,000-volt range. One of them is calibrated but the other is not. You are also given a glass rod and a piece of cloth, but you are forbidden to buy any batteries. Can you calibrate the second electrometer by connecting it to the first?

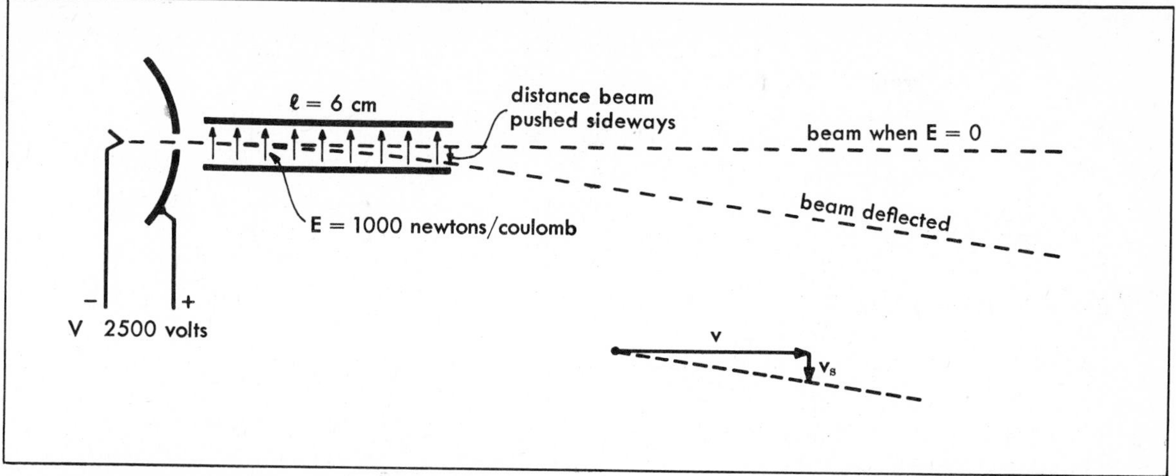

29–34. For Problem 3.

3. An electron gun shoots a stream of electrons between two deflecting plates of length l = 6.0 cm (Fig. 29–34). The electron mass is 0.91×10^{-30} kg. The potential difference between the filament and plate of the gun is 2,500 volts ($2.5 \times 10^{3} \times 1.6 \times 10^{-19}$ joules per elementary charge). The electric field E between the deflecting plates is 1,000 newtons per coulomb (1,000 newtons per 6.25×10^{18} elementary charges).

(a) If the deflecting plates are separated by 0.20 cm, what is the potential difference from one deflecting plate to the other?

(b) What is the speed of the electrons leaving the gun?

(c) How long do the electrons take to pass through the length l?

(d) As an electron passes between the deflecting plates, it picks up a sidewise velocity because of the electric force exerted on it. How big is this sidewise velocity when the electron leaves the deflecting plates?

(e) How far is the electron pushed sidewise in passing between the plates?

4. (a) For the apparatus used in Problem 3, find a formula for the sidewise displacement of any ion accelerated through the same potential difference V in the gun and deflected by the same deflecting field E. Write the formula in terms of E, V, and l, the length of the deflecting field.

(b) What is the influence of the mass of the ion?

(c) What is the influence of the charge of the ion?

5. Fig. 29–35 shows a device for calibrating the ammeter A. It is an insulated can with a coil of wire in it. Water flows in at the top of the diagram, passes thermometer No. 1. Then after flowing past the coil of wire, it flows out at the bottom of the diagram past thermometer No. 2. The difference of potential across the coil in the calorimeter is measured, using a calibrated electrometer, so that we know the potential difference between the points α and β. In an experiment (i) the flow of water is 1 gram per second, (ii) thermometer No. 2 reads a temperature 1°C higher than thermometer No. 1, and (iii) the electrometer reads a potential difference of 2.09 volts.

(a) What is the current through the ammeter?

(b) How would you calibrate an ammeter with this device?

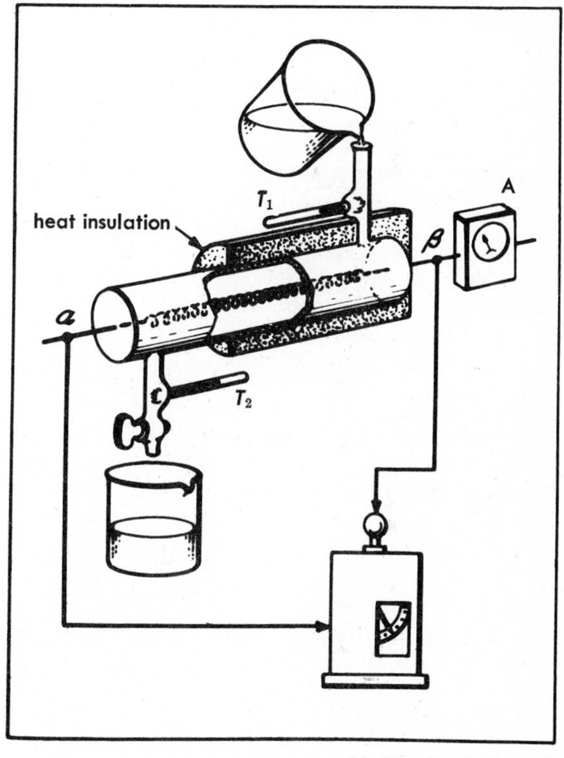

29–35. For Problem 5.

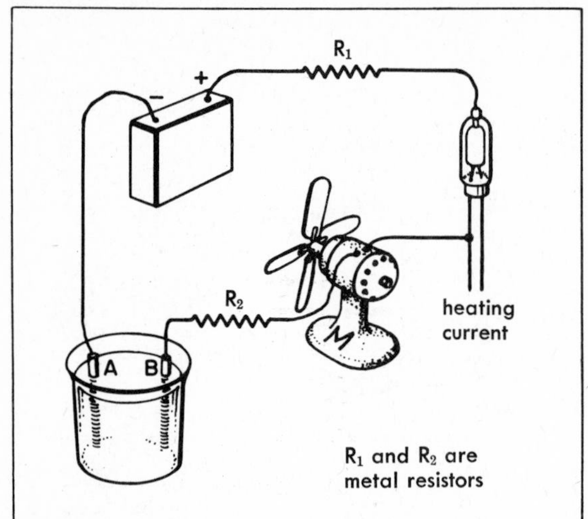

29–36. For Problem 6.

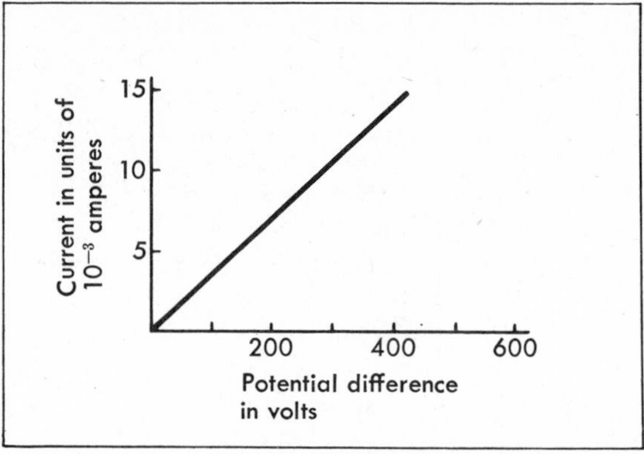

29–37 (a). For Problem 11.

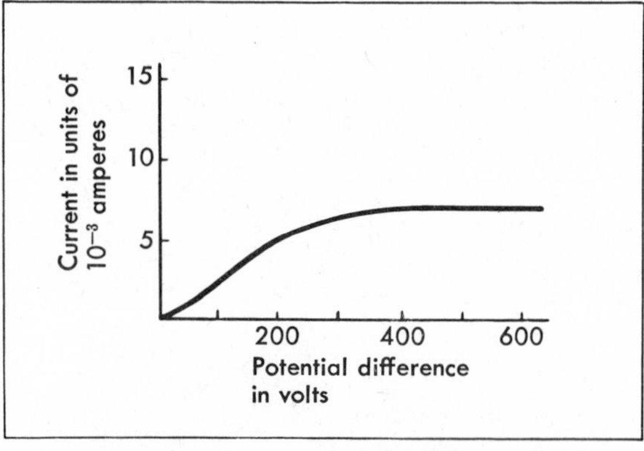

29–37 (b). For Problem 11.

6. In the circuit shown in Fig. 29–36, two resistors, a diode, an electric motor *M*, and an electrolytic cell are connected in series with a battery. The difference of potential across each of these circuit elements is measured and it is found that they are all the same. A certain amount of heat is dissipated per second in the first resistor.

(a) What can you say about the ratio of the heat dissipated in each of the other circuit elements to the heat dissipated in the first resistor?

(b) In the second resistor?

(c) In the diode?

(d) In the motor which runs a fan?

(e) If there is actually less heat dissipated in the electrolytic cell than in resistor 1, which terminal, *A* or *B*, would be positive when the cell is used as a source of potential difference?

7. Show that the energy dissipated in heat per unit time (the power used) in a metal resistor is given by the formula I^2R. (The heating rate reckoned as I^2R is called the Joule heat.)

8. (a) In Problem 5, what is the resistance in ohms of the coil?

(b) Show that the power dissipation from the coil is given by I^2R.

9. We have two lengths of wire made of exactly the same metal and of exactly the same cross-sectional area. One wire is twice as long as the other.

(a) When the same difference of potential is imposed on the ends of both wires, what is the ratio of the currents that will pass through the wires?

(b) How does the resistance of a wire depend on its length?

10. There are two wires of identical material of exactly the same length and the same cross-sectional area.

(a) If the same difference of potential is imposed across their ends, what is the ratio of the current that will pass through them?

(b) If the wires side by side are viewed as a single conductor, what is the ratio of the current through this combined conductor to the current through one of the single wires with the same potential difference across its ends?

(c) If we have a wire of twice the cross-sectional area and the same length and material as each of the original ones, what current do you expect will flow through it compared to one of the original wires, with the same potential difference across its ends?

(d) What do you expect to be the dependence of the resistance of a wire on its cross-sectional area?

11. In Fig. 29–37 (a), the current through a metal circuit is plotted as a function of the potential difference across its ends. In Fig. 29–37 (b), we plot the current through a diode as a function of the potential difference across it.

(a) If a current of 5×10^{-3} amperes passes through both circuit elements in series, what is

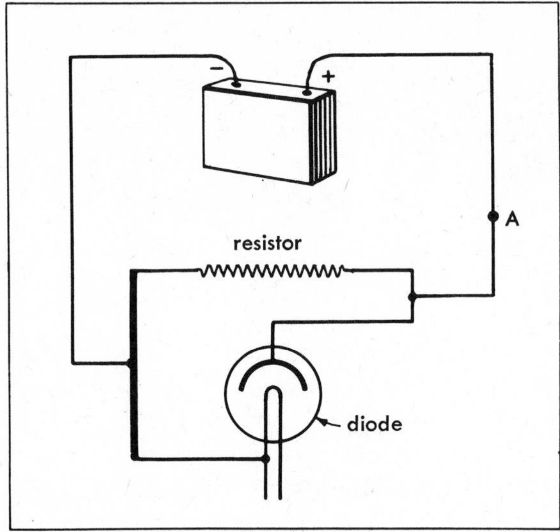

29–37 (c). For Problem 11.

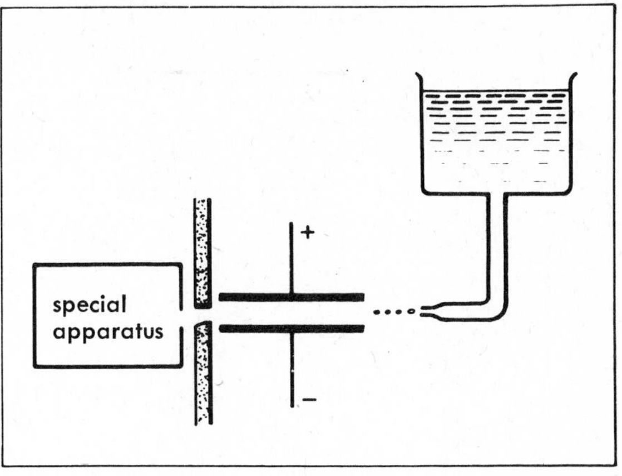

29–38. For Problem 13.

the potential difference from one end to the other of the resistor? What is the potential difference across the diode?

(b) If the diode and the resistor are connected in parallel as in Fig. 29–37 (c), and the potential difference across the diode is 100 volts, what is the current through each of the circuit elements?

(c) What then is the total current passing point *A* in the figure?

(d) What is the resistance in ohms of the resistor?

12. The same diode and resistor as were used in Problem 11 are connected in series. The potential difference from one end of the circuit to the other is 1,000 volts.

(a) What current flows through the circuit?

(b) What is the potential difference between one end and the other of the resistor?

13. An inventor devises a charge selector for picking out water drops all with one charge. This consists of a small jet of water emerging from a narrow glass tube and forming drops all of the same size. The drops are squirted horizontally through a region where a pair of charged plates provides a uniform vertical electric field. Beyond this region there is a wall with a small hole. The wall stops all the drops (and lets them run away to a drain) except those that just "hit" the hole and continue into some special apparatus that needs them. This arrangement selects water drops with a certain charge. (Fig. 29–38.)

(a) How does the charge selected depend on the velocity of the drops?

(b) Give a clear reason for your answer to (a).

(c) If some of the drops were larger, say of twice the diameter, what charge would they need to be "selected" with the rest?

(d) If the whole selector is now tilted (keeping the electric field perpendicular to the initial velocity of the stream), how does the selected charge depend on the angle of tilt?

14. Connect a 270-volt battery in series with a 1,000,000-ohm and a 2,000,000-ohm resistor.

(a) What potential difference do you expect across the megohm resistor?

(b) What potential difference do you expect across the 2,000,000-ohm resistor?

Now suppose you measure the potential differences with a voltmeter.

(c) If the voltmeter has a resistance of 10 megohms, what potential difference would you expect across the 2,000,000-ohm resistor?

(d) What potential difference would you expect to read across the megohm resistor?

FURTHER READING

FINK, DONALD G., and LUTYENS, DAVID M., *The Physics of Television.* Doubleday, 1959: A Science Study Series paperback.

FURRY, W. H.; PURCELL, E. M.; STREET, J. C., *Physics for Science and Engineering Students.* Blakiston, 1952 (Chapter 25).

HOLTON, GERALD, *Introduction to Concepts and Theories in Physical Science.* Addison-Wesley, 1952 (Chapter 21).

PANOFSKY, WOLFGANG, "The Linear Accelerator." *Scientific American,* October, 1954.

SEGRE, EMILIO, and WIEGAND, CLYDE C., "The Antiproton." *Scientific American,* June, 1956.

THE MAGNETIC FIELD

CHAPTER 30

WHEN Albert Einstein wrote his life story at the age of 67, he recalled the day when he was a little boy of four, happy to get a new toy from his father. That toy was a compass needle; and the wonder it aroused remained with Einstein all his life. Most of us have shared that wonder, and a good many of us as children experienced the fascination of a horseshoe magnet, which attracts iron. In this chapter we shall discuss magnetic forces and the concept of the magnetic field by which we can best interpret them.

30–1. The Magnetic Needle

A compass needle free to rotate about a vertical axis will line up in the north-south direction. We say that it aligns in the magnetic field of the earth (which originates deep in the core of the globe). We call the tip of the needle that points north, the northern tip.* In any region where a compass needle feels forces that tend to align it, we say that there is a *magnetic field.* (Fig. 30–1.) The direction of the field is the direction taken by a compass needle which is free to line up. We say that the field points in the direction that runs from the southern to the northern compass tip. Just as we used grass seeds to show the direction of an electric field, so we use a magnetic needle to explore the direction of a magnetic field.

When a compass needle is in a uniform magnetic field, the net force on the needle is zero. The

*Actually the northern tip of the needle points *approximately* to the geographic North Pole as long as we are south of the Arctic Circle.

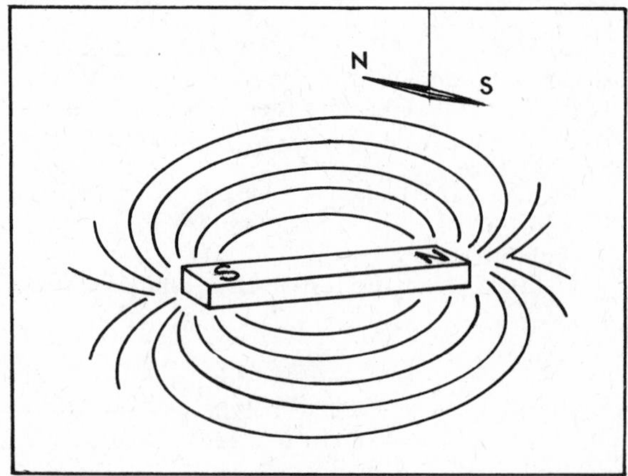

30–1. A compass needle in a magnetic field lines up in the direction of the field.

needle as a whole does not move, as a single electric charge would move in an electric field; but it does line up. (Fig. 30–2.) Magnets act as if they had equal plus and minus magnetic charges on their ends, pulled in opposite directions by the magnetic field. It therefore used to be common to talk about magnetic "poles" (that is, magnetic "charges" of opposite signs). However, if we break a magnet into two, each piece again acts as if it had opposite poles at its ends. (Fig. 30–3.) In fact, even electrons, protons, and neutrons act like tiny compass needles. This is a major difference between magnets and electrified bodies. We can put plus and minus electric charges on separate objects, because there are elementary charged particles. We have never separated positive from

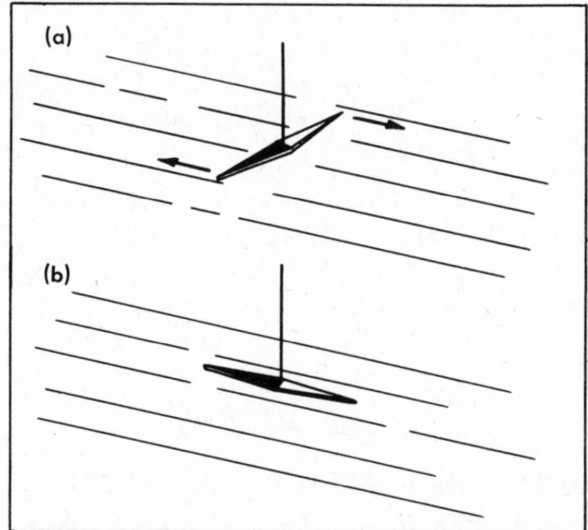

30–2. (a) In a magnetic field a compass experiences equal and opposite forces at each end. (b) These forces will turn the needle until it is lined up with the field.

negative magnetic charge. So we have no reason to believe that separate magnetic charges actually exist. The elementary magnetic unit appears to be a complete magnet which will align in a uniform magnetic field but will not be accelerated.

30–2. Magnetic Fields of Magnets and Currents — Magnetic Field Lines

We find magnetic fields around certain objects: around a piece of magnetite, for instance, or around a piece of steel that has been magnetized by contact with magnetite. A compass needle is also a magnet, usually a magnetized steel needle. Two compass needles, when placed near each other, influence each other: each pulls the other around. Each produces a magnetic field, and each lines up in the field of the other.

Such permanent magnets are not the only source of magnetic fields. Let us perform a familiar experiment. We attach a long piece of wire to the terminals of a battery through a switch as shown in Fig. 30–4. With the switch open, we hold the wire above a compass needle and parallel to it. Then we close the switch. If the current in the wire is sufficiently strong, we see the compass needle suddenly deflected. It now points across the wire. We therefore conclude that electric currents produce magnetic fields in the surrounding space.

Today this fact is common knowledge, so that it is difficult to appreciate the revolutionary im-

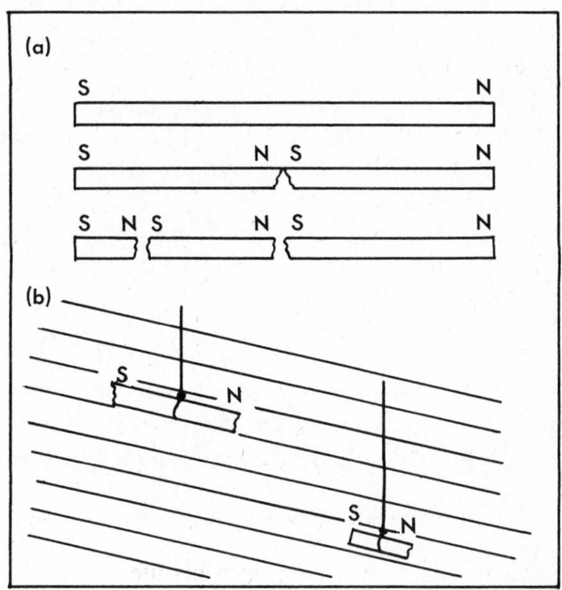

30–3. (a) When we break a magnet, each piece has opposite poles at its ends. (b) Any of these pieces will line up in a magnetic field.

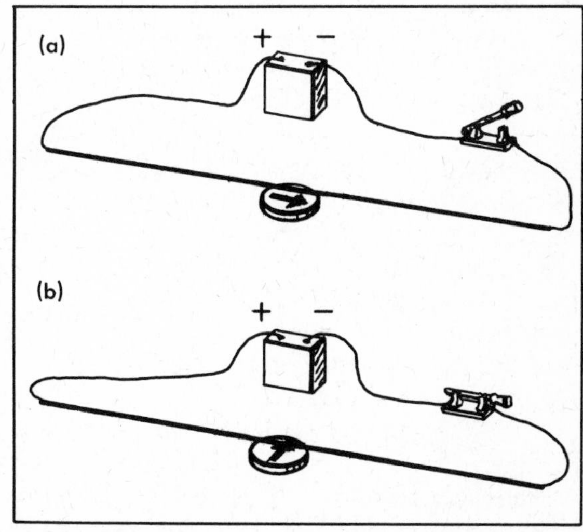

30–4 (a). A wire is placed over a compass needle and parallel to it. The switch is open, and no current flows in the wire. (b) When current flows, the needle is deflected and points across the wire.

pact of its discovery by the Danish schoolteacher Oersted early in the nineteenth century. Until that time, electric and magnetic effects had been regarded as entirely separate. Oersted's discovery revealed an unsuspected relationship: it tied the origin of magnetic fields to the motion of electric charges.

The experiment last described is one you can

do, and is probably enough to convince you that moving electric charges generate magnetic fields. But there is an even more direct experiment, though a far more difficult one. It was performed by Henry Rowland in Baltimore in 1876. He put the biggest electric charge that he could onto a hard-rubber disc about 20 cm across. Then he spun the disc at about 60 revolutions per second. In this way he could look for the magnetic effect of the moving charges directly. The magnetic field was the same as that of a very weak electric current.

We describe magnetic fields by drawing magnetic field lines, just as we describe electric fields by drawing electric field lines. Figs. 30–5 and 30–6 show the magnetic fields produced by various magnets and currents. You may compare them with Figs. 28–9 and 28–10 showing various electric fields.

Electric field lines from charges at rest begin and end at the charges producing the field; but the lines of the magnetic fields produced by currents have no beginning nor end. They encircle the wires carrying the current (Fig. 30–6). The lines of the magnetic fields produced by permanent magnets (Fig. 30–5) *appear* to begin and end at the surface of the magnets, but this is only because we have not drawn the lines inside the magnets where we cannot place an ordinary compass needle. Using neutrons as the compass needles, we can explore the inside of a permanent magnet. We then see that the lines do not stop at the surface.

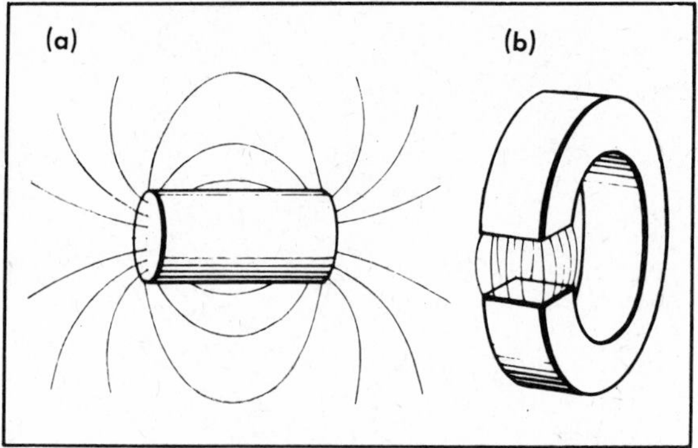

30–5. Diagrams of the magnetic field lines of permanent magnets. (a) A bar magnet. (b) A horseshoe magnet.

If a magnetic field is sufficiently strong, and if you are not interested in great accuracy, you can "see" the field lines by spreading some fine iron filings on a piece of paper. The grains of iron line up along field lines like grass seeds in an electric field (see Section 28–3). Tap the paper gently if the filings stick. The photographs in Fig. 30–7 are iron-filing pictures.

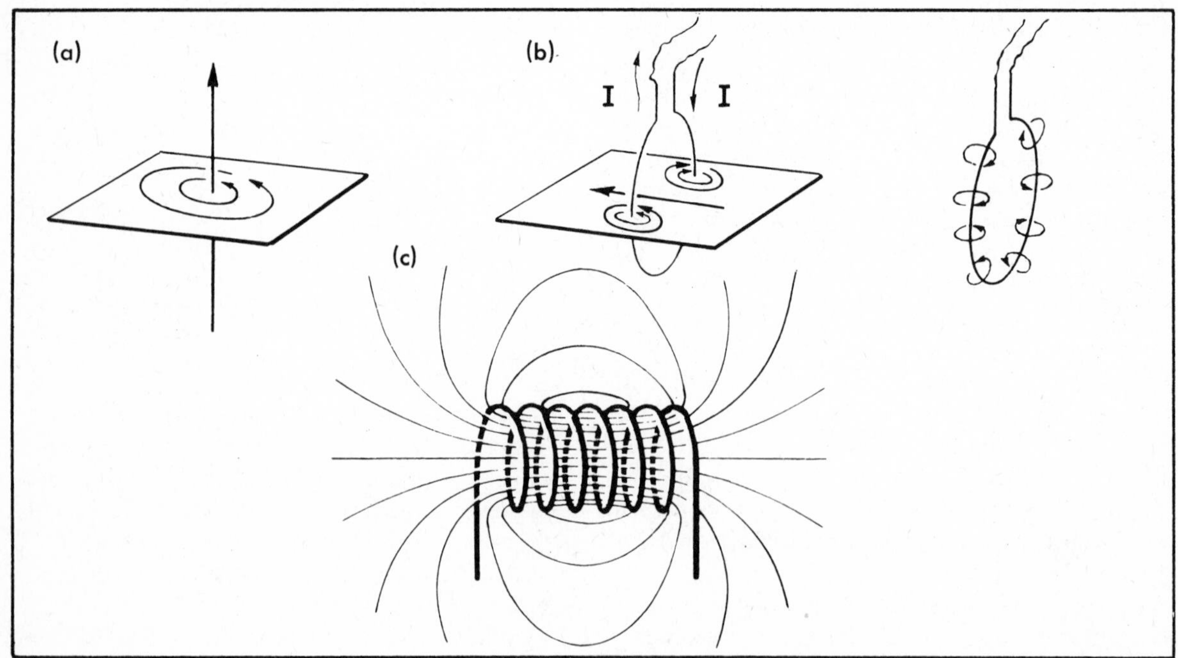

30–6. Diagrams of the magnetic field lines around current-carrying wires. (a) A long straight wire. (b) A loop of wire. (c) A solenoid.

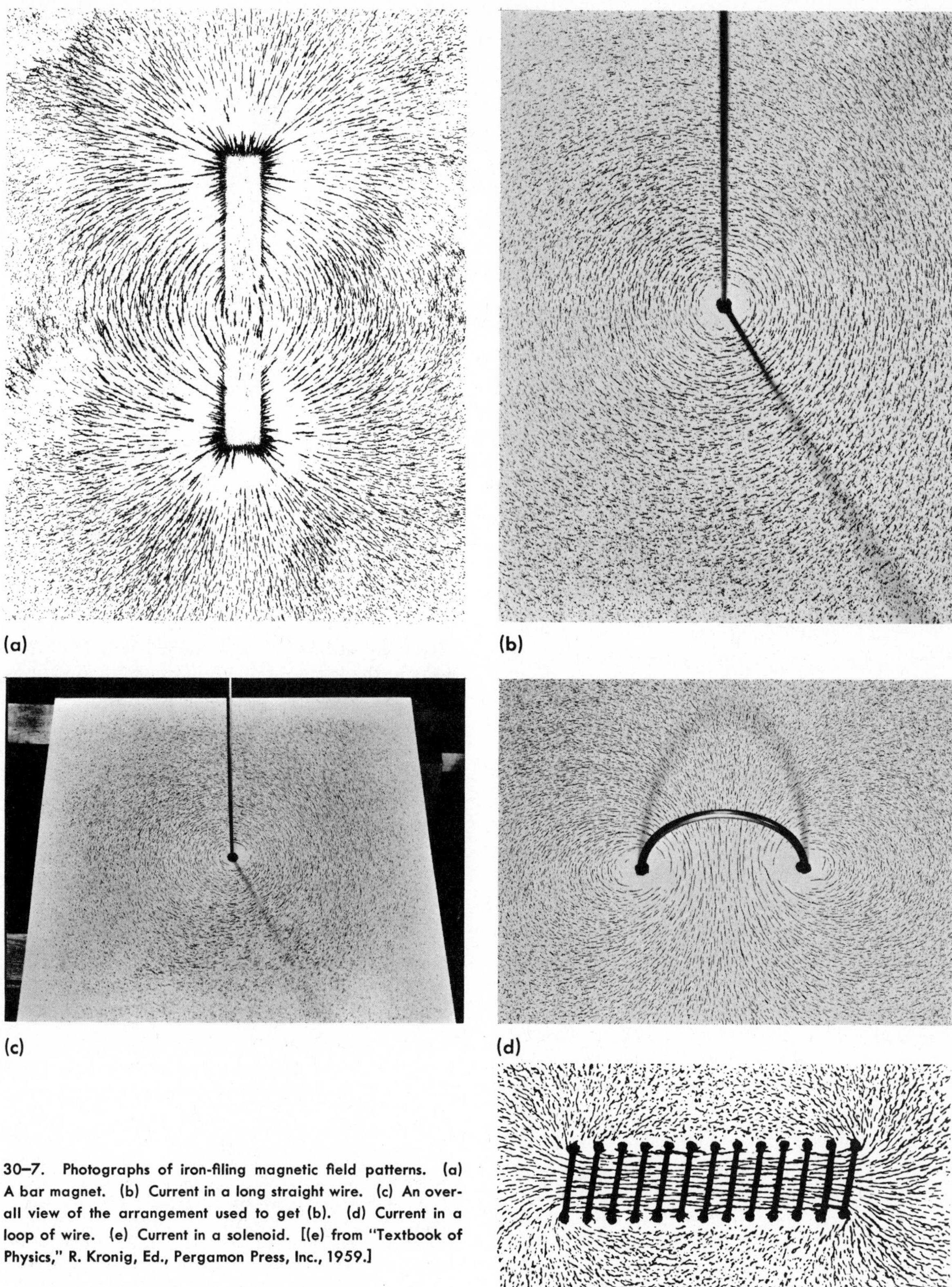

30–7. Photographs of iron-filing magnetic field patterns. (a) A bar magnet. (b) Current in a long straight wire. (c) An overall view of the arrangement used to get (b). (d) Current in a loop of wire. (e) Current in a solenoid. [(e) from "Textbook of Physics," R. Kronig, Ed., Pergamon Press, Inc., 1959.]

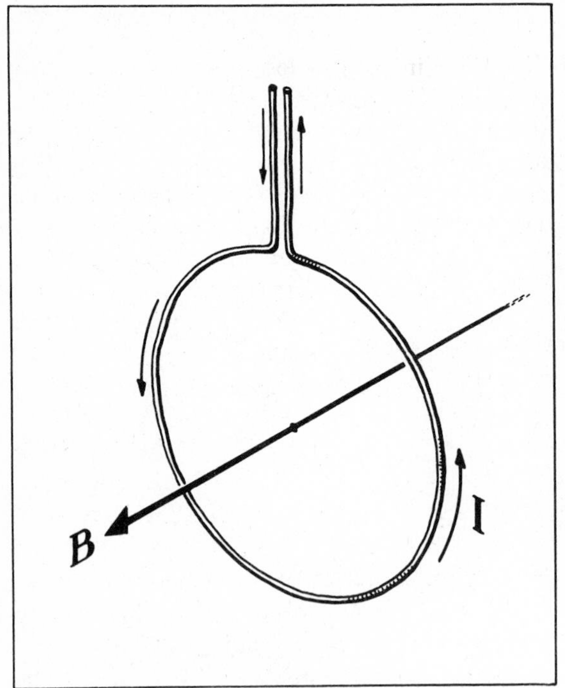

30–8. The direction of the magnetic field at the center of a loop of wire, with current flowing as indicated.

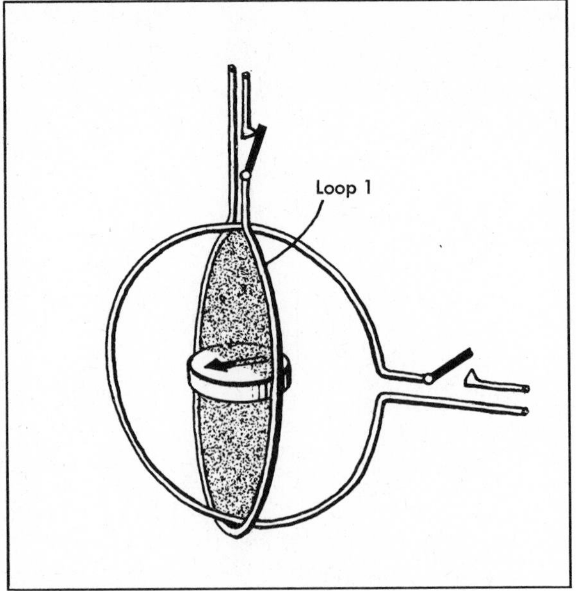

30–9. Experiments to find out if magnetic fields add vectorially. We arrange two loops of wire so that they have a common center and can be rotated with respect to each other. With current in loop 1, the compass points along the axis of the loop. This is the direction of the field.

30–3. Direction and Magnitude of Magnetic Fields; Vector Addition

We can reproduce a particular magnetic field when and where we wish by sending a specified electric current around a loop of wire. Because the source of the magnetic field is the same (as long as the loop is away from other magnets), the field at the center of the loop, for instance, should be the same no matter where it is located. Also, this field must always point in the same direction with respect to the loop.

As Fig. 30–8 indicates, this direction — measured by using a compass — is along the axis of the loop. When the current appears to be going around the loop clockwise, the direction of the field along the axis is away from you; and when you look from the other side, the current runs counterclockwise while the field comes toward you. To save words later, we shall say that the axis of the loop has the direction of the field.

If we use two loops side by side, each carrying the same current going around in the same direction, the strength of the magnetic field at the center is greater than it is with only one loop. It takes more force, for example, to twist a compass needle out of the direction of the field. If the currents in the loops circulate in opposite directions, the two loops produce fields in opposite directions, and the resultant field is zero.

In general, how do two fields add together? Since a magnetic field is characterized by both a magnitude and a direction, it is natural to suppose that magnetic fields add like vectors, just as forces or velocities do. Let us make this assumption, draw some conclusions from it, and then check up on it experimentally.*

When we assume that magnetic fields act like vectors, the first conclusion we can draw is that the magnetic field of a particular current loop must be proportional to the current. From the vector addition of two equal magnetic fields, it follows that the magnetic field of two loops, each

*Not everything with magnitude and direction is a vector. In our technical meaning of the word vector, only things that add vectorially count. A truck 2 meters wide with its direction indicator pointed down cannot be added to one 1.8 meters wide signalling for a right turn. Neither can the rotations of a book around two different axes be added vectorially. Try rotating a book 90° around a horizontal axis followed by rotating it 90° around a vertical axis. Then try doing the rotations in the opposite order. You do not get the same final result. The rotations do not add vectorially, as we know because vectors can be added in any order.

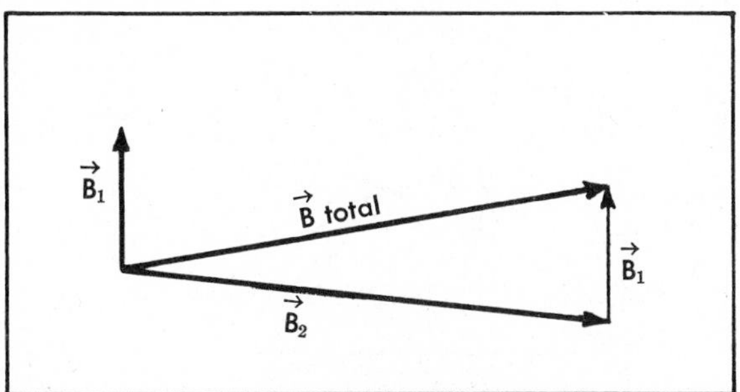

30–10. The vector addition of magnetic fields. With current in loop 1 alone, the field $\vec{B}_1$ points along the axis of loop 1 and is proportional to the current I_1. With current in loop 2 alone, the field $\vec{B}_2$ points along the axis of loop 2 and is proportional to the current I_2. When both currents are on, vector addition predicts the total field $\vec{B}_{total}$ shown. Is this prediction correct?

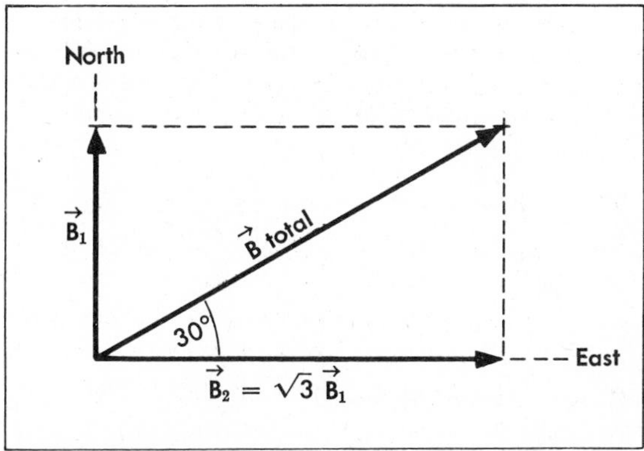

30–11. The fields $\vec{B}_1$ and $\vec{B}_2$ are produced by identical loops, but the current in loop 2 is $\sqrt{3}$ amp, while the current in loop 1 is 1 amp. The predicted $\vec{B}_{total}$ shown here is twice $\vec{B}_1$ and 30° north of east.

carrying the same current and placed right next to each other, is twice as big as the magnetic field of one of them. The two loops side by side are just a way of getting a loop with twice the current. We therefore predict that the magnetic field *is* proportional to the current that produces it.

If the above prediction is correct we should be able to use two identical current loops to produce any combination of magnetic fields. We arrange the two loops of wire so that they have a common center and so that we can change the direction of one loop with respect to the other (Fig. 30–9). At the center, the magnetic field from one loop is proportional to the current in that loop and points along its axis. The same is true for the field of the other loop. By adjusting the currents in the two loops, we should get any magnitudes we want for the two magnetic fields; and by changing the angle between the loops, we should be able to make the magnetic fields point in any directions we want. Using vector addition we can then predict the direction and the magnitude of the total field when both loops are turned on. (Fig. 30–10.) We can make these predictions for an infinite number of combinations both of direction and of magnitude.

For example, suppose $I_1 = 1$ ampere and the axis of loop 1 points north; $I_2 = \sqrt{3}$ amperes and the axis of loop 2 points east. Then by vector addition (Fig. 30–11) we predict a total field pointing 30° north of east and of magnitude just twice the field from loop 1. In other words, the total field that we expect at the center is the same as the field of an identical loop carrying a current of 2 amperes with its axis pointing along the 30° line in the figure. Every time we change the direction of a loop or the magnitude of the current in a loop, we get a new prediction for the total magnetic field.

We are now in a position to check the validity of vector addition, by comparing its predictions with experimental results. First we can check the direction of the total field from the two loops by putting a compass needle at the center. No matter how we change the currents and the directions of the loops, we find again and again that the direction of the total magnetic field is correctly given by the vector addition of the fields of the individual loops.*

Next we can check directly on the magnitude of the total field. For this purpose we introduce a third loop of identical size and shape with its center at the same place as that of the other two. We orient this loop so that its axis points in the direction opposite to the total field and adjust the current in it until the compass at the common center is no longer forced to line up in any particular direction. When the total field from the original two loops is thus canceled, the canceling field

*The magnetic field of the earth complicates quantitative experiments on magnetic fields. It may be negligible if the fields to be investigated are strong. Otherwise, we can cancel the earth's field in part of our laboratory by means of an equal and opposite field produced by a suitable current. We shall assume that in all our experiments the earth's magnetic field either is negligible or has been appropriately compensated.

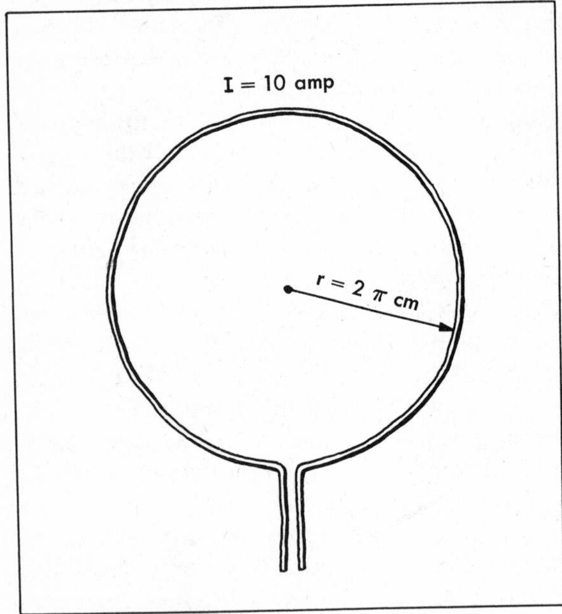

30–12. For our standard magnetic field we use the field at the center of a loop of wire of 2π cm radius, carrying a current of 10 amperes.

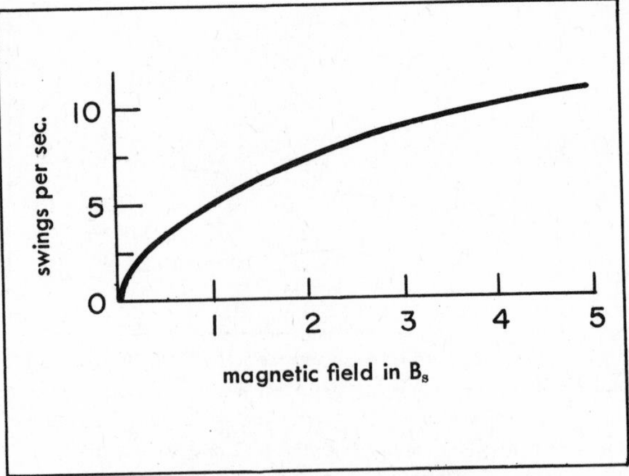

30–14. The calibration curve of a particular magnetic needle. If we twist a compass needle in a magnetic field out of its lined-up position, it will swing back and forth at a definite frequency. The frequencies were measured by putting the needle in known magnetic fields. Now with the needle we can measure the magnitude of a field by counting the swings per second. The square of the frequency is proportional to the field, but the constant of proportionality depends on the needle we use.

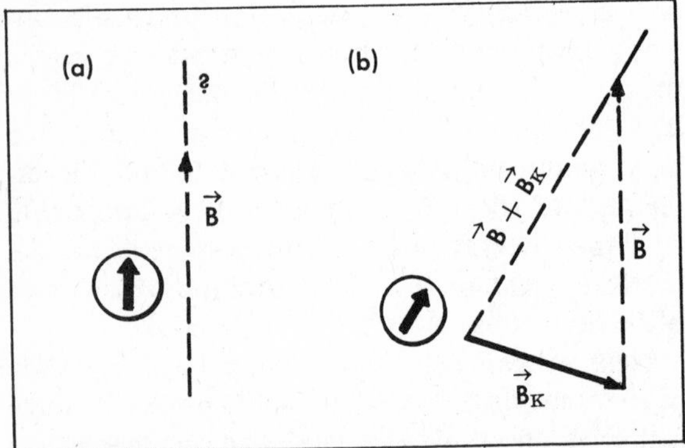

30–13. Measuring an unknown magnetic field $\vec{B}$ by adding a known field $\vec{B}_K$. (a) With a compass, we find the direction of the unknown field. (b) We then add any known field $\vec{B}_K$. The compass will change its direction, pointing in the direction of the combined field $\vec{B} + \vec{B}_K$. The vector diagram now determines the magnitude of $\vec{B}$.

from the third loop must be equal in magnitude as well as opposite in direction to the sum of the fields of the first two loops. The current in the third loop, therefore, measures the magnitude of the sum of the two magnetic fields from the original two loops. Again we can try any number of magnitudes and of directions of the original two fields. Again we always find that the magnetic fields add vectorially.

The experimental checks which we have just described show that magnetic fields add vectorially, and in particular they show that the magnetic field of a current is proportional to the magnitude of that current. With this knowledge, we can now produce a standard magnetic field wherever and whenever we want by using a particular current loop carrying a current of a given magnitude. We shall use the field B_s observed at the center of a circular loop of wire 2π centimeters in radius carrying a current of 10 amperes (Fig. 30–12). We chose the field B_s produced in this way because, as we shall see in Section 30–5, it is a convenient fraction of the basic unit that we shall introduce for magnetic field strength.

Now that we have a unit in which to measure the strength of a magnetic field, we can measure an unknown magnetic field by canceling it with the field from a standard loop. Actually, because we know that magnetic fields add vectorially, we shall do better if we add a known field from a standard loop at an angle to the unknown field (Fig. 30–13). First we use a compass to measure the direction of the unknown field. Second with the known field turned on, we use the compass to tell us the direction of the total field. We can then read off the magnitude of the original unknown field from a vector diagram.

Vector addition is not the only way we can

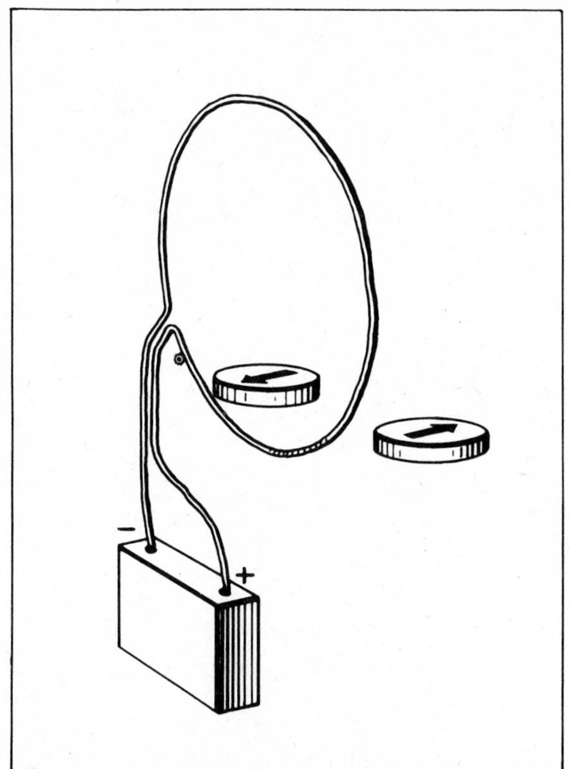

30–15 (a). The compass needles show the direction of the field at two points near a loop of metal wire. See. Fig. 30–15 (b).

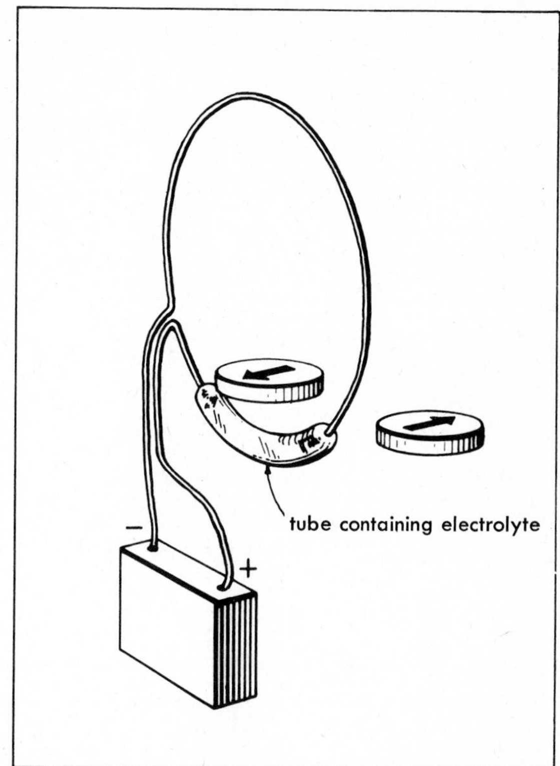

30–15 (b). If we replace part of the loop by an electrolytic conductor, the field is not changed. Magnetic effects do not depend on the sign of the charges that carry the current.

measure unknown fields. Many instruments are sensitive to the strength of a magnetic field. For instance, the frequency of oscillation of a magnetic needle about its rest position depends on the field strength (Fig. 30–14). We can calibrate any one of these devices in known magnetic fields and then use it to measure unknown field strengths.

30–4. Magnetic Fields of Steady Electric Currents

To discover the laws that relate the magnetic fields to the electric currents that produce them, we shall experiment first with *steady* electric currents, currents that do not change with time. Changing electric currents and their changing magnetic fields raise new problems, some of which we shall discuss later. Even for steady currents we shall not try to give a complete account. Rather than develop the procedure for computing the magnetic field from any system of currents, we shall concentrate on a few important examples.

We already know the magnetic field is proportional to the current I_p which produces it. Also, if we reverse the direction of current flow, we find that the magnetic field reverses its direction. In particular, when there is a current going around a wire loop in the direction indicated in Fig. 30–8, the magnetic field through the center of the loop has the direction shown.

In the last chapter we learned that positive charges moving in one direction have the same electrical effects as negative charges moving in the opposite direction. Experiment shows that they also have the same magnetic effects. Suppose that we build two geometrically identical circuits; the first, however, is made of metal wires while the second includes an electrolytic conductor [Figs. 30–15 (a) and 30–15 (b)]. With equal currents, the two circuits produce exactly equal magnetic fields even though in the first circuit the current is due entirely to the motion of negative charges, whereas in the second the current is due to the motion of both positive charges and negative charges. Thus in describing the magnetic effects of steady currents we need not worry about the sign of the particles which move.

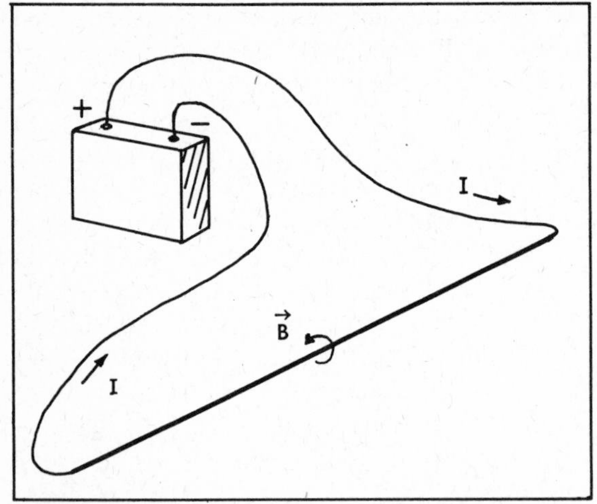

30–16. The field near the middle of the wire (where the field is shown) is uninfluenced by the parts of the circuit which are far away. See Figs. 30–6 (a) and 30–7.

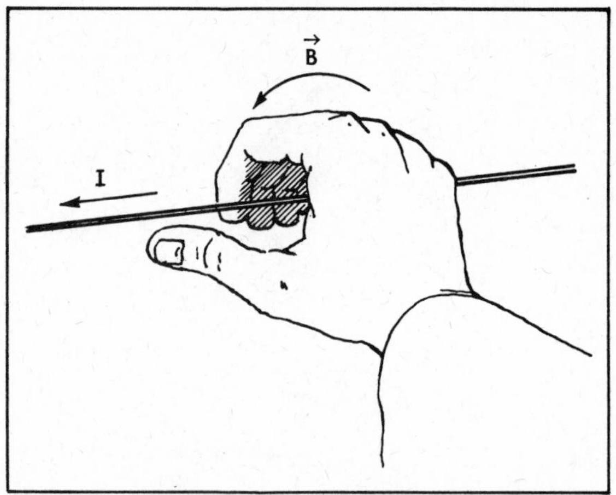

30–17. The "right-hand rule." When your right thumb points in the direction of the current in a wire, your fingers curl the way the magnetic field goes around the current.

Measurements with different loops show that the magnitude of the field at the center of the loop varies inversely with the radius of the loop. That is,

$$B_{\text{loop}} = (\text{Const})\,\frac{I_{\text{P}}}{r}.$$

Moreover, we also know the value of the constant in terms of our standard magnetic field B_s. When the loop is 2π cm ($2\pi \times 10^{-2}$ m) in radius and the current is 10 amperes, the field is B_s at the center. Consequently,

$$B_s = (\text{Const})\,\frac{10\text{ amp}}{2\pi \times 10^{-2}\text{ m}}$$

or

$$\text{Const} = \left(2\pi \times 10^{-3}\,\frac{\text{m}}{\text{amp}}\right) B_s.$$

With this value for the constant, we see that the field at the center of a loop is

$$B_{\text{loop}} = \left(2\pi \times 10^{-3}\,\frac{\text{m}}{\text{amp}}\right) B_s\,\frac{I_{\text{P}}}{r}.$$

When I is measured in amperes, r in meters, B_{loop} comes out as a multiple of B_s.

In 1820 the French physicists Biot and Savart announced the results of the first quantitative investigation of a magnetic field produced by an electric current. This was the field near a straight wire (Fig. 30–16). Near the middle of such a wire, the field arises almost entirely from the current near by. The other parts of the current do not contribute much field because the magnetic effects decrease rapidly with distance. (You check this by moving the *other* parts of the circuit.) The field lines form concentric circles around the wire [Fig. 30–6 (a) and Fig. 30–7]; and the strength B of the field at a distance d from the wire is inversely proportional to d. Consequently, B has the form

$$B = K\,\frac{I_{\text{P}}}{d}.$$

By experimentally comparing B around the long wire with the standard field B_s at the center of one of our special loops, we find that

$$B = \left(2 \times 10^{-3}\,\frac{\text{m}}{\text{amp}}\right) B_s\,\frac{I_{\text{P}}}{d}.$$

When I is measured in amperes, and d in meters, B comes out as a multiple of the standard field B_s.

You can remember how the direction of the field is related to the direction of the current by the "right hand" rule. In imagination place your *right* hand, with the thumb in the direction of the current; then your fingers curled around the wire point in the direction of the field (Fig. 30–17), the way the north tip of a compass would point. Notice that this rule also gives the direction of the field through a loop of wire.

As a last example consider a conducting wire wound in a helical coil. It is called a *solenoid.* A solenoid may have a single layer, or many layers of wire like thread on a spool. A steady current in the solenoid produces the magnetic field sketched in Fig. 30–6 (c) and photographed in Fig. 30–7. If the length of the solenoid is large compared with its diameter, the magnetic field inside is parallel to the axis and the same strength everywhere except very close to the winding or near the ends. This uniform field is proportional to the number of turns per unit length of the solenoid.

The field outside a solenoid looks very much like the field of a cylindrical bar magnet (Fig. 30–5). This suggests — as Ampère saw — that the field of a permanent magnet may be caused by electric currents. These currents arise from the motion of the charged particles inside the atoms or molecules. Perhaps, as in a planetary model of an atom, the electrons revolve like planets about the sun; perhaps the charges also spin around like the earth. In any case, their motion produces magnetic fields. In many materials the moving charges act like current loops pointing in all directions, and they give no net magnetic field. In a magnet, however, some of the moving charges act like a collection of current loops lined up the same way; then the result is an appreciable magnetic field. (For more detail of how these ideas explain the relation between a bar magnet and a solenoid, see the box below.)

Nowadays we have come to understand a great deal about the inner motions of charges in atoms — and to check them against their observed magnetic effects. Altogether, we are pretty sure that magnetism is always the effect of moving electric charge. Consequently, we do not expect to find separate magnetic poles.

Why a Bar Magnet Is Like a Solenoid

Inside a magnet there are many lined-up circulating currents — electrons moving around the atoms, for example. If we make an imaginary cut across a bar magnet we would lay bare a set of such circulating currents side by side. They are shown schematically in Fig. 30–18 (c). The field of a bar magnet resembles the field of a solenoid because each such set of atomic currents acts like one large current loop running around the outside of the bar. This current loop might just as well be one loop of the solenoid.

To see how the atomic current loops form one large loop, look first at Fig. 30–18 (a). Here we see two adjacent atomic loops. Where the loops have a common edge, the currents run in opposite directions. Therefore, the magnetic effects of these edges cancel. The two loops are magnetically equivalent to the bigger single loop in Fig. 30–18 (b).

Now look at 30–18 (c) again. Except at the outside of the bar, every current in an atomic loop is canceled by a neighboring opposite current. So the whole magnetic effect comes from the uncanceled currents around the outside of the bar. As you see, the uncanceled currents go steadily around the bar because all the little loops are lined up the same way. There might as well be current running around the surface of the magnet and nothing inside.

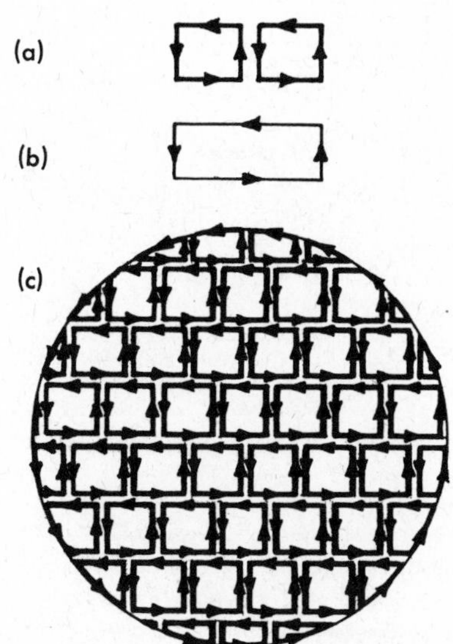

30–18. We can picture a magnet as having a large number of small current loops. In adjacent sides of different loops the currents go in opposite directions and their effects cancel. Around the outside, the currents all go in the same direction. We get the effect of a current around the magnet.

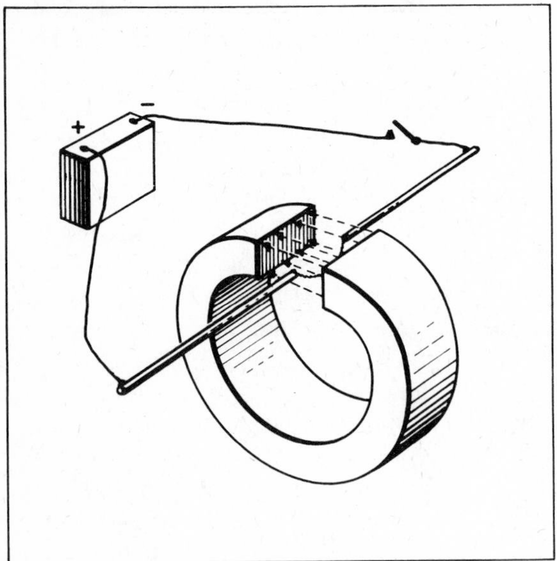

30–19 (a). A flexible wire in a magnetic field. The switch is open, no current flows, the wire hangs down.

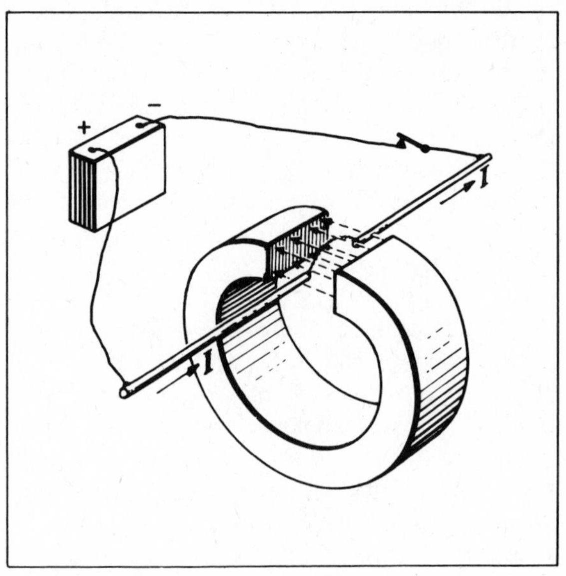

30–19 (b). When current flows, there is a magnetic force on the wire that pulls it taut.

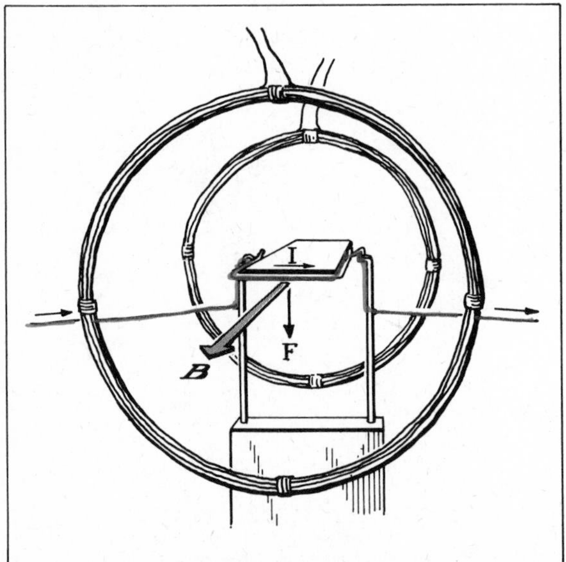

30–20. A U-shaped wire, shown in green, runs on the edge of a light balance in the center of the magnetic field of two large coils. When the coils are separated a distance equal to their radii, the magnetic field at the center is almost uniform. (Such coils are called Helmholtz coils.) The straight section of wire on the end of the balance is acted on by a force $\vec{F}$ tending to tip the balance. By putting weights on the other end we measure $\vec{F}$. By turning the balance, we find how the angle between the wire and $\vec{B}$ affects $\vec{F}$.

Because the current runs in opposite directions in the two arms of the U, in a uniform field the forces on the arms cancel. Since the field is not perfectly uniform, these forces do not cancel exactly. However, the twist they apply to the balance is very small compared to the twist applied by $\vec{F}$.

30–5. Forces on Currents in Magnetic Fields

Electric charges produce electric fields which exert forces on other electric charges. Now we find that electric currents produce magnetic fields, and we might guess that, correspondingly, magnetic fields exert forces on electric currents. They do, and with ordinary fields and currents the forces are quite sizable. It is these magnetic forces which spin the electric motors of the world.

Suppose, to begin with, that we hang a flexible wire in a magnetic field (Fig. 30–19). The field may be either the field of a permanent magnet or the field of a current which we control. When we turn on an electric current in the flexible wire, this wire is pushed across the magnetic field.

Let us try to discover the rules describing the force experienced by a current in a magnetic field. We can find this force by measuring the force needed to hold a movable section of wire in place when a magnetic field is applied. Using experimental arrangements like that in Fig. 30–20, we find the following:

(i) *The force is perpendicular to both the magnetic field and the current.* Here is a simple rule to enable you to remember the actual arrangement of directions. Stretch out your *right* arm with your hand open and your thumb sticking out at right angles to your fingers. Turn your

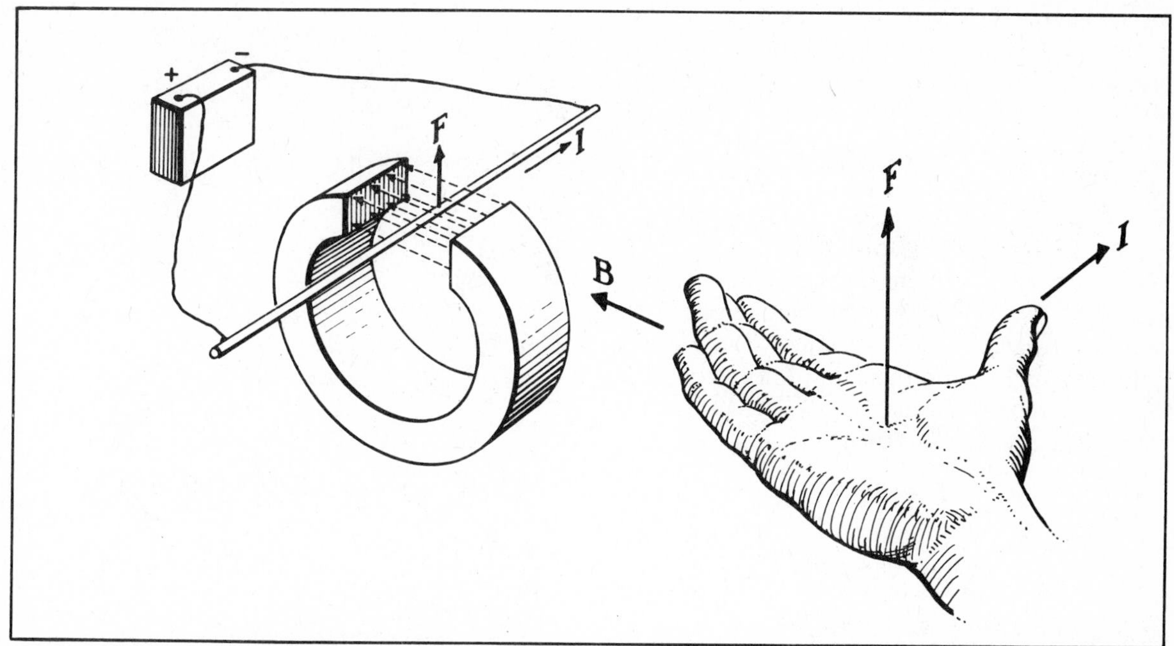

30–21. A rule to give the direction of the magnetic force on a current. Extend the fingers of your right hand in the direction of the magnetic field, and turn your hand so your thumb points along the current. The magnetic force then points out from your palm — in the direction you would push with your hand.

right hand till the *thumb points along the current* and your *fingers point along the external magnetic field.* Then the *force* on the current is in the direction pointing *straight out from the palm of your hand* — the force is in the direction in which you would slap someone. (Fig. 30–21.)

(ii) By changing the strength of the magnetic field without changing its direction, we find that the force on the current is proportional to the magnitude of the field. By changing the direction of the field we find that only the component of B perpendicular to the current contributes to the force. Therefore, *the force is proportional to* $B_{\perp}$, *the perpendicular component of the magnetic field* (Fig. 30–22).

To find how the force depends on the current and on the length of wire, we then reason as follows. Two wires placed side by side and carrying equal currents in a magnetic field together experience twice the force experienced by each wire alone. But the two wires combined carry twice the current of one wire. Thus doubling the current doubles the force:

The force, F, is proportional to current, I.

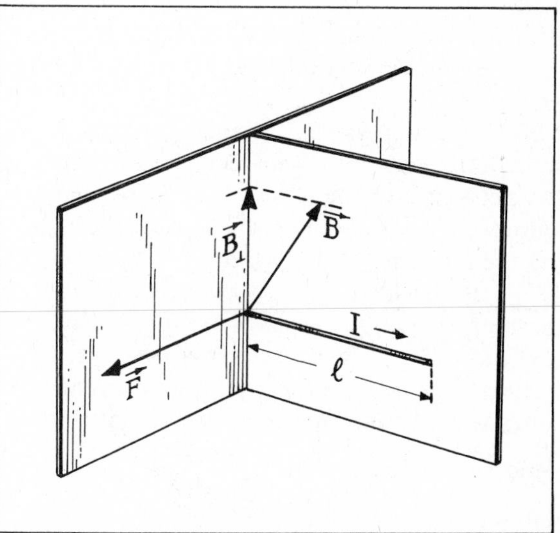

30–22. To find the magnetic force on a piece of wire carrying the current I: (i) Find the component of the magnetic field $\vec{B}$ perpendicular to the wire. (ii) Multiply $\vec{B}_{\perp}$ by the current I and by the length of the wire l. This gives the magnitude of the force $F = IlB_{\perp}$. (iii) The vector representing this force is perpendicular to the wire and to $\vec{B}$; its direction is given by the right-hand rule.

Next, two short straight wires of the same length placed end to end to form one longer wire experience together double the force experienced by each length alone. Thus doubling the length of the wire doubles the force:

The force, F, is proportional to length of wire, l.

To summarize our results, we now know the direction of the force and we know that the force is proportional to $B_\perp$, to I, and to l. In the form of an equation, we can write this as

$$F = AIlB_\perp$$

where A is a proportionality constant that depends only on the choice of units.

Now we shall settle on a definite unit of magnetic field, by defining it in terms of the units we have already adopted for F, I, and l. We measure F in newtons, I in amperes, and l in meters, and we choose the unit of magnetic field to make the constant A equal to 1. Then

$$F = IlB_\perp$$

and the unit of B is $\dfrac{1 \text{ newton}}{(1 \text{ ampere})(1 \text{ meter})}$. A magnetic field of 1 $\dfrac{\text{newton}}{\text{amp-meter}}$ exerts a force of 1 newton on a current of 1 ampere running perpendicularly across it for a distance of 1 meter.

In Section 30–3 we introduced a standard magnetic field B_s. We defined it as the field at the center of a loop 2π cm in radius carrying a current of 10 amperes. That definition relates the magnetic field to the current I_p that produces it. Here we have an entirely different way of defining the magnetic field. We do not care how the field is produced, and we measure it in newtons/amp-m by the magnetic force on a current I running a distance l across the field. This current may be an entirely different current.

What is the magnitude of the standard magnetic field strength B_s in $\dfrac{\text{newtons}}{\text{amp-meter}}$? We must find out experimentally. For instance, we can use a current I_p to generate a field which is a known multiple of B_s. Then we find the strength of that field in newtons/amp-m by measuring the force it exerts on another current I. We shall find a simple value for B_s because we chose B_s for convenience in the light of this experiment.

For our experiment let us use a standard loop, 2π cm in radius, but instead of a current $I_p = 10$ amp, let us make $I_p = 100$ amp. Since the current is 10 times standard, the field B_{loop} at the center of the loop is $B_{\text{loop}} = 10\ B_s$. Now we run a current $I = 50$ amp through a segment of wire 0.010 m (1 cm) long at the center of the loop (Fig. 30–23). We measure the force on this segment when it is perpendicular to the field B_{loop} from the loop, so $B_\perp = 10\ B_s$. The force is 5.0×10^{-4} newtons. From $F = IlB_\perp$ we therefore get

5.0×10^{-4} newtons $= 50$ amp $\times\ 0.010$ m $\times\ 10\ B_s$.

We thus learn that

$$B_s = 1.0 \times 10^{-4}\ \frac{\text{newtons}}{\text{amp-meter}}.$$

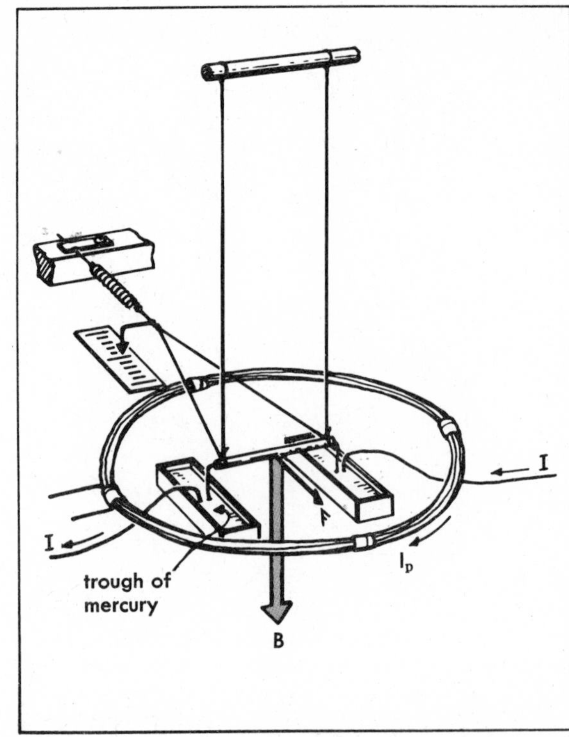

30–23. An experiment to measure the field at the center of a loop by measuring the force on a segment of a current-carrying wire. In the experiment described in the text, the total current I_p in the loop producing the field is 100 amp. The current I through the segment at the center is 50 amp. The segment itself is far shorter than shown here, so that the whole segment is in a uniform field at the center of the standard loop. For another type of current balance with which you could do the same measurement, see Fig. 30–20. The force F read on the scale is equal to IlB where l is the length of the segment.

Experiments like this have been done with great accuracy, and we shall describe another such experiment in Section 30–7. So we know that this is actually a very good value for the field at the center of the standard loop. With this value for B_s we can rewrite the formulas of Section 30–4.

The formula $B_{\text{loop}} = \left(2\pi \times 10^{-3} \dfrac{\text{meter}}{\text{amp}}\right) B_s \dfrac{I_p}{r}$

for the field produced at the center of a loop of radius r carrying a current I_p now becomes

$$B_{\text{loop}} = \left(2\pi \times 10^{-3} \frac{\text{meter}}{\text{amp}}\right)\left(1.0 \times 10^{-4} \frac{\text{newton}}{\text{amp-m}}\right) \frac{I_p}{r}$$

or $$B_{\text{loop}} = \left(2\pi \times 10^{-7} \frac{\text{newton}}{\text{amp}^2}\right) \frac{I_p}{r}.$$

In a similar way, the formula for the field around a long straight wire carrying a current I_p is

$$B_{\text{st. wire}} = \left(2 \times 10^{-7} \frac{\text{newton}}{\text{amp}^2}\right) \frac{I_p}{d}.$$

Notice that the constants have dimensions. They are in $\dfrac{\text{newtons}}{(\text{ampere})^2}\cdot$ Thus when we multiply by I_p in amperes and divide by a distance in meters, we get the B field in $\dfrac{\text{newtons}}{\text{amp-meter}}$.

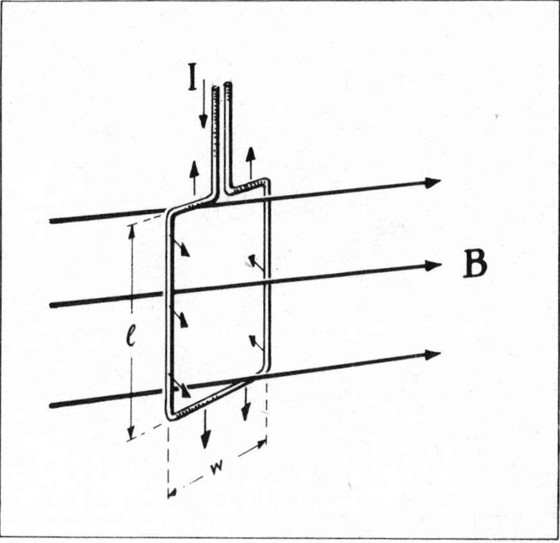

30–24. A schematic diagram of an ammeter. When current flows through the rectangular coil the magnetic forces IlB and $-IlB$ tend to twist the coil. It turns until the magnetic forces are just balanced by springs. A meter is usually made so the angle of twist is proportional to the current.

30–6. Meters and Motors

The delicate pointers which measure small currents and the big shafts that turn the rolls of a steel mill are moved by the same sort of forces: those exerted by a magnetic field on a loop or coil of wire carrying a current. Large currents mean large forces; small currents can exert only very small forces. Iron is found in most such devices; it provides the engineer with a way to increase magnetic fields from a given supply of current by lining up atomic magnets.

It is clear to anyone in our country that the use of this kind of force is very widespread, and that a great deal of understanding and skill must have been employed in inventing, designing, and building all the devices in which it is used. This is the work of electrical engineers, who have for about 75 years carried the applications of this force to constantly new uses. We are not going to try to describe the ingenious and often complex ways they have found to use the force; that is another subject. But we shall give a short account of two simple devices which depend on magnetic forces.

(a) *Moving-Coil Ammeters.* Figure 30–24 shows the forces on a loop of wire in a magnetic field. The loop coil is rectangular, with sides l and w; and its plane makes an angle with the field of strength B. When a current I runs around the loop, the forces on the sides are BIl and $-BIl$.

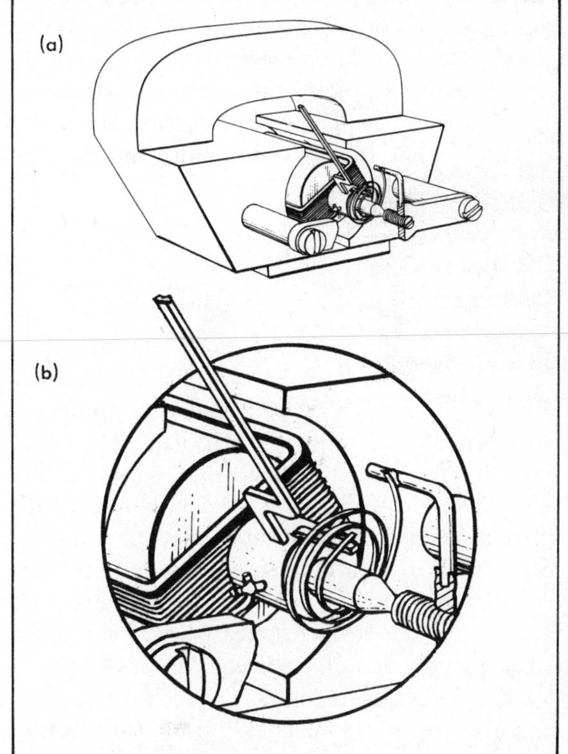

30–25. (a) An ammeter. When current enters the rectangular coil of many turns through the hairspring at the front of the shaft, the coil rotates around a fixed iron cylinder. The cylinder and the specially shaped poles of the large permanent magnet give a radial magnetic field of nearly uniform magnitude. (b) Close-up of the moving coil.

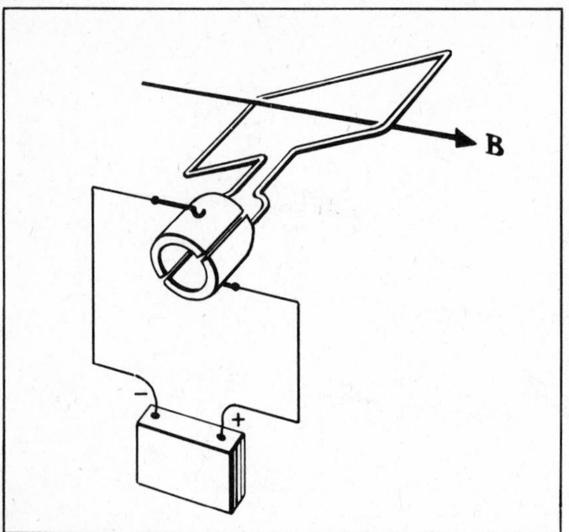

30–26. A D.C. motor is similar to a moving-coil meter. The coil is bigger, and a reversing switch or commutator is provided to reverse the direction of current flow every half turn.

They are parallel, but they do not cancel out because they do not pull along the same line. They form a "couple" which twists the coil around the vertical axis. The forces on the top and bottom are $B_{\perp}Iw$ and $-B_{\perp}Iw$, equal and opposite. They stretch the coil, but do not move it as a whole.

In an ordinary ammeter for direct currents (D.C.) the coil is carried on an axle with pivots, and its twisting is opposed by the elastic forces of a pair of hairsprings (Fig. 30–25). The current is usually led into the coil and out through the hairsprings. The magnetic field is produced by a permanent magnet whose field gives a radial pattern. (This is produced by shaped pole pieces and a cylindrical block of iron that is held in the open space inside the coil.) Then even when the coil turns, it still finds the magnetic field perpendicular to its sides in such a direction that the magnetic forces twist it equally hard no matter how far it has turned. On the other hand, the opposing forces due to the springs increase as the coil turns. Consequently, the coil turns until the spring forces balance the magnetic forces. The greater the current, the greater the magnetic forces and the farther the coil must twist to reach equilibrium. Since the spring forces are usually proportional to the angle of twist, this angle is proportional to the current: the ammeter's scale is linear. Such meters are made in a wide range of sizes and scales.

(b) *D.C. Motors.* A motor is a more robust coil, carrying current in a strong magnetic field. The D.C. ammeter's permanent magnet is replaced by an electromagnet, carrying a current from the supply driving the motor. The coil is mounted on an axle in the magnetic field of the field electromagnet. If the current just continued to flow, the coil would not continue to rotate. It would reach an equilibrium position, rock to and fro, and stop like the pointer on the meter. But a motor has a device to reverse the current in the coil every half turn. The coil is pulled around for half a turn; the current is then reversed and the coil is pulled around for another half turn. One arrangement of this reversing switch or commutator is shown in simple form in Fig. 30–26. Real motors do not have a single coil but rather a whole group of coils placed so as to give steadier turning forces. Also, the coils are wound on a block of iron to increase the magnetic field.

30–7. Forces Between Two Straight Parallel Currents

Currents produce magnetic fields, and currents are subjected to forces when magnetic fields are present. In this way currents may be said to interact with one another through the intermediary of the magnetic field. This is exactly the point of view we took for the electric field, which is the intermediary through which electric charges interact with one another. Currents repel and attract, much as charges repel and attract, with forces which depend on what currents are present and on their geometrical arrangement. The interaction of currents lies at the root of most of the myriad mechanical uses of electric energy, such as motors and generators of every type.

In Section 30–5 we computed the force between a current-carrying loop and a segment of wire at its center carrying a different current. Here let us compute the force of interaction of two currents in another simple case. Suppose a very long straight wire carries a current I_1 in the direction shown by the arrow in Fig. 30–27. A straight segment of wire MN of length l lies beside the first wire, at a distance d from it. It carries a current I_2 in the same direction. We wish to compute the force F experienced by the segment of wire MN.

We proceed in two steps. First we consider the magnetic field B, produced by the current I_1.

This field has the same magnitude B at all points of the segment MN. We also know that this field is proportional to the current I and inversely proportional to d, the distance away from the wire carrying that current, that is

$$B = \frac{KI_1}{d},$$

where $K = 2 \times 10^{-7} \frac{\text{newtons}}{(\text{ampere})^2}$ as we learned in Section 30–5. This magnetic field is perpendicular to the plane containing the currents I_1 and I_2, and it points in the direction shown by the shaded arrow in Fig. 30–27, downward across I_2.

Next we compute the force exerted by this magnetic field upon the current segment MN. This segment has a length l; it is perpendicular to the field, and it carries a current I_2. Since the B field from I_1 is perpendicular to the current I_2, the force on the segment is

$$F = BlI_2.$$

And on substituting B in this expression, we have

$$F = KI_1I_2l/d.$$

This gives us the magnitude of the force on MN.

To find the direction of the force on MN, you now apply the rule explained in Section 30–5. You place the thumb of your right hand along the direction of the current I_2 so that it points to the left in Fig. 30–27. Then move your arm until it is pointing down in the direction of the B field indicated by the shaded arrow. The force is in the direction in which you would slap someone with the palm of your hand. It points from I_2 toward I_1. We therefore conclude that two currents in the same direction attract each other. If we reverse the direction of one current, the currents now repel.

In Fig. 30–27 we have shown the magnetic field arising from I_1 and acting on I_2. There is also a magnetic field arising from I_2 and acting on I_1. If we work out its effect — or if we trust symmetry — we find the same results that we found above: when the currents are in the same direction they attract, and when they are in opposite directions they repel. And in either case the magnitude of the force is $F = KI_1I_2l/d$.

(For another way of thinking about magnetic forces see the box on the next page.)

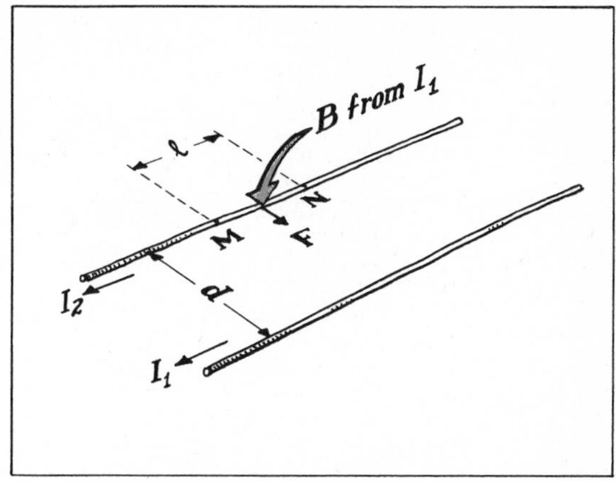

30–27. Two parallel conducting wires side by side. The segment of wire MN experiences a force F in the magnetic field of the other wire, shown by the shaded arrow.

The force between two currents is easily measured, and so are the currents and distances which occur on the right-hand side of the last equation. An experiment of this kind gives us a direct measure of the constant K. The result agrees with the value $K = 2 \times 10^{-7} \frac{\text{newtons}}{(\text{ampere})^2}$ that we obtained in Section 30–5. Indeed, this experiment and the equation $F = KI_1I_2l/d$ give us a clue to the history of electrical units. Long ago, the ampere was chosen to make the constant K have the neat, round value 2×10^{-7}. From that definition of the ampere, the measurements first done by Millikan showed that an ampere flowing for a second carried 6.25×10^{18} elementary charges. And finally, the volt was defined as the potential difference (or EMF) which delivers one watt (a joule per second) with a current of one ampere. Our definition of the volt in Chapter 29 was made to agree with these definitions.

What happens to the numerical value of the constant K in $F = KI_1I_2l/d$ when we measure the currents in our basic units of elementary charges per second instead of in amperes? Since we wish to continue measuring the force in newtons, and since in each current 1 elem. ch./sec is only 1.6×10^{-19} amperes, the constant K is multiplied by $\left(1.6 \times 10^{-19} \frac{\text{amp}}{\text{elem. ch./sec}}\right)^2$. In other words, K becomes

$$\left(2 \times 10^{-7} \frac{\text{newtons}}{\text{amp}^2}\right)\left(1.6 \times 10^{-19} \frac{\text{amp}}{\text{elem. ch./sec}}\right)^2$$

MAGNETIC FORCES AND THE TOTAL MAGNETIC FIELD

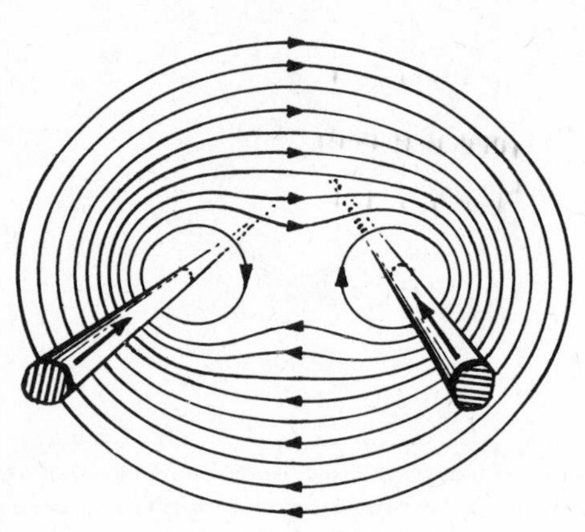

30–28 (a). The combined magnetic field patterns of two parallel conducting wires. The currents are in the same direction in both wires. They attract each other.

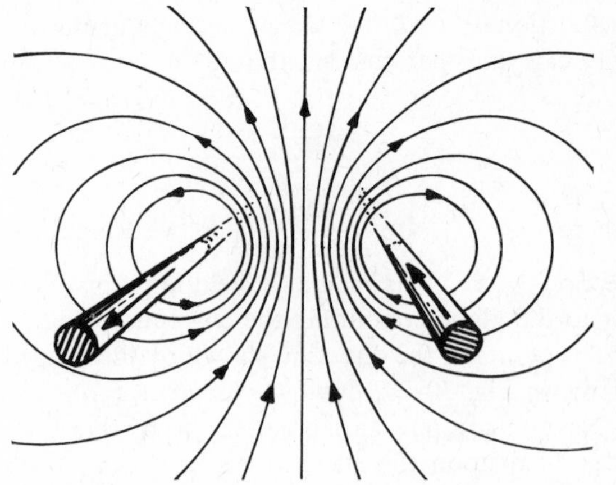

30–28 (b). The currents are in opposite directions, and the wires repel each other.

We can find the total magnetic field around two wires, the field that would act on another current or on a compass needle in the region near by, by adding the fields from the currents I_1 and I_2 vectorially. This field is sketched in Fig. 30–28. Notice that the wires repel when the field lines are denser between them than outside and they attract when the lines are denser on the outside than in between. The lines of B act as though they were so many rubber bands which resist both being stretched and being crowded together. By thinking of the total magnetic field lines in this way, we can get an idea of the forces and motions of currents in magnetic fields without doing detailed calculations.

or $$K = 5.12 \times 10^{-45}\,\frac{\text{newtons}}{(\text{elem. ch./sec})^2}.$$

Also, in these units, the field of a straight wire is

$$B_{\text{st. wire}} = \left(5.12 \times 10^{-45}\,\frac{\text{newtons}}{(\text{elem. ch./sec})^2}\right)\frac{I_p}{d}.$$

When the current I_p in the wire is measured in elem. ch. per sec and d is in meters, this gives the B field in $\frac{\text{newtons}}{(\text{elem. ch./sec})(\text{meter})}$.

This unit is useful to us when we deal with the magnetic forces on moving elementary charges. The force in newtons on a segment of wire of length l in meters carrying a current of I elementary charges per second is

$$F = IlB_{\perp}$$

where B is measured in $\frac{\text{newtons}}{(\text{elem. ch./sec})(\text{meter})}$.

On the other hand, this is not a common unit, because a B field as large as one of these units is many orders of magnitude larger than any field we can obtain. A B field of $1\,\frac{\text{newton}}{\text{ampere-m}}$ is usually considered large, but it is only

$$1.6 \times 10^{-19}\,\frac{\text{newtons}}{(\text{elem. ch./sec})(\text{meter})}.$$

30–8. Forces on Moving Charged Particles in a Magnetic Field

A conductor carrying a current experiences a force when it is placed in a magnetic field. Since an electric current is a motion of electric particles, we naturally expect that the magnetic field acts directly on the individual charged particles — on the ions or electrons whose motion produces the current. The force exerted on the conductor as a whole is simply the resultant of the forces acting on the particles.

We can check up on this idea by firing a beam of electrons from an electron gun through mercury or hydrogen gas at low pressure. The electrons emerging from the slit make the low-pressure gas glow. Thus, the path of the beam is

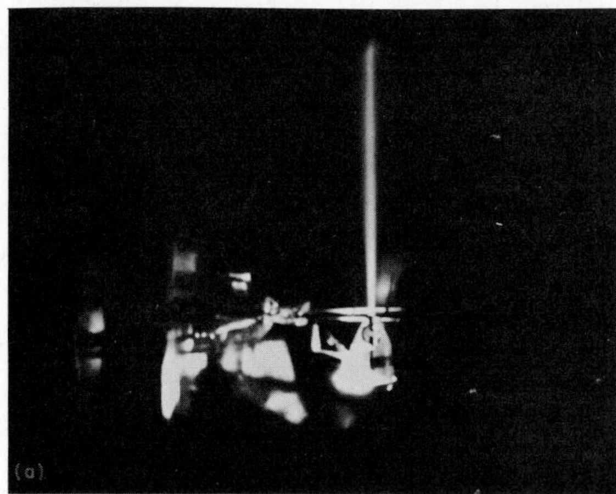

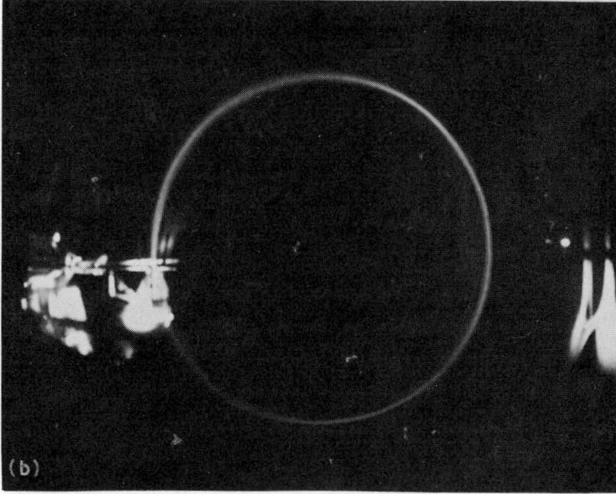

30–29. An experiment to show the deflection of moving charged particles in a magnetic field. In (a), electrons accelerated by the gun travel vertically upward, leaving a path of glowing gas. There is no magnetic field. When there is a magnetic field (b), the path of the electrons is bent into a circular arc. (We used a pair of coils rather than a bar magnet, to get a uniform field in a space into which we can look.) In (b) the beam starts to diverge but does not continue. It probably narrows down again. Can you explain why?

clearly visible in a darkened room (Fig. 30–29). Now we bring a magnet near the tube, pointed so that its magnetic field runs straight out from us across the tube. The beam is deflected at right angles to its motion and to the magnetic field. If we reverse the magnet, the beam is deflected the opposite way.

To be specific, suppose the electrons originally move vertically upward. Since electrons are negatively charged particles, this beam corresponds to a current directed vertically *downward.* Now we hold the magnet so that its field, as shown by a compass needle, is directed straight from us through the beam as we face the apparatus. Then according to our rule for directions, the force acting on the moving particles must pull them to the right. In fact, as the beam goes up it is deflected to the right.

We shall now compute the force acting on an individual charged particle moving with a given velocity in a known magnetic field. For this purpose, we shall consider a stream of elementary charges evenly spaced and all moving with the same speed v (Fig. 30–30). Then from $F = IlB_{\perp}$ we find the force F_1 on one of these elementary charges. If there are N elementary charges in the length l, then

$$F_1 = \frac{IlB_{\perp}}{N}.$$

Thus, in order to get the force F_1 in terms of the speed v of the charges, we must evaluate the current in terms of the number of charges N in the length l. To see how I is expressed in terms of N, l, and v, we imagine an observer posted at the end of the length l to count the elementary charges as they go by. Because every charge is moving at speed v, the length l of the stream takes the time $t = \frac{l}{v}$ seconds to pass him. At the beginning of that time the nearest charge is just passing the observer. At the end of that time, the last charge from the other end of l goes past him. In the time $t = l/v$, therefore, all N charges in the length l have moved past.

Now the number of elementary charges passing

last particle in ℓ

ℓ

v

N elementary charges in this length

$t = \frac{\ell}{v}$ later

$vt = \ell$

v

30–30. An imaginary observer is watching a stream of elementary charges moving with speed v. He counts N particles passing him when a length l of the stream goes by. This takes a time $t = l/v$. So the current in the stream is $\frac{N}{t} = \frac{N}{l/v} = \frac{Nv}{l}$.

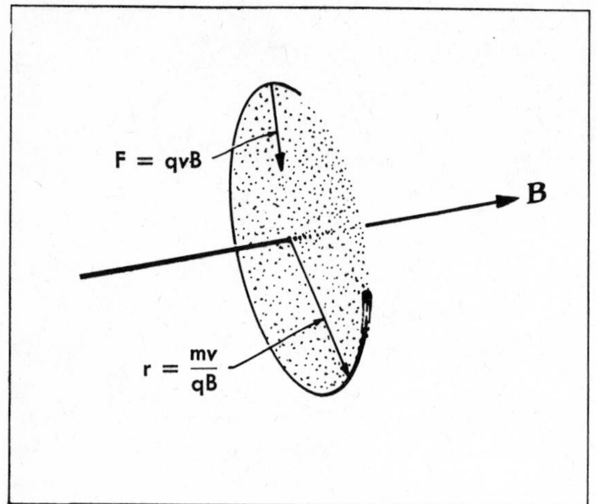

30–31. When a charged particle moves across a magnetic field, it experiences a magnetic force $F = qvB$ at right angles to its path. If the field is uniform, the particle moves in a circle of radius $r = mv/qB$.

per second is $\frac{N}{t}$, and this is the current I. By putting in $\frac{l}{v}$ for the time, we can express this as

$$I = \frac{N}{t} = \frac{N}{l/v} = \frac{Nv}{l}.$$

When we put $I = \frac{Nv}{l}$ into our expression for F_1, we get

$$F_1 = \frac{IlB_\perp}{N} = \frac{Nv}{l} \times \frac{lB_\perp}{N} = vB_\perp$$

As we should have expected, the expression for the force on an elementary charge depends only on its speed and on the magnitude of the perpendicular component of the magnetic field.

If a particle moving at speed v carries q elementary charges, the force on it is just q times as great. In other words, the force experienced by a particle carrying q elementary charges and moving with a velocity v in a magnetic field is $F = qvB_\perp$.

By shooting charged particles across a magnetic field and observing their deflection by the magnetic force, we can show experimentally that this expression for the magnetic force on a moving charge is correct. Because the magnetic force is always perpendicular to the velocity, it cannot do work on charged particles shot across the field. They therefore move at constant speed. Consequently, qvB always has the same value. In other words, as long as the field is uniform, the magnetic force is a deflecting force of constant magnitude. The particles should go around in a circle (see Fig. 30–29), and we can compute the radius of this circle by equating the magnetic deflecting force with $\frac{mv^2}{r}$, the centripetal force necessary to make a particle of mass m moving at speed v go around the arc of a circle of radius r (Fig. 30–31). From $\frac{mv^2}{r} = qvB_\perp$, we find that $r = \frac{mv}{qB_\perp}$. Therefore we can test our expression for the magnetic deflecting force by sending particles of known momentum and charge across a given magnetic field and measuring the radius of the circular arc on which they move.

We already have the information for protons with which we can make this test. In Section 29–2 we measured the mass of a proton. Accurately it is 1.66×10^{-27} kg. We also learned that when protons are accelerated from rest through a 90-volt potential difference, they emerge with a speed of 1.31×10^5 meters per second. In this way we can produce protons of known momentum

$$mv = 1.66 \times 10^{-27}\text{ kg} \times 1.31 \times 10^5\text{ m/sec}$$
$$= 2.18 \times 10^{-22}\ \frac{\text{kg-m}}{\text{sec}}.$$

Now we shoot these protons perpendicularly into a magnetic field. A good practical magnetic field, for example, might be $1.00 \times 10^{-2}\ \frac{\text{newtons}}{\text{amp-m}}$, and in elementary-charge units this is

$$1.60 \times 10^{-21}\ \frac{\text{newtons}}{(\text{elem. ch./sec})\ (\text{meter})}.$$

In that field the magnetic deflecting force should cause the protons to go around a circle of radius

$$r = \frac{mv}{qB_\perp} = \frac{2.18 \times 10^{-22}}{1 \times 1.60 \times 10^{-21}} = 0.136\text{ m}.$$

This expected radius is actually observed when protons of 90 electron volts energy are shot into that magnetic field. Thus, experiments show that the magnetic deflecting force is indeed given by $qvB_\perp$, in agreement with our reasoning from the magnetic force on currents.

30–9. Using Magnetic Fields to Measure the Masses of Charged Particles

To measure the masses of electrons and protons in Section 29–2, we used a known potential difference to accelerate electrons or protons to a known kinetic energy, $\frac{1}{2}mv^2$. Then we deter-

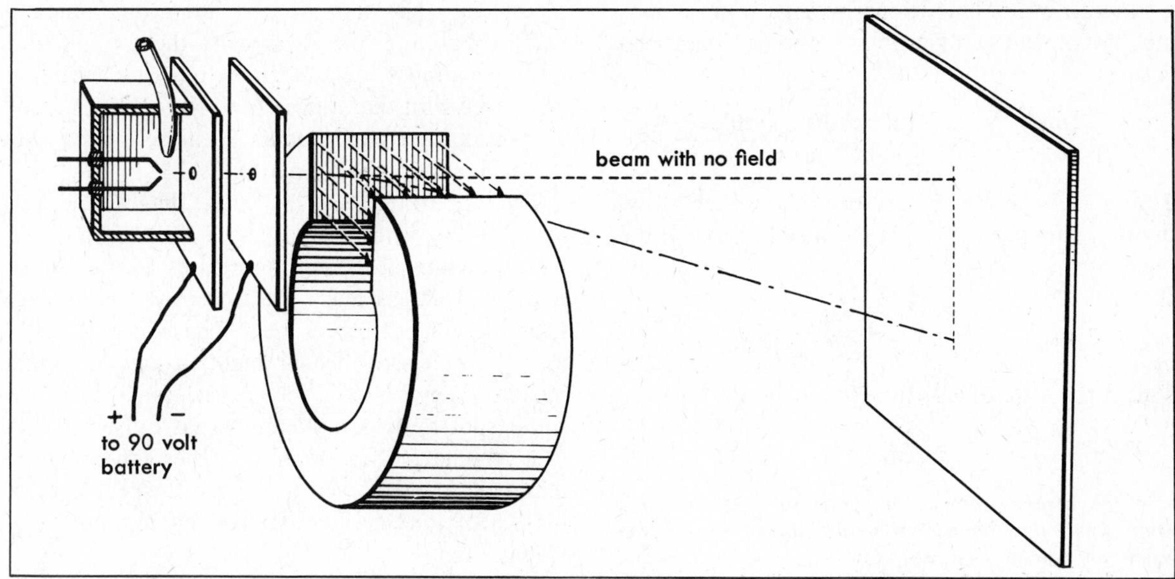

30–32. A simple mass spectrograph. Ions are accelerated to a known kinetic energy by the electric field between the plates. In the magnetic field their path is bent into a circular arc. The ions strike a screen or photographic plate, and from the deflection we can calculate the radius of the arc.

mined the speed v of these particles by doing a time-of-flight experiment.

We have another, older method of making this mass measurement. Instead of measuring the speed v of the particles we can find their momentum mv by observing their deflection in a known magnetic field. If we know their kinetic energy and momentum, we can easily compute their mass. This is the method by which our most precise measurements of the masses of ions have been made in the past. It is particularly valuable for electrons because their high speeds make time-of-flight measurements difficult.

The measurement of momentum by deflecting a beam of particles in a magnetic field is basically the same measurement that we made at the end of the last section. There we used the deflection of protons as an experimental check on the expression $F = qvB_{\perp}$ for the magnetic force. Here we shall use the known magnetic force to find unknown masses.

To use this method to measure ionic masses, we accelerate the ions of unknown mass through a known electrical potential difference, V (Fig. 30–32). This tells us their kinetic energy per elementary charge: $\frac{1}{2}mv^2 = qV$. Then we allow the ions to go perpendicularly into the known magnetic field and measure the radius of the circular arc on which they move. Because the centripetal force $\frac{mv^2}{r}$ *is* the magnetic deflecting force qvB — that is, $\frac{mv^2}{r} = qvB$ — we get $mv = qBr$. Consequently, by measuring the radius of the circular arc, we can evaluate the momentum of the particle.

Let us take a specific example. We accelerate singly charged sodium ions through an electric potential difference of 90 volts. Any singly charged ion accelerated through 90 volts acquires 1.44×10^{-17} joules of kinetic energy. With this kinetic energy the sodium ions enter a uniform magnetic field of strength

$$1.00 \times 10^{-20} \frac{\text{newtons}}{(\text{elem. ch./sec})\,(\text{meter})}$$

at right angles to their direction of motion. Now we measure the radius of the arc through which they travel in the magnetic field, and we find that it is 0.105 meters. Since the ions are singly charged,

$$qBr = \underset{(\text{elem. ch.})}{1} \times \underset{\left(\frac{\text{newtons}}{(\text{elem. ch./sec})\text{-m}}\right)}{100 \times 10^{-20}} \times \underset{(\text{meter})}{0.105}$$

$$= 1.05 \times 10^{-21} \text{ newton-sec.}$$

This is the momentum of the ions.

Now from the kinetic energy $\frac{1}{2}mv^2$ and the momentum mv, we can get both m and v. The speed is easy:

$$v = \frac{2(\frac{1}{2}mv^2)}{mv} = \frac{2(1.44 \times 10^{-17} \text{ joules})}{1.05 \times 10^{-21} \text{ newton-seconds}}.$$

That is 2.74×10^4 meters per second. Finally, dividing this speed into the momentum, we get the mass of the ions:

$$m = \frac{mv}{v} = \frac{1.05 \times 10^{-21}}{2.74 \times 10^4} = 3.84 \times 10^{-26} \text{ kg}.$$

This is the mass of a sodium ion — good to within a per cent. The mass of a sodium atom, which is made by adding one electron to the sodium ion, must be almost identical. So our value can be compared with the values obtained for the mass of sodium in other experiments. The accepted value for the mass of a sodium atom is 3.82×10^{-26} kg.

The apparatus that we have diagrammed in Fig. 30–32 is known as a mass spectrograph, and the procedure of measuring masses with such apparatus is called mass spectroscopy. Our mass spectrograph is very crude. One which is made for high-precision measurements usually contains auxiliary devices to "focus" the particles on a small spot and to make sure that only particles in a very narrow range of velocities can enter the magnetic field. With a good spectrograph masses of ions can be determined to many significant figures.

Ever since J. J. Thomson introduced mass spectroscopy about fifty years ago, it has been a powerful tool of atomic research. In particular, because mass spectrographs sort the ions by their individual masses, the masses of the isotopes of a single element were largely determined by mass spectrographic measurement. Although some evidence for the existence of isotopes among the heavy radioactive elements was pointed out in the first few years of this century, it was Thomson's measurement showing the existence of the isotopes of neon that clinched the idea and started the accumulation of systematic data on isotopes. By now we have accumulated so much information that a huge table would be needed to exhibit it. Only a small sample of the known masses of isotopes is shown in Table 1.

Table 1

A few of the isotopes of some common elements. One atomic mass unit is $\frac{1}{16}$ of the atomic mass of the most common oxygen isotope.

Element	Mass of the isotopes in atomic mass units	Relative abundance: per cent
Hydrogen	1.008	99.98
	2.015	0.02
Lithium	6.017	7.5
	7.018	92.5
Carbon	12.004	98.9
	13.008	1.1
	14.008	unstable
Nitrogen	14.008	99.6
	15.005	0.4
Oxygen	16.000 (standard)	99.76
	17.004	0.04
	18.005	0.20
Neon	19.999	90.8
	21.000	0.26
	21.998	8.9
Magnesium	23.993	78.8
	24.994	10.1
	25.991	11.1
Chlorine	34.980	75.53
	36.978	24.47
Iron	53.957	5.9
	55.953	91.6
	56.954	2.2
	57.952	0.3
Silver	106.939	51.4
	108.939	48.6
Lead	204.036	1.3
	206.038	26
	207.040	21
	208.041	52

30–10. What Alpha Particles Are

In Chapter 32 we shall take a look at some of the evidence about structure of atoms accumulated by Rutherford and his co-workers in the first few decades of this century. Rutherford's chief experiments were done with alpha particles. We already know how Rutherford and Geiger determined that alpha particles carry two elementary charges (see Section 28–9). Now we shall describe two experiments equivalent to those done by Rutherford and Robinson to determine the mass of the alpha particle. In one of these experiments we determine the momentum of an ion by measuring its deflection in a magnetic field. Because we have just described this kind of ex-

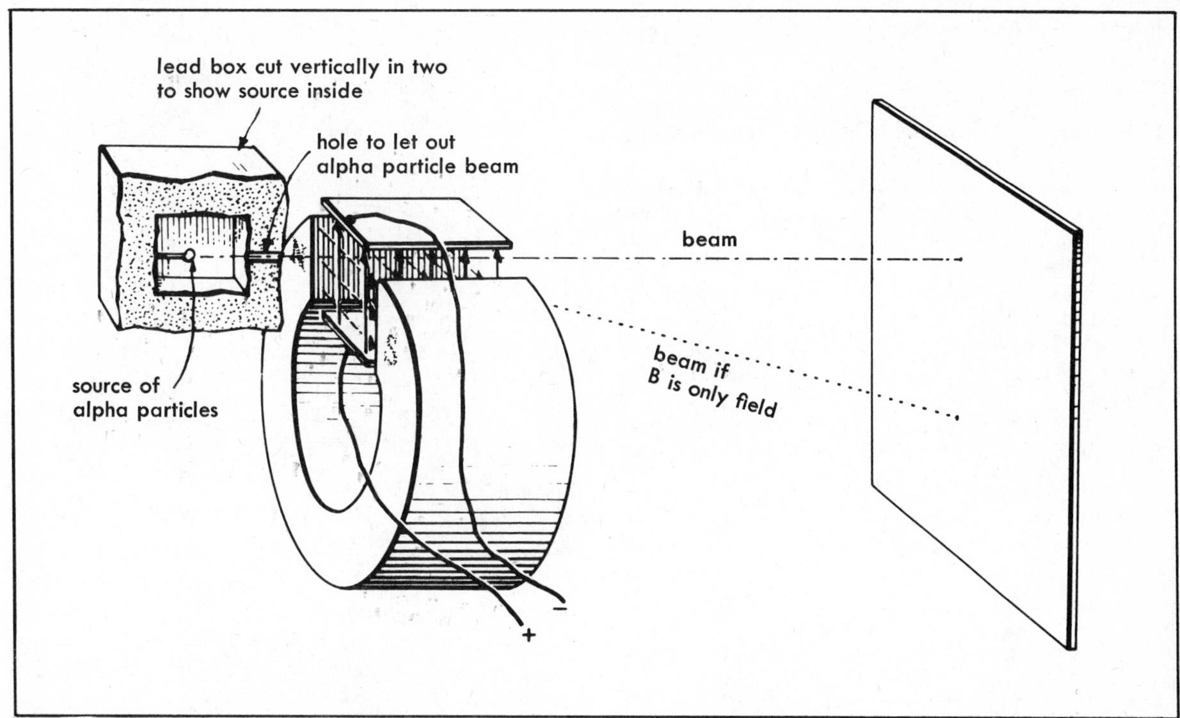

30–33. Measuring the speed of alpha particles. With a pair of metal plates placed horizontally in the tube we can apply an electric force equal and opposite to the magnetic force. Then the particles are not deflected, and their speed $v = \frac{E}{B}$. This figure is schematic. In a real experiment, we must change the dimensions to obtain known uniform electric and magnetic fields. Also, the apparatus is in a vacuum system to avoid scattering and energy loss by alpha particles hitting air molecules.

periment in the last section, we only mention the result. When we do this experiment using polonium as the source of alpha particles, we find that their momentum is $mv = 1.06 \times 10^{-19}$ kg-meters/sec.

Now, to obtain the mass of the alpha particle, we must measure the velocity. We could make this measurement by stopping the alpha particles with a retarding electric potential difference, thus determining their kinetic energy. This would require a potential difference of a million volts or so. But we can get the velocity more directly by applying an electric field across the motion of the alpha particles at the same time that we apply a magnetic one. We put on this electric field so that the electric force on the alpha particles is just opposite to the magnetic force. Then the net force on the moving particles is zero, and they move straight ahead, following the same path that they take in the absence of both fields (Fig. 30–33). The electric force on the particles is qE, and the magnetic force qBv; and when these forces balance, $qBv = qE$. The speed of the particles is therefore given by $v = \frac{E}{B}$, and since we know both the magnetic and the electric field, we know the answer. For polonium alpha particles the measured speed is $v = 1.6 \times 10^7$ meters per second. Consequently, the mass

$$\frac{mv}{v} = \frac{1.06 \times 10^{-19}}{1.6 \times 10^7} = 6.6 \times 10^{-27} \text{ kg}.$$

Within the experimental accuracy, this mass is almost exactly equal to the mass of a helium atom. It is thus natural to conclude that alpha particles are doubly charged helium ions. We can test this conclusion directly by placing a strong source of alpha particles in an evacuated glass tube. Such an experiment was done by Rutherford and Royds in 1908. After waiting for a sufficiently long time, they found a detectable amount of helium. Now, like Rutherford, we are ready to use alpha particles as probes to explore the structure of atoms.

FOR HOME, DESK, AND LAB

1. You are given a compass needle and a wire loop 2π cm in radius. You can regulate the current as you wish, and you can place the wire loop wherever you want. You are to determine the direction and magnitude of an unknown magnetic field at a definite point in a room.
   (a) How would you find the direction of the field to be measured?
   (b) How would you arrange the wire loop so that its magnetic field could cancel the unknown field?
   (c) If the current needed in your loop to cancel the unknown magnetic field is 6.0 amperes, how large is the magnetic field?

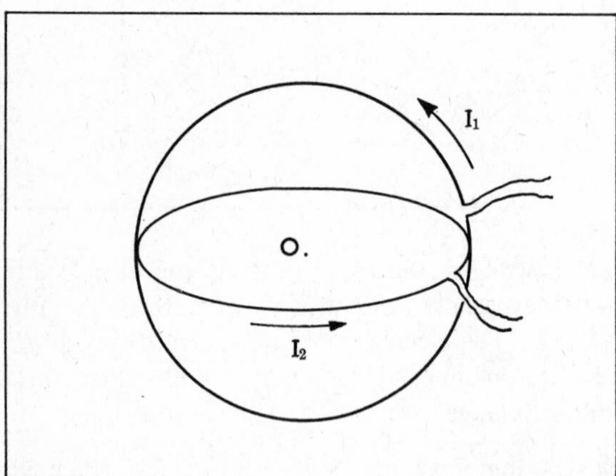

30–34. For Problem 2.

2. Two circular wire loops, each of radius 2π cm, are set up at right angles to each other with a common center (Fig. 30–34).
   (a) If $I_1 = 3.0$ amperes and $I_2 = 4.0$ amperes, what are the magnitude and direction of the magnetic field at the center O?
   (b) How is the field changed if we make $I_1 = 4.0$ amperes and $I_2 = 3.0$ amperes?

3. A uniform magnetic field $\vec{B}$ is perpendicular to the horizontal component of the earth's magnetic field $\vec{B}_e$ and points east.
   (a) The ratio $B/B_e = \sqrt{3}$; in which direction will a compass needle point?
   Note: the compass needle rotates in a horizontal plane.
   (b) If the compass needle points northeast, what is now the magnitude of $\vec{B}$?

4. Three circular wire loops with radii r_1, r_2, and r_2 are arranged as shown in Fig. 30–35. The two loops with I_1 and I_2 are in the same horizontal plane; and the third loop with current I_3 is perpendicular to the other two. The radii r_1 and r_2 are 5.0 cm and 15 cm, respectively.
   (a) If $I_3 = 20$ amperes and $I_2 = 10$ amperes, how big must I_1 be and in what direction, so that the magnetic field at O points directly out of the page?
   (b) What can you say about this value of B?

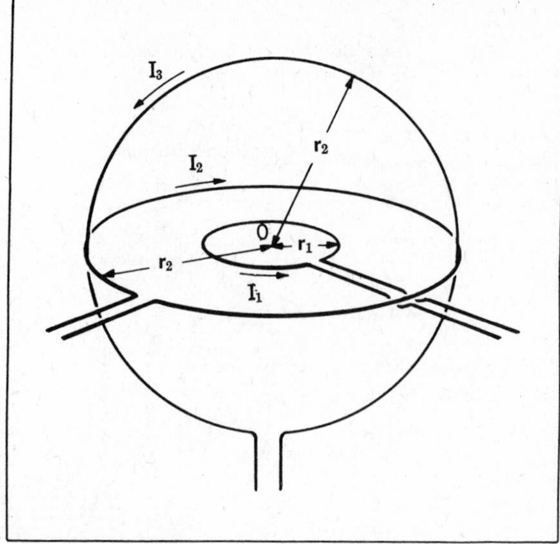

30–35. For Problem 4.

5. In Problem 4, how must the small loop be tilted and what current must it carry if the resultant magnetic field at the center is to be zero?

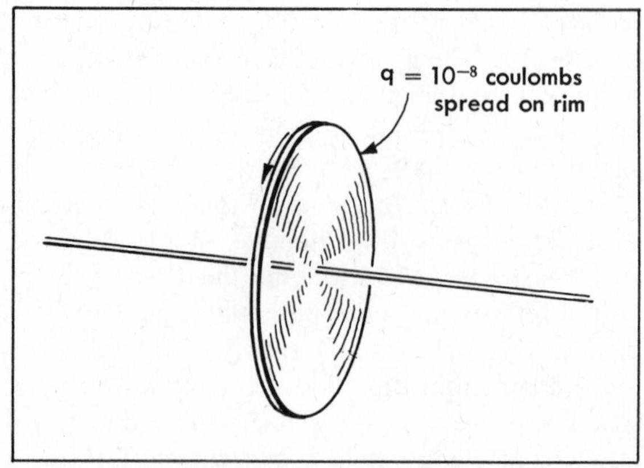

30–36. For Problem 6.

6. A ring 2π cm in radius is uniformly charged and is rotating about an axis through its center as shown in Fig. 30–36. If the total charge on the ring is $q = 1.0 \times 10^{-8}$ coulombs and the ring rotates at 100 revolutions per second, what is the magnetic field at the center?

7. Two very long straight parallel wires, one carrying 10 amperes and the other 20 amperes, are separated by a distance of 10 cm (Fig. 30–37). Find the magnitude and direction of $\vec{B}$ at the points P, Q, and R shown in the figure.

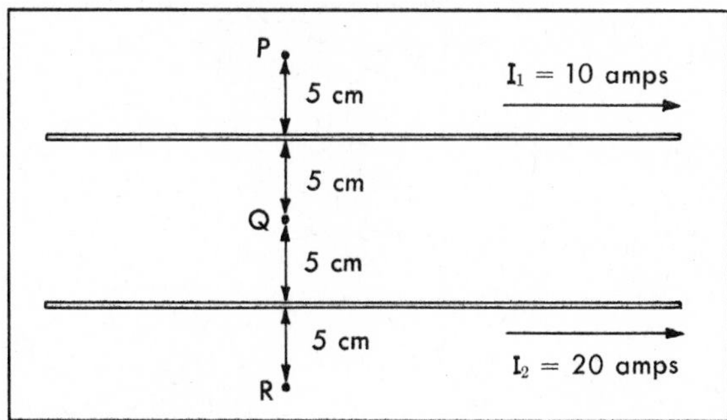

30–37. For Problem 7.

8. Suppose in Fig. 30–37 that the direction of I_2 is reversed. Find $\vec{B}$ (magnitude and direction) at the points P, Q, and R.

9. Refer to Fig. 30–37.

(a) Find the magnetic field produced by I_1 at a point on the wire which carries the current I_2.

(b) What is the force per meter acting on the wire carrying the current I_2?

(c) What do you think is the force per meter acting on the wire carrying I_1? Why?

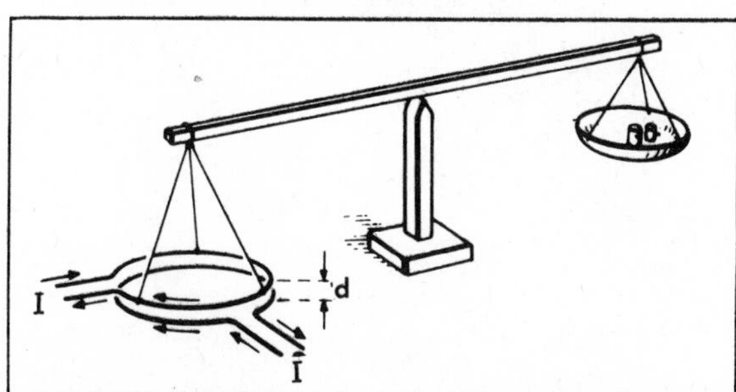

30–38. For Problem 10.

10. The two parallel circular loops of wire shown in Fig. 30–38 each have a radius $R = 20$ cm and are separated by a distance $d = 0.5$ cm. The bottom loop is held fixed and the top loop hangs from one end of the arm of an equal-arm balance. Since d is much smaller than R, the magnetic field produced by one loop at the other is practically the same as if both were long straight wires.

(a) If the current in each loop is 20 amperes, how big is the force of attraction of one loop for the other?

(b) How much additional mass m must be added to the right-hand balance pan to keep the loops separated by 0.5 cm when the currents are turned on?

(c) How can you use this device to measure an unknown current?

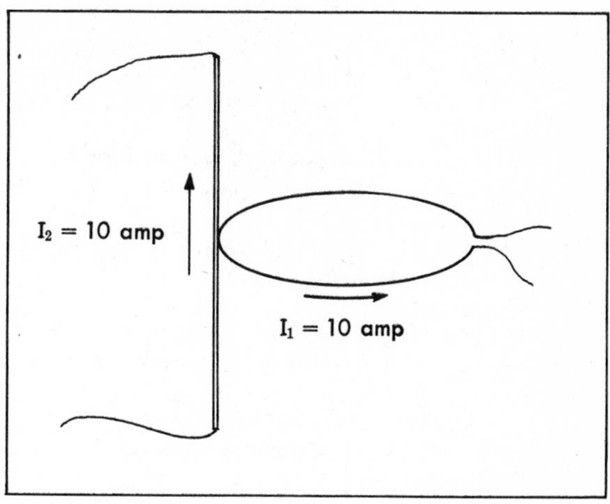

30–39. For Problem 11.

11. A circular loop of wire carries a current of 10 amperes (Fig. 30–39). A long straight wire also carrying a current of 10 amperes is placed parallel to the axis of the loop and passes through a point on the circumference. In what direction will a compass needle point if it is placed at the center of the loop?

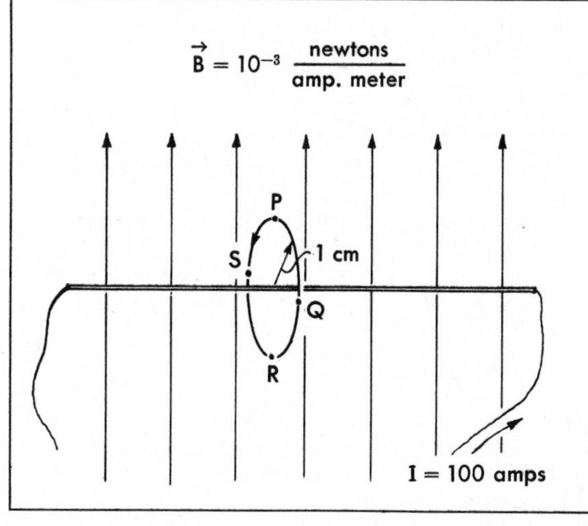

30–40. For Problem 12.

12. A long straight wire carrying a current $I = 100$ amperes is perpendicular to a uniform magnetic field of strength $B = 1.0 \times 10^{-3} \dfrac{\text{newtons}}{\text{ampere-meter}}$ (Fig. 30–40). What is the strength and direction of the resultant $\vec{B}$ field at the points P, Q, R, S on a circle of radius 1 cm around the wire?

13. A square coil 10 cm on a side carrying a current of 1.0 ampere is placed 10 cm from a long wire which also carries 1.0 ampere (Fig. 30–41).

(a) How does the force on AB compare with that on CD?

(b) Compute the net force on the coil.

14. A rubber band is covered with a conducting coating. Electrical connections are made to the rubber band so that a current runs through it (Fig. 30–42). What happens when it is placed in the magnetic field B shown in the figure?

15. The magnetic field inside a long solenoid is uniform and parallel to the axis of the solenoid.

(a) What is the force on a current-carrying wire inside the solenoid and parallel to the axis?

(b) What is the force on the wire shown in Fig. 30–43 which carries a current of 1.0 ampere, if the field B in the solenoid is $1.0 \times 10^{-2} \frac{\text{newtons}}{\text{ampere-meter}}$ and the length CD is 2 cm?

(c) How much mass m should be placed on the other end of the balance to keep it from tilting?

(d) Describe how you could use this set-up as an ammeter.

16. Two long parallel wires are placed perpendicular to a uniform magnetic field (Fig. 30–44).

$$B = 2 \times 10^{-7} \frac{\text{newtons}}{\text{ampere-meter}}.$$

A current $I = 1$ ampere runs in opposite directions along the wires. At what separation d will there be no net force on either wire?

17. (a) Show that a square loop of wire carrying a current will always tend to align itself in a magnetic field so that the plane of the loop is perpendicular to the field.

(b) What do the magnetic forces tend to do to the loop in this position? (Hint: draw a side view.)

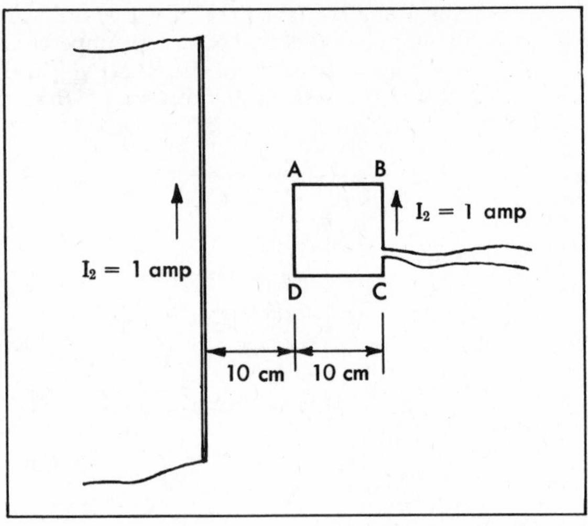

30–41. For Problem 13.

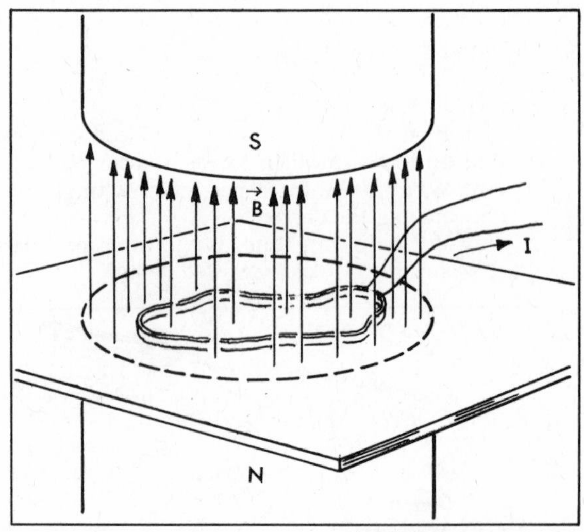

30–42. For Problem 14.

30–43. For Problem 15.

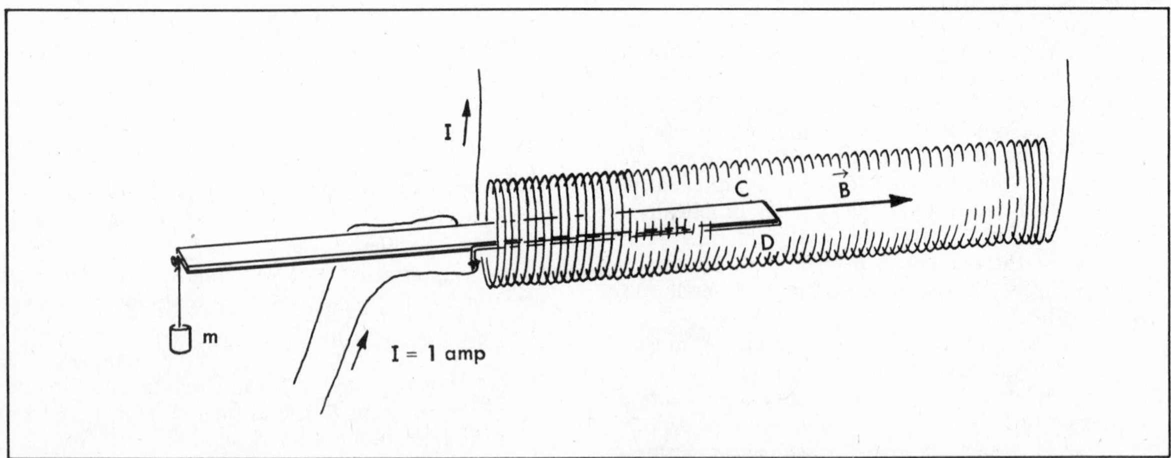

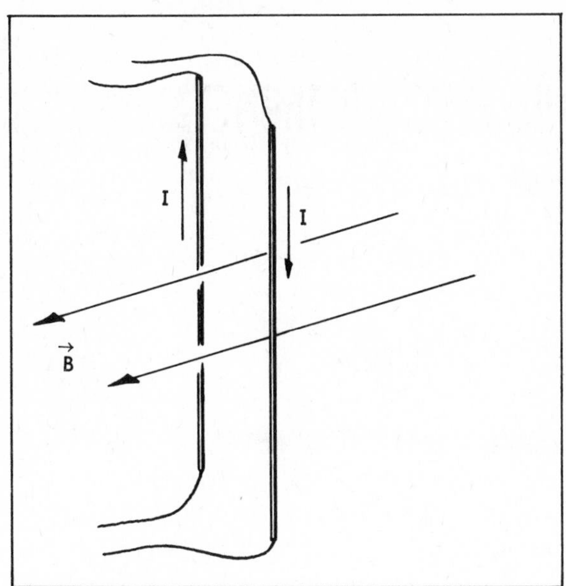

30–44. For Problem 16.

18. A singly charged helium ion which has been accelerated through an electric potential difference of 180 volts travels in a magnetic field of $2.00 \times 10^{-20} \frac{\text{newtons}}{\text{(elem. ch. /sec)(meter)}}$ on the arc of a circle of radius 0.031 m.

(a) What is its velocity?

(b) What is its mass?

19. Suppose we have a beam of electrons moving at a velocity $v = 3.00 \times 10^6$ m/sec and carrying a current of 1.00 microampere.

(a) How many electrons per second pass a given point?

(b) How many electrons are in 1.00 meter of the beam?

(c) What magnetic field does the beam produce at 1.00 m distance?

(d) What is the total force on all of the electrons in 1.00 m of the beam if it passes through a field of $0.10 \frac{\text{newtons}}{\text{ampere-meter}}$?

(e) What is the force on a single electron if you assume that each electron experiences the same force?

20. A beam of singly charged ions moves into a region of space where there is a uniform electric field $E = 1.0 \times 10^3$ newtons per coulomb and a uniform magnetic field

$$B = 2.0 \times 10^{-2} \frac{\text{newtons}}{\text{ampere-meter}}.$$

The electric and magnetic fields are at right angles to each other and both are perpendicular to the beam so that the electric and magnetic forces on an ion oppose each other. What is the speed of those ions which move *undeflected* through these crossed electric and magnetic fields?

21. The undeflected ions of Problem 20 are passed through a slit and move into a region where there is a uniform magnetic field $B = 0.09 \frac{\text{newtons}}{\text{ampere-meter}}$ at right angles to their motion. If the ions are a mixture of neon ions of mass 20 and 22 atomic mass units, how far apart will these ions land on a photographic plate after they have moved through a semicircle?

22. An electron is accelerated from rest through a potential difference of 2,000 volts. It then enters a region where there is a uniform magnetic field at right angles to its motion. The magnetic field is $1.00 \times 10^{-3} \frac{\text{newtons}}{\text{ampere-meter}}$.

(a) What is the period of the circular motion of the electron?

(b) What is the radius of the circle it moves in?

(c) If the accelerating potential difference were 8000 volts, what would the period and radius be?

23. A beam of charged particles, accelerated from rest by a potential difference of 320 volts enters a uniform magnetic field of strength $6.0 \times 10^{-4} \frac{\text{newtons}}{\text{ampere-meter}}$ at right angles to its initial direction of travel. The radius of the circle in which this beam moves is found to be 10.0 cm.

(a) What is the ratio of mass to charge of these charged particles?

(b) What kind of particles do you think they are?

FURTHER READING

BITTER, FRANCIS, *Magnets.* Doubleday, 1959: A Science Study Series paperback.

PAKE, GEORGE E., "Magnetic Resonance." *Scientific American*, August, 1958.

TAYLOR, LLOYD, *Physics, the Pioneer Science.* Dover, 1959 (Chapters 39, 42, and 43).

THOMSON. J. J., *Moments of Discovery.* Edited by G. Schwartz and P. Bishop. Basic Books, 1958 (pp. 913 ff.).

ELECTROMAGNETIC INDUCTION AND ELECTROMAGNETIC WAVES

CHAPTER 31

LOOKING BACK at the contents of the previous chapters, you will realize that we have dealt so far with electric fields produced by electric charges at rest, and with the magnetic fields produced by steady currents. Such fields are constant in time. We must again turn to experiment to learn what happens when electric and magnetic fields vary with time.

31–1. Induced Current and Induced EMF

What happens when electric circuits move in magnetic fields? Such motions result in changing relations between the circuits and the fields. We can understand the effect of these changes on the basis of what we already know about the motions of charges in magnetic fields. Later we shall see how this kind of change is related to changes of the fields themselves.

We have seen that there are magnetic fields around moving charges and that any electric charge moving across a magnetic field is acted on by a force perpendicular to its motion. Suppose that instead of running a current through a wire in a magnetic field and getting a force, we apply a force to a wire, dragging it across a magnetic field; will we get a current?

Take a big magnet and a single loop of wire with a current meter A, *but no battery*. Arrange them as in Fig. 31–1, so that part of the wire is in the magnet's field. Then drag the whole loop of wire steadily to one side. As we pull the loop of wire so that the length l is dragged at a steady speed across the magnetic field, the meter A shows a current running around the loop in the direction indicated. If we stop moving the loop, the current stops; and when we move the loop in the opposite direction the current runs the other way around the circuit.

It is not difficult to understand what is going on. The metal wire is full of electrons free to move along the wire. In dragging the wire l sideways we are moving these electrons across the magnetic field B — the green arrow in Fig. 31–1 shows the direction of this motion. Each of these elementary electric charges moving across the magnetic field experiences a force, perpendicular to its motion and to the field. This force there-

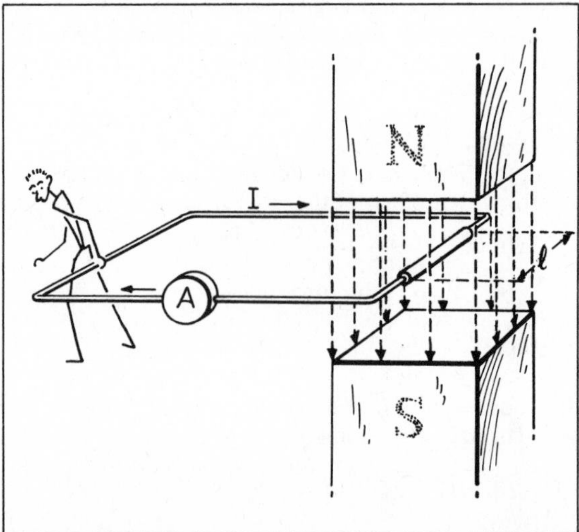

31–1. When we pull a wire loop so part of it passes through a magnetic field, a current flows in the loop. Because the wire l moves sideways, the electrons in it are moving across the magnetic field and are pushed along the wire by the magnetic forces.

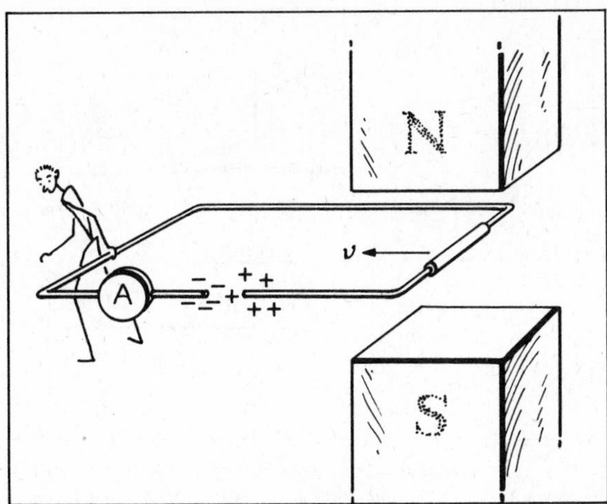

31–2. If there is a break in the loop, charges will build up at the break.

fore pushes each electron along the wire. So, as we drag the circuit across the field, the magnetic forces drive the whole horde of movable electrons along the wire — much as a battery there would drive them. And if the loop of wire is closed, a current is driven around it.* This is the essential principle of electric generators. Faraday discovered it when he looked for just such a "reverse effect" between magnets and currents. He knew that currents make magnetic fields, and he asked whether magnetic fields would make currents. Therefore he tried placing a loop of wire in a magnetic field. He found no effect until he moved the wire. Then he found the induced current resulting from the magnetic force on the moving electrons.

The current driven around the circuit depends on the resistance. If we add resistance we get less current, just as we do with a battery in the circuit. If there is a break in the wire, there is no current. Electrons will simply pile up on one side of the break and there will be a shortage of them at the other side (Fig. 31–2). Charges will build up near the ends of the wire until there is a potential difference across the break. Again, this is just what happens with a battery in an open circuit.

In fact, what we are really generating by moving the loop across the magnet's field is not a definite current — that depends on the resistance — but a definite EMF. If we put different resistors into the loop but always move the same length of wire through the given magnetic field at the same speed, we find that the current times the resistance of the circuit always stays the same. The value of I times R measures the induced EMF; which depends only on the motion through the magnetic field. We call this method of producing an EMF *electromagnetic induction.* When there is a complete circuit, the induced EMF forces an induced current to flow.

Electromagnetic induction of this kind is of basic importance in practical electric power generation. If we rotate a wire loop steadily in a uniform magnetic field (Fig. 31–3), we shall obtain an induced current that changes direction periodically. The single loop in the uniform field is an alternating-current generator. Other generators are usually fancier versions of the same thing.

*Of course the positive particles of the metal atoms are also dragged across the magnetic field, but as they are anchored and not free to move, the forces on them produce no current. If they *were* free to move, they would be driven the opposite way along the wire and would also contribute to the effects we are discussing.

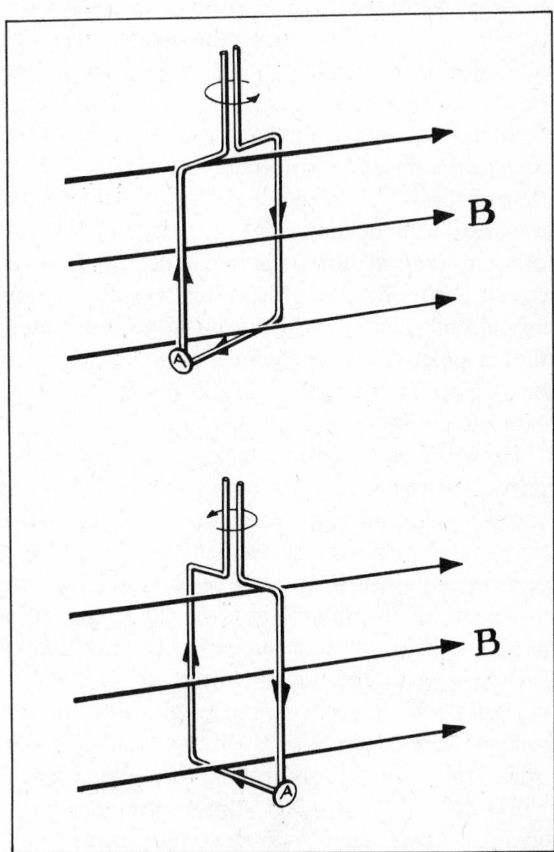

31–3. When a wire loop rotates in a magnetic field, the induced current flows alternately in opposite directions.

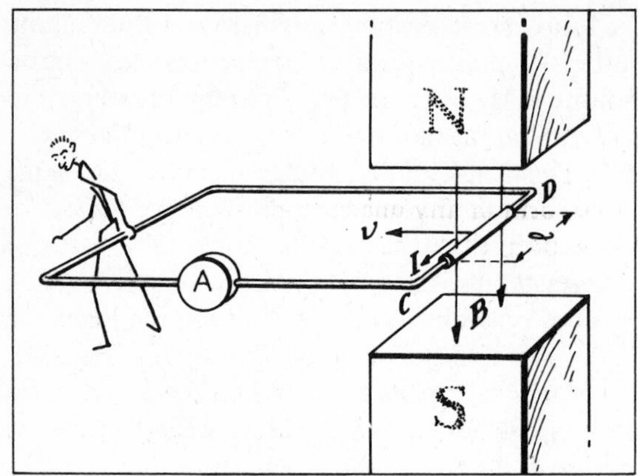

31–4. Direction of the induced current.

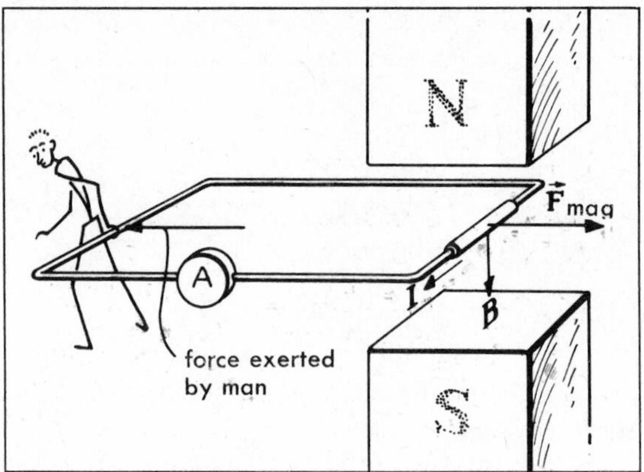

31–5. When we pull a wire loop through a magnetic field, the magnetic force on the induced current is opposite to the force we apply. We therefore must do work pulling the loop. We transfer energy into the circuit.

31–2. Direction and Magnitude of the Induced EMF

Study the diagram of Fig. 31–4 and apply your "right-hand rule" carefully to find which way the induced current will flow. The magnetic field B runs vertically down, from north to south pole faces of the magnet. Suppose we drag the wire l (the part of the loop that is in the region of B) across to the left. Then all the elementary charges in it are moving from right to left in a downward field B. A positive elementary charge moving in this way is therefore subjected to a magnetic force that pushes it out of the diagram toward you, and a negative elementary charge is pushed in the other direction along the segment CD into the paper. In either case the result will be to move any electric charges which are free to respond, so that a positive current comes along the segment of wire out of the paper. This is just what we find experimentally.

How big is this force on an electron? Any particle moving across the magnetic field with speed v experiences a force qvB. Since the charge on each electron is one elementary charge, each electron is pushed with the force $F_1 = vB$. As long as it is in the length l of the wire, the length in the magnetic field, the electron experiences this force.

Now we can find the EMF induced in the moving wire. If an electron moves through the distance l from one side of the magnetic field to the other, the energy transferred to it is given by the work $F_1 l = vBl$. In fact, this is the amount of energy transferred by the magnetic force to *any* elementary charge moving through a length l of the wire as it is dragged across the magnetic field.

The energy per elementary charge provided by a battery is what we mean by $\mathcal{E}$, the EMF of the battery. And the energy per elementary charge vBl provided by electromagnetic induction is the induced EMF between the ends of the length of wire l being dragged across the magnetic field. From the point of view of the rest of the circuit, the points C and D of the wire act like the terminals of a battery. Indeed, we could take away the magnet and replace the segment l of the wire by a battery with an EMF equal to vBl without affecting the current in the rest of the circuit.

31–3. Where Does the Energy Come From?

There is one big difference between the EMF supplied by a battery and the induced EMF that we have just found. The energy supplied to an elementary charge passing through a battery is supplied from stored chemical energy. The energy supplied per elementary charge passing through the length of the wire l that is dragged across the magnetic field comes in through the magnetic force. It is eventually supplied by us, through the force we exert in dragging the length of wire l sidewise across the magnetic field.

To see that we really supply the energy when we drag the loop through the magnetic field, let us suppose that the induced EMF, that is $\mathcal{E} = vBl$, drives a current I around the circuit. As this current passes through the length l of wire in the magnetic field, there is a magnetic force on the current in the direction perpendicular both to the current and to the field (Fig. 31–5). By looking at the direction of the current and the direction of the magnetic field, you can see that this force is opposite to the direction of motion of the wire across the field. The magnitude of the force is IlB. To move the wire at a constant speed we must exert a counter force of exactly the same magnitude. Consequently we do work feeding the energy into the circuit at the rate

$$F \times \frac{\text{distance}}{\text{time}} = IlBv.$$

Since vBl is $\mathcal{E}$, the induced EMF, and I is the current in the circuit, we are feeding energy into the circuit at the rate $I\mathcal{E}$. This is exactly the rate $I\mathcal{E}$ that the induced EMF feeds energy into the current. In place of a battery, *we* supply the power in exactly the right amount.

31–4. Relative Motion

Suppose that, instead of dragging a loop across a magnetic field at speed v, we drag a magnetic field across the same loop. We place the magnet on a cart moving at speed v to the right and hold the loop at rest with respect to the ground (Fig. 31–6). Then from the point of view of an observer on the ground, the magnet and its field are moving off to the right, while the wire loop is standing still. But to an observer on the cart the magnet is at rest and the wire loop is being dragged to the left. In his view the experiment is exactly the same as the first experiment that we did. He therefore expects to find the same induced EMF as before. When we measure it, we do find the same value. Apparently it is the relative velocity of the loop and magnet that determines the EMF.

From our experience with dynamics we know that Newton's laws hold in any frame of reference that does not accelerate with respect to the fixed stars. Consequently all dynamical behavior must fall into the same patterns in any unaccelerated frame of reference, and we would naturally expect that electromagnetic induction would take the same form in any unaccelerated frame. In detail, we expect that the whole system of loop and magnet can move at any constant velocity relative to the fixed stars without changing the induced EMF. Otherwise we could use the differences in the EMF to identify different frames of reference even though we know that mechanical behavior will not distinguish one from another.

Every day, on fast-moving trains and airplanes, motors and generators run. Although the results are not normally measured with great precision, they reveal *no* measurable differences in the effects observed. Carrying the whole apparatus in any direction, going fast or slow, does not seem to affect electromagnetic induction. The earth rushes around the sun at 30 km/sec, but we do not observe seasonal variation in electromagnetic induction. Instead, the EMF is unaffected. The induction works according to the relative motions of the moving parts.

We shall now assume that electromagnetic induction depends on relative motion alone, and in the next section we shall build that assumption into our description of induction. From that description and some other electrical laws, we can eventually make many predictions — including a prediction of the speed of light. That these predictions agree with experimental observations

31–6. We are standing on the ground watching the magnet move off to the right. To us, the loop is at rest. The observer on the cart sees the magnet at rest and the loop moving away to the left. Both observers read the same current on the ammeter. Apparently, it is the relative motion that counts.

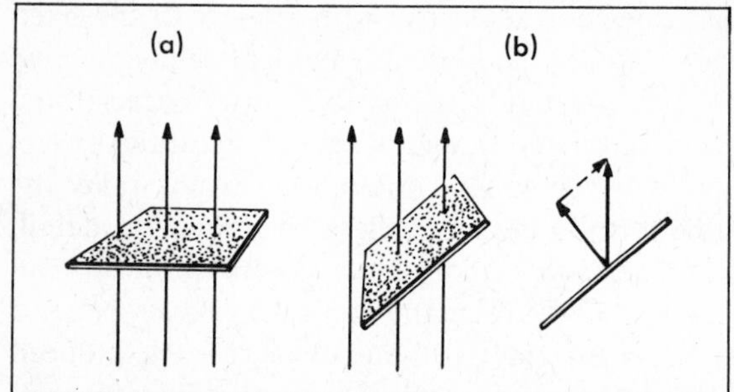

31–7. (a) The magnetic flux φ through an area is measured by field strength times area when the area is perpendicular to the field. (b) When the area is not perpendicular, we multiply the area times the perpendicular component of the B-field.

is still more evidence that the induced electromagnetic effects depend only on the relative motions. We can view the motions of wire loop and magnet in any unaccelerated frame of reference we want and predict the same correct results.

31–5. Magnetic Flux and the Induction Law

We can generate the same EMF in many ways. For example, consider another motion made with the same loop and magnet as before. Instead of moving the loop to the left as in Fig. 31–4, move it out of the page. If in this motion a segment of wire of length l' passes through the field B' at the speed v', we get an induced EMF equal to $B'l'v'$. We can easily adjust v' so that $B'l'v'$ is equal to Blv — or to any other induced EMF we wish. Indeed, there are all sorts of different relative motions of the loop and the magnet that result in the same induced EMF.

We shall now express the induced EMF — the energy fed in per unit charge — in a way that brings out the common feature of all the motions that generate the same EMF. This formulation will also make it possible to consider the electromagnetic induction that goes on when one part of the loop moves with respect to another, as, for example, when we have a flexible wire loop and change its shape [Fig. 31–9 (b)].

If we look back at the previous sections, we see that the induced voltage depends on the amount of the magnetic field moved in or out of the loop in a given time. We measure the amount of magnetic field through a given area as the field strength times that area as long as the area is perpendicular to the magnetic field. If the area is cocked at an angle so that the magnetic field does not run straight across it, less of the magnetic field passes

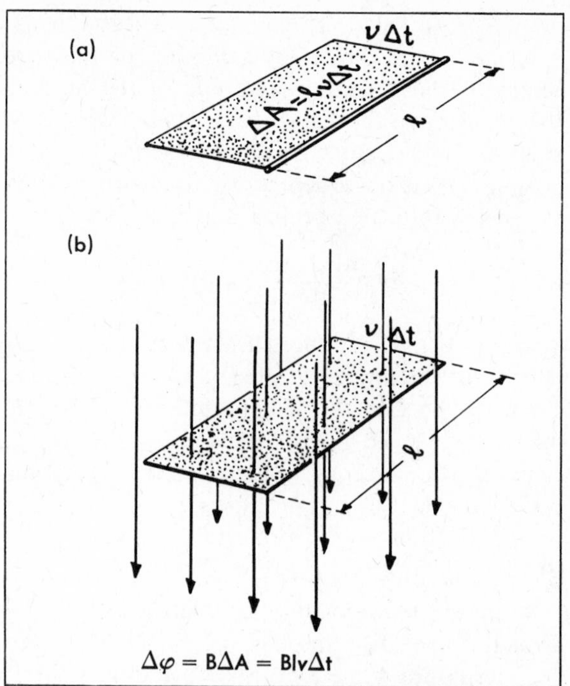

31–8. When a wire and a magnetic field move relative to one another with speed v, the wire sweeps out an area $lv\Delta t$ in the time Δt. The change in magnetic flux $\Delta\varphi$ is $Blv\Delta t$.

through it (Fig. 31–7). For example, when we look at an area which is parallel to the lines of magnetic field, no magnetic field crosses it. It is only the component of the magnetic field perpendicular to a given area that carries magnetic field through that area. So we shall measure the amount of magnetic field crossing an area as the product of the area times the perpendicular component of the magnetic field. This is called the *magnetic flux* φ through the area: $\varphi = B_{\perp}A$.

The induced EMF — the energy we feed in per elementary charge driven around the wire loop — can always be expressed as the rate of change of the flux of magnetic field through the loop. (Look at Fig. 31–5.) When we pull either the wire or the magnet so that one moves with respect to the other with the speed v, the area swept out by the length of wire l in time Δt is $lv\Delta t$, because $v\Delta t$ is the distance the wire travels sidewise with respect to the magnet in the time Δt (Fig. 31–8). When the magnetic field perpendicular to this area is of strength B, the magnetic flux moved out from the loop is $Blv\Delta t$. This is the change $\Delta\varphi$ in the flux. The rate of change of the flux φ is therefore

$$\frac{\Delta\varphi}{\Delta t} = Blv.$$

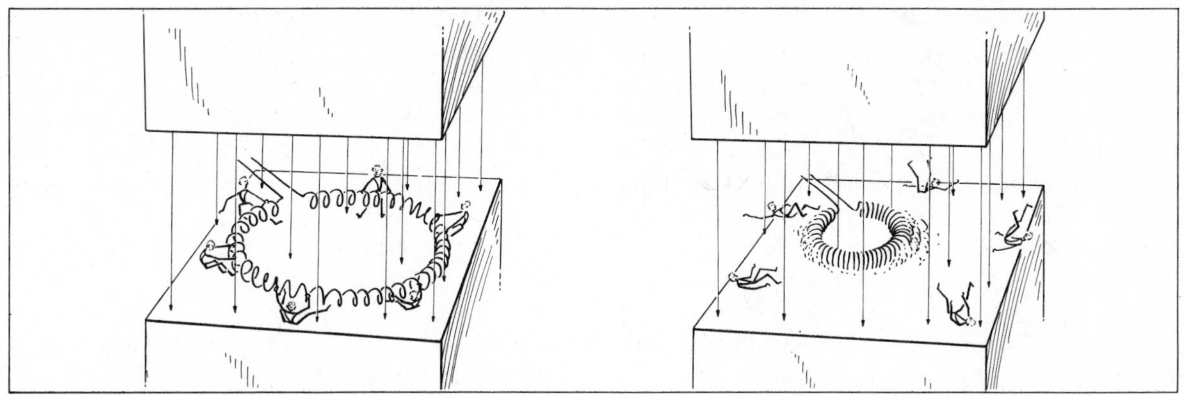

31–9 (a). The induced EMF depends only on the rate at which the flux changes $\Delta\varphi/\Delta t$, no matter how the change is produced. Here an extended spring is allowed to contract to a smaller area.

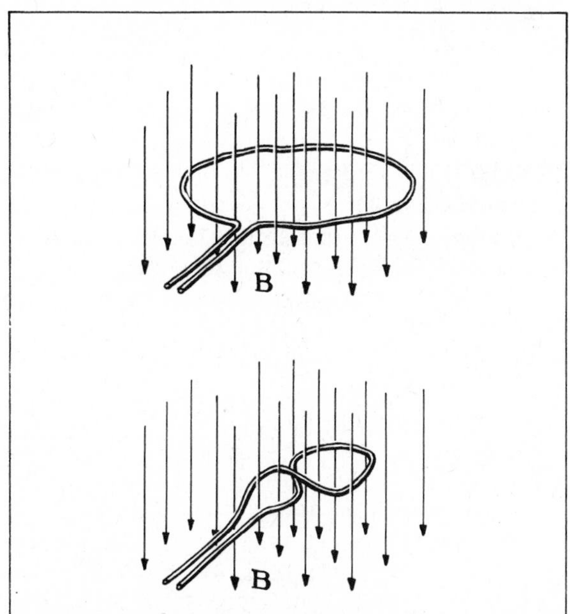

31–9 (b). Twisting a loop to a different area.

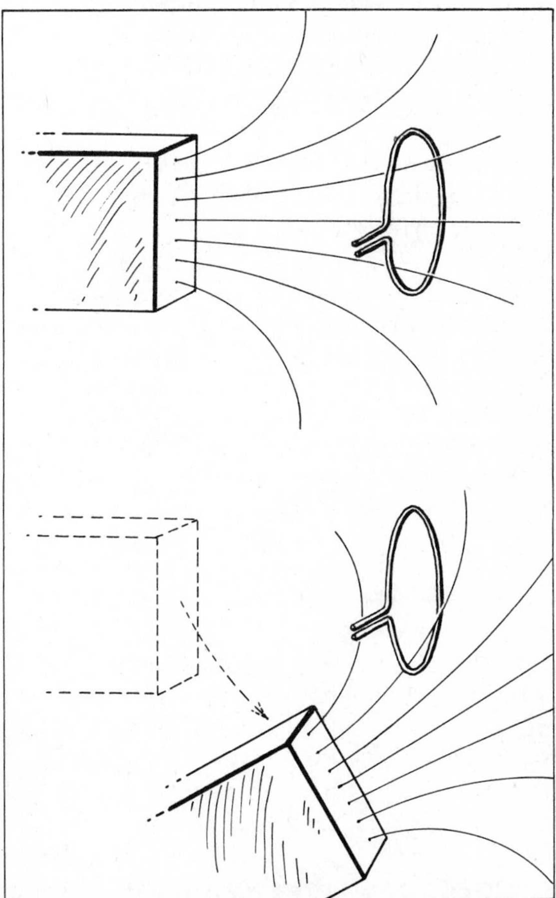

31–9 (c). Changing the direction of the magnetic field.

But this is exactly the expression for the energy fed in per elementary charge which we previously obtained by considering the magnetic force on the individual charges. The induced voltage $\mathcal{E}$ is therefore $\frac{\Delta\varphi}{\Delta t}$. This evaluation of the energy fed in per elementary charge as a rate of change of flux is the more general form that Faraday gave to the induction law. It applies equally well whether the circuit moves or the magnet moves.

You can test out the expression $\mathcal{E} = \frac{\Delta\varphi}{\Delta t}$ for the induced voltage by letting a wire spring change its size in a region of uniform magnetic field [Fig. 31–9 (a)], by twisting loops of wire into various areas in a magnetic field [Fig. 31–9 (b)], by moving a magnet around so that the flux changes because of the change in direction of the magnetic field passing through a loop [Fig. 31–9 (c)], or by any combination of these maneuvers. You will find that only the rate of change of flux counts in producing the induced voltage.

31–6. Electromagnetic Induction When the Circuits Do Not Move

Moving either a circuit or a magnet is not the only way to change the flux through a wire loop. We can leave the loop at rest and change the magnetic field through it by changing the electric currents that produce the field. In other words, we can use an electromagnet as in Fig. 31–10. Then by changing the current in the electromagnet at the right rate, we can make the magnetic flux through the loop change at any rate we want. If experiments with an electromagnet give the same EMF for the same rate of change of flux produced by moving a loop, it will make the picture of magnetic flux changes as the agents producing the effects on the wire loop much more convincing.

Experiments with electromagnets do show that we get just the same electromagnetic induction for the same change of flux whether that change is made by an obvious motion of the magnet or loop or by turning on or off a current. Any currents or magnets may be used to produce the flux through the loop, and the loop may be of any shape or size. A particular change of the magnetic flux gives the same effect independent of the mechanism which calls that flux change into being. The flux changes, therefore, are an essential link through which electromagnetic induction takes place.

31–7. Electric Fields Around Changing Magnetic Fluxes

A wire loop may enclose a magnetic flux in such a way that the magnetic field has appreciable strength only near its center (Fig. 31–11). The magnetic field then never seems to cross the wire at all. Nevertheless, a given rate of change of the magnetic flux results in the same electromagnetic induction. How does this happen?

In order to find out, let us examine the electrical mechanism that drives charges around any current loop which is standing still. In this case, the magnetic forces cannot be responsible because they act at right angles to the motion of the electrons and cannot feed in energy. Nevertheless, the electrons are being pushed around the circuit by some kind of electrical force.

What kind of electrical force pushes the electrons around? Notice that this force will start them moving even when they are at rest. Notice also that it will feed energy to them. Apparently this force comes from an electric field, acting on the charges. When there is a battery in the circuit the electric field arises from the charges forced onto the battery terminals and distributed along the wires. When the driving mechanism is electromagnetic induction there is also an electric field, an E-field, pushing the electrons around. Let us accept that for a moment. Then we can ask: how big is the electric field which arises

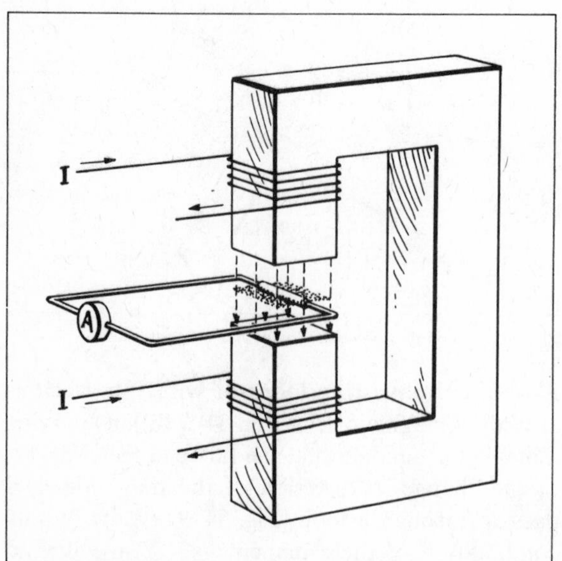

31–10. We can change the magnetic flux by using an electromagnet and changing the current in its coils.

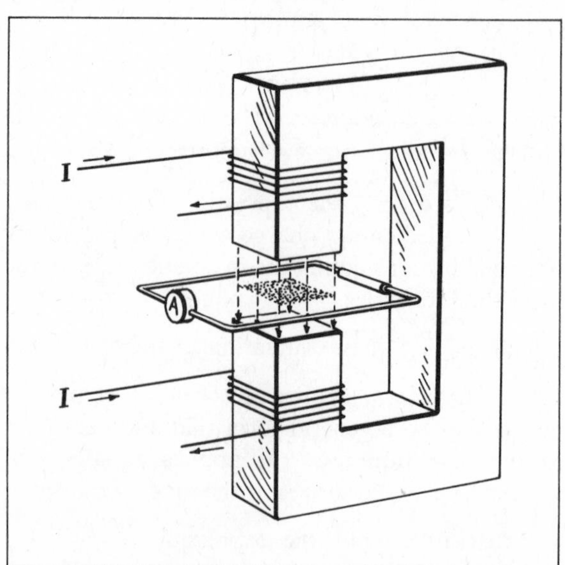

31–11. An EMF is induced in a wire loop even though the region of changing flux is entirely inside the loop.

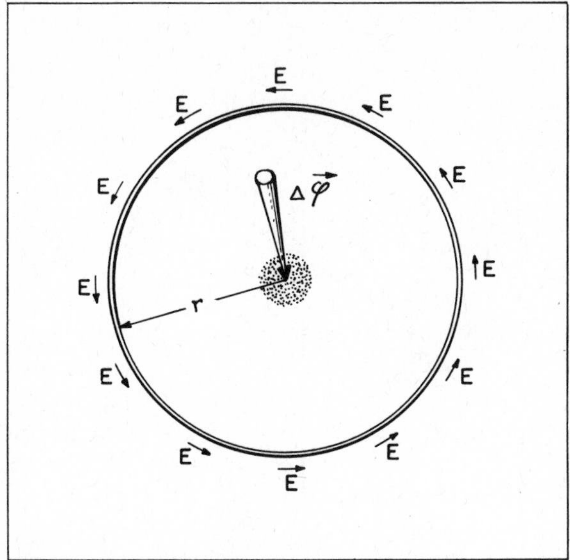

31–12. When the flux changes through the shaded area, the magnitude of the E-field that circles around it must be the same anywhere on the wire. Therefore an elementary charge must receive energy E2πr as it is pushed around the wire.

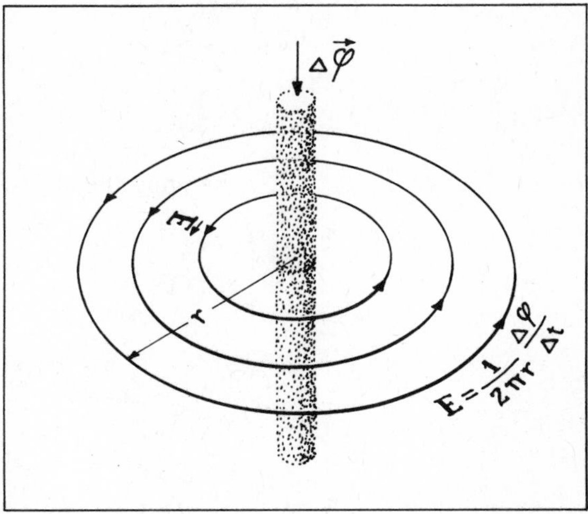

31–13. The induced electric field around a changing magnetic flux runs around in circles. Its magnitude varies inversely with the distance.

from a change of the magnetic flux through a circuit?

Let us take a nice symmetrical example in order to do an easy calculation. Take a circular wire loop of radius r, and assume that the magnetic flux through this circle is being changed by changing the magnetic field through a much smaller concentric circle (Fig. 31–12). In this situation, the electric field pushing charge along the wire at one point should be just the same as the electric field pushing it along the wire at any other point. The electric field produced by the change in magnetic flux must circle that flux, pointing along the wire. As an elementary charge is moved all the way around the wire loop, it is therefore pushed by the field of constant strength E through the distance $2\pi r$. Consequently, it must receive from the induced electric field the energy $E \times 2\pi r$. This energy per elementary charge is the induced voltage — that is, $\mathcal{E} = E2\pi r$. But we already know that the induced voltage is given by the rate of change of the flux: $\mathcal{E} = \frac{\Delta\varphi}{\Delta t}$. So the electric field is related to the rate of change of the flux by

$$E2\pi r = \frac{\Delta\varphi}{\Delta t}.$$

Notice that this electric field has constant magnitude around any circle of radius r. Also, if we have a wire loop of greater radius, the electric field at that greater radius must be smaller since the product of the field times the circumference of the circle must come out to the same induced voltage — to the same value of $\frac{\Delta\varphi}{\Delta t}$. In summary, the induced electric field around the changing flux therefore must run around in circles, and the magnitude of this induced field must decrease inversely with the distance away from the central region (Fig. 31–13).

We have just brought in a completely new kind of electric field, one that circles around instead of starting and stopping on charges. This may look like a desperate attempt to save an obviously wobbly theory. We invented this new kind of field solely to make sense out of the observation that energy is fed in and drives currents around any loop through which magnetic flux is changing. Is there any reality to this new electric field — a reality that we can test independently? The answer is "yes." The electric field is really there, for we can shoot individual charged particles into the region around a changing magnetic flux, and by following their paths we can see that they are indeed acted upon by just this electric force. There is even one modern high-energy accelerating machine which speeds up the individual charged particles to high energies by using exactly this

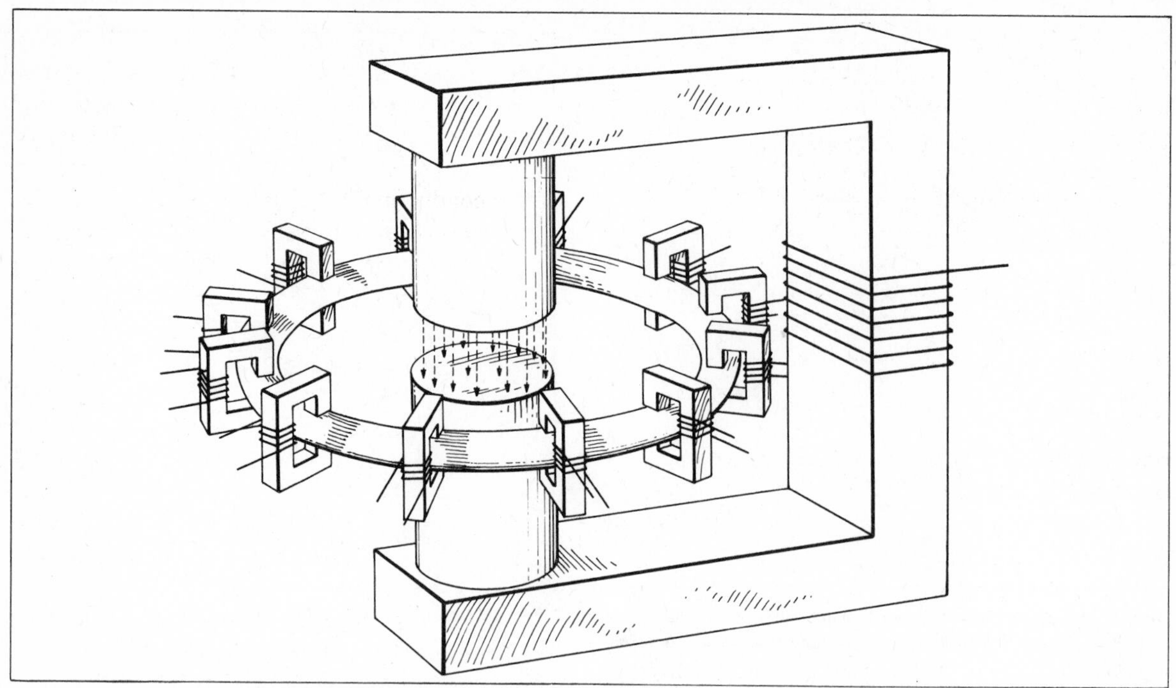

31–14. A schematic diagram of a betatron. The changing flux in the center produces an electric field which accelerates electrons. The electrons are made to move in circular paths by the outer ring of magnets. We correctly predict the paths from the local magnetic field for deflection and from the induced electric field giving the acceleration along the path.

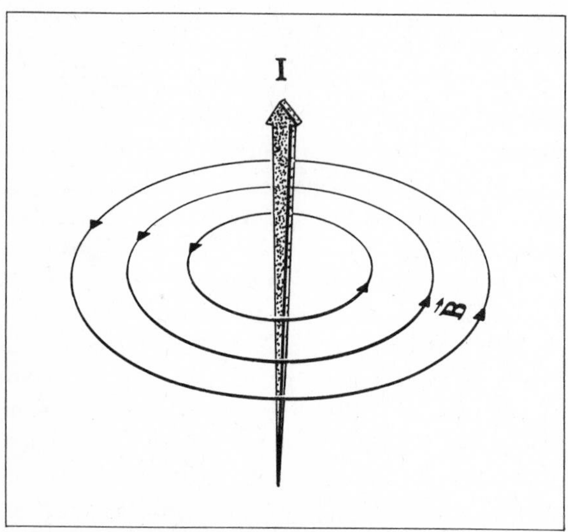

31–15 (a). The magnetic field of an electric current circles the current, falling off in magnitude as 1/r.

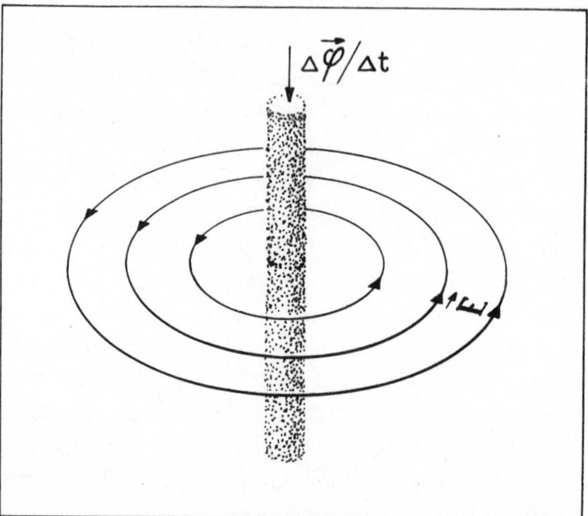

31–15 (b). Similarly the electric field around a changing magnetic flux circles the flux and falls off as 1/r. The electric field extends far beyond the region of this change.

electric force. In a betatron, electrons in an evacuated ring are caused to rush around a changing magnetic flux (Fig. 31–14). They speed up in exactly the way we predict from the action of the circular electric field that arises from electromagnetic induction.

The electric field which surrounds (but is well away from) a changing magnetic field may still appear strange. Perhaps the situation will seem more reasonable if we think for a moment about the magnetic field around an electric current (Fig. 31–15). This magnetic field circles the electric current and falls off inversely with the distance. Also, its strength is proportional to the rate of transfer of electric charge. Similarly, a changing magnetic flux acts as a kind of "magnetic current" around which an electric field is produced. Like the magnetic field around a current of moving charged particles, the *E*-field around the changing magnetic flux falls off inversely as the distance from the changing flux. Also, its strength is proportional to the rate of change of magnetic flux. This rate of change of the magnetic flux is the strength of the "magnetic current."

31–8. Direction of Induced Electric Fields

To determine the direction of circulation of an induced electric field E around a changing flux $\Delta\varphi$, let us go back to the experiment of Section 31–1. When we pull a wire loop out of a magnetic field as in Fig. 31–16 (a), we know the direction of the induced voltage and of the induced current. The induced current goes around as indicated in the figure and the induced *E*-field as seen in the wire must go round the same way to drive it. By pulling the loop out of the magnetic field we are diminishing the magnetic flux φ passing down through the loop. The change in flux $\Delta\varphi$ therefore points upward [Fig. 31–16 (b)]. If we look down on the loop, the induced current generated by this change in flux runs around clockwise, and so must the induced electric field. The same thing happens if the magnet is an electromagnet and we turn off the downward field. Indeed, whenever the change in flux is toward us, the induced *E*-field around it is clockwise; and if the change in flux is away from us, the induced field runs counterclockwise from our point of view. You can check this conclusion on any example of changing flux and induced electric field. All experiments agree with it.

Let us look again at Fig. 31–1. Notice there that the induced current produces a magnetic field down through the loop of wire. Consequently, there is an induced change of flux through the loop which tends to offset the change of the flux of the field from the magnet. Also, if we think of the induced current in the loop as making a magnet, we see that this induced magnet points down through the loop with its north pole near the south pole of the big magnet, and its south pole near the big magnet's north pole. The two magnets attract each other. By working against this attraction as we drag the loop out of the magnetic field of the big magnet we feed energy into the loop. This is another way of describing the mechanism of providing the induced EMF.

This analysis gives us a general method for determining the direction of induced electromagnetic effects. Whenever we bring a magnet and a conducting loop toward each other, the induced *E*-field in the loop will generate a current in the direction that makes a repelling magnet of the loop. You must therefore force the magnet and the loop together, feeding in the needed energy to drive the induced current. On the other hand, if a magnet and a loop are pulled apart, the loop will always become an attracting magnet and again we must do work against this attraction to drive the induced current.

We have just seen that the induced electric field is always in a direction that causes an induced flux through the loop opposing the over-all change in flux. This observation is often called Lenz's law, after the Russian physicist Lenz. As we have seen, Lenz's law is related to the flow of energy. If the induced electromotive force or the induced fluxes and magnets were oriented in the opposite direction, we would have an absurd situation in which a magnet moving toward a loop would be *attracted* by the current it induced in the loop. That attraction would speed up the approach, making still bigger induced currents, taking a still bigger flow of energy both into the motion and

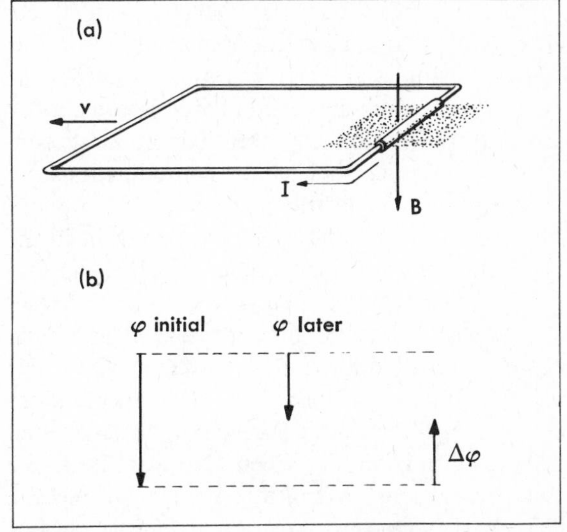

31–16 (a). When we pull a wire loop out of a magnetic field, the induced electric field drives a current in the direction indicated. (b) We are reducing the amount of downward flux, so the change in flux $\Delta\varphi$ is upward toward us. As we look at this $\Delta\varphi$ pointing at us, the E-field circulates around it clockwise.

into the magnetic field of the induced current. All this energy would come from nowhere. So Lenz's law is really an expression of the conservation of energy, telling us that induced electric fields deal with known sources of energy and do not derive energy from nowhere.

31–9. Self-Induction and Electric Oscillators

A potential difference V applied across the ends of a wire results in an electric field which accelerates electrons in the wire. By means of the electric field, the energy V is provided per elementary charge moving past any point in the wire. As the electrons move around, this energy is dissipated as heat, and at the same time the motions give an electric current $I = V/R$, where R is the resistance of the wire.

We can rewrite the last equation as $V = IR$. Now on the left we have the energy provided per elementary charge and on the right we have the energy that goes into heat per elementary charge. The expression IR always gives the heat dissipated per elementary charge. If the electrons move faster, the current I increases and the kinetic energy of the electrons increases. Therefore, more energy is dissipated as heat in the wire. Each elementary charge is picking up more energy from the electric field and as it collides with the atoms of the wire it transfers this greater energy into thermal energy.

On the other hand, the energy provided per elementary charge need not come solely from the source of potential difference applied across the ends of the coil. For example, suppose that V arises from charges concentrated on large conductors. From the same concentrations of charge, the same electric field is always produced in the coil. In addition, when the current in the coil is changing, an induced electric field is also present. The changing current in the coil causes a changing magnetic flux through it, and the changing flux induces an electric field which acts on the current. Since this field may induce changes in the current, the whole effect is often called self-induction. When the current in the coil rises, the increasing flux induces an electric field in the opposite direction from the current (Fig. 31–17). This induced field must be subtracted from the electric field of the charges at the ends of the wire to get the electric field which is causing the current and actually feeding energy into heat. Just as the electric field from the charges at the ends of the wire times the length of the wire gives us the applied potential difference, so the induced electric field times the length of the wire gives us the induced EMF. The effective potential difference which accounts for the energy per elementary charge fed into heat is the difference between the potential applied across the ends of the wire and the induced EMF. Consequently, the heat dissipated per elementary charge is given by

$$V - \mathcal{E},$$

where $\mathcal{E}$ is the induced potential arising from the rate of change of the flux. As always, this thermal energy yielded per elementary charge is given by IR. Consequently,

$$V - \mathcal{E} = IR.$$

When the current is steady, $\mathcal{E} = 0$ and this last equation becomes $V = IR$. All the energy per elementary charge supplied by the applied potential difference V at the ends of the wires is dissipated in heat. But when the current is changing, we see that only a part of the energy V per elementary charge goes into heat; the rest goes into changing the current and thus building up the magnetic fields. How much energy goes into building up the magnetic fields is measured by $\mathcal{E}$ — that is, by the rate of change of the flux.

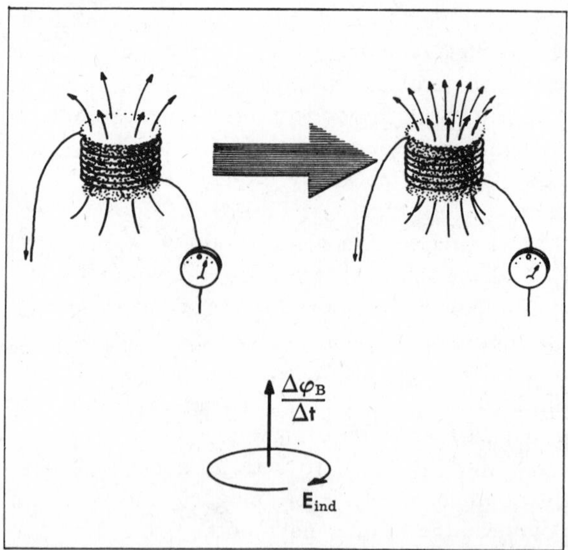

31–17. While the current increases, the flux increases. Consequently an electric field is induced which opposes the electric field of the battery.

A crude analogy may help us to understand what is happening. When we push a mass through the air at steady speed, all the energy fed in by the force we exert goes into heating up the air. But if we push a little bit harder, the mass will speed up. While the mass speeds up, only a fraction of the energy goes into heating up the air; the rest of it goes into increasing the kinetic energy as the mass picks up speed. In this case, the force we apply is the energy fed in per unit distance, and it may be considered to be analogous to the applied potential difference V which represents the energy fed in per unit charge. The kinetic energy that the mass gains per unit distance may be thought of in analogy with the gain in magnetic energy per unit charge passing through our coil. It is because of this analogy that the applied potential difference and the induced EMF are sometimes called electromotive forces, although they are really energies per unit charge.

In the analogy, when there is no viscous drag on the mass, the external force feeds all the energy directly into the kinetic energy of the mass. In the same way, when there is extremely low resistance in our circuit, the applied potential difference feeds energy exclusively into the magnetic field surrounding the coil. In the analogy, if the external force is removed from the mass after it is set in motion, the mass will continue to move. In fact, in order to remove the kinetic energy, we must exert a counter force. In the same way, in our circuit, if the external potential is removed, the current will continue to flow; and there must be an EMF in the opposite direction through which the magnetic energy is removed from the field as the current decreases.

In the mechanical system, by using a spring to exert a force on the mass, we can get the mass to oscillate back and forth. First the spring exerts a force in one direction, accelerating the mass, feeding in kinetic energy. Then, after the spring passes through its equilibrium position, it exerts a force in the opposite direction, taking the kinetic energy out of the motion of the mass and storing it in potential energy of the spring. The mass on the spring will oscillate back and forth. We can make an electric oscillator in an analogous way. In addition to the coil in which we can store up the magnetic energy — the energy which acts like the kinetic energy of the mass — we must introduce a springy electric potential energy.

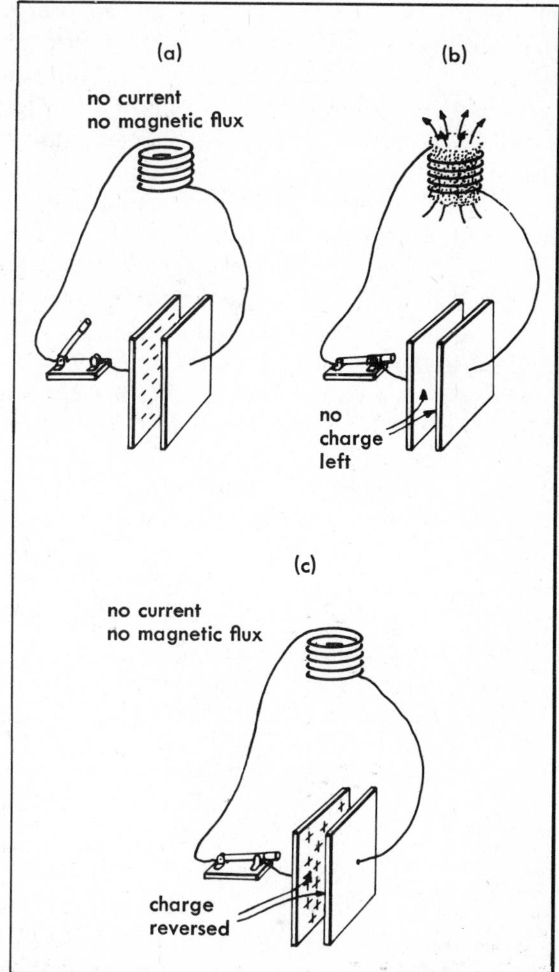

31–18. (a) We begin by charging a pair of parallel metal plates with the switch open. (b) After the switch is closed, the potential difference between the plates drives a current through the coil, as the plates discharge. When the maximum current is flowing, the potential energy of the charges has been transferred into magnetic energy. (c) As the magnetic flux begins to decrease, an induced electric field continues to drive the current in the same direction. Charges of opposite sign build up on the plates.

We can make a springlike electric potential by connecting the coil to two parallel conducting plates, as in Fig. 31–18. We charge the plates with the switch open. Then we close the switch. The electric potential energy of the charges concentrated on the plates will drive a current around through the loop. As the plates discharge and the electric potential energy decreases, the magnetic energy of the current passing through the loop will increase. When the plates are discharged and the electric potential energy has disappeared, the current and the magnetic energy will be at the maximum value. After this, the magnetic energy in the coil will be fed back into the circuit through the induced electric field. This field, as you can easily check up, now drives the current on in the same direction. Consequently, charges will be forced onto the plates at the ends of the circuit, and an electric potential difference will be built up there in the opposite direction from the original potential difference. All the magnetic energy in the coil will come back out and be transferred to electric potential energy when the plates are fully charged in the opposite direction.

The process does not stop when the plates are fully charged. The magnetic field continues to change, passing through zero and building up in the opposite direction. The current reverses. The electric potential energy is fed back into the circuit, and the magnetic energy builds up again. The whole process repeats again and again. We have made an electrical pendulum which will oscillate like a mass on a spring.

There is always some resistance in the wires of our circuit. Some energy is always dissipated in heat as the current sloshes back and forth through the coil. Each time charges are driven onto the plates, the maximum charge is slightly smaller. Each time the current rushes through the coil, its maximum value decreases a little bit. Gradually all the energy is transferred from electrical potential and magnetic energy into heat. This, of course, is the same thing that happens with a mechanical oscillator. As the mass moves back and forth through the air, it gradually loses its potential and kinetic energy into the random motions of the molecules of the gas.

Electric oscillators of the kind that we have just described are the basic element in radio transmitters and in radio receivers. By selecting plates and coils of different sizes, we can change the "spring" of the potential and the "inertia" of the current through the coil. We can even adjust plate size or coil dimensions while the oscillator is working. In this way we can tune to oscillations of any desired frequency. To keep an electric oscillator going in a radio transmitter, we must feed in some energy periodically from an outside source that gives a little boost to the current as it goes in the right direction. The power used by a radio transmitting station is used to maintain the oscillations despite heat losses and despite the loss of the energy which is radiated away from the oscillating circuit in the form of electromagnetic waves. The oscillating circuit in a radio receiver is driven by oscillating electric fields in the radio signal itself as it goes through space, and the power used in the radio receiver need not come from any other source, as those of you who have made batteryless radios know.

31–10. Magnetic Fields Produced by Changes of Electric Flux

A changing magnetic flux — a region with a changing B-field through it — generates an induced electric field around it. The E-field is much like the magnetic field B around a current. What happens around a region with a changing E-field through it — that is, what happens around a changing electric flux? Does it generate a magnetic field that goes around it, just like the one around a current of moving electric charges?

There is a way of showing, by direct experiment, that this is actually so. Suppose that we charge two parallel conducting plates so that they carry equal charges of opposite sign. Between them there is a practically uniform electric field (Fig. 31–19). Now imagine that we suddenly turn on a strong X-ray source near the plates. The air in the gap between them becomes ionized and the ions begin to move, carrying electric charges from one plate to the other until the plates are dis-

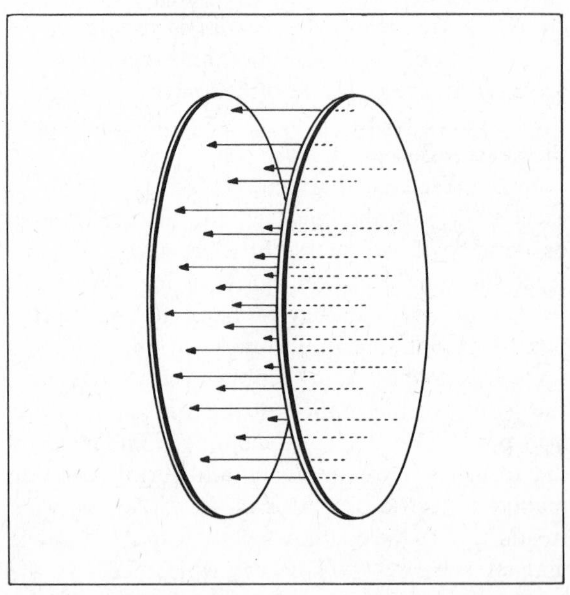

31–19. There is a nearly uniform electric field between two charged metal plates.

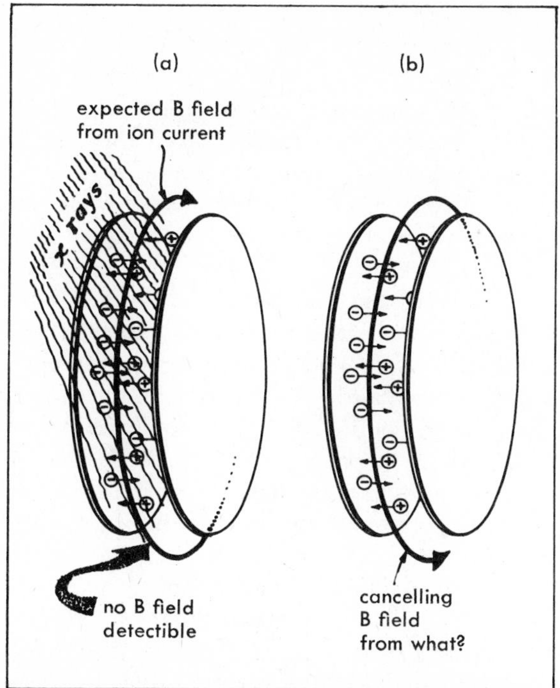

31–20. (a) When the air between the plates is ionized, a current flows, and we would expect to find a magnetic field circling the gap between the plates. A magnetic field detector, however, sees nothing. (A practical *B*-field detector would probably be a small coil of many turns connected to a sensitive ammeter or amplifier. This would actually detect *changes* of field — which would be just as useful to us.) (b) Consequently there must be a canceling magnetic field in the opposite direction. This canceling magnetic field arises from the changing electric field between the plates.

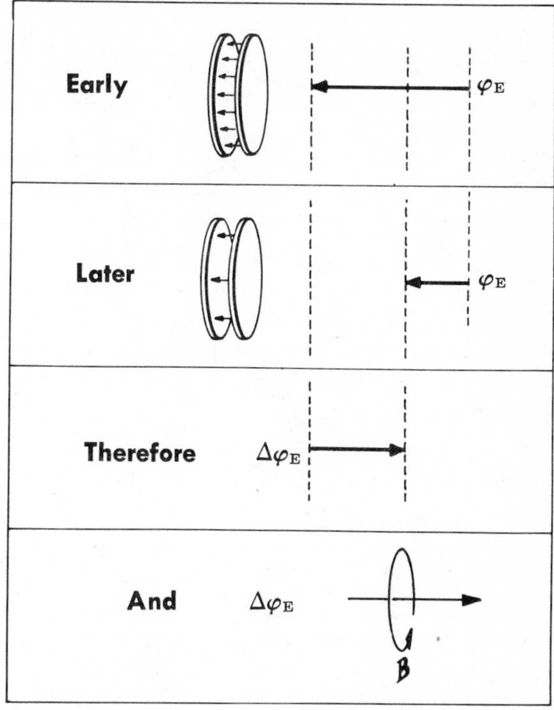

31–21. When there is a change of electric flux, a magnetic field is induced whose magnitude is proportional to the rate of change of flux. The direction of the magnetic field is the same as that from a current flowing in the direction of the flux change.

charged. While this happens, there is an electric current flowing in the gap from the positive to the negative plate. This current, as we know, should produce a magnetic field whose lines encircle the current, as indicated in Fig. 31–20.

If, however, we try to measure this magnetic field by placing a detector a little distance beyond the edges of the plates where the large arrow is in Fig. 31–20, we do not find anything, no matter how sensitive our detector is.

Since we know that a magnetic field must be produced by the current, we are obliged to conclude that this field is exactly canceled by an equal and opposite magnetic field arising from some other source. The only other significant thing, besides the flow of charges, that happens during the discharge of the capacitor, is a *change in the electric field between the plates.* Thus the additional magnetic field, the field which cancels the magnetic field of the current, must be due to this change of electric flux.

Our hunch that changing electric fields produce magnetic fields is correct. Moreover, we now see that a decrease of electric flux, such as that occurring in the gap during the discharge, is magnetically equivalent to a current flowing from the negative to the positive plate. The equivalent current producing the magnetic field is in the direction of the *change* of the electric flux (Fig. 31–21). Also, the magnitude of the magnetic field must depend on the *rate of change* of electric flux. If the ionization current is small, the electric flux changes slowly; if the ionization current is large, the electric flux changes rapidly. A slowly varying electric flux produces the small magnetic field that cancels the field of a small ionization current. A fast-varying electric flux produces the large magnetic field that cancels the field of a large ionization current. Consequently, the magnetic field from the flux change is proportional to the rate of change of the electric flux.

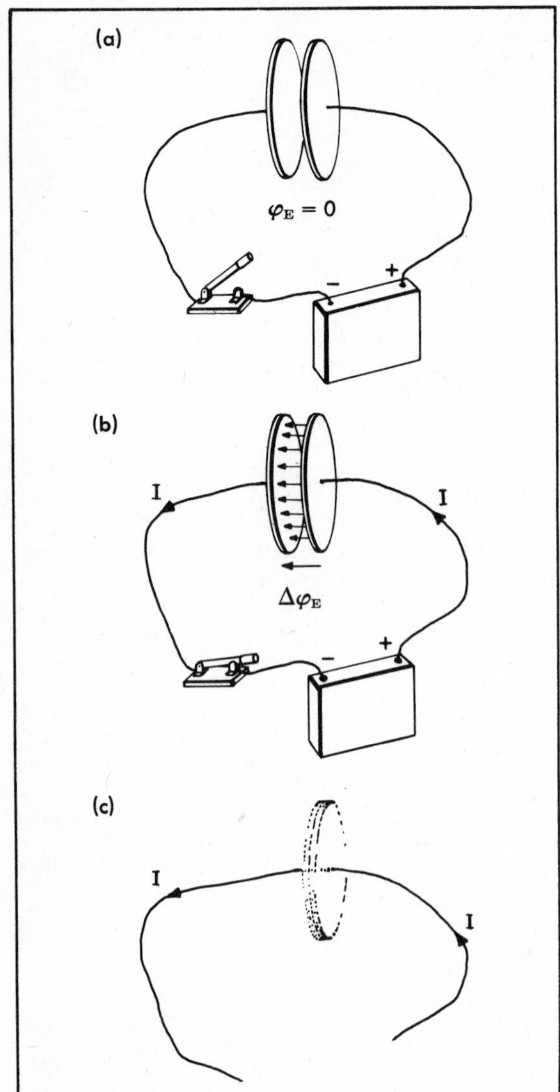

31–22. (a) The conducting plates are connected to a battery through a switch. (b) We close the switch and current flows, charging up the plates and increasing the electric flux between them. The magnetic field is just the same as if the changing flux were a continuation of the current in the gap. (c) If we fill in the gap with a conductor, we get the same magnetic effect.

Suppose now that we connect the conducting plates through a switch to a battery (Fig. 31–22). When we close the switch, current flows from the positive battery terminal to one plate and from the other plate to the negative battery terminal, until the plates are fully charged. At the same time the electric flux in the gap *increases* from zero to the final value. This change of the electric flux produces the same magnetic field as a current flowing from the positive to the negative plate, and therefore in the same direction as the real current in the wires. We may therefore think of the change of the electric flux as the continuation through the gap of the real current in the wires. Experimentally the magnetic field in this case is indistinguishable from the magnetic field of a similar circuit with the same current flowing but no gap between the plates [Fig. 31–22 (c)].

Although the experiments we have described are feasible, it is extremely hard to do them with enough accuracy to be completely convincing. In the case of the plates discharging internally through ionized air in the gap, each of the canceling magnetic fields — that from the current and that from the changing flux of electric field — would be very small. In the experiment, when the plates are being charged, the absence of a magnetic effect from the gap would only make a small difference in the total magnetic field.

Historically, the fact that a changing electric flux produces a magnetic field was not discovered in such experiments. It was first asserted by Clerk Maxwell in 1864 as a logical necessity, as something needed to make the formal statement of electromagnetic theory consistent. From it he showed that there should be electromagnetic waves. Even today the existence of electromagnetic waves behaving just as Maxwell predicted is the most convincing proof of the equivalence between current and changes of electric flux.

31–11. The Mechanism of Electromagnetic Radiation

How is the generation of magnetic fields by changing electric flux connected with the existence of electromagnetic waves? We shall not attempt to follow the details here, but we can get a qualitative understanding. With Maxwell's description of the induction of magnetic fields by changing electric flux we must combine Faraday's description of the induction of electric fields by changing magnetic flux. Neither of these laws separately will lead to electromagnetic radiation. But if both are true, then it is possible for moving electric fields to produce moving magnetic fields while these moving magnetic fields are generating the electric fields. The change of flux of each field generates the other. So the whole package of electric and magnetic fields will move along, propelling itself through space.

A magnetic field pointing toward us, for in-

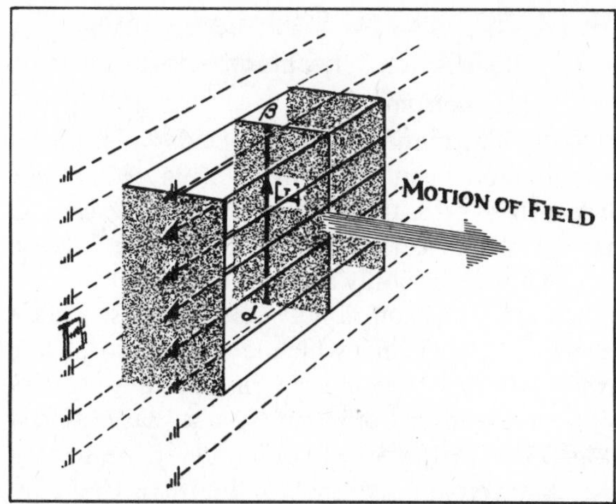

31–23. A piece cut out of a large slab of magnetic field pointing toward us. The magnetic field is moving to the right, across the path $\alpha\beta$. This change of flux generates an upward electric field along $\alpha\beta$. Since we could choose any path anywhere in the slab, the slab will be filled with electric field which moves along with it.

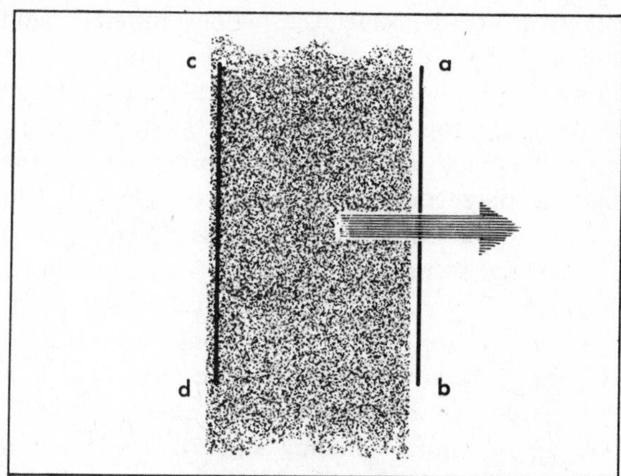

31–24. Imagine that the shaded area is a cross section through a slab of magnetic field. The magnetic field is pointing toward you, and the whole slab is moving to the right. As the slab crosses the path *ab*, what electric field is generated on it? Notice that when the slab moves to the right so that it just covers *ab* and just leaves *cd*, the electric field lost at *cd* is just the field we gain on *ab*. In its motion there is no change in the total amount of the electric field induced inside of the slab. It neither increases nor decreases. Can you show the same thing about *B*-field induced by a moving slab of electric field?

stance, and sweeping to the right, generates an induced electric field. In Section 31–4 we studied the effect of such a moving magnetic field. If you look back at Fig. 31–6 and think where the induced EMF is produced, you can see that there is an induced electric field in the portion of the wire loop past which the magnetic field is moving. In just the same way there is an induced electric field in the slab of moving magnetic field shown in Fig. 31–23. Since the magnetic field is moving to the right, the electric field generated by the Faraday induction mechanism actually runs upward in the region where the moving magnetic field is present. You can check this by thinking of the induced voltage on a wire extending from α to β in the figure. The upward path $\alpha\beta$ can be put anywhere in the region of the moving magnetic field. Consequently, we see that the whole slab of moving magnetic field will be filled with a vertical electric field generated by the Faraday induction mechanism (Fig. 31–24).

Since the slab is kept full of electric field, as it moves to the right the electric field moves with it. But the motion of the electric field will generate magnetic field through the Maxwell induction mechanism. The Maxwell induction law is similar to the Faraday law. It connects moving electric fields with induced magnetic fields in the way the Faraday law connects moving magnetic fields with induced electric fields. Aside from numerical constants, the only difference is that induced fields from a given flux change point in opposite directions. (Compare the directions of the flux changes and induced fields in Figs. 31–19 and 31–21.) Consequently, when the electric flux is spread out in a moving slab, it generates magnetic field along any path across which the electric field is moving, along $\gamma\delta$ in Fig. 31–25 for instance. The vertical electric fields moving to the right in the slab therefore generate a horizontal

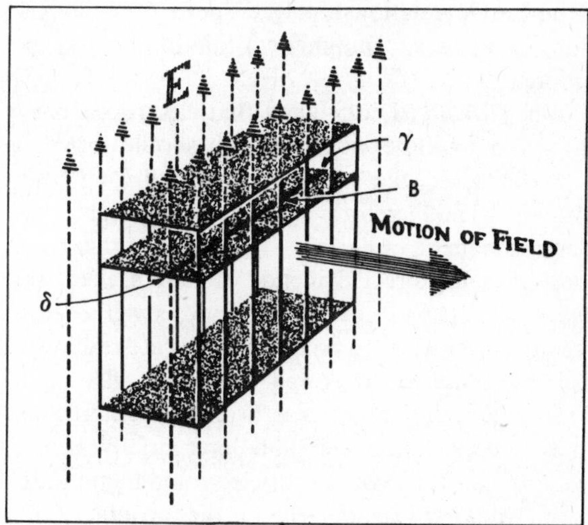

31–25. The moving electric field produces magnetic field along any path across which it moves.

magnetic field inside the whole moving field region. And if we check out the directions we find that the horizontal field generated is indeed in the same direction as the magnetic field toward us with which we started. In other words, the moving magnetic field generates the electric field moving into new regions, and this electric field is in turn the source of the moving magnetic field. A package of moving crossed electric and magnetic fields thus sweeps itself along as each field change continuously generates the other.

In order to make a moving electromagnetic package, we must somehow start the fields out in the right way. Just making some stationary crossed electric and magnetic fields will not do. Unless the fields are moving at the right speeds, they will not generate each other. We shall have a look at the problem of starting a package in the next section. Once the moving package is set up, however, the speed at which it moves can be computed from the exact numerical factors in Faraday's and Maxwell's induction laws. In the box (page 567) we have worked out the speed that follows from them. As Maxwell first found, it is 3×10^8 m/sec. All electromagnetic radiation must propagate at this speed.

We can now see why the existence of electromagnetic radiation, and measurements of its speed, are such decisive tests of the generation of magnetic fields by changing electric fluxes. If changing electric fields did not generate magnetic fields, there would be no electromagnetic radiation at all. If they generated magnetic fields in any other quantitative relationship, the speed of propagation of all electromagnetic radiation would be different.

When Maxwell concluded that electromagnetic radiation should exist and that it should move at 3×10^8 m/sec, the speed of light had long been known. He therefore suspected that light was electromagnetic radiation. However, at that time there was no direct evidence of light's electrical character. It was not until after Maxwell's death that Heinrich Hertz was able to generate radiation using machinery that was obviously electrical. Then Maxwell's theory was brilliantly confirmed. In the next section we shall look briefly at the evidence for the existence of electromagnetic radiation, looking particularly at the proofs of its electrical nature.

31–12. Evidence for Electromagnetic Radiation; the Electromagnetic Spectrum

All electric and magnetic fields arise from charges and their motions. When should we expect these fields to radiate away from the electric particles from which they originate? An electric charge at rest has only a Coulomb field around it, a field which falls off rapidly (as the inverse square of the distance) and which does not propagate away from it. A charge in constant-velocity motion is really no different from a charge at rest (Fig. 31–26). If we walk alongside it, we see the charge at rest and the field around it is a Coulomb field. If we move past it, or it moves past us, because of the changes of electric flux through any region, we shall also see a magnetic field. But this magnetic field is localized in the region of the Coulomb field. So the electric and magnetic fields stay with a charge in constant-velocity motion. They do not radiate away.

On the other hand, if we accelerate a charge, it cannot stay at rest in any dynamical frame of reference in which Newton's laws and the laws of electromagnetism apply. When we accelerate a charge, we have a chance of breaking some electric and magnetic fields away from the charge into a new relation. We may make it possible for some of the electromagnetic field to move away as radiation. Also, when we accelerate a charge, we do work. At that moment, we have our only opportunity to feed energy into the electromagnetic fields. We have our only chance to start a pulse of crossed electric and magnetic fields moving away. To find electromagnetic radiation, then, we should look for radiation from accelerated charges.

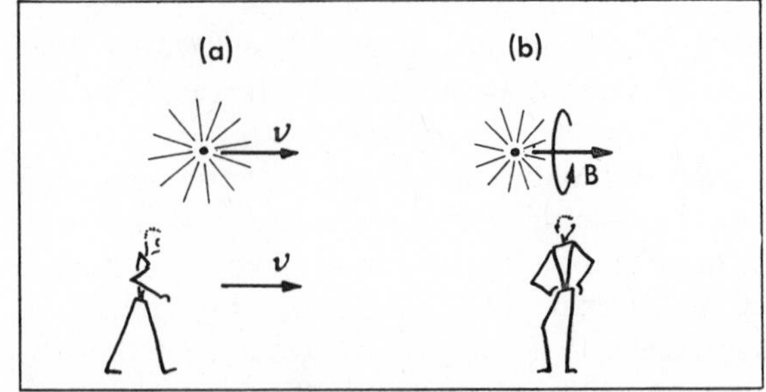

31–26. (a) If we walk along beside a moving charge, we see only its Coulomb field. (b) If the charge moves past us, we also see a magnetic field in the same region.

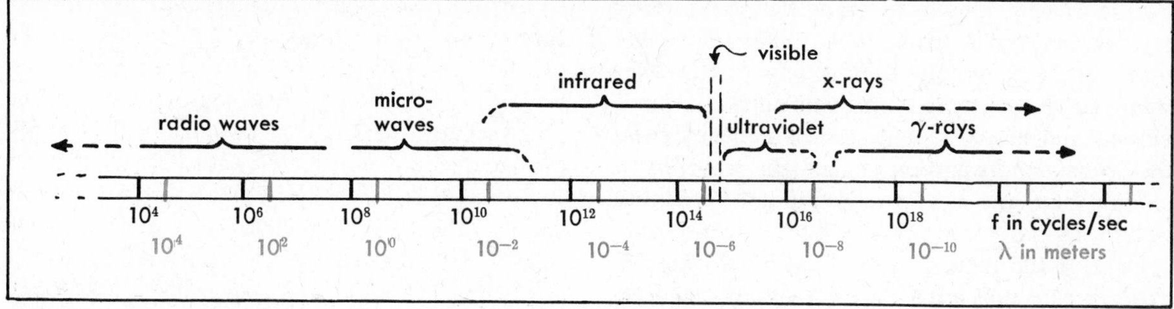

31–27. The electromagnetic spectrum: this is a continuous range of radiation spreading from gamma rays to radio waves. The descriptive names for sections of the spectrum are historical; they merely give a convenient classification according to the source of the radiation. The physical nature of radiation is the same throughout the whole range. In all sections it has the same velocity, the same electromagnetic nature, and the only difference from one part of the spectrum to another is in frequency and wave length. The regions with historical names overlap, but the names still give a hint of the common sources: radio waves and microwaves from electrons moving in conductors; infrared from hot objects; visible light from very hot objects; ultraviolet from arcs and gas discharges; X rays from electrons striking a target; gamma rays from nuclei of radioactive atoms

Let us check up experimentally on what happens when we accelerate charges. A radio transmitting station pumps charges along an antenna, first in one direction and then in the other direction. They do not move at constant velocity but go back and forth, accelerated first one way and then the other. The radio waves which break away from the antenna travel at 3×10^8 meters per second. Evidently they arise from the accelerated motions of the charges pushed back and forth along the antenna. When we stop high-speed electrons on the target of an X-ray tube, we give them a rapid backward acceleration to bring them to rest. X rays radiate away from the region where the charges are accelerated. On measuring the speed of propagation of X rays, we find that it also is 3×10^8 meters per second.

In a synchrotron — a machine to supply high-speed electrons — electrons of tremendous energies are forced around large orbits by deflecting magnetic fields. If we look around the orbit, we see light coming out. Indeed, the energy to which we can bring the electrons is practically limited by the energy they radiate in light as they are accelerated by the deflecting magnetic forces. We feed in energy from a huge electrical oscillator as rapidly as we can, but at some speed of motion of the electrons it is radiated away as fast as we can supply it. Ordinary visible light is therefore an electromagnetic radiation with its origin in the acceleration of electric particles. The coincidence between the speed of light and the speed of electromagnetic radiation as calculated by Maxwell was no accident. All the radiations we have mentioned travel at 3×10^8 meters per second; all of them are electrical in origin. They are all electromagnetic radiation (Fig. 31–27).

The common speed of these radiations and their origin from accelerated charges is not the only evidence we have for their electromagnetic nature. There is other evidence connecting the whole spectrum of radiation from X rays to radio waves. If we accelerate charged particles back and forth with a given frequency, the radiant electric fields that we shake off from them should have this frequency of oscillation. Each radio transmitting station pumps charge back and forth through its antenna at a definite frequency. It must impart this frequency to the radio waves which it sends out. The oscillating electric field in these waves should in turn drive charges back and forth in the receiving antenna at the same frequency. Are those oscillating currents really there? We detect the radio signals by tuning an oscillating circuit in the radio receiver, and we pick up a particular radio station when we have tuned our receiver to exactly the same frequency that the transmitter puts out. The oscillation frequency has been carried from the transmitter to us by the electromagnetic radiation.

With various circuits and antennas we can make transmitters that will send out radio waves of frequencies from about 10^4 cycles per second to about 3×10^{11} cycles per second. All send out electromagnetic waves that travel with the speed of light.

So the wave lengths — which we can measure by interference — run from about 30 kilometers down to the region of a millimeter. At the long-wave-length end these waves will diffract around any normal obstacle; but as the frequency rises, they behave more and more like light, traveling in straight lines and clearly reflecting and refracting as light does.

Even at the highest radio frequencies that we can generate, the wave length of electromagnetic radiation is many times longer than the longest wave length of visible light. In between lies the region of heat radiation. This radiation is emitted by colliding molecules in hot gases or solids. The collisions of the molecules cause charges in them to vibrate, emitting electromagnetic radiation of higher frequencies than we can produce with electrical circuits of man-made sizes.

At still higher temperatures, in arcs and sparks for instance, the disturbed atoms emit light — infrared, visible, or even ultraviolet light. The visible part of the spectrum corresponds to frequencies of between 4×10^{14} cycles per second and 8×10^{14} cycles per second. Here we have long passed the region where we can directly measure the frequency, but we can identify the frequencies in light of a single spectral color by measuring the wave lengths. In this way, by using spectroscopes with the air pumped out, we can find the frequencies of the ultraviolet radiations emitted by atoms. These frequencies run up to a few times 10^{15} cycles per second. Are these the frequencies that we would expect for the motions of electrons in the excited atoms? We can make an estimate by taking an electron running around an atom of 1 angstrom radius. We assume that the electron is held there by the Coulomb force exerted by one positive elementary charge, the net charge of the rest of the atom. The frequency we thus compute is about 2×10^{15} cycles per second, in good qualitative agreement with the highest frequencies of light normally emitted from atoms.

As well as emitting light, atoms absorb it. An atom of a particular kind will absorb light of only certain very definite frequencies. Presumably these are the frequencies of the natural motions of the electrons in the atom. The atom is only tuned to these frequencies and will only respond to electric fields which oscillate with them. We cannot tune atoms in the way that we can tune an oscillatory circuit that we build ourselves. But by looking for the right kind of atom, we may be able to find an electronic motion tuned in a frequency region in which we want to absorb light.

At higher frequencies we come to the region of X rays. Here we can make a crude estimate of the frequencies expected by calculating the time during which the high-speed electrons in an X-ray tube are decelerated when they crash into the target of heavy metal in the tube. We expect that the frequencies of the X rays generated will run up to approximately one divided by this time. If the frequency of the X ray is not too high, its wave length will be about the size of an atom. Then we can use the regular gratings ruled in crystals by the natural repetitious spacing of the atoms to get a measurement of the wave length. Also, indirect measurements, measurements that you will be able to understand from the discussion in Chapter 33, agree with the frequencies we compute from the crystal-grating measurements of wave length. These indirect measurements can be extended to still higher frequencies, and they show that the X-ray frequencies observed are those we predict from our estimates of the stopping time of the accelerated charges.

Finally, at enormously high frequencies, we come to gamma rays. They are emitted spontaneously in some radioactive decay processes. Like light, they travel in straight lines at 3×10^8 m/sec and cannot be deflected by electric or magnetic fields. The same kind of measurement that we use to determine high X-ray frequencies shows that there are gamma rays with a frequency of 10^{21} cycles per second.

All these electromagnetic radiations carry energy. When they are absorbed, the body absorbing them heats up. This means that electromagnetic radiation, as we expected, can only be emitted in a process in which energy is supplied. As we assumed at the beginning, the radiating electric and magnetic fields must be set up when a force accelerates a charge. The evidence that electromagnetic radiation arises from accelerated charges is now overwhelming. Electromagnetic radiation exists; it is propagated with the speed of light, and it arises from accelerated charges.

More About Electromagnetic Theory and Electromagnetic Radiation

1. THE QUANTITATIVE EQUIVALENCE OF CHANGING ELECTRIC FLUX AND ELECTRIC CURRENT

As a pair of parallel plates are charged up by a current, the rate of change of electric flux between the plates acts magnetically as a continuation of that current. The current, a certain number of elementary charges per second, tells us exactly how fast the charge on the plates changes. Since the charge on the plates determines the electric flux between them, the rate of change of the electric flux is proportional to the rate of change of the charges, and therefore proportional to the current. That is: Since $\varphi_E \propto Q$,

$$\frac{\Delta\varphi_E}{\Delta t} \propto \frac{\Delta Q}{\Delta t} = I$$

We can find the constant relation between current and rate of flux change by finding the constant of proportionality between the charge on the plates and the flux between them. This proportionality factor between flux and charge is independent of the size of the plates, for if we concentrate the charge on an area half as big, the electric field will double in the smaller area between the plates, and the flux will remain the same. To determine the constant of proportionality, therefore, we need only make one measurement.

Let us take plates of area 1 meter^2, with $Q = 4.85 \times 10^{12}$ positive elementary charges on one and 4.85×10^{12} negative elementary charges on the other. Then we find experimentally that the electrical field between the plates is $1.4 \times 10^{-14} \frac{\text{newtons}}{\text{elem. charge}}$. Since the field between the plates is uniform, the flux of electric field between them is given by the field times the area of the plates. It is

$$\varphi_E = 1.4 \times 10^{-14} \frac{\text{newton-meters}^2}{\text{elem. charge}}.$$

On dividing φ_E by Q, we find that the ratio is

$$\frac{\varphi_E}{Q} = 2.9 \times 10^{-27} \frac{\text{newton-meters}^2}{(\text{elem. charge})^2}.$$

This relation between flux and charge is general. We could prove it by using nothing more than Coulomb's law and some arithmetic. Here we shall content ourselves with carrying out the computation for a special case, and in so doing we shall discover the meaning of the proportionality constant in the equation above. We consider a small body with a charge Q, and, in imagination, we put a sphere of radius r around it. The flux of the electric field passing through this sphere is the same no matter what the radius of the sphere. The electric field which passes straight outward along the radii is of strength

$$E = k\frac{Q}{r^2}.$$

The area of the sphere through which it passes is $4\pi r^2$. Consequently, the total outward flux — field times area — is

$$\varphi_E = E4\pi r^2 = 4\pi kQ,$$

and therefore $\frac{\varphi_E}{Q} = 4\pi k$. When we put in for k its value, $2.3 \times 10^{-28} \frac{\text{newton-meters}^2}{(\text{elem. charge})^2}$, we find that the proportionality constant $4\pi k$ is actually $2.9 \times 10^{-27} \frac{\text{newton-meters}^2}{(\text{elem. charge})^2}$ as we found experimentally in the case of the charged parallel plates. In fact, the shape of the body and the distribution of charge on it make no difference. The flux away from a charged body is always given by this relation. Other charges in the neighborhood may pull the E-field around so that it changes its direction, but the total flux is unchanged.

From the general relation between flux and charge we see that the rate of change of flux between the plates must be given by

$$\frac{\Delta\varphi_E}{\Delta t} = 4\pi k \frac{\Delta Q}{\Delta t}.$$

Finally, since the rate of change of charge is the current, this tells us that the rate of electric flux change $\frac{\Delta\varphi_E}{\Delta t}$ acts in producing magnetic effects like an equivalent current of magnitude

$$I_{eq} = \frac{1}{4\pi k}\frac{\Delta\varphi_E}{\Delta t}.$$

2. THE CIRCULATION OF MAGNETIC FIELD AROUND A CHANGING ELECTRIC FLUX

Now from Chapter 30 we already know the magnetic effect of a current. Around a current I, the circling magnetic field a distance d away is

$$B = \left(5.12 \times 10^{-45} \frac{\text{newtons}}{(\text{elem. ch./sec})^2}\right)\frac{I}{d}.$$

The B-field at distance d around the changing electric flux is therefore

$$B = \frac{5.12 \times 10^{-45}}{d} \frac{1}{4\pi k} \frac{\Delta\varphi_E}{\Delta t}.$$

(Remember that the 5.12×10^{-45} has the dimensions of $\frac{\text{newton}}{(\text{elem. ch./sec})^2}$.)

On putting in

$$k = 2.3 \times 10^{-28} \frac{\text{newton-meters}^2}{(\text{elem. ch.})^2},$$

we get

$$B = \frac{1}{9 \times 10^{16}\ \text{m}^2/\text{sec}^2} \frac{\Delta\varphi_E/\Delta t}{2\pi d}.$$

Here we have saved out the 2π in the denominator so as to write our result in exactly the same form as the Faraday induction law for the induced electric field around a changing magnetic flux. As we found in Section 31–7, that law is

$$E = \frac{\Delta\varphi_B/\Delta t}{2\pi d}.$$

Actually, as you can check, both of these results stay exactly the same — including the same constant — if we use practical units or the units based on the elementary charge.

The constant factor $\frac{1}{9 \times 10^{16}\ \text{m}^2/\text{sec}^2}$ depends only on the choice of units in measuring time and space. Notice that in either system of units the dimensions of E are m/sec times those of B $\left(\frac{\text{newtons}}{\text{coulomb}} = \frac{\text{m}}{\text{sec}} \times \frac{\text{newtons}}{\text{ampere-meter}}\right.$ and $\left.\frac{\text{newtons}}{\text{elem. ch.}} = \frac{\text{m}}{\text{sec}} \times \frac{\text{newtons}}{(\text{elem. ch./sec})\text{-meter}}\right)$.

As a result of the experiments described at the beginning of this chapter, we know that the Faraday induction law really gives the circulation of the E-field around a region of changing magnetic flux. If the region is small and circularly symmetrical, the E-field runs around in circles, but if the region is extended and odd-shaped, the E-field on any path may have different values at different points. Nevertheless, we get the same circulation of E, the same induced potential around a closed path through which the magnetic flux is changing, by mentally dividing the circuit of the path into small lengths over which the electric field is approximately constant, multiplying each length by the value of the electric field along the path there, and adding up all those products.

In just the same way, the Maxwell induction law really determines the circulation of B-field around a changing electric flux. Again, if the region of flux change is a circle, the field around it also goes around in circles, but if the region of flux change is extended, the induced B-field on any path will change from point to point, and we must add up the magnetic circulation in just the way that we have to add up the electric circulation in a similar situation. In general, therefore, we can write the two induction laws as:

$$\begin{pmatrix}\text{the circulation} \\ \text{of } B\end{pmatrix} = \frac{1}{9 \times 10^{16}\ \text{m}^2/\text{sec}^2} \frac{\Delta\varphi_E}{\Delta t}.$$

$$\begin{pmatrix}\text{the circulation} \\ \text{of } E\end{pmatrix} = \frac{\Delta\varphi_B}{\Delta t}.$$

Remember that when a magnetic flux changes toward you, the circulation of E around it is clockwise, but when an electric flux change is toward you, like a current toward you, the circulation of B around it is counterclockwise.

3. THE SPEED OF ELECTROMAGNETIC RADIATION

From the induction laws we can now show that electromagnetic radiation must move at 3×10^8 meters per second. Let us do this by taking a slab of crossed electric and magnetic fields moving along by itself at some speed c. By using the induction laws, we shall determine the value of c.

Suppose that the slab contains the magnetic field B in Fig. 31–23. By taking the path $\alpha\beta$ in that figure to be of length l, we now find from the Faraday induction law the magnitude of the E-field generated by the changing magnetic flux. It must be

$$lE = lcB.$$

Here the left side is the circulation of E, and the right side is the rate at which magnetic flux moves across the path. Consequently,

$$E = cB$$

The electric field generated in this way is vertical in the figure.

In the same way using the path $\alpha\delta$ in Fig. 31–25, we find the strength of the regenerated B-field from Maxwell's induction law. This regenerated field B' is

$$B' = \frac{cE}{9 \times 10^{16}\ \text{m}^2/\text{sec}^2}.$$

The reasoning is exactly the same as before. The additional factor $\dfrac{1}{9 \times 10^{16}\ \text{m}^2/\text{sec}^2}$ is contained in Maxwell's induction law. Furthermore, B' is in the same direction as the original B-field.

Now let us express B' in terms of the original B-field by putting $E = cB$ into the last equation. The result is

$$B' = \frac{c(cB)}{9 \times 10^{16}\ \text{m}^2/\text{sec}^2}.$$

In order that the slab of electric and magnetic field shall maintain itself while it moves along, it is necessary that the regenerated B-field B' be equal to the original B-field. If B' were less, the fields would rapidly vanish. All the electromagnetic energy in the radiation would disappear mysteriously. On the other hand, if B' were greater than B, the total amount of the fields would increase. Energy would be coming into the electromagnetic radiation without any source. The slab of electromagnetic radiation just maintains itself when the regenerated field B' equals the original field B. By letting $B = B'$ in the last equation, we see that the speed of propagation of the fields must be 3×10^8 m/sec.

In summary, the fields in the slab must be at right angles to each other and to the direction of propagation. The relative size of the E- and B-fields is given by

$$E = (3 \times 10^8\ \text{m/sec})B$$

and the radiation moves with the speed of light.

FOR HOME, DESK, AND LAB

1. Fig. 30–26 is a diagram of an electric motor.
   (a) Explain how you could use the same arrangement of magnetic field and wire loop to make a generator that would produce current in only one direction in an external circuit.
   (b) How should the wire loop be oriented in the magnetic field when the commutator interchanges the connections between the ends of the loop and the wires of the outside circuit?

2. The rectangular wire loop shown in Fig. 31–28 is in a uniform magnetic field.
   (a) In what direction (clockwise or counterclockwise) is the induced current when the loop is in the plane of the paper and BC is moving into the page about P_1 as an axis? About P_2?
   (b) For a given speed of rotation, how would the induced currents compare when the loop is rotated about P_1 and then P_2?

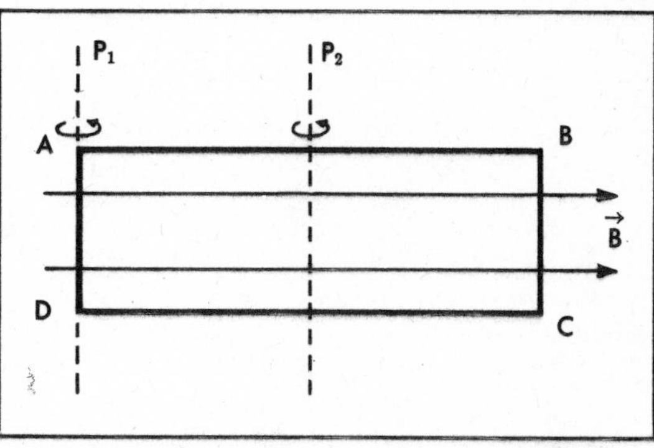

31–28. For Problem 2.

   (c) For a given speed of rotation, how does the induced voltage depend on the area of the loop?
   (d) If the magnetic field has a magnitude of 1.5 newtons per ampere-meter, $AB = 10$ cm, and $BC = 4$ cm, what is the maximum induced voltage when the loop is rotating about P_1 at 19.1 revolutions per second $\left(\dfrac{120}{2\pi}\text{ r.p.s.}\right)$?

3. Draw a graph of the voltage induced in the loop in Fig. 31–28 as a function of the angle through which it is rotated, assuming it rotates at constant speed.

4. What would be the result of keeping the loop in Fig. 31–28 stationary and rotating the magnetic field?

5. In Problem 2, part (d) what maximum force must be applied to the edge *BC* of the loop to keep it rotating around P_1 so that the maximum induced voltage is $\frac{1}{2}$ volt if the loop has a resistance of 1 ohm?

6. In Problem 5:

(a) How fast is the edge *BC* moved?

(b) What power do we put in at the time the voltage is maximum? (Compute it from Fv.)

(c) What power is dissipated into heat at that time? [Compute it from $I\mathcal{E}$ and compare with your answer to (b).]

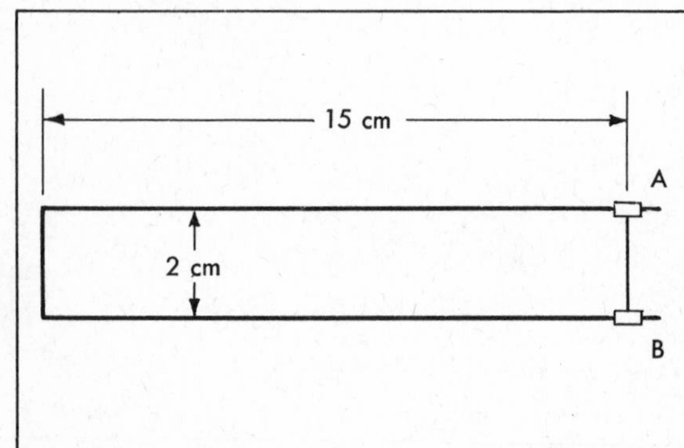

31–29. For Problem 7.

7. A U-shaped wire (Fig. 31–29) has a movable wire *AB* connected to it. This arrangement is in a uniform field perpendicular to, and into, the page.

(a) If the magnetic field strength is 40 newtons per ampere-meter, what is the induced voltage when *AB* is in the position shown and moving at 20 cm per sec? Calculate this first from the rate of flux change and then from the magnetic force on the elementary charges in the wire.

(b) What is the induced voltage when *AB* is 5.0 cm from the left end and moving at 20 cm per sec? At 10 cm per sec?

(c) At what rate is energy fed into the loop when *AB* moves at 20 cm per sec and the induced current is 2.0 amperes?

(d) If the induced current is 2.0 amperes, what force is needed to move *AB* at 20 cm per sec?

8. In the circuit of Problem 7, all the wires and the contacts have very little resistance except the left-hand wire. Therefore, as *AB* moves, the resistance of the circuit does not change appreciably.

(a) What is the ratio of the induced currents when a total change of magnetic flux $\Delta\varphi$ is made in 1 second and in 2 seconds?

(b) What is the ratio of the total numbers of charges moved past any point in the circuit in each case?

(c) If in any such circuit you double the total flux change, what happens to the total charge moved past any point in the circuit?

9. In a betatron electrons are accelerated to very high energies by a changing magnetic flux. The electrons move in a circle around the inside of an evacuated glass doughnut and speed up when the flux through the hole in the doughnut increases. A separate magnetic field passes through the doughnut perpendicular to its plane to keep the electrons moving in a circle.

An electron is traveling in a circle of 50 cm radius at 98 per cent of the speed of light in the "doughnut" of a betatron. If the flux inside the doughnut increases at a rate of 24 $\frac{\text{newton-meters}}{\text{ampere-sec}}$ for $\frac{1}{240}$ second how much energy (in electron volts) will be transferred to the electron? Note: Assume that the speed stays constant at approximately the speed of light.

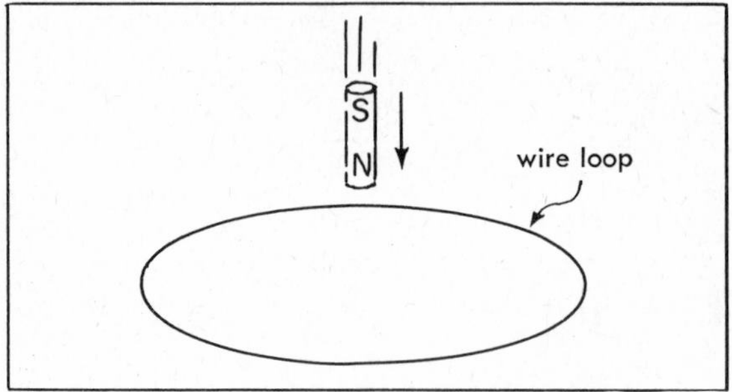

31–30. For Problem 10.

10. A bar magnet is dropped through a wire loop as shown in Fig. 31–30.

(a) Describe the changes in the direction and magnitude of the induced current in the loop as the magnet falls through the loop.

(b) Neglecting air resistance, will the acceleration of the falling magnet be constant?

11. (a) Will the earth's magnetic field induce currents in an artificial satellite with a metal surface that is in orbit around the equator? Around the poles?

(b) If so, how would these currents affect the motion of the satellite?

12. (a) In Fig. 31–31, *L* is a large electromagnet. When the switch is closed, the lamp glows dimly.

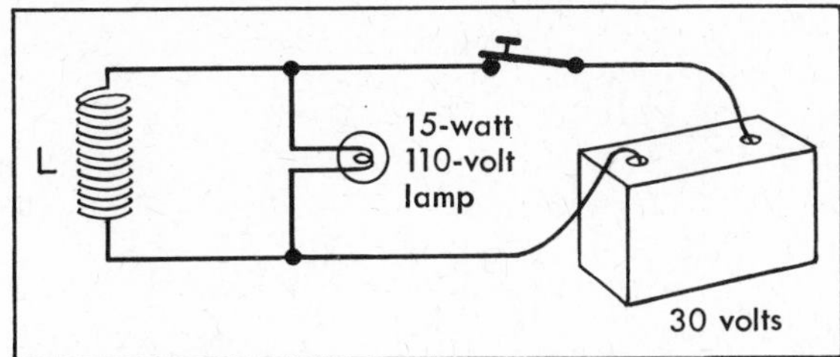

31–31. For Problem 12.

When the switch is suddenly opened, the lamp flashes for an instant to much greater brightness. How can you explain this?

(b) Explain why, when you switch off a circuit with a big coil of wire in it, you may see a spark jump across the switch or get a shock if your hand is across the switch. (This can even happen with a small electric bell.)

13. We charge two circular parallel plates, $\frac{1}{2}$ m in diameter, like those in Fig. 31–22, through long straight wires. When the current in the wires is 1 ampere, what is the magnetic field at a point $\frac{1}{2}$ m from the center of the plates in the plane midway between them?

14. A package of electromagnetic radiation is traveling straight toward you. At the moment there is no electric field where you are, but a short time later there will be an *E*-field pointing vertically down, later still an *E*-field pointing vertically up, and finally no field. When the *E*-field pointing vertically down has reached you, what direction will the *B*-field have at your position?

15. (a) Suppose a slab of magnetic field is moving with only the electric field it generates by induction. If it were moving at half the speed of light, would it generate more electric field or less than it does when moving with the speed of light?

(b) Would this moving electric field regenerate more or less than the original magnetic field?

(c) If the energy in the electric and magnetic fields must be conserved, can the electromagnetic package move at any speed other than that of light?

(d) What would happen to the energy in the electromagnetic package if the package moved faster than light?

16. What evidence is there that sound is not electromagnetic radiation?

17. As you no doubt have observed, crashes of static are heard on a radio when a lightning flash occurs — even if the lightning occurs far away.

(a) Why does this happen?

(b) If thunder is heard 15 seconds after a static crash is heard, how long did it take the light from the flash to reach you?

Note: The speed of sound is about 330 m/sec.

18. When electrons moving at 3×10^7 m/sec hit the target in an X-ray tube, they are brought to rest in about an atomic diameter — in about 10^{-10} m.

(a) What is the stopping time?

(b) If we use one divided by this time to estimate the frequencies we might expect to see in the electromagnetic radiation arising from this deceleration, what frequency do you get?

(c) What wave length does this frequency give?

19. What would be the order of magnitude of the minimum frequency of electromagnetic waves that could be used to detect the presence of:

(a) the planet Venus?

(b) an airplane 50 meters long?

(c) a bird 10 cm long?

(d) atoms of a noble gas?

(e) an atomic nucleus?

From what sources of electromagnetic radiation would you be able to generate radiation of these wave lengths?

20. Radio transmitting stations often use more than one antenna in order to put more signal in particular directions and less where they have no audience.

Two vertical radio transmitting antennas have alternating currents flowing in them at a frequency of 10^6 cycles per second. The antennas are 300 meters apart along a north-south line.

In what horizontal directions will the radiation intensity be (1) a maximum and (2) a minimum when

(a) the currents in the two antennas are in phase — run up together and down together?

(b) they differ in phase by $\frac{1}{2}$ period — when one current is up the other is down?

FURTHER READING

FARADAY, MICHAEL, *Moments of Discovery*. Edited by G. Schwartz and P. Bishop. Basic Books, 1958 (p. 856).

FINK, DONALD G. and LUTYENS, DAVID M., *The Physics of Television*. Doubleday, 1959: A Science Study Series paperback.

HERTZ, HEINRICH, *Moments of Discovery*. Cited above (p. 901).

ROENTGEN, WILHELM, *Moments of Discovery*. Cited above (p. 867).

TAYLOR, LLOYD, *Physics, the Pioneer Science*. Dover, 1959 (Chapter 45).

EXPLORING THE ATOM

CHAPTER 32

We already know a lot about atoms — about their masses and the chemical compounds they form. We also know that they contain electrons which are far lighter than any atom. We can rip off electrons, leaving positive ions of almost the entire atomic mass, and sometimes we can add an electron to a neutral atom, producing a negative ion. But what does an atom look like? How is it built? About these questions we have said rather little.

Much of the early information on the structure of atoms came from probing very thin sheets of matter with moving charged particles. You can understand how we use high-energy charged particles to probe the internal structure of atoms if you think about the following analogy. For some reason, we suspect that a bale of hay may conceal some valuable contraband goods, perhaps a large block of irreplaceable platinum metal, perhaps even several pieces of platinum which have been distributed around inside. If the platinum is inside the hay, we may think of the bale as having an internal structure: so much platinum at such and such a point, none in some other region, and perhaps some in still a third position. With platinum in a bale of hay, it would clearly pay us to rip the bale apart and comb through the fragments. But it is not so easy to rip an atom apart in order to see what is inside, and we would like to know where the particles that make up the atom are located. So in our model for atomic experiments, we shall now try to find the platinum in the hay without untying the bale. We therefore get out a rifle and start shooting bullets through the hay (Fig. 32–1). When a bullet passes straight through, we can conclude that nothing very massive was in its way. And since most of the bullets do pass straight through, we can conclude that most of the bale is in fact pure hay. From our point of view, since we are looking for platinum, most of the bale is just empty. But if we are right and the contraband platinum is really somewhere inside, eventually one of the bullets will hit a piece of it. Then it will bounce off and come out at some angle to its original path. From the path of the bullet on the way in and the path of the bullet after it ricochets, we can work backward and locate some of the platinum.

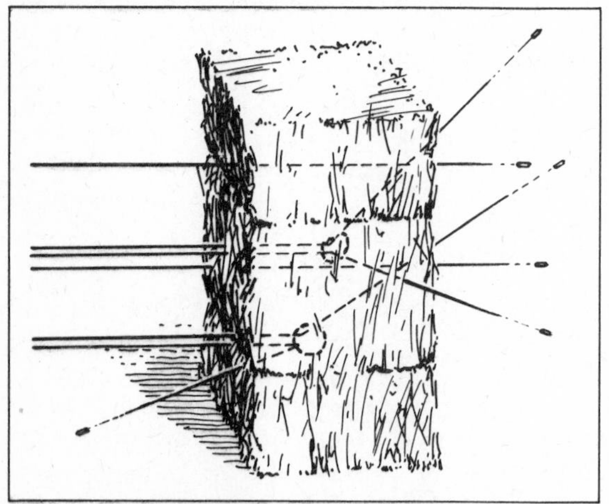

32–1. Probing inside a bale of hay with bullets. The paths of the bullets tell us where pieces of matter may be located in the hay, and something about their shapes.

If we want to, we can do a great deal more. If we shoot a lot of bullets into the general vicinity of the platinum, we can tell something about the

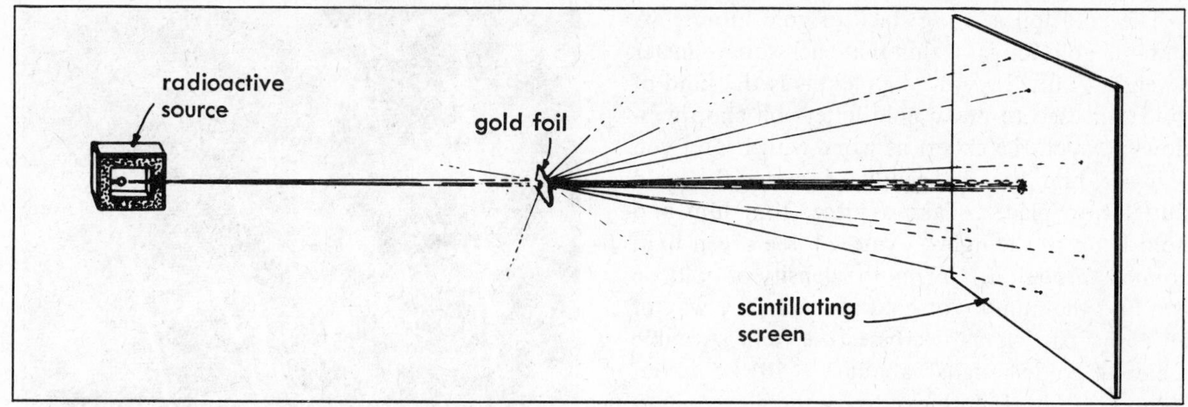

32–2. An experiment to probe the interior of atoms with alpha-particle "bullets."

shape of the piece of platinum from the angles at which the bullets ricochet. If there is a big flat surface of platinum dead ahead of us, the bullets will all ricochet at the same angle. If the platinum has been cast into a sphere, the bullets will ricochet equally often in all directions around the original direction of motion. By spraying the whole bale with bullets and looking at all the ricochets, we can tell a good deal about the positions of platinum pieces inside the bale and about their shape.

Of course, an atom is not a bale of hay with hunks of platinum embedded inside. When we shoot charged-particles bullets at an atom, we do not expect to get exactly the same kind of information that we got from our search for contraband. Nevertheless, by probing the atoms with charged particles and looking at the directions in which they come back out, we can hope to learn a good deal about the inside of atoms.

In many ways atoms are a lot more regular than chunks of platinum in bales of hay. The laws of chemical composition, the characteristic spectra (the same for all atoms of the same species), and, as we shall see, the evidence gained by bombarding atoms with charged particles to probe their depths — all these things indicate that atoms are built on about one hundred standard patterns; and in some ways these patterns are pretty simple. For this reason, with relatively few probing experiments, we can learn a good deal about the structure of atoms.

In order to bring back information about the inside of an atom, our probes must get in. Consequently, other atoms and molecules, which bounce off the atomic surface, are poor probes. Also low-energy charged particles are not much use, for they, too, do not penetrate very far. On the other hand, a probe that passes straight through anything will tell us nothing about the place it has been. Highly penetrating X rays or the even more penetrating gamma rays from radioactive disintegration are hard to use because of this defect. In the early years of this century, the most suitable probes for poking in atoms were alpha particles. They come out of radioactive materials with high enough energy to penetrate well into an atom; and although they often pass on through with little change of direction, they sometimes are violently deflected. Then we assume that they have hit something relatively massive inside and bounced away.

32–1. The Deflection of Alpha Particles and the Rutherford Model of Atoms

Fig. 32–2 shows the set-up for an experiment to probe gold atoms with high-speed alpha particles. The alpha particles are emitted in radioactive disintegration of a piece of polonium. This is our gun. As we know from Section 30–10, it shoots out the alpha particles, which are doubly charged helium ions, with a speed of 1.6×10^7 meters per second. Some of the alpha particles pass through a hole, so that we know their direction as well as their speed. These particles then hit a thin gold foil.

On the far side of the gold foil there is a detector of alpha particles, a scintillating screen such as we used in Chapter 7, or a bank of modern counters which will give us a signal telling us where the alpha particles go after passing through the foil.

The gold foil is a big stack of gold atoms. A suitable gold foil is so thin that each square meter "weighs" only 2×10^{-3} kg. (This is the kind of gold foil used to make gold letters on shop windows; watch the expert at work with it and you will see him breathe gently to make the gold flutter into place. Take a piece from him and hold it up to the light — you will see green light coming through it.) From the density of gold we can find the number of gold atoms in the way of an alpha particle as it crosses the foil. A cubic meter of gold "weighs" about 2×10^4 kg, about 20 tons. The foil thickness is therefore about

$$\frac{2 \times 10^{-3} \text{ kg/m}^2}{2 \times 10^4 \text{ kg/m}^3} = 1 \times 10^{-7} \text{ meters.}$$

Also, we know that the mass of a gold atom is about 3.3×10^{-25} kg (197 atomic mass units per gold atom times 1.66×10^{-27} kg per atomic mass unit). In this way, we learn that each atom — stacked in contact with its neighbors — has a volume of

$$\frac{3.3 \times 10^{-25} \text{ kg/atom}}{2 \times 10^4 \text{ kg/m}^3} = 1.65 \times 10^{-29} \text{ meters}^3.$$

If we think of the atoms as boxes, the side of each of the little boxes must be about 2.5×10^{-10} meters. Therefore the thickness of the gold foil measured in little atomic gold boxes is

$$\frac{1 \times 10^{-7} \text{ meters}}{2.5 \times 10^{-10} \text{ meters}}.$$

The foil is about 400 gold atoms thick.

In our analogy, each gold atom is represented by a bale of hay with contraband buried inside. Because we know that gold atoms all behave identically, and all weigh the same, we represent them by bales of hay all with the same internal structure. The gold foil then is modeled by a wall of identical bales, 400 bales thick.

The first thing we learn with this apparatus is that most of the alpha particles pass through the gold leaf without appreciable change in their direction of motion. In other words, an alpha particle usually passes right through some 400 atoms. Just as we concluded by shooting bullets through a bale of hay that most of the inside of the bale is hay, here we can conclude that most of the inside of the atom is empty of hard massive objects from which the alpha particles would bounce off at an angle. The atom does, however, have something like atomic hay inside, for we see that the alpha particles gradually lose their energy in passing through gold. With any ordinary thickness of gold the alpha particles would never come out of the far side. As we can easily tell in other experiments, the alpha-particle energy is rubbed off, ionizing the gold atoms. When an alpha particle moves through the atoms, losing energy to rip off electrons, it is slowed up much as a bullet is slowed up when it goes through many bales.

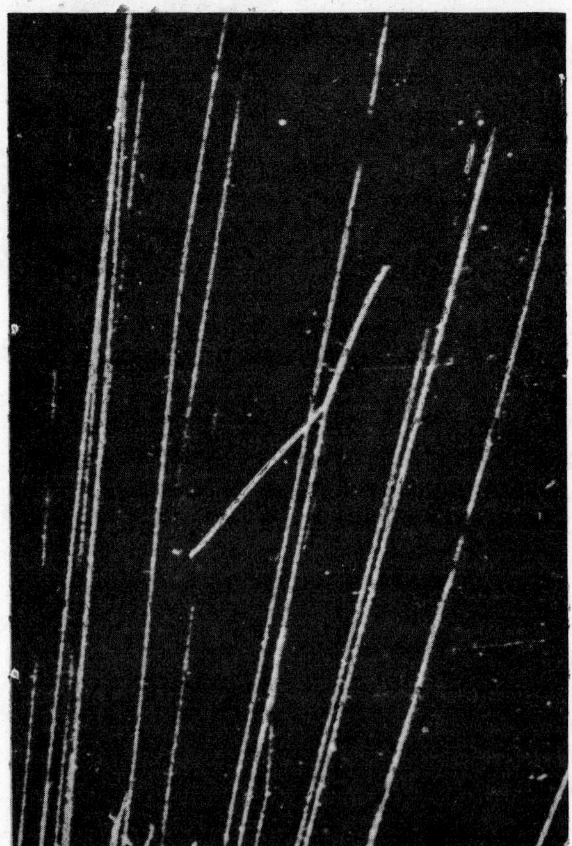

32–3. A cloud-chamber photograph showing the tracks of alpha particles moving through nitrogen. The alpha particles are moving upward from a source in the lower left. Notice the particle which collided with a nitrogen atom near the center of the picture. It was deflected back through an angle of nearly 142 degrees, while the nitrogen atom recoiled. (From P. M. S. Blackett and D. S. Lee, in Proceedings of the Royal Society, 134A, 658, 1931.)

Because we have weighed atoms, however, we know that something massive must be located somewhere in the atom. We can hardly believe that this mass is made of electrons. Many thousands would be required for a light atom, and at most we can get only a few when we disrupt the atom. A gold atom has a mass about 50 times that of an alpha particle, and if an alpha particle hits such a mass head on, it should bounce straight back. Let us, therefore, look again at the beam of alpha particles passing through the gold foil. If we look carefully all around in every direction, we find that in passing through the gold foil, about 1 out of 10,000 of the incident alpha particles is actually knocked off its original course and deflected by an angle of more than 10 degrees. Every once in a while, one out of some astronomical number of alpha particles is bounced out of its course by 90 degrees or more. The same kind of event happens once in a while when alpha particles are passing through the gas in a cloud chamber. There, if we look at myriads of cloud-chamber pictures, we eventually find a few in which the alpha particles clearly ricochet from an atom, having made almost an about-face. Fig. 32–3 is such a photograph.

The alpha particles that are sharply deflected in the gold foil also have made just one violent collision with some part of one atom in the foil. We can be sure that it is one collision which is important, because most of the alpha particles pass straight through. Consequently, we know that the chance of even one big collision is tiny and the chance of more than one real hit on the way through is absolutely negligible.

An alpha particle which has undergone such a large deflection has been acted upon by strong forces. Somewhere inside the atom, therefore, there is at least one heavy massive center, and those alpha particles which come right at it interact strongly with it.

To account for these observations any atomic model must have two features: Because almost all the alpha particles pass right through an atom, most of the atom must be empty of anything but atomic hay. Because an occasional alpha particle bounces off backward, somewhere inside the atom there must be at least one lump of mass with which alpha particles can interact strongly. In addition, we would like to associate the atomic hay with the electrons which are ripped off when alpha particles pass through atoms and ionize them. So we are tempted to associate the main mass of the atom with the positive charge which must be present in order that the atom as a whole shall normally be neutral.

In 1911 Rutherford invented an atomic model which incorporated all these features and in addition called only upon the Coulomb force to explain the interaction of alpha particles with the positive massive atomic core. His model describes an atom as a miniature solar system with a core, or *nucleus*, at the center and a number of electrons around it. The nucleus is positively charged and carries almost all of the atomic mass. The light, negatively charged electrons revolve around the nucleus, held by the Coulomb attraction, much as the planets revolve around the sun, held by gravitational attraction. Outside the atom, these negative electrons cancel the effect of the positive charge of the nucleus, so that the atom as a whole is neutral. This means that the nucleus carries a number of positive elementary charges equal to the number of electrons.

We have already concluded that the hydrogen atom is composed of a proton and an electron (Section 29–2). Thus, in the Rutherford model of the hydrogen atom (Fig. 32–4), the proton is the nucleus, and there is one electron moving around it in an orbit. Similarly, the helium atom consists of an alpha particle and two electrons. In helium the alpha particle is the nucleus, and two electron planets revolve about it.

In the Rutherford model of any atom the dimensions of the nucleus and of the electrons are assumed to be very small compared with the overall size of the atom, so that most of the atom's volume is actually empty space. In this space near the nucleus, the electric field is essentially that of the nuclear charge, a Coulomb's-law field whose strength varies as the inverse square of the distance from the nucleus. The planetary elec-

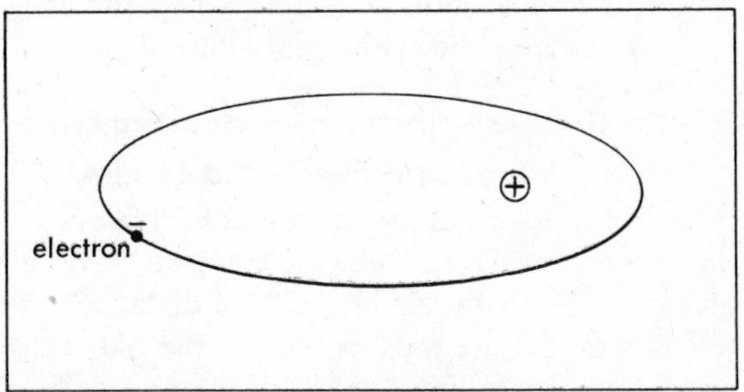

32–4. The Rutherford model of the hydrogen atom. On this scale both the electron and the nucleus are so very small that in fact you could not see them at all, even though the linear magnification is 10^9 times.

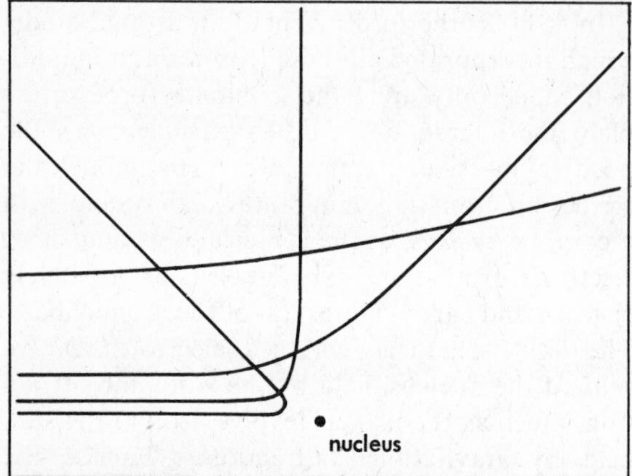

32–5. The computed paths of alpha particles approaching a nucleus. These were computed using an inverse-square force of repulsion.

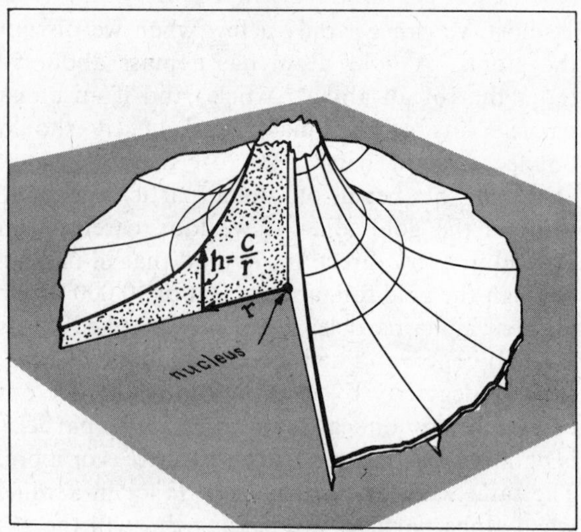

32–6. A mechanical model to illustrate the paths of alpha particles near a nucleus. Alpha particles have a potential energy proportional to $1/r$, where r is the distance from the nucleus. The hill is so constructed that the height of any point on its surface is proportional to $1/r$, where r is the distance on the plane from the center. Consequently, a ball on the hill will have gravitational potential energy proportional to $1/r$. Its motion then resembles the motion of a charge moving on the plane in the electric field of the nucleus.

trons are found in the outer regions of the atom and there these negative charges will also contribute to the electric field. Outside the atom these negative charges completely screen the positive charge of the nucleus, and the electric field vanishes.

In this model, an alpha particle fired through an atom some distance off center will pass through without appreciable deflection. It will just brush the electrons aside. But in a stream of alpha particles fired at gold leaf, a few will pass so near the center of an atom that they encounter the strong electric field close to its heavy nucleus — they will be "scattered" through a large angle.

We see that Rutherford's model accounts, at least qualitatively, for the experimental facts. It explains why atoms let most alpha particles go through almost unaffected, and why a few alpha particles are strongly deflected. Before we place more confidence in this model, however, we must submit it to a quantitative test. This Rutherford and his students did with great skill.

32–2. The Trajectories of Alpha Particles in the Electric Field of a Nucleus

In Rutherford's model an alpha particle near a nucleus experiences a force of repulsion, inversely proportional to the square of the distance. To test this model, we must work out the paths that an alpha particle would take in such a force field.

Examples of the computed trajectories are shown in Fig. 32–5. Although we shall not reproduce the long computations of these paths, they involve nothing more mysterious than Coulomb's law, Newton's law of motion, and the detailed geometrical arrangement. The curves are hyperbolas, all with the nucleus at the focus. (The hyperbolic orbits here are related to the elliptic orbits of planets in the inverse-square gravitational force field. For some remarks on this relation, see the box on page 578.)

You may also convince yourself that the computed results are sensible by looking at a mechanical model which reproduces the essentials of alpha-particle scattering in the Coulomb-force field. You may even want to construct such a model and experiment with it. In the mechanical model the alpha particle is represented by a steel ball which rolls with little friction on a smooth curved hill rising from a level table (Fig. 32–6). We make the gravitational potential energy of the ball on the hill correspond to the electric potential energy of the alpha particle near the nucleus; so this model pictures a plane through the center of an atom with the third dimension, the height in the model, representing not space but potential energy. The electric potential energy of the alpha particle varies as $1/r$, where r is its distance from the nucleus. There-

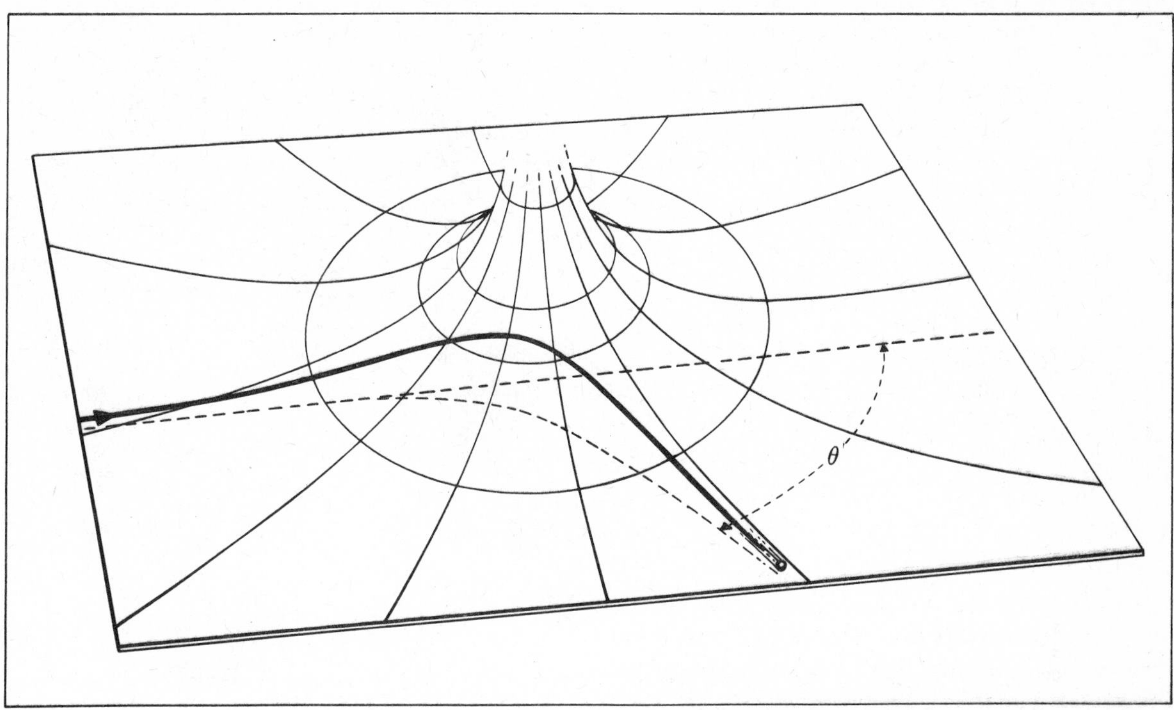

32–7. The solid line shows a possible path of a rolling ball in the "hill" model of the Coulomb field. The dashed straight line on the plane below the hill shows the direction in which one ball was originally aimed. If you look straight down on the hill, the apparent path of a ball models the path of an alpha particle moving in the horizontal plane. This path is the dashed curved line on the plane.

fore we build our hill so that above any point on the plane the height is inversely proportional to the distance r of that point from the center.*

With this model, the motion of an alpha particle on the green shaded plane through the nucleus in Fig. 32–6 is modeled by the motion of a ball on the potential-energy hill above. If we look down on a ball rolling on a real hill of this shape, the path we see will closely approximate that of an alpha particle near the nucleus. (See Fig. 32–7.)

An alpha particle aimed head-on at a nucleus will be scattered in exactly the backward direction. Similarly, in the mechanical model, if we start the ball rolling exactly toward the center of the hill, it will go straight up, to a height where its potential energy equals its original kinetic energy. There it reverses its motion and returns to the starting point. If, however, we aim the alpha particle at a point to the right of the nucleus, Coulomb repulsion pushes the alpha particle to the right, changing its direction as it passes the nucleus (Fig. 32–7). The angle θ between the final direction of motion and the original line of flight is called the scattering angle (Fig. 32–8). The closer the alpha particle comes to the nucleus, the stronger the Coulomb force it feels and the more nearly that force pushes straight backward against the original direction of motion.

*Actually this mechanical model is a little wrong because the ball will have some kinetic energy upward which must be robbed from its kinetic energy in the horizontal directions. But if the ball is rolled slowly, it will never rise much and the kinetic energy associated with its vertical motion will be a small fraction of the energy. By choosing the right speed the model can be made as accurate as you want.

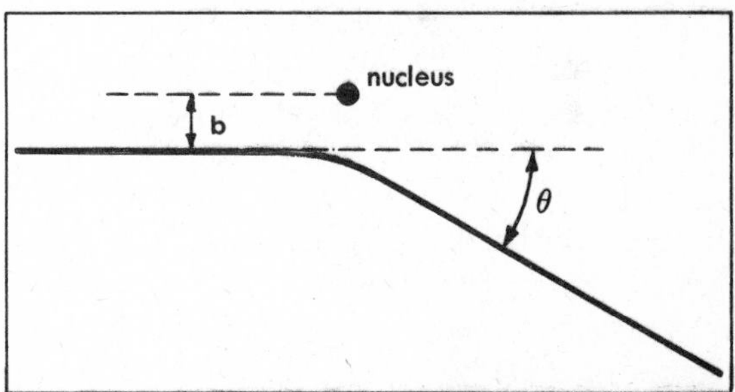

32–8. The aiming error b is the distance by which a particle would miss the nucleus if it were not deflected. The scattering angle θ is the angle between the original direction and the direction after deflection.

Therefore, the scattering angle θ will *increase* when the "aiming error," represented by the distance b, *decreases*. Fig. 32–10 shows the corresponding motions of the ball in our mechanical model.

32–3. Angular Distribution of Scattering

For particles of the same energy a definite aiming error leads to a particular angle of scattering under the influence of the Coulomb force from the nucleus. By computing the paths for a number of aiming errors, b (or by more elegant methods), we can plot a graph of the aiming error b against the resulting scattering angle θ. For the Coulomb force this relation is shown in Fig. 32–11.

Now if we could see the center of an atom and aim an alpha particle with complete precision so that we picked our aiming error b, we could test the relation between b and θ by a direct experiment. However, the alpha particles in the most accurately aimed beam will hit at random all over a region many times the area presented by an atom. Consequently, we must do a slightly less direct experiment.

Because smaller aiming errors lead to larger scattering angles (Fig. 32–12) we can take advantage of our uncontrollably poor aim by com-

CONIC SECTIONS AND INVERSE SQUARE FORCE FIELDS

Whenever a mass moves under the influence of a force that varies as the inverse square of the separation from a fixed center, the orbit is a conic section: it is a curve which can be made by a plane slicing through the surface of a cone. If the plane slices through the cone perpendicular to its axis, the surface of the cone is cut in a circle. As you know, this orbit is a possible planetary orbit. If the plane is now tipped slightly, the surface of the cone is sliced in an ellipse (Fig. 32–9). Again we have a possible planetary orbit. As the plane is tipped farther, the ellipse becomes more eccentric and the orbit resembles the orbit of a comet.

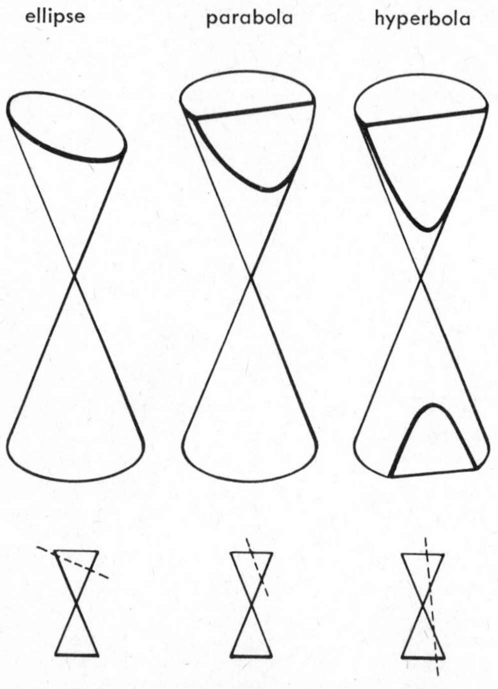

ellipse parabola hyperbola

32–9. The conic sections. Plane figures such as the ellipse, the parabola, and the hyperbola are formed by the intersections of planes at various angles with a cone.

As we see in Fig. 32–9, when the plane is tipped far enough, the intersection with the cone becomes a hyperbola, a curve like those computed for the orbit of an alpha particle in the electric field of the nucleus. The same kind of curve also gives the orbit of a mass which moves past the sun so fast that it will never come back.

Just in between the closed orbits which are ellipses, and the open hyperbolic orbits on which the mass never returns, there is one angle at which the plane cuts the cone in a parabola. This curve is the orbit of a particle with barely enough energy to get infinitely far from the center of force. It divides the orbits of masses that return from those that make a single trip.

Ellipses, parabolas, and hyperbolas are all possible orbits when the force is attractive. Only hyperbolas will be found with a repulsive force, because the mass is shoved away and does not come back.

All the curves are interrelated because they are the orbits of masses moving in inverse-square force fields, and they are all related geometrically as conic sections.

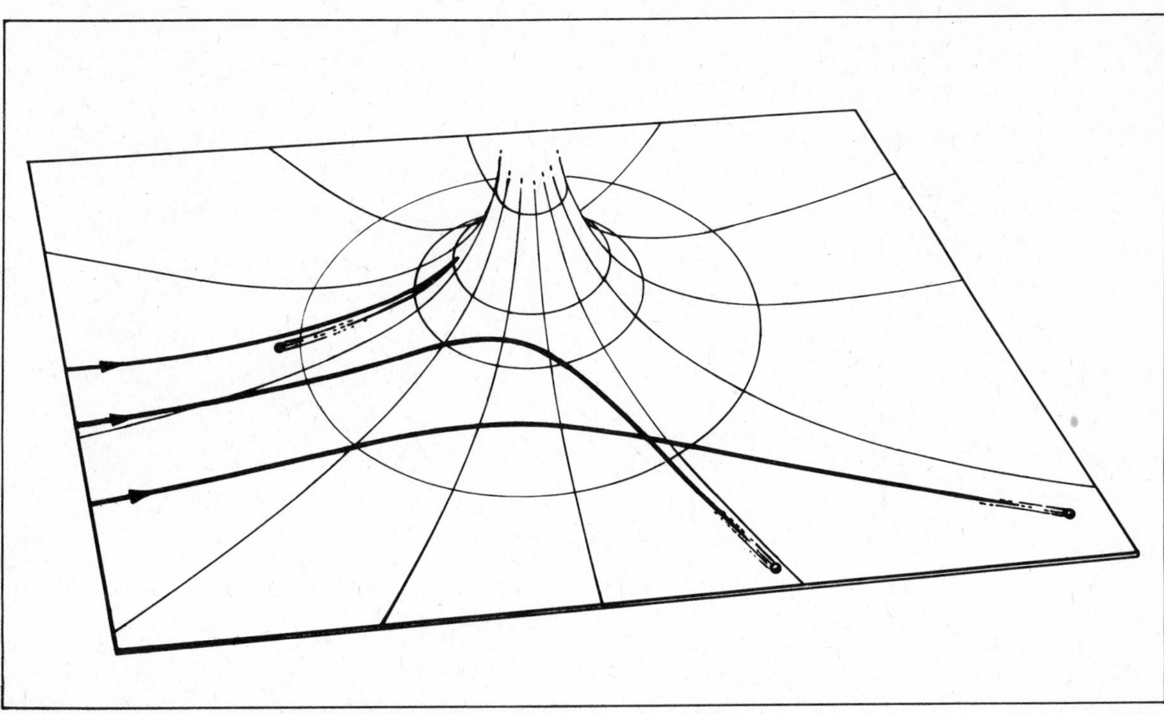

32–10. Paths of a rolling ball on the hill model. The ball is sent with the same energy each time, but with a different aiming error. Note that the smaller the aiming error is, the larger is the scattering angle.

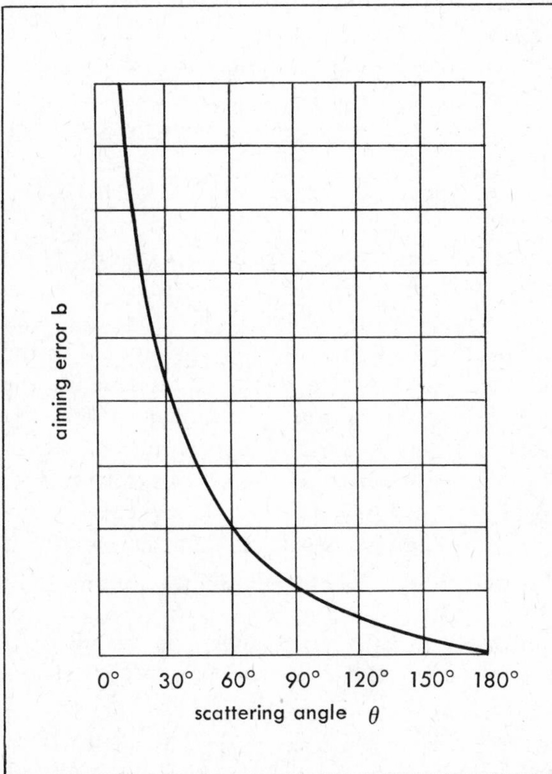

32–11. A graph of the relation between *b* and θ for a Coulomb force of repulsion.

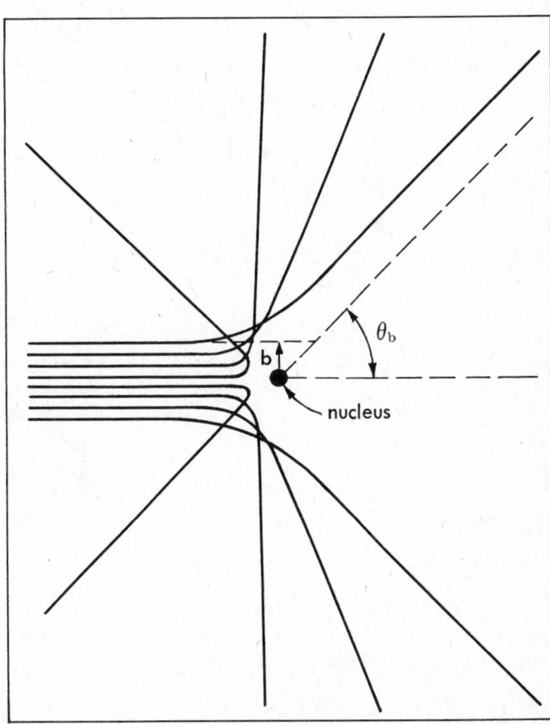

32–12. As the aiming error *b* decreases, the scattering angle θ increases. Therefore, all particles aimed within a distance *b* of the nucleus will be scattered through angles greater than θ. You can see this same relation in Figs. 32–10 and 32–11.

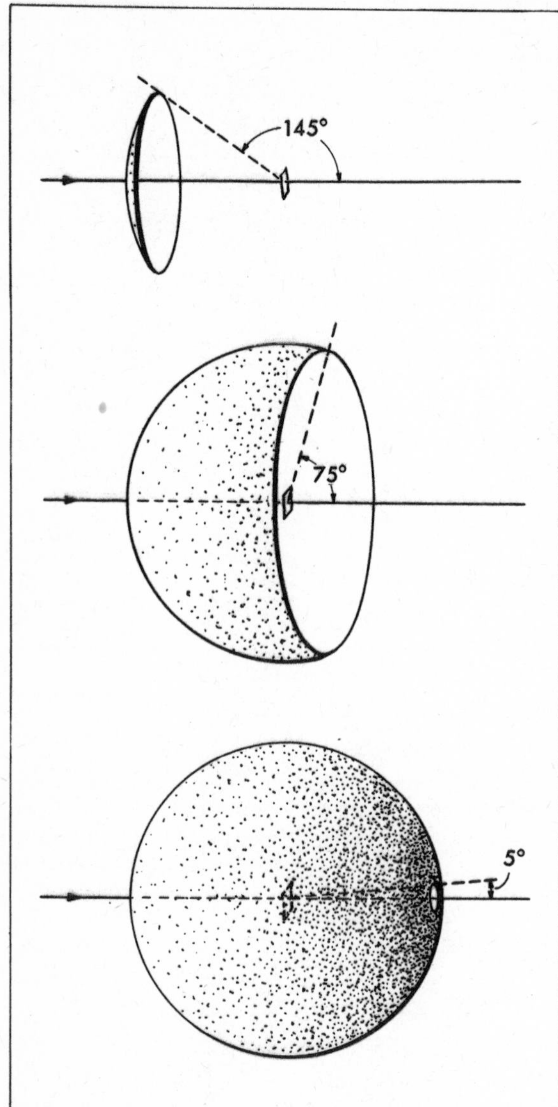

32–13. Since the particles are scattered in all directions, they spread out over the surface of a sphere. When we count all those particles scattered by more than a given angle θ, we are counting the particles that fall on a cap, on a segment of the sphere. The caps for $\theta = 145°$, $\theta = 75°$, and $\theta = 5°$ are shown. N_θ is the number of particles scattered onto the appropriate cap.

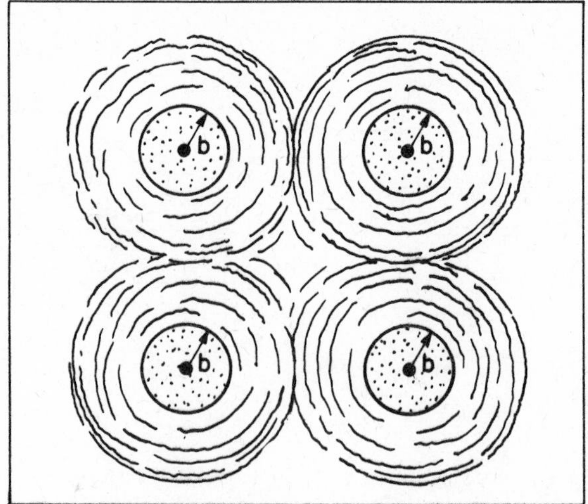

32–14. Alpha particles are sprayed uniformly over the target area of many atoms. Therefore the number of particles coming within a distance b of any nucleus is proportional to πb^2 — the area of a circle of radius b.

puting the number of alpha particles that will hit with less than a certain aiming error b. All these alpha particles (and no others) should then be scattered by more than the corresponding scattering angle θ. Since we can measure experimentally the number of alpha particles N_θ scattered by more than any particular angle θ, we can then find experimentally whether the scattering is produced by a Coulomb force. Another force might produce the same number N_θ scattered by more than one particular angle θ, but as we shall see, it could not produce the same relation between N_θ and θ over many angles. In detail, therefore, our experiment will be to measure N_θ as a function of θ (Fig. 32–13) and to compare the experimental results with those we predict from the Coulomb force.

To compute the number of alpha particles that hit within a certain distance b of the center of an atom, we take advantage of the fact that the beam sprays uniformly all over the target area of an atom. Because the number of alpha particles aimed at a small area of an atom is equal to the number aimed at any other equal area in the same atom, the number of alpha particles that pass within a distance b of a given nucleus is proportional to the area of a circle of radius b (Fig. 32–14). This area is πb^2. Consequently, the number of alpha particles that are scattered through more than the angle θ is proportional to b^2.

Now we already know how b is related to θ. By using the graph of b vs. θ we can construct a graph of b^2 vs. θ. Since the number of particles N_θ scattered through more than the angle θ is proportional to b^2, a plot of b^2 vs. θ and a plot of N_θ vs. θ are the same (except for a factor to adjust the vertical scale). Fig. 32–15 shows this graph.

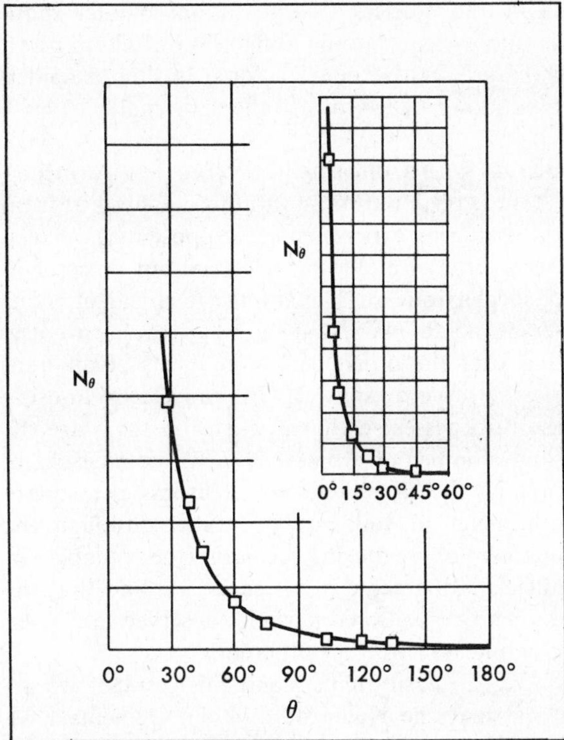

32–15. A graph of N_θ (the number of particles scattered through an angle greater than θ) vs. θ. The curved line shows what we would expect with a Coulomb force. The points in small squares represent the data collected by Geiger and Marsden in their scattering experiments. The insert shows the curve for small angles on a different scale.

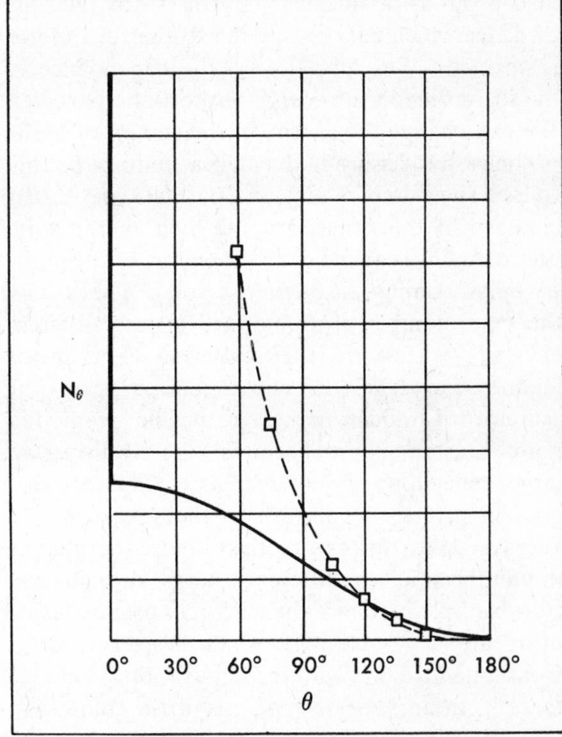

32–16. The solid line is the curve of N_θ vs. θ for a force that rises abruptly. The dashed line connects Geiger and Marsden's experimental points. The curves were adjusted so that they coincided at $\theta = 120°$. No adjustment will make them fit together.

We are now in a position to make an experimental test of the Rutherford model. By counting the number of alpha particles scattered out of the beam into all various directions, we can find out experimentally whether or not the number of alpha particles N_θ — the number scattered through all angles larger than θ — looks like the graph. Detailed experiments on the angular distribution were performed by Geiger and Marsden (1913). The square boxes in Fig. 32–15 show some of their results. Within the accuracy of the measurements, the experimental points fall on the computed curve for the Coulomb force.

We can now conclude that the scattering of alpha particles is the result of a Coulomb force; but to be more certain of this conclusion, we shall see what kind of graph of N_θ versus θ would result from a different force. It is easy to calculate the paths and find the relation between aiming error and scattering angle for a force which is zero at large distances from the center of the atom and then rises abruptly to large values if an alpha particle gets within a certain distance of the center. For this reason we have chosen to construct the graph of N_θ versus θ for such an abrupt force. This curve shown in Fig. 32–16 is different from the curve that results from a Coulomb force, so different that we clearly cannot get it to agree with the experimental results of Geiger and Marsden.

In general we may assume that any force we fancy is acting on the alpha particles, then we can compute the graph of N_θ versus θ for that force. For each different force, we get a different graph — and we can identify the force by the shape of the graph. The shape of the graph of the experimental results is the same as that for the Coulomb force. Consequently this is the force that acts on the alpha particles.

The test of the Rutherford model provided by the measurements of the angular distribution of scattered alpha particles is convincing evidence that the scattering takes place in a Coulomb-force field around the nucleus. But it is not the only evidence which tells us that the Rutherford model is correct. We can also use the dependence of the scattering on the energy of the alpha particles. We can change the energy of the stream of alpha particles by passing it through a number of thin foils. The numbers of alpha particles are hardly changed by this procedure, but their energy is reduced, and we can measure the energy of the alpha particles coming through the foil. Then, with the same number of alpha particles but different energy, we can do the scattering experiments again. For less energetic alpha particles, the Rutherford model makes a specific prediction about the angular deflections. The number of large deflections should increase. This number goes in inverse proportion to the square of the energy. With forces of other kinds, the change in numbers has a different energy dependence. For example, with an abrupt force, the scattering of an alpha particle is the same at every energy. Consequently, we can distinguish one kind of force from another on the basis of the changes in the angular distribution that occur when the energy of the alpha particle is altered. Geiger and Marsden also carried out an experiment to check the Rutherford model in this way. Again, the experimental results agree with the Rutherford model. In changing the energy by a factor of 10, they found that the number of particles scattered into any given range of large angles increases as the inverse square of the energy. The force doing the scattering must be the Coulomb force.

This is indeed a most remarkable result. Using alpha particles as probes, we have explored the electric field *inside* individual atoms and found that it obeys an inverse-square law. In the first place, this means that the positive charge of the atom is actually concentrated in a much smaller volume than the complete atom. In the second place, we find evidence that Coulomb's law, which we had previously verified experimentally only down to distances of the order of centimeters, holds in fact with high accuracy down to distances much smaller than atomic dimensions. As we shall see in the next section, those alpha particles with which we probe closest to the nucleus and for which we get the largest angles of deflection penetrate far inside the atoms. They only turn around when they are about 10^{-14} meters away from the nuclear charge, about one-ten-thousandth of an atomic dimension. The known domain of the Coulomb force is thus extended by a factor of 10^4 toward the very small.

32–4. More Information from Scattering

There is more information to be obtained from the scattering experiments. Suppose that we keep our source of alpha particles and our detector in fixed positions and we change to a leaf of a different metal (Fig. 32–17). Suppose that we use, one after the other, very thin sheets of different elements (gold, silver, platinum, etc.), choosing the thicknesses so that in each foil there are the same number of atoms in the way of the beam, that is, the same number of atoms per square centimeter of foil surface. Now although the number of scattering centers (the number of nuclei) is the same in all cases, we find that the numbers of scattered particles observed in a given time interval are very different.

We can easily understand this result if we assume that the nuclei of different elements have different electric charges. For a larger nuclear charge, the force pushing the particle out of its original direction is greater. Therefore, if we shoot in alpha particles with a given speed and the same aiming error, we expect them to undergo

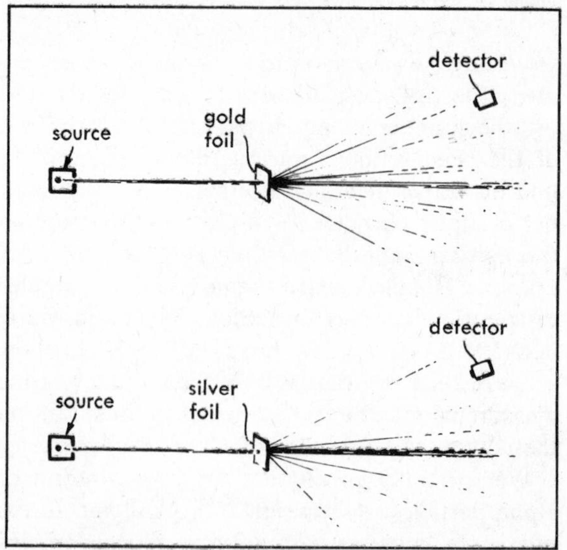

32–17. If we use foils of different metals, but each with the same number of atoms per cm² of surface, the observed scattering is different. Using the same beam for equal times, the number of alpha particles scattered into any given angle by the gold foil is 2.8 times the number scattered into the same angle by the silver foil.

a larger deflection (Fig. 32–18). Detailed computations (Newton's law, Coulomb's law, and geometry) show that the number of alpha particles scattered within a given range of angles is proportional to the square of the nuclear charge. Therefore, we can actually compare by our experiments the electric charges of the nuclei of different elements. We can go further still and compute the actual charge in elementary electric charges.

According to other evidence, the nucleus of copper has 29 positive elementary charges, the nucleus of silver 47, the nucleus of platinum 78. From alpha-particle scattering, Chadwick found almost these results. His experimental measurements yielded 29.3, 46.3, and 77.4 $\pm$ $1\frac{1}{2}$%. This means that the nuclear charges must be 29 or 30, 46 or 47, and between 76 and 79 elementary charges respectively — a masterpiece of prying information out of atoms with simple apparatus.

Also we know from other evidence that the nuclei of hydrogen and helium have one and two elementary charges respectively. (See Chapters 29 and 30.) Scattering experiments with hydrogen and helium gases (e.g., in a cloud chamber) confirm this result.

The number of elementary charges in the nucleus is called the *atomic number* of the element. Earlier in the development of chemistry this number was used for the serial number of the element in the chemical list. It is obviously a quantity of great physical significance. As we have mentioned, it can be measured by other methods as well as by alpha-particle scattering. They all agree and they give a new meaning to the serial numbers in the table of elements. Table 1 gives the atomic numbers of all known elements. Because atoms are neutral, the atomic number tells both the number of positive elementary charges on the nucleus and the number of electrons that surround it.

We still have not exhausted the information we can get from scattering. We have said several times that the radius of the nucleus must be much smaller than the radius of the atom. But how small is it? We found experimentally that in gold foils the scattering of alpha particles from a radioactive source corresponds to the predictions we made from Coulomb's law. This means that these alpha particles never "hit" a gold nucleus. For, if they did, forces other than the Coulomb repulsion would come into play and the resultant

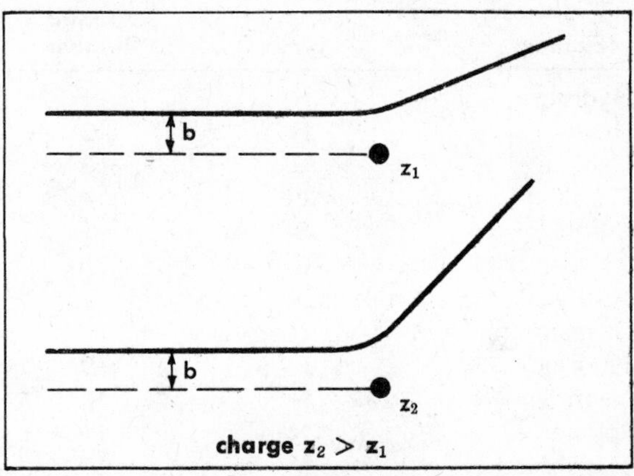

32–18. Alpha particles of a given energy and aiming error are deflected more by nuclei of larger charge.

scattering would certainly differ from that computed from the inverse-square law. Thus the gold nucleus must be smaller than the distance of closest approach of the alpha particles to the center of the nucleus.

Alpha particles of a given energy come closest to the nucleus when they are aimed directly at its center. (They move then on a straight line until their potential energy equals their initial kinetic energy, and then retrace their path backward. See Section 32–2.) Let r_0 be the distance of closest approach. Since the gold nucleus has 79 elementary charges and the alpha particle 2, the potential energy at the distance r_0 is:

$$U = k\,\frac{79 \times 2}{r_0} = \frac{3.6 \times 10^{-26}}{r_0}\ \text{joules}$$

$$\text{since } k = 2.3 \times 10^{-28}\ \frac{\text{newton-m}^2}{(\text{elem. ch.})^2}$$

and r_0 is measured in meters.

On the other hand, alpha particles from a polonium source have a velocity of 1.6×10^7 m/sec and a mass of 6.62×10^{-27} kg. (See Chapter 30.) Therefore, their kinetic energy is

$$\tfrac{1}{2}mv^2 = 8.47 \times 10^{-13}\ \text{joules.}$$

By equating the potential energy gained to the original kinetic energy, we obtain

$$r_0 = 4.3 \times 10^{-14}\ \text{meters.}$$

Thus we can assert that the radius of the gold nucleus is certainly less than 4.3×10^{-14} m.

Table 1 The Elements

Element	Symbol	Atomic Number	Element	Symbol	Atomic Number
Hydrogen	H	1	Iodine	I	53
Helium	He	2	Xenon	Xe	54
Lithium	Li	3	Cesium	Cs	55
Beryllium	Be	4	Barium	Ba	56
Boron	B	5	Lanthanum	La	57
Carbon	C	6	Cerium	Ce	58
Nitrogen	N	7	Praseodymium	Pr	59
Oxygen	O	8	Neodymium	Nd	60
Fluorine	F	9	Promethium	Pm	61
Neon	Ne	10	Samarium	Sm	62
Sodium	Na	11	Europium	Eu	63
Magnesium	Mg	12	Gadolinium	Gd	64
Aluminum	Al	13	Terbium	Tb	65
Silicon	Si	14	Dysprosium	Dy	66
Phosphorus	P	15	Holmium	Ho	67
Sulfur	S	16	Erbium	Er	68
Chlorine	Cl	17	Thulium	Tm	69
Argon	A	18	Ytterbium	Yb	70
Potassium	K	19	Lutetium	Lu	71
Calcium	Ca	20	Hafnium	Hf	72
Scandium	Sc	21	Tantalum	Ta	73
Titanium	Ti	22	Tungsten	W	74
Vanadium	V	23	Rhenium	Re	75
Chromium	Cr	24	Osmium	Os	76
Manganese	Mn	25	Iridium	Ir	77
Iron	Fe	26	Platinum	Pt	78
Cobalt	Co	27	Gold	Au	79
Nickel	Ni	28	Mercury	Hg	80
Copper	Cu	29	Thallium	Tl	81
Zinc	Zn	30	Lead	Pb	82
Gallium	Ga	31	Bismuth	Bi	83
Germanium	Ge	32	Polonium	Po	84
Arsenic	As	33	Astatine	At	85
Selenium	Se	34	Radon	Rn	86
Bromine	Br	35	Francium	Fr	87
Krypton	Kr	36	Radium	Ra	88
Rubidium	Rb	37	Actinium	Ac	89
Strontium	Sr	38	Thorium	Th	90
Yttrium	Y	39	Protactinium	Pa	91
Zirconium	Zr	40	Uranium	U	92
Niobium	Nb	41	* * * * * * *		
Molybdenum	Mo	42			
Technetium	Tc	43	Neptunium	Np	93
Ruthenium	Ru	44	Plutonium	Pu	94
Rhodium	Rh	45	Americium	Am	95
Palladium	Pd	46	Curium	Cm	96
Silver	Ag	47	Berkelium	Bk	97
Cadmium	Cd	48	Californium	Cf	98
Indium	In	49	Einsteinium	E	99
Tin	Sn	50	Fermium	Fm	100
Antimony	Sb	51	Mendelevium	Mv	101
Tellurium	Te	52	Nobelium	No	102

Similar results are obtained for the nuclei of the other elements. Alpha-particle experiments therefore also bear out Rutherford's hypothesis that the nucleus is a minute heavy speck.

32–5. Troubles

Looking back at what we have learned in this chapter, we find good reason to be pleased with the new insight that we seem to have gained.

The Rutherford model, describing the atom as a tiny but massive positively charged nucleus surrounded by a number of electrons, seems essentially correct. Moreover, we have learned how to measure the charge on the nucleus and how to estimate at least an upper limit for its "radius." Knowing the charge of the nucleus, we also know the number of electrons which complete the atom.

And yet, as we continue our study, our complacency begins to be shaken. Suppose, for example, that in an effort to determine the size of nuclei, we bombard them with faster and faster alpha particles. The distance of closest approach decreases. When it becomes smaller than the nuclear radius, deviations from the simple scattering laws should appear. Since the particles that come closest to the nucleus are those that suffer largest deflections, the theoretical scattering distribution should fail at the largest angles first. This, however, is not always in agreement with the observations. Deviations from the computed scattering law occur for sufficiently high energies of the alpha particles, but when they do, often small angles as well as large angles are affected.

An even more serious flaw in the Rutherford model becomes evident as soon as we start considering the behavior of the electrons. In the atom, as imagined by Rutherford, the electrons move around the nucleus like planets around the sun. In fact, under the urging of the Coulomb force, they can avoid falling immediately into the nucleus only by continuously revolving around it. This motion is an accelerated motion, and therefore should be accompanied by the emission of electromagnetic waves. But the electromagnetic waves drain away energy. So, like an earth satellite which loses energy in the atmosphere, the electrons must spiral into the nucleus. By imagining that they move like planets, we have only stretched the time for electrons to fall in. Instead of falling into the nucleus in about 10^{-17} sec, as an electron would if it started from rest at the outside of an atom, an electron spiraling in while radiating away its energy should take about 2×10^{-11} sec to get to the nucleus. This time is still far too short to make the atom look stable at the dimensions we know. Consequently, Rutherford's model is not consistent with our knowledge of the process of electromagnetic radiation.

Atoms do emit light, and that light must come from the accelerated motion of the charge in the atom. Therefore our whole picture of the atom is clouded by the conflicting demands. The emission of light is consistent with the Rutherford model — but it also destroys that model, for the atoms should all shrink to nuclear dimensions long before we can blink at their light. The normal atom should have the electrons stuck in the nucleus into which they have fallen. But this is in direct conflict with the evidence of alpha-particle scattering and with the size of atoms as seen in collisions in gases and in their packing in solids and liquids.

The more we probe into these questions, the more we become aware of serious troubles. Let us consider for simplicity the hydrogen atom, consisting of a single proton and a single electron. The frequency of the light emitted by the atom should be related to the number of revolutions per second of the electron around the nucleus. But the period of revolution depends on the diameter of the orbit, just as in the case of the planets in the solar system (Chapter 22). Electrons rotating in a smaller orbit have a shorter period and therefore should emit light of a higher frequency than electrons rotating in larger orbits.

As an electron emits light, its energy must decrease. Therefore, the diameter of its orbit must decrease and the frequency of the emitted wave must increase. A light source contains a huge number of atoms, and many are emitting light at one time. Some of these atoms are at one stage in the process of light emission, and some at another. Consequently, the source should be emitting light of practically all frequencies. Thus, hydrogen gas made to glow, for example, by an electric discharge should emit a continuous spectrum of light. In contrast to this prediction, spectral analysis of the hydrogen light reveals a number of sharp "lines" — that is, a number of separate wave lengths or frequencies. (Chapter 7.)

These and other difficulties cannot be solved by a mere revision of the atomic model. The understanding of atoms requires a revolutionary change in all our basic physical concepts. The new physics born of this revolution forms the subject of the next chapters. In that new physics the Rutherford atom is vindicated. The tiny, but massive, charged nucleus remains. So do the electrons spread through the far larger atomic volume. What changes is the very basis of dynamics. Newton's mechanics must be replaced by a more subtle quantum mechanics — a mechanics which includes Newton's as a special case, as an approximation good enough for the world of bulk motions but startingly inadequate in the atomic world.

FOR HOME, DESK, AND LAB

1. Suppose you have a large collection of small steel balls which you can fire at different targets in turn. You cannot see the targets directly, but you can observe the paths of the balls before and after striking. In each case below, tell what you know about the targets from the behavior of the balls. The balls are all fired at the target in the same direction.

(a) All the balls bounce off the target with angle of reflection equal to angle of incidence.

(b) All the balls bounce back, but with no definite relation between angle of reflection and angle of incidence.

(c) Practically all of the balls go through the target, but a few are lost in it.

(d) All the balls are lost in the target.

(e) The paths of all the balls cross after reflection at a point in front of the target.

2. You have a wall made of cubical bales of hay, each 2 meters on a side, with a platinum ball of radius r somewhere inside each bale. The wall is 4 bales thick. Machine-gun bullets are fired at the wall so that they spread uniformly over a large area covering many bales. If a bullet misses the platinum it goes straight through; if it hits a platinum "nucleus" it bounces away and is not recorded by the "counter" at the other side. The platinum "nuclei" are not exactly one behind the other in the line of fire, so that they do not shield each other from the rain of bullets.

(a) A counter on the far side of the wall records that 314 bullets out of every 10,000 fired fail to come straight through. Estimate the radius of the nucleus.

(b) If 4 times as many bullets (1,256 bullets per 10,000) fail to get straight through, what would be your estimate of nuclear radius?

Suppose the platinum was replaced with equally hard and massive steel, and the bullets were strong steel magnets. Then an attractive force would be felt outside the nuclei.

(c) Would you expect this change to increase or decrease the number of bullets that do not go straight through?

(d) Would you expect this new effect to be more noticeable with low-speed bullets or high-speed bullets?

3. In a scattering experiment using gold foil, 4 alpha particles in 10,000 are scattered through an angle of more than 5°.

(a) How many particles would be scattered through more than 5° if we doubled the thickness of the foil?

(b) If we made the foil a thousand times thicker?

4. (a) To construct the curve of b vs. θ for an abrupt force draw a fairly large circle to represent a plane cut through a rigid sphere, and measure the scattering angles for various aiming errors. (Assume the angle of reflection of a ball hitting the surface equals the angle of incidence. Why?)

(b) From your curve of b vs. θ construct a graph of N vs. θ and compare it with Fig. 32–16.

(c) Explain why this relationship is independent of the energy of the particles fired at the sphere.

5. From the graph in Fig. 32–15, determine the ratio of the number of particles scattered through an angle greater than 15° to those scattered through an angle greater than 22.5°.

6. Suppose we wish to probe the interior of atoms with light waves.

(a) What is the wave length of X rays?

(b) What size would a nucleus have to be to reflect them?

7. Three experiments were done with the same alpha particle beam, the same counters at the same positions, and different foil targets. Five counters were arranged with respect to each target and the beam to count particles scattered by the angles given in the table. The time interval of counting was the same for all three experiments. The foils were designed so that the beam passed through the same number of atoms per square centimeter regardless of which target was used. The results presented in the table below give the numbers of particles scattered into the same range of scattering angles. For example, the count at 30° includes all particles scattered in any direction in the range between 29° and 31°; the count at 60°, all those scattered in any direction in the range between 59° and 61°, etc.

SCATTERING ANGLE	NUMBER COUNTED		
	Target 1	Target 2	Target 3
30°	2,790	35,920	102,810
60°	346	4,451	12,760
90°	100	1,288	3,685
120°	39	496	1,423
150°	14	187	532

(a) Plot the number scattered versus the scattering angle for each target. (Plot all three graphs on the same axes.)

(b) Target 1 was aluminum. What were the other targets?

8. (a) Explain why the gravitational force between an alpha particle and a gold nucleus has little effect on the scattering of alpha particles by gold.

(b) What is the ratio of the electric force on an alpha particle to the gravitational force when the separation of an alpha particle and a gold nucleus is 10^{-14} m? When it is 10^{-13} m?

9. An alpha particle whose kinetic energy is 10^{-12} joules is scattered by a gold nucleus.

(a) What is the minimum possible distance of closest approach?

(b) What must be the aiming error if the alpha particle is to get this close?

(c) How close could a proton of the same energy approach? A neutron?

10. In one scattering experiment a proton beam strikes a gold target. In a second experiment a beam of deuterons (atomic mass = 2, atomic number = 1) is used. The kinetic energy of the particles is the same in both beams. How will the minimum distance of closest approach to gold nuclei of the two kinds of beams compare?

11. What is the change in velocity of (a) a nitrogen atom and (b) a helium atom when struck head-on by an alpha particle whose velocity is 1.6×10^7 m/sec? Assume that the atoms are at rest when they are hit. See Section 24–8.

12. (a) What fraction of its energy is lost by an alpha particle in a head-on collision with an electron? (The mass of an alpha particle is about 7,200 times that of an electron.)

(b) Approximately how many such collisions must occur before the energy of the alpha particle is reduced by 1 per cent.

13. A student wants to make an approximate scale model of the arrangement of the gold nuclei in a monolayer of gold. He decides to use marbles (diameter 1.5 cm) to represent the nuclei. About how far apart should he place them? Note: The radius of the gold nucleus is about 7×10^{-15} meters.

14. An alpha particle whose velocity is 10^7 m/sec is scattered by a gold nucleus at rest through an angle of 60°. Assume that so little kinetic energy is transferred to the gold nucleus that the speed of the alpha particle after the scattering is the same as it was before.

(a) What is the momentum transferred to the gold atom?

(b) What is the velocity given to the gold nucleus?

(c) What is the kinetic energy given to the gold nucleus?

(d) Was your initial assumption a good one? Explain.

15. (a) If the distance of closest approach of the alpha particle in problem 14 was 10^{-13} m, what was its speed at this point?

(b) At what speed was it moving toward the nucleus at that point?

FURTHER READING

ANDRADE, E. N. DA C., *An Approach to Modern Physics*. Doubleday, 1956 (Chapter 8).
BORN, MAX, *The Restless Universe*. Dover, 1951.
FERMI, LAURA, *Atoms in the Family*. University of Chicago Press, 1954.
HECHT, SELIG, *Explaining the Atom*. Viking, 1954.
HUGHES, DONALD J., *The Neutron Story*. Doubleday, 1959: A Science Study Series paperback.
OLDENBERG, OTTO, *Introduction to Atomic Physics*. McGraw-Hill, 1954. (See section on Rutherford.)
PEIERLS, R. E., *The Laws of Nature*. Scribner, 1956 (Chapter 4).
ROMER, ALFRED, *The Restless Atoms*. Doubleday, 1960: A Science Study Series paperback.
WHITTAKER, SIR EDMUND, *History of the Theories of Aether and Electricity*. Nelson, 1953 (Chapter 1).

PHOTONS AND MATTER WAVES

CHAPTER 33

WITH the Rutherford model, classical physics went as far as it could into the understanding of the atom. The troubles discussed at the end of the last chapter made it clear that only fundamental new ideas about the principles of physics could carry us further. But the troubles uncovered by the Rutherford model were by no means the only nor the first indication that fundamental changes were needed in physics. At the end of the last century, the successes of the classical wave theory of light were tempered by troubles similar to those met by the Rutherford model with regard to dynamical laws. With a series of new discoveries, including the photoelectric effect, X rays, and radioactivity, the new physics began. Although this new physics was to make a revolutionary change in dynamics, the original clues to this change came from the radiation of light and its interaction with matter.

We now shall examine the experimental evidence which called for a good hard look at the wave theory of light. Later we shall see how the ideas coming from this study eventually led to an extension of Newtonian dynamics. Then you can see how really revolutionary the statements of the new physics are, and at the same time how this new physics was built upon and successfully conserved the great gains of the physics of the past.

33–1. The Graininess of Light

The wave theory has had convincing successes in describing all forms of electromagnetic radiation, from radio waves measured in kilometers down to the light waves which in our microscopes bring us a view of the smallest cell. We shall now give an account of experiments, some actually as they were done, some only illustrative of what might be done, in which the wave picture was subjected to a new kind of test.

That test was to see what light did to the atomic structure of matter. In the Millikan experiment, discussed for a very different purpose in Section 28–5, X rays — high-frequency light — expel individual electrons from tiny specks of matter. A good many tries were made of a related experi-

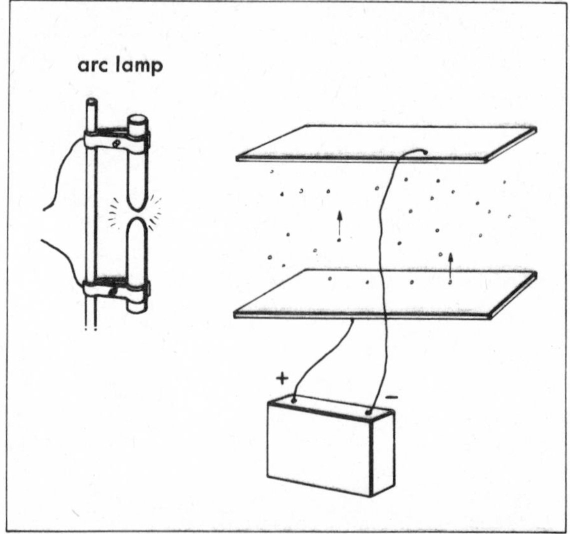

33–1. The light from the arc lamp illuminates a large number of droplets or specks of metal. These specks have been allowed to charge, and are floating between charged parallel plates; they are nothing but a large crowd of "Millikan oil drops." As the light strikes the specks, they may lose electrons. Each time an electron is lost, the speck will begin to drift upward toward the negative plate, for it is now positively charged by more than enough to balance its weight. Here and there, at random over the whole lighted region, a speck will suddenly start upward.

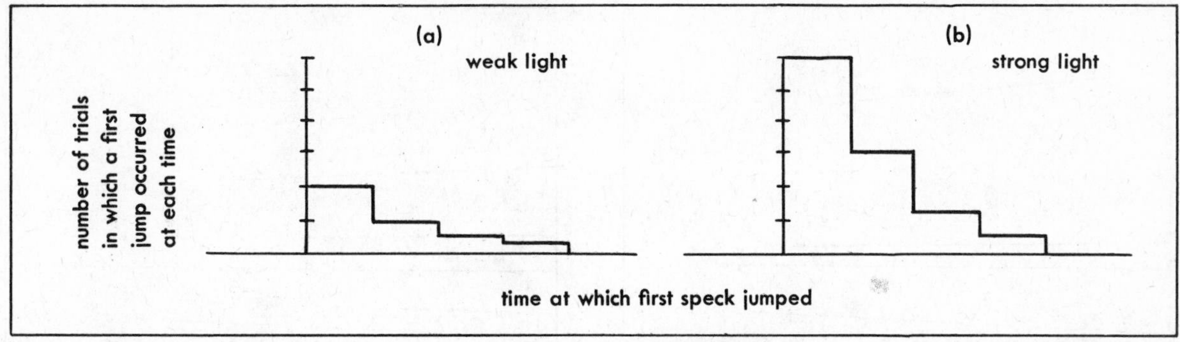

33–2. In the apparatus of Fig. 33–1, we turn the light on suddenly, and watch for the first speck to start upward. This time is then recorded. The graphs show the results of many such time-lag measurements. In (a) the experiment was done with weak light; in (b) with much stronger light. Everything else remained unchanged. On the average, the strong light ejects electrons more quickly than the weak light, but even in weak light, some electrons are ejected with no appreciable lag. Experiments of more advanced sort have pushed this minimum lag time down below 10^{-8} seconds.

ment: a kind of Millikan experiment in which X rays or ultraviolet light from an arc lamp falls upon large numbers of specks of material drifting between a pair of charged plates (Fig. 33–1). We ask what the wave picture of light predicts about the ejection of electrons from the tiny specks, and compare the prediction with what actually happens.

When light — that is, electromagnetic radiation — shines on a speck of matter, the electric field in the light wave pushes on the electrons in the atoms. If an electron is ejected from an atom, its ejection must be an effect of the electric field which forces it out of its normal motion within the atom. (You may want to figure out why the *magnetic* field is not important for electron ejection.)

Now, the electric field is rapidly changing in time, but at a given instant it has the same strength everywhere along the front of the electromagnetic wave. When such a wave hits an atom, therefore, it starts to shake the electrons. Since the wave looks the same over a large region of space, it shakes electrons in the little specks of matter in the same way at almost exactly the same time all over the region between the plates. If the light is weak, it will take the light wave considerable time to shake any electrons loose. Then, since there are many electrons in identical atoms pushed in the same way by the electric field of the light wave, a large number of electrons should be ejected at almost the same time. We thus expect to see, for rather weak light, a time during which nothing happens. Then, at one time all over the front of the light beam, individual specks should begin to lose electrons. With stronger light, the loss should come sooner; with weak light, later.

The actual result is astonishingly different. Instead of a definite wait, after which all the specks begin to lose electrons, it is found that a speck or two may jump immediately. These jumps show that the specks have already lost electrons and are now moving like the Millikan spheres under the influence of the electric field between the plates. The first specks to jump may be found anywhere in the beam. After them others will jump — one here, one there, with no particular pattern. After a while most of the specks will have lost electrons, but in a quite random way. Some may have lost several electrons; a few will have lost none at all.

If the light is made weaker, the waiting period is sometimes no longer. If the light is stronger, the wait is sometimes no shorter. We can make the specks as similar as can be, use our best identical spheres, and yet the individual specks behave differently (Fig. 33–2). Only the average behavior seems to be what we expect. On the average the specks will lose electrons as well in one part of a uniform light beam as in another. On the average, more electrons are driven out in one second by strong than by weak light; but this refers only to the average over many specks and many trials. In any particular case, how long it takes the first speck to respond seems to be a matter of chance. Once in a while, even the weakest light will cause the immediate loss of an electron; once in a while, even in the strongest beam, you will wait a fairly long time to see the first electron removed. The whole nature of this result seems to belie our well-founded view of the smooth oscillating wave front,

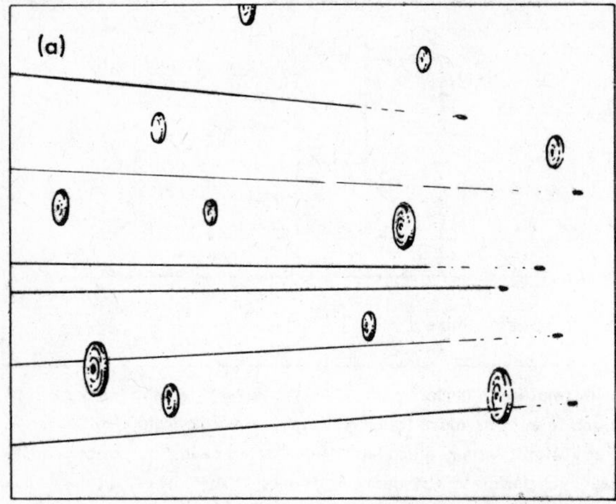

33–3. The close analogy between bullets fired in a random volley at a set of targets, and a light beam ejecting electrons. If the volley comes from only a few guns (a), the "beam" of bullets is weak. Most of the time, you would wait a long time to see a direct hit. But occasionally a lucky hit would immediately follow the start of firing. With many rifles firing (b), the "beam" is intense. Hits become frequent, and on the average you wait less time for the first one. But the first hit might come no sooner, or even later, than an early first hit in a weak beam. Just which target would be hit next, of course, is a matter of chance.

everywhere uniform and moving in phase, displacing electrons in every speck by the cumulative action of the varying electric field.

The predictions of our picture of electromagnetic waves do not fit the facts, but we know of another simple model, long discarded, which we can now revive. Suppose that instead of the smooth plane wave front, the beam of light is represented by a collection of fast-moving tiny particles, like a volley of bullets or an air-driven blast of sand (Fig. 33–3). In such a beam, a speck would be hit squarely by a single particle of light only by chance. The hits would appear now here, now there, over the whole of the beam. The moment when the first speck was hit would also be a matter of chance. Even if the beam was weak — with only a few particles crossing a given area in a second — it might happen that a particle of light strikes one speck immediately after the beam is turned on. On the other hand, in a strong beam, the dense rain of particles might fail to make any direct hit for a noticeable time. Only on the average would it be true that in a strong beam the first hit would come soon, and the others follow in rapid sequence. This picture gives an accurate and convincing description of the way light really ejects electrons from the little specks of matter.

On this picture light comes in grains. It arrives in little bundles which we shall call *photons*. The photons are the bullets or particles of light; and when they hit a speck of matter, they may eject an electron.

Our experiment directly detecting the ejection of electrons by a light beam is not the only means of displaying the grainy character of the beam of light. A photographic plate bears a layer of very small crystals, each one of which can be changed by the impact of light into a form which the developer solution can blacken. The image is not formed smoothly, but by the random accumulation of blackened grains. This process is too complex to lead us to interpret light from it alone — the film grains differ in their atomic constitution, for example — but it adds support to the direct electron-ejection experiment. With other devices using ejection — the photoelectric cell, the television-camera image tube — one can watch an image being formed point by point by light. In very weak light, the successive "hits" are so slow that the eye can easily follow them. The image, whatever it may be, is painted slowly by the accumulation of random hits, which gradually pile up, many wherever much light falls, few wherever the illumination is weak. Only when very many particles of light have struck every little area — in a strong beam, quickly, or in a weak beam after sufficient time — does the accumulation become so dense that all trace of its grainy structure is lost.

33–2. The Orderliness of Chance

It is easy to convince yourself that the accumulation of individual events, all going on by chance, but some of them more probable than others, will form in the end a regular and smooth pattern. There is no substitute for actually performing an experiment in which you watch meaning emerge from what appears to be a sequence of wholly meaningless and sporadic events. It is not practical to simulate the myriad grains of light which form a good photographic image, but we can consider a crude pattern formed by a smaller number instead.

Suppose the bombardment of some receiving plate by a light beam results in the bar pattern of Fig. 33–4 (a). More of the "grains" of light must in the end fall on the regions of the photographic plate that become dark than on those that remain lighter. We can represent this pattern by the graph of Fig. 33–4 (b), where the height of the graph is proportional to the total number of hits on that same region in the picture of Fig. 33–4 (a). Now we prepare a set of cards, marked *L*, *C*, and *R* for the left-, center-, and right-hand bars of the pattern. We prepare cards in a number proportional to the total number of hits expected; say, 3 marked *L*, 1 marked *C*, and 6 marked *R*. This fairly expresses the assumed probability of a hit in each of the three places we distinguish. Now draw a single card blindly from a well-shuffled mixture. Read what it is, then put it back, reshuffle, and draw again. Do this over and over again. At each draw, note the letter the card bears, and plot the results of each draw by adding to the height of the appropriate vertical bar on a graph constructed like Fig. 33–4 (b). At first, no clear sign of the pattern will be present, except very rarely by a remarkable accident. Later on, the pattern will begin to emerge, and if you are patient enough to draw several thousand times, the pattern thus randomly built up is almost sure to be regular as any graph you could deliberately construct. The results of one such experiment are plotted in Fig. 33–4 (c), and your own experiment should give you a still better idea of how such patterns can arise. Of course, the grains of light are not cards; we are not really experimenting with light, but with the laws of chance and probability. But many experiments have demonstrated that the formation of images by light follows in quantitative detail exactly the laws obeyed by the random draw of shuffled cards.

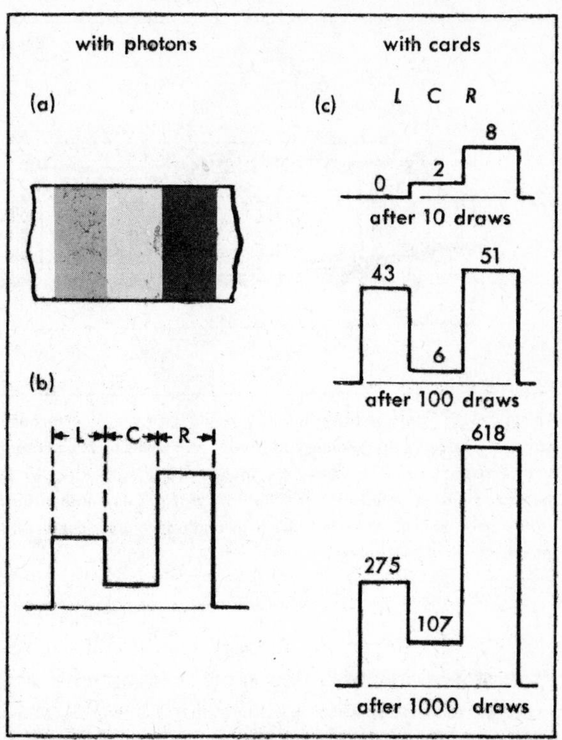

33–4. The growth of pattern out of chance. In (a) we see a bar pattern of light and dark, representing some sort of interference fringes. In (b) the same pattern has been graphed, showing how the light intensity varies with position. In (c) we see plots of an analogous experiment in which a similar pattern is built up by random chance draws from a collection of cards whose probability of draw has been correctly adjusted. The patterns made with more and more individual draws come closer and closer to the expected pattern, beginning with an apparently disorderly arrangement showing no resemblance to the final result. The ordinary light source presents us images which are painted out by some 10^{12} or even many more photons per second.

With this model we produced the final regular pattern and also the irregular fluctuating build-up of the pattern that can actually be observed.

It is just for this reason that the finely detailed images caught by a TV camera or a photographic camera can be formed only in sufficient light. The inviolable minimum of light needed is set by the graininess of light. No matter how sensitive the receivers of the light may be, the image cannot be made unless there are enough of the light packets to form it accurately. It is striking that the effects of the intrinsic graininess of light have been demonstrated to occur for the eye just about at the dimmest light which a man can see. Our

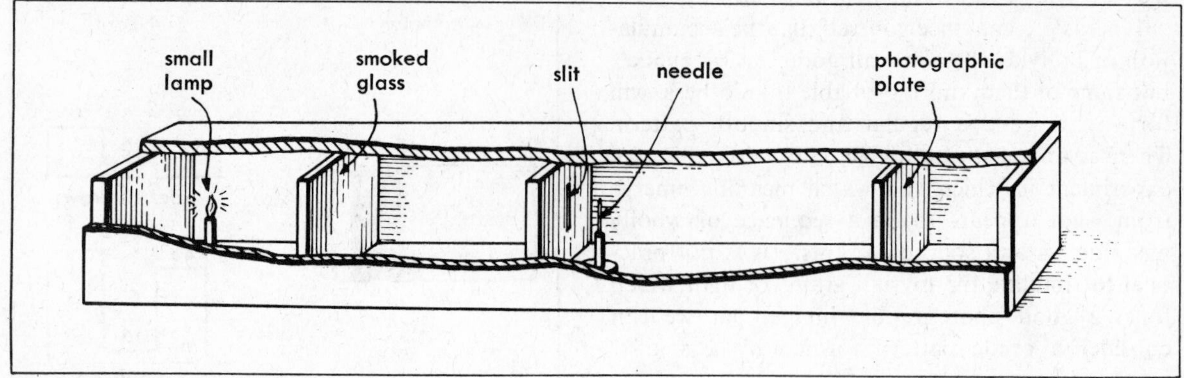

33–5. G. I. Taylor's experiment, proving that the interference pattern was correctly given even if only one photon was present in the apparatus at a time. He found good, sharp fringes in the shadow of a needle cast by light from a slit, even when that light came from a dim gas flame through such absorbers that an exposure of three months was needed.

eyes are developed about as far as any light receivers working with the same size of lens, the same time of response, and the same band of wave lengths can possibly be. They have reached very close to the natural limit.

33–3. Graininess and Interference

In weak light we find the individual effects of grains. Little bundles of light come along at random, now here and now there, arriving in greater number where the intensity is higher and in smaller number where the light is weaker. This grainy picture of light is far different from our usual view of waves. It seems to have nothing to do with interference and diffraction. Can it be that the wave properties demonstrated so clearly in interference experiments apply only to strong light, where somehow the many individual "grains" of light interact one with another to produce the wavelike results? Or do the patterns built up by weak light also show interference? This question was directly tested fifty years ago by Geoffrey Taylor, a young student at the University of Cambridge, who later become Sir Geoffrey for his lifetime of successful work in physics.

In a light-tight box Taylor set up a small lamp which cast the shadow of a needle on a photographic plate (Fig. 33–5). He chose the dimensions so that the diffraction bands around the shadow of the needle were plainly visible. Then he reduced the intensity of the light. Longer and longer exposures were needed to get a well-exposed plate. Finally, he made an exposure lasting a couple of months (which, the story goes, he spent sailing). Even on this plate the diffraction bands were perfectly clear, though he could show for this very faint light that only one photon — one of the packets of light — was in his box at a time. Interference therefore takes place even for single particles of light. It works for every single photon.*

Taylor's experiment is not the only experiment that points to this conclusion. There are many. Nowadays a photo-cell working an amplifier can make the arrival of the photons audible. It is interesting to hear the clicks which signal the painting out by individual photons of a two-slit diffraction pattern. While you watch and listen, the pattern is formed by photons coming in one by one. All interference experiments work this way: the photons come one at a time. So we are forced by direct experimental evidence to believe that wave behavior applies to individual photons.

What do we mean by the wave behavior of an individual photon? We shall have more to say on this by no means simple point. For the moment, we shall be satisfied to say that the electromagnetic wave must somehow fix the probability of appearance of a photon. Where the field in the wave is strong, there we shall very probably find photons; where the field is weak, photons will occur with small probability; where the field

*Taylor knew that there was only one (and often no) photon in his box at one time because from the energy of one photon and the intensity of the light he could find the number of photons in any given length of light beam. He found the photons must be spaced farther apart on the average than the length of the box. So usually there was not even one photon in the box. You can do this kind of calculation after studying the next section.

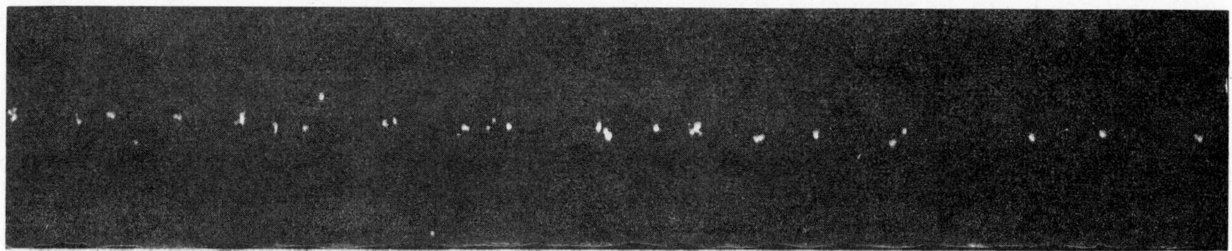

33–6. The cloud chamber shows the absorption of photons, one by one, and the weakening of the beam as photons are removed. The photons enter from the left, and are absorbed by the argon atoms of the gas. They eject photo-electrons, whose tracks acquire little fog droplets, which show white in the photograph. Notice the similarity of all the short photo-electron tracks. The "light" is actually an X-ray beam of wave length about 0.2 angstroms. (W. Gentner, H. Maier-Leibnitz and W. Bothe, "Atlas Typischer Nebelkammerbilder," Springer Verlag, Berlin, 1940.)

vanishes, no photons occur at all. When it interacts with the photographic emulsion or the photoelectric cell, no single photon is spread out over a whole interference pattern. The photon hits at a definite place. But for each photon, the probability is highest that it will arrive where the interference pattern is most intense. The probability of arrival at a region of half that intensity is half as big, and so on. The probabilities of arrival for each photon have just the pattern of the intensity of the interference fringes (the bright and dark interference bars). So when many photons have arrived, the interference picture is painted out by their cumulative effect.

33–4. The Photoelectric Effect

Where a photon hits, and when it arrives, are matters of probability. On the other hand, a photon behaves *every single time*, and not just on the average, like a particle of definite energy and momentum.

This is shown directly by watching the ejection of an electron by a photon, not from a speck of matter, but from a single atom. In Fig. 33–6 a beam of photons coming from the left strikes the gas in a cloud chamber. As the beam penetrates, here and there a photon ejects an electron from an atom of the gas. The little clusters of water drops form at the place where the electrons come out. After a while the beam of photons is noticeably weakened; indeed, for each electron produced, a photon has been removed from the beam. This can be verified by watching the photons penetrate so far into the gas that the original beam has all but been absorbed. The energy of the beam of light has passed into the gas. In fact, most of that energy appears as the kinetic energy of the ejected electrons.

Each electron makes a track of about equal length wherever it may start. So each of the emitted electrons must have had almost the same energy. From this point of view all the events are the same. And in particular each photon that causes an event is the same. A weaker beam means fewer photons, rather than photons of different energy. When we study the energy balance more closely we find that the energy is conserved in each individual event, and we again check that a weaker beam only means less photons.

Such a cloud-chamber study cannot be made with photons of visible light. In the experiment shown in Fig. 33–6, X rays were used, forming a beam of electromagnetic radiation of wave length only a few tenths of an angstrom. At this wave length the individual process is then made obvious. With X rays of shorter wave length the photoelectrons are knocked out harder and the identical nature of the individual events is even easier to see.

The use of a beam of ultraviolet light allows a more detailed, if a less direct, study of the process of ejection of an electron by light. This process is called the photoelectric effect. It can occur at a metallic surface, in a liquid, or in the individual atoms of a gas.

To study the photoelectric effect, we can use a simple device (though not an easy one to build). It is a glass bulb, evacuated to a first-class vacuum, with two small and really clean copper plates mounted inside (Fig. 33–7), and two leads for electrical connections to the plates. We apply a potential difference of several volts between the plates, and shine light on the inner surface of one plate. If we illuminate the positive plate, no measurable current will flow within the vacuum.

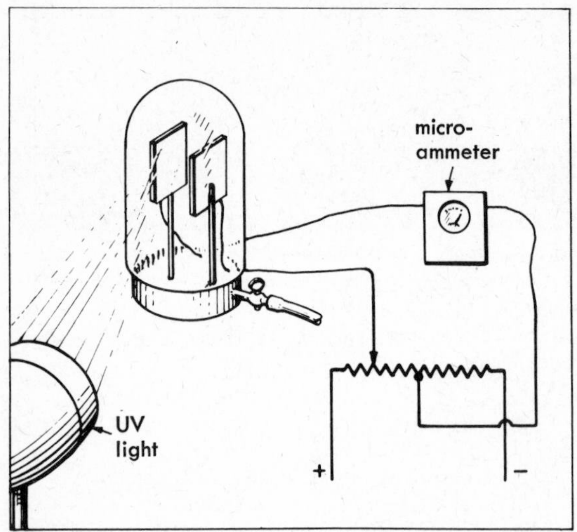

33–7. The photoelectric cell. Two copper electrodes are mounted in a well-evacuated glass bulb, and leads are brought out as shown. The circuit allows for adjustment of the potential difference between the plates; the moving contact is connected to the unilluminated plate, and can be arranged to make it either positive or negative in potential compared to the illuminated plate.

But if instead we illuminate the negative plate, a current will flow. Evidently electrons are flowing across the vacuum. If the light is cut off, the current ceases. If the beam of light is turned on again, the current begins without delay — direct measurement has shown that the lag in the photoelectron emission is certainly shorter than 10^{-8} seconds. The current is not large, but it is within easily measurable range; a copper plate a few square centimeters in area will yield microamperes of photoelectric current in direct sunlight. The current will increase and decrease in proportion to the intensity of light over a very wide range. Similar tubes are widely used in practical applications, from opening doors to reading the sound from movie film.

Our simple photo-tube confirms what we knew: when light strikes, electrons are released from the surface of a substance. The stronger the light, the greater the number of electrons ejected. The number of electrons ejected is proportional to the number of photons. All this makes sense, but we are in for a surprise when we change the wave length of the light used. The copper photo-cell will give no current in even the strongest beam of red or of green light; only ultraviolet light, or light of still shorter wave length, will work.

Perhaps this effect only occurs in copper. Let us try another substance. We continue the experiment with a tube in which the plate surfaces are coated with potassium. Now visible blue light will give a photoelectric current but red light will not. A threshold, as it is called, exists in green light. (In copper the threshold was between the visible and the ultraviolet.) Light with a wave length slightly longer than the threshold value will give no photo-current even if it floods the surface; while some current will flow in even the weakest beam of light with wave length shorter than the threshold value.

All substances have photoelectric thresholds. The wave length of the threshold depends on the nature of the substance. But there is one common point: for long waves the photoelectric effect does not take place, and for short waves — for light of high-enough frequency — it does. No picture of a wave will suffice to explain these results, but they fit well with the idea of photons. An individual electron is ejected by one particular photon. The strength of the beam determines the number of photons. Therefore the current is proportional to the light intensity. But the character of each photon collision, its ability to eject an electron, does not depend at all on how many others are present. It is a property of every single photon, and must somehow depend on wave length of the light. Light of short wave length seems more effective than that of long. Every surface will let electrons go when hit by the photons of light which is blue enough; a few surfaces will let electrons go for the photons of red light — and those of any light of shorter wave length. Some artful combinations, notably the alkali metal cesium dissolved with oxygen in a silver surface, have a threshold in the infrared; but metals like platinum will not respond to any of the light that passes through glass; only use of the deep ultraviolet will suffice to generate a photo-current from them.

33–5. Einstein's Interpretation of the Photoelectric Effect

We have seen a little way into the mechanism of the photoelectric effect. We know that it involves some detail of the photoelectric surface. We also know that it always requires light of high rather than low frequency. This suggests that the photons differ in some way dependent on the frequency. That photons of red light are different from those of blue light is only reasonable. Photons must somehow carry the information which shows up as the wave length when light waves interfere. To find out in what way the frequency is contained in the photons we must do something new. We must find out how violently the photo-electrons are ejected.

In the apparatus of Fig. 33–7 we can adjust the magnitude of the applied potential. We get the maximum current for any particular choice of surface and any given illumination by making the receiving plate slightly positive with respect to the emitting one. No increase in current follows upon increasing the voltage; evidently we are picking up all the photo-electrons ejected (Fig. 33–8). Now we can turn the voltage down and reverse the potential, making the emitting plate the positive one. Then the electrons are attracted back to the plate as they seek to leave it; but the photo-current does not vanish. Apparently the ejection of photo-electrons by light imparts to some of the electrons enough energy to overcome the retarding electric potential difference between the plates. Finally, as the retarding potential is increased, at some particular retarding potential difference, the current stops. Even stronger light (if the wave lengths remain unchanged) will not restore any photo-current. None of the photo-electrons have enough energy to cross between the plates against this retarding potential difference. We call it the cut-off potential. (See Fig. 33–8.)

The cut-off potential V_c is a means of studying the energy imparted in each single act of electron ejection. The cut-off potential difference, measured in joules per elementary charge, times the one elementary charge of each electron tells us the energy that must be taken from the fastest electrons to stop them from going all the way across from one plate to the other. It therefore tells us the maximum kinetic energy E_{el} with which these photo-electrons are emitted:

$$E_{el} = (1 \text{ elementary charge}) \times V_c.$$

With the cut-off potential as a tool, we can measure the maximum kinetic energy of the photo-electrons ejected in a series of experiments on light beams of different colors. When we are at the cut-off potential difference with one wave length, we find that we can always

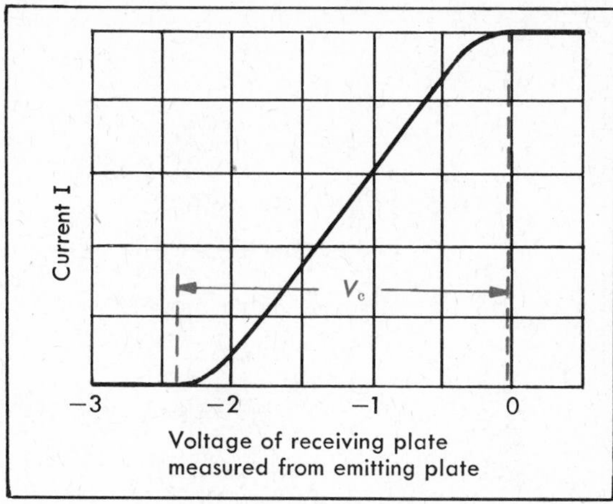

33–8. Current of photo-electrons vs. potential difference between the plates for a given kind of light. Note that the current does not stop until the receiving plate is a volt or so negative. This value is the cut-off potential V_c.

restore some photo-current by using light of shorter wave length. This observation tells us that the shorter the wave length of the light we use, the more energy the photons can give to the ejected electrons. We can measure just how much more by finding the cut-off potentials at shorter and shorter wave lengths.

If we plot the results of a series of experiments with light beams of different colors, a simple and fundamental relation emerges. It is shown in Fig. 33–9, where we plot the cut-off potential against the frequency ν (rather than the wave length) of the light.* For any particular substance, the curve of cut-off potential difference versus frequency is a straight line with a slope which we shall call h. And this slope h is the same for all materials. Only the intercept, B, changes from one material to another. Consequently, the graphs for all substances can be described by the relation:

$$E_{el} = (1 \text{ elem. charge}) \times V_c = -B + h\nu,$$

where h is always the same, B is constant in any particular experiment, and ν is the frequency of the light which changes with the spectral color.

*In modern physics the frequency is almost always represented by the Greek letter ν (read nu) rather than by the letter f. We shall follow this standard practice throughout the rest of the book. When you read modern physics in other books, the symbols will then be familiar to you. For example, the relation between the speed of light, its frequency and its wave length is written $c = \nu\lambda$, meaning just the same thing as $c = f\lambda$ which you used in Part II.

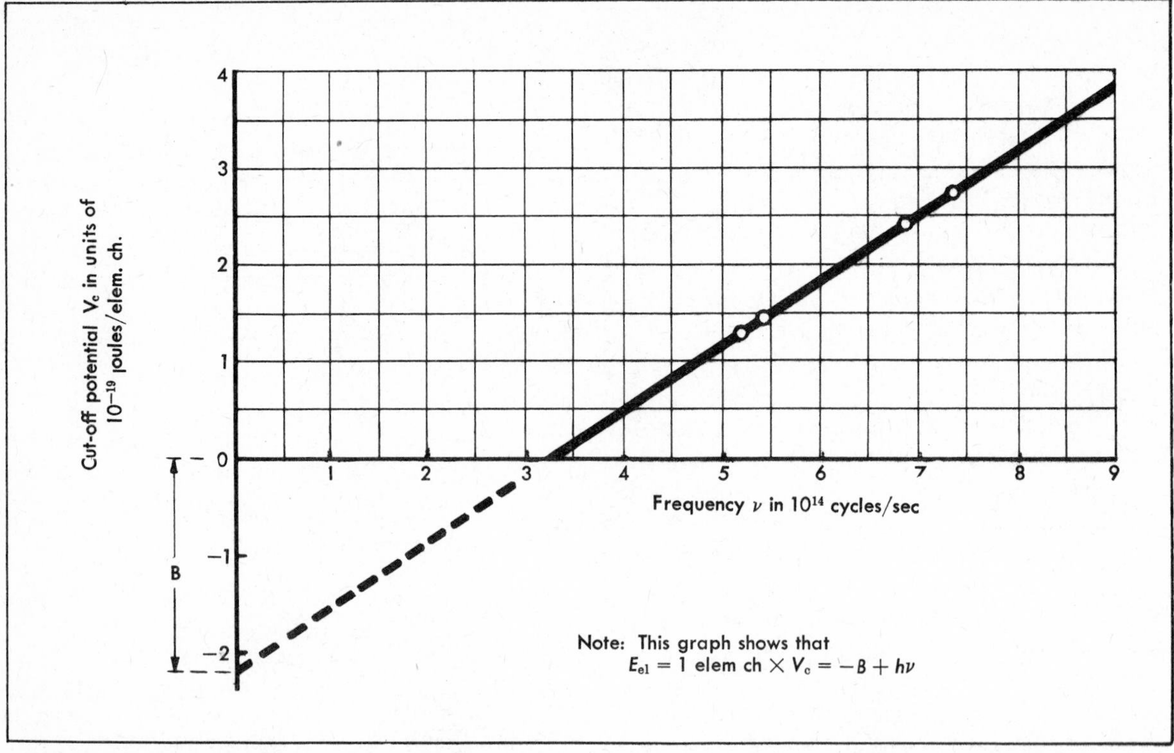

33–9. The results of experiments with the apparatus of Fig. 33–7, augmented by the use of various light sources and filters of different color. The cut-off potential difference V_c is plotted against the frequency ν of the light used.

Here we see that the experimental information clearly distinguishes between the role of the light and the role of the photoelectric surface. The surface is represented solely by the term $-B$, which is the intercept of the photoelectric curve indicated on the left in Fig. 33–9. This term is independent of the light, for we can change the frequency ν as much as we like without influencing it. Consequently, it only contains information about the nature of the surface. On the other hand, the light is described by the term $h\nu$, which is always the same for light of the same frequency. (Because the slope h is the same for all substances, this term has nothing to do with the nature of the photoelectric surface.) This term tells us in what way the photon carries the information about the frequency of light. Each photon is able to give more energy to an emitted photo-electron in direct proportion to the frequency, that is, E_{el} increases with ν.

On the photon picture we can interpret the last equation completely. Each photon carries (or perhaps the photon *is*) the energy $h\nu$. When the photon hits the surface it disappears, and the energy $h\nu$ is transferred. Some of this energy is needed to bring the photo-electron out of the surface. That becomes the threshold value B. Photons with less energy than that value can eject no electrons. But if a photon has more energy than the threshold value, the surplus appears as kinetic energy of the emitted electron. Not all electrons come straight out of the metal surface; some go more deeply into the metal, and never come out at all. Others come out by indirect paths, having lost some energy in atomic collisions on the way out. A few come nearly directly out with the full surplus of kinetic energy donated by the photon; these are the electrons which still flow when the retarding potential difference is not quite so great as the cut-off value.

The photon interpretation of the photoelectric effect was first given by Einstein in 1905, and the equation we have found which represents the conservation of energy in the photoelectric process is known as Einstein's photoelectric equation. But the experimental evidence that we used to establish this relation was not available to Einstein. He invented the whole picture on the basis of far less evidence, and predicted the experimental results which we have used. In this work Einstein built upon a result obtained by Planck. In 1900 Planck had explained the spectrum of light inside an insulated enclosure at constant temperature.* His explanation implied that light was emitted and absorbed in energy bundles $h\nu$ in size. Einstein now pointed out a number of pieces of evidence for the reality of these bundles. He made them into particles of light, into photons; and at the same time he used them to found the theory of photochemistry and forecast the results of later photoelectric experiments.

33–6. The Mechanics of the Photon; Photon Momentum

The photoelectric effect has been explained by the photon picture. In any beam of light of frequency ν, each photon carries an energy

$$E = h\nu.$$

This is the famous Einstein-Planck relation. A beam of light is more or less intense according as it has more or fewer photons per unit time; but the energy per photon, the quantum energy, is always the same for a definite frequency or wave length of the light.

The Einstein-Planck relation is the key to the photon. The proportionality constant h is called Planck's constant, after the great German physicist who first proposed this relation in 1900, a few years before Einstein showed that it would clarify the photoelectric effect. This constant is directly measurable from the last experiment; for as we saw in the last section, h is the slope of all photoelectric curves. The result is

$$h = 6.62 \times 10^{-34} \text{ joule-sec.}$$

From the value of h, we can quickly find the energy of ordinary photons. Visible light has a wave length of about 5,000 A or 5×10^{-7} m. (Recall that the A stands for angstroms. Each A is 10^{-10} m, so this is 5×10^{-7} m.) Its frequency is

$$\nu = \frac{c}{\lambda} = \frac{3 \times 10^{8} \text{ m/sec}}{5 \times 10^{-7} \text{ m}} \approx 6 \times 10^{14} \text{ cycles/sec.}$$

Consequently, an average visible photon carries the energy $E = h\nu$, which is

$(6.62 \times 10^{-34}$ joule-sec$) \times (6 \times 10^{14}$ cycles/sec$)$ or 4×10^{-19} joules.

When we write this in ordinary units, the enormous negative power of ten involved suggests at once how small is the energy of a single photon compared to the energies of everyday mechanical systems. This is a pretty clear case for the desirability of using the energy units suited to electron energies, the electron volt of Chapter 29. Since there are 1.6×10^{-19} joules per electron volt, the energy of our visible photon is about 2.5 electron volts. (The relation between wave length and photon energy is worked out in the box.) The whole range of visible-light photons extends from an energy of around two electron volts for the red to somewhat above three for the blue.

These energies, of a few electron volts per photon, are exactly in the lowest energy range which can cause important chemical changes, presumably — as we shall see in the next chapter

*An insulated enclosure with a small hole in one wall is commonly called a "black body," because it absorbs radiation almost perfectly through the hole. Previous theories about the frequency distribution of radiant energy in a black body had been in violent disagreement with the experimental facts.

THE RELATION OF PHOTON ENERGY AND THE WAVE LENGTH OF LIGHT

The relation between photon energy and the wave length of the corresponding light can be derived as follows:

$$\lambda = \frac{c}{\nu} = \frac{hc}{h\nu} = \frac{hc}{E_{\text{photon}}}$$

$$hc = (6.62 \times 10^{-34} \text{ joule-sec}) \times (3 \times 10^{8} \text{ m/sec}) = 1.99 \times 10^{-25} \text{ joule-meters.}$$

Also, there are 10^{10} angstroms/meter and 6.25×10^{18} ev/joule. Therefore,

$hc = (1.99 \times 10^{-25}$ joule-meters$) \times (10^{10}$ angstroms/meter$) \times (6.25 \times 10^{18}$ ev/joule$) = 1.24 \times 10^{4}$ ev-angstroms.

This means that

$$\lambda \text{ in angstroms} = \frac{1.24 \times 10^{4}}{E},$$

where E is the energy of the photon in electron volts. Accurately, the energy in electron volts possessed by a single photon of wave length λ measured in angstrom units is given by:

$$\lambda E = 12{,}397 \text{ electron volt-angstroms.}$$

— because they are energies high enough to disturb the electrons within an atom or even to eject them. For these energies, then, but not for lower values, photographic chemicals, photoelectric surfaces, and the retina of the eye itself are sensitive. The differences among the "visible" ranges for such devices are exciting, but they are really rather small. No known photo-surface will respond to infrared light which is even ten times longer in wave length than the limiting response of the human eye.

From the value for the energy of a single photon, we can find the number of photons streaming by in any radiation beam whose total energy rate we know. Then it is interesting to compare the total number of photons striking a photoelectric surface with the number of photo-electrons ejected. Even for a very good surface, only a few percent of the photons eject electrons. The rest send electrons deeper into the surface, or are wasted in some other way. Of course, photons with less than the threshold energy cannot eject electrons at all.

Energy is not all that is transferred from light to matter when a photon collides with an atom. The hail of photons impacting on a surface transfers momentum as well. From the photon point of view, we must think of the pressure of light exactly as we think of the gas pressure in the kinetic theory. The apparently smooth and continuous pressure is the result of a myriad of little collisions, each one transferring momentum to the surface. Then, by measuring the pressure of light from photons of a single "frequency" and dividing the corresponding momentum up equally among photons, we find that each photon carries $\frac{h\nu}{c}$ momentum in its direction of motion.

Although the electromagnetic theory of Maxwell contained no photons, it agrees with the photon momentum. According to the electromagnetic theory, any radiant energy E going in one direction should carry the momentum E/c in the same direction. Photons of energy $h\nu$ and momentum $h\nu/c$ "obey" this relation. Consequently, a large number of photons can lead to the same effects as a supposedly continuous wave of light.

We can verify the photon momentum directly when a single photon collides with an electron. For this experiment we need to observe the motion of the electron, and we can do this in the cloud chamber. The electrons are supplied by the atoms of the gas or by a thin sheet of matter placed in the cloud chamber. They do not come to us in free form, and the photon must knock them out of the atom. So the energy of the photon must be high compared to the energy with which the electron is bound to the rest of the atom.

Even with photons which are energetic enough to remove an electron from the atom, we may not get the kind of collision we want to study. Unless we use an X-ray photon — a photon of really high energy — we shall see the ordinary photoelectric effect in which the energy of the photon is shared between the residual kinetic energy of the electron and the energy required to break the electron away from the atom, the quantity B, which fixes the photo-threshold. In the photoelectric effect, the momentum also goes partly to the atom, and the momentum conservation does not take place between electron and photon alone. But if we use much more energetic photons, those of high-voltage X rays or those of nuclear gamma rays, the atomic binding energy becomes small in comparison. Then the electron is knocked out with nearly all the energy and all the momentum lost by the photon. This new process is called the Compton effect, named for the American physicist A. H. Compton.

In a Compton collision the photon is not absorbed. It appears after the collision scattered off with reduced energy and momentum, moving in some new direction. The electron recoils from the collision, also carrying off some energy and some momentum. In each collision of this kind, the energy brought in by the original photon is accounted for by the energy of the recoiling electron and that of the scattered photon. The momentum is also conserved. The momentum of the original photon becomes the total momentum of the recoil electron and of the scattered photon. Fig. 33–10 shows two photographs of recoil electrons which have been given momentum when struck by a photon. We see directly that the photon has brought in momentum. In addition we can check the conservation of momentum by adding up the momentum vectors as is done in the diagram of Fig. 33–10. The conservation of momentum checks out in each such collision, and

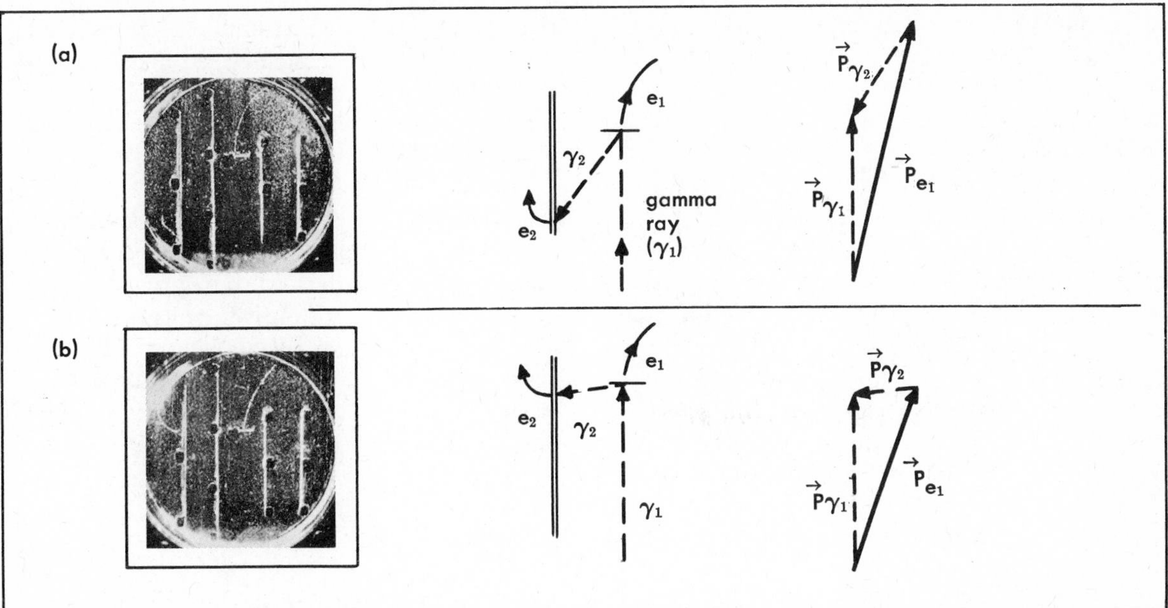

33–10. The Compton effect. To the left are cloud-chamber photographs; next are diagrams showing the paths of gamma-ray photons and electrons; to the right are vector diagrams showing the momentum changes. In both sets of pictures a gamma-ray beam, with energy of around 2 Mev, enters the cloud chamber from below. A gamma ray strikes the mica foil, and occasionally a Compton recoil electron is ejected, mostly near the forward direction. The re-emitted photon, having lost energy and momentum, goes off in another direction, and ejects a photo-electron from the lead strips put into the cloud chamber. This reveals its path, and the measurement of the curvature of the electron tracks in the known applied magnetic field makes possible the check on the conservation of energy and momentum. (Photographs from: Crane, Gaerttner, and Turin, "A Cloud-Chamber Study of the Compton Effect," Physical Review, Vol. 50, 1936.)

in each we use the photon momentum $p = \frac{h\nu}{c}$. As a result we have a convincing check that

$$p = \frac{h\nu}{c} = \frac{h}{\lambda}$$

is the photon momentum.

The relations

$$p = mv \text{ and } E_k = \frac{mv^2}{2} = \frac{pv}{2}$$

which we learned for slow-moving particles *do not apply* here. Instead $p = \frac{h\nu}{c}$ and $E = h\nu$ give $E = pc$. This is *not* something peculiar to a photon; it is a verification of the theory of relativity, which modifies mechanical laws for motions which are close to the speed of light. The photon indeed moves at the speed of light; its mechanical behavior is to be described not by Newton's, but by Einstein's slightly modified equations of motion. Relativity is outside of our present topic; we only can pause to remark that in the atomic domain the laws of relativity mechanics have been amply verified. Of course they must agree with Newton's mechanics whenever they are applied to bodies which move slowly compared with the speed of light, and they do.

33–7. Photons and Electromagnetic Waves

Where is the wave picture in all this? It may seem to have no relationship to what we have just been discussing, but we cannot forget all the evidence for light waves that we discussed in Part II, nor the evidence for electromagnetic waves of all kinds in Section 31–12. Somehow photons and electromagnetic waves must fit together, and we already noticed that this is possible for average effects involving great numbers of photons. In Section 33–3 we saw that interference patterns — a typical wave effect — are painted by photons landing one at a time at many different points. Here we shall look again at the relation between waves and photons.

First we must establish that photons are compatible with all we know about electromagnetic waves in the region of wave lengths from millimeters to miles. We make and detect these waves, not by using single electrons or atoms, but with radio tubes and antennae, through which currents flow back and forth. And we have plenty of evidence that the wave picture agrees with the facts of radio transmission.

In that range the frequencies are small, relative to atomic values. A frequency of a few kilocycles represents the low frequency limit of radio technique, while a frequency of a million megacycles is beyond the most advanced radar and microwave techniques, and lies at the margin of the deep infrared. Yet even these highest radio frequencies, with the tiny atomic constant h, give a photon energy which is really very small.

At one megacycle, for example, the photons in a radio wave have the energy

$$h\nu = (6.62 \times 10^{-34} \text{ joule-sec})(10^6 \text{ cycles/sec}) = 6.62 \times 10^{-28} \text{ joules.}$$

Because there are 6.25×10^{18} ev/joule, this is

$$h\nu = 4 \times 10^{-9} \text{ electron volts.}$$

Such small photon energies mean that a radio signal cannot be detected unless it contains very many photons. The lower limit of a good communications receiver is about 10^{10} photons/second. Among so many photons the average behavior alone is detectable. The result is the smooth transfer of energy from wave to matter which we would expect on the wave theory. The large numbers of photons guarantee that the graininess will not usually show up unless we try very hard to detect it.

We might even suspect that there are no photons in light of long wave length. But we now have experimental evidence of the absorption and emission of "radio-frequency" photons by atoms and molecules (see Section 34–3). So we know that both the photon and the wave description apply.

As we go to higher frequencies, we pass to the region of visible light. Here the number of photons is large in any light beam that appears bright to our eye. Sunlight, for example, represents a rain of some 10^{17} photons per square centimeter per second. In such a burst the individual arrivals of photons are not easily noticed. At the other extreme, however, we can still make out the glow of a faint luminous source which sends to our dark-adapted eye a hundred photons on the area of the pupil each second. So for visible light, both the wave and the photon sort of observation is possible.

The photographic plate and the photoelectric cell are, like the eye, capable of responding to the smooth flow of intense or moderate beams no less than to the fluctuating and chancy arrival of a few photons every second. It is for this reason that it was with the study of visible light, and not in the study of the long-wave-length portions of the electromagnetic wave spectrum, that the photon idea was first conceived and found satisfactory.

As the frequency of light increases and the photon energy and momentum rise, the photon description appears more and more dominant. The photon energy in the X-ray region is large enough so that single photons are easily detectable. The arrival of a single gamma-ray photon — associated with still higher frequency and correspondingly shorter wave length — is energetically a sizable event. It can be noted with good probability in a whole variety of "counters." Gamma-ray photons, which have energies as great as 10^{14} electron volts, have been found in the high atmosphere. There they are produced by cosmic-ray particles reacting with the atoms of the air. Such a photon produces tens of millions of recoil electrons.

On the other hand, as the frequency rises and the wave length correspondingly diminishes, wave effects are less obvious. For example, interference and diffraction become more difficult to demonstrate. The wave lengths of X rays are no longer than the dimensions of atoms. For them we can hardly make slits narrow enough to exhibit interference maxima of detectable width. Although X-ray interference is widely used, the essential diffracting apparatus is rarely man-made. Instead we employ the regular atomic patterns of crystals. For gamma rays, not even crystals will work as diffraction obstacles; only the nucleus of a single atom can be employed, and the procedure has become very indirect.

We have no choice; electromagnetic radiation of every kind must be understood from two points of view. If we wish to view the over-all pattern it makes in space or time, we can do so by the theory of electromagnetic waves described in Chapter 31.

We can design antennas, lenses, and gratings. They all function just as the wave theory predicts. But we must admit that we cannot say exactly when or where the energy will be transferred to the detector or the recoil momentum given to the screen or to the electron. The wave theory gives us only the probability of finding the photon. It tells only the probability that a photon will transfer its energy and momentum to a given object within a definite time. Here we are subject to the laws of chance. The photon cannot be pinned down by any wave prediction. In an interference experiment, a particular photon may occur in any bright bar, and we cannot trace its path through the slits of the apparatus. But wherever and whenever it interacts, there and then we can be certain that energy and momentum are precisely conserved.

In the older mechanics and classical physics, we thought that we could know the energy and momentum of a particle and at the same time tell when and where it was going to hit. That was naive, and the study of the photon was the hard school in which physicists became more sophisticated in the ways of the world. For photons at least, when we know the energy and momentum, we cannot do any more than assign probabilities to the time and place of arrival. These probabilities follow from the associated wave properties of light. We can therefore use only part of the ideas that we formerly associated with particles and their motions, and at the same time we must add new ideas from the wave picture and the probability interpretation to fill out our description of what actually happens.

Sometimes only one of the older pictures is needed. When many photons take part in any detectable change, it is the wave picture alone. On the other extreme, when a single photon is so energetic that it can easily be observed, and when it has as well so short a wave length that interference studies are nearly impossible, then the photon picture is sufficient. But the real nature of light is more subtle. It shows us both wave and photon behavior. We have therefore been forced to make a new picture of light, one which combines some aspects of wave behavior as we previously understood it with some aspects of photon or particle behavior. This new picture is forced upon us, for this is the way the world is. Newton's corpuscular picture of light is by no means restored by the photon. It is no more true than the pure electromagnetic picture, with its waves of continuously distributed energy and momentum. Light is to be understood fully only by a novel scheme of the kind we have tried to outline.

33–8. Matter Waves

By 1923 the photon lesson was well learned. In the next years it was learned again in a new and unexpected connection. At about that time, the French physicist Louis de Broglie asked the following question. Since light, which we had thought was a continuous wave, has also a photon nature, can it be that the particles of matter have wavelike properties associated with them? De Broglie's proposal was little more than pure speculation, but he was able to draw some conclusions from it. In particular, he could assign a wave length to his hypothetical matter waves. Particles of momentum p should have the same wave length associated with them as photons of the identical momentum. λ should be $\frac{h}{p}\cdot$ Then, within a few years' time, the question he raised was settled by a wide variety of experiments. The answer was yes — there are waves associated with moving material particles.

The idea of matter waves came at the same time as a number of other theoretical ideas which changed Newtonian mechanics, extending and refining it to fit the facts of the world of atoms. Soon it was found that all these ideas fitted together. Together they form our most powerful theory, quantum mechanics, which had extended its proper domain over all of physics within a single decade from its birth. Today this theory is the basis of our knowledge of both matter and radiation. Although the ideas of quantum mechanics can be profitably studied in the light of the improvements on Newtonian dynamics introduced by Bohr, Heisenberg, and other members of the Copenhagen school of physics, here we shall penetrate a little way into them by following de Broglie's wave ideas.

The most direct evidence for matter waves is the observation that beams of particles are diffracted. Electrons make elegant diffraction and interference patterns (Figs. 33–11 and 33–12). They are easily controlled; so beams of them,

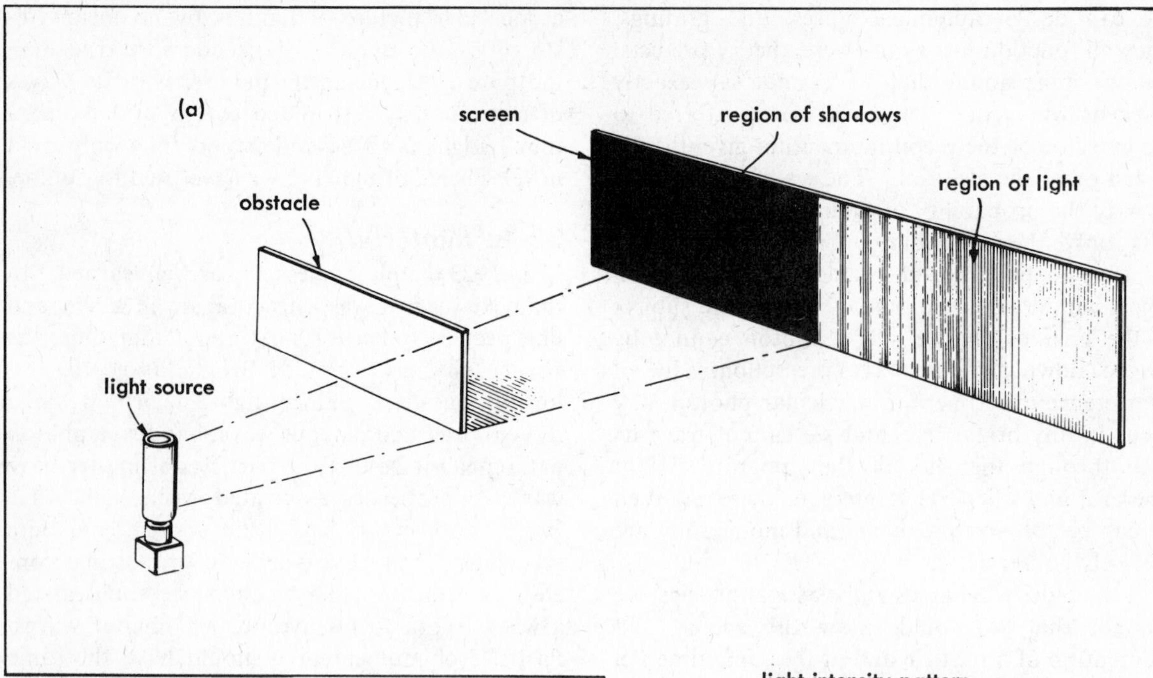

(a)

screen

region of shadows

region of light

obstacle

light source

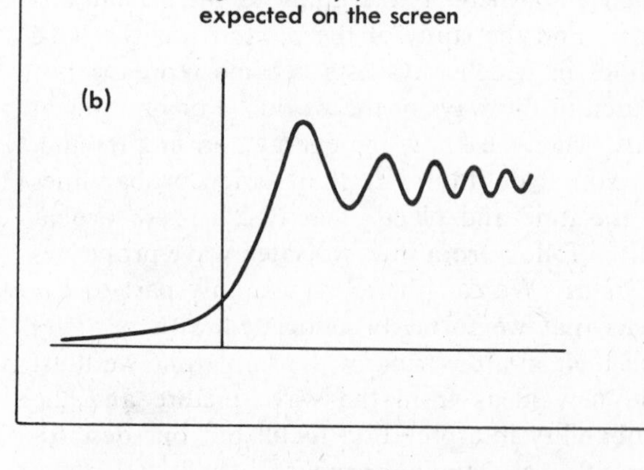

33–11. Electron diffraction compared with the corresponding fringes made by visible light in the shadow of an edge. (a) Diagram of the set-up used with visible light. An ordinary carefully made straightedge will serve; the fringes are closely spaced and must be studied a meter or so behind the obstacle. The small graph (b) shows the expected pattern of light intensity on the screen. (c) The pattern painted by light. (From: Valasek, "Introduction to Theoretical and Experimental Optics," John Wiley & Sons, New York, 1949.) (d) The pattern painted by electrons. For the electrons, the straightedge is a small cubical crystal of MgO, much smaller than a micron, and the fringes have been photographed with the aid of an electron microscope. (From: H. Raether, "Elektroninterferenzen," Handbuch der Physik, Volume XXXII, Springer Verlag, Berlin, 1957.)

(c)

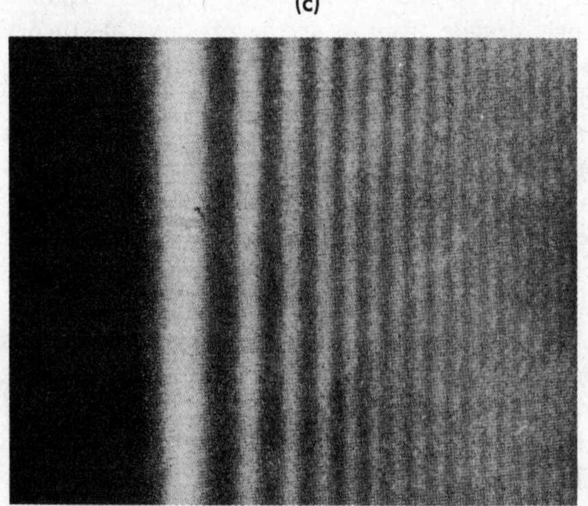

(d)

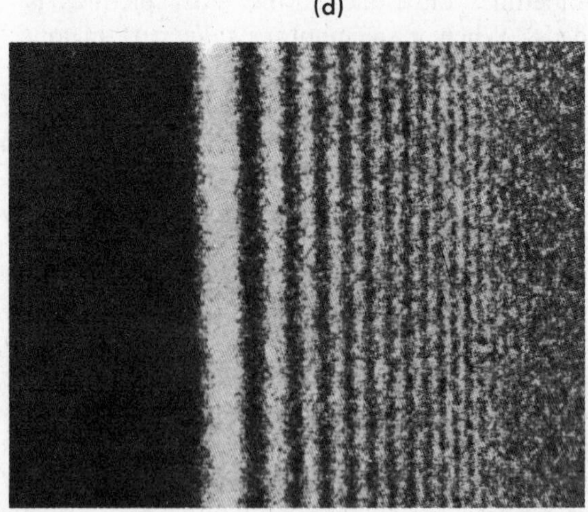

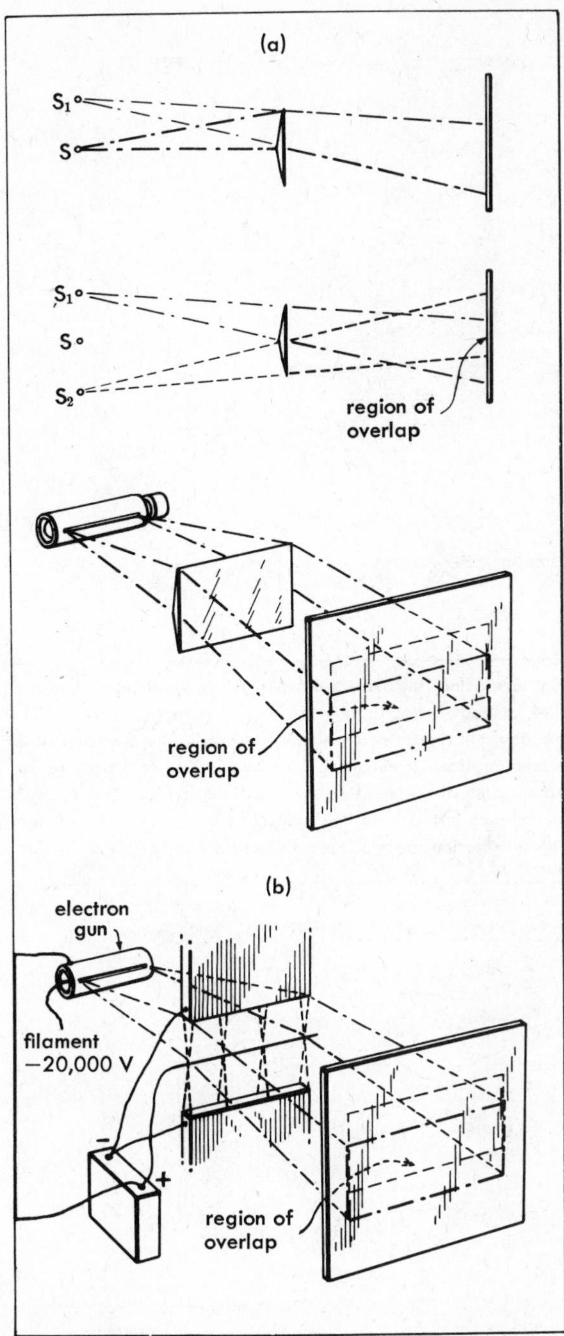

33–12. Two analogous experiments showing the interference of waves. Both show interference fringes from a biprism — a device that takes waves from a single slit as the source and produces the effect of waves from two slits. The likeness of the patterns obtained with light and with electrons is striking. The bending would happen in just the same way if electrons behaved simply as charged particles; but the peculiarity is that where the two streams of electrons overlap there are bright and dark bands just like those of light waves, though on a very small scale.

(a) With visible light, a glass biprism (two wedges of glass pointing opposite ways) bends the two halves of the beam of light from the original slit so that they overlap on a remote photographic film. The light passing through the upper half is bent down and the lower half bent up so that in the region of overlap on the photographic film light appears to come from two slits S_1 and S_2. Interference is observed in this region of overlap. At some places on the photographic plate, crests that seem to come from S_1 arrive along with troughs that seem to come from S_2, making a dark fringe. At other places crests arrive together, making a bright fringe.

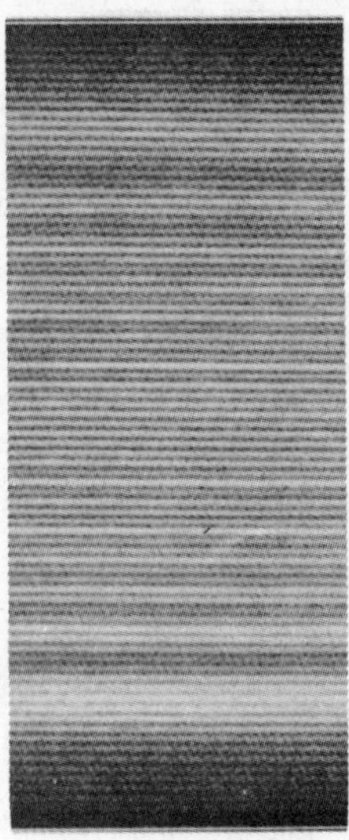

(Above) The interference pattern painted by light. (Valasek, op. cit.)

(b) The electron source is a 20,000-volt gun which provides electrons with a de Broglie wave length of 0.086 angstroms. The electric field "biprism" is made by a fine silvered quartz thread, a few microns in diameter, suspended in a wide slit in a metal screen. The thread is kept about 6 volts positive with respect to the slit. The diagrams show the electrostatic biprism and its electric field lines. The electric field bends the streams of electrons that pass each side of the wire. They overlap on the photographic film, arriving there as if they came from two sources.

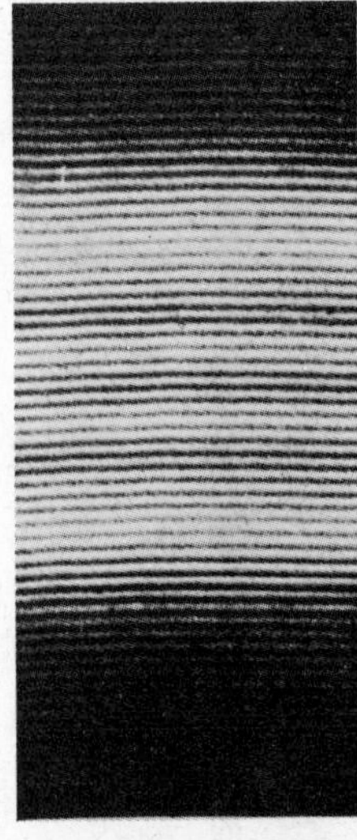

(Above) The interference pattern painted by electrons. It has been hugely magnified by an electron microscope. (From: H. Düker, "Lichtstarke Interferenzen mit einem Biprisma für Elektronenwellen," Zeitschrift für Naturforschung, Volume 10A, 1955.)

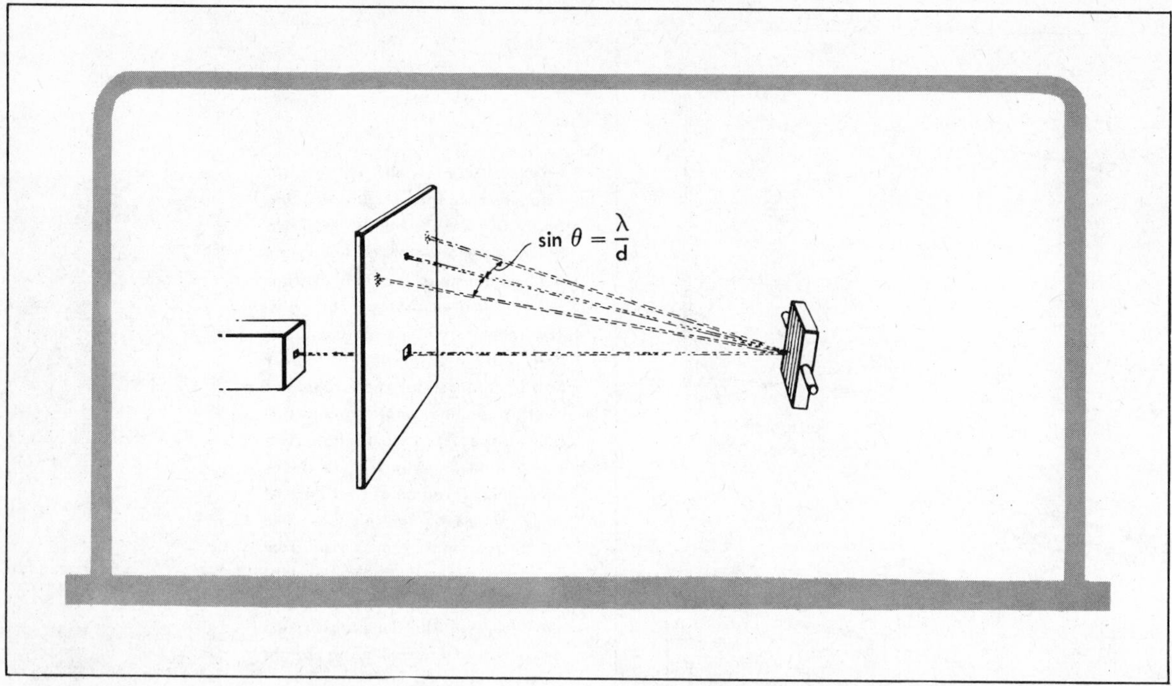

33–13 (a). The general idea of an atomic beam experiment for observing the interference of helium matter waves reflected from a grating spectroscope. A beam of helium is directed at the surface of a crystal which acts as the grating because of the natural repeated spacing of its molecules. The source of the beam is a slightly warmed box fed with a very small amount of gas. Because of the regular vertical "rulings" made by the atomic spacing, the reflected waves show constructive interference at angles that depend on the wave length. When used this way, the crystal acts for helium waves in the same way that a ruled optical grating does for light. You can measure the wave length of the matter waves from the angles of constructive interference just as you can measure the wave length of light with a reflection grating. See Figs. 33–13 (b) and 33–13 (c).

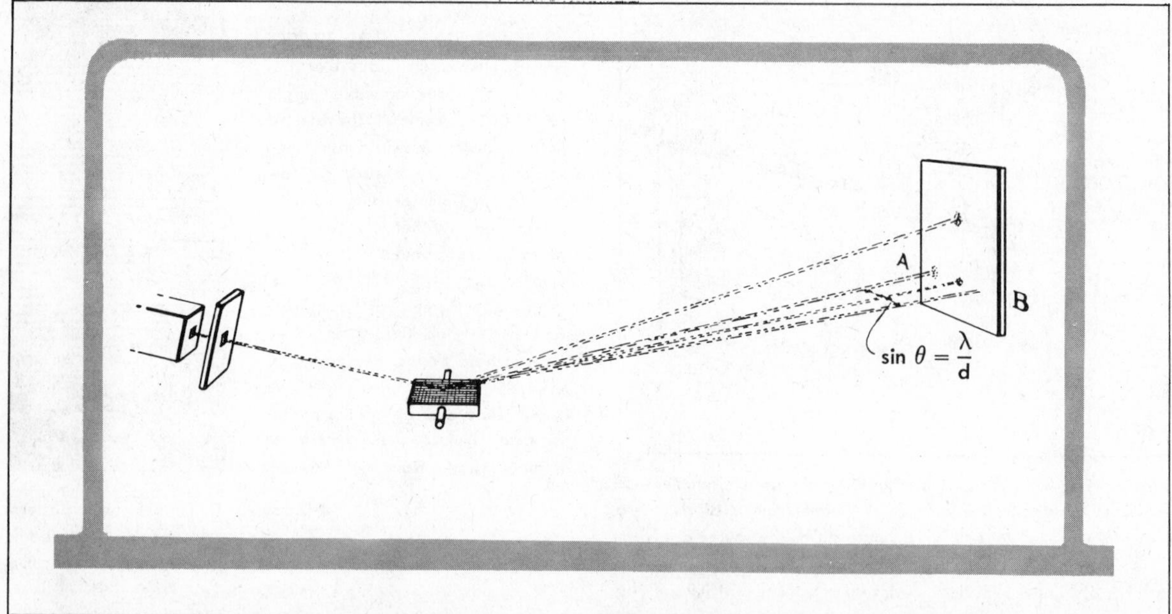

33–13 (b). In the actual experiment the whole apparatus is in a highly evacuated chamber, constantly being pumped. The helium beam strikes the crystal at a low grazing angle to increase the amount of reflection. The beam deviated upward comes from first-order constructive interference of the waves scattered from atomic rulings perpendicular to those producing the beams deviated toward *A* and *B*. The intensity is measured along the line *AB*.

all of nearly the same definite momentum, are easy to obtain. With such beams the intensity patterns look like the optical patterns of diffraction and interference of light of one wave length — like the patterns we obtain from any kind of waves of one wave length. Furthermore, by changing the momentum we can change the apparent wave length. Then we find that the wave length is inversely proportional to the momentum. The relation is

$$\lambda = \frac{h}{p},$$

where h is again Planck's constant. Just as de Broglie had predicted, this is the same as the relation between photon momentum and the wave length of the associated light wave.

This de Broglie relation holds good for everything. What sort of particles are used is irrelevant. In an early investigation helium atoms were used. Fig. 33–13(c) shows the beautiful pattern they make when they reflect from the molecular grating that nature rules on the surface of a lithium fluoride crystal. Here the beam did not have a single well-defined momentum. It was made of atoms coming out of a warm box of helium gas. Nevertheless, the interference maxima are clearly visible, humped up around the wave length expected from the thermal energy and the corresponding momentum of the atoms.

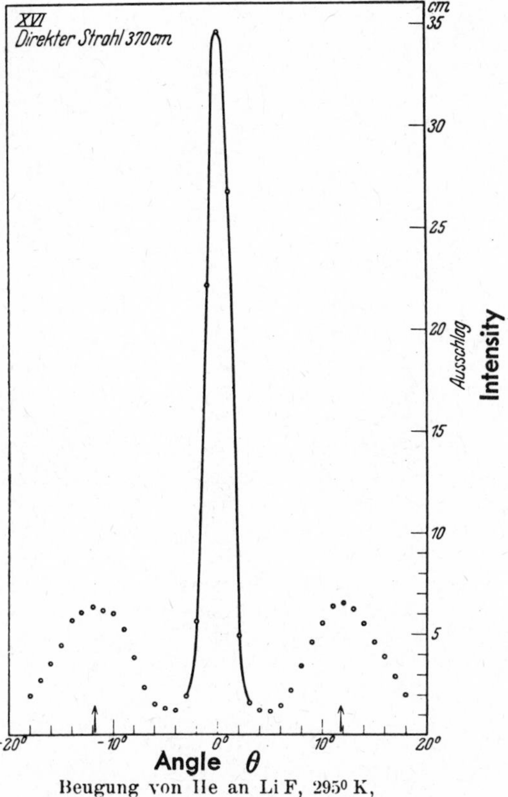

33–13 (c). The graph shows the result of an experiment with a beam of helium directly at a freshly cut surface of a lithium fluoride crystal. The existence of interference shows the wave nature and the angle measures the wave length.* (From "Beugung von Molekularstrahlen," I. Estermann and O. Stern, Zeitschrift für Physik, Volume 61, 1930, p. 107, Springer Verlag, Berlin.)

*The beam of helium atoms came from a sample of gas at about room temperature; not all atoms have the same velocity, but they tend to cluster about some central value, which determines the angle at which the maximum is seen in the diffracted beam. From the crystal lattice spacing of 2.85 angstrom units, and from the measured angle, about 11.8°, the de Broglie wave length is calculated to be about 0.57 angstrom units. The de Broglie wave length calculated from $\lambda = \frac{h}{mv}$ for helium at velocities corresponding to room temperature is also 0.57 angstrom units.

Since this experiment, all sorts of particles have been tried. In recent years, with the intense neutron beams from nuclear reactors, even the neutron has been put to test. With high-speed mechanical velocity selectors — whirling wheels that eat up all the neutrons passing down a channel at any but a preselected speed — beams of almost a single momentum are produced. Alternatively, and this is often the more practical method, we may send a beam of neutrons at the face of an interference grating where the slits or the reflecting regions have a known spacing. Then the neutron waves coming off the grating in a given direction will have a definite wave length — the wave length for which a maximum wave disturbance is obtained at this angle. By investigating this particular neutron beam with a second interference grating, we can easily confirm the success of this procedure. Then we can use the beam of neutrons to perform new diffraction and interference experiments. The results are so good that we now use neutron interference patterns to find out more about the positions of atoms in crystal gratings. Hydrogen atoms, for instance, whose regular spacing will not show up well in X-ray interference, form a far more effective part of the grating as seen by neutrons. Locating them in their regular repetitive array in a crystal is only one of the jobs neutrons can do because of their wave nature

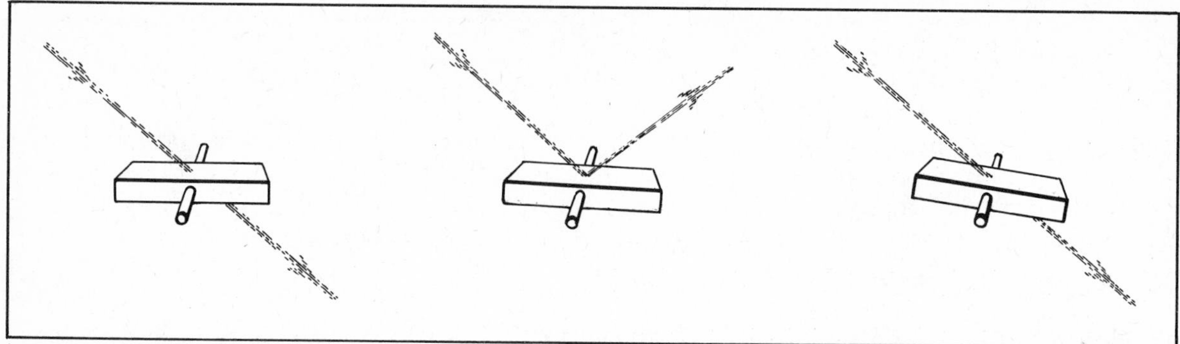

33–14 (a). An interference experiment to show the wave properties of neutrons. A neutron beam is directed at a salt crystal mounted so it can be rotated about an axis. At most angles of incidence the beam will go right through. However, if we rotate the crystal (keeping the beam direction constant) there will be an angle at which a reflected beam will suddenly flash out. If we rotate the crystal further, reflection will cease and the neutrons will again go through. The reflection flashes out when the path differences between the regularly spaced layers of the crystal give constructive interference for the neutron waves. This is analogous to the thin-film interference described in Chapter 19. See Figs. 33–14 (b) and 33–14 (c).

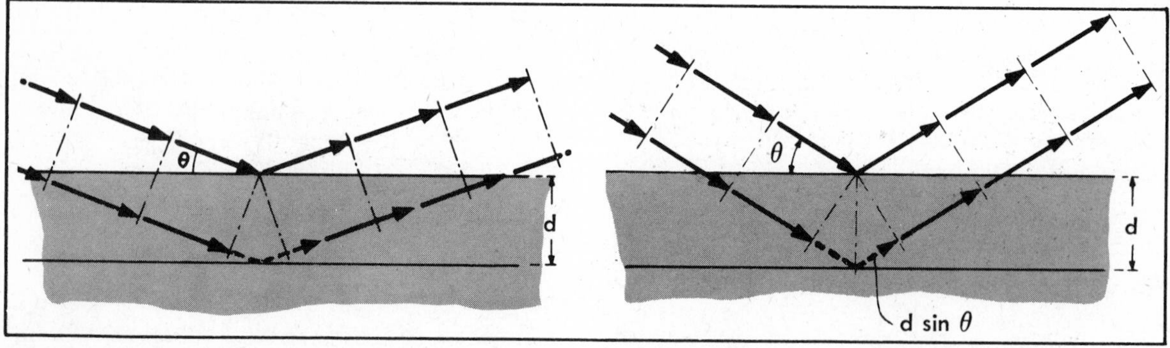

33–14 (b). The line shown dotted is the extra distance traveled by a neutron wave that reflects from the second layer of the crystal instead of the first. If the beams from each layer are to interfere to give a maximum reflection, this dotted distance must be a whole number of wave lengths. The dotted distance is also $2d \sin \theta$, where d is the spacing between the reflecting layers of atoms. Therefore the first flashout should occur when $2d \sin \theta = \lambda$.

and their own special way of interacting with other particles of matter. Fig. 33–14 shows the interference maximum of a neutron beam.

Neutrons will travel a long way in air, but the experiments with atoms and electrons must be done in vacuum. Otherwise the air molecules would scatter and diffuse the beam beyond any possible use for sharp measurement. Also, when crystals are used as gratings, the particles penetrate only very slightly into the solid matter before losing their energy. Only those few particles which lose very little energy before passing out of the target material can yield a well-marked diffraction pattern. When beams of atoms are used, most of the atoms which come back from a crystal surface have in fact been somewhat disturbed internally by their collisions within the crystal, or have imparted differing fractions of their kinetic energy to the crystal. These do not make clear the wavelike behavior. In the diffracted wave there are to be found only those atoms which have behaved throughout the process as simple structureless masses, not changing in any way their internal condition. All the particles diffracted into a definite direction have the same velocity; this was directly checked to verify the point. Every moving particle, as long as it behaves as a whole, and has no change internally, or in its kinetic energy, diffracts as though it has a single wave length given by the de Broglie relation:

$$\lambda = \frac{h}{p}.$$

The de Broglie wave length applies to the motion of the center of mass of the whole "particle."

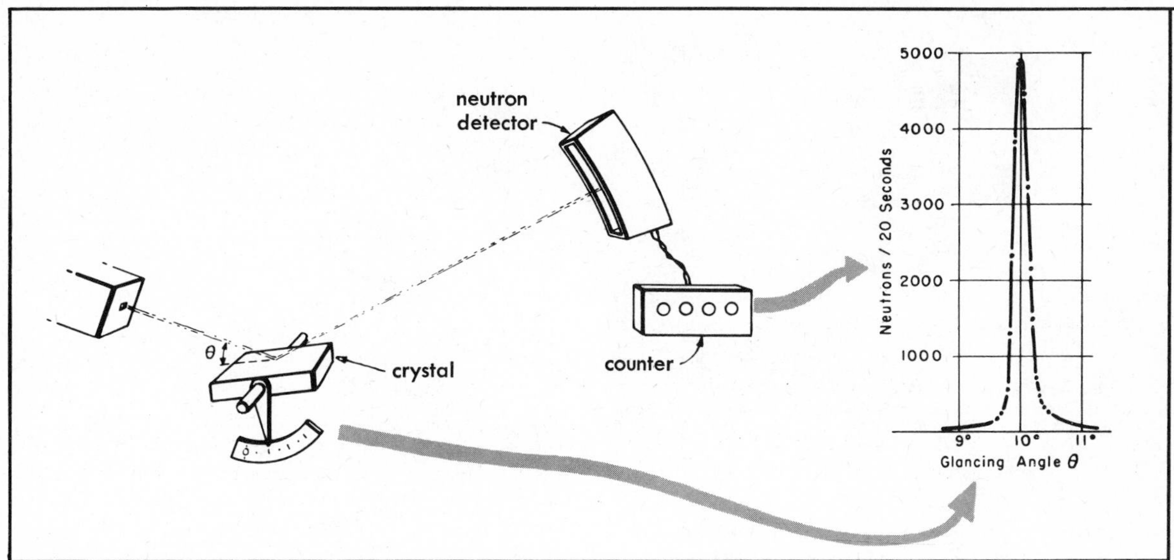

33–14 (c). The experimental arrangement. A beam of neutrons selected to have speed 4.04×10^4 meters per second (or a de Broglie wave length 0.98 angstrom units) falls on the crystal from the left. When the beam is reflected, the detector responds by sending a signal to the counter for each neutron caught. We plot the neutron count against crystal angle, as measured by the pointer on the crystal mounting. The flash-out angle is $\theta = 10.01°$. The spacing d for a salt crystal is 2.815 angstrom units. Compute the wave length. Is it the expected de Broglie wave length? (Experiment by Prof. Clifford G. Shull.)

33–9. When Is the Wave Nature of Matter Important?

Observe how short are the waves of matter. If we take the mass of a microbe, about 10^{-15} kg, and a velocity appropriate to a lethargic snail, say of about 10 centimeters per day, the de Broglie wave length which results is

$$\lambda = \frac{6.62 \times 10^{-34} \text{ joule-sec}}{(10^{-15} \text{ kg})(10^{-6} \text{ m/sec})}$$
$$= 6 \times 10^{-13} \text{ m} = 6 \times 10^{-3} \text{ A}.$$

The particle involved in this sort of motion, which is about as small a mechanical system as we might expect to find outside of atomic physics, has a wave length as short as that of a photon of several million electron volts of energy. Such a photon is a nuclear gamma ray, and its wave length is one-millionth that of visible light. Even for visible light the wave properties are usually unimportant. To know where it will go and what shadows it will cast, a ray approximation is usually sufficient. The nuclear gamma ray is far more raylike. It is almost impossible to find its wave properties through diffraction or interference. Similarly, the moving microbe of the same wave length shows us only normal particle properties. We cannot detect its wave nature. Its physical behavior is quite perfectly described by Newtonian mechanics. An ordinary body like a baseball has a mass about 10^{14} times as much. There is no hope of seeing its wave properties at all, and we can understand why the wave nature of matter took so long to discover.

To observe effects which show us the wave nature of matter, we must have much longer de Broglie wave lengths. How could we lengthen the de Broglie wave length? We can try to reduce the velocity; but this is not practical. Thermal agitation itself limits the slowness of motion which can in fact be realized. The only other factor we have left to change is the mass; we *can* take smaller masses. The smallest masses are the particles of which matter is composed: the molecules, the atoms, the electrons, and the particles within the nucleus. As we have seen, their wave lengths can be long enough so that we can see their diffraction patterns. Because an electron has a mass of only 10^{-30} kg, at a reasonable speed it will have a wave length of the size of an atom. An electron moving with 90 electron volts of kinetic energy, as we found out in Section 29–2, moves at a speed of 5.6×10^6 meters per second.

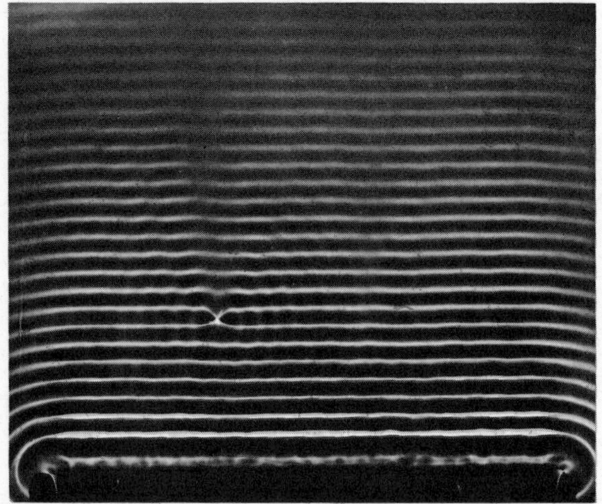

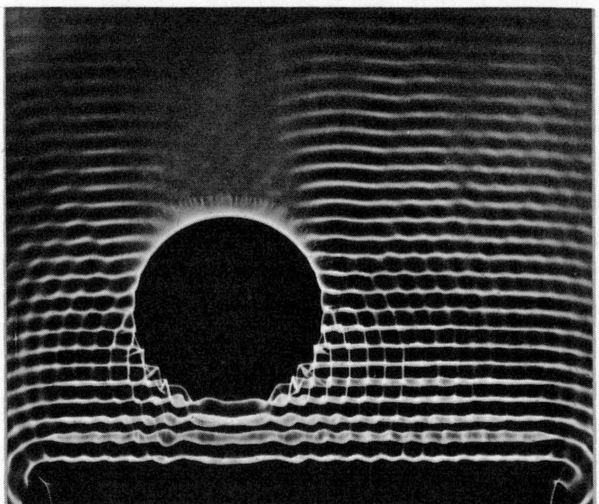

33–15. Ripple-tank photographs of waves meeting obstacles. On the left a small object is located where the waves seem to bend together. Notice that this small barrier disturbs the waves very little. On the right there is a large obstacle in the ripple tank. The waves are strongly reflected and there is a definite "shadow" region.

Its momentum is therefore

$$(0.91 \times 10^{-30} \text{ kg}) \times (5.6 \times 10^{6} \text{ m/sec}) = 5.0 \times 10^{-24} \text{ kg-m/sec}.$$

Consequently, its de Broglie wave length is about 1.3×10^{-10} meters, which is in the range of atomic dimensions. A reasonably slow-moving electron with one electron volt of kinetic energy moves at about a tenth of the speed, and has a wave length of about 10 atomic dimensions. Atoms are small obstacles for such an electron. The associated waves can easily diffract around them. (Fig. 33–15.) These examples show that wave behavior is essential whenever an electron of small kinetic energy moves in or near an atom. For these motions our ordinary experience with Newton's particle mechanics is not an adequate guide.

The situation is the same for protons and neutrons with respect to the size of the atomic nucleus. The wave length of a proton or neutron with 100 electron volts of kinetic energy is about 3×10^{-12} meters. This wave length is large compared to nuclear dimensions, which are 10^{-14} meters or less. Consequently, such a neutron approaching the nucleus from the outside will find it a small obstacle around which it diffracts. Neutrons with ten million electron volts have a wave length of 10^{-14} meters, comparable to the nuclear size. Consequently, neutrons of this energy just get inside the nucleus. A neutron that stays inside a nucleus, forming a part of it with practically no chance of being found outside, must have a wave length of this size or smaller. Consequently, we expect that the neutrons and protons in nuclei have kinetic energies of about ten million electron volts or more. Even at these energies their wave nature is important as they move about inside the nucleus.

The alpha particles emitted from nuclei show similar kinetic energies, and their wave lengths are also of the same order of magnitude. When we use them in scattering experiments, a wave effect explains why the whole pattern of alpha-particle scattering can be modified at energies at which the alpha particles get near certain nuclei. The alpha-particle waves may then diffract around the nucleus so that scattering at many angles differs from the Coulomb scattering, although only scattering in the backward direction would be modified according to ordinary Newtonian mechanics. This effect correctly removes one of the apparent troubles we mentioned in Section 32–5 in discussing the planetary model of the atom.

Once again we have found that the atomic world cannot be fully described by the simple models of the older physics. The little particles cannot be followed like so many bullets as they fly about within the atom; they obey rather the laws followed by waves. The waves determine the probable location of the particles, and the motion of wave trains determines the probable motion of the particles. Where the amplitude of the wave is large, there the particle is probably to be found; where it is small, there it will be found rarely. But all we can learn is a probability. Exactly where the electrons will be found in an atom we cannot predict. Inside the atom we must be prepared to use a new version of mechanics which combines parts of Newton's particle mechanics with the effects of the wave nature of matter.

33–10. Light and Matter

The circle has closed. Waves of light proved to describe the probability of the appearance of certain particle-like photons; the particles of matter turn out to be governed by a wavelike quantity. Planck's constant controls the magnitudes involved in both cases. We cannot follow the path of a particle through the slits of a diffraction grating any better than we can follow the path of a photon. The associated waves diffract and from these waves we can calculate probable locations of a particle and probable numbers of arrivals. But, just as in the photon picture, the particles transfer energy and momentum in every single collision in the same way as they are expected to do from the mechanics of Newton. The wave nature does not modify that at all. Therefore, whenever the wave lengths are small compared to the dimensions of slits or obstacles, small compared to the dimensions of atoms or of measuring instruments, we get results identical with the predictions of ordinary mechanics. Indeed, it is for this reason that we can use ordinary measuring instruments, and it is for this reason that ordinary measurements will only allow us to measure the same quantities which are dealt with in Newtonian mechanics.

For all objects of everyday size, or for objects like the planets, the mechanics of Newton is without any important error, but if we look with great refinement, or if we ask questions on the scale of the atom, the classical physics (as physics before 1900 is often called) is found wanting. It remains the foundation of physics, because the very instruments and apparatus with which we measure are well understood in classical terms, but it is powerless to explain the atom. Only the quantum theory can do that, with its orders of magnitude proclaimed by Planck's constant, and its more subtle picture of the atomic world. The photon governed in space and time by its electromagnetic wave of probability, the particle and its matter wave of probability — all with the de Broglie wave length — are the keys with which we propose to enter the interior of the atom.

In all that we have said, the analogies between the behavior of light and matter have been striking. Light behaves both as waves and as particles — photons. Matter behaves both as particles and as waves. But the similarities have their limitations. There is one sharp distinction between a photon and a particle of the sort we usually think of, between a photon and a little bit of matter. Photons are not conserved in number; they are easily created and easily destroyed. To turn on the light creates photons by the swarm; they rush to the walls. Some are reflected, but in the end all die, giving their energy to the atoms they strike. Energy is conserved, for heat or chemical changes will reveal the photon energy content, but the number of "particles" is not. This behavior is sharply different from the behavior of electrons and atoms. Those particles cannot be created or destroyed (not in any commonplace way, at least). They are permanent as a photon is not. In this sense photons differ very much from little grains or bullets of matter.

In physics today we regard the wave-particle relationship as fundamental for every one of the objects we deal with on the atomic scale; the main distinction between light and matter is between the permanence of particles and easy creation or absorption of photons.

33–11. What It Is That Waves

In the ripple tank it is quite plain that the "waves" are waves of water. The water moves, the shape of its surface changes, the orderly nature of the patterns is in the end the orderly behavior of little masses of water. But in the electromagnetic wave, there is no material changing its shape or its motion or its density. The emptiest of vacuums will transmit light or radio waves just as well as — indeed, better than — a region filled with any material we know. The waves are patterns of electric and magnetic fields formed in space. In the last century there was for a while a fashion of thinking that the empty space was filled with some strange substance — the "luminiferous" or light-bearing ether — and that waves of light were motions of that curious substance. Gradually physicists came to feel that it added very little to say that space was filled with ether. We now regard it just as a property of space itself that electromagnetic disturbance can travel within it. "Empty" space is devoid of atoms, of any material things at all, but that no longer means that we try to think of it as empty of properties. One of the properties of space is its ability to carry energy in electromagnetic form, and to support the waves of electric and magnetic field which we find to make up radio or light.

The same view holds for the de Broglie waves. The de Broglie waves are not changes of shape or of motion of the electrons whose positional probabilities they describe. They are simply patterns of probability which behave in most respects as analogies to the waves we studied in the ripple tank. There is no reason to say that any substance is waving to and fro. We have been able to show that the fundamental properties of the world resemble some simple models we can build up in the laboratory. But we do not need to carry that to extremes: electromagnetic waves and matter waves are not, as far as we now know, waves of any substance. The wonderful thing is that these things are so much like the waves we can see in the ripple tank; there is no point in insisting that every feature of the ripple tank be found in atom or in photon.

The physicists of the early twentieth century who lived through the development of modern physics found it a magical but a terrible time. It seemed full of paradox: things were both waves and particles, waves of no substance at all, particles without definite paths through space. The novelty of combining these ideas in a new, consistent picture was often mistaken for impossibility. But we have learned that the old models based on experience with matter more or less on our own scale do not completely suit the world on the scale of the atom. The new picture is much better. The astonishing thing is that we can use a large part of our everyday experience as a guide to the atom. The quantum theory — the combination of wave and particle — was the greatest of triumphs. For a physics willing to face the facts squarely and to be neither frightened nor dazzled by novelty, it opened up a whole new domain. How it revealed the interior of the atom is the topic of the next chapter.

FOR HOME, DESK, AND LAB

1. Take the instructions from Section 33–2. Carry out the experiment with cards marked *L*, *C*, and *R*, and make a graph like Fig. 33–4 (c). (You can use any distinguishable cards.)

2. * Make a table showing the various ways the numbers can come up when you throw a pair of dice. (Assume you are using one green and one red die.) The table might start like this:

Green die	Red die	Sum
1	1	2
1	2	3
2	1	3

(a) In how many different ways can they come up?

(b) In how many of these different ways do the numbers add up to 7?

(c) In how many of these different ways do the numbers add up to 2?

(d) Actually throw a pair of dice a number of times. Record the number of times you throw, the number of 7's that come up, and the number of 2's — always using the sum of the spots on the tops of the dice. Watch the distribution build up in your record.

(e) From your record compute the fraction

$$\frac{\text{Number of throws with 7}}{\text{Total number of throws}}$$

and the corresponding fraction for throws totaling 2. Compute the values you would *expect* for these fractions from your answers to (a), (b), and (c). Compare your experimental fractions with these expectations.

3. * In the usual pair of cubical dice, each die has six sides labeled with one to six spots. See how many times you have to cast one die in order to feel confident that each side comes up with equal probability. (Don't expect a simple answer.)

4. Look at Fig. 33–6. Divide the photograph into four equal sections along the beam of photons, and count the number of photo-electrons ejected in each section. Make a rough prediction of the number you would expect in one section more to the right.

5. Suppose you are experimenting to find out whether light behaves as a stream of bullets or as continuous waves. You place a small electric lamp several meters from a photocell. The photocell is a glass tube containing a sensitive photoelectric surface and a collecting rod in a vacuum. Any electron ejected from the surface is driven across to the collector by an electric field and an amplifier is arranged to show the collecting of single electrons. Suppose you reduce the light falling on the photocell to an extremely faint stream by introducing a number of pieces of blackened photographic film. (A film that has been exposed to light and developed will transmit only about one-hundredth of the light falling on it. Then how much would be transmitted by three such films placed one after the other?) You first run the experiment for an hour and count the number of electrons collected. You find that with the very weak light you have provided, only 1,800 electrons have been collected. Thus the stream of light received in one hour is able to provide the energy to eject 1,800 electrons.

(a) In how much time does the stream bring enough energy to eject 1 electron from that sensitive surface?

Now suppose you start with the apparatus in complete darkness. (If the collecting system records any electrons, they are strays or "background effects" due to unwanted events in the apparatus. You should subtract an allowance for that background in any measurements you make.) Turn on the weak light suddenly, and notice how long it takes until an electron is ejected.

(b) If the light consists of a smooth stream of waves, how soon after turning on the light would you expect to see an electron ejected?

(When such an experiment is actually done and repeated many times, on some occasions an electron is ejected at about the time you have just calculated, but on some occasions much later, and on other occasions very much earlier — almost immediately.)

6. Copy Fig. 33–9 in a rough sketch, with any scale you like. Draw another graph with the same scale for a different photoelectric surface, for example a metal that requires two or three times as much energy to remove an electron.

7. Red light has a wave length of about 6,500 angstroms.

(a) Estimate its frequency.

(b) Estimate the energy in joules of one photon of red light.

(c) Estimate the energy in electron volts of one such photon.

(d) Find out approximately the longest and shortest wave lengths you can see, and compute the energy of the corresponding photons.

8. Light of 5,000-angstrom wave length illuminates a surface. What voltage is needed to stop all the photo electrons emitted from the surface if their binding energy to the surface is 2.0 electron volts?

9. A typical FM radio station broadcasts with a wave length of 3 meters. Estimate:

(a) the energy in one photon of this radiation.

(b) the number of photons broadcast per second if the radiated power is 10 kilowatts.

(c) roughly the number of photons received by a receiving set during one vibration of the letter "s" in the audio pattern, if the receiver is 100 km from the station. (Make the following simplifying assumptions:

(i) the radiation spreads uniformly in all directions along radii from the source so that an inverse-square law holds for energy flow — this is not true for any ordinary antenna.

(ii) the receiving antenna collects radiation from an area of 1 meter^2 perpendicular to the line of travel of waves.

(iii) the sound of the letter "s" involves air oscillations of frequency about 4,000 cycles per second.)

(d) Will you ordinarily notice the individual photons in receiving the letter "s"?

10. (a) Find from Part III of this book the average kinetic energy of center-of-mass motion of a mole of a monatomic gas at room temperature, and its increase of energy when its temperature is raised 1°C.

(b) Suppose photons of 3-meter radio waves are given to the gas molecules. How many would raise the temperature 1°C?

11. (a) How much energy is carried by an "average" photon of visible light with wave length of about 5,000 angstroms? How much momentum?

(b) Estimate the number of photons of visible light emitted per second from a 100-watt light bulb emitting 1 per cent of its power in the visible region.

(c) What is the light *pressure* exerted by the photons from that bulb when they strike a black body 2 meters away head-on?

12. The layers of atoms in crystals are known (from density and Avogadro's number) to be a few angstroms apart, say 3×10^{-10} m. X rays from ordinary commercial X-ray tubes are found to be diffracted at quite large angles, such as 10°, by such crystals acting as interference gratings. Make a rough estimate of the energy of photons in such X rays.

13. In a particular X-ray tube electrons hit a target after they have been accelerated by a potential difference of 20,000 volts. As they decelerate to a stop in the target, a few of them emit X-ray photons.

(a) Why is there a definite minimum wave length of photons observed from this tube? (This limit is known as the Duane-Hunt limit.)

(b) Calculate that minimum wave length.

14. In the three-months experiment described in Section 33–3, G. I. Taylor estimated the energy of the light reaching his photographic plate. He found it was 5×10^{-13} joules per second. (He obtained that value by comparing the average blackening of the plate with that produced in 10 seconds by a candle 2 yards away, without any absorbing screens of smoked glass.) From that estimate, calculate the average distance between photons, as follows:

(a) Assume the wave length of the useful light was about 5,000 angstrom units. What energy did each photon carry?

(b) Calculate from the given flow of energy the average time that elapsed between the arrival of one photon and the next.

(c) From the average time, calculate the average distance between one photon and the next in the beam of light.

(d) If you were asked, "How many photons are in the box at any chosen instant?" you would have to answer "None, most of the time, but on looking again and again and again, you should expect to 'see' one photon in the box about once in so many trials." How many? Assume the box was 1.2 meters long.

(e) On the same basis, you might expect to "see" two photons in the box about once in how many trials? (All we want is the order of magnitude.)

15. A stream of radiation falls on the completely absorbing surface of a small object of mass 10^{-3} kg that is free to move in space (e.g., sunlight on a small meteor somewhere near the sun). The stream reaching the object carries energy to it at a rate of 3,000 watts. Calculate the momentum reaching the object in 10 seconds. (Assume, if you like, that the stream of radiation is a shower of photons.)

(a) Assuming that momentum and energy are conserved, calculate the kinetic energy acquired by the object in 10 seconds, starting at rest.

(b) What fraction of the total energy received by the object becomes its kinetic energy?

(c) What happens to the rest of the energy received by the object?

16. A photon of wave length 1 angstrom hits an electron "at rest." The photon bounces away at right angles to its original path.

(a) Draw a vector diagram of the photon momentum before the collision and the photon and electron momentum after the collision.

Note: For such a collision the fractional loss of energy is small: ν' is nearly equal to ν, so in drawing a vector diagram for momenta, you can take the momentum of the photon after collision to have practically the same magnitude as the momentum of the photon before collision when you are finding the direction of the electron's recoil. Taking the electron recoil given by that assumption, use conservation of momentum and conservation of energy to compute the answers asked for.

(b) Calculate the momentum of the photon after the collision.

(c) Calculate the kinetic energy of the electron after the collision.

(d) Calculate the energy of the photon after the collision.

(e) Is ν' very different from ν?

17. A narrow stream of 100-volt electrons is fired at two parallel slits very close together. The distance between the slits is estimated to be 10 angstrom units. The electrons passing through the slits reach a screen 3 meters away, and form a pattern of interference fringes.

[It seems almost impossible to make such a pair of slits in any real sheet of matter, made of atoms which are themselves 1 angstrom or more in diameter; and even more impossible to measure their separation, since light has a wave length of thousands of angstroms. Yet the equivalent of this pair of slits can be made — has been made and used. It is the "biprism" of Fig. 33–12 (b).]

(a) Estimate the distance between one bright fringe and the next.

(b) The bright fringes would appear as bright marks on a fluorescent screen sufficiently sensitive to glow when bombarded with 100-volt electrons (or as dark marks on a photographic film, or as large pointer readings on some meter attached to an electron collector). What is the essential difference between the bright-fringe electrons and those that reach the screen in a dark fringe: Are they bigger? More massive? Of better quality? Of greater charge, or what?

18. Electrons passing through a double slit (fantastic but possible, as discussed in the previous question) make an interference pattern on a remote screen.

If the gun voltage used to provide the original stream of electrons with kinetic energy is changed from 50 volts to 5,000, what does this do to the spacing of the fringes?

19. The sizes of atomic nuclei are hard to measure with alpha particles, because we have to look for small differences from Coulomb scattering. Neutrons are often used.

(a) What are the de Broglie wave lengths of neutrons with kinetic energy 10^4 electron volts? 10^6 electron volts? 10^8 electron volts?

(b) Compare these wave lengths with the diameter of a gold nucleus (15×10^{-15} m).

(c) Look back at Fig. 33–15 to see how waves behave when they meet an obstacle. Suppose we fire a stream of neutrons at a small target of gold. For which of the neutron waves in (a) do you expect to find

(i) most of the neutrons pass by the nuclei undisturbed while some are absorbed and some bounce off, all like balls in Newtonian mechanics?

(ii) most of the neutrons pass the nucleus apparently undisturbed and the rest come out of the gold target equally in all directions, regardless of the shape of the nucleus?

(d) With neutrons of which energy would you prefer to try measuring the nuclear size?

20. (a) What is the wave length of X rays whose photons each carry 40,000 electron volts of energy?

(b) About what energy electrons have a de Broglie wave length equal to that of 40,000-volt X rays? (Give your answer in electron volts.)

(c) What energy baseballs?

(d) What is the wave length of a baseball moving at 10 meters per second?

21. The wave picture of matter describes how a proton and an electron are put together to form a hydrogen atom. We already know that the diameter of a hydrogen atom is about 10^{-10} m.

(a) If we assume that a de Broglie matter wave one wave length long will just encircle the outside of the atom, how large is the wave length?

(b) How big is the kinetic energy of the electron if it has that wave length?

(c) Compute the potential energy of the electron. It will be negative as measured from zero when electron and proton are infinitely far apart.

(d) Compute the kinetic energy of an electron circling at that radius and compare your answer with that of (b).

(e) According to your estimates in (b), (c), and (d), how much energy is needed to ionize a hydrogen atom? (Measurements give 13.6 electron volts.)

FURTHER READING

DE BROGLIE, LOUIS, *Matter and Light*. Norton, 1939.

GAMOW, GEORGE, "The Principle of Uncertainty." *Scientific American*, January, 1958.

ROSSI, BRUNO, "Where Do Cosmic Rays Come From?" *Scientific American*, September, 1953.

SCHRÖDINGER, ERWIN, "What Is Matter?" *Scientific American*, September, 1953.

James Clerk Maxwell

Michael Faraday

Michael Faraday (1791–1867) was one of the great electrical pioneers. Among his discoveries were electromagnetic induction and the laws of electrolysis. He emphasized the significance of the ideas of electric and magnetic fields.

James Clerk Maxwell (1831–1879) built on the work of Faraday; he developed the formal electromagnetic theory. He introduced the idea that a changing electric flux produces a magnetic field equivalent to that produced by an electric current. His theory shows that electromagnetic waves should behave like light.

J. J. Thomson (1856–1940) contributed further to electromagnetic theory: for example, he introduced the idea of electromagnetic momentum. He established the existence of the electron and showed that it must be a particle with a negative electric charge and a mass very small compared to even the lightest atom. He pointed out that electrons are one of the building blocks of all atoms.

The experiments done by *Ernest Rutherford* (1871–1937) and his students established the nature of alpha particles. He then used these particles to explore the structure of atoms, establishing the nuclear model.

Niels Bohr (1885—) applied the ideas of photons and energy states to understanding the structure of atoms. He and his students have been at the center of the development of modern quantum ideas.

(Pictures of Faraday, Maxwell, and Thomson, courtesy British Information Services. Picture of Rutherford from *British Scientists of the Twentieth Century*, 1952, Routledge & Kegan Paul Limited. Picture of Bohr, courtesy Royal Danish Ministry of Foreign Affairs.)

J. J. Thomson

Ernest Rutherford

Niels Bohr

QUANTUM SYSTEMS AND THE STRUCTURE OF ATOMS

CHAPTER 34

WITH Chapter 33 we began twentieth-century physics. There direct and convincing experiment showed that the old picture of the world with waves for light and particles for matter was too simple. Nature is more subtle than these early models: the photons on the one hand, and the de Broglie waves on the other, show that subtlety. The older mechanics proved inadequate. Energy and momentum are conserved in every individual event, but the wave picture is necessary to describe the over-all patterns of events. For example, each electron that hits a detector transfers the right amount of momentum and energy, but to know where electrons hit most often we need the wave picture. With the aid of the idea of probability, we found a single view combining wave and particle behavior. Chapter 33 ended with a quiet note of victory.

Chapter 32, however, ended with a jangling enigma. Scattering experiments, using alpha particles as probes, showed the atom to be a loose structure, somewhat like that giant Newtonian machine, the solar system. The electrons were there, all right, flying about like tiny planets. This much seemed to be established, but it led to a troublesome problem. As the electrons fly about in their orbits, they ought to spend their energy in radiation (Section 32–5). Unlike the earth, an electron should not remain indefinitely on the same orbit. Instead, the energy it loses in electromagnetic radiation should have just the mechanical effect of energy lost by a satellite in air friction; the steady loss should shrink the orbit toward the attracting center. In other words, because accelerated charges radiate, an atom built according to Rutherford's planetary model could not be stable, and the world could not remain as it does. That impossibility spotlighted the ultimate limitation of classical physics. The combination of Newton's mechanics and classical electromagnetism cannot describe atoms as they are.

Apart from this basic trouble — energy loss by radiation — physicists had another reason to fear that the Newtonian laws of mechanics could never explain a Rutherford atom. The solar system and the atom may both be planetary systems, but in changing the scale to the very small a qualitative difference appears.

We can picture some agent (such as a visiting star) changing our own solar system by any amount, small, medium, or large — short of a major break-up — and when the disturbing agent is removed the new arrangement would just continue. We can imagine a solar system of planets built to any size over a wide range — with orbits, masses, and numbers of planets different from ours, and yet equally stable. A collection of similar solar systems, such as we might find around other stars, would be like the other things we see in nature, like a set of roses or of raindrops; they would bear a strong family resemblance, but with different-sized suns, and planetary orbits of different sizes, no two would be precisely alike.

Atoms are not like that. Their most remarkable property is the likeness they bear one to another. All hydrogen atoms act the same, all helium atoms are alike, and so on. Atoms of one kind are far more alike than any Grade A peas. Yet they have different histories; different stories of collisions and ionizations and chemical combination lie behind each one. Through it all they remain one and the same, showing the same spectral lines and making the same chemical reactions with the same amounts of energy.* The atom may be a planetary system, but it is a planetary system that comes in myriad identical copies.

The identity of the atoms, and the stability of their internal motions, makes no sense on the basis of Newton's laws of mechanics. This repetitive quality requires a new explanation, a fundamental change in the theory. Here a wonderful thing happens. The ideas we introduced to make sense of photons and matter waves also supply a clear and powerful explanation of atomic stability and atomic sameness. To take account of the wave behavior of matter, we must modify Newton's mechanics, making it into the newer quantum mechanics. Then we find a way to understand all that we have yet seen of the structure of matter. The combined view of wave and particle behavior covers all we know about nature.

34–1. The Experiments of Franck and Hertz; Atomic Energy Levels

For a planetary system, according to Newtonian mechanics, motions at all total energies are possible. For an atom, on the other hand, we suspect that only a limited set of motions can take place. This limitation is suggested by the repetitious behavior and by the stability of atoms. The identity of the members of an atomic species suggests the same thing.

If only certain distinct patterns of motion are possible, we would expect that an atomic system can take on only the separate total energies corresponding to those motions. Then there should be gaps between the possible energies; and in that case the internal energy of an atom can be changed only by certain definite amounts of energy transferred from the outside.

Are there really gaps between the possible energies that an atom may have? A direct test of this idea is important. It can be made by trying to change the energy of atoms directly by bombarding them with electrons. Can an atom that is hit by an electron take in some energy and keep it as a gain of internal energy? And if so, can it retain *any* gain from small to large, or is it limited to a selection of sharply defined amounts? In Germany in 1914 such a test was made. James Franck and Gustav Hertz performed an electron-bombardment experiment for which they later received the Nobel Prize. This experiment — and the many similar ones that stem from it — are a key to the problems of atomic stability and structure. Here we shall describe an experiment somewhat different from the original Franck and Hertz experiments which gets the same information by closely related means. We choose this particular experiment because it is easier to interpret though harder to carry out.

Like Franck and Hertz we shall use electrons to bombard the atoms. We can do this by using an electron gun like the ones we described in Chapters 27 and 28. The electron gun gives kinetic energy to the electrons boiled out of the filament. If the accelerating voltage in the gun is V_A, the electrons leave the gun with kinetic energy of one electronic charge times V_A volts, or V_A electron volts.

When the electrons leave the gun they pass into a chamber containing a gas. They enter this chamber through a small hole, and the electron gun operates in a good vacuum because we continually and rapidly pump away any gas that escapes from the chamber into the gun (Fig. 34–1). The chamber containing the gas is made of a conducting material so it is all at one potential and there is no electric field inside it which could change the energy of the electrons. Consequently, any change in the electrons' energy arises because of their interaction with the gas atoms.

Now to investigate what happens to the electrons when they collide with the gas atoms, we allow some of the electrons to come out of the gas chamber through another small hole leading out on a slant into a second evacuated space. There we measure the energy of the electrons which have passed through the gas. We can make this measurement with any one of a number of devices. For example, we can use a magnetic mass spectrograph like that described in Chapter 30. Then, since we know the mass of the electron, the curvature of the electron path in the magnetic

*Although the atoms of an element are all alike in essential structure, they can take in energy, as we shall see, and change to an "excited state." However, unlike a solar system which would keep any change imposed on it, an excited atom snaps back to exactly the same original form when it is left alone.

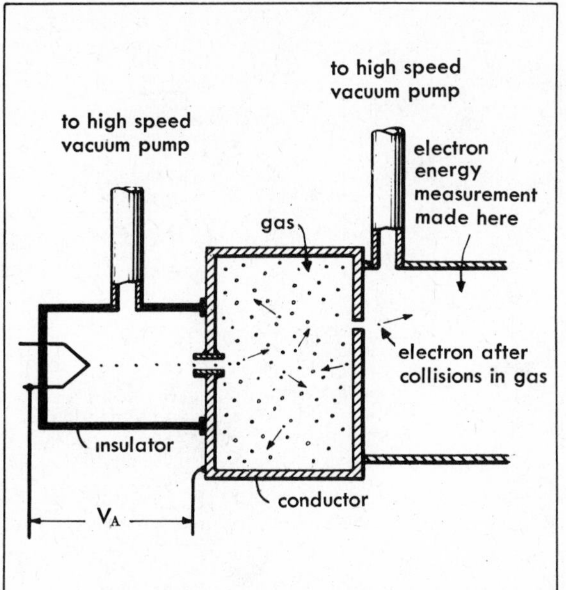

34–1. The general idea of an experiment to measure the changes in the energy of electrons when they collide with gas atoms. The electrons pass through a sample of gas (mercury vapor) in the middle chamber. Electrons leave the gun with energy given by the accelerating voltage. Their energy remaining after collisions is measured in the right-hand chamber. Note that the opening into the energy-measuring region is not in the direct line of the original beam of electrons. This is to insure catching only those electrons that have been deflected by collisions.

field allows us to determine the energy. Alternatively, we can determine the electron's energy by making the electron move against a retarding potential difference and measuring what potential difference just prevents the electrons from reaching the collector. We could even use time-of-flight measurements in the detecting chamber to find electron speed and therefore kinetic energy. The practical details of these measurements turn out to be difficult and complicated, but despite the complications we emerge with the knowledge we want of the energy of electrons after interaction with the gas atoms.

What kind of information do we get from this apparatus? Let us take a specific example. What happens when we have mercury vapor in the gas chamber? As long as the accelerating potential in the electron gun is only a few volts, we find that the electrons entering our detector after colliding with the gas atoms have almost exactly the same energy that is imparted to them by the gun. The collisions with gas atoms at this low energy are elastic. (In such collisions the massive atoms take a negligible share of kinetic energy.) However, when the accelerating potential in the gun passes 5 volts, so that the electrons bombard the atoms with 5 electron volts or more kinetic energy, a dramatic change occurs. The electrons entering the detector no longer have the energy with which they left the gun. Instead the electrons entering the detector have practically no kinetic energy.

Now we increase the gun potential further so that the kinetic energy of the bombarding electrons is greater. We find that the energy of electrons reaching the detector is also greater. When we raise V_A from 5 to 6 electron volts, the kinetic energy measured in the detector rises from a small fraction of an electron volt to one electron volt more than that. Careful measurements in which we determine the gun voltage accurately and the kinetic energy in the detector accurately show that in their collisions with the atoms the electrons are losing almost exactly 4.9 electron volts. This loss only sets in when the bombarding electrons have 4.9 electron volts of kinetic energy, and the amount of the loss stays the same while we increase the bombarding energy through the next couple of electron volts. The mercury atom cannot accept anything less than 4.9 electron volts of energy, and even when it is offered somewhat more energy it still accepts exactly this amount.

However, 4.9 electron volts is not the only amount of energy the atom can take in. If the bombarding energy is 6.7 electron volts or more, the electrons can lose either 4.9 electron volts or 6.7 electron volts. On increasing the bombarding energy still further, we find other thresholds at which greater losses can occur and beyond which any of several different amounts of energy can be robbed from the electrons. This is the essential property Franck and Hertz looked for: atoms can change their internal energy, but the changes are restricted to sharply defined steps.

The smallest amount of energy which can be accepted by an atom is called its first *excitation energy*. For mercury the excitation energy is 4.9 electron volts. For helium, which has the highest excitation energy, the value is 19.8 electron volts. The lowest excitation energy of all the atoms goes to cesium, which will accept a bundle of 1.4 electron volts. Other atoms will also accept certain definite bundles of energy, and these bundles are characteristic of the kind of atom.

The experiment we have described is an idealization; the results we have quoted were collected in a number of similar experiments, all of which agree. Thus the Franck-Hertz experiment and its later modifications have shown us that atoms can accept only parcels of energy. The internal energy content of an atom cannot be continuously changed. It changes only in steps. The successive internal energies which an atom can take on are called its *energy levels.* Often they are diagrammed as we show them in Fig. 34–2.

The ground state is the state in which we normally find the atom before any excitation energy has been fed into it. Above it lie the various excited states, separated by gaps. These excited states are formed when enough energy is supplied by the impinging electrons. Finally, when an atom is hit by an electron of sufficient energy, the atom is in fact disrupted. An electron is ejected from the atom and a positive ion left behind. Since the energy of the ejected electron can take on any value, the atom can accept any parcel of energy larger than the ionization energy. For mercury, as we have indicated in Fig. 34–2, the ionization energy turns out to be 10.4 electron volts.

The atoms of many elements have been studied by electron collision. From these experiments, we find that every kind of atom has its own set of energy levels and its own ionization energy. They identify the atom much as its chemical reactions or its optical spectra identify it.

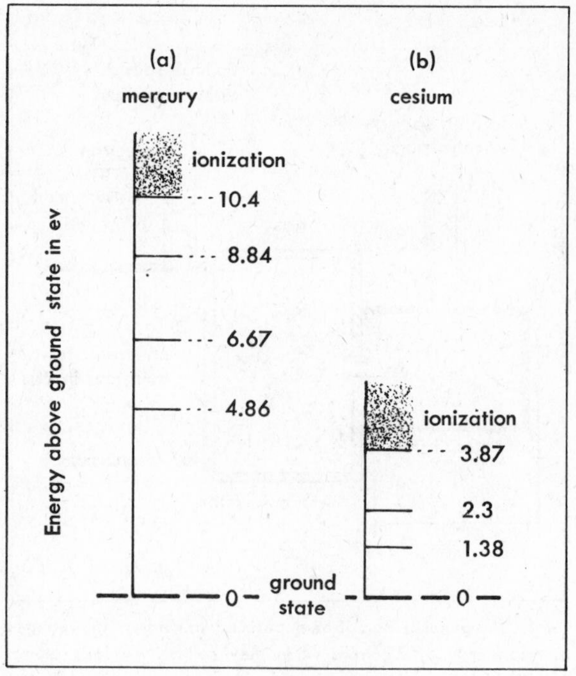

34–2. (a) Some of the energy levels of the mercury atom. In this diagram the normal "ground state" is taken as the zero of energy; and we have plotted a few of the amounts of energy that the atom will accept. (b) A similar diagram for the cesium atom.

34–2. Dissecting Atomic Spectra: Excitation and Emission

A completely different means of measurement fully confirms the existence of energy levels. While we are bombarding a gas with electrons, we observe the light emitted by the gas. At low bombarding energies, we see no appreciable light emitted by the gas. But when we pass the first excitation energy, light suddenly appears. Examining the light with a spectroscope, we see a sharp line indicating light of a definite wave length and frequency, photons of a single energy.

With mercury, for example, when the energy of the bombarding electrons passes 4.9 electron volts, a spectroscope with which we are observing the gas will suddenly show the presence of ultraviolet light having a wave length of 2537 angstroms. This strong spectral line is one of the lines by which the mercury spectrum is recognized. But this single-line mercury spectrum is most unusual. From a discharge tube filled with mercury vapor we usually see many characteristic mercury spectral lines, many lines of definite wave length which identify the element mercury. We have produced only one part of the normal mercury spectrum.

The experiments we described in the last section tell us that we have succeeded in feeding energy bundles of 4.9 electron volts to some of the mercury atoms in the gas. Only when such energy bundles have been transferred do we see any light from the mercury. Apparently the excitation energy which we feed in from the kinetic energy of the electrons is radiated as photons by the individual atoms as they return to the ground state. (Remember that the ground state is the lowest energy state, the state in which the mercury atom is normally found before the 4.9 electron volts of energy are transferred to it by a colliding electron.) If all the energy taken in by an individual atom is radiated in one lump, the photons should have 4.9 electron volts energy, and the wave length of the corresponding light should be*

$$\lambda = \frac{12{,}400 \text{ ev-A}}{E} = \frac{12{,}400 \text{ ev-A}}{4.9 \text{ ev}} = 2530 \text{ A.}$$

*This expression is derived in the box in Section 33–6.

34–3. The changes of energy when an atom is bombarded by electrons.

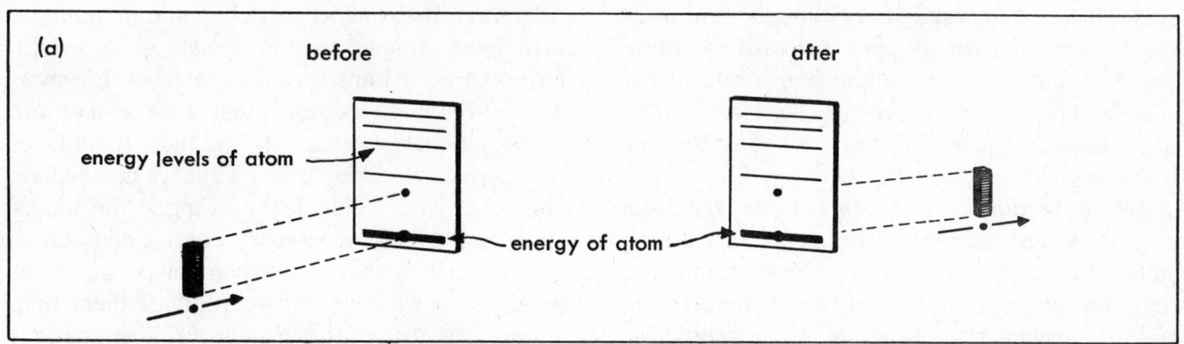

(a). An elastic collision between a bombarding electron and an atom. The arrow shows the path of the incoming electron. The "load" above the electron represents its kinetic energy. The atom and its energy levels are represented by the rectangular "billboards." In this case the electron does not have enough energy to raise the atom to the next higher energy level so it scatters off elastically, keeping its kinetic energy.

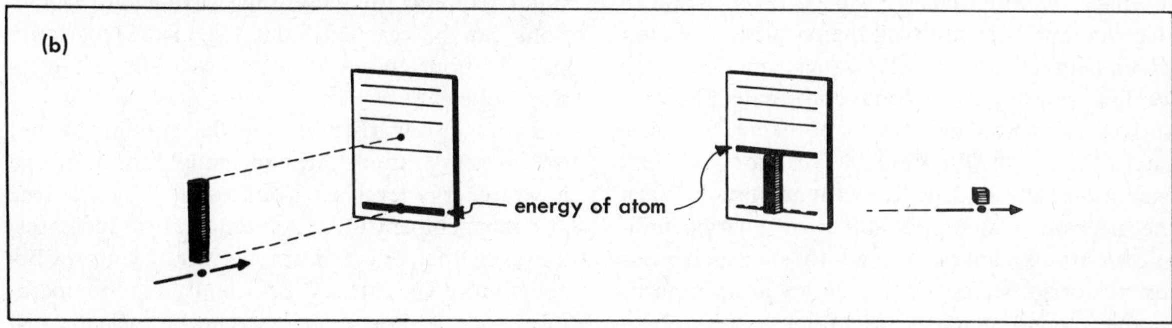

(b). Here the electron has more energy. The atom absorbs just the right amount of energy to reach its second level, and the electron goes on with only the surplus kinetic energy. The collision is inelastic.

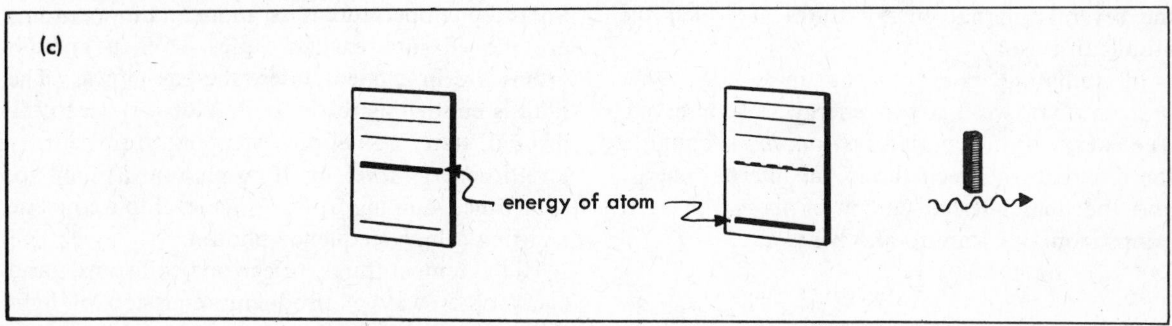

(c). The atom is at its second energy level, an "excited state." In returning to the ground state, the atom emits a photon with energy equal to the difference in energy between the two states.

If a mercury atom could radiate its extra energy in more than one photon, light of longer wave lengths would be visible. The experiment with the spectroscope therefore shows that the atoms not only take a definite amount of energy from the electrons but that they can only radiate exactly this amount of energy in returning to the ground state. Both in accepting energy from electron bombardment and in emitting energy as light, the atoms change in one jump between two energy states a little less than 4.9 electron volts apart (Fig. 34–3). This is a magnificent confirmation of the idea that atoms can make only definite shifts of internal energy.

Let us continue to experiment with the spectroscope, increasing the energy with which the electrons bombard the mercury atoms and observing the light they emit. As we increase the bombarding energy, the rest of the familiar lines of the mercury spectrum appear. They enter in groups as the bombarding energy rises successively above the thresholds for excitation of higher and higher energy states. This procedure therefore allows us to dissect the mercury spectrum and to see how it arises.

Before an atom is hit by an electron, the atom is in its lowest internal energy state, the ground state. When an atom is hit by an electron of less than the energy difference between the ground state and its first excitation state, nothing happens. A higher-energy electron, however, may transfer energy into the atom. If there is only sufficient energy to reach the first excited atomic state, just the first excitation energy will be taken from an electron, and the atom will then radiate a photon which helps to make the 2537-angstrom line which we first saw. Many atoms contribute photons, and each photon has the same energy because each of the individual atoms falls from the first excitation state back to the ground state. When the electrons can supply still more energy, individual atoms can be excited to still higher internal energy states. Then as an atom returns to the ground state, it can radiate a photon of greater energy or possibly several photons with energies equal to the energy differences between the several internal energy states at which the atom can exist.

In radiating photons — as in every other process that we know — energy is conserved. The energy of the emitted photon, $h\nu$, is equal to the difference between the initial internal energy and the final internal energy of the atom as it jumps from one state to another:

$$E_{\text{photon}} = h\nu = E_{\text{initial}} - E_{\text{final}}.$$

Each spectral line consists of the radiation from many atoms, all jumping between the same internal energy states independently of each other. Fig. 34–4, in the box, shows the analysis of the mercury spectrum and its connection with the energy levels of the mercury atom. The vertical lines on the energy-level diagrams show the energies of the photons that can be emitted. For each photon emitted, some single atom must jump from a higher state down to a lower state, and the photon carries off the energy given up.

Notice that the longer wave-length lines of mercury correspond to jumps between states both of which are above the ground state. Their energy differences are smaller, so the photons emitted have lower frequency and longer wave length. To make such long wave-length lines, however, some of the mercury atoms must first be sent into the higher energy states. To get them there takes more than 5 electron volts. Thus we can explain what otherwise would seem strange: the longer wave-length lines of mercury consist of photons of lower energy than 5 electron volts. Yet more electron energy is needed to produce them than to produce the strong line at 2537 angstroms. The reason is clear: spectral lines are formed by the transitions of atoms between particular internal energy states. And none of the initial states required for these long wave-length transitions can be reached from the mercury ground state without energy transfers well above 5 electron volts.

So far in our discussion we have assumed that the mercury atoms are normally found in the lowest energy level, or ground state. This is true at room temperature. As temperature increases, however, the collisions among mercury atoms become more violent. At sufficiently high temperature, some atomic collisions can be inelastic just as electron collisions can. They leave one or both of the colliding atoms in an excited state. So as the temperature rises, more and more atoms are moved into excited states. When enough atoms are in excited states, the gas glows. The light is emitted as the atoms rapidly return to the ground state, sometimes stepping from energy level to energy level, emitting photons as they go, sometimes jumping from a high level to a low one emitting a high-frequency photon.

High temperatures, electron collisions, and every other way of producing emission of light from gas atoms are all means of promoting atoms to excited states. The atoms then emit the photons whose energies correspond to the energy differences between the atomic energy levels. These emitted photons make up the atom's spectrum. A given kind of atom can emit only the lines which have the characteristic frequencies:

$$\nu = \frac{E_{\text{initial}} - E_{\text{final}}}{h}$$

determined by the differences between its energy levels.

Of course, different ways of putting energy into

The Dissection of the Spectrum of Mercury

34–4. The photographs show the spectral lines that appear when mercury vapor is bombarded with electrons. In each case the bombarding electrons have a definite energy which is recorded at the side of the photograph. (Photos from: John A. Eldridge, "The Spectrum of Mercury below Ionization," Physical Review, Vol. 23, Series 2, 1924.)

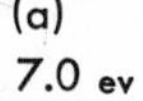

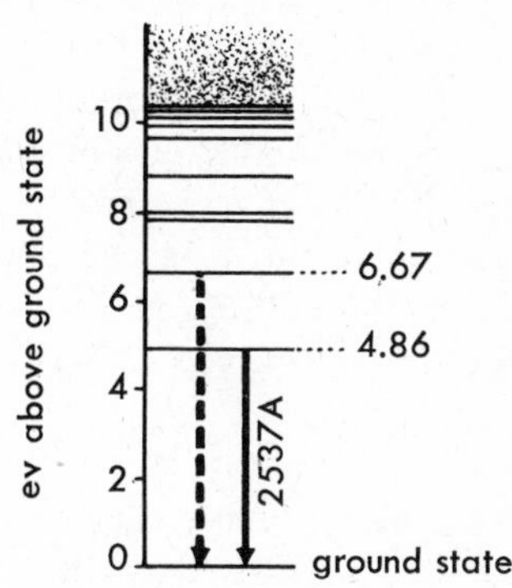

(a). With electrons of any energy above 4.9 ev, the strong ultraviolet line of wave length 2537 angstroms is emitted. This corresponds, as shown at the right, to an energy change in the atom from the first excited state to the ground state. By the time the energy is 7 ev, there is also an energy change from 6.67 ev to the ground state, giving a line of wave length 1849 angstroms. The wave length of this light, however, is too short to affect the photographic plate. Here this transition is shown by a dotted arrow. In the subsequent figures that arrow is omitted.

(b)
8.4 ev

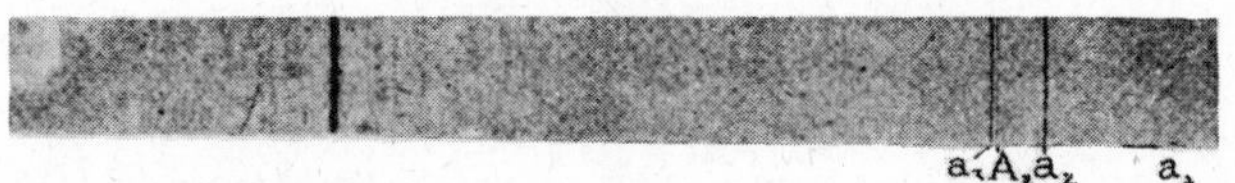

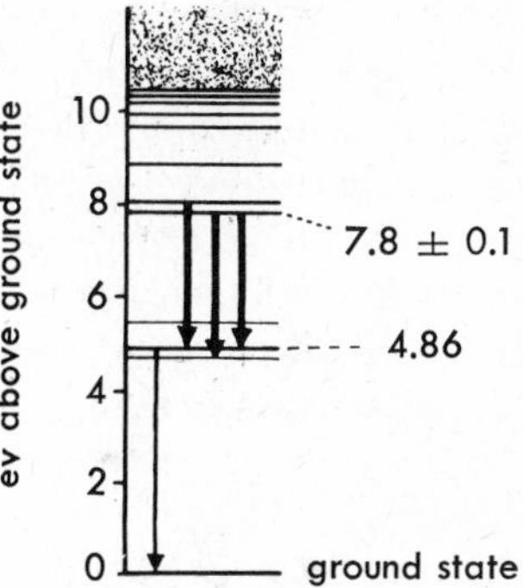

(b). At 8.4 ev three new lines of longer wave length show up in the region photographed. The photons of this light have energy given by the transitions from the levels around 7.8 ev to the levels around 4.9 ev.

(c)
8.9 ev

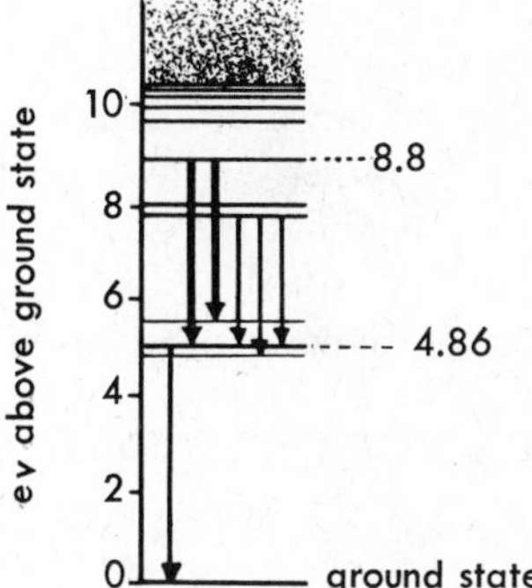

(c). With bombarding energy raised to 8.9 ev, two more lines of intermediate wave length appear. The photons have energies given by the transitions from the levels around 8.8 ev to the levels around 4.9 ev.

(d). As the electron-accelerating voltage is further increased, more and more lines appear. At 10 4 ev the atom is ionized and the complete spectrum is produced. In this case the classifications above and below the photo help to sort out the various sets of lines.

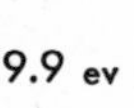

9.9 ev

10.4 ev

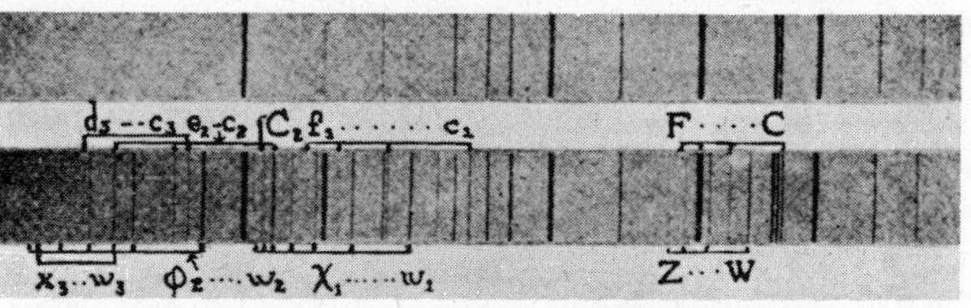

the gas can result in different proportions of atoms in the various excited states. As we shall see in the next section, photons from light of a single wave length can excite atoms to a single high energy state; and only a few other states may be reached as the atoms radiate their way back to the ground state. The carefully adjusted electron beam of 5 electron volts excites only the first excitation state of mercury. High temperatures act differently. The collisions of the randomly moving atoms raise the internal energies of a few atoms to high energy levels, but there are more atoms in lower states. Thus the brightness of lines can vary, but an individual line of an atom always has the same frequency whenever it is present.

34–3. Absorption Spectra

Emission spectra — the bright lines we see in the spectra of excited atoms — are not the only spectra which reveal the internal energy states of the atoms. We get similar information about those states when we send white light through a gas and then analyze it with a spectroscope. The white light is a mixture of all frequencies; it contains photons of all energies. Most of these photons pass through the gas and show up in the spectrum on the spectrographic plate. They are not absorbed, because the energy of the photon cannot be taken up by the atom as it makes a transition from one internal energy level to another. But some of the photons are taken up. Their absence is shown by narrow gaps in the spectrum of the light which passes through the gas. Each missing photon has been absorbed by an atom, causing a transition from one internal energy level to another. These gaps in the spectrum then tell us about the internal energy states (Fig. 34–5).

Here the same interpretation and the same rule of energy conservation apply; only the order of the process is different. (Fig. 34–6.) In this case

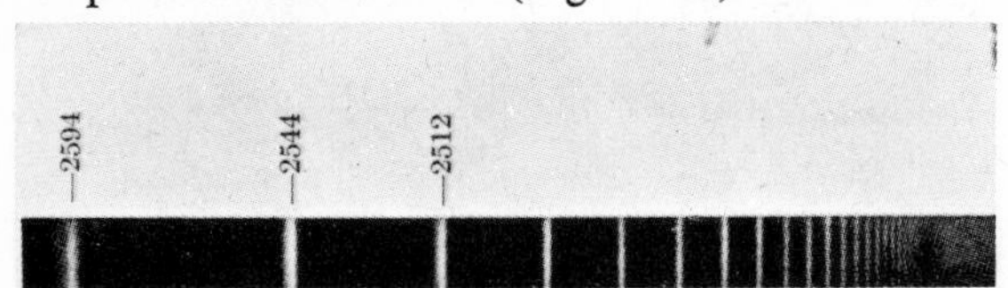

34–5. The short wave-length region of the absorption spectrum of sodium. Since this is a reproduction of a photographic negative, the wave lengths absorbed appear as light lines on a continuous dark background. (From: H. Kuhn, "Über Spektren von unecht gebundenen Molekülen (Polarisationsmolekülen) K_2, Na_2, Cs_2, und Verbreiterung von Absorptionslinien," Zeitschrift für Physik, Vol. 76, 1932.)

the initial state of the atom is the lower internal energy state; the final state is the higher, because it must have the full energy of the original atom plus that of the absorbed light photon:

$$E_{\text{final}} = E_{\text{initial}} + E_{\text{photon}} = E_{\text{initial}} + h\nu$$

In this way, one can see, for example, why mercury vapor at room temperature is transparent to visible light. No photon in visible light has enough energy to promote the mercury atom from the ground state to its first excited state. The right photons only come in ultraviolet light of 2537 angstroms wave length. As we should expect, that particular light is very strongly absorbed. The same argument applies to the other common colorless gases — oxygen, nitrogen, helium, and the rest. They can absorb light only in the ultraviolet. And there we find a series of absorption lines.

Once the frequency of the light is sufficiently high, in the deep ultraviolet or beyond, a photon can take an electron completely out of an atom. The atom is ionized, and any surplus energy is carried away by the electron as kinetic energy. This *is* the photoelectric effect. There is no limitation on the amount of kinetic energy the electron can be given. So there are no restrictions on the frequency of the light that ejects electrons provided it exceeds a certain minimum "threshold" value. The observed threshold of the photoelectric effect in atoms is just the minimum frequency required to break an electron loose from the atom. The evidence of spectra in this matter agrees perfectly with the evidence obtained by observing the photo-electrons.

All light, all electromagnetic radiation can excite atoms, or be emitted by them in jumps or transitions between energy levels. Consider one example far outside the range of visible light. Although we are apt to think of radio waves interacting with antennas rather than with atoms, the study of atomic spectra at radio and microwave frequencies is a modern and powerful tool for physicist and chemist. Because radio waves are long, their photons carry little energy, so they arise from levels which lie very close together in energy. All the alkali metals, lithium, potassium, rubidium, and cesium, have pairs of close-lying energy levels. The photons from transitions between these pairs of energy states are in the radio-frequency part of the spectrum. In particular, the ground state of the element cesium is really a

34–6. The change in energy when an atom is bombarded by light photons of various energies. The "load" sketched above the photon represents its energy.

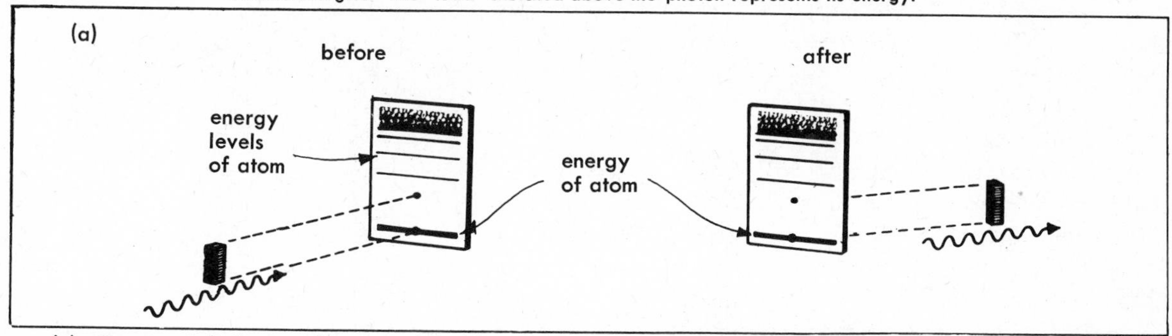

(a). The atom is in the ground state, and the photon has too little energy to change the atom to the next excited state. The photon simply passes through or scatters off elastically.

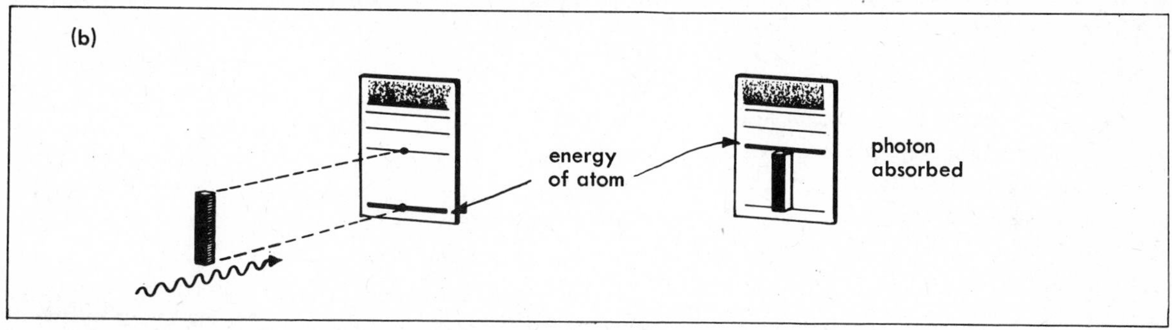

(b). The photon is one that has exactly the right energy to raise the atom to its first excited state. The atom absorbs the photon, taking on all the energy of the photon.

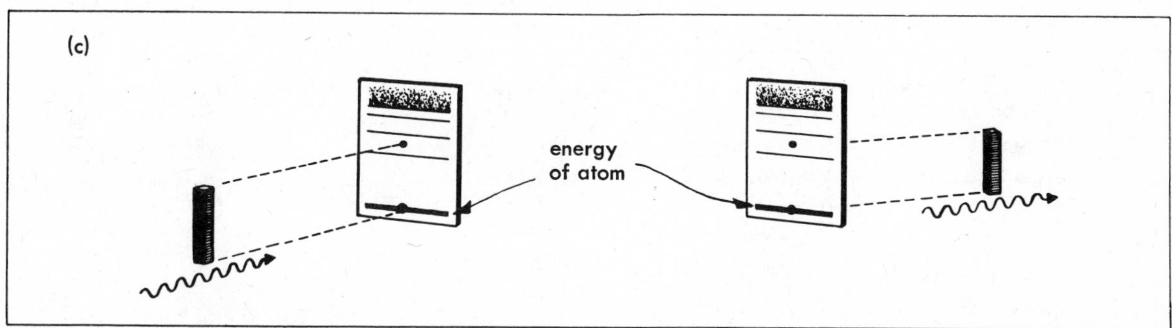

(c). The photon is one that has more than enough energy to excite the atom but not enough to reach another excited state. This photon, too, must scatter elastically, for if it were absorbed the atom could not both conserve energy and be in an allowed energy level. The only alternative is the re-emission of the photon.

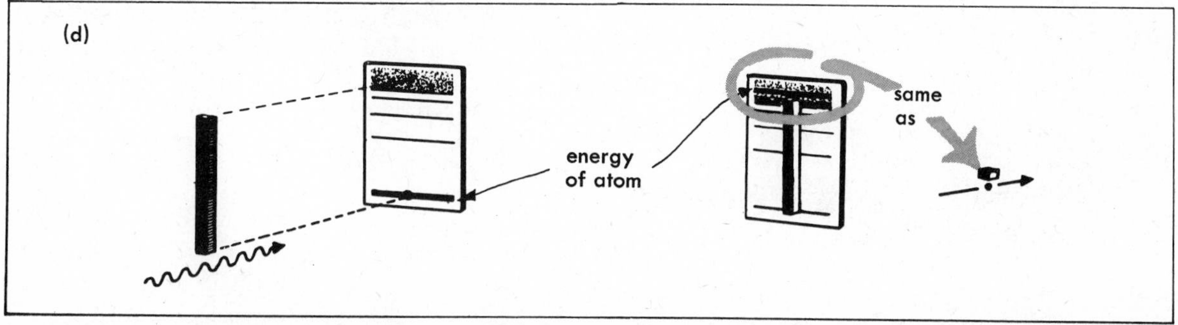

(d). In this case the photon is one with enough energy to ionize the atom. It raises the atom to a region filled with positive energy levels. This is another way of saying that the atom is broken up and the electron carries away the energy above the ionization threshold as kinetic energy. (Note that an atom which is already excited can be ionized by a photon of lower energy which would simply have been scattered elastically from an atom in its ground state.)

pair of energy levels separated by about 4.14 $\times 10^{-5}$ electron volts. Precisely, the radiation from this transition between energy levels has the frequency of

$$\nu = 9.19263177 \times 10^9 \text{ cycles per second.}$$

This frequency is now used as a standard of frequency and time. Clocks working directly with it are commercially available.

The spectrum has become the best clue to the energy levels of any radiating atom. But realizing this and establishing the energy levels from these clues required great ingenuity. Once the spectral wave lengths are known, they must be converted to frequencies, and the frequencies examined and fitted together to find the energy levels themselves. Each spectral line gives a difference of two energy levels, and a few levels can give quite a complicated collection of lines. So the job is not easy. To disentangle the levels, absorption spectra help. So does excitation by photon absorption, and other special forms of excitation. Following up all these clues, the spectroscopist finally presents his results in the form of a table or diagram of energy levels belonging to the atom he is studying. As the result of his labor, many internal energy states have been precisely established for practically all kinds of atoms.

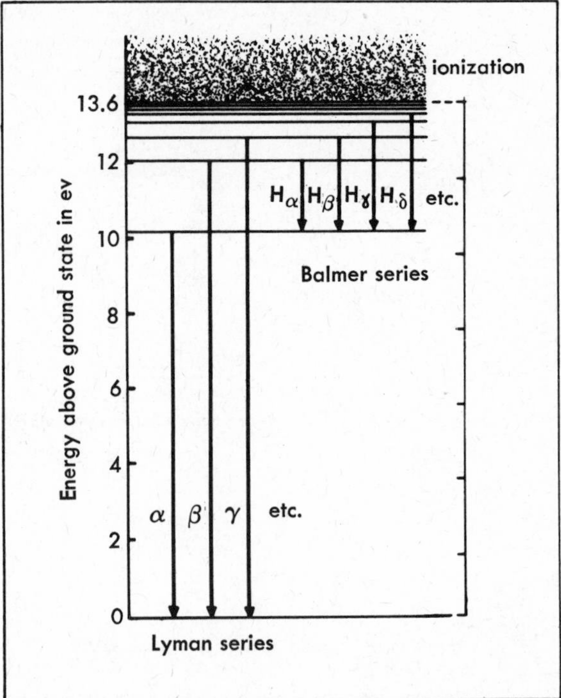

34–7 (a). The energy level diagram of the simplest atom, hydrogen. The arrows show the energy changes for two of the sets of spectral lines characteristic of hydrogen. The jumps marked H_α, H_β, etc. are called the Balmer series. The lines of the Lyman series in the ultraviolet are also shown. This diagram is considerably simplified, because the scale does not permit drawing the "fine structure."

34–7 (b). A photograph of the first dozen lines in the Balmer series produced by glowing hydrogen gas.

34–7 (c). A photograph of the Balmer series, from $n = 6$ to as high as $n = 20$ or more. Their positions fit the predicted values to within one part in ten thousand or even better. (Photos from: G. Herzberg, "Über die Spektren des Wasserstoffs," Annalen der Physik, Vol. 84, 1927.)

34–4. The Energy Levels of Hydrogen

The energy levels of atomic hydrogen and some of the spectral lines with which each one is associated are displayed in Fig. 34–7. It is the fruit of the work of a generation or two of spectroscopists; in it we see displayed the level structure of the simplest of atoms.

What is remarkable is that these many energy levels, which gave rise to still more numerous spectral lines, all can be represented by a very simple formula

$$E_n = E_I - \frac{E_I}{n^2},$$

where E_I is the ionization energy of 13.6 electron volts, and n is any positive whole number. When $n = 1$, this formula gives $E_1 = 0$, setting our zero of energy at the ground state. When $n = 2$, we

get $$E_2 = 13.6 \text{ ev} - \frac{13.6 \text{ ev}}{(2)^2} = 10.2 \text{ ev},$$

which is the energy of the first excited state. For other values of n we get the other observed energy states. Scores of levels have been identified at their predicted positions. The formula works wonderfully well, fit ing experiments to one part in ten thousand or better.

In all these energy states, the electron and proton are bound together. They cannot get infinitely far apart. For higher values of n, however, the energy states approach the ionization energy, and as n becomes infinitely large we reach the energy at which the electron can just escape from the proton.

At still higher energies the electron and proton are no longer bound together. The electron is just moving past the proton. At these energies, even when the electron gets infinitely far from the proton, there will be kinetic energy left over. On the energy-level diagram you will notice the essential difference between these energy states in which the electron moves freely away with any energy and the bound states (beneath the ionization energy). There are free states at all energies above ionization, while there are gaps between the individual bound energy states.

In Chapter 32, we saw that the atom resembled a planetary system. In particular on the Rutherford model, the hydrogen atom consists of a proton sun with a single electron planet. The Coulomb force between them goes with the inverse square of their separation just like the force between the sun and a planet, or satellite-earth, and the force between the earth and a satellite. In Section 25–5 we studied the binding and the escape of satellites in just these systems. There we found that it was natural to choose the zero of energy when the sun and planet, the earth and satellite, or the proton and electron are standing still infinitely far apart. That energy marks the border between bound states and free states. For the atom it is the ionization energy.

When we shift the zero of energy to the ionization energy, the formula for the energy states of hydrogen becomes even simpler. It is

$$E_n = \frac{-13.6 \text{ electron volts}}{n^2}.$$

$E_1 = -13.6$ ev now tells us directly that the ground state is 13.6 ev lower than the ionization energy. The atom is bound together by 13.6 electron volts.

$E_2 = \dfrac{-13.6 \text{ ev}}{(2)^2} = -3.4$ ev says that the first excited state is only 3.4 electron volts below ionization level; and so on. On the right-hand edge of Fig. 34–7 we have added an energy scale with its zero at the ionization energy. You can compare these answers with the energy levels measured against that scale.

Originally the simple formula for the energy states was obtained from the measurements of spectral lines. The spectroscopists Balmer and Rydberg developed it in fitting the spectra into a neat pattern, and what we now call the energy levels were called the term values in their purely spectroscopic analysis. Then in 1913 Niels Bohr showed the connection between the planetary model and the formula $E_n = \dfrac{-13.6 \text{ ev}}{n^2}$. He was actually able to derive the value 13.6 from the fundamental constants of nature: the Coulomb constant k, Planck's constant h, and the mass m of the electron. We may take Bohr's success as marking the beginning of our present theory of the structure of matter.*

Despite their similarities, the description of a hydrogen atom must be different from that of a planet moving around the sun. The description must account for the stability of the ground state, for the existence of special excited states, and for

*Bohr justified his derivation by appealing to a general principle which we now name his Correspondence Principle. Suppose we have a successful theory — a theory developed to deal with the known facts in some region of knowledge. As new knowledge is gained, the theory may show difficulties; it may fail to fit all the new facts. Then a new theory has to be developed to replace the old. But, the new theory has no hope of success unless it agrees with the old theory in all matters where the old theory itself agreed with the facts. In other words, new theory must make the same predictions, in the same form, as old theory in the region where the old was adequate. In this way the structure and content of old theory can provide an essential check on new theory and may even go further and show the direction in which unknown new theory must develop.

Bohr's first use of this Correspondence Principle was in justifying his derivation of the constant for hydrogen energy levels. He imagined the atom excited until it is almost ionized so that the electron moves around the proton in a huge orbit of man-sized dimensions, a meter or so across (n = 10,000 or so). An orbit like that is the size of a radio antenna or a synchrotron, and we know that in such cases the frequency radiated is the frequency of the motion (up and down the antenna, or around the race track). Therefore, the frequency of photons emitted in a hydrogen atom's quantum jumps between levels near ionization must be the same as the frequency of the orbital motion. Equating the photon frequency and the orbital frequency tells us the combination of k, h, and m which must appear in the expression for these energy states and for all other energy states of the hydrogen atom. In this way, Bohr derived his result by relying on an over-all principle of fitting together new theory and old. Here, however, we shall derive the result from other considerations in Section 34–6.

the identity of all the individual hydrogen atoms in the universe. An atom can remain for any length of time only in one or another of its separate energy levels. If the atom is in any energy level above the ground state, it will not stay there forever. Sooner or later it will radiate; it will lose energy, not until the electron coincides with the proton, but only until it reaches the ground state. In the next sections we shall see how the properties of the de Broglie waves which describe the electron moving in the electrostatic field of its proton allow us to calculate the values of the internal energy states of hydrogen.

34–5. The Origin of Energy Levels

How can we understand the presence of definite internal energy levels, and the simple numerical relations they sometimes have? We hope to do this by using the ideas of the last chapter. In it we learned of matter waves, waves whose intensity at any place indicates the probability of finding a particle there. How does that idea explain separate, well-defined energy levels?

The matter wave for a particular energy level must stay the same for a very long time. We know from Franck-Hertz experiments and from the definite line spectra of elements that there are definite separate energy states in atoms. We should not find that behavior if the matter wave for a particular energy level wobbled around and did not remain the same for a long time. Also, there must be a different matter wave corresponding to each separate energy level, because the energy levels are different. We must therefore look for several distinct wave patterns, each one different from the others and each unchanging. The only waves which show the same patterns all the time and do not travel away are standing waves. These are the stationary waves that you find on vibrating strings or in tubs of water. They do not move about. Instead, they stay in place and keep their shape while the displacements periodically grow and collapse without moving along. Look at Fig. 34–8, for example, at the second picture from the left. At the two ends of the tube and in the middle there are nodes — points which do not move. In between each pair of nodes are regions of maximum displacement. These regions always stay at the same place along the tube, but as *time* goes on the displacement ranges from maximum in one direction through zero to maximum in the other direction. Everywhere, the displacement oscillates back and forth in the same way, but nothing appears to move along the tube.

There is no substitute for making standing waves yourself. Tie a rubber tube between two firm supports. Wiggle the tube up and down with your hand near one support. By choosing the right frequency for the motion of your hand, you can set up a standing wave pattern in which the tube oscillates up and down but the pattern does not travel along. It may be a pattern with one loop between the end supports, or two loops, three loops, four loops, and so on (Fig. 34–8). Now stop moving your hand and watch the motion. Except for friction losses, the motion persists with the tube oscillating in the same fixed pattern. The standing wave stays in place and continues unchanging. That is the kind of wave motion we are going to picture for a stable state of an atom.

Notice that these standing waves are naturally determined. With the ends held fixed, only the patterns with a whole number of loops (and corresponding definite frequencies) will stand on the tube. If you try to drive the tube with any other frequency you will find that the motion of your hand undoes some of the tube's existing motion rather than being in step and increasing the motion. So, unless you use the right frequency, your efforts produce very little effect. You fail to build up a standing wave that can stay on the tube. The set of distinct standing waves with whole numbers of loops is the only set of unchanging wave patterns.

Although standing waves just oscillate up and down, we can view them as the superposition of two equal traveling wave-trains moving in opposite directions. If you draw two wave patterns, move them across each other, and add their displacements to find the resultant, you will find that they make a standing wave. Also, you will find that the loops of the standing wave are just $\frac{1}{2}\lambda$ long, where λ is the wave length of either wave-train. We did something like this in Section 16-3.

If it is hard to see that standing waves are thus made by two separate equal wave-trains traveling in opposite directions across each other, you should try it experimentally with real waves. Get a long rope and have two people hold it. Then let each of them send out a train of, say, a dozen wave lengths along the rope. Watch what hap-

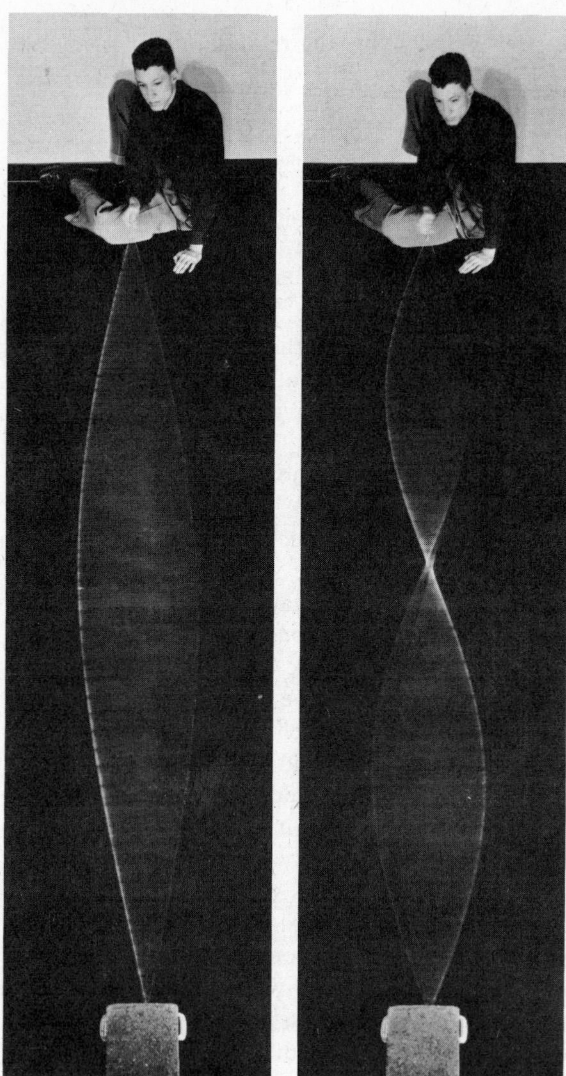

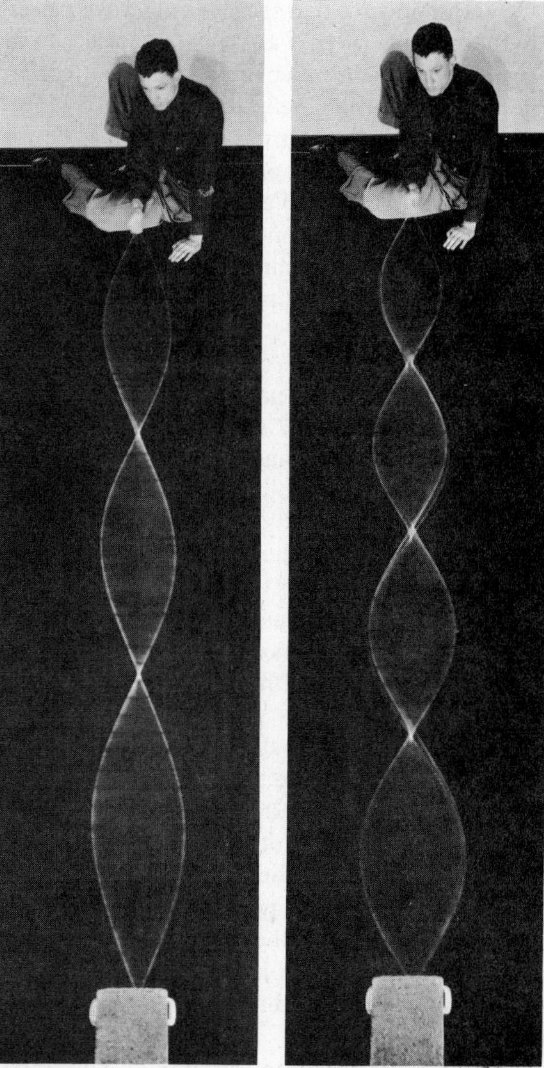

34–8. Standing waves. As one end of the tube is moved from side to side with increasing frequency, patterns with more and more loops are formed. Note, however, that there are only certain definite frequencies that will produce fixed patterns.

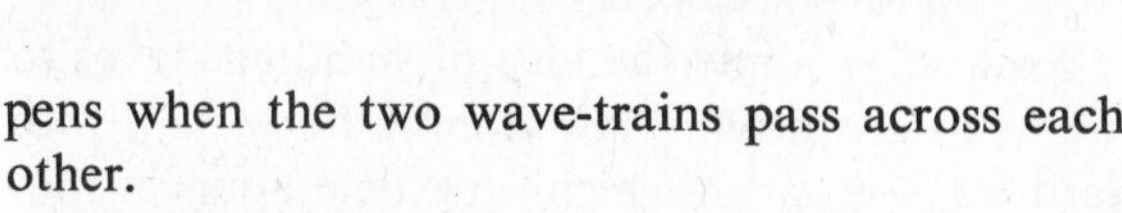

pens when the two wave-trains pass across each other.

On this view the standing waves between two supports are just like standing waves you have already seen in front of a reflecting wall in a ripple tank. There, you can drive the wave toward the wall with any frequency; and the reflected waves returning from the wall combine with your forward waves to make standing waves. However, for a given position of driver and wall you must choose the "right" frequency or you will find you have to give the driver a large motion to get a big effect. With the right frequency, a very small motion of the driver builds up a large effect.

As you can see from Fig. 34–8, we can make good standing waves on a rubber tube by tying one end to a rigid support and wiggling the other end very slightly with the "right" frequency. Then, the reflection by the support at the other end supplies the opposite wave-train which combines with the forward one to make standing waves. When such a standing wave is established, we may imagine that two rigid reflecting walls are suddenly installed at nodes in the standing wave pattern. Because we install the walls at places of no motion, they would trap a section of standing wave between them. In any such section we would see the standing wave as a pattern of oscillation instead of a moving wave pattern.

You can now see that the standing wave pattern on the tube between the rigid supports can be generated by adding two wave-trains, a forward one and a returning reflected train. To trap a standing wave pattern the supports must be one half wave length apart, or two half wave lengths, or three, and so on. We shall now use standing waves in discussing atom models.

We know there are matter waves. And when they are confined to a limited region of space, as they are in atoms, they must take the form of standing wave patterns. We shall see how these standing matter-wave patterns explain the observed energy levels in atoms. But to get the general idea, we shall start with an example that is simpler than any atom. We shall consider a particle traveling steadily to and fro between reflecting walls and we shall look for the standing wave pattern which fits that motion. When the particle moves at constant speed in one direction between the walls, it has constant momentum, so there is a definite de Broglie wave length associated with its motion. When it rebounds and moves in the opposite direction, the magnitude of the momentum is the same, so that a reflected wave with the same de Broglie wave length is also associated with the motion. We picture both these matter waves existing together in the region between the walls. The wave length is determined by the magnitude of the particle's momentum. And if that wave length is suitable, the two wave trains will set up a standing wave pattern between the walls.

This is where the wave nature enters in an essential way. Between fixed end walls only certain standing waves can exist, so only certain particular motions of the particle with corresponding definite magnitudes of momentum can take place. The simplest standing wave looks like the first photograph in Fig. 34–8. There the wave length is twice the distance between the walls: $\lambda = 2d$. This is the wave length belonging to one of the possible motions of the particle. (Other patterns of several loops give shorter wave lengths and bigger momentum. Therefore this "one loop" wave gives the slowest motion a particle can have.) We can find the energy of the particle in this motion from the relation

$$E = \tfrac{1}{2}mv^2 = \frac{\tfrac{1}{2}(mv)^2}{m} = \frac{p^2}{2m}.$$

By using the de Broglie relation, $p = \frac{h}{\lambda}$, we then find

$$E = \frac{h^2}{2m\lambda^2}.$$

And since $\lambda = 2d$, we get a definite value

$$E = \frac{h^2}{8md^2}$$

for the kinetic energy of the particle bouncing back and forth in a "box" of length d. This is the lowest energy at which the de Broglie standing wave can maintain itself. At lower energy the wave length is too long and no wave associated with a particle of mass m can stand in the box. Although in Newtonian mechanics the particle could move with less energy, in our wave mechanics there is no possible state of motion at lower energy. So this lowest energy is the ground state.

Now when we think back to the hydrogen atom, we can see that we are following a promising road. For just such reasons, the hydrogen atom must have a ground state — although Newtonian mechanics would allow it indefinitely lower energies. Thus an explanation of the stability of atoms is already in sight. Furthermore, there are many matter waves of higher energy that can stand in the box. There are the standing waves with 2 loops, 3 loops, . . . n loops, and so on. These stationary wave states, with their definite values of energy, provide a model for the excited states of the atom.

34–6. The Wave Theory of Hydrogen Energy Levels

Now let us apply the idea of standing waves to the hydrogen atom. An atom is not a box with hard walls between which a particle bounces, but the Coulomb force between the nucleus and the electron prevents the electron from running away. This force makes the electron bounce back and forth or run around inside a small region near the nucleus. The hydrogen atom therefore sets us the problem of a standing wave in three dimensions, a wave in a region of changing Coulomb force in place of the simpler wave in the space between hard walls. This problem is like the problem of finding the standing wave patterns on water in a cup. (You can see these beautiful symmetrical patterns in the cup just by jiggling the

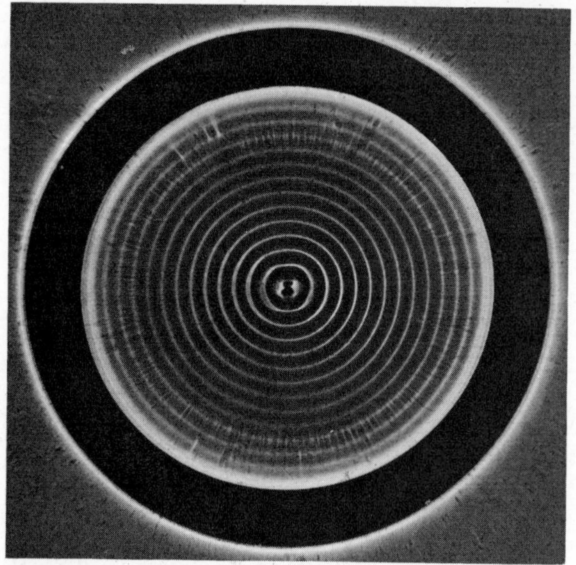

34–9 (a). A time exposure of standing waves in a circular ring in a ripple tank. The whole tank was vibrated, but the moving waves outside the ring are blurred out.

34–9 (b). Standing wave patterns in a metal plate held rigidly at the center. Such patterns (often called Chladni's figures) are formed by fine sand sprinkled on the plate when it is set into vibration. The sand accumulates on the stationary nodal lines.

cup. See also Fig. 34–9.) The mathematical theory of waves is fully able to handle such wave patterns, and in the same way it can handle the waves in the hydrogen atom. Here we shall take a few short cuts; we shall try to make the result plausible, though we cannot claim a perfectly logical demonstration.

To start with, we consider an electron moving in a circular orbit at distance r from the center of the atom. The centripetal force needed to keep the electron moving on the circle is the electrostatic attraction $k\,\frac{q_1q_2}{r^2}$. Consequently,

$$\frac{mv^2}{r} = \frac{kq_1q_2}{r^2} \quad \text{or} \quad mv^2 = \frac{kq_1q_2}{r}.$$

This equation relates the speed v to the radius r.

Because the electron moves at a constant distance from the nucleus and therefore at constant speed, the magnitude of its momentum around the orbit stays constant. In such an orbit, therefore, the matter wave associated with electronic motion has a well-defined de Broglie wave length:

$$\lambda = \frac{h}{mv}.$$

Of course the matter wave cannot really move around a classical orbital path, for all waves in the atom, like those in a cup, extend over some region

34–9 (c). Sand patterns formed by standing waves on the diaphragm of a telephone receiver. (Photos b and c from F. A. Saunders, "A Survey of Physics for College Students," Henry Holt & Co., New York, 1930.)

sidewise as well as along the orbit. But we can hope to approximate the behavior of the matter wave by thinking of it as a wave around a narrow circular channel of radius r. In this channel a standing wave can persist only if there is a whole number of wave lengths around the circumference of the "orbit." Then the traveling waves moving in opposite directions which make up the standing wave come back around the orbit with a

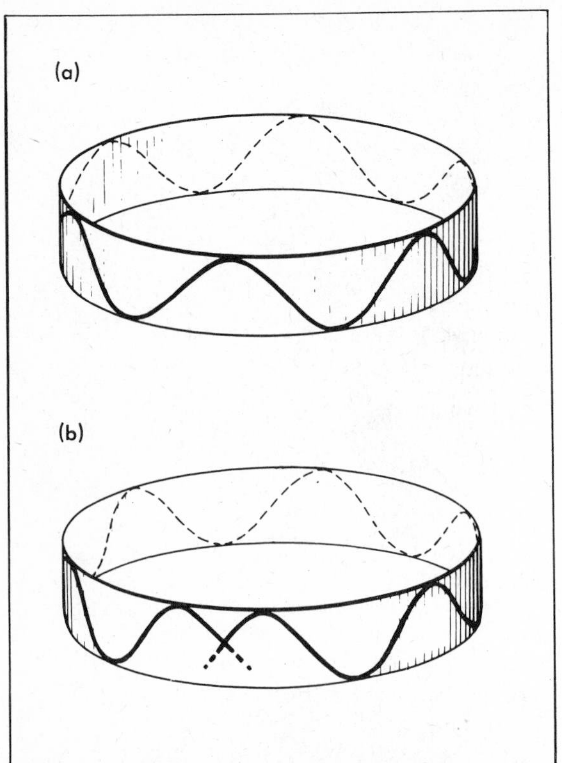

34–10. (a) A schematic diagram of water waves in a narrow circular channel producing a standing wave pattern. A wave moving around the channel comes back to its starting point so that crest meets crest and trough meets trough. This will happen when the channel is a whole number of wave lengths long. (b) The channel is not a whole number of wave lengths long. In this case, when the wave comes back to its starting point, crests and troughs do not exactly come together. The waves tend to cancel and no fixed pattern is produced.

maximum on top of a maximum in the wave displacement and a minimum on top of a minimum. (Fig. 34–10.) If there were not a whole number of wave lengths around the orbit, on going around a number of times we would find that a minimum now lies on top of a maximum, so that no standing wave can actually exist. There are therefore only certain orbits or channels in which the waves can stand; and, for the circular channels in particular, we must have

$$n\lambda = 2\pi r.$$

Because the de Broglie wave length is determined by the momentum $\left(\lambda = \frac{h}{mv}\right)$, this condition gives us a second relation between the radius r of the orbit and the velocity of the electron: $\frac{nh}{mv} = 2\pi r.$

From the two conditions, the one for standing waves in a channel and the other which tells us how the channels fit into the box made by the Coulomb force, we can find the velocities and the corresponding radii for which standing wave patterns can exist. The algebra by which we evaluate the velocities and radii is shown on the next page. Once we know the velocity and the radius, we can compute both the kinetic energy $\frac{1}{2}mv^2$ and the electric potential energy $-\frac{kq_1q_2}{r}$. This gives us the energies of the standing wave states. The result (obtained opposite) is

$$E = -\tfrac{1}{2}m\left(\frac{2\pi kq_1q_2}{nh}\right)^2.$$

Now in order to compare these energies for the standing wave patterns with the actual energy states in hydrogen, we must put in the values of Planck's constant, the constant in Coulomb's law, and the mass of the electron:

$$h = 6.62 \times 10^{-34} \text{ joule-sec}$$
$$k = 2.3 \times 10^{-28} \text{ newton (meters)}^2/(\text{elem. ch.})^2$$
$$m = 0.911 \times 10^{-30} \text{ kg}$$

Then remembering that the charges of electron and proton are each one elementary unit of charge, we get

$$E = -\tfrac{1}{2}\,\frac{0.911\times10^{-30}(2\pi\times2.3\times10^{-28}\times1\times1)^2}{(6.62\times10^{-34})^2}\times\frac{1}{n^2}$$

$$E = -\frac{2.17\times10^{-18}}{n^2} \text{ joules where } n = 1, 2, 3 \ldots$$

Since each joule is 6.25×10^{18} electron volts, this gives

$$E_n = \frac{-13.6}{n^2}\text{ ev}$$

for the energies of the standing wave states in hydrogen. This is exactly the same as the expression for the energy levels of the hydrogen atom which we had in Section 34–4. There the expression came from the experimental work of the spectroscopists. It represents the energy states of hydrogen which lead to the observed spectral lines in the light it emits and absorbs. It also agrees with the measured energy necessary to ionize the hydrogen atom; 13.6 electron volts is just the energy necessary to take a hydrogen atom from its ground state, the lowest-energy standing-wave state in which $n = 1$, and bring it to zero

COMPUTATION OF THE STANDING WAVE ENERGIES

Two conditions relate the velocity to the radius of the orbit on which a charged particle travels around the nucleus. Because the Coulomb force must provide the necessary deflecting force to keep the particle on the orbit, we have

$$\frac{mv^2}{r} = \frac{kq_1q_2}{r^2}$$

or

$$mv^2 = \frac{kq_1q_2}{r}. \qquad (1)$$

For matter waves that can form a standing pattern

$$n\lambda = 2\pi r \text{ and } \lambda = h/mv,$$

so

$$\frac{nh}{mv} = 2\pi r. \qquad (2)$$

By multiplying equations (1) and (2) together, left side with left side and right side with right side, we get

$$[mv^2]\left[\frac{nh}{mv}\right] = \left[\frac{kq_1q_2}{r}\right][2\pi r]$$

$$nhv = 2\pi kq_1q_2.$$

This gives us the possible speeds of the orbiting particle

$$v = \frac{2\pi kq_1q_2}{nh} \quad \text{where } n = 1, 2, 3 \ldots . \qquad (3)$$

On substituting (3) into (2), we obtain the corresponding radii of the orbits

$$r = \frac{nh}{2\pi mv} = \frac{n^2h^2}{(2\pi)^2mkq_1q_2} \qquad (4)$$

where $n = 1, 2, 3 \ldots .$
The total internal energy is

$$E = \text{kinetic energy} + \text{potential energy}$$
$$E = (\tfrac{1}{2}mv^2) + (-kq_1q_2/r).$$

On putting the possible values of v from (3) into $\frac{1}{2}mv^2$ and the corresponding values of r from (4) into $\frac{-kq_1q_2}{r}$, we obtain for the total internal energies

$$E = -\tfrac{1}{2}m\left(\frac{2\pi kq_1q_2}{nh}\right)^2. \qquad (5)$$

Finally, if we put the numerical values of the constants

$$k = 2.3 \times 10^{-28} \frac{\text{newton(meters)}^2}{\text{(elem. ch.)}^2}$$
$$h = 6.62 \times 10^{-34} \text{ joule-sec}$$
$$m = 0.911 \times 10^{-30} \text{ kg}$$

into (3), (4), and (5), we get

$$v = 2.18 \times 10^6 \frac{q_1q_2}{n} \text{ meters/sec}$$

$$r = 0.53 \times 10^{-10} \frac{n^2}{q_1q_2} \text{ meters}$$

$$E = -\frac{2.17 \times 10^{-18}(q_1q_2)^2}{n^2} \text{ joules.}$$

Note that the units of electric charge have all been included in the constants. q_1 and q_2 are pure numbers counting the numbers of elementary charges on the nucleus and the circling electron. The quantum number n of the state measures the complexity of the standing wave pattern.

energy which we set at the point where the hydrogen atom is just ionized. Our standing-wave result therefore agrees completely with the experimental evidence.

We can check up on our theoretical result in several other ways. According to our analysis of the standing-wave states, the energies should be proportional to the square of the number of elementary charges on the nucleus. Therefore, any atomic structure with a central nucleus and only one electron should give a spectrum like that of hydrogen, but with all the energies increased in proportion to the square of the nuclear charge. For example, a helium atom may lose one of its two electrons. The helium ion then consists of an electron moving around a nucleus with two positive elementary charges. This ion of helium is present where an atom of helium has been excited beyond its ionization energy. Its spectrum has been observed in the atmospheres of blue-hot stars, and in the laboratory when intense sparks are sent through helium. Fig. 34–11 displays some of its spectral lines. They are exactly represented by our formula for hydrogen energy levels with a factor of 4 for the square of the nuclear charge. The observed spectrum of doubly ionized lithium is also in agreement with the wave-mechanical formula, but there the nuclear charge is 3 rather than 2 elementary charges. Consequently, the energies are all nine times those for hydrogen.

Actually, hydrogen itself comes in three different forms. In addition to normal hydrogen, there are two rare heavy isotopes. The spectra of these isotopes look almost exactly like those of ordinary hydrogen, but there are minute differences. To understand them, we must look more closely at our computations for the energy levels in hydrogen. In finding the energy states, we assumed that the heavy nucleus remained at rest. But this is only approximately true. The two attracting masses, nucleus and electron, rotate about their mutual center of mass, like earth and sun. This center of mass nearly coincides with the nucleus, because it is so much heavier than its partner. But the small distance between center of mass and the nucleus implies that the energy levels depend just a little bit on the nuclear mass. The size of this effect was calculated by Bohr in his original paper in which he used an approach entirely different from the one we have discussed. For a nucleus of mass M (instead of infinite mass), every energy should be multiplied by the factor

$$\frac{1}{\left(1 + \frac{m}{M}\right)}.$$

Since the proton is about 2000 times as massive as the electron, this means that each frequency in the spectrum of ordinary hydrogen should be about one part in 2000 less than we previously predicted. (Indeed it is after making this correction that the predictions and the experimental results agree to better than a part in 10,000.) For the other isotopes we now get slightly different predictions. For example, the mass of the deuterium nucleus — the deuteron — is about double that of the proton. Consequently, the deuterium frequencies are lower than those for an atom with an infinitely heavy nucleus by only one part in 4000. The frequencies in the spectrum of deuterium should thus be slightly greater than those for ordinary hydrogen. Spectroscopy is so

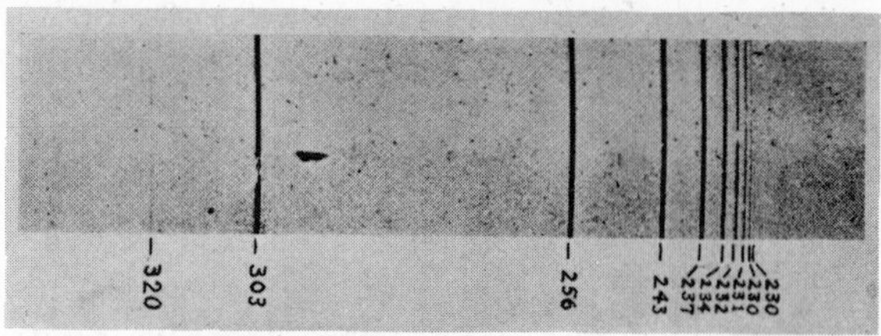

34–11. The spectrum of singly ionized helium with the wave lengths marked in angstroms. These lines correspond to the Lyman series of hydrogen (see Fig. 34–7) modified for a nuclear charge of 2 units. Notice that they are in the extremely short ultraviolet range. (From: P. G. Kruger, "Arc and Spark Spectrum of He," Physical Review, Vol. 36, Series 2, July–December, 1930.)

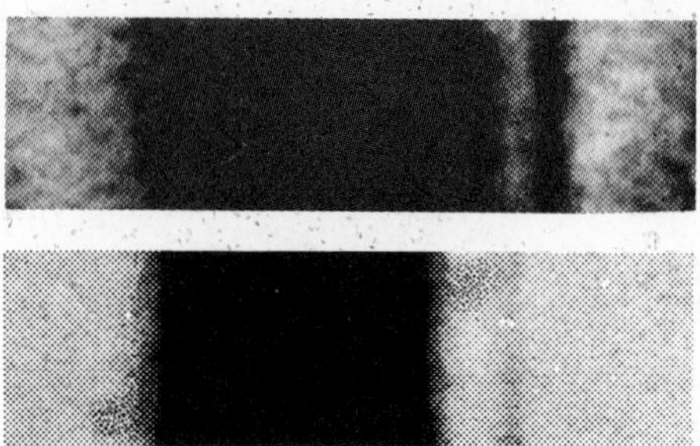

34–12. Photos showing the details of two different hydrogen spectral lines. The faint spectral lines of deuterium are seen slightly to the right (one or two angstroms shorter wave length) of the much overexposed lines of ordinary hydrogen. This experiment showed for the first time that the heavy isotope of hydrogen did exist. The deuterium lines are faint because the concentration of deuterium atoms in natural hydrogen is only about 1 in 6500. For these photographs the concentration was increased somewhat by evaporating liquid hydrogen. With modern techniques one can separate the isotopes and produce relatively pure deuterium, and that makes it easier to check the wave length of the line. (From: H. C. Urey, F. G. Brickwedde, and G. M. Murphy, "A Hydrogen Isotope of Mass 2 and its Concentration," Physical Review, Vol. 40, Series 2, April–June, 1932.)

refined a tool that this small difference can be detected. In fact it played a role in the discovery of deuterium (Fig. 34–12).

34–7. Conclusion

In a certain sense the story that we have been telling is now complete. Waves, which we first met in Part II, have turned out to be associated with the energy and momentum we met in Part III. However, this association was not revealed until Part IV, where the probing of the atom required us to refine Newtonian mechanics by the more subtle quantum theory. In the world of the atom and the photon, both the wave and particle aspects of nature are essential to our understanding.

In the last section we found the energy states of hydrogen, using a standing-wave model that supplies some of the possible wave patterns. There are other standing-wave patterns that do not correspond to circular channels, but the full wave theory shows that those other patterns give the same energy levels that we have computed. Our success here is important, both because of the quantitative agreement of our theoretical calculation of the constant, 13.6 electron volts, with its observed value, and even more because the general picture of standing wave states gives us confidence that the matter waves are essential to the description of all atoms. In successfully describing hydrogen on the combined picture of waves and particles we are not at the end. Instead we are really at the beginning of our ability to understand nuclei, atoms, molecules, . . .: the structure of matter. Energy levels with significant separations occur in all these physical systems and all of them can be understood in terms of standing-wave patterns. In these fields questions arise that could never be properly answered within the framework of Newtonian dynamics. Other questions could not even be formulated without the insight we get from wave mechanics.

But this is not all. Wave behavior differs from the behavior of particles as predicted from Newtonian mechanics, not only in leading to definite separated energy states (and an irreducible ground state), but also in other unexpected ways. One example may suggest some of the new insights into the behavior of particles that arise from considering the associated matter waves. The wave patterns often spread into regions where, according to Newtonian mechanics, particles would never penetrate at all. For light a Newtonian particle picture would make us expect to have *either* reflection *or* transmission at a surface between air and glass, but not both. The waves, however, split up: they are partially reflected and partially transmitted, and photons are found with some probability in either the reflected or the transmitted light. In the same way, matter waves may undergo partial reflections and partial transmissions where, according to Newtonian mechanics, only one or the other would take place. In just this way matter waves have led to an understanding of radioactive decay by the transmission of particles through a region where no particle would penetrate in Newtonian mechanics. A similar mechanism also explains some chemical reactions.

We have therefore come to the threshold of many new developments. In the years since 1925 (when wave mechanics was formally stated) wave mechanics has given us a great deal of understanding of the physics that was previously mysterious. There is much to be studied in these new fields, some of it already fairly well understood and a great deal of it the subject of present work. This book is barely an introduction. A life can be well spent in study of the physical world.

FOR HOME, DESK, AND LAB

1. (a) With electrons of what energy would you bombard hydrogen atoms to excite them to the first excitation state shown in Fig. 34–7? This state is 10.2 electron volts above the ground state.

(b) If you send in electrons of 12.1 electron volts kinetic energy (just enough to excite the second excited state), what energies can they lose in inelastic collisions with the hydrogen atoms?

2. Suppose you are going to bombard a vapor of cesium atoms with 4.00-electron-volt electrons. Use Fig. 34–2 to predict some of the things that you would expect to happen.

3. If we heat helium gas to a high-enough temperature, the average kinetic energy of an atom in its thermal motion will be so high that an inelastic collision between two helium atoms can easily excite one of them to its first excited state at 19.8 electron volts above the ground state. Estimate this temperature, obtaining any data you need from Part III.

4. (a) What energy electrons would you have to use in a Franck-Hertz experiment in order to "see" the Lyman α line? (See Fig. 34–7.)

(b) In order to "see" the H α line?

(c) What other spectral line would you expect to "see" if you can see the H α line?

5. (a) What wave length of light is necessary to excite hydrogen atoms in their ground state so that they emit the H_2 α line (Fig. 34–7)?

(b) What is the longest wave length that can be absorbed by the hydrogen atoms in making a transition from the ground state (Fig. 34–7)?

(c) Compare this with the H_2 α wave length. (You need only one really significant figure.)

6. * Fig. 34–9 (a) shows standing waves produced in a circular ripple tank. These standing waves have circular nodal lines. You can also make standing waves by using a straight generator with its edge along a radius. Then there will be radial nodal lines, and the patterns are more like the standing electron waves discussed in Section 34–6. Try this in your ripple tank.

7. Suppose the particle between fixed walls (Section 34-5) is charged and can, therefore, radiate, what is the frequency of its radiation as it goes from the first excited state to the ground state? Express your answer in terms of h, m, and d.

8. A blood corpuscle has a diameter about 10^{-5} meter. Suppose hydrogen atoms could be excited to a state for which the circular standing wave makes them about as big as blood corpuscles. Make a rough estimate of the value of n for such a state.

9. Excited hydrogen atoms are "larger" than hydrogen atoms in the ground state. Their standing-wave patterns extend out farther so that two atoms cannot easily approach each other so closely. Suppose you had a gas consisting of hydrogen atoms at atmospheric pressure (this is possible, though hydrogen usually forms molecules of two atoms, H_2). Suppose these atoms could be excited until neighboring atoms just elbow each other with their wave patterns.

(a) Make an estimate of the value of n for the excited state in which neighbors would elbow each other. [Use the following estimate of the spacing of gas molecules: One mole of any gas has 6×10^{23} molecules and, at atmospheric pressure and room temperature, occupies about 2.4×10^{-2} cubic meters. If we imagine these molecules arranged in an array of small cubical cells each containing one molecule, we find that each cell must have a side about 30×10^{-10} meter. (This is obtained by dividing volume by the number of molecules and taking the cube root.) So we may take the average distance between a molecule and its nearest neighbors as about 30 angstroms or 30×10^{-10} meter in any gas of atmospheric pressure and room temperature.]

(b) If you started with a sample of unexcited hydrogen gas, in a closed bottle, and excited it to such a state, how would its density change?

(This problem deals with a gas of excited H atoms. In fact, H_2 molecules similarly excited would show much the same behavior — the electron looking in from its large "orbit" in the excited state would experience almost the same electric field.)

10. (a) Estimate the kinetic energy of a neutron in a nucleus of radius

$$R = 6 \times 10^{-15} \text{ m.}$$

(This is a big nucleus.) Assuming the nucleus is a box of length R will be good enough.

(b) If the nucleus is smaller, should the kinetic energy be smaller?

11. (a) Compute the first two wave lengths that you expect for the Lyman series of hydrogen.

(b) Compare these with the spectrum of single ionized helium (Fig. 34–11). Explain why your comparison indicates that Fig. 34–11 is the Lyman series for ionized He.

FURTHER READING

BENADE, ARTHUR H., *Horns, Strings, and Harmony*. Doubleday, 1960: A Science Study Series paperback.

DARROW, KARL K., "The Quantum Theory." *Scientific American*, March, 1952.

DE BENEDETTI, SERGIO, "Mesonic Atoms." *Scientific American*, October, 1956.

HOFFMAN, BANESH, *The Strange Story of the Quantum*. Harper, 1947.

LIFSHITZ, EUGENE M., "Superfluidity." *Scientific American*, June, 1958.

APPENDIX

APPENDIX 1

Table of Trigonometric Functions

sin (read down)

	.0	.1	.2	.3	.4	.5	.6	.7	.8	.9		
0°	.0000	.0017	.0035	.0052	.0070	.0087	.0105	.0122	.0140	.0157	.0175	89°
1°	.0175	.0192	.0209	.0227	.0244	.0262	.0279	.0297	.0314	.0332	.0349	88°
2°	.0349	.0366	.0384	.0401	.0419	.0436	.0454	.0471	.0488	.0506	.0523	87°
3°	.0523	.0541	.0558	.0576	.0593	.0610	.0628	.0645	.0663	.0680	.0698	86°
4°	.0698	.0715	.0732	.0750	.0767	.0785	.0802	.0819	.0837	.0854	.0872	85°
5°	.0872	.0889	.0906	.0924	.0941	.0958	.0976	.0993	.1011	.1028	.1045	84°
6°	.1045	.1063	.1080	.1097	.1115	.1132	.1149	.1167	.1184	.1201	.1219	83°
7°	.1219	.1236	.1253	.1271	.1288	.1305	.1323	.1340	.1357	.1374	.1392	82°
8°	.1392	.1409	.1426	.1444	.1461	.1478	.1495	.1513	.1530	.1547	.1564	81°
9°	.1564	.1582	.1599	.1616	.1633	.1650	.1668	.1685	.1702	.1719	.1736	80°
10°	.1736	.1754	.1771	.1788	.1805	.1822	.1840	.1857	.1874	.1891	.1908	79°
11°	.1908	.1925	.1942	.1959	.1977	.1994	.2011	.2028	.2045	.2062	.2079	78°
12°	.2079	.2096	.2113	.2130	.2147	.2164	.2181	.2198	.2115	.2233	.2250	77°
13°	.2250	.2267	.2284	.2300	.2317	.2334	.2351	.2368	.2385	.2402	.2419	76°
14°	.2419	.2436	.2453	.2470	.2487	.2504	.2521	.2538	.2554	.2571	.2588	75°
15°	.2588	.2605	.2622	.2639	.2656	.2672	.2689	.2706	.2723	.2740	.2756	74°
16°	.2756	.2773	.2790	.2807	.2823	.2840	.2857	.2874	.2890	.2907	.2924	73°
17°	.2924	.2940	.2957	.2974	.2990	.3007	.3024	.3040	.3057	.3074	.3090	72°
18°	.3090	.3107	.3123	.3140	.3156	.3173	.3190	.3206	.3223	.3239	.3256	71°
19°	.3256	.3272	.3289	.3305	.3322	.3338	.3355	.3371	.3387	.3404	.3420	70°
20°	.3420	.3437	.3453	.3469	.3486	.3502	.3518	.3535	.3551	.3567	.3584	69°
21°	.3584	.3600	.3616	.3633	.3649	.3665	.3681	.3697	.3714	.3730	.3746	68°
22°	.3746	.3762	.3778	.3795	.3811	.3827	.3843	.3859	.3875	.3891	.3907	67°
23°	.3907	.3923	.3939	.3955	.3971	.3987	.4003	.4019	.4035	.4051	.4067	66°
24°	.4067	.4083	.4099	.4115	.4131	.4147	.4163	.4179	.4195	.4210	.4226	65°
25°	.4226	.4242	.4258	.4274	.4289	.4305	.4321	.4337	.4352	.4368	.4384	64°
26°	.4384	.4399	.4415	.4431	.4446	.4462	.4478	.4493	.4509	.4524	.4540	63°
27°	.4540	.4555	.4571	.4586	.4602	.4617	.4633	.4648	.4664	.4679	.4695	62°
28°	.4695	.4710	.4726	.4741	.4756	.4772	.4787	.4802	.4818	.4833	.4848	61°
29°	.4848	.4863	.4879	.4894	.4909	.4924	.4939	.4955	.4970	.4985	.5000	60°
30°	.5000	.5015	.5030	.5045	.5060	.5075	.5090	.5105	.5120	.5135	.5150	59°
31°	.5150	.5165	.5180	.5195	.5210	.5225	.5240	.5255	.5270	.5284	.5299	58°
32°	.5299	.5314	.5329	.5344	.5358	.5373	.5388	.5402	.5417	.5432	.5446	57°
33°	.5446	.5461	.5476	.5490	.5505	.5519	.5534	.5548	.5563	.5577	.5592	56°
34°	.5592	.5606	.5621	.5635	.5650	.5664	.5678	.5693	.5707	.5721	.5736	55°
35°	.5736	.5750	.5764	.5779	.5793	.5807	.5821	.5835	.5850	.5864	.5878	54°
36°	.5878	.5892	.5906	.5920	.5934	.5948	.5962	.5976	.5990	.6004	.6018	53°
37°	.6018	.6032	.6046	.6060	.6074	.6088	.6101	.6115	.6129	.6143	.6157	52°
38°	.6157	.6170	.6184	.6198	.6211	.6225	.6239	.6252	.6266	.6280	.6293	51°
39°	.6293	.6307	.6320	.6334	.6347	.6361	.6374	.6388	.6401	.6414	.6428	50°
40°	.6428	.6441	.6455	.6468	.6481	.6494	.6508	.6521	.6534	.6547	.6561	49°
41°	.6561	.6574	.6587	.6600	.6613	.6626	.6639	.6652	.6665	.6678	.6691	48°
42°	.6691	.6704	.6717	.6730	.6743	.6756	.6769	.6782	.6794	.6807	.6820	47°
43°	.6820	.6833	.6845	.6858	.6871	.6884	.6896	.6909	.6921	.6934	.6947	46°
44°	.6947	.6959	.6972	.6984	.6997	.7009	.7022	.7034	.7046	.7059	.7071	45°
		.9	.8	.7	.6	.5	.4	.3	.2	.1	.0	

cos (read up)

Table of Trigonometric Functions

sin (read down)

	.0	.1	.2	.3	.4	.5	.6	.7	.8	.9		
45°	.7071	.7083	.7096	.7108	.7120	.7133	.7145	.7157	.7169	.7181	.7193	**44°**
46°	.7193	.7206	.7218	.7230	.7242	.7254	.7266	.7278	.7290	.7302	.7314	**43°**
47°	.7314	.7325	.7337	.7349	.7361	.7373	.7385	.7396	.7408	.7420	.7431	**42°**
48°	.7431	.7443	.7455	.7466	.7478	.7490	.7501	.7513	.7524	.7536	.7547	**41°**
49°	.7547	.7559	.7570	.7581	.7593	.7604	.7615	.7627	.7638	.7649	.7660	**40°**
50°	.7660	.7672	.7683	.7694	.7705	.7716	.7727	.7738	.7749	.7760	.7771	**39°**
51°	.7771	.7782	.7793	.7804	.7815	.7826	.7837	.7848	.7859	.7869	.7880	**38°**
52°	.7880	.7891	.7902	.7912	.7923	.7934	.7944	.7955	.7965	.7976	.7986	**37°**
53°	.7986	.7997	.8007	.8018	.8028	.8039	.8049	.8059	.8070	.8080	.8090	**36°**
54°	.8090	.8100	.8111	.8121	.8131	.8141	.8151	.8161	.8171	.8181	.8192	**35°**
55°	.8192	.8202	.8211	.8221	.8231	.8241	.8251	.8261	.8271	.8281	.8290	**34°**
56°	.8290	.8300	.8310	.8320	.8329	.8339	.8348	.8358	.8368	.8377	.8387	**33°**
57°	.8387	.8396	.8406	.8415	.8425	.8434	.8443	.8453	.8462	.8471	.8480	**32°**
58°	.8480	.8490	.8499	.8508	.8517	.8526	.8536	.8545	.8554	.8563	.8572	**31°**
59°	.8572	.8581	.8590	.8599	.8607	.8616	.8625	.8634	.8643	.8652	.8660	**30°**
60°	.8660	.8669	.8678	.8686	.8695	.8704	.8712	.8721	.8729	.8738	.8746	**29°**
61°	.8746	.8755	.8763	.8771	.8780	.8788	.8796	.8805	.8813	.8821	.8829	**28°**
62°	.8829	.8838	.8846	.8854	.8862	.8870	.8878	.8886	.8894	.8902	.8910	**27°**
63°	.8910	.8918	.8926	.8934	.8942	.8949	.8957	.8965	.8973	.8980	.8988	**26°**
64°	.8988	.8996	.9003	.9011	.9018	.9026	.9033	.9041	.9048	.9056	.9063	**25°**
65°	.9063	.9070	.9078	.9085	.9092	.9100	.9107	.9114	.9121	.9128	.9135	**24°**
66°	.9135	.9143	.9150	.9157	.9164	.9171	.9178	.9184	.9191	.9198	.9205	**23°**
67°	.9205	.9212	.9219	.9225	.9232	.9239	.9245	.9252	.9259	.9265	.9272	**22°**
68°	.9272	.9278	.9285	.9291	.9298	.9304	.9311	.9317	.9323	.9330	.9336	**21°**
69°	.9336	.9342	.9348	.9354	.9361	.9367	.9373	.9379	.9385	.9391	.9397	**20°**
70°	.9397	.9403	.9409	.9415	.9421	.9426	.9432	.9438	.9444	.9449	.9455	**19°**
71°	.9455	.9461	.9466	.9472	.9478	.9483	.9489	.9494	.9500	.9505	.9511	**18°**
72°	.9511	.9516	.9521	.9527	.9532	.9537	.9542	.9548	.9553	.9558	.9563	**17°**
73°	.9563	.9568	.9573	.9578	.9583	.9588	.9593	.9598	.9603	.9608	.9613	**16°**
74°	.9613	.9617	.9622	.9627	.9632	.9636	.9641	.9646	.9650	.9655	.9659	**15°**
75°	.9659	.9664	.9668	.9673	.9677	.9681	.9686	.9690	.9694	.9699	.9703	**14°**
76°	.9703	.9707	.9711	.9715	.9720	.9724	.9728	.9732	.9736	.9740	.9744	**13°**
77°	.9744	.9748	.9751	.9755	.9759	.9763	.9767	.9770	.9774	.9778	.9781	**12°**
78°	.9781	.9785	.9789	.9792	.9796	.9799	.9803	.9806	.9810	.9813	.9816	**11°**
79°	.9816	.9820	.9823	.9826	.9829	.9833	.9836	.9839	.9842	.9845	.9848	**10°**
80°	.9848	.9851	.9854	.9857	.9860	.9863	.9866	.9869	.9871	.9874	.9877	**9°**
81°	.9877	.9880	.9882	.9885	.9888	.9890	.9893	.9895	.9898	.9900	.9903	**8°**
82°	.9903	.9905	.9907	.9910	.9912	.9914	.9917	.9919	.9921	.9923	.9925	**7°**
83°	.9925	.9928	.9930	.9932	.9934	.9936	.9938	.9940	.9942	.9943	.9945	**6°**
84°	.9945	.9947	.9949	.9951	.9952	.9954	.9956	.9957	.9959	.9960	.9962	**5°**
85°	.9962	.9963	.9965	.9966	.9968	.9969	.9971	.9972	.9973	.9974	.9976	**4°**
86°	.9976	.9977	.9978	.9979	.9980	.9981	.9982	.9983	.9984	.9985	.9986	**3°**
87°	.9986	.9987	.9988	.9989	.9990	.9990	.9991	.9992	.9993	.9993	.9994	**2°**
88°	.9994	.9995	.9995	.9996	.9996	.9997	.9997	.9997	.9998	.9998	.9998	**1°**
89°	.9998	.9999	.9999	.9999	.9999	1.000	1.000	1.000	1.000	1.000	1.000	**0°**
		.9	.8	.7	.6	.5	.4	.3	.2	.1	.0	

cos (read up)

Table of Trigonometric Functions

tan (read down)

	.0	.1	.2	.3	.4	.5	.6	.7	.8	.9		
0°	.0000	.0017	.0035	.0052	.0070	.0087	.0105	.0122	.0140	.0157	.0175	**89°**
1°	.0175	.0192	.0209	.0227	.0244	.0262	.0279	.0297	.0314	.0332	.0349	**88°**
2°	.0349	.0367	.0384	.0402	.0419	.0437	.0454	.0472	.0489	.0507	.0524	**87°**
3°	.0524	.0542	.0559	.0577	.0594	.0612	.0629	.0647	.0664	.0682	.0699	**86°**
4°	.0699	.0717	.0734	.0752	.0769	.0787	.0805	.0822	.0840	.0857	.0875	**85°**
5°	.0875	.0892	.0910	.0928	.0945	.0963	.0981	.0998	.1016	.1033	.1051	**84°**
6°	.1051	.1069	.1086	.1104	.1122	.1139	.1157	.1175	.1192	.1210	.1228	**83°**
7°	.1228	.1246	.1263	.1281	.1299	.1317	.1334	.1352	.1370	.1388	.1405	**82°**
8°	.1405	.1423	.1441	.1459	.1477	.1495	.1512	.1530	.1548	.1566	.1584	**81°**
9°	.1584	.1602	.1620	.1638	.1655	.1673	.1691	.1709	.1727	.1745	.1763	**80°**
10°	.1763	.1781	.1799	.1817	.1835	.1853	.1871	.1890	.1908	.1926	.1944	**79°**
11°	.1944	.1962	.1980	.1998	.2016	.2035	.2053	.2071	.2089	.2107	.2126	**78°**
12°	.2126	.2144	.2162	.2180	.2199	.2217	.2235	.2254	.2272	.2290	.2309	**77°**
13°	.2309	.2327	.2345	.2364	.2382	.2401	.2419	.2438	.2456	.2475	.2493	**76°**
14°	.2493	.2512	.2530	.2549	.2568	.2586	.2605	.2623	.2642	.2661	.2679	**75°**
15°	.2679	.2698	.2717	.2736	.2754	.2773	.2792	.2811	.2830	.2849	.2867	**74°**
16°	.2867	.2886	.2905	.2924	.2943	.2962	.2981	.3000	.3019	.3038	.3057	**73°**
17°	.3057	.3076	.3096	.3115	.3134	.3153	.3172	.3191	.3211	.3230	.3249	**72°**
18°	.3249	.3269	.3288	.3307	.3327	.3346	.3365	.3385	.3404	.3424	.3443	**71°**
19°	.3443	.3463	.3482	.3502	.3522	.3541	.3561	.3581	.3600	.3620	.3640	**70°**
20°	.3640	.3659	.3679	.3699	.3719	.3739	.3759	.3779	.3799	.3819	.3839	**69°**
21°	.3839	.3859	.3879	.3899	.3919	.3939	.3959	.3979	.4000	.4020	.4040	**68°**
22°	.4040	.4061	.4081	.4101	.4122	.4142	.4163	.4183	.4204	.4224	.4245	**67°**
23°	.4245	.4265	.4286	.4307	.4327	.4348	.4369	.4390	.4411	.4431	.4452	**66°**
24°	.4452	.4473	.4494	.4515	.4536	.4557	.4578	.4599	.4621	.4642	.4663	**65°**
25°	.4663	.4684	.4706	.4727	.4748	.4770	.4791	.4813	.4834	.4856	.4877	**64°**
26°	.4877	.4899	.4921	.4942	.4964	.4986	.5008	.5029	.5051	.5073	.5095	**63°**
27°	.5095	.5117	.5139	.5161	.5184	.5206	.5228	.5250	.5272	.5295	.5317	**62°**
28°	.5317	.5340	.5362	.5384	.5407	.5430	.5452	.5475	.5498	.5520	.5543	**61°**
29°	.5543	.5566	.5589	.5612	.5635	.5658	.5681	.5704	.5727	.5750	.5774	**60°**
30°	.5774	.5797	.5820	.5844	.5867	.5890	.5914	.5938	.5961	.5985	.6009	**59°**
31°	.6009	.6032	.6056	.6080	.6104	.6128	.6152	.6176	.6200	.6224	.6249	**58°**
32°	.6249	.6273	.6297	.6322	.6346	.6371	.6395	.6420	.6445	.6469	.6494	**57°**
33°	.6494	.6519	.6544	.6569	.6594	.6619	.6644	.6669	.6694	.6720	.6745	**56°**
34°	.6745	.6771	.6796	.6822	.6847	.6873	.6899	.6924	.6950	.6976	.7002	**55°**
35°	.7002	.7028	.7054	.7080	.7107	.7133	.7159	.7186	.7212	.7239	.7265	**54°**
36°	.7265	.7292	.7319	.7346	.7373	.7400	.7427	.7454	.7481	.7508	.7536	**53°**
37°	.7536	.7563	.7590	.7618	.7646	.7673	.7701	.7729	.7757	.7785	.7813	**52°**
38°	.7813	.7841	.7869	.7898	.7926	.7954	.7983	.8012	.8040	.8069	.8098	**51°**
39°	.8098	.8127	.8156	.8185	.8214	.8243	.8273	.8302	.8332	.8361	.8391	**50°**
40°	.8391	.8421	.8451	.8481	.8511	.8541	.8571	.8601	.8632	.8662	.8693	**49°**
41°	.8693	.8724	.8754	.8785	.8816	.8847	.8878	.8910	.8941	.8972	.9004	**48°**
42°	.9004	.9036	.9067	.9099	.9131	.9163	.9195	.9228	.9260	.9293	.9325	**47°**
43°	.9325	.9358	.9391	.9424	.9457	.9490	.9523	.9556	.9590	.9623	.9657	**46°**
44°	.9657	.9691	.9725	.9759	.9793	.9827	.9861	.9896	.9930	.9965	1.000	**45°**
		.9	.8	.7	.6	.5	.4	.3	.2	.1	.0	

cot (read up)

Table of Trigonometric Functions

tan (read down)

	.0	.1	.2	.3	.4	.5	.6	.7	.8	.9		
45°	1.000	1.003	1.007	1.011	1.014	1.018	1.021	1.025	1.028	1.032	1.036	**44°**
46°	1.036	1.039	1.043	1.046	1.050	1.054	1.057	1.061	1.065	1.069	1.072	**43°**
47°	1.072	1.076	1.080	1.084	1.087	1.091	1.095	1.099	1.103	1.107	1.111	**42°**
48°	1.111	1.115	1.118	1.122	1.126	1.130	1.134	1.138	1.142	1.146	1.150	**41°**
49°	1.150	1.154	1.159	1.163	1.167	1.171	1.175	1.179	1.183	1.188	1.192	**40°**
50°	1.192	1.196	1.200	1.205	1.209	1.213	1.217	1.222	1.226	1.230	1.235	**39°**
51°	1.235	1.239	1.244	1.248	1.253	1.257	1.262	1.266	1.271	1.275	1.280	**38°**
52°	1.280	1.285	1.289	1.294	1.299	1.303	1.308	1.313	1.317	1.322	1.327	**37°**
53°	1.327	1.332	1.337	1.342	1.347	1.351	1.356	1.361	1.366	1.371	1.376	**36°**
54°	1.376	1.381	1.387	1.392	1.397	1.402	1.407	1.412	1.418	1.423	1.428	**35°**
55°	1.428	1.433	1.439	1.444	1.450	1.455	1.460	1.466	1.471	1.477	1.483	**34°**
56°	1.483	1.488	1.494	1.499	1.505	1.511	1.517	1.522	1.528	1.534	1.540	**33°**
57°	1.540	1.546	1.552	1.558	1.564	1.570	1.576	1.582	1.588	1.594	1.600	**32°**
58°	1.600	1.607	1.613	1.619	1.625	1.632	1.638	1.645	1.651	1.658	1.664	**31°**
59°	1.664	1.671	1.678	1.684	1.691	1.698	1.704	1.711	1.718	1.725	1.732	**30°**
60°	1.732	1.739	1.746	1.753	1.760	1.767	1.775	1.782	1.789	1.797	1.804	**29°**
61°	1.804	1.811	1.819	1.827	1.834	1.842	1.849	1.857	1.865	1.873	1.881	**28°**
62°	1.881	1.889	1.897	1.905	1.913	1.921	1.929	1.937	1.946	1.954	1.963	**27°**
63°	1.963	1.971	1.980	1.988	1.997	2.006	2.014	2.023	2.032	2.041	2.050	**26°**
64°	2.050	2.059	2.069	2.078	2.087	2.097	2.106	2.116	2.125	2.135	2.145	**25°**
65°	2.145	2.154	2.164	2.174	2.184	2.194	2.204	2.215	2.225	2.236	2.246	**24°**
66°	2.246	2.257	2.267	2.278	2.289	2.300	2.311	2.322	2.333	2.344	2.356	**23°**
67°	2.356	2.367	2.379	2.391	2.402	2.414	2.426	2.438	2.450	2.463	2.475	**22°**
68°	2.475	2.488	2.500	2.513	2.526	2.539	2.552	2.565	2.578	2.592	2.605	**21°**
69°	2.605	2.619	2.633	2.646	2.660	2.675	2.689	2.703	2.718	2.733	2.747	**20°**
70°	2.747	2.762	2.778	2.793	2.808	2.824	2.840	2.856	2.872	2.888	2.904	**19°**
71°	2.904	2.921	2.937	2.954	2.971	2.989	3.006	3.024	3.042	3.060	3.078	**18°**
72°	3.078	3.096	3.115	3.133	3.152	3.172	3.191	3.211	3.230	3.251	3.271	**17°**
73°	3.271	3.291	3.312	3.333	3.354	3.376	3.398	3.420	3.442	3.465	3.487	**16°**
74°	3.487	3.511	3.534	3.558	3.582	3.606	3.630	3.655	3.681	3.706	3.732	**15°**
75°	3.732	3.758	3.785	3.812	3.839	3.867	3.895	3.923	3.952	3.981	4.011	**14°**
76°	4.011	4.041	4.071	4.102	4.134	4.165	4.198	4.230	4.264	4.297	4.331	**13°**
77°	4.331	4.366	4.402	4.437	4.474	4.511	4.548	4.586	4.625	4.665	4.705	**12°**
78°	4.705	4.745	4.787	4.829	4.872	4.915	4.959	5.005	5.050	5.097	5.145	**11°**
79°	5.145	5.193	5.242	5.292	5.343	5.396	5.449	5.503	5.558	5.614	5.671	**10°**
80°	5.671	5.730	5.789	5.850	5.912	5.976	6.041	6.107	6.174	6.243	6.314	**9°**
81°	6.314	6.386	6.460	6.535	6.612	6.691	6.772	6.855	6.940	7.026	7.115	**8°**
82°	7.115	7.207	7.300	7.396	7.495	7.596	7.700	7.806	7.916	8.028	8.144	**7°**
83°	8.144	8.264	8.386	8.513	8.643	8.777	8.915	9.058	9.205	9.357	9.514	**6°**
84°	9.514	9.677	9.845	10.02	10.20	10.39	10.58	10.78	10.99	11.20	11.43	**5°**
85°	11.43	11.66	11.91	12.16	12.43	12.71	13.00	13.30	13.62	13.95	14.30	**4°**
86°	14.30	14.67	15.06	15.46	15.89	16.35	16.83	17.34	17.89	18.46	19.08	**3°**
87°	19.08	19.74	20.45	21.20	22.02	22.90	23.86	24.90	26.03	27.27	28.64	**2°**
88°	28.64	30.14	31.82	33.69	35.80	38.19	40.92	44.07	47.74	52.08	57.29	**1°**
89°	57.29	63.66	71.62	81.85	95.49	114.6	143.2	191.0	286.5	573.0	∞	**0°**
		.9	.8	.7	.6	.5	.4	.3	.2	.1	.0	

cot (read up)

APPENDIX 2

PHYSICAL CONSTANTS

Avogadro's number: $N_0 = 6.0247 \times 10^{23}$

Atomic mass unit: $1 \text{ amu} = 1.660 \times 10^{-27} \text{ kg}$

Ice point: $273.15°\text{K}$

Gravitational constant: $G = 6.670 \times 10^{-11} \dfrac{\text{m}^3}{\text{kg-sec}^2}$

Boltzmann's constant: $k = 1.3804 \times 10^{-23} \dfrac{\text{joules}}{°\text{K}}$

Mechanical equivalent of heat: $1 \text{ calorie} = 4.1855 \text{ joules}$

EMF: $1 \text{ volt} = 1.602 \times 10^{-19} \dfrac{\text{joules}}{\text{elem. ch.}}$

Charge: $1 \text{ coulomb} = 6.2425 \times 10^{18} \text{ elem. ch.}$

Mass of electron: $m_e = 9.108 \times 10^{-31} \text{ kg}$

Planck's constant: $h = 6.625 \times 10^{-34} \text{ joule-sec}$

Speed of light: $c = 2.99793 \times 10^8 \text{ m/sec}$

Ratio of mass of proton to mass of electron: $\dfrac{m_p}{m_e} = 1836$

Constant in Coulomb's law: $k = 2.3063 \times 10^{-28} \dfrac{\text{newton-m}^2}{(\text{elem. ch.})^2}$

$$= 8.9876 \times 10^9 \frac{\text{newton-m}^2}{(\text{coulomb})^2}$$

Constant in $F = \dfrac{KI_1I_2l}{d}$: $K = 5.1322 \times 10^{-45} \dfrac{\text{newton}}{(\text{elem. ch./sec})^2}$

$$= 2 \times 10^{-7} \frac{\text{newtons}}{(\text{ampere})^2}$$

(exact, by definition)

APPENDIX 3

THE DEVELOPMENT OF THIS BOOK

This book and the coordinated development of laboratory materials, teachers' resources, and films are the cooperative work of many people. Any brief summary of its development is bound to be unsatisfactory. Even the basic outline and aims were formulated by a large number of people at several centers, and teachers all over the country shared the desire to make a fundamental change in the presentation of physics for beginning students.

The present book is the result of innumerable individual contributions, of extensive trials in many schools, and of a process of revision over three years. To assign detailed credit for the creation and formulation among the hundreds of contributions is impossible. Nevertheless, as the person who took the responsibility for the selection that now appears, I should like to sketch some of the stages. Above all, both on behalf of the PSSC and also personally, I wish to thank my many coworkers for their part in the difficult but pleasurable experience of working together to bring forth a new physics course.

During the fall of 1956 and the winter of 1957, under the leadership of the PSSC Steering Committee, research physicists and physics teachers — often they are the same people — outlined, drafted, and discussed many of the ideas that now appear in this book. Then at Massachusetts Institute of Technology during the summer of 1957 some 60 physicists, teachers, apparatus designers, writers, artists, and other specialists pooled their knowledge and experience to produce a pilot model of the PSSC physics course.

In common with every section of the course, Part I of this book benefited from the work and the discussions of the group as a whole. In particular, it arose largely from the initial discussions of a group at Cornell University, especially Professors K. I. Greisen, Philip Morrison, and Hans A. Bethe. The job of making a complete first draft was carried out during the summer by Professor Morrison, with the help of George L. Carr now of Milford Mill High School, Baltimore, Maryland, and John Marean of Reno High School, Reno, Nevada. With slight rewriting, this draft, edited by Judson Cross of Phillips Exeter Academy, Curtis Hinckley of Woodstock Country School and me, formed the basis of the first school try-outs.

From the beginning, work in school has been a major part of the program. The teachers have been among the authors. To keep in touch, there has been an extensive program of school visiting and meetings between teachers and editors. Every part of the book has been improved by this process of testing and revision. For example, several sections of Part I have been revised three times. On the whole, the revisions, again tested in school, have proved their worth, and at the same time an astonishing amount of the original conception remains basically unchanged. We are particularly grateful for the efforts of the teachers who tried the earliest versions and who spent large amounts of time analyzing their experience. By now we have benefited by the experience of over 600 teachers and innumerable students. Their impressions and suggestions were collected and digested by a feedback team. Professor Gilbert Finlay of the College of Education at the University of Illinois has been in charge of this part of the job, and has contributed to the whole project in many ways.

In revising Part I at various times the special work of the group at the University of Illinois, that of Walter Michels at Bryn Mawr, and Sherman Frankel at the University of Pennsylvania was combined with more contributions from Professor Morrison and with the work of the staff at the central office of

PSSC. For the present edition, further revision based on more experience in school has been provided by Malcolm K. Smith, Thomas Dillon of Concord High School, Concord, Massachusetts, Professors Eric M. Rogers of Princeton University, Nathaniel H. Frank of MIT, and me.

Most of the discussions and the preliminary development of apparatus that led to Part II of this book took place at the Massachusetts Institute of Technology. There, with the aid of Professor Walter Michels and Elbert P. Little, later assistant to the president of Educational Services Incorporated, I prepared an extensive outline. Following this, the first half of the volume was drafted by Professor Michels and Charles Smith of the Radnor High School, Radnor, Pennsylvania; the second half by Professors Uri Haber-Schaim and Arthur Kerman of MIT with Richard Jones of Indian Springs School, Helena, Alabama, and Darrel Tomer of Hanford High School, Hanford, California. Judson Cross and I edited the preliminary edition. Since that time it has had a history of try-out and revision similar to that of all the other parts. In particular, revisions for the present edition were carried out by Professor Haber-Schaim, Malcolm K. Smith, Professor Kerman, and me.

Most of the preliminary discussions leading to Part III took place in a group working at the University of Illinois. Then at MIT in the summer of 1957, Professors E. L. Goldwasser, Peter Axel, David Lazarus, Leon Cooper, and Allen C. Odian of the Illinois group worked with Thomas J. Dillon, Richard G. Marden of Worcester Classical High School, and John H. Walters of Browne and Nichols School to produce the first complete draft. Later Part III was considerably redrafted at PSSC to take advantage of the first draft, of suggestions from many physicists and teachers, and of new laboratory developments carried out by the PSSC staff in Cambridge. In this process Professor Bruno B. Rossi, Professor Frank, and I (all of MIT), were joined by Professor Eric M. Rogers and Malcolm K. Smith. So many members of the PSSC staff, both at MIT and the University of Illinois, contributed that it is even less possible here than elsewhere to give a fair impression of their joint efforts.

The first half of Part IV, dealing with electricity and magnetism, was originally drafted by Professor Rossi with the help of Alexander Joseph of the Bronx Community College, Bronx, New York, Thaddeus P. Sadowski of North Quincy High School, Quincy, Massachusetts, and Edwin Smith, Withrow High School, Cincinnati, Ohio. Also, starting in the summer of 1957, Professors Herman Feshbach and Roy Weinstein of MIT worked on the job of bringing as much modern atomic physics as possible from the last years of college physics to within reach of beginning students. Following after this and other preliminary work, Professor Morrison, Professor Rossi, and I laid out most of the present structure of Part IV, and drafts of the text were produced mainly by Rossi and Morrison. Malcolm K. Smith, Professor Rogers, Professor Frank, and I have been responsible for bringing the comments of teachers to bear on these drafts and for such rewriting and editing as has resulted in the present edition. Here we must particularly thank Professor James H. Smith of the University of Illinois, who tried some of these materials in preliminary form and pointed out the advantage of one radical change in order. We are also especially indebted to Richard Brinckerhoff of Phillips Exeter Academy for detailed commentary not only in this part but throughout the text, and to David A. Page of the University of Illinois, whose careful classroom observations were of great value especially in improving the earlier parts. To their names a great number should be added if space permitted.

In this kind of sketch, it is clear that many people are left out, especially if there is no one thing to which their names are obviously attached. Such omissions are painful: often enough, wise advice has been as valuable as an identifiable draft of text. Along these lines, then, I would like to mention the overall contributions of many others. Professor I. Bernard Cohen of Harvard University has read successive drafts and supplied historical materials. Stephen White, whose main concern has been with the PSSC films, has helped with other jobs from time to time since the beginning of the Committee's work. Paul Brandwein of Harcourt, Brace & Company and the Conservation Foundation has supplied detailed criticism, encouragement, and aid at many times. For instance, along with George H. Waltz, Jr., he helped to set up the effective system which turned authors' scrawls into respectable preliminary editions. In this process we benefited from the editorial experience of Judy Meyer and Lee Wertheim. Judson Cross and Malcolm Smith acted as executive editors of the preliminary volumes. For three years their work and mine has been lightened and made effective by the efforts of Benjamin T. Richards, who supervised the production of the texts for schools. Over the last year we have been joined by Richard T. Wareham, of D. C. Heath and Company, who smoothed the transition into this edition.

In this book the illustrations are essential. They were created by cooperative work between the illustrators, photographers, and physicists. Peter Robinson and Percy Lund have worked hard to make their illustrations meet our needs. James Strickland and Berenice Abbott have worked together to produce many of the excellent photographs; others were taken by Charles Smith, Ben Diver, Phokion Karas, Robin Hartshorne, Paul Larkin, and (in Part III) by Professor Chalmers Sherwin and Louis Koester of the University of Illinois. Special film clips were supplied by the Educational Services Incorporated film studio, where work on the related films has gone on in close collaboration.

The preliminary editions and the classroom work of teachers were essential to the process of developing this course. In utilizing them to bring about further improvements, the work of Gilbert Finlay and his co-workers who stayed in close touch with teachers, was supplemented by information gathered directly from testing of students. Here Walter Michels made another of his many contributions. With Frederick L. Ferris, Jr., of Educational Testing Services and a group of physicists and teachers from the region around Philadelphia, he is responsible for a large set of standardized tests from which we learned much. Professor Hulsizer of the University of Illinois provided a teacher's guide to the test answers; and he and several others at Illinois and MIT have helped with test revisions. The Illinois group has taken the major part in development of detailed resource books for teachers, and in this they have been joined by the PSSC staff in Cambridge, who (with the usual aid from all sources) worked out both the student laboratory and the laboratory parts of the teacher's materials.

It is impossible for me to express my thanks adequately to those people whose continuing wisdom has been my chief reliance. The trouble — and pleasure — is that there are too many. Professor J. R. Zacharias has restrained himself with admirable control when, as often happened, the text or laboratory was not sufficiently settled to ease his job of making an accompanying film. He has encouraged us with his confidence despite the inevitable problems that arose in some of the new developments. Professors Morrison, Rogers, Frank, and Rossi have been among the major creators and selectors of material at every point. The whole process has been a continuing cycle and I can only stop where I began, by acknowledging our indebtedness to more people than I could make clear with ten times this space.

FRANCIS LEE FRIEDMAN

STEERING COMMITTEE

PAUL BRANDWEIN
Harcourt, Brace & Company; the Conservation Foundation

VANNEVAR BUSH
Honorary Chairman of the Corporation, MIT

FRANK CAPRA
President, Frank Capra Productions

ROBERT H. CARLETON
Executive Secretary, National Science Teachers' Association

HENRY CHAUNCEY
President, Educational Testing Service

MARTIN DEUTSCH
Professor of Physics, MIT

BRADLEY DEWEY
Member of the Corporation, MIT

NATHANIEL H. FRANK
Head of the Department of Physics, MIT

FRANCIS L. FRIEDMAN
Professor of Physics, MIT

MERVIN KELLY
President, Bell Telephone Laboratories

JAMES R. KILLIAN, JR.
Chairman of the Corporation, MIT

EDWIN H. LAND
President, Polaroid Corporation

ELBERT P. LITTLE
Assistant to the President, Educational Services, Inc.

JAMES MCCORMACK, JR.
Vice President, MIT

MORRIS MEISTER
President, Bronx Community College

WALTER C. MICHELS
Chairman, Department of Physics, Bryn Mawr College

EDWARD M. PURCELL
Gerhard Gade University Professor, Harvard University

I. I. RABI
Higgins Professor of Physics, Columbia University

JERROLD R. ZACHARIAS
Professor of Physics, MIT
Chairman

TEACHERS IN FIRST TRY-OUT PROGRAM, 1957–58

WILLIAM S. BURTON
George School
Bucks County, Pennsylvania

GEORGE P. CARPENTER
Taunton High School
Taunton, Massachusetts

JUDSON B. CROSS
Phillips Exeter Academy
Exeter, New Hampshire

ALEXANDER JOSEPH
Bronx High School of Science
New York City, New York

CLIFFORD C. LITTLE
The Hill School
Pottstown, Pennsylvania

DAVID A. PAGE
University High School
Champaign, Illinois

CHARLES C. SMITH
Radnor High School
Radnor, Pennsylvania

JOHN H. WALTERS, JR.
Browne and Nichols School
Cambridge, Massachusetts

FEEDBACK GROUP

(Other members of the staff have helped with this program from time to time.)

Anne Coulter
Thomas Dingman
Gilbert C. Finlay
Ervin H. Hoffart
Alexander Joseph
John H. Marean
George J. Pallrand
Robert C. C. St. George
John J. Seiler

UNIVERSITY OF ILLINOIS GROUP

Giulio Ascoli
Peter Axel
James Connell
Gilbert C. Finlay
Edwin L. Goldwasser, Chairman 1958–
Robert I. Hulsizer
Kenneth B. Hunt
Louis J. Koester, Jr.
Leo S. Lavatelli
David Lazarus
F. Wheeler Loomis, Chairman 1957–58
Allen C. Odian
David A. Page
David G. Ravenhall
Chalmers Sherwin
Charles P. Slichter
James H. Smith
Alice Summerbell

TEST DEVELOPMENT GROUP

(Others contributed from time to time.)

William S. Burton
George School, Bucks County, Pa.
Max Caspari
University of Pennsylvania
Fred L. Ferris, Jr.
Educational Testing Service
Sherman Frankel
University of Pennsylvania
Thomas H. Glover
Overbrook Regional High School, N.J.
Robert Hulsizer
University of Illinois
Walter Michels
Bryn Mawr College
Charles Smith
Radnor High School, Pa.
Thomas H. Wood
University of Pennsylvania

CONTRIBUTORS TO THE PSSC PROGRAM

ABBOTT, BERENICE — ESI*
ALDRICH, JAMES L. — ESI
ALEXANDER, EDNA S. — ESI
ASCOLI, GIULIO — University of Illinois
AXEL, PETER — University of Illinois
BAEZ, ALBERT V. — Smithsonian Astrophysical Observatory
BAKER, PHILIP S. — Oak Ridge National Laboratory
BARTA, JOHN J. — ESI Film Division
BARTZ, ROBERT V. — Associated Rocky Mountain Universities, Inc.
BEGLE, E. G. — Yale University
BEISER, ARTHUR — New York University
BELESON, ABRAHAM — Bronx High School of Science, N.Y.
BELL, LAIRD — Bell, Boyd, Marshall, and Lloyd (Trustee, ESI)
BENADE, ARTHUR H. — Case Institute of Technology
BENJAMIN, THEODORE — DeWitt Clinton High School, Bronx, N.Y.
BETHE, HANS A. — Cornell University
BITTER, FRANCIS — MIT†
BLOOM, NORTON — Film director
BOHMER, JOSEF — Educational Film Production
BONDI, HERMANN — Kings College, London, England
BOVA, BENJAMIN — Technical writer
BOYD, WATSON F. — Harvard University
BOYLAN, PAUL J. — Boston State Teachers College, Mass.
BRANDWEIN, PAUL F. — Harcourt, Brace & Company; The Conservation Foundation
BRINCKERHOFF, RICHARD F. — Phillips Exeter Academy, N.H.
BRONK, DETLEV W. — National Academy of Sciences (Trustee, ESI)

* Educational Services Incorporated
† Massachusetts Institute of Technology

BROWN, HARRISON — California Institute of Technology
BROWN, MARY CHALLIS — Cambridge, England
BROWN, QUENTIN — ESI Film Division
BRUNER, JEROME S. — Harvard University
BURNS, CYNTHIA P. — ESI
BURTON, WILLIAM S. — George School, Bucks County, Pa.
BURWASH, NATHANIEL — Cambridge Pattern Works
BUSH, VANNEVAR — MIT
BUTCHER, WILLIAM S. — Arthur D. Little, Inc.
CAPRA, FRANK — Frank Capra Productions
CARLETON, N. P. — Harvard University
CARLETON, ROBERT H. — National Science Teachers Association
CARPENTER, GEORGE — Wayland High School, Mass.
CARR, GEORGE L. — Milford Mill High School, Baltimore, Md.
CASPARI, MAX E. — University of Pennsylvania
CHASE, FRANCIS F. — University of Chicago
CHAUNCEY, HENRY — Educational Testing Service
CHURCHILL, JOHN D. W. — Anderson-Nichols & Co.
CHURCHILL, JOHN M. B., JR. — ESI Film Division
CLAWSON, LAWRENCE D. — ESI Film Division
CLOUD, DUDLEY H. — Wilbraham Academy, Mass.
COHEN, I. BERNARD — Harvard University
COLBY, WALTER F. — National Academy of Sciences
CONNELL, JAMES R. — University High School, Urbana, Ill.
COONS, STEVEN A. — MIT
COOPER, LEON F. — Brown University
COULTER, ANNE — ESI
CREUTZ, EDWARD — General Atomics

CROSS, JUDSON B. — Phillips Exeter Academy, N.H.
CUMMINGS, JOAN M. M. — ESI Film Division
CUSICK, PAUL V. — MIT
DAHL, NORMAN C. — MIT
DAMERY, THOMAS A. — ESI
DAVID, EDWARD E., JR. — Bell Telephone Laboratories
DAVIS, KENNETH S. — Reed College, Oregon
DE BRUNNER, CLARICE — ESI Film Division
DEUTSCH, MARTIN — MIT
DEWEY, BRADLEY — Dewey & Almy Chemical Co.
DILLON, THOMAS J. — Concord High School, Mass.
DINGMAN, THOMAS — South Kent School, Conn.
DIVER, BEN — MIT
DONALDSON, ROBERT — State University Teachers College, N.Y.
DUBOS, RENÉ — The Rockefeller Institute
DURSTON, JOHN H. — Writer and editor
EAGLESON, PETER S. — MIT
EDGERTON, HAROLD E. — MIT
ENGEL, HERMAN J. — Film producer
EVEROTE, WARREN P. — Encyclopaedia Britannica Films, Inc.
FELD, BERNARD T. — MIT
FERMI, LAURA — Writer
FERRIS, FREDERICK L., JR. — Educational Testing Service
FESHBACH, HERMAN — MIT
FINK, DONALD — Philco Corporation
FINLAY, GILBERT C. — University of Illinois
FITZPATRICK, JOSEPH P. — WNAC–TV
FOGELSON, JOHN — ESI Film Division
FORNOFF, FRANK J. — Educational Testing Service
FRANK, NATHANIEL H. — MIT
FRANKEL, SHERMAN — University of Pennsylvania
FRIED, CHARLES — MIT
FRIEDMAN, FRANCIS L. — MIT
FRIEDMAN, JOHN R. — Bell Telephone Laboratories
FRISCH, DAVID — MIT
GAZAN, MARGARET M. — MIT
GENOVESE, FRANK C., JR. — MIT
GIBNEY, HARRIET H. — Harvard University
GLOVER, THOMAS H. — Overbrook Regional High School, N.J.
GLUCKSTERN, ROBERT — Yale University
GOLDEN, RUTH U. — Buckingham School, Cambridge, Mass.
GOLDWASSER, EDWIN L. — University of Illinois
GOUDSMIT, SAMUEL A. — Brookhaven National Laboratory
GRANGER, ROBERT A. — Shoreham High School, Vt.
GREENBERG, JACK S. — Yale University
GREENBERGER, DANIEL — U.S. Army
GREISEN, KENNETH I. — Cornell University
GRIFFIN, DONALD R. — Harvard University
GRISDALE, RICHARD O. — Bell Telephone Laboratories
GROSS, HARVEY — McGraw-Hill Book Company
HABER-SCHAIM, URI — MIT
HAFNER, EVERETT M. — University of Rochester
HANF, MARY D. — ESI
HARTSHORNE, ROBIN — Photographer
HELLMAN, CHARLES — Bronx High School of Science, N.Y.
HENRY, JAMES M. — ESI
HERZOG, MILAN — Encyclopaedia Britannica Films, Inc.
HESBURGH, THEODORE M. (REV.) — Notre Dame University (Trustee, ESI)
HINCKLEY, CURTIS — Woodstock Country School, Vt.
HITCHCOCK, CURTISS — Lawrenceville School, N.J.
HOFFART, ERVIN H. — ESI
HOLDEN, ALAN — Bell Telephone Laboratories
HOVDE, FREDERICK L. — Purdue University (Trustee, ESI)
HUGHES, DONALD J. — Brookhaven National Laboratory

HULSIZER, ROBERT I. — University of Illinois
HUME, PATTERSON — University of Toronto
HUNT, KENNETH B. — Lyons Township High School, Ill.
HURLEY, PATRICK M. — MIT
INGARD, K. UNO — MIT
IVEY, DONALD — University of Toronto
JAFFE, BERNARD — Writer
JONES, KENNETH — Anderson-Nichols & Co.
JONES, RICHARD N. — Indian Springs School, Ala.
JONES, THOMAS F., JR. — MIT
JOSEPH, ALEXANDER — Bronx Community College, N.Y.
JUBENVILLE, ARTHUR R. — Apparatus designer
KANEFSKY, VICTOR — ESI Film Division
KARAS, PHOKION — MIT
KATZ, LEONHARD — Woburn Engineering Co.
KATZEFF, ROBERT J. — ESI Film Division
KAUFMAN, JACK — ESI Film Division
KEARNEY, GENE R. — ESI Film Division
KELLY, MERVIN — Bell Telephone Laboratories
KENNEDY, MURIEL B. — ESI
KERMAN, ARTHUR K. — MIT
KERR, CLARK — University of California (Trustee, ESI)
KILLIAN, JAMES R., JR. — MIT (Trustee, ESI)
KING, JOHN G. — MIT
KINGSBURY, BRUCE F. — ESI
KNAUSS, HAROLD P. — University of Connecticut
KOESTER, LOUIS J., JR. — University of Illinois
KOESTLER, ARTHUR — Writer
KOPEL, HAL — Encyclopaedia Britannica Films, Inc.
KUDZMA, THOMAS G. — Clinton High School, Iowa
LACROIX, ARTHUR — New England Electric System
LAITIN, JOSEPH — Writer
LAND, EDWIN H. — Polaroid Corporation
LANDECKER, LOUIS — Bronx High School of Science, N.Y.
LANGMUIR, ROBERT V. — California Institute of Technology
LARKIN, R. PAUL — ESI Film Division
LAVATELLI, LEO S. — University of Illinois
LAWSON, PEGGY — CBS–TV
LAZARUS, DAVID — University of Illinois
LEACOCK, RICHARD — Film director
LEATHERMAN, BLANCHE — ESI Film Division
LECORBEILLER, PHILIPPE — Harvard University
LESUER, GEORGE W. — University of Buffalo
LEUNG, GEORGE Y. — MIT
LEWIS, LESTER C. — Wagner Lutheran College
LEWIS, ROBERT B. — Aspen Public Schools, Colo.
LITTAUER, RAPHAEL — Cornell University
LITTELL, ANDREW — MIT
LITTLE, CLIFFORD C. — The Hill School, Pottstown, Pa.
LITTLE, ELBERT P. — ESI
LITTLE, NOEL C. — Bowdoin College
LOOMIS, F. WHEELER — University of Illinois
LOUD, CAROL — ESI Film Division
LUND, PERCY — MIT
LUTYENS, W. DAVID M. — Harvard University
MACLACHLAN, JAMES H. — Earl Haig Collegiate Institute, Canada
MADSEN, BORGE S. — University of Copenhagen
MARDEN, RICHARD G. — Worcester Classical High School, Mass.
MAREAN, JOHN H. — Reno High School, Nev.
MARSH, CHARLES R. — Pennsylvania State University
MARSH, PAUL E. — MIT
MASON, RICHARD F. — Madison High School, N.J.
MCCORMACK, JAMES, JR. — MIT
MEISTER, MORRIS — Bronx Community College, N.Y.

MENZEL, DONALD — Harvard University
MEYER, JUDITH — Harcourt, Brace & Company
MICHELS, WALTER C. — Bryn Mawr College
MILES, CLIFFORD L. — University of Connecticut
MILLER, RAY L. — Hunter College High School, N.Y.
MILLMAN, SIDNEY — Bell Telephone Laboratories
MITCHELL, DALE — Columbia University
MOLARSKY, OSMOND — Film editor
MONTGOMERY, DOROTHY D. — Hollins College
MOROCHNIK, ABRAHAM — ESI Film Division
MORRIS, JOSEPH C. — Tulane University (Trustee, ESI)
MORRISON, PHILIP — Cornell University
MORSE, PHILIP M. — MIT
MOTZ, LLOYD — Columbia University
MULDAWER, LEONARD — Temple University
MULLER, ERWIN — Pennsylvania State University
NEDELSKY, LEO — University of Chicago
NEWSOM, CARROLL V. — New York University (Trustee, ESI)
OAKLEY, GILBERT, JR. — ESI
ODIAN, ALLEN C. — University of Illinois
OFFENBACHER, ELMER — Temple University
OKOOMIAN, HOWARD — Hermes Electronics Co.
PAGE, DAVID A. — University of Illinois
PAIGE, JOSEPH C. — Arlington Senior High School, Mass.
PALLRAND, GEORGE J. — Moses Brown High School, Providence, R.I.
PERKINS, NANCY — Cambridge Acoustical Associates
PERRY, WESLEY G. — Hermes Electronics Co.
PESETSKY, ALAN H. — ESI Film Division
PIEL, EMIL J. — East Orange High School, N.J.
PIEL, GERARD — Scientific American
PIERCE, JOHN R. — Bell Telephone Laboratories
PIOCH, RAYMOND C. — Artist
PROTHEROE, CHESTER F. — Needham Senior High School, Mass.
PURCELL, EDWARD M. — Harvard University
RABI, I. I. — Columbia University
RANDALL, COURTLAND S. — ESI
RAVENHALL, D. G. — University of Illinois
REDFIELD, ALFRED G. — International Business Machines Corp.
RICHARDS, BENJAMIN T. — ESI
RICHARDSON, BARBARA B. — ESI
ROBERTS, LAURENCE H., JR. — Woodstock Country School, Vt.
ROBINSON, PETER — Artist
ROGERS, ERIC M. — Princeton University
ROMER, ALFRED — St. Lawrence University
ROSSI, BRUNO — MIT
SADOWSKI, THADDEUS P. — North Quincy High School, Mass.
SAFFORD, J. CAROLYN — ESI
ST. GEORGE, ROBERT C. C. — The Cambridge School, Weston, Mass.
SALMEN, STANLEY S. — Columbia University
SCHAADT, JAMES G. — ESI Film Division
SCHMIDT, STEPHEN — Kenco Films, Inc.
SCHWARZ, GUENTER — Florida State University
SCOTT, MARY JEAN — Brookhaven National Laboratory
SCOTT, WILLIAM T. — Smith College
SEARLE, CAMPBELL — MIT
SEHNERT, MARION P. — ESI Film Division
SEILER, JOHN J. — Cambridge, Mass.
SHAPIRO, ASCHER — MIT
SHEERS, J. — Writer and editor
SHERWIN, CHALMERS W. — University of Illinois
SHIVE, JOHN N. — Brookhaven National Laboratory
SIEBERT, WILLIAM — MIT
SILK, LAWRENCE N. — ESI Film Division
SINGER, PHYLLIS — Bell Telephone Laboratories
SLICHTER, CHARLES P. — University of Illinois
SLICHTER, WILLIAM P. — Bell Telephone Laboratories

SMITH, ALISON V. — Rutgers University
SMITH, CHARLES C. — Radnor High School, Pa.
SMITH, EDWIN M. — Withrow High School, Cincinnati, Ohio
SMITH, JAMES H. — University of Illinois
SMITH, KENNETH A. — Watertown, Mass.
SMITH, KEVIN H. — ESI Film Division
SMITH, M. DANIEL — ESI Film Division
SMITH, MALCOLM K. — ESI
SOULE, ANDREW J. — Topsfield High School, Mass.
STABLER, HOWARD P. — Williams College
STANTON, FRANK — CBS (Trustee, ESI)
STARK, LEONARD — ESI Film Division
STETSON, ROBERT — Watertown, Mass.
STRATTON, JULIUS A. — MIT
STRICKLAND, JAMES S. — ESI
SUMMERBELL, ALICE — University of Illinois
TESSMAN, JACK — Tufts University
TOMER, DARREL W. — Hanford Union High School, Calif.
VAN BERGEIJK, WILLEM A. — Bell Telephone Laboratories
VAN BORK, BERT — Encyclopaedia Britannica Films, Inc.
VARNEY, HAROLD W., JR. — ESI Film Division
VERBRUGGE, FRANK — University of Minnesota
WALL, NATHAN S. — MIT
WALTERS, JOHN H. — Browne and Nichols School, Cambridge, Mass.
WALTZ, GEORGE H., JR. — Writer and editor
WATSON, FLETCHER — Harvard University
WAYMOUTH, JOHN — Sylvania Company
WEBB, JAMES E. — ESI (President, Trustee)
WEINSTEIN, ROY M. — MIT
WERTHEIM, LEO — Technical editor
WESTERVELT, PETER — Brown University
WHITE, CHARLES L., JR. — Encyclopaedia Britannica Films, Inc.
WHITE, STEPHEN — ESI
WILKES, DANIEL M. — University of California
WILLIAMS, JOHN A., JR. — ESI Film Division
WILLIAMS, ROBERT W. — MIT
WILSON, M. MITCHELL — Editorial consultant
WILSON, ROBERT R. — Cornell University
WINE, EMERY C. — Western Interstate Commission for Higher Education
WOLGA, GEORGE — MIT
WOOD, THOMAS H. — University of Pennsylvania
WORSLEY, WALLACE, JR. — International Production Associates, Inc.
YOUTZ, BYRON L. — Reed College, Oregon
ZACHARIAS, JERROLD R. — MIT (Trustee, ESI)
ZIGMAN, JOSEPH — International Production Associates, Inc.
ZIM, HERBERT S. — Simon & Schuster

INDEX